Data for Biochemical Research

DATA for BIOCHEMICAL RESEARCH

Edited by

R. M. C. DAWSON *et al.*

DAPHNE C. ELLIOTT

W. H. ELLIOTT

K. M. JONES

Second Edition

OXFORD
AT THE CLARENDON PRESS

Oxford University Press, Ely House, London W. 1

GLASGOW NEW YORK TORONTO MELBOURNE WELLINGTON
CAPE TOWN IBADAN NAIROBI DAR ES SALAAM LUSAKA ADDIS ABABA
DELHI BOMBAY CALCUTTA MADRAS KARACHI LAHORE DACCA
KUALA LUMPUR SINGAPORE HONG KONG TOKYO

First edition 1959
Second edition 1969
Reprinted (with corrections) 1972

Printed in Great Britain
at the University Press, Oxford
by Vivian Ridler
Printer to the University

Preface to Second Edition

THE range of compounds and experimental procedures available to biochemists has widened greatly in recent years. The reception accorded to the first edition of this book has encouraged us to produce a new edition which takes account of this growth and includes data on many new compounds and techniques. Inevitably, there has been a considerable increase in the size of the book and some material has been rearranged into new sections. In order to limit the increase in size, we have omitted the section on 'Enzymes commonly used as laboratory reagents', since we believe that the information it contained is now more than adequately covered in other works.

Our policy has continued to be that which guided the compilation of the first edition, particularly that all the information contained in the book should be useful in the laboratory and that the best way to ensure this is that the contributors should be biochemists with practical experience in the fields covered by their contributions. We are most grateful to our contributors for the way in which they have fulfilled their tasks of collection and selection of data. The responsibility for any deficiencies in the material selected, however, rests solely with the editors.

There are many others whom we should also like to thank: the contributors to the first edition, whose work has formed the foundation upon which the present edition has been built; the many people who offered criticisms of the first edition and suggestions for its improvement—we have tried to put into practice their good advice; and those who have offered us encouragement and advice during the preparation of this edition, particularly Sir Hugh Ennor, F.A.A., and Professor H. L. Kornberg, F.R.S. We are indebted to Mrs. Elizabeth Dawson, who compiled the index, and to the staff of the Clarendon Press, who have once again given generously of their time and expert knowledge.

Finally we are indebted to Professor M. Dixon, F.R.S., and the Biochemical Society for permission to reproduce the nomograms which appear on pp. 612, 613, and 615, and to Measuring and Scientific Equipment Ltd. for permission to reproduce the nomogram which appears on p. 627.

R. M. C. D.
D. C. E.
W. H. E.
K. M. J.

November 1968

Preface to First Edition

MOST biochemists find a need for a readily available source of information about the compounds and reagents which they use in their everyday research. In this book an attempt has been made to bring together much of this information without producing a treatise of unwieldy size. To achieve this, the editors have been constantly guided by the principle that the information contained in the book should be useful in the laboratory, and any material not meeting this criterion has been deliberately omitted. This book is not intended therefore to be an exhaustive work of reference, and consequently it does not contain all the data that may be required in a specialized field of biochemistry. Nevertheless, the references given may serve as an introduction to the more exhaustive literature on particular subjects.

The book contains a number of sections written by biochemists with practical experience in the fields covered by their contributions. The selection of material is, however, often open to individual interpretation, and consequently, in order to conform to a consistent policy in keeping with the aims of the book, major editorial changes by cutting, adding to, or rearranging individual contributions have had to be made. Responsibility for the final selection of material must, therefore, rest with the editors.

We should like to thank particularly our contributors and also the many other colleagues who have given advice about the contents of the book, especially the following: Dr. R. B. Clayton, Professor A. H. Ennor, Dr. J. A. Fewster, Mr. R. Hems, Sir Hans Krebs, F.R.S., Mr. J. R. P. O'Brien, Sir Rudolph Peters, F.R.S., Professor D. D. Woods, F.R.S., and Dr. P. F. V. Ward. We are indebted to the Academic Press Inc., New York, for permission to include material from *Methods in Enzymology*, vol. 1, edited by S. P. Colowick and N. O. Kaplan, in section 20. We wish to thank Mrs. Elizabeth Dawson who has undertaken the preparation of the index. Finally, we should like to acknowledge the very helpful assistance given to us during the preparation of the book by the staff of the Clarendon Press.

R. M. C. D.
D. C. E.
W. H. E.
K. M. J.

January 1959

Contents

Notes on the Use of this Book

I. TABLES OF BIOCHEMICAL COMPOUNDS AND COMPREHENSIVE INDEX OF COMPOUNDS

1. The tables of biochemical compounds are arranged in sections according to the type of compound. In some instances ambiguity existed as to the correct section for a particular compound and here the Editors have made arbitrary decisions as to their designation. No cross-references between sections or to synonyms have been included, but **there is a comprehensive index of all compounds and of their commonly used synonyms (p. 639). It is strongly advised that this index be used to determine whether a compound is included in the tables and to ascertain its location.**

2. *Melting-points and boiling-points*

The value given is that at a pressure of 760 mm of mercury, unless otherwise stated.

3. *Optical rotations*

The optical activity quoted is the specific rotation, generally for the sodium D line, with the temperature of the measurement indicated by a superscript. Where other wavelengths have been employed, the wavelength is given in Å as a subscript. Where given, the concentration of the substance is in g/100 ml.

4. *Solubility*

Solubilities are given as grams of solute dissolving in 100 ml of solvent. The temperatures at which solubility data were determined are given as superscripts. Where there is no temperature indicated, the data are for room temperature, that is in the range 15° to 25° C.

II. REFERENCES

In general, references are intended to enable readers to find the relevant literature on methods and not necessarily to give credit to the main workers in the field. References are usually not given to methods of preparation of compounds which can be readily obtained commercially at a reasonable price. An abbreviated system of references has been used throughout the volume. Authors of individual papers have been omitted and for those journals and books which are mentioned most frequently the titles have been specially abbreviated as follows:

Ann.	*Liebig's Annalen der Chemie.*
Arch. B.B. (or *Arch. B.*)	*Archives of Biochemistry and Biophysics* (or *Archives of Biochemistry*).
B.B.A.	*Biochimica et Biophysica Acta.*
B.B.R.C.	*Biochemical and Biophysical Research Communications.*
Ber.	*Chemische Berichte* (prior to 1947 *Berichte der deutschen chemischen Gesellschaft*).
Biochem. Preps.	*Biochemical Preparations* (Wiley & Sons Inc., N.Y.).
B.J.	*Biochemical Journal.*
B.P.	*British Pharmacopaeia.*
B.Z.	*Biochemische Zeitschrift.*
C.A.	*Chemical Abstracts.*
J.A.C.S.	*Journal of the American Chemical Society.*
J.B.C.	*Journal of Biological Chemistry.*
J.C.S.	*Journal of the Chemical Society.*
Meth. biochem. Anal.	*Methods of Biochemical Analysis*, ed. D. Glick (Wiley-Interscience Inc., N.Y.).

Meth. Enzymol.	*Methods in Enzymology*, ed. S. P. Colowick and N. O. Kaplan (Academic Press).
Org. Synth.	*Organic Syntheses.*
Org. Synth. **Coll.**	Collective Volumes of *Organic Syntheses.*
P.S.E.B.M.	*Proceedings of the Society for Experimental Biology and Medicine.*
U.S.P.	*United States Pharmacopaeia.*
Z.P.C.	*Hoppe-Seyler's Zeitschrift für physiologische Chemie.*

For other journals the conventional system of abbreviation has been adopted. In certain sections, works of reference which have been quoted extensively in that section only have been abbreviated and a note to this effect is included in the preamble to the section.

Abbreviations

$[\alpha]_D^t$	specific optical rotation for sodium D line at temperature *t*
abs.	absolute, absorbance
acet.	acetone
alk.	alkaline
amorph.	amorphous
anhyd.	anhydrous
approx.	approximately
aq.	aqueous
benz.	benzene
B.p.	boiling-point
Bu	butyl
c	concentration (g/100 ml)
ca.	circa = approximately
C.N.S.	central nervous system
col.	colourless
comp.	competitive(ly)
compd.	compound
conc.	concentrated, concentration
cryst.	crystals, crystalline, crystallization
C.S.F.	cerebrospinal fluid
d.	with decomposition (after M.p. or B.p.), density
decomp.	decomposition point, decomposes
deliq.	deliquescent
deriv.	derivative
dil.	dilute
ed.	editor, edited by, edition
efflor.	efflorescent
ENZ.	enzymic
equiv.	equivalent
esp.	especially
EST.	estimation, estimated
Et	ethyl
eth.	ether
evap.	evaporates, evaporation
F.p.	freezing point
fluor.	fluorescence
G.I.T.	gastro-intestinal tract
gl. acetic	glacial acetic acid
gp.	group
hex.	hexagonal
hr	hour
hygr.	hygroscopic
i.	insoluble
IDENT.	identification
i.m.	intramuscular
inorg.	inorganic
i.p.	intraperitoneal
i.r.	infra-red
ISOL.	isolation, isolated
i.v.	intravenous
liq.	liquid
max.	maximum
Me	methyl
min.	minimum, minute
misc.	miscible
mod.	moderately
monocl.	monoclinic
M.p.	melting-point
M.wt.	molecular weight
no.	number
OD	optical density
org.	organic
orthorh.	orthorhombic
p.	page
path.	pathological(ly)
pet. eth.	petroleum ether
ppt.	precipitate
Pr	propyl
pract.	practical(ly)
PREP.	preparation, prepared
prism.	prismatic
pyr.	pyridine
q.v.	quod vide
recryst.	recrystallize
rect.	rectangular
ref.	reference
rel.	relative(ly)
rh.	rhombic
R.T.	room temperature
s.	soluble
sat.	saturated
s.c.	subcutaneous
sens.	sensitivity
s.g.	specific gravity
sl.	slightly
sl. s.	slightly soluble
sol.	solubility
soln.	solution
sp.	sparingly, species
sp. s.	sparingly soluble
suppl.	supplement
SYN.	synthesis, synthetic
temp.	temperature
tricl.	triclinic
u.v.	ultra-violet
v.	very
visc.	viscous

vol.	volume	wh.	white
v.s.	very soluble	yel.	yellow
v. sl. s.	very slightly soluble	∞	completely miscible

In conformity with established practice the following abbreviations are used for some biochemical compounds:

ACTH	adrenocorticotrophic hormone
AMP, ADP, ATP	adenosine monophosphate, diphosphate, and triphosphate
CMP, CDP, CTP	cytidine monophosphate, diphosphate, and triphosphate
CoA, CoA.SH	coenzyme A
DNA	deoxyribonucleic acid
DNP-	dinitrophenyl-
EDTA	ethylenediaminetetra-acetate
FAD	flavin adenine dinucleotide
FMN	riboflavin 5′-phosphate, flavin mononucleotide
GMP, GDP, GTP	guanosine monophosphate, diphosphate, and triphosphate
GSH, GSSG	glutathione, reduced, and oxidized
IMP, IDP, ITP	inosine monophosphate, diphosphate, and triphosphate
MSH	melanocyte stimulating hormone
NAD	nicotinamide adenine dinucleotide
NADP	nicotinamide adenine dinucleotide phosphate
P_i	inorganic phosphate
PMS	phenazine methosulphate
RNA	ribonucleic acid
TMP, TDP, TTP	thymidine monophosphate, diphosphate, and triphosphate
UMP, UDP, UTP	uridine monophosphate, diphosphate, and triphosphate

1. Amino Acids, Amines, Amides, Peptides, and their Derivatives

Revised by D. O. GRAY (*Department of Botany, Westfield College, University of London*) *and* P. D. J. WEITZMAN (*Department of Biochemistry, University of Leicester*)

General references

J. P. Greenstein and M. Winitz, *Chemistry of the Amino Acids*, 3 volumes, Wiley (1961), referred to in this table as Greenstein & Winitz.

A. Meister, *Biochemistry of the Amino Acids*, 2 volumes, Academic Press (1965).

Nomenclature

Rules of nomenclature for amino acids are given in *Handbook for Chemical Society Authors* (1961), p. 186 and *J.A.C.S.* **82,** 5575 (1960). Nomenclature of amino acids with two or more asymmetric centres, *J. org. Chem.* **28,** 291 (1963).

Symbols for amino-acid derivatives and peptides, *B.J.* **126,** 773 (1972); *Eur. J. Biochem.* **27,** 201 (1972).

Estimation

Methods of estimation of amino compounds are described in:

R. J. Block and D. Bolling, *Amino Acid Composition of Proteins and Foods*, 2nd ed., Charles C. Thomas (1951), referred to in this table as Block & Bolling.

R. J. Block and K. W. Weiss, *Amino Acid Handbook*, Charles C. Thomas (1956).

Greenstein & Winitz.

S. P. Colowick and N. O. Kaplan (eds.), *Methods in Enzymology*, particularly vols. 3 (1957) and 6 (1963), referred to in this table as *Meth. Enzymol.*

Meth. biochem. Anal. **4,** 285 (1957). Use of bacterial decarboxylases.

Where only a single amino compound is present it is frequently more convenient to use a method of estimation specific for the amino group, e.g.

Ninhydrin method	*J.B.C.* **211,** 907 (1954)
	Analyst **80,** 209 (1955)
	Arch. B.B. **67,** 10 (1957)
Copper salt method	*Meth. Enzymol.* **3,** 471, 474 (1957)

With mixtures it is usual to separate the amino compounds first and then apply a non-specific method of estimation. Separation procedures may use:

Ion-exchange chromatography	*J.B.C.* **211,** 893 (1954)
	Analyt. Chem. **30,** 1185, 1190 (1958)
	Analyt. Biochem. **1,** 187 (1960)
	Analyt. Chem. **32,** 1551 (1962)
	Analyt. Chem. **35,** 2055 (1963)
Paper chromatography	*Meth. Enzymol.* **3,** 504 (1957)
	Reference works on paper chromatography, see p. 512
Electrophoresis	*Meth. biochem. Anal.* **13,** 1 (1965)

pK_a *Values*

Most of the values quoted are from D. D. Perrin, *Dissociation Constants of Organic Bases in Aqueous Solution*, Butterworth (1965).

Peptides

A few peptides which either occur naturally or are used as substrates for the assay of peptidases are included in this table. For further information on the synthesis and properties of peptides, see:

1. Amino Acids, Amines, Amides, Peptides, and their Derivatives

Greenstein & Winitz, vol. 2, p. 763
Adv. Protein Chem. **12,** 465 (1957)
Adv. org. Chem. **3,** 159 (1963)
H. Neurath (ed.), *The Proteins*, 2nd ed., vol. 1, p. 53, Academic Press (1963)

Abbreviations

The abbreviations 'Greenstein & Winitz' and 'Block & Bolling' are used in this table for the books by these authors, the full references to which are given above.

No.	*Name*	*Synonyms*	*Formula*	*M. wt.*	*Physical form*	*M.p.*
1	Acetamide	Ethanamide	$CH_3\cdot CO\cdot NH_2$	59·1	col. hex. or rhombohedral deliq. needles from $CHCl_3$	81–83, B.p. 22
2	*N*-Acetylaspartic acid		$HOOC\cdot CH_2\cdot CH\cdot COOH$ | $NH\cdot CO\cdot CH_3$	175·1	L-, oil from aq. acetic acid, slowly becoming microcryst. solid (2 months)	DL-, 15 L-, 142 D-, 142
3	Acetylcholine bromide	A.C.H. bromide; (β-Acetoxyethyl)-trimethylammonium bromide	$(CH_3)_3\overset{+}{N}\cdot CH_2\cdot CH_2\cdot O\cdot CO\cdot CH_3$ Br^-	Free base as hydroxide, 163·2; Bromide, 226·1; Iodide, 273·1	Bromide, hygr. prisms from aq. EtOH. Iodide, non-hygr.	Bromi 143–6; Iodide
4	*N*-Acetylglutamic acid		$HOOC\cdot CH_2\cdot CH_2\cdot CH\cdot COOH$ | $NH\cdot CO\cdot CH_3$	189·2	cryst.	DL-, 1 L-, 19 D-, 19
5	*N*-Acetyl-5-methoxytryptamine	Melatonin; 5-Methoxy-*N*-acetyltryptamine; *N*-[2-(5-Methoxyindol-3-yl)-ethyl]acetamide	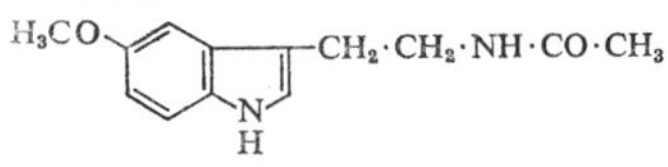	232·3	pale yellow leaflets from benz.	116–1
6	Acetyl-β-methylcholine chloride	(2-Acetoxypropyl)-trimethylammonium chloride; Methacholine chloride; Mecholyl chloride	$(CH_3)_3\overset{+}{N}\cdot CH_2\cdot CH(CH_3)\cdot O\cdot CO\cdot CH_3$ Cl^-	Chloride, 195·7; Iodide, 287·1	Chloride, v. deliq. needles. Iodide, non-hygr. cryst.	Chlo 172–3 Iodid 177·5

)	pK_a *at 25°*	*Solubility*	*Preparation*	*Estimation*	*General remarks*
		97·5^{20}, 178^{60} H_2O; 25·0^{20}, 257·1^{60} EtOH; v.s. glycerol; s. $CHCl_3$; sl. s. eth.	*Org. Synth.* Coll. 1, 3 (1932)	*Pharmazie* **12,** 488 (1957); *C.A.* **52,** 5742*g* (1958) *Analytica chim. Acta* **24,** 397 (1961) *J. Biochem., Tokyo* **50,** 46 (1961)	Can be absorbed by cation exchange resins, *Naturwissenschaften* **42,** 580 (1955). Picrate, M.p. 117. *N*-Xanthydryl deriv., M.p. 238–45. *N*-Diphenylmethyl deriv., M.p. 147.
+57 (in gl. ic) −57 (in gl. ic)		v.s. H_2O; s. gl. acetic, methyl-cellosolve; v. sl. s. acet.	SYN. *J.C.S.* **1953,** 453 ISOL. *J.B.C.* **219,** 257 (1956)	*J. gen. Physiol.* **43,** 331 (1959–60) *C.A.* **57,** 2699*b* (1962)	*N*-Acetylaspartic anhydride, M.p., DL-, 143–4; L-, 173. *N*-Acetyl-DL-aspartic acid β-anilide, M.p. 197–8. *N*-Acetyl-L-aspartic acid bis-*p*-nitrobenzyl ester, M.p. 122–5, $[\alpha]_D^{27}$ −12·1 (c = 2·1 in methyl-cellosolve).
		Bromide, v.s. H_2O, EtOH; i. eth., benz.	*Arch. Pharm., Berl.* **232,** 266 (1894) *Acta chem. scand.* **10,** 145 (1956) SYN. ^{14}C. *J. gen. Chem. U.S.S.R.* **28,** 3040 (1958) *J.A.C.S.* **73,** 2968 (1951)	*P.S.E.B.M.* **81,** 5 (1952) *Scientia pharm.* **25,** 1 (1957); *C.A.* **51,** 11934*b* (1957) *Meth. med. Res.* **9,** 125 (1961) *J. Pharm. Pharmac.* **13,** 510 (1961) *Br. J. Pharmac. Chemother.* **19,** 286 (1962)	Ganglionic and neuromuscular transmitter. Action prolonged by anticholinesterases. 'Nicotinic' action blocked by nicotine, hexamethonium and *d*-tubocurarine (ganglia) and by *d*-tubocurarine and decamethonium (skeletal muscle). 'Muscarinic' action (smooth and cardiac muscle, exocrine glands) blocked by atropine. Unstable in aq. soln. at alkaline pH or when heated. Most stable at pH 4. Reacts with hydroxylamine to form acethydroxamic acid. Platinichloride, M.p. 256–7. Aurichloride, M.p. 154. Dipicrylaminate, M.p. 125. Tetraphenylboron deriv., M.p. 185–7.
-16·6^{25} 2 in H_2O) ^{25} (c = 2 NaOH) -16·6 (in)		s. H_2O, alkalis	*J.A.C.S.* **73,** 3533 (1951) Greenstein & Winitz, vol. 3, p. 1948 ^{14}C and ^{18}O. *J.B.C.* **234,** 1534 (1959)		Dimethyl ester of L-, $[\alpha]_D$ −20 (c = 2·3 in MeOH). This preparation was probably not quite optically pure.
		s. EtOH; sl. s. H_2O, benz.; v. sl. s. pet. eth.	ISOL. *J.A.C.S.* **80,** 2587 (1958) SYN. *J. org. Chem.* **25,** 857 (1960)	*J.A.C.S.* **80,** 2587 (1958) *Meth. biochem. Anal.* **8,** 295 (1960) *Analyt. Biochem.* **5,** 51 (1963)	Occurs in mammalian pineal gland and reverses effect of M.S.H. Sublimes. λ_{max} (in 95% EtOH) 223 and 278 mμ.
27·0$^{22·5}$ 2 iodide % EtOH)		v.s. H_2O, EtOH; s. $CHCl_3$; i. eth.	*J. gen. Chem. U.S.S.R.* **28,** 181 (1958) *Archs int. Pharmacodyn. Thér.* **125,** 216 (1960) *J. Pharm. Pharmac.* **15,** 349 (1963)	*B.P.* 1953, 341	Biologically active compd. is L-isomer. Rapid decomp. by alkalis. Aq. soln. slowly decomp. on standing.

No.	*Name*	*Synonyms*	*Formula*	*M. wt.*	*Physical form*	*M.p.*
7	*S*-Adenosyl-homocysteine	*S*-(5′-Deoxy-adenosine-5′)-homocysteine	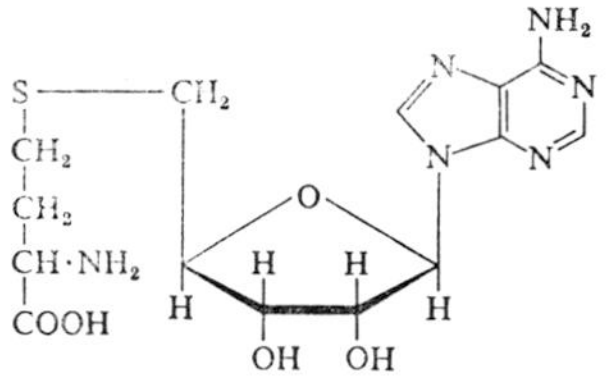	384·4	DL-, small prisms from aq. EtOH. L-, col. tufts of needles from H_2O	L-, 210
8	*S*-Adenosyl-methionine chloride	Active methionine chloride; *S*-(5′-Deoxyadenosine-5′)-methionine chloride; Methyl (5-deoxyribosyl-adenine) (2-aminobutyro)-thetin chloride	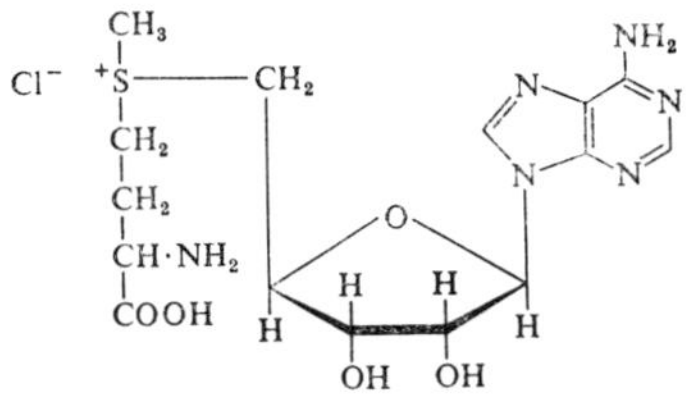	Free cation, 398·4; Chloride, 434·9; Bromide, 479·3; Iodide, 526·4	Chloride, cryst. solid	L-, Chlo 118–22
9	D-Adrenaline	3,4-Dihydroxy-α-[(methylamino)-methyl]-benzyl alcohol; 1-(3,4-Dihydroxy-phenyl)-2-methylamino-ethanol; Epinephrine; Suprarenine	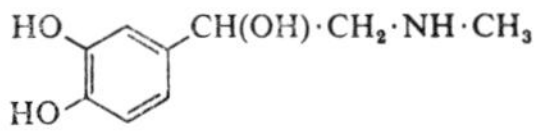	183·2	cryst. solid	211–16
10	DL-Alanine	α-Amino-propionic acid	$CH_3\cdot CH(NH_2)\cdot COOH$	89·1	needles or prisms from H_2O	295 d.
11	D-Alanine			89·1	wh. needles or prisms from EtOH	295 d.
12	L-Alanine			89·1	rh. cryst. from H_2O	297 d.
13	*β*-Alanine	*β*-Amino-propionic acid	$H_2N\cdot CH_2\cdot CH_2\cdot COOH$	89·1	col. rh. prisms from EtOH; col. prisms from H_2O	196 d. (206– rapid heatir

	p*K* at 25°	*Solubility*	*Preparation*	*Estimation*	*General remarks*
37[25] (c = 1·3 N-H_2SO_4) (c = 1 in H_2SO_4) [23] (c = 1 in HCl)		s. hot H_2O; sl. s. cold H_2O, EtOH; v. sl. s. eth.	*J.C.S.* **1955**, 1085 *Bull. Soc. Chim. biol.* **40**, 1787 (1958) *Arch. B.B.* **96**, 70 (1962) *Biochem. Preps.* **8**, 8 (1961) ^{14}C. *Arch. B.B.* **96**, 575 (1962)	*J.B.C.* **234**, 603 (1959) *Arch. B.B.* **96**, 575 (1962)	Decomp. by hot dil. mineral acids to *S*-ribosylhomocysteine. Picrate, M.p., DL-, 170; L-, 175–7.
8·5[24] (c = 1·8 le in 5N-HCl) [24] (c = 1 le in H_2O)		L- chloride, v.s. MeOH at pH 2; s. H_2O; sl. s. MeOH at pH 6	*J.B.C.* **229**, 1051 (1957) *Arch. B.B.* **83**, 28 (1959) *J.A.C.S.* **81**, 3975 (1959) *Biochem. Preps.* **5**, 58 (1957) ^{14}C. *J.B.C.* **233**, 425 (1958)	*J.B.C.* **229**, 1037 (1957) *B.B.A.* **59**, 700 (1962) *Analyt. Biochem.* **6**, 289 (1963)	Unstable at room temperature both as a dry solid and in aq. soln. Frozen aq. soln. stable for months providing pH does not exceed 7. Compound has 4 possible stereo-isomers due to asymmetry of sulphonium centre. $[\alpha]_D$ is given for the natural form. See *J.A.C.S.* **81**, 3975 (1959) for synthesis and properties of other isomers. Iodide is less deliq. than bromide.
[22–25] (c = 1·2 -HCl) [17] (c = 7·5 in ICl)	1. 8·55–8·88 (OH gps.) 2. 9·8–9·9 (NH)	s. gl. acetic, mineral acids, alkalis; sl. s. H_2O, EtOH; i. eth., acet. $CHCl_3$	*Am. J. Physiol.* **5**, 457 (1901) *Z.P.C.* **58**, 581 (1908) *Ber.* **59**, 1068 (1926) *C.A.* **28**, 4398[6] (1934) ^{14}C. *Bull. Soc. chim. Fr.* **1961**, 2255	*Endocrinology* **59**, 260 (1956) *Z. analyt. Chem.* **149**, 355 (1956) *J. Pharm. Pharmac.* **9**, 464 (1957) *Pharmac. Rev.* **11**, 241 (1959) *Meth. med. Res.* **9**, 125 (1961) Dorfman, *Methods in Hormone Research*, vol. 1, p. 337, Academic Press (1962)	Sympathomimetic, predominant hormone of suprarenal (adrenal) medulla. Configuration of natural adrenaline is D- by relation to D-mandelic acid, *J.C.S.* **1958**, 2069. Unstable in aq. soln. at alkaline pH and when heated. Relatively stable at pH 5 in cold. 3,4-Diacetyl deriv., M.p. 168. L-Adrenaline, $[\alpha]_D^{20}$ +50·5 (in HCl).
	1. 2·35 2. 9·87	16·6[25], 32·2[75] H_2O; 0·57[75] 75% EtOH; 0·084[25] 90% EtOH; 0·0087[25] EtOH; i. eth.	*Org. Synth.* Coll. **1**, 20 (1932)	Block & Bolling, p. 352 *Acta physiol. scand.* **13**, 297 (1947) *See also* General methods	Sublimes. *N*-Acetyl-DL-alanine, M.p. 137. *N*-Benzoyl-DL-alanine, M.p. 165–6. *N*-DNP-DL-alanine, M.p. 172–3. Phenylthiohydantoin, M.p. 185.
(c = 2·0 in) (c = 2·0 in		15·78[20] H_2O; 0·2 cold 80% EtOH; i. eth.	*J.B.C.* **178**, 503 (1949)		Sublimes. Benzoyl-D-alanine, M.p. 151, $[\alpha]_D^{20}$ −36·9 (c = 0·753 in KOH). *N*-Acetyl-D-alanine, M.p. 125, $[\alpha]_D$ +66·5 (c = 2 in H_2O).
(c = 2·0 in (c = 2·0		16·65[25], 28·5[75] H_2O; 0·16[20] EtOH; i. eth., acet.	ISOL. *Biochem. Preps.* **1**, 9 (1949) *J.B.C.* **227**, 871 (1957)		Benzoyl-L-alanine, M.p. 152–4, $[\alpha]_D^{20}$ +37·12 (c = 0·668 in KOH). *N*-Acetyl-L-alanine, M.p. 125, $[\alpha]_D$ −66·2 (c = 2 in H_2O). Copper salt, $(C_3H_6O_2N)_2Cu$. *N*-DNP-L-alanine, M.p. 178.
	1. 3·55 2. 10·24	54·5[25] H_2O; 0·017[25] EtOH; i. eth., acet., $CHCl_3$	*Org. Synth.* Coll. **2**, 19 (1943); Coll. **3**, 34 (1955) *Ber.* **86**, 749 (1953) *J. org. Chem.* **26**, 262, 376 (1961)	*Analyt. Chem.* **19**, 207 (1947) *B.Z.* **333**, 302 (1960) *See also* General methods	Sublimes. Decomposes in alkali at 37° yielding ammonia and acrylic acid. Benzyloxycarbonyl-β-alanine, M.p. 106. *N*-DNP-β-alanine, M.p. 146–7. β-Alanine monohydrochloride, M.p. 122·5. Copper salt, $(C_3H_6O_2N)_2Cu \cdot 6H_2O$.

No.	Name	Synonyms	Formula	M. wt.	Physical form	M.p.
14	Allantoic acid	Diureidoacetic acid	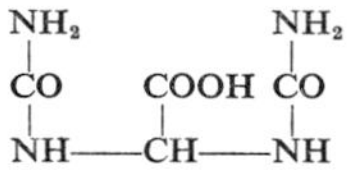	176·1	cryst. as Na salt	172 d.
15	Allantoin	5-Ureido-hydantoin	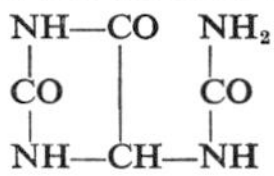	158·1	wh. monocl. prisms	230–1 (slow heatin
16	Amino-acetone	1-Amino-2-propanone; Acetonylamine	$CH_3\cdot CO\cdot CH_2\cdot NH_2$	73·1	needles from EtOH	
17	α-Amino-adipic acid	2-Amino-hexanedioic acid	$HOOC\cdot(CH_2)_3\cdot CH(NH_2)\cdot COOH$	161·1	cryst. solid	DL-, v variat range 165–2 L-, 20
18	DL-α-Amino-butyric acid	2-Amino-butanoic acid; Butyrine	$CH_3\cdot CH_2\cdot CH(NH_2)\cdot COOH$	103·1	col. leaflets from H_2O; fibrous cryst. when pptd. from H_2O with EtOH	283–9 (307 tube)
19	D-α-Amino-butyric acid			103·1	leaflets from $EtOH/H_2O$	292 d
20	L-α-Amino-butyric acid			103·1	col. leaflets from $EtOH/H_2O$	292 (303 tube

	pK_a at 25°	*Solubility*	*Preparation*	*Estimation*	*General remarks*
		sl. s. H_2O; s. EtOH; sl. s. most organic solvents	SYN. *C.A.* **44**, 1418*h* (1950)	*Arch. B.B.* **44**, 468 (1953) *Modern Methods of Plant Analysis* (eds. Paech & Tracey), vol. **4**, p. 128, Springer (1955) *C.r. hebd. Séanc. Acad. Sci., Paris* **250**, 2424 (1960) *See also under* allantoin	Hydrolysed to glyoxylic acid and urea by 0·05N-HCl at 100° in 2 min. Not affected by dil. alkali.
	8·96	0·525 H_2O; sl. s. EtOH; i. eth.	SYN. *Org. Synth.* **Coll. 2**, 21 (1943)	*Modern Methods of Plant Analysis* (eds. Paech & Tracey), vol. 4, p. 128, Springer (1955) *J. Biochem., Tokyo* **50**, 46 (1961) *B.Z.* **337**, 525 (1963) *J.B.C.* **155**, 161 (1944)	Hydrolysed to allantoic acid by alkali.
		v.s. H_2O; s. MeOH, EtOH, eth.	*Ber.* **35**, 3805 (1902) *J.A.C.S.* **76**, 4561 (1954) ISOL. *B.J.* **74**, 478 (1960)	*J.B.C.* **238**, 811 (1963) *B.J.* **74**, 90 (1960)	Very difficult to obtain free base in pure form. Spontaneously oxidizes in cold alkaline aq. soln. Hydrochloride, v. hygr. plates from EtOH-eth., M.p. 75 (73–81). Platinichloride, orange-yellow needles from EtOH, v.s. H_2O, M.p. 188–9. Semicarbazone hydrochloride, M.p. 212. *p*-Toluenesulphonic acid salt, M.p. 130–1.
^{25} (c = 2 (c = 2 Cl) ·0^{25} (c = 2 Cl)	1. 2·14 2. 4·21 3. 9·77	0·22^{40} H_2O; sl. s. EtOH, eth.	*J. gen. Chem. U.S.S.R.* **30**, 69 (1960) Greenstein & Winitz, vol. 3, p. 2408 ^{14}C. *B.J.* **86**, 284 (1963)	*See* General methods	Free acid cyclizes in boiling water to piperidone carboxylic acid; DL-, M.p. 177–8; D-, $[\alpha]_D^{25}$ −16·5 (c = 2 in H_2O), −41·5 (c = 2 in 6N-HCl). Benzyloxycarbonyl-DL-α-aminoadipic acid, M.p. 124. *N*-Chloroacetyl-DL-α-aminoadipic acid, M.p. 129. *N*-Benzoyl-D-α-aminoadipic acid, M.p. 181–2, $[\alpha]_D^{20}$ −25 (c = 1 in 2N-NaOH). 6-Ethyl ester, M.p. 201–3.
	1. 2·29 2. 9·83	28 H_2O; 0·182^{78} EtOH; i. eth.	*J.A.C.S.* **81**, 505 (1959) Greenstein & Winitz, vol. 3, p. 2381	*Analyt. Chem.* **30**, 293 (1958) *Analyt. Chem.* **32**, 162 (1960) *See also* General methods	Sublimes. I.r. spectrum, *Ann. N.Y. Acad. Sci.* **69**, 94 (1957). Acetyl-DL-α-aminobutyric acid, M.p. 132. Chloroacetyl-DL-α-aminobutyric acid, M.p. 128. *N*-Benzoyl-DL-α-aminobutyric acid, M.p. 142.
(c = 1–2 Cl) : = 1–2		s. H_2O	*J.B.C.* **182**, 451 (1950) *J.B.C.* **194**, 455 (1952) *Ber.* **87**, 1279 (1954) *J.A.C.S.* **78**, 4636 (1956)		Acetyl-D-α-aminobutyric acid, M.p. 131, $[\alpha]_D$ +40·0 (in H_2O). Chloroacetyl-D-α-aminobutyric acid, M.p. 118, $[\alpha]_D$ +31·0 (c = 1 in H_2O).
(c = 1–2 Cl) : = 1–2 c = 1–2 tic)		s. H_2O, gl. acetic	*J.B.C.* **182**, 451 (1950) *J.B.C.* **194**, 455 (1952) *Ber.* **87**, 1279 (1954) *J.A.C.S.* **78**, 4636 (1956)		Sublimes. I.r. spectrum, *Ann. N.Y Acad. Sci.* **69**, 94 (1957). Chloroacetyl-L-α-aminobutyric acid, M.p. 118, $[\alpha]_D$ −31·5 (c = 1 in H_2O).

1. Amino Acids, Amines, Amides, Peptides, and their Derivatives

No.	Name	Synonyms	Formula	M. wt.	Physical form	M.p.
21	γ-Amino-butyric acid	Piperidinic acid; Piperidic acid; 4-Amino-butanoic acid	$H_2N\cdot CH_2\cdot CH_2\cdot CH_2\cdot COOH$	103·1	monocl. tablets, plates or needles from $EtOH/H_2O$	203 d. (183–203
22	α-Amino-*iso*-butyric acid	α-Methylalanine; α-Amino-α-methylpropionic acid	$(CH_3)_2C(NH_2)\cdot COOH$	103·1	col. monocl. plates or prisms	200 d., sublime 280
23	β-Amino-*iso*-butyric acid	α-Methyl-β-alanine	$H_2N\cdot CH_2(CH_3)CH\cdot COOH$	103·1	(±)-, col. prisms	(±)-, 17 (−)-, 19 (+)-, 19
24	5(4)-Amino-imidazole-4(5)-carboxamide	AICA	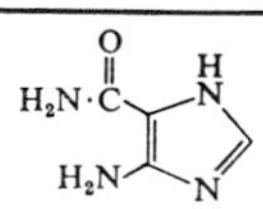	126·1; Hydro-chloride, 162·6	needles from EtOH. Hydrochloride, wh. needles	170–1; Hydro-chloride 255–6 d
25	δ-Amino-laevulinic acid hydrochloride	δ-Amino-levulinic acid hydrochloride	$HOOC\cdot CH_2\cdot CH_2\cdot CO\cdot CH_2\cdot NH_2\cdot HCl$	167·6	cryst.	Free base, 118–19 Hydro-chloride 144–51
26	L-Anserine	β-Alanyl-1-methyl-L-histidine	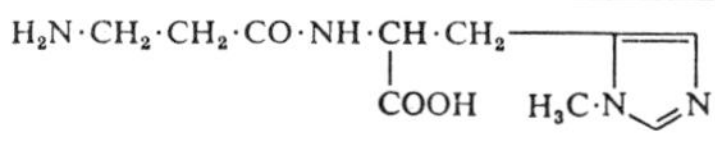	240·3	col. needles from H_2O; v. hygr.	240–2
27	Anthranilic acid	*o*-Amino-benzoic acid	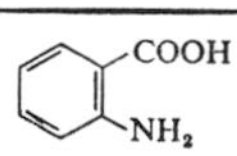	137·1	cryst. leaflets	144–6

	pK_a at 25°	*Solubility*	*Preparation*	*Estimation*	*General remarks*
	1. 4·03 2. 10·56	v.s. H_2O; i. eth., EtOH, benz.	SYN. *Org. Synth.* **Coll. 2,** 25 (1943) *Arch. B.B.* **46,** 248 (1953) ISOL. *B.J.* **48,** 429 (1951)	*J.B.C.* **187,** 55 (1950) *Analyt. Chem.* **28,** 1679 (1956) *Acta chem. scand.* **12,** 1332 (1958) *Meth. med. Res.* **9,** 192 (1961) *See also* General methods	Monohydrochloride, M.p. 135–6, v.s. H_2O. *N*-DNP-γ-aminobutyric acid, M.p. 80.
	1. 2·36 2. 10·21	13·72^{25} H_2O; 0·483^{25} 80% EtOH; i. eth.	*Org. Synth.* **Coll. 2,** 29 (1943) *J.C.S.* **1955,** 1632 *J.B.C.* **180,** 29 (1949) Greenstein & Winitz, vol. 3, p. 2559	*See* General methods	
−15·3^{27} in H_2O) +15·4^{23} in H_2O)		s. H_2O	SYN. (±)-, *J.A.C.S.* **65,** 1335 (1943) *Biochem. Preps.* **7,** 20 (1960) (+)- and (−)-, *J.B.C.* **236,** 3283 (1961) ISOL. *J.B.C.* **234,** 343 (1959)	*J.B.C.* **234,** 343 (1959) *Clinica chim. Acta* **5,** 528 (1960) *B.J.* **80,** 616 (1961) *See also* General methods	Sublimes. Hydrochloride, (±)-, M.p. 128–9; (−)-, M.p. 134–8, $[\alpha]_D^{24}$ −10·7 (c = 1 in H_2O). Benzenesulphonyl-(±)-β-amino-*iso*-butyric acid, M.p. 80–83. Natural isomer is laevorotatory. Absolute configuration, see *J.B.C.* **236,** 3283 (1961).
		s. H_2O	ISOL. *J.B.C.* **161,** 333 (1945) SYN. *J.B.C.* **181,** 89 (1949) *J.C.S.* **1959,** 1648 *J. org. Chem.* **24,** 256 (1959) *J.A.C.S.* **82,** 3144 (1960)	*J.B.C.* **172,** 67 (1948) *Meth. Enzymol.* **6,** 55 (1963) *Can. J. Biochem. Physiol.* **39,** 591 (1961)	Spectrum; λ_{max} (ε), 240 mμ (9050) and 267 mμ (11 200) at pH 1; 266 mμ (12 700) at pH 7; 277 mμ (12 500) at pH 13. Bratton-Marshall chromophore, λ_{max} 540 mμ ε 26 400. Picrate, M.p. 240 d.
	1. 4·05 2. 8·90	s. H_2O, EtOH; v. sl. s. Et acetate	*J.C.S.* **1954,** 1820 *J.B.C.* **215,** 613 (1955) *J. org. Chem.* **24,** 556 (1959) *Biochem. Preps.* **10,** 6 (1963) ^{14}C. *Bull. Soc. chim. Fr.* **1957,** 673	*B.J.* **64,** 101 (1956) *J.B.C.* **219,** 435 (1956) *B.J.* **74,** 90 (1960) *J.B.C.* **238,** 811 (1963)	Spectrum, λ_{max} 266·5 mμ ε 23·0. Forms a 2,5-disubstituted pyrazine in alkali. Ethyl ester, M.p. 101.
(c = 5	1. 2·64 (COOH) 2. 7·04 (imidazole) 3. 9·5 (NH_2)	v.s. H_2O; sl. s. MeOH; v. sl. s. EtOH	SYN. *J. org. Chem.* **29,** 1968 (1964) ISOL. *J. Biochem., Tokyo* **54,** 349, 355, 363 (1963)	*Nature, Lond.* **179,** 209 (1957) *J.B.C.* **225,** 325 (1957) *J.B.C.* **235,** 1398 (1960) *B.J.* **81,** 98 (1961) *See also* General methods	Nitrate, M.p. 226–8 d. Picrolonate, M.p. 245 d. Copper salt, $C_{10}H_{16}O_3N_4{\cdot}CuO$, M.p. 238, hygr.
	1. 2·05 2. 4·95	0·35^{14} H_2O; 10·7^{9} EtOH; 16·0^{7} eth.	^{14}C. *J. org. Chem.* 27, 2274 (1962)	*Analyt. Biochem.* **8,** 82 (1964) *Naturwissenschaften* **50,** 643 (1963) *Analytica chim. Acta* **21,** 555 (1959)	Spectrum, λ_{max} 310 mμ at pH 7.

1. Amino Acids, Amines, Amides, Peptides, and their Derivatives

No.	*Name*	*Synonyms*	*Formula*	*M. wt.*	*Physical form*	*M.p.*
28	Arcain	Tetramethylene-diguanidine; α,δ-Diguanidino-butane	$HN{=}C(NH_2)\cdot NH\cdot(CH_2)_4\cdot NH\cdot C(NH_2){=}NH$	172·2; Hydrate, 190·3	cryst. + 1H_2O	172
29	DL-Arginine	α-Amino-δ-guanidino-valeric acid; *N*-δ-Amidino-ornithine	$(HN{=})(H_2N)C\cdot NH\cdot(CH_2)_3\cdot CH(NH_2)\cdot COOH$	174·2		238 d.
30	D-Arginine			174·2		238 d.
31	L-Arginine			174·2; Hydrate, 210·2	prisms + 2H_2O from H_2O; anhyd. plates from EtOH	Loses 105; n 238 d.
32	L-Arginino-succinic acid		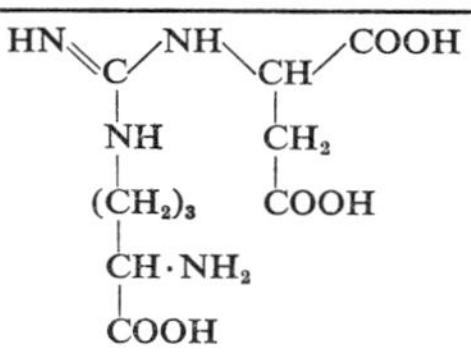	290·3	v. hygr. powder. Ba salt, amorphous powder	
33	DL-Asparagine	α-Amino-succinamic acid; Aspartic acid β-monoamide	$H_2N\cdot CO\cdot CH_2\cdot CH(NH_2)\cdot COOH$	132·1; Hydrate, 150·1	triclinic tablets + 1H_2O	Deco 213–1
34	D-Asparagine			132·1; Hydrate, 150·1	col. rh. cryst. + 1H_2O	Hydr 215 d
35	L-Asparagine			132·1; Hydrate, 150·1	col. rh. hemi-hedra + 1H_2O	Hyd 236 d (seal 226

	pK_a *at 25°*	*Solubility*	*Preparation*	*Estimation*	*General remarks*
			SYN. *Z.P.C.* **118**, 277, 284 (1922) *C.A.* **41**, 4455*e* (1947) ISOL. *Z.P.C.* **199**, 273 (1931) *Z.P.C.* **203**, 132 (1931)	*Bull. Soc. Chim. biol.* **21**, 1381 (1939) *See also Meth. biochem. Anal.* **7**, 193 (1959)	Lowers blood sugar level. Dihydrochloride, M.p. 228, v.s. H_2O. Sulphate, M.p. 297 d., solubility 0·64[21] H_2O, v.s. hot H_2O. Diaurichloride, M.p. 172·5. Dipicrate, M.p. 253–4 d.
	1. 1·82 (COOH) 2. 8·99 (NH_2) 3. 12·48 (guanido)		*J.B.C.* **180**, 1253 (1949)	Block & Bolling, p. 40 *J.B.C.* **141**, 711 (1941) *B.J.* **40**, 470 (1946) *Z.P.C.* **286**, 248 (1950) *B.J.* **63**, 153 (1956) *Experientia* **13**, 21 (1957) *B.J.* **66**, 603 (1957) *See also* General methods	Dipicrate, M.p. 196 d. Flavianate, M.p. 258–9 d. Picrate, M.p. 200 d. Picrolonate, M.p. 248. Acetyl-DL-arginine·$2H_2O$, M.p. 266.
[25] (c = 2·0 in Cl) [25] (c = 2·0 in			*J.B.C.* **188**, 643 (1951) *J.B.C.* **194**, 455 (1952)		Hydrochloride, M.p. 215. Picrate, M.p. 205. Picrolonate, M.p. 231.
[25] (c = 2·0 in Cl) [25] (c = 2·0))		15[21] H_2O; i. EtOH, eth.	*Org. Synth.* Coll. **2**, 49 (1943) *J.B.C.* **194**, 455 (1952)	*J.B.C.* **160**, 35 (1945) *J.B.C.* **161**, 705 (1945) *Nature, Lond.* **157**, 265 (1946) *B.J.* **41**, vii (1947)	Loss of arginine occurs during protein hydrolysis in the presence of carbohydrate. Unstable to hot alkali. Hydrochloride, M.p. 220. Picrate+$2H_2O$, M.p. 217 d., solubility 0·5[16] H_2O. Picrolonate, M.p. 231. Monoflavianate, M.p. 255–60 d., solubility 0·0177[19] H_2O. N^1-DNP-L-arginine, M.p. 252 d. Phenylthiohydantoin, M.p. 189.
[24] (c = 2·9 in [24] (c = 2·9 in aOH)	1. 1·62 (COOH) 2. 2·70 (COOH) 3. 4·26 (COOH) 4. 9·58 (α-NH_2) 5. > 12 (guanido)	v.s. H_2O. Ba salt, v.s. H_2O; i. EtOH	*J.B.C.* **204**, 95 (1953) *J.B.C.* **203**, 143 (1953) *B.J.* **77**, 135 (1960)	*J.B.C.* **204**, 115 (1953) *Nature, Lond.* **192**, 555 (1961)	Forms enzymically inactive anhydrides (two forms, s. H_2O, EtOH), rapidly on heating or at acid pH; anhydrides slowly hydrolysed to argininosuccinic acid under mildly alkaline conditions, see *B.J.* **77**, 135 (1960). Free amino acid and Ba salt stable for months as solid if kept dry and at 0°. Neutral aq. solns. do not cyclize appreciably over several weeks at −18°. Prolonged alkaline hydrolysis, e.g. 0·5N-$Ba(OH)_2$ at 100° for 24 hr, forms DL-aspartic acid and DL-ornithine.
	1. 2·1 2. 8·84	2·16[25] H_2O; i. EtOH, eth.	*J.B.C.* **148**, 151 (1943) *J.A.C.S.* **75**, 330 (1953)	*Analyt. Chem.* **23**, 1300 (1951) *See also* General methods	Stable at 100° in H_2O. 23% hydrolysed in 5 min at 100° in 5% H_2SO_4. Phenylthiohydantoin, M.p. 234.
[25] (c = 2 in (c = 2 in		Monohydrate, 2·989[25] H_2O; 0·02[20–55] EtOH			
[25] (c = 2 in (c = 2 in		Monohydrate, 2·989[25], 24·09[75] H_2O; 0·0003[25] EtOH; s. NH_4OH; i. eth.	*J.B.C.* **145**, 45 (1942)	*B.J.* **47**, 605 (1950)	*N*-DNP-L-asparagine, M.p. 180.

No.	*Name*	*Synonyms*	*Formula*	*M. wt.*	*Physical form*	*M.p.*
36	DL-Aspartic acid	α-Amino-succinic acid	$HOOC\cdot CH_2\cdot CH(NH_2)\cdot COOH$	133·1	col. monocl. prisms	278–80
37	D-Aspartic acid			133·1	cryst. from H_2O	251
38	L-Aspartic acid			133·1	col. rh. leaflets	269–71
39	Aspartic semi-aldehyde	2-Aminosuccin-aldehydic acid; 4-Aspartal	$OHC\cdot CH_2\cdot CH(NH_2)\cdot COOH$	117·1	solid	
40	Asterubin	*N,N*-Dimethyl-guanidino-ethanesulphonic acid	$HN{=}C\begin{smallmatrix}\diagup N(CH_3)_2 \\ \diagdown NH\cdot CH_2\cdot CH_2\cdot SO_3H\end{smallmatrix}$	195·2	prisms or needles from $MeOH/H_2O$	272–3 d
41	Betaine	Glycine betaine; (Carboxy-methyl)-trimethyl-ammonium hydroxide anhydride; Lycine; Oxyneurine; Trimethyl-glycocoll	$(CH_3)_3\overset{+}{N}\cdot CH_2\cdot COO^-$	117·2; Hydrate, 135·2	col. monocl. prisms or leaflets $+1H_2O$ from aq. solvents	loses H 100; 29
42	Betaine aldehyde chloride		$(CH_3)_3\overset{+}{N}\cdot CH_2\cdot CHO$ Cl^-	137·6; Hydrate, 155·6; Free base as hydroxide, 119·2	cryst. $+1H_2O$	142–4
43	Butyryl-choline chloride		$(CH_3)_3\overset{+}{N}\cdot CH_2\cdot CH_2\cdot O\cdot CO\cdot (CH_2)_2\cdot CH_3$ Cl^-	209·7	wh. deliq. cryst.	
44	Cadaverine	1,5-Pentane-diamine; Pentamethylene-diamine	$H_2N\cdot CH_2\cdot CH_2\cdot CH_2\cdot CH_2\cdot CH_2\cdot NH_2$	102·2; Hydrate 138·2	syrupy fuming liq., d_4^{25} 0·873; forms oily hydrate $+2H_2O$	9, B.p. 1
45	Canaline	α-Amino-γ-(aminooxy)-*n*-butyric acid	$H_2N\cdot O\cdot CH_2\cdot CH_2\cdot CH(NH_2)\cdot COOH$	134·1	needles from EtOH	DL-, 19 (190–8 L-, 21

	pK_a at 25°	*Solubility*	*Preparation*	*Estimation*	*General remarks*
	1. 1·99 2. 3·90 3. 9·90	$0{\cdot}82^{25}$, $4{\cdot}79^{75}$ H_2O; $0{\cdot}032^{25}$ 75% EtOH; i. eth.	*Org. Synth.* Coll. **4**, 55 (1963) *J.A.C.S.* **75**, 330 (1953)	*B.B.A.* **3**, 417 (1949) *P.S.E.B.M.* **74**, 446 (1950) *See also* General methods	*N*-DNP-DL-aspartic acid, M.p. 196 d. Acetyl-DL-aspartic, M.p. 150. Phenylthiohydantoin, M.p. 229.
$\cdot4^{25}$ (c = 2 in ICl) 05^{25} (c = 2 in)		s. H_2O, HCl; i. EtOH, eth.	*J.B.C.* **194**, 455 (1952)		*N*-Benzoyl-D-aspartic acid, M.p. 184–5.
$\cdot4^{25}$ (c = 2 in ICl) 05^{25} (c = 2 in)		$0{\cdot}5^{25}$, $2{\cdot}875^{75}$ H_2O; $0{\cdot}00016^{25}$ EtOH	*Biochem. Preps.* **2**, 71 (1952)	*B.J.* **47**, 605 (1950) *J.B.C.* **189**, 591 (1951)	Stable to hot mineral acids in presence of carbohydrate. *N*-DNP-L-aspartic acid, M.p. 186. *N*-Acetyl-L-aspartic acid, M.p. 139–41.
		s. H_2O, mineral acids	*J.C.S.* **1962**, 3963 *Recl Trav. chim. Pays-Bas Belg.* **75**, 29 (1956)	*J.B.C.* **213**, 39 (1955)	Has probably never been obtained pure in solid state. Reasonably stable in aq. soln. at acid pHs. Unstable when neutral both as a dry solid and in aq. soln. *N*-Benzyloxycarbonyl-L-aspartic semialdehyde, stable, M.p. 135–7 $[\alpha]_D^{21}$ −19·8 (c = 1·7 in Et acetate), s. mineral acids, Et acetate.
		s. H_2O; i. EtOH	SYN. *Z.P.C.* **235**, 233 (1935) ISOL. *Z.P.C.* **232**, 206 (1935)		With hot $Ba(OH)_2$ yields dimethylamine and carbamyltaurine (M.p. 185).
	1. 1·83	Hydrated form, 157^{19} H_2O; $8{\cdot}6^{18}$ EtOH; v. sl. s. eth.		*Analyt. Chem.* **23**, 1309 (1951) *B.J.* **55**, 189 (1953) *Analyst* **85**, 272 (1960) *Analyt. Chem.* **32**, 870, 874 (1960)	Isomerizes at M.p. giving methyl ester of dimethylaminoacetic acid. Hydrochloride, M.p. 227–8 d., solubility 60 H_2O, 5 90% EtOH, i. eth. I.r. spectrum, *Spectrochim. Acta* **16**, 1322 (1960)
		v.s. H_2O	*J.B.C.* **234**, 1171 (1959) *J.B.C.* **209**, 511 (1954) *Bull. Soc. chim. Fr.* **45**, 1016 (1929)	*J.B.C.* **209**, 511 (1954) *J.B.C.* **234**, 1171 (1959)	Free base difficult to crystallize because of polymerization of the aldehyde. Stable to alkalis. Picrate of 2,4-dinitrophenylhydrazone, M.p. 181–3. Forms bisulphite complex at acid pHs, complex dissociates at pH 8.
		v.s. H_2O, EtOH; s. $CHCl_3$; i. eth.		*Meth. biochem. Anal.* **1**, 265 (1954)	Rancid odour. Rapid hydrolysis in boiling acids. Substrate for pseudocholinesterase, hydrolysed much more slowly by acetylcholinesterase.
	At I = 0·1, 1. 10·0 2. 11·0	s. H_2O; sl. s. EtOH, eth.	*J.C.S.* **1943**, 561 *J.C.S.* **1946**, 782 *Ber.* **90**, 1251 (1957) ^{14}C. *Z. Chemie, Lpz.* **2**, 336 (1962); *C.A.* **59**, 1583*d*. (1963)	*Nature, Lond.* **197**, 290 (1963)	Dihydrochloride, hygr. prisms, M.p. 255, s. H_2O, MeOH, sl. s. EtOH. Dipicrate, M.p. 237 d. (221 d.), i. H_2O.
$3{\cdot}31^{21}$ (in	1. 2·4 (COOH) 2. 3·7 (ONH_2) 3. 9·2 (αNH_2)	v.s. H_2O; s. gl. acetic; sl. s. EtOH	SYN. *J.C.S.* **1958**, 1632 *Nature, Lond.* **186**, 1047 (1960) SYN. & ISOL. Greenstein & Winitz, vol. 3 p. 2623	*Experientia* **14**, 332 (1958)	Dihydrochloride, L-, cryst. from EtOH, M.p. 166. Dipicrate, M.p., DL-, 189–91 d.; L-, 192–4 d. Dihydrochloride of ethyl ester, L-, M.p. 172–3.

1. Amino Acids, Amines, Amides, Peptides, and their Derivatives

No.	*Name*	*Synonyms*	*Formula*	*M. wt.*	*Physical form*	*M.p.*
46	Carbamyl-aspartic acid	Ureidosuccinic acid	$HOOC \cdot CH_2 \cdot CH(NH \cdot CO \cdot NH_2) \cdot COOH$	176·1		178–80
47	Carbamyl-choline chloride	Carbachol; Doryl; (2-Hydroxy-ethyl)-trimethyl-ammonium chloride carbamate	$(CH_3)_3\overset{+}{N} \cdot CH_2 \cdot CH_2 \cdot O \cdot CO \cdot NH_2 \quad Cl^-$	182·6	hard prism. cryst.; v. hygr.	210–12
48	Carnitine	γ-Trimethyl-β-hydroxybutyro-betaine; Vitamin B_T; (3-Carboxy-2-hydroxypropyl)-trimethyl-ammonium hydroxide inner salt; Novain	$(CH_3)_3\overset{+}{N} \cdot CH_2 \cdot CH(OH) \cdot CH_2 \cdot COO^-$	161·2	hygr. solid	DL-, 195–7 (195–215); L-, 197–212 d.; D-, 210–12
49	L-Carnosine	β-Alanyl-L-histidine	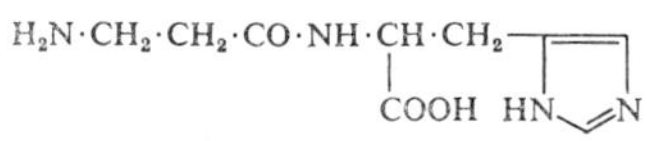	226·2	col. needles	260–2 d.
50	Choline	(2-Hydroxy-ethyl)-trimethyl-ammonium hydroxide; Bilineurine; Sincaline	$(CH_3)_3\overset{+}{N} \cdot CH_2 \cdot CH_2OH \quad OH^-$	121·2	col. viscous syrup or col. cryst.	
51	DL-Citrulline	α-Amino-δ-ureidovaleric acid; N-δ-Carbamyl-ornithine; N^5-Carbamoyl-ornithine; 5-Ureidonor-valine	$O{=}C(NH_2) \cdot NH \cdot (CH_2)_3 \cdot CH(NH_2) \cdot COOH$	175·2	wh. needles from $EtOH/H_2O$	220–1 d.

	pK_a at 25°	*Solubility*	*Preparation*	*Estimation*	*General remarks*
+24·1[25] (c = 3 salt in H_2O)		s. H_2O	*J.A.C.S.* 69, 1382 (1947)	*J.B.C.* 237, 891 (1962)	L-isomer does not crystallize readily but can be purified by ion-exchange chromatography, see *Acta chem. scand.* **10**, 548 (1956).
		v.s. H_2O; s. MeOH; sl. s. EtOH; i. $CHCl_3$, eth.			Neutral aq. soln. stable even when heated. Parasympathomimetic action, activity not prolonged by eserine or neostigmine. Not attacked by choline esterases.
−30·9 +30·9		v.s. H_2O, EtOH; sl. s. acet., isopropanol; i. eth.	*Z.P.C.* 238, 183 (1936) *Ber.* 86, 525 (1953) *Arch. B.B.* **66**, 10 (1957) ISOL. *Biochem. Preps.* **7**, 26 (1960) *Z.P.C.* **318**, 129 (1960) ^{14}C. *Acta chem. scand.* **15**, 701 (1961)	*Z.P.C.* 298, 27 (1954) *Arch. B.B.* 75, 24 (1958) *Analyt. Chem.* **32**, 870, 874 (1960)	Hydrochloride, v.s. H_2O, sl. s. EtOH, i. eth.; DL-, M.p. 190, solubility in H_2O 146·4[16], 234[56]; D-, M.p. 139, $[\alpha]_D^{20}$ +23·7; L-, M.p. 142, $[\alpha]_D^{20}$ −23·7. Sulphate, DL-, M.p. 156–7. Nitrate, DL-, M.p. 79–81. Tetrachloroaurate, orange yellow needles, M.p., DL-, 145–55 d.; L-, 155. Platinichloride, orange cryst., M.p., DL-, *ca.* 200 d.; D-, 192–4 d.; L-, 191–3 d. *O*-Acetyl-L-carnitine, M.p. 145, $[\alpha]_D^{20}$ −19·5.
·9[20] (c = 1 in	1. 2·64 (COOH) 2. 6·87 (imidazole) 3. 9·51 (NH_2)	32 H_2O; i. EtOH	SYN. *Biochem. Preps.* **4**, 38 (1955) *J.A.C.S.* **75**, 2388 (1953) *Ber.* **94**, 2768 (1961) *J. org. Chem.* **29**, 1968 (1964) ISOL. *Ergebn. Physiol.* **41**, 917 (1939) *J. Biochem., Tokyo* **53**, 271 (1963), **54**, 349 (1963)	DL-, *J.B.C.* 225, 325 (1957) *J.B.C.* **235**, 1398 (1960) *Nature, Lond.* 179, 209 (1957) *B.J.* **81**, 98 (1961) L-, *J.B.C.* **196**, 443 (1952) *B.J.* **48**, 487 (1951) *See also* General methods	Nitrate, col. needles, 222–3 d., $[\alpha]_D^{20}$ +23·0 (c = 5·2 in H_2O), v.s. H_2O. Copper salt, $C_9H_{14}O_3N_4 \cdot CuO$, decomp. 221.
	13·9	v.s. H_2O; s. EtOH; sl. s. amyl alcohol; i. eth., $CHCl_3$		*Meth. biochem. Anal.* **1**, 265 (1954) *J.B.C.* **205**, 803 (1953) *J.B.C.* **206**, 647 (1954) *Chem. pharm. Bull., Tokyo* **10**, 533 (1962) *Analytica chim. Acta* **29**, 510 (1963) *B.Z.* **339**, 281 (1964)	Strongly alkaline; absorbs CO_2 from air. Chloride, cryst. from EtOH, v. hygr. Picrate, M.p. 240 s. H_2O, EtOH. Reineckate, M.p. > 250, solubility 0·02[18] H_2O, in presence of NH_4 reineckate 0·0015 H_2O.
		s. H_2O; i. EtOH, MeOH, eth.	*Biochem. Preps.* 3, 100 (1953) Greenstein & Winitz, vol. 3, p. 2491	*B.J.* 35, 650 (1941) *B.J.* 56, 606 (1954) *J.B.C.* **156**, 121 (1944) *J.B.C.* **209**, 145 (1954) *Clin. Chem.* **6**, 291 (1960) *See also* General methods	Stable to acid; unstable to alkali forming ornithine, NH_3 and CO_2.

No.	*Name*	*Synonyms*	*Formula*	*M. wt.*	*Physical form*	*M.p.*
52	D-Citrulline			175·2	cryst. solid	
53	L-Citrulline			175·2	wh. long thin prisms from EtOH/H_2O	220 d.
54	Cortico-trophin	ACTH; Adrenocortico-trophin; Adrenocortico-trophic hormone	1 5 Ser–Tyr–Ser–Met–Glu–His–Phe–Arg–Try– 10 15 Gly–Lys–Pro–Val–Gly–Lys–Lys–Arg–Arg– 20 25 Pro–Val–Lys–Val–Tyr–Pro–Asp–Gly–Ala– 30 35 Glu–Asp–Gln–Leu–Ala–Glu–Ala–Phe–Pro– 39 Leu–Glu–Phe	4566	solid	
55	Creatine	(β-Methyl-guanido)-acetic acid; Methylglycocy-amine; *N*-Amidino-sarcosine	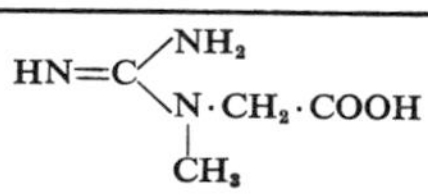	131·1; Hydrate, 149·2	col. monocl. prisms+1H_2O from H_2O	loses H_2O 100 295 d.
56	Creatinine	1-Methylglyco-cyamidine; 2-Imino-1-methyl-4-imidaz-olidinone	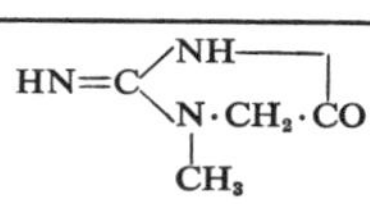	113·1; Hydrate, 149·2	col. rh. prisms +2H_2O on slow evap. of sat. aq. soln., or monocl. prisms, or H_2O-free leaflets from hot sat. soln.	Anhyd., 260 d.

	pK_a *at 25°*	*Solubility*	*Preparation*	*Estimation*	*General remarks*
·2[25] (c = 2 in Cl)		s. H_2O; i. MeOH, EtOH	*J.B.C.* **188**, 643 (1951)		I.r. spectrum, *J.A.C.S.* **77**, 5708 (1955).
)[25] (c = 2 in) ·2[25] (c = 2 in Cl) ·8 (c = 1·1 in -NaOH)	At I = 0·1, 1. 2·43 2. 9·41	s. H_2O; i. EtOH, MeOH	*Biochem. Preps.* **3**, 100, 104 (1953) *J.B.C.* **188**, 643 (1951) Greenstein & Winitz, vol. 3 p. 2491		Stable to acid; unstable to alkali, giving ornithine, NH_3 and CO_2. I.r. spectrum, *J.A.C.S.* **77**, 5708 (1955). Cu salt, $(C_6H_{12}N_3O_3)_2$ Cu, blue prisms, M.p. 249–58. Hydrochloride, M.p. 185 d., $[\alpha]_D^{22}$ +17·9 (in H_2O). Monopicrate, M.p. 206 d. Monoflavianate, M.p. 218 d.
	Ionization, *J.A.C.S.* **81**, 415 (1959)	v.s. H_2O; s. anhyd. HF; sl. s. *n*-BuOH; i. cold acet.	ISOL. (SHEEP) *J.B.C.* **213**, 171 (1955) (BEEF PITUITARY) *Science* **124**, 934 (1954) (HOG) *J.A.C.S.* **78**, 5051 (1956) SYN. *Nature, Lond.* **199**, 172 (1963)	*Endocrinology* **42**, 379 (1948) *Endocrinology* **56**, 523 (1955) *Acta Endocr.* **29**, 70 (1958) *Endocrinology* **71**, 13 (1962) Dorfman, *Methods in Hormone Research*, vol. 2, p. 641, Academic Press (1962)	Pituitary hormone. The material is defined according to its biological activity, and corticotrophins obtained from different sources, or even from the same source by different methods, do not have identical amino acid sequences. Structure given is that of the main component of the preparation from hog pituitary (β-corticotrophin), *J.A.C.S.* **76**, 5565 (1954); structure of other corticotrophins, *Nature, Lond.* **183**, 464 (1959). Unstable to u.v. light in aq. soln. at basic pHs. Aq. soln. slowly loses biological activity due to oxidation, but process is reversed by mild reducing agents (e.g. Na_2SO_3). β-Corticotrophin acetate (β-ACTH·2HOAc·32H_2O), $[\alpha]_D^{23}$ − 140 (in N-HOAc in 3·2% NaCl), $[\alpha]_D^{23}$ − 150 (c = 0·5 in 0·1N-HOAc).
	1. 2·63[12] 2. 14·3[12]	1·09[10], 1·35[18] H_2O; 0·0063 cold EtOH; i. eth.		*Meth. biochem. Anal.* **7**, 193 (1959) *B.J.* **42**, 557 (1948) *B.Z.* **323**, 480 (1953) *B.J.* **67**, 258 (1957) *J.B.C.* **234**, 3201 (1959) *Clin. Chem.* **6**, 537 (1960) *Standard Methods of Clinical Chemistry*, vol. 3, p. 93, Academic Press (1961)	Unstable in mineral acids, giving creatinine. Solubility in H_2O enhanced by urea. *N,N*-Diacetylcreatine, M.p. 165.
	1. 4·80[20] 2. 9·2[20]	8·7[16] H_2O; 0·98[16] EtOH	*Org. Synth.* Coll. **1**, 166 (1932)	*Meth. biochem. Anal.* **7**, 193 (1959) *J.B.C.* **110**, 481 (1935) *J.B.C.* **171**, 363 (1947) *Analyt. Chem.* **25**, 1859 (1953) *Standard Methods of Clinical Chemistry*, vol. 1, p. 55, Academic Press (1953) *J.B.C.* **222**, 225 (1956) *J.B.C.* **233**, 530 (1958) *Analyt. Chem.* **34**, 854 (1962) *See also* General methods	Spectrum, λ_{max} 217 mμ ε 4500 below pH 3; λ_{max} 234 mμ ε 6900 at pH 6·5–12·3; λ_{max} 225 mμ ε 11 100 in N-KOH; *Acta chem. scand.* **7**, 445 (1953). I.r. spectrum, *J.A.C.S.* **76**, 5169 (1954), *J.A.C.S.* **77**, 178 (1955). Flavianate, decomp. 250, solubility 0·198[19] H_2O. Picrate, M.p. 220–1, sl. s. H_2O.

No.	Name	Synonyms	Formula	M. wt.	Physical form	M.p.
57	L-β-Cyano-alanine		$CH_2 \cdot CH(NH_2) \cdot COOH$ (with CN on CH_2)	114·1	rectangular needles from H_2O	214–18 d
58	Cystamine	Cystinamine; 2,2′-Dithiobis-ethylamine; 2,2′-Diamino-diethyldisulphide	$S \cdot CH_2 \cdot CH_2 \cdot NH_2$ / $S \cdot CH_2 \cdot CH_2 \cdot NH_2$	152·3; Dihydro-chloride, 225·2	oil. Dihydro-chloride, needles or plates	B.p. 106- Dihydro chloride, 217 (219- 20, 212)
59	L-Cysta-thionine	S-(β-Amino-β-carboxyethyl)-homocysteine; 2-Amino-4-[(2-amino-2-carboxyethyl) thio]-butyric acid	S with $CH_2 \cdot CH_2 \cdot CH(NH_2) \cdot COOH$ and $CH_2 \cdot CH(NH_2) \cdot COOH$	222·3	col. cryst.	Darkens 270–4; decomp. 301–12
60	Cysteamine	2-Mercapto-ethylamine; Thioethanol-amine; 2-Amino-ethanethiol	$HS \cdot CH_2 \cdot CH_2 \cdot NH_2$	77·1; Hydro-chloride, 113·6	wh. solid. Hydrochloride hygr. wh. plates	97–98·5; Hydro-chloride 70–72
61	L-Cysteic acid	α-Amino-β-sulphopropionic acid; 3-Sulpho-L-alanine	$HO_3S \cdot CH_2 \cdot CH(NH_2) \cdot COOH$	169·2; Hydrate, 187·2	col. rh. octahedra from aq. EtOH; prisms or needles $+1H_2O$ from H_2O	Hydrate 289 d.; Anhyd., 260 d.
62	DL-Cysteine	β-Mercapto-alanine	$HS \cdot CH_2 \cdot CH(NH_2) \cdot COOH$	121·2; Hydro-chloride, 157·6		
63	D-Cysteine			121·2; Hydro-chloride, 157·6		

	pK_a at 25°	*Solubility*	*Preparation*	*Estimation*	*General remarks*
^{26} (c = 1·4 in Ac)	1. 1·7 2. 7·4	s. H_2O; v. sl. s. dioxane	ISOL. *J.B.C.* 237, 733 (1962) SYN. *J. org. Chem.* **26**, 3356 (1961)		Benzyloxycarbonyl deriv., M.p. 136, $[\alpha]_D^{23}$ −46·0 (c = 0·47 in dimethylformamide).
	At I = 1, 1. $8{\cdot}82^{30}$ 2. $9{\cdot}58^{30}$	s. H_2O; sl. s. EtOH	*J.A.C.S.* **63**, 2361 (1941) *J. gen. Chem. U.S.S.R.* **28**, 3027 (1958) *J. org. Chem.* **26**, 3780 (1961)	*Bull. Soc. Chim. biol.* **41**, 1207 (1959) *Ital. J. Biochem.* **10**, 42 (1961)	*N,N′*-Dibenzoylcystamine, M.p. 134. Dipicrate, M.p. 204.
^{24} (c = 1 in)		s. H_2O, mineral acids; i. EtOH	SYN. *J.B.C.* **143**, 59 (1942) *Ann.* **599**, 23 (1956) Greenstein & Winitz, vol. 3 p. 2682 ISOL. *J.B.C.* **171** 255(1947)	*See* General methods	Configuration of molecule is designated according to configuration of 'cysteine' centre. In the *allo* isomers the two optical centres have opposite configurations. *N,N′*-Di-benzoyl-L-cystathionine, M.p. 228–34. D-Cystathionine, $[\alpha]_D^{21.5}$ −23·5 (c = 1 in N-HCl). *N,N′*-Dibenzoyl-D-cystathionine, M.p. 232–40. L-*allo*-Cystathionine, $[\alpha]_D^{21}$ −25 (c = 1 in N-HCl). *N,N′*-Dibenzoyl-L-*allo*cystathionine, M.p. 186–7. D-*allo*cystathionine, $[\alpha]_D^{21}$ +24·5 (c = 1 in N-HCl). *N,N′*-Dibenzoyl-D-*allo*cystathionine, M.p. 184–9. Separation and i.r. spectra of cystathionine and *allo*cystathionine, *Z.P.C.* 305, 105 (1956).
	At I = 0·15, 1. 8·35 2. 10·81	s. H_2O, 95% EtOH	*J.A.C.S.* **62**, 1173 (1940) *J. gen. Chem. U.S.S.R.* **28**, 3027 (1958) *J.A.C.S.* **81**, 4322 (1959)	*Meth. biochem. Anal.* **1**, 1 (1954) *Arch. B.B.* **74**, 443 (1958)	Confers protection against radiation damage. Free base v. unstable and should be used immediately after preparation. Hydrochloride more stable. Picrate, M.p. 125–6. *N*-Acetylcysteamine, hygr. oil, B.p. $138\text{–}40^{7}$.
(c = 7·4 in	At c = 0·1, 1. 1·3 (SO_3H) 2. 1·9 (COOH) 3. 8·70 (NH_2)	v.s. H_2O; i. EtOH	*Org. Synth.* Coll. **3**, 226 (1955) *B.B.A.* **78**, 126 (1963)	*Analyt. Chem.* **31**, 1204 (1959) *B.J.* **74**, 37P (1960) *See also* General methods	Heated under pressure with water gives taurine. Phenylthiohydantoin, M.p. 193–7 d. I.r. spectrum, *Spectrochim. Acta* **16**, 910 (1960).
		s. H_2O, gl. acetic, NH_4OH	Greenstein & Winitz, vol. 3, p. 1901	Block & Bolling, p. 187 *J.B.C.* **173**, 407 (1948) *J.B.C.* **202**, 551 (1953) *B.J.* **56**, 417 (1954) *Analyt. Biochem.* **11**, 190 (1965) *Meth. biochem. Anal.* **1**, 1 (1954) *Analyt. Biochem.* **6**, 486 (1963) *Arch. B.B.* **82**, 70 (1959) *Adv. Protein Chem.* **14**, 255 (1959) *See also* General methods	Aq. soln. oxidizes to cystine on contact with air at neutral or alkaline pH. Relatively stable at acid pH; store as hydrochloride. *N*-Acetyl-*S*-benzyl-DL-cysteine, M.p. 157. *S*-Benzyl-DL-cysteine, M.p. 215, PREP. *J.C.S.* **1953**, 580.
(c = 2 in) ^{5} (c = 2 in		v.s. H_2O, EtOH; s. gl. acetic, NH_4OH			Aq. soln. oxidizes to cystine on contact with air at neutral or alkaline pH. Relatively stable at acid pH; should be kept as hydrochloride.

No.	*Name*	*Synonyms*	*Formula*	*M. wt.*	*Physical form*	*M.p.*
64	L-Cysteine			121·2; Hydro-chloride, 157·6	cryst. powder. Hydrochloride, cryst.	240 d.; Hydro-chloride, 178 d.
65	L-Cysteine sulphinic acid	α-Amino-β-sulphino-propionic acid; 3-Sulphino-L-alanine	$HO_2S\cdot CH_2\cdot CH(NH_2)\cdot COOH$	153·2	octahedral cryst.	Decomp. 152–3 (foams)
66	L-Cysteinyl-glycine		$H_2N\cdot CH\cdot CO\cdot NH\cdot CH_2\cdot COOH$ | CH_2 | SH	178·2; Hydrate, 196·2	rect. prisms $+1H_2O$	184–5
67	DL-Cystine	3,3′-Dithiobis-(2-amino-propionic acid); Dicysteine	$S\cdot CH_2\cdot CH(NH_2)\cdot COOH$ | $S\cdot CH_2\cdot CH(NH_2)\cdot COOH$	240·3	needles	260
68	D-Cystine			240·3	wh. hexagonal plates	247–9
69	L-Cystine			240·3	hexagonal plates from dil. HCl or hexagonal prisms	258–61
70	DL-α,γ-Diamino-butyric acid	2,4-Diamino-butanoic acid; γ-Amino-butyrine	$H_2N\cdot CH_2\cdot CH_2\cdot CH(NH_2)\cdot COOH$	118·1; Mono-hydro-chloride, 154·6; Dihydro-chloride, 191·1	Monohydro-chloride, prisms from $EtOH/H_2O$. Dihydrochloride, hex. prisms from conc. HCl/gl. acetic	Monoh- chlorid 228–30 (246–8 Dihydr- chlorid 202–6
71	L-α,γ-Di-aminobutyric acid			118·1; Mono-hydro-chloride, 154·6; Dihydro-chloride, 191·1	Monohydro-chloride, plates from $EtOH/H_2O$. Dihydrochloride, prisms from conc. HCl/gl. acetic	Monoh chlorid 228–30 Dihyd chlorid 197–8

	pK_a at 25°	*Solubility*	*Preparation*	*Estimation*	*General remarks*
5^{25} (c = 2 in HCl) ·5^{25} (c = 2 in)	At I = 0·15, 1. 1·92 (COOH) 2. 8·35 (NH_2) 3. 10·46 (SH) See *Adv. Protein Chem.* **14**, 272 (1959)	v.s. H_2O, EtOH; s. gl. acetic, NH_4OH	Greenstein & Winitz, vol. 3, p. 1901 *B.J.* **93**, 1 (1964)	*J.B.C.* **185**, 839 (1950)	Aq. soln. oxidizes to cystine on contact with air at neutral or alkaline pH. Relatively stable in acid; store as hydrochloride. *N,S*-BisDNP-L-cysteine, M.p. 155–69 d. *S*-Benzyl-L-cysteine, flat plates, M.p. 208–11, $[\alpha]_D^{24-26}$ −20·0 (c = 0·5–2·0 in 5N-HCl). *N*-DNP-*S*-benzyl-L-cysteine, M.p. 111. *S*-Carboxymethyl-L-cysteine, M.p. 197–203, $[\alpha]_D^{25}$ 0·0, PREP. *J. org. Chem.* **23**, 1251 (1958), EST. *B.B.A.* **31**, 417 (1959), *Analyt. Biochem.* **5**, 433 (1963). Phenylthiohydantoin of *S*-carboxymethyl-L-cysteine, M.p. 164.
(in H_2O) (c = 1 in Cl)	*ca.* 2·1	s. H_2O	SYN. *J.A.C.S.* **55**, 3336 (1933) *J.B.C.* **113**, 583 (1936) *Bull. Soc. chim. Fr.* **1959**, 1887	*Analyt. Biochem.* **4**, 252 (1962)	Forms cystine by reacting with cysteine in H_2O.
·1^{28} (c = 2·9 O)	1. 7·07 2. 9·55	s. H_2O	*Biochem. Preps.* **2**, 74 (1952) *J.B.C.* **202**, 551 (1953) *J.A.C.S.* **80**, 1185 (1958)	*Meth. biochem. Anal.* **1**, 1 (1954) *J.B.C.* **186**, 159 (1948) *J.B.C.* **202**, 551 (1953)	Readily oxidized in air to cystinyl-diglycine, prisms+$2H_2O$, M.p. 210 d., $[\alpha]_D^{25}$ −68·5 (c = 1 in H_2O) −84·2 (c = 0·5 in N-HCl), v.s. H_2O, PREP. *J. org. Chem.* **22**, 805 (1957), *J.C.S.* **1950**, 3461. *S*-Benzyl-L-cysteinylglycine, M.p. 165–7, $[\alpha]_D$ +27 to +29 (c = 2 in N-NaOH).
	At I = 0·1 and 35°, 1. < 1 2. 2·1 3. 8·02 4. 8·71	0·003^{20}, 0·010^{50} H_2O	*J.B.C.* **98**, 577 (1932)	Block & Bolling, p. 187 *Analyt. Chem.* **24**, 1164 (1952) *Analytica chim. Acta* **21**, 190 (1959) *See also* General methods	ϵ_{249} 340 (in 0·1N-NaOH). *N,N'*-Diacetyl-DL-cystine, M.p. 121. *meso*-Cystine, decomp. 200–18, solubility 0·0056^{25} H_2O, ISOL. *J.B.C.* **102**, 287 (1933).
^{25} (c = 1 in Cl)		0·011^{25} H_2O; s. mineral acids and alkalis; i. EtOH	*J.B.C.* **130**, 109 (1939) *J.B.C.* **184**, 55 (1950)		*N,N'*-Dimethyl-D-cystine, M.p. 216–18, $[\alpha]_D^{26·5}$ −75 (c = 1 in N-HCl).
^{25} (c = 1 in Cl)		0·011^{25}, 0·052^{75} H_2O; s. mineral acids, alkalis, NH_4OH; i. eth., benz., $CHCl_3$	*Org. Synth.* Coll. **1**, 188 (1932) *J.B.C.* **184**, 55 (1950)	*J.B.C.* **185**, 839 (1950)	Extensive losses occur during acid hydrolysis of proteins in the presence of carbohydrate. *N,N'*-Dimethyl-L-cystine, M.p. 216–18, $[\alpha]_D^{23}$ +75·7 (c = 1 in N-HCl). *N,N'*-bisDNP-L-cystine, M.p. 109.
		s. H_2O, mineral acids	Greenstein & Winitz, vol. 3, p. 2469 *J.B.C.* **178**, 325 (1949) *Can. J. Chem.* **36**, 593 (1958) ^{14}C. *J.B.C.* **238**, 2460 (1963)	*See* General methods	Dipicrate, M.p. 191–3 d. *N,N'*-Dibenzoyl-DL-diaminobutyric acid, needles, M.p. 200. *N,N'*-Dichloro-acetyl-DL-diaminobutyric acid, M.p. 128.
^{25} (c = 2 free n H_2O) ^{25} (c = 2 hydrochloride HCl) ^{18} (c = 3·67 rochloride O)	1. 1·85^{20} (COOH) 2. 8·28^{20} (NH_2) 3. 10·50^{20} (NH_2)	s. H_2O, mineral acids	SYN. Greenstein & Winitz, vol. 3, p. 2469 *J.B.C.* **199**, 207 (1952) ^{14}C. *J.B.C.* **238**, 2460 (1963) ISOL. *J.B.C.* **181**, 95 (1949) *B.J.* **70**, 626 (1958)	*B.B.A.* **90**, 401 (1964)	Dipicrate, M.p. 180–1 (187). Diflavianate, M.p. 239 d. γ-Chloro-acetyl-L-diaminobutyric acid, $[\alpha]_D^{25}$ +24·0 (c = 2 in 5N-HCl). BisDNP-L-diaminobutyric acid, M.p. 120–2 d.

No.	Name	Synonyms	Formula	M. wt.	Physical form	M.p.
72	*Meso*-Diamino-pimelic acid	2,6-Diamino-heptanedioic acid	HOOC·CH(NH_2)·(CH_2)$_3$·CH(NH_2)·COOH	190·2	wh. anhyd. needles from H_2O	> 305 (313–15)
73	DD-Diamino-pimelic acid			190·2; Hydrate 208·2	+1H_2O from H_2O	
74	LL-Diamino-pimelic acid			190·2; Hydrate 208·2	wh. powder +1H_2O when pptd. from H_2O with EtOH; cryst.+1H_2O from H_2O	
75	L-β-(3,4-Di-hydroxy-phenyl)-alanine	2-Amino-3-(3,4-dihydroxy-phenyl)-propionic acid; DOPA	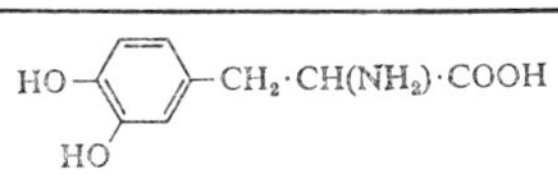	197·2	wh. needles or prisms from H_2O	275–86 d
76	3,5-Diiodo-tyrosine	Iodogorgoic acid; β-(*p*-Hydroxy-3,5-di-iodophenyl)-alanine	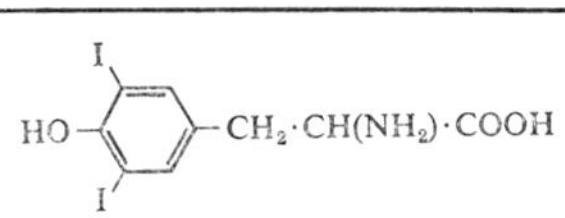	433·0; Di-hydrate, 469·0	DL-, prisms; L-, wh. cryst. +2H_2O	DL-, 201 L-, 194 d
77	Dimethylamine		CH_3·NH·CH_3	45·1	col. liq. or gas	−96·0, B.p. 7·4
78	Dimethyl-ethanolamine	Dimethyl-2-hydroxy-ethylamine; *N,N*-Dimethyl-2-amino-ethanol	$(CH_3)_2N$·CH_2·CH_2OH	89·1	liq., d_4^{20} 0·887	B.p. 13

D	pK_a *at* 25°	*Solubility*	*Preparation*	*Estimation*	*General remarks*
(in 2N-NaOH, and 12N-HCl)	1. 1·8 (COOH) 2. 2·2 (COOH) 3. 8·8 (NH_2) 4. 9·9 (NH_2)	0·92^{21} H_2O; s. dil. mineral acids, alkalis; i. EtOH	Greenstein & Winitz, vol. 3, p. 2512 *J.A.C.S.* **79**, 648 (1957) ISOL. *B.J.* **61**, 562 (1955) *J.B.C.* **234**, 2955 (1959)	*Analyst* **86**, 673 (1961) *Meth. Enzymol.* **6**, 632 (1963) *J.B.C.* **233**, 1501 (1958) *See also* General methods	The *meso*-compd. is less soluble in H_2O than the other stereoisomers and can easily be obtained from a mixture by crystallization. Separation of isomers by paper chromatography of amino acids and DNP derivs., *J.A.C.S.* **77**, 4844 (1955), *Can. J. Biochem. Physiol.* **41**, 817 (1963). Hydrochloride, hex. plates from H_2O, M.p. 240 d. *N,N'*-Dibenzoyl-*meso*-diaminopimelic acid, M.p. 195. *N,N'*-Dibenzyloxycarbonyl-*meso*-diaminopimelic acid, M.p. 123–5.
nohydrate, ·4^{24} (c = 5 in)) 5·5^{26} (c = 1 in Cl) 4·6^{24} (c = 2·6 N-HCl)		v.s. H_2O; i. EtOH	*J.A.C.S.* **79**, 648 (1957) Greenstein & Winitz, vol. 3, p. 2519	*J.B.C.* **233**, 1501 (1958)	Monohydrochloride, $[\alpha]_D^{24}$ −38·0 (c = 2·6 in 5N-HCl). Identification of DD-form in presence of other stereoisomers, *B.J.* **65**, 441 (1957).
nohydrate, 1^{25} (c = 5 in) ·0^{26} (c = 1 in Cl) ·1^{24} (c = 2·6 N-HCl)	1. 1·8 (COOH) 2. 2·2 (COOH) 3. 8·8 (NH_2) 4. 9·9 (NH_2)	v.s. H_2O; i. EtOH	*J.A.C.S.* **79**, 648 (1957) Greenstein & Winitz, vol. 3, p. 2512 ISOL. *B.J.* **61**, 562 (1955) *J.B.C.* **234**, 2955 (1959)	*Meth. Enzymol.* **6**, 632 (1963) *J.B.C.* **233**, 1501 (1958)	Monohydrochloride, $[\alpha]_D^{24}$ +38·5 (c = 2·6 in 5N-HCl). *N,N'*-Dibenzyloxycarbonyl-DL-diaminopimelic acid, M.p. 164–5.
·5 (in H_2O) ·1^{20} (c = 1 in N-HCl) ·0^{25} (c = 2 in Cl)	1. 2·32 (COOH) 2. 8·72 (NH_3) 3. 9·96 (OH) 4. 11·79 (OH)	0·5^{20}, 2·5^{100} H_2O; s. acids and alkalis; i. EtOH, eth.	*Biochem. Preps.* **1**, 25 (1949) *Helv. chim. Acta* **35**, 1776 (1952) Greenstein & Winitz, vol. 3, p. 2713	*J.B.C.* **118**, 531 (1937) *Ber.* **90**, 1687 (1957) *Biochem. Pharmac.* **7**, 181 (1961) *See also* General methods	Rapidly oxidized in aq. solns., which become green. The solid should be stored away from light. Hydrochloride, M.p. 209 d. *O,O,N*-Tribenzoyl deriv., M.p. 170. Picrolonate, M.p. 241 d. DL-3,4-Dihydroxyphenylalanine, M.p. 265–80 d., solubility 0·36 H_2O. D-3,4-Dihydroxyphenylalanine, M.p. 274–5 d., solubility 0·165 H_2O, $[\alpha]_D$ +11·9 (in N-HCl).
1·5^{26} (c = 5 HCl)	1. 2·12 (COOH) 2. 6·48 (OH) 3. 7·82 (NH_2)	DL-, 0·034^{25} H_2O; s. alkalis. L-, 0·062^{25} H_2O; s. alkalis	Greenstein & Winitz, vol. 3, p. 2259 SYN. *B.J.* **39**, 157 (1945) *J.C.S.* **1949**, S 185 ^{131}I and ^{14}C. *Biochem. Preps.* **10**, 171 (1963) *Meth. Enzymol.* **4**, 856 (1957)	Dorfman (ed.), *Methods in Hormone Research*, vol. 1, p. 351, Academic Press (1962) Gray and Bacharach (eds.), *Hormones in Blood*, p. 93, Academic Press (1961) *Meth. Enzymol.* **4**, 856 (1957) *Meth. biochem. Anal.* **12**, 143 (1964)	Unstable in light, losing iodine. De-iodination occurs during protein hydrolysis, esp. with acid. Spectrum, λ_{max} 310 mμ ϵ 5920 in 0·04N-KOH; λ_{max} 285 mμ ϵ 2730 in 0·04N-HCl.
	10·92^{20}; 10·63^{30}; 10·35^{40}	v.s. H_2O; s. EtOH, eth.		*J. Chromat.* **12**, 358 (1963) *Analytica chim. Acta* **24**, 397 (1961)	Hydrochloride, deliq., M.p. 171, s. EtOH, $CHCl_3$. Picrate, M.p. 155–6, sl. s. cold H_2O.
	9·24	∞ H_2O, EtOH, eth.	*Ber.* **34**, 3482 (1901) *J. org. Chem.* **26**, 3536 (1961) *Mh. Chem.* **82**, 621 (1951)	*Nature, Lond.* **184**, 550 (1959) *Meth. Enzymol.* **3**, 358 (1957)	Tetrachloroaurate, M.p. 195. Picrate, M.p. anhyd. 96–97. Picrolonate, M.p. 196 d.

1. Amino Acids, Amines, Amides, Peptides, and their Derivatives

No.	*Name*	*Synonyms*	*Formula*	*M. wt.*	*Physical form*	*M.p.*
79	Dimethyl-glycine	Dimethylamino-acetic acid	$(CH_3)_2N \cdot CH_2 \cdot COOH$	103·1	cryst. hygr.	182–3 (176–8)
80	Dipicolinic acid	2,6-Pyridine dicarboxylic acid; α,α′-Dipicolinic acid	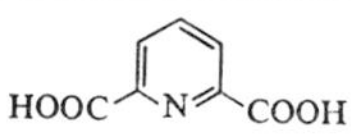	167·1; Hydrate, 194·1	col. needles $+1\frac{1}{2}H_2O$; prisms when sublimed	232 d. (225–37)
81	L-Djenkolic acid	3,3′-Methylene-dithiobis(2-aminopropanoic acid)	$CH_2(S \cdot CH_2 \cdot CH(NH_2) \cdot COOH)_2$ $S \cdot CH_2 \cdot CH(NH_2) \cdot COOH$ / CH_2 / $S \cdot CH_2 \cdot CH(NH_2) \cdot COOH$	254·3	needles	Decomp. 300–50
82	L-Ergo-thioneine	Thioneine; Thiasine; β-2-Thiolimidazolyl-propiobetaine; 2-Mercapto-histidine tri-methylbetaine	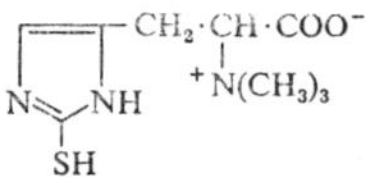	229·3; Hydrate, 265·3	leaflets $+2H_2O$ from H_2O; anhyd. needles from EtOH	Anhyd. 256–7 d.
83	Ethanol-amine	2-Amino-ethanol; 2-Hydroxy-ethylamine; Colamine	$H_2N \cdot CH_2 \cdot CH_2OH$	61·1	col. oily liq., d_4^{20} 1·018	10·5, B.p. 172·
84	*N*-Formimino-L-glutamic acid	*N*-Formimidoyl-glutamic acid; α-Formamidino-glutaric acid	$HOOC \cdot CH_2 \cdot CH_2 \cdot CH(NH \cdot CH{=}NH) \cdot COOH$	174·2	col. hygr. cryst. from EtOH	80–87 d. (70–100)
85	*N*-Formimino-glycine	*N*-Formimidoyl-glycine; Formamidino-acetic acid	$HN{=}CH \cdot NH \cdot CH_2 \cdot COOH$	102·1	wh. cryst. from aq. EtOH	217 d.
86	*N*-Formyl-L-glutamic acid		$HOOC \cdot CH_2 \cdot CH_2 \cdot CH(NH \cdot CHO) \cdot COOH$	175·1	rosettes of fragile cryst. from EtOH/benz.	112–13
87	General methods		General methods of estimation of amino acids and other amino compounds are discussed together with other general topics at the beginning of this table.			

	pK_a at 25°	*Solubility*	*Preparation*	*Estimation*	*General remarks*
	1. 2·08 2. 9·94	v.s. H_2O, EtOH; sl. s. eth., dioxane; i. gl. acetic	*J.B.C.* **115**, 221 (1936) *J.A.C.S.* **73**, 4452 (1951)		Can be sublimed. Hydrochloride, M.p. 189–90. Methyl ester, B.p. 135. Ethyl ester, B.p. 150. Benzyl ester, M.p. 116.
	1. 2·16 2. 4·76	sl. s. H_2O; v. sl. s. EtOH	*Ber.* **67**, 751 (1934) *J. org. Chem.* **14**, 17 (1949) *B.J.* **54**, 205 (1953) *C.A.* **59**, 14542*a* (1963)	*Arch. Mikrobiol.* **31**, 171 (1958) *Science* **127**, 26 (1958) *J. Cell Biol.* **16**, 579 (1963)	Can be sublimed. Spectrum, λ_{max} 270 mμ, shoulders at 262·5 mμ and 277·5 mμ (pH 7–13). Calcium salt, v.s.H_2O. Dimethyl ester, M.p. 121. Diethyl ester, M.p. 41–42. Diphenyl ester, M.p. 179.
·0$^{20.5}$ (c = 1 HCl)		< 0·05^{30}, 0·5^{100} H_2O	*J.B.C.* **168**, 373 (1947)	*See* General methods	Easily racemized in presence of alkali. Decomposed by dil. sulphuric acid to cysteine and formaldehyde. Monohydrochloride, M.p. 250 d. *N,N'*-Dibenzoyl-L-djenkolic acid, M.p. 85.
$^{27.5}$ (c = 1 in		11·6^{20} H_2O; sl. s. hot EtOH; i. cold EtOH, $CHCl_3$, benz.	*Vitams Horm.* **17**, 155 (1959) SYN. *J.C.S.* 1951, 2215 Greenstein & Winitz, vol. 3, p. 2766 ISOL. *B.J.* **53**, 140 (1953) *Can. J. Res.* **E27**, 226 (1949)	*Vitams Horm.* **17**, 155 (1959) *J.B.C.* **206**, 221 (1954) *Can. J. Res.* **E27**, 230 (1949) *B.J.* **47**, 513 (1950) *Z. analyt. Chem.* **153**, 268 (1956) *B.J.* **70**, 656 (1958)	Synthesis in *J.C.S.* 1951, 2215 gives partially racemized product. Ergothioneine is a more powerful reducing substance than cysteine and glutathione. Yields trimethylamine and thiolimidazoyl-4-acrylic acid with strong alkali. Spectrum, λ_{max} 258 mμ ε 16 000 (pH 2–9).
	9·65^{20}, 9·35^{30}, 9·07^{40}	∞ H_2O, EtOH; 0·72 eth.; s. $CHCl_3$; sl. s. benz., ligroin		*Meth. biochem. Anal.* **7**, 111 (1959) *B.B.A.* **40**, 118 (1960) *J. Biochem., Tokyo* **50**, 151 (1961) *Analyt. Biochem.* **4**, 69, 433 (1962) *J. Chromat.* **12**, 358 (1963) *See also* General methods	Hydrochloride, deliq. cryst., M.p. 76. Flavianate, M.p. 211–12. Picrate, M.p. 159·5.
^{28} (c = 0·8 Cl)	1. 2·7 2. 4·4 3. 11·3	v.s. H_2O; s. MeOH, EtOH; i. eth., acet., $CHCl_3$, CCl_4, dimethylformamide	*Biochem. Preps.* **5**, 100 (1957) *J.A.C.S.* **76**, 6205 (1954) ^{14}C. *Nature, Lond.* **176**, 830 (1955)	*Lancet* 1961–I, 112 *J. clin. Path.* **14**, 345 (1961) *Br. med. J.* **1**, 27 (1962) *J. clin. Invest.* **41**, 1472 (1962) *Aust. J. exp. Biol. med. Sci.* **38**, 239 (1960)	Unstable in aq. soln. at alkaline pHs or when heated; neutral and acid solns. stable. Barium salt, $[\alpha]_D^{20}$ −9·8 (c = 2·5 in H_2O). Mercuric salt, i. H_2O, EtOH, eth.
	1. 2·2 2. 11·6	s. H_2O, mineral acids, alkalis; v. sl. s. EtOH	*Biochem. Preps.* **5**, 100 (1957) *Ann.* **577**, 234 (1952)	*J.B.C.* **222**, 537 (1956)	Unstable in aq. soln. at alkaline pHs; neutral and acid solns. stable. I.r. spectrum, *J.B.C.* **222**, 537 (1956). Phenethyl ester hydrochloride, M.p. 120.
^{0} (c = 2 in (c = 2 in	1. 3·4 (COOH) 2. 4·9 (COOH)	s. H_2O, EtOH; i. benz.	*J.B.C.* **210**, 559 (1954)	*J.B.C.* **210**, 559 (1954) *Z. Naturf.* **17b**, 785 (1962)	Ammonium salt, M.p. 133–5. γ-Benzyl ester, M.p. 132–4.

No.	Name	Synonyms	Formula	M. wt.	Physical form	M.p.
88	DL-Glutamic acid	α-Amino-glutaric acid	$HOOC \cdot CH_2 \cdot CH_2 \cdot CH(NH_2) \cdot COOH$	147·1	col. tetragonal plates	225–7 d.
89	D-Glutamic acid			147·1	col. rh. plates from H_2O	247–9 d.
90	L-Glutamic acid			147·1	col. tetragonal plates	247–9 d. (208 d., 213 d.)
91	L-Glutamine	α-Amino-glutaminic acid	$H_2N \cdot CO \cdot CH_2 \cdot CH_2 \cdot CH(NH_2) \cdot COOH$	146·2	wh. needles	184–5
92	L-γ-Glutamyl-L-cysteine		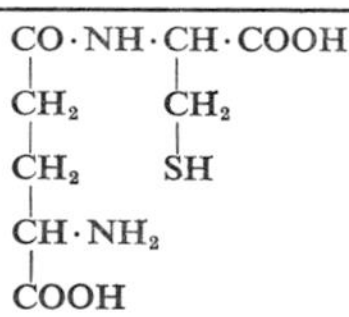	250·3	prisms	167 d.
93	L-Glutathione, oxidized	GSSG	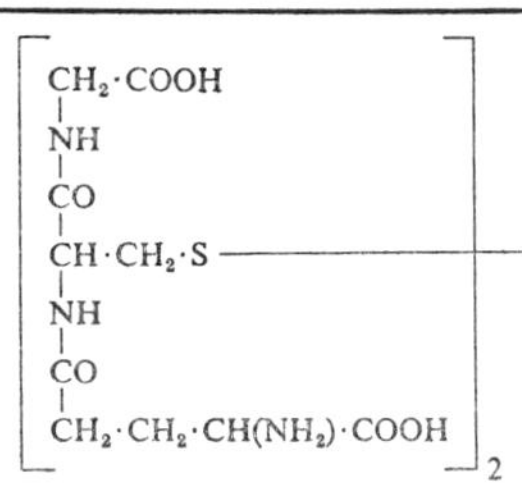	612·6	wh. cryst. powder	182–5 (170–95)
94	L-Glutathione, reduced	L-γ-Glutamyl-L-cysteinylglycine; GSH	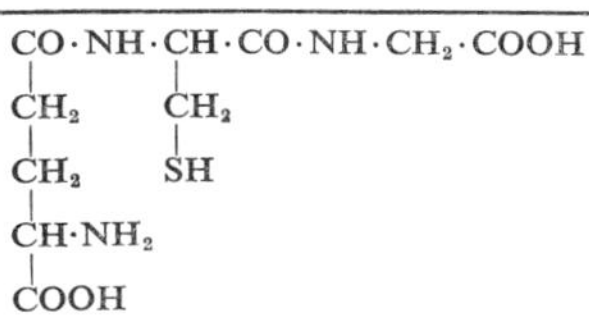	307·3	rh. cryst. from H_2O, prisms from EtOH	190–2 d.

	pK_a at 25°	*Solubility*	*Preparation*	*Estimation*	*General remarks*
	1. 2·10 2. 4·07 3. 9·47	2·054[25], 11·86[75] H_2O; v. sl. s. EtOH, eth.	*Biochem. Preps.* **2**, 69 (1949)	Block & Bolling, p. 325 *B.J.* **33**, 551 (1939) *See also* General methods	In aq. neutral soln. forms pyrrolidone carboxylic acid (q.v.) at 100° and slowly at room temp. Monohydrate, M.p. 197–9. Acetyl-DL-glutamic acid, M.p. 185. *N*-DNP-DL-glutamic acid, M.p. 155–62.
·8[25] (c = 2 in HCl) 2·0[25] (c = 2 in)		1·5[20] H_2O; 0·07[15] EtOH; i. eth.	*J.B.C.* **194**, 455 (1952) *Biochem. Preps.* **4**, 91, 97 (1955)	*B.J.* **55**, 46 (1953)	Acetyl-D-glutamic acid, M.p. 201.
·8[25] (c = 2 in HCl) 2·0[25] (c = 2 in)		0·864[25], 5·53[75] H_2O; 0·032[25] 75% EtOH; 0·00027[25] EtOH; i. gl. acetic; 0·007[25] MeOH	*Org. Synth.* Coll. **1**, 281 (1932)	*B.J.* **43**, 51 (1948) *J.B.C.* **189**, 591 (1951) *B.J.* **79**, 21P (1961)	Stable to hot mineral acids in presence of carbohydrates. Monohydrochloride, M.p. 214. Copper salt, $C_5H_7O_4NCu{\cdot}2\frac{1}{2}H_2O$, solubility 0·03 cold H_2O. *N*-Carbamoyl-L-glutamic acid, M.p. 160. *N*-DNP-L-glutamic acid, M.p. 134–6. Phenylthiohydantoin, M.p. 166–7.
·8[25] (c = 2 in Cl) 3[25] (c = 2 in)	1. 2·17 2. 9·13	3·6[18], 4·25[25] H_2O; 0·00046[25] EtOH; 0·0035[27] MeOH; i. eth., $CHCl_3$, ethyl acetate, acet., gl. acetic	SYN. *J.B.C.* **165**, 333 (1946) ISOL. *Biochem. Preps.* **1**, 44 (1949); **5**, 79 (1957) *Arch. B.B.* **35**, 176 (1952)	*B.J.* **43**, 51 (1948) DL-, *J.B.C.* **176**, 1199 (1948)	Rapidly converted in boiling neutral aq. soln. or in weak acid soln. to the ammonium salt of pyrrolidone carboxylic acid. Phenylthiohydantoin, M.p. 201–11 d.
·4[28] (c = 1·7 O)		s. H_2O	*Biochem. Preps.* **9**, 52 (1962) *J.A.C.S.* **80**, 1158 (1958)	*J.B.C.* **186**, 159 (1950) *Meth. biochem. Anal.* **1**, 1 (1954)	Hydrochloride, fine needles, M.p. 173–4, $[\alpha]_D^{28}$ +2·9 (c = 2·5 in H_2O).
·9 (c = 1 in 1·0$^{16}_{5461}$ (c = 1 O)		s. H_2O; i. EtOH, eth.	*J.B.C.* **90**, 409 (1931) *J.B.C.* **194**, 119 (1952) *Biochem. Preps.* **9**, 52 (1962)	Bergmeyer, *Methods of Enzymatic Analysis*, p. 363, Academic Press (1963) As GSH after reduction, see *J.B.C.* **129**, 393 (1939)	Solid binds approx. 2 moles solvent (H_2O, EtOH, acet.) per mole GSSG; solvent removed only with some decomp. at high temp. (> 100°) in v. high vacuum; not removed by lyophilization. *N,N'*-Dibenzenesulphonyl-GSSG, M.p. 123.
3[27] (c = 2 in	At I = 0·15, 1. 2·12 (COOH) 2. 3·59 (COOH) 3. 8·75 (NH_2) 4. 9·65 (SH) See *Adv. Protein Chem.* **14**, 272 (1959)	s. H_2O; i. EtOH, eth.	SYN. *Biochem. Preps.* **2**, 87 (1952) *J.C.S.* **1957**, 880 *Ber.* **97**, 2434 (1964) ISOL. *B.J.* **33**, 1180 (1939) *Meth. Enzymol.* **3**, 603 (1957)	*Meth. biochem. Anal.* **2**, 259 (1955) Bergmeyer, *Methods of Enzymatic Analysis*, p. 363 Academic Press (1963) *Analyt. Biochem.* **8**, 217 (1964) *Arch. B.B.* **82**, 70 (1959) *Adv. Protein Chem.* **14**, 255 (1959)	Solid stable in air over long periods; aq. soln. readily oxidized in air to GSSG. Phenylcarbamylglutathione, M.p. 210. REVIEW. Boyer, *et al.* (eds.), *The Enzymes*, vol. 2, p. 253 (1960).

1. Amino Acids, Amines, Amides, Peptides, and their Derivatives

No.	*Name*	*Synonyms*	*Formula*	*M. wt.*	*Physical form*	*M.p.*
95	Glycine	Aminoacetic acid; Glycocoll	$H_2N\cdot CH_2\cdot COOH$	75·1	wh. monocl. cryst.	292 d.; darkens at 232–3
96	Glycocyamine	Guanidoacetic acid; *N*-Amidino-glycine	$HN{=}C(NH_2)\cdot NH\cdot CH_2\cdot COOH$	117·1	leaflets or needles from H_2O	Decomp. > 300
97	Glycylglycine	Diglycine	$H_2N\cdot CH_2\cdot CO\cdot NH\cdot CH_2\cdot COOH$	132·1	col. plates	215–20 d (> 250 d
98	Glycylglycyl-glycine	Diglycylglycine; Triglycine	$H_2N\cdot CH_2\cdot CO\cdot NH\cdot CH_2\cdot CO\cdot NH\cdot CH_2\cdot COOH$	189·2	monocl. cryst. from H_2O	244–6 d.
99	Glycyl-L-proline		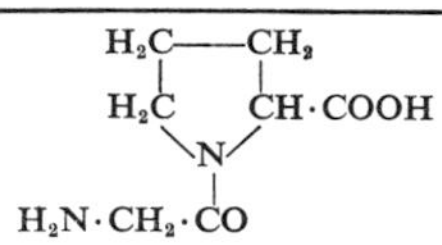	172·2; Hydrate, 181·2	hygr. prisms $+\frac{1}{2}H_2O$	185
100	Guanidine	Carbamamidine; Aminoform-amidine	$HN{=}C(NH_2)_2$	59·1; Hydro-chloride, 95·5; Carbon-ate, 180·2	deliq. cryst. Hydrochloride cryst. Carbonate, prisms	Carbon 197
101	Hippuric acid	*N*-Benzoyl-glycine	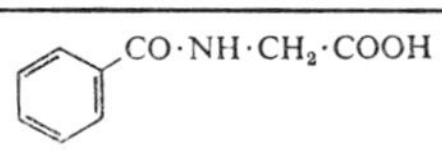	179·2	col. rh. cryst.	187·5 d

	pK_a at 25°	*Solubility*	*Preparation*	*Estimation*	*General remarks*
	1. 2·35 2. 9·78	25^{25}, $54{\cdot}4^{75}$ H_2O; $0{\cdot}043^{25}$ 90% EtOH; $0{\cdot}0029^{25}$ EtOH; $0{\cdot}61^{20}$ pyr.; $0{\cdot}032^{25}$ MeOH; $0{\cdot}00023^{25}$ acet.	*Org. Synth.* Coll. **1**, 292 (1932) *J. org. Chem.* **6**, 349 (1941)	Block & Bolling, p. 343 *J.B.C.* **160**, 51 (1945) *Analyt. Chem.* **23**, 1521 (1951) *Analyt. Chem.* **34**, 196 (1962) *Clin. Chem.* **9**, 79 (1963) *See also* General methods	Acetylglycine, M.p. 206. Benzoylglycine, M.p. 187. *N*-DNP-glycine, M.p. 203. Phenylthiohydantoin, M.p. 245–8 d.
	2·82	$0{\cdot}45^{15}$ H_2O; v. sl. s. EtOH, eth.	*Org. Synth.* Coll. **3**, 440 (1955) *Angew. Chem.* **67**, 275 (1955)	*Meth. biochem. Anal.* **7**, 193 (1959) *J.B.C.* **141**, 711 (1941) *Nature, Lond.* **183**, 1053 (1959) *Analyt. Chem.* **33**, 853 (1961)	Spectrum, λ_{max} 214 mμ ϵ 310 (in BuOH/EtOH/H_2O, 1:1:2, pH 8). Picrate, M.p. 199–200, sl. s. H_2O.
	1. 3·14 2. 8·25	$13{\cdot}4^{25}$, v.s. hot H_2O; v. sl. s. EtOH; i. eth.	Greenstein & Winitz, vol. 2, pp. 763, 1215	*Analyt. Biochem.* **9**, 158 (1964)	Substrate for the assay of glycylglycine dipeptidase, see *Meth. Enzymol.* **2**, 107 (1955), *Meth. biochem. Anal.* **2**, 215 (1955). Used as a buffer. Hydrochloride needles + $1H_2O$. *N*-Acetylglycylglycine, M.p. 186–7.
	1. 3·23 2. 8·09	$6{\cdot}2^{25}$, v.s. hot H_2O; i. EtOH, eth.	Greenstein & Winitz, vol. 2, pp. 763, 1215 *Meth. Enzymol.* **3**, 528 (1957)		Substrate for the assay of aminotripeptidase, see *Meth. Enzymol.* **2**, 83 (1955), *Meth. biochem. Anal.* **2**, 215 (1955).
2^{24} (c = 1)	1. 2·81 2. 8·65	v.s. H_2O; sl. s. EtOH	*Meth. Enzymol.* **3**, 528 (1957) *Ber.* **95**, 1031 (1962)		Soln. keeps only a few days at 5° due to diketopiperazine formation. Substrate for the assay of prolidase (imidodipeptidase), see *Meth. Enzymol.* **2**, 100 (1955), *Meth. biochem. Anal.* **2**, 215 (1955).
	13·6	Free base and hydrochloride, v.s. H_2O, MeOH, EtOH; i. eth. Carbonate, s. H_2O; i. EtOH, eth.		*Meth. biochem. Anal.* **7**, 193 (1959) *Nature, Lond.* **183**, 1053 (1959) *Analyt. Biochem.* **1**, 221 (1960) *C.r. hebd. Séanc. Acad. Sci., Paris* **257**, 2552 (1963)	Soln. of free base alkaline, absorbs CO_2 from air. Soln. of hydrochloride neutral. Flavianate, decomp. *ca.* 274, solubility $0{\cdot}25^{19}$ H_2O. Picrate, darkens 280, M.p. 333 d., solubility 0·037 H_2O.
	3·62	$0{\cdot}37^{25}$ H_2O; sl. s. EtOH, eth.; $0{\cdot}11^{20}$ $CHCl_3$; i. benz., pet. eth.	*Org. Synth.* Coll. **2**, 328 (1943)	*J.B.C.* **206**, 695 (1954) *Analyt. Chem.* **29**, 1712 (1957) *J. Lab. clin. Med.* **57**, 813 (1961) *Analyt. Biochem.* **4**, 423 (1962) *Clin. Chem.* **9**, 102 (1963)	Spectrum, λ_{max} 230 mμ ϵ 10 300.

No.	*Name*	*Synonyms*	*Formula*	*M. wt.*	*Physical form*	*M.p.*
102	Histamine	β-Aminoethyl-imidazole	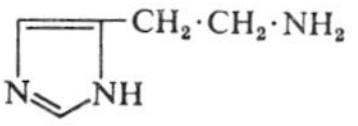	111·2	wh. deliq. cryst.; col. needles from $CHCl_3$	83–84, B.p. 209
103	DL-Histidine	α-Amino-4(5)-imidazole-propionic acid	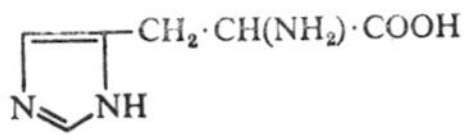	155·2	tetragonal prisms	285–6 d
104	D-Histidine			155·2	long plates	287–8
105	L-Histidine			155·2	leaflets from H_2O	277 d.
106	Histidinol dihydro-chloride	β-Amino-imidazole-4(5)-propanol; 4-(2-Amino-3-hydroxypropyl)-imidazole	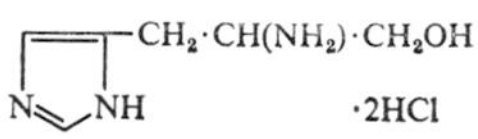	214·1; Free base, 141·2	DL-, rh. plates when pptd. from MeOH with eth.	DL-, 19 L-, 198
107	DL-Homo-cysteine	2-Amino-4-mercapto-butyric acid	$HS \cdot CH_2 \cdot CH_2 \cdot CH(NH_2) \cdot COOH$	135·2	platelets from H_2O/EtOH	263–5 (232–
108	D-Homo-cysteine			135·2	cryst. solid	
109	L-Homo-cysteine			135·2	cryst. solid	

	pK_a at 25°	*Solubility*	*Preparation*	*Estimation*	*General remarks*
	1. 5·78 (imidazole) 2. 9·76 (NH_2)	s. H_2O, EtOH, hot $CHCl_3$; i. eth.		*Meth. biochem. Anal.* **3**, 49 (1956) *J. Lab. clin. Med.* **62**, 506 (1963) *J. Chromat.* **12**, 358 (1963) *Scand. J. clin. Lab. Invest.* **15**, 173 (1963) *Biochem. Pharmac.* **12**, 251 (1963) *Clinica chim. Acta* **7**, 488 (1962)	Dihydrochloride, M.p. 240, s. H_2O, MeOH, 0·005 hot $CHCl_3$. Diflavianate, decomp. 262–3, solubility $0{\cdot}102^{21}$ H_2O.
	1. 1·80 (COOH) 2. 6·04 (imidazole) 3. 9·33 (NH_2)	s. H_2O; i. EtOH, eth., acet., $CHCl_3$	*J.A.C.S.* **67**, 308, 502 (1945)	Block & Bolling, p. 51 *B.J.* **36**, 59 (1942) *B.J.* **40**, 470 (1946) *See also* General methods	Acetyl-DL-histidine monohydrate, M.p. 148.
^{25} (c = 2 in l) ^{25} (c = 2 in		i. EtOH, $CHCl_3$, eth., acet.	*J.B.C.* **184**, 55 (1950) *J.B.C.* **202**, 339 (1953)		
^{25} (c = 2 in) ^{5} (c = 2 in		$4{\cdot}16^{25}$ H_2O; v. sl. s. EtOH; i. eth.	SYN. *J.B.C.* **184**, 55 (1950) ISOL. *Org. Synth.* Coll. **2**, 330 (1943)	*B.J.* **39**, 46 (1945) *B.J.* **41**, vii (1947) *J.B.C.* **161**, 669 (1945) *J.B.C.* **160**, 35 (1945)	Losses occur during protein hydrolysis. Readily racemized on heating with H_2SO_4. Dihydrochloride, rh. plates, M.p. 245–6, v.s. H_2O. Diflavianate, $+\frac{1}{2}H_2O$, M.p. 254 d. *N,N'*-BisDNP-L-histidine, M.p. 232. Phenylthiohydantoin monohydrochloride, M.p. 200–6 d.
(c = 10 in (c = 10 in		s. H_2O; sl. s. EtOH, MeOH: i. eth.	DL-, *Helv. chim. Acta* **44**, 206 (1961) L-, *Biochem. Preps.* **4**, 46 (1955) *Helv. chim. Acta* **36**, 570 (1953)	*J.B.C.* **209**, 829 (1954)	*N*-Benzoyl-L-histidinol, M.p. 207, $[\alpha]_D^{19}$ −47·6 (in EtOH). Histidinol dipicrate, M.p., DL-, 207–8; L-, 194–7.
	1. 2·22 (COOH) 2. 8·87 3. 10·86	s. H_2O; sl. s. EtOH; i. eth.	*Biochem. Preps.* **5**, 93 (1957) Greenstein & Winitz, vol. 3, p. 2656	*P.S.E.B.M.* **43**, 104 (1940) *B.J.* **59**, 234 (1955) *J.B.C.* **222**, 249 (1956) *Analyst* **83**, 422 (1958) *See also* General methods	Readily oxidizes to homocystine and can only be obtained pure in the absence of O_2. Forms thiolactone hydrochloride (in a few minutes) in presence of hot 20% HCl, *J.B.C.* **112**, 149 (1935–6). Thiolactone hydrochloride, M.p. 197–201, hydrolysed to homocysteine at pH 8·3. *S*-Benzyl-DL-homocysteine, irregular plates from H_2O, M.p. 240–50 (190–1), sl. s. H_2O, i. MeOH, EtOH.
			Greenstein & Winitz, vol. 3, p. 2668 *Biochem. Preps.* **5**, 93 (1957) *Arch. B.B.* **42**, 212 (1953)		Too readily oxidized to have been completely characterized. *S*-Benzyl deriv., M.p. 240–3 (247–52), $[\alpha]_D^{26}$ −25 (c = 1 in N-HCl), −27·3 (c = 2 in 2N-HCl), sl. s. H_2O, s. mineral acids.
		s. H_2O; sl. s. EtOH	Greenstein & Winitz, vol. 3, p. 2668 *Biochem. Preps.* **5**, 93 (1957) *Arch. B.B.* **42**, 212 (1953)		Too readily oxidized to have been completely characterized. *S*-Benzyl deriv., M.p. 241–4, $[\alpha]_D^{25}$ +27·2 (c = 1–2 in 5N-HCl) +16·0 (c = 1–2 in gl. acetic), sl. s. H_2O, s. gl. acetic.

No.	Name	Synonyms	Formula	M. wt.	Physical form	M.p.
110	DL-Homo-cystine	4,4′-Dithio-bis(2-amino-butanoic acid)	$S\cdot CH_2\cdot CH_2\cdot CH(NH_2)\cdot COOH$ $\vert$ $S\cdot CH_2\cdot CH_2\cdot CH(NH_2)\cdot COOH$	268·4	thin irregular hex. plates from H_2O	Decomp. 260–5
111	D-Homo-cystine			268·4		281–4 d.
112	L-Homo-cystine			268·4		282–3 d.
113	DL-Homo-serine	2-Amino-4-hydroxy-*n*-butyric acid; γ-Hydroxy-butyrine	$HOCH_2\cdot CH_2\cdot CH(NH_2)\cdot COOH$	119·1	cryst. solid	184–7 d.
114	D-Homo-serine			119·1		203 d.
115	L-Homo-serine			119·1	flat prisms from H_2O/EtOH	203 d.
116	3-Hydroxy-anthranilic acid	2-Amino-3-hydroxybenzoic acid	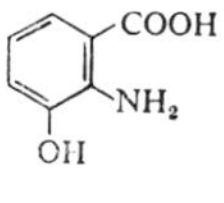	153·1	leaflets from H_2O; wh. needles after sublimation	250–2 (230–6

	pK_a at 25°	*Solubility*	*Preparation*	*Estimation*	*General remarks*
	At I = 0·1, 1. 1·59 (COOH) 2. 2·54 (COOH) 3. 8·52 (NH_2) 4. 9·44 (NH_2)	$0·02^{25}$ H_2O; s. mineral acids, alkalis	*Biochem. Preps.* 5, 93 (1957) Greenstein & Winitz, vol. 3 p. 2656	*P.S.E.B.M.* 43, 104 (1940) (not in presence of cystine) *Analyst* **83**, 422 (1958) *J.B.C.* **125**, 115 (1938) *See also* General methods	Preparations may contain *meso*-compound. Dibenzoyl-DL-homocystine, M.p. 184–5, s. EtOH.
^{25} (c = 1–2 in Cl) ^{21} (c = 0·06 O)			*Arch. B.B.* **42**, 212 (1953) *Biochem. Preps.* **5**, 93 (1957) Greenstein & Winitz, vol. 3, p. 2668		I.r. spectrum, *J.A.C.S.* **77**, 5708 (1955).
(c = 1–2 in Cl))^{21} (c = 0·06 O)			*Arch. B.B.* **42**, 212 (1953) *Biochem. Preps.* **5**, 93 (1957) Greenstein & Winitz, vol. 3 p. 2668		I.r. spectrum. *J.A.C.S.* **77**, 5708 (1955).
	1. 2·71 2. 9·62	125^{30} H_2O; v. sl. s. EtOH, eth.	Greenstein & Winitz, vol. 3, p. 2612 *J.A.C.S.* **70**, 1756 (1948)	*See* General methods	Stable in neutral and alkaline aq. soln. but at acid pHs is converted to a γ-lactone and/or a diketopiperazine. *N*-Benzoyl deriv., M.p. 126–7. γ-Methyl ether, M.p. 240. γ-Ethyl ether, M.p. 235–8. γ-Lactone hydrobromide, M.p. 225–8.
^{26} (c = 2 in) (c = 1–2 in prepared as)		v.s. H_2O; i. EtOH	*J.A.C.S.* **70**, 1756 (1948) *Arch. B.B.* **42**, 212 (1953) Greenstein & Winitz, vol. 3, p. 2615		D-γ-Lactone hydrochloride, $[\alpha]_D^{26}$ +26·7 (c = 5 in H_2O). D-γ-Lactone hydrobromide, M.p. 241 d., $[\alpha]_D^{24}$ +21·0 (c = 1 in H_2O). *O*-Phenyl-D-homoserine, M.p. 241 d., $[\alpha]_D^{26}$ −23·5 (c = 1 in N-HCl).
(c = 2 in) (c = 1–2 prepared as)		110^{30} H_2O; i. EtOH	*J.A.C.S.* **70**, 1756 (1948) *Arch. B.B.* **42**, 212 (1953) Greenstein & Winitz, vol. 3, p. 2615		L-γ-Lactone hydrochloride, $[\alpha]_D^{26}$ −27·0 (c = 5 in H_2O). L-γ-Lactone hydrobromide, M.p. 242 d., $[\alpha]_D^{24}$ −21·3 (c = 1 in H_2O). *O*-Phenyl-L-homoserine, M.p. 241–2 d., $[\alpha]_D^{26}$ +23·5 (c = 1 in N-HCl). α-Benzoyl-L-homoserine, M.p. 140–4.
		s. hot H_2O, alkalis; sl. s. cold H_2O, EtOH; i. eth.	*J.A.C.S.* **70**, 1847 (1948) *Helv. chim. Acta* **34**, 611 (1951) *Biochem. Preps.* **6**, 20 (1958) ^{14}C. *J.B.C.* **234**, 880 (1959) *Biochem. Preps.* **9**, 59 (1962)	*J.B.C.* **218**, 241 (1956) *Analytica chim. Acta* **21**, 555 (1959) *Analytica chim. Acta* **24**, 438 (1961)	Sublimes under reduced pressure. Spectrum, λ_{max} (ε) 298 mμ (3000) and 235 mμ (6400) in 0·1N-HCl, λ_{max} 315–20 mμ at pH 7, *Z. Naturf.* **4b**, 327 (1949). Hydrochloride, M.p. 227. Methyl ester, M.p. 94.

1. Amino Acids, Amines, Amides, Peptides, and their Derivatives

No.	Name	Synonyms	Formula	M. wt.	Physical form	M.p.
117	β-Hydroxy-aspartic acid	2-Amino-3-hydroxy-butanedioic acid	$HOOC\cdot CH(OH)\cdot CH(NH_2)\cdot COOH$	149·1	*erythro*-DL-, cubic, tricl., or monocl. cryst.; *threo*-DL-, prisms	*erythro*-DL decomp. 225–45; *threo*-DL-, decomp. 220–60
118	β-Hydroxy-glutamic acid	2-Amino-3-hydroxy-pentanedioic acid	$HOOC\cdot CH_2\cdot CH(OH)\cdot CH(NH_2)\cdot COOH$	163·1	anhyd. rh. prisms or needles from H_2O; cryst.+$3H_2O$ lose H_2O at 100°	*erythro*-, DL-, 198 d; D-, 200 d; L-, 187 d; *threo*-, DL-, 193-; D-, 203 d; L-, 203 d
119	5-Hydroxy-indoleacetic acid	5-Hydroxy-indole-3-acetic acid; 5-Hydroxy-(hetero)auxin	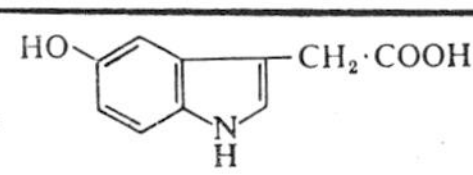	191·2	solid	160–6
120	3-Hydroxy-kynurenine	3-(3-Hydroxy-anthraniloyl)-alanine	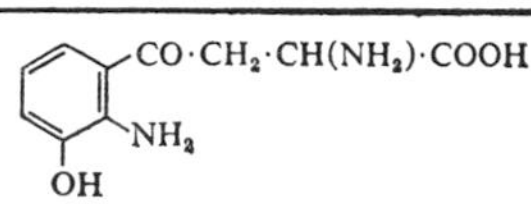	224·2; Hydrate, 242·2	L-, golden-yellow needles+$1H_2O$ from water	DL-, 22[illegible] (213–38); L-, 180
121	DL-δ-Hydroxy-lysine	2,6-Diamino-5-hydroxy-caproic acid	$CH_2(NH_2)\cdot CH(OH)\cdot CH_2\cdot CH_2\cdot CH(NH_2)\cdot COOH$	162·2; Hydro-chloride, 198·6	Hydrochloride, wh. cryst.	Hydro-chloride 223–7

D	pK_a at 25°	*Solubility*	*Preparation*	*Estimation*	*General remarks*
thro-L-, 3·0 (c = 2·46 N-HCl) 1·4 (c = 2·43 H_2O) *eo*-L-, ·3 (c = 3·12 N-HCl) ·5 (c = 1·76 H_2O)	*erythro*-DL-, 1. < 2 2. 3·55 3. 9·0 *threo*-DL- 1. < 2 2. 3·04 3. 8·75	*erythro*-DL-, 2·1 H_2O; i. EtOH. *threo*-DL-, 0·2 H_2O; i. EtOH	*Biochem. Preps.* **10**, 67 (1963) *Bull. chem. Soc. Japan* **36**, 899 (1963) *Arch. B.B.* **104**, 79 (1964) *C.A.* **57**, 16732*g* (1962)	*See* General methods	The *erythro*-D- and *threo*-D-isomers have rotations equal in magnitude but opposite in sign to those of the corresponding L-isomers. Assignment of D- and L-configuration is related to serine. The naturally occurring isomer is *erythro*-β-hydroxy-L-aspartic acid. Interconversion of *erythro*- and *threo*-forms occurs slowly at 120° in H_2O or 6N-HCl. Separation of *erythro*- and *threo*- forms by electrophoresis, *J.B.C.* **236**, 1121 (1961), by ion-exchange, *Arch. B.B.* **91**, 39 (1960).
hro-L-, ·8[20] (c = 2 in HCl) 6[8] (in H_2O) *o*-L-, ·8[22] (c = 2 in HCl)	*erythro*-DL-, 1. 2·27 (COOH) 2. 4·29 (COOH) 3. 9·66 (NH_2)	v.s. hot H_2O, acetic acid; i. EtOH, eth.	*J.B.C.* **201**, 377 (1953) Greenstein & Winitz, vol. 3, p. 2419 *C.A.* **56**, 8837*a* (1962)	*J.B.C.* **142**, 139 (1942) *See also* General methods	The *erythro*-D- and *threo*-D-isomers have rotations equal in magnitude but opposite in sign to those of the corresponding L-isomers. The naturally occurring isomer is *erythro*-β-hydroxy-L-glutamic acid. *allo*-β-Hydroxyglutamic acid has the *threo*- configuration. Separation of *erythro*- and *threo*- forms, *J.B.C.* **201**, 377 (1953). Cyclizes to corresponding pyrrolidone carboxylic acid in boiling aq. soln. Hydrochloride, *erythro*-DL- and *threo*-DL-, M.p. 193–4 d.; *erythro*-D-, M.p. 192–3 d., $[\alpha]^8_D$ −18·7 (in H_2O).
		s. H_2O, EtOH, Et acetate; sl. s. eth.	*J.A.C.S.* **76**, 5579 (1954) *J. org. Chem.* **24**, 179 (1959)	*Meth. biochem. Anal.* **6**, 95 (1958) *J.B.C.* **216**, 499 (1955) *Analyt. Chem.* **32**, 666 (1960) *Analyt. Biochem.* **4**, 423 (1962) *Clinica chim. Acta* **7**, 714 (1962)	Spectrum, λ_{max} 277 and 300 mμ (in EtOH). 5-Benzyloxy-3-indole-acetic acid, M.p. 146.
34[27] (c = 0·17 O) [27] (c = 0·17 in N-HCl)		s. hot H_2O, acids; sl. s. cold H_2O, MeOH, EtOH	*Biochem. Preps.* **7**, 62 (1960) *Ber.* **90**, 1120 (1957) *Ber.* **92**, 2676 (1959) ^{14}C. *Biochem. Preps.* **9**, 79 (1962) *J.B.C.* **237**, PC2043 (1962)	*C.A.* **49**, 10536*g* (1955) *Mikrochim. Acta* **1956**, 1818 *J.B.C.* **227**, 649 (1957) *Clinica chim. Acta* **5**, 415 (1960)	Soln. oxidizes spontaneously in air. Aq. soln. colourless at acid pH, yellow in alkali. Spectrum, λ_{max} (ε) 368 mμ (4050), 267 mμ (7630), 228 mμ (19 000) at pH 7. Hydrobromide, DL-, s. H_2O, M.p. 233 d. Sulphate, DL-, M.p. 175.
		s. H_2O; i. MeOH, EtOH, acet., eth.	*Biochem. Preps.* **8**, 62 (1961) *Bull. chem. Soc. Japan* **35**, 2006 (1962) *Ber.* **91**, 1359 (1958)	Block & Bolling, p. 69 *B.J.* **40**, 470 (1946) *B.J.* **53**, 431 (1953) *See also* General methods	Most methods of synthesis yield initially a mixture of DL-hydroxylysine (*threo*-configuration) and DL-*allo*hydroxylysine (*erythro*-configuration). Separation of normal and *allo*- forms by ion exchange, *J.B.C.* **213**, 249 (1955). *N,N′*-Dibenzoyl-DL-hydroxylysine, M.p. 139–41. *N,N′*-BisDNP deriv., M.p. 80–100. Dibenzyloxycarbonyl-δ-lactone, M.p. 137–41. Monopicrate, M.p. 237 d. Dipicrate, M.p. 198 d.

No.	Name	Synonyms	Formula	M. wt.	Physical form	M.p.
122	L-δ-Hydroxy-lysine		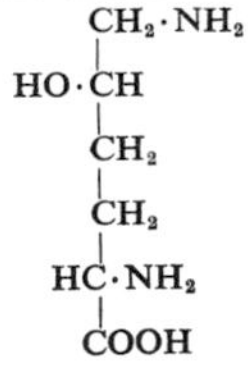	162·2; Hydro-chloride, 198·6	Hydrochloride, non-hygr. wh. cryst.	Hydro-chloride, 225 d.
123	*allo*-δ-Hydroxy-lysine		L-, 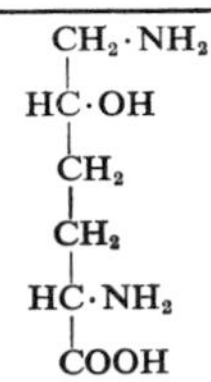	162·2; Hydro-chloride, 198·6	Hydrochloride, wh. cryst.	Hydro-chloride, 239–41 d.
124	DL-Hydroxy-proline	4-Hydroxy-DL-proline; 4-Hydroxy-2-pyrrolidine carboxylic acid	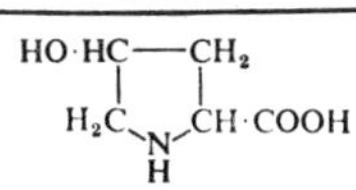	131·1		247 d. (255)
125	L-Hydroxy-proline		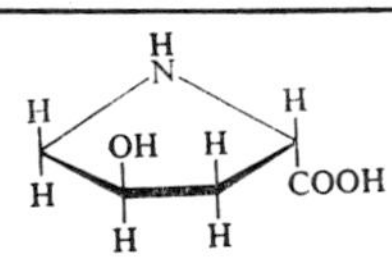	131·1	rh. plates or fine needles	273–4 d.
126	*allo*Hydroxy-proline		L- 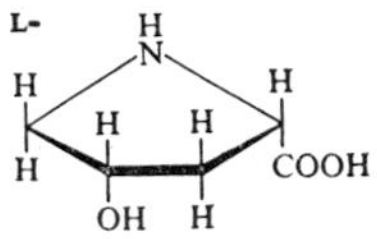	131·1		DL-, 238 (245 d.) L-, 240
127	5-Hydroxy-tryptamine	Serotonin; 5-Hydroxy-3-(2-amino-ethyl)-indole; 5-HT	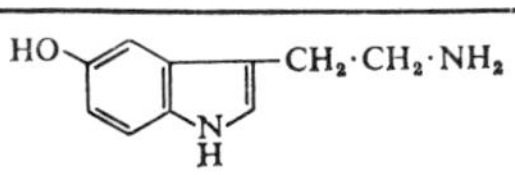	176·2; Creatin-ine sulphate salt hydrate, 405·4	small whitish lamellae. Creatinine sulphate salt, wh. prisms or plates + $1H_2O$	Creati[illegible] sulpha[illegible] salt, 219–21

	pK at 25°	Solubility	Preparation	Estimation	General remarks
8^{25} (c = 2 ase in Cl) ^{25} (c = 2 free n H_2O)	At I = 0·1, 1. 2·13[38] 2. 8·62[38] 3. 9·67[38]	s. H_2O; i. MeOH, EtOH, acet., eth.	ISOL. *Biochem. Preps.* **8**, 55 (1961) SYN. *Biochem. Preps.* **8**, 62 (1961)		Isomerizes in 6N-HCl at 120° to D-*allo*hydroxylysine, 10% in 12 hr, 25% in 24 hr, so that isolated material is partly isomerized and gives variable values for $[\alpha]^{25}_D$ of +14·9 to −4·5 for different preparations. *N,N'*-Dibenzoyl-L-hydroxylysine, M.p. 172. D-Hydroxylysine, SYN. *Biochem. Preps.* **8**, 62 (1961), rotations equal in magnitude but opposite in sign to those for L-hydroxylysine.
^{25} (c = 2 ase in Cl) ^{25} (c = 2 ase in H_2O)		s. H_2O; i. MeOH, EtOH, acet., eth.	*Biochem. Preps.* **8**, 62 (1962) *Bull chem. Soc. Japan* **35**, 2006 (1962) *Ber.* **91**, 1359 (1958)	*See* DL-Hydroxylysine and General methods	*N,N'*-BisDNP-DL-*allo*hydroxylysine, M.p. 97. Dibenzyloxycarbonyl-δ-lactone, M.p. 154–5·5. Monopicrate, M.p. 208–9 d. Dipicrate, M.p. 245–8 d. D-*allo*-Hydroxylysine has rotations equal in magnitude but opposite in sign to those for L-*allo*hydroxylysine.
		s. H_2O; v. sl. s. EtOH; i. eth.	Greenstein & Winitz, vol. 3, p. 2018 *Ber.* **90**, 1721 (1959) *J.A.C.S.* **76**, 139 (1954)	*J.B.C.* **184**, 299 (1950) *Z.P.C.* **311**, 41 (1958) *Analyt. Chem.* **35**, 1963 (1963) *Acta chem. scand.* **17**, 2499 (1963) *J.B.C.* **206**, 553 (1954) *J.B.C.* **223**, 687 (1956) *See also* General methods	Copper salt, i. H_2O, may be separated from copper salt of *allo*hydroxyproline by crystallization.
^{25} (c = 2 in l) ^{25} (c = 2 in	1. 1·82 2. 9·66	36·1^{25}, 51·7^{65} H_2O; v. sl. s. EtOH; i. eth.	Greenstein & Winitz, vol. 3, p. 2018 *J.B.C.* **234**, 1731 (1959) *Biochem. Preps.* **8**, 114 (1961)		*N*-Acetyl-L-hydroxyproline, M.p. 135, $[\alpha]^{25}_D$ −118·5 (c = 2 in H_2O). D-Hydroxyproline, SYN. *J.B.C.* **195**, 383 (1952), M.p. 274–5 d., rotations equal in magnitude but opposite in sign to those of L-hydroxyproline.
^{5} (c = 2 in l) ^{5} (c = 2 in		s. H_2O; v. sl. s. EtOH; i. eth.	Greenstein & Winitz, vol. 3, p. 2018 DL-, *J.A.C.S.* **85**, 1835 (1963) *Recl Trav. chim. Pays-Bas Belg.* **80**, 557 (1961) L-, ISOL. *Indian J. Chem.* **2**, 88 (1963); *C.A.* **58**, 13711*d* (1963) SYN. *Ber.* **92**, 2106 (1959)	*See* DL-Hydroxyproline and General methods	Cu salt, s. H_2O, i. EtOH. *N*-Acetyl-L-*allo*hydroxyproline, M.p. 144–5, $[\alpha]_D$ −91·5 (in H_2O). D-*allo*-Hydroxyproline, SYN. *J.B.C.* **195**, 383 (1952), rotations equal in magnitude but opposite in sign to those of L-*allo*hydroxyproline.
	1. 9·8 (NH_2) 2. 11·1 (OH)	Creatinine sulphate salt, 2^{27}, 10^{100} H_2O; s. gl. acetic; sl. s. MeOH, 95% EtOH; i. EtOH, acet., pyr., eth., benz., $CHCl_3$	*J. gen. Chem. U.S.S.R.* **34**, 1605 (1964) *J.C.S.* **1961**, 2919 *J. org. Chem.* **24**, 894 (1959) *J.C.S.* **1958**, 3493	Garattini & Valzelli, *Serotonin*, p. 9, Elsevier (1965) *Standard Methods of Clinical Chemistry*, vol. 4, p. 197, Academic Press (1963) *Meth. Enzymol.* **6**, 598 (1963) *Meth. biochem. Anal.* **6**, 95 (1958) *Analyt. Biochem.* **6**, 393 (1963)	Creatinine sulphate salt, soln. stable at all pHs under anaerobic conditions, oxidizes readily in air esp. at alkaline pHs; at neutral pH, soln. stable several hours at room temp. Spectrum, λ_{max} 275 and 295 mμ at pH 3·5, 275 and 322 mμ at pH 11·6, ϵ_{275} 5800 at pH 7. Hydrochloride, M.p. 167–8, hygr., unstable at room temp., photolabile. Picrate, M.p. 185–94 d. 5-Benzyloxytryptamine·HCl, M.p. 253–5.

No.	Name	Synonyms	Formula	M. wt.	Physical form	M.p.
128	DL-5-Hydroxy-tryptophan		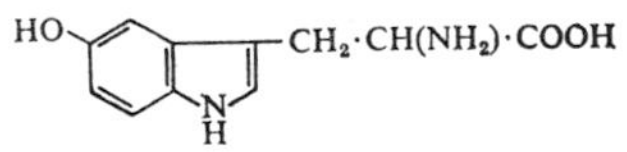	220·2	col. rods	DL-, 293… L-, 273 d… D-, 274 d…
129	Hydroxy-tyramine	DOPA amine; 4-(2-Amino-ethyl)pyro-catechol; 2-(3,4-Dihydroxy-phenyl)-ethylamine	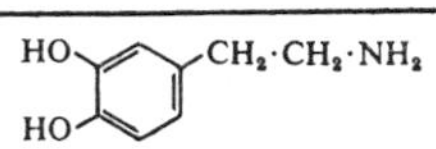	153·2	short wh. prisms from H_2O, rapidly darkening on exposure to air	
130	Hypotaurine	2-Aminoethane-sulphinic acid	$H_2N\cdot CH_2\cdot CH_2\cdot SO_2H$	109·1; Hydro-chloride, 145·6	wh. needles. Hydrochloride, sl. yel. in dry state	171–8
131	Indole	2,3-Benzo-pyrrole	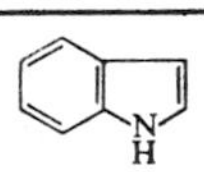	117·1	pale yel. leaflets	52–53, B.p. 2…
132	Indoleacetic acid	3-Indolylacetic acid; Hetero-auxin	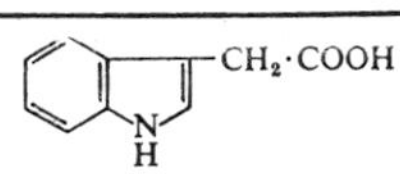	175·2	leaflets; rh. micro-cryst. from dichloroethane	165 d. (162–…
133	3-Iodotyrosine	β-(p-Hydroxy-3-iodophenyl)-alanine; Mono-iodotyrosine; MIT	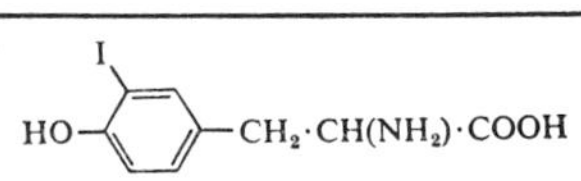	307·1	DL-, rounded plates+1H_2O; L-, anhyd. needles	DL-, … L-, 2…

	pK_a *at 25°*	*Solubility*	*Preparation*	*Estimation*	*General remarks*
5^{22} (c = 1 in ^{22} (c = 1 in Cl) ^{22} (c = 1 in		1^{5}, $5{\cdot}5^{100}$ H_2O	*J.A.C.S.* **76,** 5579 (1954) *J. org. Chem.* **22,** 306 (1957) Greenstein & Winitz, vol. 3 p. 2734 *Biochem. Preps.* **9,** 92 (1962)	*J.B.C.* **224,** 803 (1957) *Meth. biochem. Anal.* **6,** 95 (1958) *See also* General methods	Cryst. solid stable. Acid soln. stable for a year or more at −10° in air. At higher temps. and neutral or alkaline pH, increasingly sensitive to O_2. Decomp. avoided by inert atmosphere, aq. soln. may be autoclaved in absence of O_2. Spectrum, λ_{max} 278 mμ ε 5560, inflexions at 291 and 299 mμ at pH 6. At pH 11, λ_{max} 278 and 324 mμ. 5-Benzyloxytryptophan, M.p. 280 d. *N*-Benzyloxycarbonyl-5-benzyloxytryptophan, DL-, M.p. 132–3; L-, M.p. 97–99, $[\alpha]^{22}_{D}$ −10·1 (c = 1 in EtOH). Picrolonate, L-, M.p. 184–6 d.
	1. 8·9 (OH gps) 2. 10·6 (NH_2)	s. H_2O	*Ber.* **43,** 189 (1910) *Helv. chim. Acta* **6,** 54 (1923) ^{14}C. *J.C.S.* **1954,** 381	*Pharmac. Rev.* **11,** 300 (1959) *Biochem. Pharmac.* **7,** 181 (1961) *Meth. med. Res.* **9,** 130 (1961)	Spontaneously oxidizes in aq. soln. at alkaline pHs. Hydrochloride, needles from H_2O, v.s. H_2O, M.p. 237–41 d. Hydrobromide, plates, M.p. 212. Picrate, M.p. 189.
	1. 2·16 2. 9·56	v.s. H_2O, EtOH, acet.	*B.B.A.* **14,** 543 (1954) *B.B.A.* **18,** 358 (1955) *Acta chem. scand.* **12,** 146 (1958) ^{35}S. *Bull. Soc. chim. Fr.* **1958,** 820	*Analyt. Biochem.* **4,** 378 (1962)	Zn and Ba salts are hygr. and s. organic solvents.
		v.s. EtOH, eth.; s. hot H_2O, benz., pet. eth.	*Org. Synth.* Coll. **3,** 479 (1955)	*Analyt. Biochem.* **8,** 82 (1964) *B.J.* **78,** 790 (1961) *Meth. Enzymol.* **2,** 233, 238 (1955)	Intense faecal odour unless highly purified. β-Methylene group highly reactive, coupling readily with aldehydes and phenols.
	4·54	0·16 H_2O; v.s. EtOH; s. acet., eth.; sl. s. benz., dichloroethane; i. $CHCl_3$	*Ber.* **85,** 324 (1952) *J.A.C.S.* **75,** 3589 (1953) *Ber.* **91,** 1141 (1958) *J. org. Chem.* **28,** 589, 1246 (1963)	*Encyclopaedia of Plant Physiology,* vol. 14, pp. 501, 513, 521, Springer-Verlag (1961) *Modern Methods of Plant Analysis,* vol. 3, p. 565, Springer-Verlag (1955) *C.r. hebd. Séanc. Acad. Sci., Paris* **250,** 4035 (1960) *Analyt. Biochem.* **4,** 423 (1962)	Plant growth hormone. Aq. solns. are decomposed by u.v. radiation but are stable to visible light. Picrate, M.p. 128.
c = 5 in	1. 2·2 (COOH) 2. 8·7 (OH) 3. 9·1 (NH_2)	sl. s. cold H_2O; $6{\cdot}7^{100}$ H_2O	Greenstein & Winitz, vol. 3, p. 2259 *B.J.* **38,** 320 (1944) *Chemy. Ind.* **1956,** 21 ^{131}I. *Meth. Enzymol.* **4,** 856 (1957) *Nature, Lond.* **197,** 180 (1963)	Dorfman (ed.), *Methods in Hormone Research,* vol. 1, p. 351, Academic Press (1962) Gray and Bacharach (eds.), *Hormones in Blood,* p. 93, Academic Press (1961) *Meth. biochem. Anal.* **12,** 143 (1964)	Unstable in light, losing iodine.

No.	*Name*	*Synonyms*	*Formula*	*M. wt.*	*Physical form*	*M.p.*
134	DL-Isoleucine	α-Amino-β-methylvaleric acid	$(CH_3\cdot CH_2)(CH_3)CH\cdot CH(NH_2)\cdot COOH$	131·2	rh. or monocl. plates from dil. EtOH	292 d.
135	D-Isoleucine		CH_3 CH_2 $H_3C\cdot CH$ $H_2N\cdot CH$ $COOH$	131·2	plates	283–4 d.
136	L-Isoleucine		CH_3 CH_2 $HC\cdot CH_3$ $HC\cdot NH_2$ $COOH$	131·2	rh. leaflets from EtOH or plates	285–6 d
137	D-*allo*Iso-leucine	*allo*-α-Amino-β-methylvaleric acid	CH_3 CH_2 $HC\cdot CH_3$ $H_2N\cdot CH$ $COOH$	131·2	leaflets or wh. plates	274–5 d
138	L-*allo*Iso-leucine		CH_3 CH_2 $H_3C\cdot CH$ $HC\cdot NH_2$ $COOH$	131·2	leaflets or wh. plates	278–81
139	Kynurenic acid	γ-Hydroxy-quinoline-α-carboxylic acid; 4-Hydroxy-quinaldic acid	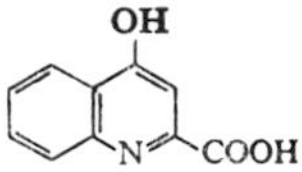	189·2	needles	Lose H 140–5, decom 277 (257–8
140	Kynurenine	3-Anthraniloyl-alanine	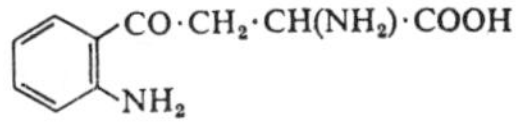	208·2; Hydrate, 214·2; Sulphate, 306·3; Sulphate hydrate, 324·3	leaflets + $\frac{1}{2}H_2O$ from H_2O; anhyd. needles from H_2O/EtOH. Sulphate, col. needles + $1H_2O$ from aq. solvents	DL-, 2 Sulph 173; L-, 19 Sulph 190 (178–

	pK at 25°	Solubility	Preparation	Estimation	General remarks
	1. 2·32 2. 9·76	2·23^{25}, 4·61^{75} H_2O; s. hot EtOH, hot gl. acetic; i. eth.	*See* General remarks	Block & Bolling, p. 295 *B.Z.* **320**, 115 (1950) *See also* General methods	Commercial preparations may contain DL-*allo*isoleucine. Method in *Org. Synth.* Coll. **3**, 495 (1955) gives such a mixture. Chromatographic separation of isoleucine and *allo*isoleucine, *J.B.C.* **207**, 77 (1954). Acetyl-DL-isoleucine, M.p. 116. *N*-DNP-DL-isoleucine, M.p. 168–72.
5^{25} (c = 1 in Cl) 4^{25} (c = 1 in		s. H_2O; i. eth.	*Biochem. Preps.* **3**, 84 (1953)		Acetyl-D-isoleucine, M.p. 150, $[\alpha]^{25-27}$ −15 (c = 4 in EtOH).
5^{25} (c = 1 in Cl) 4^{25} (c = 1 in		4·12^{25}, 6·08^{75} H_2O; s. hot gl. acetic; 0·072^{20} EtOH; i. eth.	*Biochem. Preps.* **3**, 84 (1953)	*J.B.C.* **160**, 35 (1945) *J.B.C.* **161**, 705 (1945) *J.B.C.* **180**, 695 (1949)	Stable to hot mineral acid in the presence of carbohydrate. The method of estimation in *J.B.C.* **180**, 695 (1949) takes into account the presence of the *allo*- isomer in the standard. Acetyl-L-isoleucine, M.p. 150, $[\alpha]_D^{25-27}$ +15 (c = 4 in EtOH). *N*-DNP-L-isoleucine, M.p. 113. Phenylthiohydantoin, M.p. 173–5.
^{25} (c = 1 in Cl) ^{25} (c = 1 in			*J.B.C.* **188**, 647 (1951) *Biochem. Preps.* **3**, 84 (1953)	*See* DL-Isoleucine and General methods	Acetyl-D-*allo*isoleucine, M.p. 155–6, $[\alpha]_D^{25-27}$ −21·5 (c = 4 in EtOH). Acetyl-DL-*allo*isoleucine, M.p. 168.
^{25} (c = 1 in l) ^{25} (c = 1 in	1. 2·27 2. 9·62	2·9^{20} H_2O; 0·1^{20} EtOH; i. eth.	*Biochem. Preps.* **3**, 84 (1953)		Acetyl-L-*allo*isoleucine, M.p. 155–6, $[\alpha]_D^{25-27}$ +21·5 (c = 4 in EtOH). *N*-DNP-L-*allo*isoleucine, M.p. 119.
		0·9^{100} H_2O; s. hot EtOH, alkalis; sl. s. eth., mineral acids, 50% aq. acetic	*J.A.C.S.* **68**, 2685 (1946) *J.B.C.* **113**, 125 (1936)	*J.B.C.* **131**, 469 (1939) *Z.P.C.* **293**, 106 (1953) *J.B.C.* **230**, 781 (1958) *J.B.C.* **219**, 985 (1956) *Mikrochim. Acta* **1956**, 1818	Extremely difficult to obtain pure. Spectrum, λ_{max} (ϵ) 332 mμ (9800) and 344 mμ (7920) at pH 7, *B.J.* **52**, 8 (1952). Methyl ester, M.p. 225. Ethyl ester, M.p. 215.
(c = 1 in (c = 1 sulphate		s. H_2O	*Biochem. Preps.* **3**, 108 (1953) Greenstein & Winitz, vol. 3, p. 2723 *J.A.C.S.* **76**, 1708 (1954) ISOL. *C.A.* **47**, 12489*d* (1953)	*J.B.C.* **195**, 515 (1952) *B.J.* **53**, 379 (1953) *Z.P.C.* **293**, 106 (1953) *Mikrochim. Acta* **1956**, 1818 *Analytica chim. Acta* **21**, 170 (1959) *J.B.C.* **219**, 985 (1956) *See also* General methods	Spectrum, λ_{max} (ϵ) 360 mμ (4500) 257 mμ (7500) 230 mμ (18 900) at pH 7, little change in range pH 2–12. *N'*-Formylkynurenine, M.p. 162, spectrum λ_{max} (ϵ) 260 mμ (10 980) 321 mμ (3750) at pH 7, SYN. *J.C.S.* **1952**, 137, ISOL. *B.B.A.* **31**, 301 (1959). N^{α}-Acetylkynurenine, DL-, M.p. 171; L-, M.p. 188, $[\alpha]_D^{25}$ +136·5 (c = 0·5 in 95% EtOH). Picrate, L-, M.p. 181d. D-Kynurenine and derivs. have similar properties to L-kynurenine but rotations have opposite sign.

1. Amino Acids, Amines, Amides, Peptides, and their Derivatives

No.	Name	Synonyms	Formula	M. wt.	Physical form	M.p.
141	DL-Lanthionine	β-Amino-β-carboxyethyl sulphide; β,β′-Thiodialanine	$S(CH_2\cdot CH(NH_2)\cdot COOH)_2$	208·2	hex. plates from NH_4OH; prisms or hex. plates from H_2O	290–2, decomp. 283–4
142	DL-Leucine	α-Amino*iso*caproic acid	$(CH_3)_2CH\cdot CH_2\cdot CH(NH_2)\cdot COOH$	131·2	leaflets from H_2O	293–5 d.
143	D-Leucine			131·2	plates from EtOH	293 d.
144	L-Leucine			131·2	col. leaflets from H_2O	293–5 d.
145	L-Leucylglycine		$(CH_3)_2CH\cdot CH_2\cdot CH(NH_2)\cdot CO-NH\cdot CH_2\cdot COOH$	188·2	needles from EtOH/H_2O	236
146	DL-Lysine	α,ε-Diaminocaproic acid	$H_2N\cdot CH_2\cdot (CH_2)_3\cdot CH(NH_2)\cdot COOH$	146·2; Monohydrochloride, 182·7; Dihydrochloride, 219·1		
147	D-Lysine			146·2	needles or hexagonal plates from EtOH	224 d.
148	L-Lysine			146·2	flat hexagonal plates from EtOH; needles from H_2O	224 d.
149	DL-Methionine	α-Amino-γ-methylmercaptobutyric acid	$CH_3\cdot S\cdot CH_2\cdot CH_2\cdot CH(NH_2)\cdot COOH$	149·2	clusters of narrow platelets from EtOH	281 d

	pK_a at 25°	*Solubility*	*Preparation*	*Estimation*	*General remarks*
…^{22} (c = 5 in …NaOH) …^{22} (c = 5 in …NaOH)		0·15^{25} H_2O; i. EtOH, eth.; s. acids, alkalis	SYN. *J.B.C.* **140**, 767 (1941) *J.C.S.* **1953**, 580 Greenstein & Winitz, vol. 3, p. 2675 ISOL. *J.B.C.* **144**, 93 (1942) *B.J.* **39**, 7 (1945)	*Arch. B.B.* **35**, 305 (1952) *Analyst* **80**, 875 (1955) Greenstein & Winitz, vol. 3, p. 2681 *See also* General methods	*meso*-Lanthionine, M.p. 306 (283–306 d.), triangular plates, solubility 0·022^{25} H_2O, SYN. *J.B.C.* **140**, 767 (1941), *Ber.* **94**, 2157 (1961), ISOL. *J.B.C.* **144**, 87 (1942). *N,N'*-Dibenzoyl-lanthionine, M.p. DL-, 184; *meso*-, 205; L-, 202–4; D-202–4.
	1. 2·33 2. 9·74	0·991^{25}, 2·276^{75} H_2O; 0·155^{25} 75% EtOH; 0·13^{25} 90% EtOH; i. EtOH	*Org. Synth.* Coll. **3**, 523 (1955)	Block & Bolling, p. 295 *P.S.E.B.M.* **45**, 289 (1940) *See also* General methods	Acetyl-DL-leucine, M.p. 159. *N*-DNP-DL-leucine, M.p. 132.
…0^{25} (c = 2·0 …HCl) …0^{25} (c = 2·0 …O)		2·20^{25}, 2·66^{50} H_2O	*J.B.C.* **194**, 455 (1952)		Acetyl-D-leucine, M.p. 185, $[\alpha]_D$ +21·3 (c = 2 in EtOH).
…^{25} (c = 2·0 …HCl) …^{25} (c = 2·0 …O)		2·19^{25}, 3·82^{75} H_2O; 0·017^{25} EtOH; 10·9 gl. acetic; i. eth.	*J.B.C.* **194**, 455 (1952)	*J.B.C.* **161**, 705 (1945) *J.B.C.* **160**, 35 (1945)	Sublimes. Stable to hot mineral acids in presence of carbohydrate. Copper salt, $(C_6H_{12}O_2N)_2Cu$. Acetyl-L-leucine, M.p. 185, $[\alpha]_D$ −21·3 (c = 2 in EtOH). β-Naphthalenesulphonate, M.p. 187–9. *N*-DNP-L-leucine, M.p. 94. Phenylthiohydantoin, M.p. 178.
…^{21} (c = 2·4 …O)	1. 3·25 2. 8·28	s. H_2O	Greenstein & Winitz, vol. 2, pp. 763, 1221 *Ber.* **93**, 2387 (1960) *Ber.* **94**, 2644 (1961)		Substrate for the assay of peptidases, especially leucine aminopeptidase, see *Meth. biochem. Anal.* **2**, 215 (1955); *Meth. Enzymol.* **2**, 88 (1955).
	At I = 0·1, 1. 2·16 2. 9·18 3. 10·79 (ε-NH_2)	s. H_2O; v. sl. s. EtOH	*Org. Synth.* Coll. **2**, 374 (1943) *J.A.C.S.* **71**, 1837 (1949)	Block & Bolling, p. 62 *See also* General methods	Monohydrochloride, M.p. 263–4. Dihydrochloride, M.p. 187–9. Diacetyl-DL-lysine, M.p. 141.
…^{25} (c = 2·0 …HCl) …^{25} (c = 2·0 …)		s. H_2O, acids; sl. s. EtOH, eth., $CHCl_3$	*J.B.C.* **182**, 451 (1950) *J.B.C.* **194**, 455 (1952)		
…^{25} (c = 2·0 …HCl) …^{25} (c = 2·0 …)		v.s. H_2O; v. sl. s. EtOH; i. eth.	*Biochem. Preps.* **1**, 63 (1949)	*B.J.* **39**, 46 (1945) *B.J.* **41**, vii (1947) *J.B.C.* **160**, 35 (1945) *J.B.C.* **161**, 705 (1945) *J.B.C.* **156**, 715 (1944)	Monohydrochloride, M.p. 263–4, v.s. H_2O, s. MeOH. Dihydrochloride, M.p. 192–3, v.s. H_2O, s. MeOH, i. EtOH. α-*N*-DNP-L-lysine, M.p. 260 d. ε-*N*-DNP-L-lysine·HCl+1H_2O, M.p. 186. α,ε-*N*-BisDNP-L-lysine, M.p. 170–4. ε-Phenylthiohydantoin, M.p. 162–4.
	1. 2·13 2. 9·28	3·38^{25}, 10·52^{75} H_2O	*Org. Synth.* Coll. **2**, 384 (1943) *Ber.* **83**, 265 (1950)	Block & Bolling, p. 214 *J.B.C.* **141**, 871 (1941) *J.B.C.* **156**, 293 (1944) *J.B.C.* **188**, 1 (1951) *See also* General methods	Acetyl-DL-methionine, M.p. 112. *N*-DNP-DL-methionine, M.p. 107–12. Phenhyltiohydantoin, M.p. 132.

No.	Name	Synonyms	Formula	M. wt.	Physical form	M.p.
150	D-Methionine			149·2		
151	L-Methionine			149·2	hexagonal plates	281 d.
152	Methionine sulphone	α-Amino-γ-methyl-sulphonyl-butyric acid	$CH_3\cdot SO_2\cdot CH_2\cdot CH_2\cdot CH(NH_2)\cdot COOH$	181·2	hex. cryst. from H_2O	DL-, 248–50 d L-, 257–8 D-, 256–8
153	Methionine sulphoxide	α-Amino-γ-methyl-sulphinyl-butyric acid	$CH_3\cdot SO\cdot CH_2\cdot CH_2\cdot CH(NH_2)\cdot COOH$	165·2	wh. powder	Decomp. 225–31 (mixture all four isomers)
154	Methylamine	Aminomethane	CH_3NH_2	31·1; Hydro-chloride 67·5	col. gas	−92·5, B.p. −6
155	β-Methyl-aspartic acid	3-Methyl-aspartic acid	COOH | $CH\cdot CH_3$ | $CH\cdot NH_2$ | COOH	147·1	DL-*threo*-, hex. prisms from H_2O; wh. cryst. from aq. EtOH	DL-*threo*, 274–5; L-*threo*, 254–6
156	Methyl-guanidine		$HN{=}C(NH\cdot CH_3)(NH_2)$	73·1	deliq. alkaline mass	
157	L-1-Methyl-histidine	*N*-Methyl-imidazole-5-alanine; α-Amino-β-(1-methyl-5-imidazole)-propionic acid	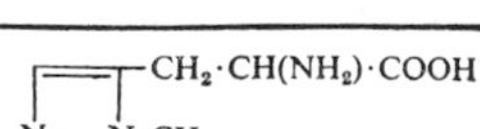	169·2; Hydrate, 187·2	needles + $1H_2O$, loses H_2O *in vacuo*	Loses H_2O 100; 248–9

]$_D$	pK_a at 25°	*Solubility*	*Preparation*	*Estimation*	*General remarks*
23·2[25] (c = 0·5– 0 in 5N-HCl) 10·0[25] (c = 0·5– 0 in H_2O)			*J.B.C.* **194,** 455 (1952)	*Science* **106,** 319, 589 (1947)	Acetyl-D-methionine, M.p. 105.
23·2[25] (c = 0·5– 0 in 5N-HCl) 10·0[25] (c = 0·5– 0 in H_2O)		s. H_2O; i. eth., EtOH	*J.B.C.* **194,** 455 (1952)	*J.B.C.* **160,** 35 (1945) *J.B.C.* **166,** 321 (1946) *J.B.C.* **166,** 161 (1946)	Losses occur during hydrolysis of protein in presence of carbohydrate. Acetyl-L-methionine, M.p. 104.
, +13·5[28] (c = 2·1 H_2O) 30·3[28] (c = 2·1 N-HCl) , −11·6[18] (c = 2·4 H_2O)		s. H_2O (< sulphoxide, >methionine); i. 95% EtOH	*Biochem. Preps.* **4,** 83 (1955) *Helv. chim. Acta* **44,** 61 (1961) D- & L-, *C.A.* **51,** 17747*i* (1957)	*B.J.* **74,** 37P (1960) *See also* General methods	More stable than the sulphoxide. *N*-Formyl-DL-methionine sulphone, M.p. 107–9.
, 71·6[24-26] (c = 0·5–) in H_2O) 57·6[24-26] (c = 0·5–) in 5N-HCl) -, 99·0[24-26] (c = 0·5–) in H_2O) 127·2[24-26] (c = 0·5– in 5N-HCl)		> 66[25] H_2O; sl. s. EtOH; i. acet., eth.	*Biochem. Preps.* **4,** 80 (1955) All isomers, *C.A.* **54,** 13010*g* (1960)	*See* General methods	Stable in aq. soln. Four possible stereoisomers, as S atom forms asymmetric centre. These isomers are sometimes written as L*l*-, L*d*-, D*l*-, D*d*-. *N*-Benzylmethionine sulphoxide, M.p. 181–2 (mixture of isomers).
	10·79[20], 10·47[30] 10·16[40]	1153·9[12·5] ml gas per ml H_2O; v. s. MeOH; ∞ eth.	*Org. Synth.* **Coll. 1,** 340 (1932)	Conway, *Micro-diffusion Analysis and Volumetric Error*, p. 195, Crosby, Lockwood & Son, London (1962) *Nature, Lond.* **197,** 290 (1963) *J. Chromat.* **12,** 358 (1963)	Methylamine hydrochloride, deliq. leaflets from EtOH, M.p. 226, B.p. 230[15], v.s. H_2O, 23[78] EtOH, i. eth., acet., $CHCl_3$. Picrate, M.p. 215.
hreo-, 12·4[26] (c = 1 in O) 13·3[24] (c = 3 in HCl) *rythro-*, 24·5 (in H_2O) 2·5 (in 3N-HCl)	1. — 2. 3·5 (COOH) 3. 9·9 (NH_2)	sl. s. (L-*threo-*, 0·57[25]) H_2O, EtOH; i. eth., acet.	*Biochem. Preps.* **8,** 89, 93, 96 (1961) *J. org. Chem.* **27,** 2959 (1962) Greenstein & Winitz, vol. 3, p. 2423	L-*threo-*, *Arch. B.B.* **78,** 468 (1958) *See also* General methods	Natural compd. is L-*threo-* isomer. Rotations of D-*threo-* and D-*erythro*-isomers are equal in size but opposite in sign to those of the corresponding L-isomers. Separation of *threo-* and *erythro*-isomers, *J.B.C.* **234,** 320 (1959). Derivs. of *threo-β*-methyl-DL-aspartic acid; *N*-Acetyl, sl. s. acet., M.p. 181–2; *N*-Chloroacetyl, M.p. 157–8; *N*-Benzoyl, M.p. 181–2; *N*-Benzyloxycarbonyl, M.p. 149–50.
	13·4	v.s. H_2O; s. EtOH		*Meth. biochem. Anal.* **7,** 193 (1959) *Nature, Lond.* **183,** 1053 (1959) *Analyt. Biochem.* **1,** 221 (1960)	Poisonous. Monohydrochloride, v. hygr. cryst., v.s. H_2O, sl. s. EtOH. Sulphate, cryst., M.p. 239–40, v.s. H_2O, i. EtOH. Picrate, M.p. 201·5.
5·8[18] (c = 3·9 H_2O)	1. 1·69 (COOH) 2. 6·48 (imidazole) 3. 8·85 (NH_2)	20[25] H_2O	SYN. *J.A.C.S.* **79,** 2249 (1957) ISOL. *Z.P.C.* **189,** 80 (1930)	*See* General methods	Appears to be some racemization during synthesis. Pauly reaction positive. Dihydrochloride, $[\alpha]_D^{20}$ −17·6 (c = 0·66 in H_2O). Diflavianate, M.p. 235 d. Picrolonate, M.p. 246 d.

No.	Name	Synonyms	Formula	M. wt.	Physical form	M.p.
158	L-3-Methyl-histidine	1-Methyl-imidazole-4-alanine; α-Amino-β-(1-methyl-4-imidazole)-propionic acid	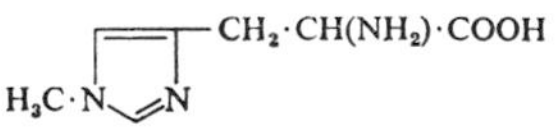	169·2		
159	N^6-Methyl-DL-lysine	ε-*N*-Methyl-lysine	$CH_3\cdot NH\cdot (CH_2)_4\cdot CH(NH_2)\cdot COOH$	160·2; Anhyd, Hydro-chloride, 196·7	hygr. syrup; Hydrochloride, rosettes + $1H_2O$ from H_2O	Hydro-bromide, 234–5
160	Methyl-methionine sulphonium bromide	Methionine methyl sulphonium bromide; (3-Amino-3-carboxy-propyl)-dimethyl-sulphonium bromide	$(CH_3)_2\cdot \overset{+}{S}\cdot CH_2\cdot CH_2\cdot CH(NH_2)\cdot COOH$ Br^-	Free cation, 163·2; Chloride, 199·7; Bromide, 244·2	Bromide, white needles or platelets from aq. EtOH	Bromide, L-, 139 d.; DL-, 139–41 d.
161	Monomethyl-ethanolamine	2-Methylamino-ethanol; Methylhydroxy-ethylamine	$CH_3\cdot NH\cdot CH_2\cdot CH_2OH$	75·1	thick oil	B.p. 169–70
162	Noradrenaline	Arterenol; Norepinephrine; 1-(3,4-Di-hydroxyphenyl)-2-aminoethanol; 4-(α-Hydroxy-β-aminoethyl)-catechol	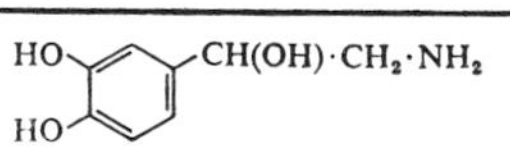	169·2; Hydro-chloride, 205·6	col. cryst. solid	D-, 216–18; L-, 215–17; DL-, 188–91
163	DL-Norleucine	2-Amino-hexanoic acid; α-Butylglycine; Glycoleucine	$CH_3\cdot (CH_2)_3\cdot CH(NH_2)\cdot COOH$	131·2	shiny leaflets	295 d. (273–327)
164	D-Norleucine			131·2	leaflets from H_2O	301 d.
165	L-Norleucine			131·2	hex. leaflets from H_2O	301 d.
166	DL-Norvaline	α-Amino-*n*-valeric acid; α-Propyl-glycine	$CH_3\cdot CH_2\cdot CH_2\cdot CH(NH_2)\cdot COOH$	117·1	leaflets from H_2O	303 (sealed tube), 285-

$]_D^t$	pK_a at 25°	*Solubility*	*Preparation*	*Estimation*	*General remarks*
-26·5[26] (c = 2·1 H₂O)		s. H_2O	*J.B.C.* **206**, 825 (1954) *J.A.C.S.* **79**, 2249 (1957)	*See* General methods	Appears to be some racemization during synthesis. Pauly reaction negative. Hydrochloride, $[\alpha]_D^{27}$ +13·5 (c = 1·9 in N-HCl).
		s. H_2O, mineral acids, EtOH. Hydrochloride, s. H_2O, mineral acids, EtOH; v. sl. s. pyr.; i. benz.	*B.J.* **38**, 125 (1944) *Can. J. Chem.* **40**, 1626 (1962)	*See* General methods	Very difficult to obtain cryst. in free state. ε-*N*-Benzoyl-ε-*N*-methyl-lysine, prisms, v.s. EtOH, s. H_2O, mineral acids, M.p. 232. Picrate, M.p. 227–9 d., s. H_2O, v.s. EtOH. Picrolonate, +1H_2O from H_2O, M.p. 228.
		s. H_2O; 0·439[25] MeOH; 0·012[25] EtOH; i. eth., acet.	ISOL. *J.A.C.S.* **76**, 115 (1954) *Chemy Ind.* **1954**, 729 SYN. *J.B.C.* **207**, 97 (1954) *J. org. Chem.* **25**, 804 (1960)	*J.A.C.S.* **76**, 115 (1954) *See also* General methods	Dry bromide slowly decomp. especially in light. The free base and its salts decomp. to homoserine, methionine sulphoxide, and dimethyl sulphide in boiling aq. soln. especially in presence of alkalis. Chloride, DL-, M.p. 134–8 d. Iodide, DL-, M.p. 150 d. Picrate, L-, M.p. 153–8. Chloroplatinate, L-, M.p. 193–201.
	9·77 (NH)	s. H_2O, EtOH, eth., $CHCl_3$	*Ber.* **31**, 1069 (1898)	*Nature, Lond.* **197**, 290 (1963)	Hydrochloride, wh. cryst. powder, i. eth. Tetrachloroaurate, prisms, M.p. 145–6. Platinichloride, M.p. 125–30 d. Picrate, M.p. 149. 3,5-Dinitrobenzoyl ester, M.p. 196–7.
37·3[25] (c = 5 in O+1 equiv. HCl) 37·4[26] (c = 5 in O+1 equiv. HCl)	1. 8·82 (OH) 2. 9·98 (NH_2)	s. mineral acids, alkalis; sl. s. H_2O, MeOH, EtOH, eth.	ISOL. *Acta chem. scand.* **3**, 305 (1949) SYN. *J.A.C.S.* **70**, 2067 (1948) *J.A.C.S.* **77**, 2896 (1955) ^{14}C. *Bull. Soc. chim. Fr.* **1961**, 2255 *J.A.C.S.* **75**, 1757 (1953)	*Br. J. Pharmac. Chemother.* **4**, 401 (1949) *Pharmac. Rev.* **11**, 241 (1959) *Arch. B.B.* **85**, 345 (1959) *Meth. med. Res.* **9**, 125 (1961) *Meth. biochem. Anal.* **2**, 57 (1955)	Sympathomimetic action. Major adrenergic effector at post-ganglionic effector junctions. Pressor effect, mainly due to peripheral vasoconstriction. Natural compd. has D-configuration relative to mandelic acid. Aq. solns. slowly racemize and oxidize. Stability maximal at about pH 4. Solns. may be autoclaved under anaerobic conditions at pH 3·6. Hydrochloride, DL-, M.p. 141; D-, M.p. 145–7, $[\alpha]_D^{25}$ −40 (c = 6 in H_2O). Oxalate, DL-, M.p. 175.
	1. 2·34 2. 9·83	1·07[20], 5·23[100] H_2O; 0·267[25] 75% EtOH; 0·0137[25] EtOH; 0·112[25] MeOH; 0·00104[25] acet.	*Org. Synth.* Coll. 1, 40 (1932) *J. org. Chem.* **24**, 1397, 1726 (1959) Greenstein & Winitz, vol. 3, p. 2381	*Analyt. Chem.* **32**, 162 (1960) *Analytica chim. Acta* **25**, 136 (1961) *See also* General methods	Copper salt, i. H_2O. *N*-Acetyl-DL-norleucine, rhombs from acet., M.p. 105–8. *N*-Benzoyl-DL-norleucine, M.p. 132–6.
4·5[25] (c = 1–2 N-HCl) 2·1[25] (c = 4 in Cl) ·7[25] (c = 1–2 H_2O)		1·6[19] H_2O	*J.B.C.* **182**, 451 (1950) *J.A.C.S.* **73**, 3366 (1951) *Ber.* **91**, 2410 (1958)		Sublimes. Hydrochloride, M.p. 270 (sublimes), $[\alpha]_D^{20}$ −23·3 (c = 1·5 in 10% HCl). *N*-Acetyl-D-norleucine, M.p. 114–15, $[\alpha]_D^{25}$ +5·0 (c = 4 in H_2O) −0·8 (c = 2 in EtOH) +19·6 (c = 4 in MeOH).
4·5[25] (c = 1–2 N-HCl) 1·8[25] (c = 4 in Cl) 7[25] (c = 1–2 H_2O)		1·5[25] H_2O; i. EtOH	*J.B.C.* **182**, 451 (1950) *J.A.C.S.* **73**, 3366 (1951) *Ber.* **91**, 2410 (1958)		Sublimes. Hydrochloride, M.p. 280–5 (sublimes), $[\alpha]_D^{20}$ +23·9 (c = 1·2 in 10% HCl). *N*-Acetyl-L-norleucine, $[\alpha]_D^{25}$ −19·4 (c = 4·0 in MeOH).
	1. 2·32 2. 9·81	10·7[15] H_2O; sl. s. EtOH; i. $CHCl_3$, eth., acet., pet. eth.	*J.A.C.S.* **82**, 4422 (1960) Greenstein & Winitz, vol. 3, p. 2381	*Analytica chim. Acta* **11**, 559 (1954) *Analyt. Chem.* **32**, 162 (1960) *See also* General methods	Acetyl-DL-norvaline, M.p. 115. *N*-Benzoyl-DL-norvaline, M.p. 152. Benzyloxycarbonyl-DL-norvaline, M.p. 83–85.

No.	Name	Synonyms	Formula	M. wt.	Physical form	M.p.
167	L-Norvaline			117·1	leaflets or needles from H_2O	291–5 d. (300–3 in sealed tube)
168	D-Octopine	N^{α}-(1-Carboxyethyl)-arginine: α,α′-Imino-(δ-guanido-valeric acid)-propionic acid; Formerly L-Octopine	$(HN)(H_2N)C \cdot NH \cdot (CH_2)_3 \cdot CH(COOH)-NH-CH(CH_3) \cdot COOH$	246·3	col. needles from dil. EtOH	262–3 d. (283–4 d.)
169	DL-Ornithine	α,δ-Diaminovaleric acid; 2,5-Diaminopentanoic acid	$H_2N \cdot CH_2 \cdot CH_2 \cdot CH_2 \cdot CH(NH_2) \cdot COOH$	132·2; Hydrochloride, 168·6; Dihydrochloride 205·1	syrup, cryst. only with difficulty. Hydrochloride, wh. granular solid	195; Monohydrochloride, 225–32 d.
170	D-Ornithine			132·2		
171	L-Ornithine			132·2; Monohydrochloride, 168·6; Dihydrochloride, 205·1	syrup, cryst. only with difficulty	226–7; Monohydrochloride, 230–2 d.; Dihydrochloride, 190–203

)	pK_a *at* 25°	*Solubility*	*Preparation*	*Estimation*	*General remarks*
·1^{25} (c = 1–2 N-HCl) ·0^{25} (c = 1–2 $_2$O)		10·75^{15} H_2O; sl. s. EtOH; i. eth., $CHCl_3$, acet., pet. eth.	*J.B.C.* **182**, 451 (1950) *J.B.C.* **194**, 455 (1952) *Ber.* **91**, 2410 (1958)		Hydrochloride, M.p. 223–4, $[\alpha]_D^{20}$ +23·7 (c = 5·3 in 5N-HCl). Copper salt, i. H_2O. Chloroacetyl-L-norvaline, M.p. 104, $[\alpha]_D$ −25·8 (c = 2 in H_2O). Acetyl-D-norvaline, M.p. 100, $[\alpha]_D$+35·0 (in H_2O).
·6^{24} (c = 1 in) ·0^{25} (c = 2 in Cl)	1. 1·36 (COOH) 2. 2·40 (COOH) 3. 8·76 (imino) 4. 11·3 (guanido)	s. H_2O; i. EtOH, acet.	SYN. *J. org. Chem.* **11**, 368 (1946) Greenstein & Winitz, vol. 3, p. 2548 *J.A.C.S.* **79**, 652 (1957) ISOL. *J.B.C.* **127**, 565 (1939)	See *Meth. biochem. Anal.* **7**, 193 (1959)	In *iso*octopine, the 'arginine centre' and the 'alanine centre' have the same configuration; in octopine the configurations are opposite. Isomers named from the configuration of the 'alanine centre'; hence natural form is D-octopine. Prep. and properties of all stereoisomers, *J.A.C.S.* **79**, 652 (1957). L-*iso*-Octopine, M.p. 258–9, $[\alpha]_D^{25}$ +26·0 (c = 2 in H_2O), +26·0 (c = 2 in 5N-HCl). D-Octopine monopicrate, M.p. 222–30 d.
	1. 1·71 (COOH) 2. 8·69 (α-NH_2) 3. 10·76 (δ-NH_2)	Monohydrochloride, s. H_2O, acids, alkalis; i. MeOH, EtOH, eth. Dihydrochloride, v.s. MeOH, EtOH	*Biochem. Preps.* **3**, 96 (1953) *J. org. Chem.* **26**, 2602 (1961) *J. org. Chem.* **28**, 1942 (1963) Greenstein & Winitz, vol. 3, p. 2477 ^{14}C. *J.A.C.S.* **73**, 1000 (1951)	*J.B.C.* **199**, 91 (1952) *See also* General methods	Dichloroacetyl-DL-ornithine, M.p. 105. Dibenzoyl-DL-ornithine, M.p. 184–8. α-*N*-DNP-DL-ornithine, M.p. 227 d. Dipicrate, M.p. 198 (196–208).
^{25} (c = 2·0 HCl) ^{25} (c = 2·0))		s. H_2O, acids	*J.B.C.* **188**, 643 (1951) *J.B.C.* **194**, 455 (1952) *Ber.* **91**, 2418 (1958) *Colln. Czech. chem. Commun.* **24**, 1993 (1959); *C.A.* **53**, 19904*i* (1959) Greenstein & Winitz, vol. 3, p. 2477		Monohydrochloride, M.p. 236–7, $[\alpha]_D^{20}$ −22·5 (c = 5·5 in 6N-HCl). Dihydrochloride, M.p. 194–5, $[\alpha]_D^{27}$ −16·4 (c = 4 in H_2O) −18·2 (in 5N-HCl). Dichloroacetyl-D-ornithine, M.p. 112, $[\alpha]_D$ −15·1 (c = 2 in EtOH).
^{25} (c = 2·0 HCl) ^{5} (c = 2·0) ochloride, ^{5} (c = 4)		v.s. H_2O, EtOH; sl. s. eth. Monohydrochloride, s. H_2O; i. MeOH, EtOH, eth. Dihydrochloride, v.s. MeOH, EtOH	*Biochem. Preps.* **3**, 97 (1953) *Ber.* **91**, 2418 (1958) *Colln. Czech. chem. Commun.* **24**, 1993 (1959); *C.A.* **53**, 19904*i* (1959) Greenstein & Winitz, vol. 3, p. 2477	*B.J.* 39, 46 (1945) *B.J.* **41**, vii (1947)	Sulphate+1H_2O, M.p. 182. Monopicrate, M.p. 208. Dipicrate, M.p. 206–8 d. δ-Acetyl-L-ornithine, $[\alpha]_D$ +24·0 (c = 1 in 5N-HCl). α-Acetyl-L-ornithine, $[\alpha]_D$ −7·5 (c = 2 in 5N-HCl). δ-*N*-DNP-L-ornithine·HCl+1H_2O, M.p. 223 d. α-Benzoyl-L-ornithine, M.p. 225–6.

No.	*Name*	*Synonyms*	*Formula*	*M. wt.*	*Physical form*	*M.p.*
172	Oxytocin	Oxytocic hormone	CyS → Tyr → Ile → Gln → Asn → CyS → Pro → Leu → Gly—H_2N (disulfide bridge CyS–CyS)	1007	amorph. powder	
173	DL-Phenyl-alanine	α-Amino-β-phenyl-propionic acid; α-Aminohydro-cinnamic acid	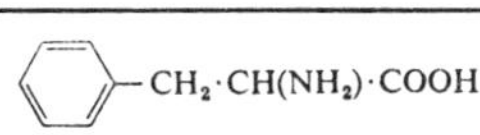	165·2	leaflets or prisms from H_2O or EtOH	271–3 d.
174	D-Phenyl-alanine			165·2	leaflets from H_2O	283–4 d. (196 d.)
175	L-Phenyl-alanine			165·2	leaflets from conc. aq. soln., needles from dil. soln.	283–4 d.
176	Picolinic acid	Pyridine-2-carboxylic acid	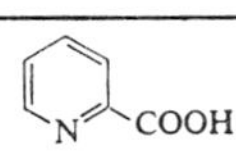	123·1	needles from H_2O, EtOH and benz.	136 (133–8)
177	L-Pipecolic acid	Pipecolinic acid; Piperidine-2-carboxylic acid; Homoproline	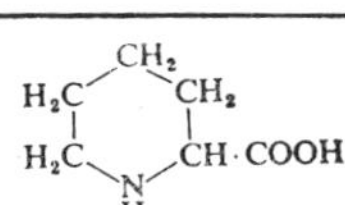	129·2	col. needles after sublimation *in vacuo*; plates from EtOH	260 d. (260–7

	pK_a at 25°	*Solubility*	*Preparation*	*Estimation*	*General remarks*
2^{22} (c = 0·53 O)	Isoelectric point, 7·7	s. H_2O; sl. s. acet.	SYN. *J.A.C.S.* **81**, 2504 (1959) *Helv. chim. Acta* **38**, 1491 (1955) ISOL. *J.B.C.* **233**, 116 (1958)	Caldeyro-Barcia & Heller (eds.), *Oxytocin*, p. 380, Pergamon (1961) Dorfman (ed.), *Methods in Hormone Research*, vol. 2, p. 495, Academic Press (1962) Gray & Bacharach (eds.), *Hormones in Blood*, p. 149, Academic Press (1961) *Endocrinology*, **71**, 196 (1962) *Br. J. Pharmac. Chemother.* **19**, 136 (1962)	Principal actions; causes contraction of uterine muscle, ejection of milk from lactating mammary gland and, in birds, lowering of blood pressure. Pure material contains *ca.* 500 units/mg. Stable in acid, unstable in alkali. Activity destroyed by reducing agents, e.g. thioglycollate. Flavianate, silky needles, M.p. 182–7.
	1. 2·16 2. 9·18	1·42^{25}, 3·71^{75} H_2O; sl. s. EtOH; v. sl. s. eth.	*Org. Synth.* Coll. **2**, 489 (1943) *Org. Synth.* Coll. **3**, 705 (1955)	Block & Bolling, p. 136 *See also* General methods	Spectrum, λ_{max} 257·5 mμ ϵ 195 in 0·1N-HCl, little change with pH; spectrum contains several minor peaks between 240 and 270 mμ, see *Adv. Protein Chem.* **7**, 319 (1952). Acetyl-DL-phenylalanine, M.p. 146. *N*-DNP-DL-phenylalanine, M.p. 204–6 d. Phenylthiohydantoin, M.p. 187.
^{5} (c = 1–2 Cl) ^{5} (c = 1–2)		3^{25} H_2O; v. sl. s. hot EtOH; i. eth., acet.	*J.B.C.* **180**, 473 (1949) *J.B.C.* **194**, 455 (1952)	*J.B.C.* **181**, 273 (1949)	Benzoyl-D-phenylalanine, M.p. 146–8.
^{5} (c = 1–2 Cl) ^{5} (c = 1–2)		2·96^{25}, 6·624^{75} H_2O; i. EtOH, eth.	*J.B.C.* **143**, 121 (1942) *J.B.C.* **180**, 473 (1949) *J.B.C.* **194**, 455 (1952)	*J.B.C.* **181**, 273 (1949) *J.B.C.* **160**, 35 (1945) *J.B.C.* **161**, 643 (1945)	Unstable to alkali; 75% destruction in 5 hr at 110–15° in 5N-NaOH. *N*-DNP-L-phenylalanine, M.p. 189.
	1. 1·0 2. 5·42	v.s. gl. acetic; s. H_2O, MeOH, toluene; 5·44^{25} EtOH; sl. s. benz.; i. eth., $CHCl_3$, CS_2, pet. eth.	*Ber.* **50**, 385 (1917) *Org. Synth.* Coll. **3**, 740 (1955) *J.A.C.S.* **74**, 5515 (1952) *C.r. hebd. Séanc. Acad. Sci., Paris* **248**, 252 (1959)		Sublimes. Hydrochloride, sl. s. EtOH, i. eth., M.p. 225–30 d. (210–12, slow heating). Methyl ester, M.p. 14, B.p. 232. Phenyl ester, M.p. 82. Anilide, M.p. 76. Platinichloride, M.p. 215–16.
(c = 5 in (c = 2 in		v.s. H_2O; s. MeOH; sl. s. EtOH; i. acet., eth.	SYN. *Ber.* **65**, 927 (1932) *Can. J. Chem.* **37**, 829 (1959) Greenstein & Winitz, vol. 3, p. 2533 ^{14}C. *C.r. hebd. Séanc. Acad. Sci., Paris* **257**, 788 (1963) *J.A.C.S.* **81**, 4756 (1959) ISOL. *B.J.* **53**, 474 (1953) *J.A.C.S.* **76**, 2908 (1954)	DL-, *J.B.C.* **208**, 603 (1954) *Analyt. Chem.* **28**, 855 (1956) *J.B.C.* **223**, 687 (1956) *See also* General methods	Monohydrochloride, M.p. 258–9, $[\alpha]^{23}_D$ −10·5 (c = 9·8 in H_2O). *N*-Benzoyl-L-pipecolic acid, M.p. 145. DL-Pipecolic acid, M.p. 264 (258–80), SYN. *B.J.* **53**, 474 (1953); monohydrochloride, M.p. 257–64. D-Pipecolic acid, $[\alpha]_D$ +26·0 (in H_2O); monohydrochloride, $[\alpha]^{25}_D$ +15·5 (in H_2O).

1. Amino Acids, Amines, Amides, Peptides, and their Derivatives

No.	Name	Synonyms	Formula	M. wt.	Physical form	M.p.
178	DL-Proline	Pyrrolidine-2-carboxylic acid	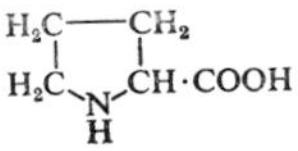	115·1	hygr. prisms from hot EtOH	213
179	D-Proline			115·1	hygr. prisms	206 (215–20
180	L-Proline			115·1	prisms from H_2O; needles from EtOH	220–2 d.
181	L-Prolyl-glycine		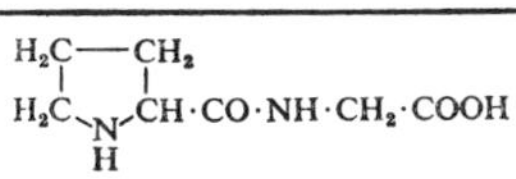	172·2; Hydrate, 190·2	rods or needles $+1H_2O$, sl. hygr.	236 d.
182	Propionyl-choline chloride		$(CH_3)_3\overset{+}{N}\cdot CH_2\cdot CH_2\cdot O\cdot CO\cdot CH_2\cdot CH_3$ Cl^-	195·7	hygr.	
183	Putrescine	1,4-Butane-diamine; Tetramethylene-diamine	$H_2N\cdot CH_2\cdot CH_2\cdot CH_2\cdot CH_2\cdot NH_2$	88·2; Dihydro-chloride, 161·1	col. leaflets melting to col. liq., d_4^{25} 0·877	27–28, B.p. 1[illegible]
184	L-2-Pyrrolidone-5-carboxylic acid	Glutaminic acid; Pyroglutamic acid; 5-Oxo-2-pyrrolidine-carboxylic acid; 5-Oxoproline	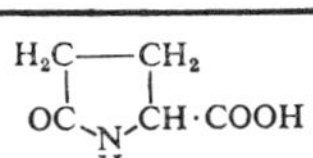	129·1	col. cryst.	159 (155–6
185	Δ^1-Pyrroline-5-carboxylic acid	1-Pyrroline-5-carboxylic acid	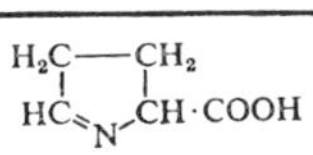	113·1; Hydro-chloride, 149·6	Hydrochloride, wh. solid	Hydr[illegible] chlor[illegible] chars 150
186	Quinolinic acid	Pyridine-2,3-dicarboxylic acid	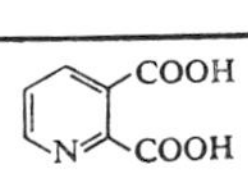	167·1	monocl. prisms from H_2O	190 d (rapi[illegible] heati[illegible] 110 d (slow heati[illegible]

...6	pK_a at 25°	*Solubility*	*Preparation*	*Estimation*	*General remarks*
	1. 1·95 2. 10·64	s. H_2O, EtOH; sl. s. $CHCl_3$, acet., benz.; i. eth.	*J.B.C.* **198**, 587 (1952)	*J.B.C.* **208**, 603 (1954) *B.B.A.* **5**, 81 (1950) *Z.P.C.* **328**, 111 (1962) *See also* General methods	DL-Proline monohydrochloride, M.p. 159. DL-Bisproline hydrochloride, M.p. 200. Acetyl-DL-proline, M.p. 106. DL-Prolinamide, M.p. 104.
...0·4^{25} (c = 1–2 ...5N-HCl) ...6·2^{25} (c = 1–2 ...H_2O)		s. H_2O, EtOH	*J.B.C.* **198**, 587 (1952) *J.B.C.* **193**, 81 (1951)		*N-m*-Nitrobenzoyl-D-proline, M.p. 137–40, $[\alpha]^{20}_D$ +120 (in N-NaOH).
...0·4^{25} (c = 1–2 ...N-HCl) ...6·2^{25} (c = 1–2 ...H_2O)		162·3^{25}, 239^{65} H_2O; 1·18^{19} EtOH; i. eth., *n*-propanol, *n*-butanol	*J.B.C.* **227**, 871 (1957) *J.B.C.* **194**, 455 (1952) *J.B.C.* **198**, 587 (1952)		L-Proline monohydrochloride, M.p. 115. L-Bisproline hydrochloride, M.p. 156. Acetyl-L-proline, M.p. 118, $[\alpha]^{23}_D$ −115 (c = 2 in H_2O). L-Prolinamide, M.p. 99. *N*-DNP-L-proline, M.p. 138. Phenylthiohydantoin, M.p. 179.
...2·5^{20} (c = 0·1–2 ...yd. in H_2O)	At I = 0·16, 1. 3·19 2. 8·97	s. H_2O	Greenstein & Winitz, vol. 2, pp. 763, 1226 *Ber.* **97**, 1024 (1964) *Ber.* **91**, 449 (1958)		Substrate for assay of iminodipeptidase (prolinase), see *Meth. biochem. Anal.* **2**, 215 (1955), *Meth. Enzymol.* **2**, 97 (1955). Soln. keeps only a few days at 5° due to diketopiperazine formation. Ethyl ester hydrochloride, M.p. 119–20, $[\alpha]^{25}_D$ −39·5 (c = 2·4 in H_2O).
		s. H_2O, EtOH; i. eth.	SYN. *J. Physiol.* **121**, 55 (1953) ISOL. *B.J.* **58**, 24 (1954)	*B.J.* **58**, 24 (1954) *Meth. biochem. Anal.* **1**, 265 (1954)	Substrate for pseudocholinesterase, hydrolysed much more slowly by acetylcholinesterase. Rapidly hydrolysed in boiling acids. Unstable in soln. Perchlorate is more stable and preferable as a standard.
	1. 9·35^{20}, 9·04^{30}, 8·83^{40} 2. 10·80^{20}, 10·50^{30}, 10·26^{40}	v.s. H_2O, EtOH; sl. s. eth.	*Org. Synth.* Coll. **4**, 819 (1963) *J.B.C.* **233**, 907 (1958)	*Meth. Enzymol.* **6**, 615 (1963) *Nature, Lond.* **197**, 290 (1963)	Dihydrochloride, col. needles or tablets, M.p. > 290, v.s. H_2O, v. sl. s. EtOH, i. eth. Dipicrate M.p. 263 d.
...·3 (c = 2 in ...) ...9 to −13·1 ...O)	3·32	s. H_2O, EtOH, gl. acetic; sl. s. Et acetate; i. eth.	*B.J.* **8**, 481 (1914) *J.B.C.* **58**, 105 (1923) *J.A.C.S.* **76**, 4615 (1954) *J. org. Chem.* **21**, 1353 (1956)	*B.J.* **71**, 654 (1959) *Analyt. Chem.* **25**, 1507 (1953) *C.A.* **52**, 6067*d* (1958) *Bull. Soc. chim. Fr.* **1957**, 376	Hydrolysed almost completely to glutamic acid by boiling for 1–2 hr at 100° in 2N-HCl or 0·5N-NaOH. DL-2-Pyrrolidone-5-carboxylic acid, M.p. 178-83.
		s. mineral acids, EtOH; i. acet. Hydrochloride, s. H_2O; i. acet.	*J.A.C.S.* **74**, 109 (1952) *J.B.C.* **235**, 2045 (1960)	*J.B.C.* **235**, 2045 (1960) *J.B.C.* **225**, 825 (1957)	Never isolated in pure state. Aq. solns. unstable at room temp. and at −15°, but stable for a few days at 3°. Hydrochloride stable as solid, loses biological activity when dissolved in EtOH, probably due to esterification.
	1. 2·43 2. 5·06	0·55$^{6·5}$ H_2O; sl. s. EtOH, eth., benz.	*Ber.* **12**, 747 (1879) *J.A.C.S.* **71**, 3020 (1949)	*J.B.C.* **191**, 543 (1951) *Arch. B.B.* **42**, 197 (1953) *J.B.C.* **234**, 880 (1959) *J. Bact.* **85**, 222 (1963)	Decomp. to nicotinic acid at 110–90, so mixture resolidifies and melts again at 225–36. Spectrum, λ_{max} 268 mμ ε 4000 (in acid). Copper salt, less soluble in H_2O than free acid. Dimethyl ester, M.p. 52–55.

1. Amino Acids, Amines, Amides, Peptides, and their Derivatives

No.	*Name*	*Synonyms*	*Formula*	*M. wt.*	*Physical form*	*M.p.*
187	Sarcosine	*N*-Methyl-glycine	$CH_3 \cdot NH \cdot CH_2 \cdot COOH$	89·1	deliq. col. rh. cryst. from dil. EtOH	210 d. (198–210)
188	DL-Serine	α-Amino-β-hydroxy-propionic acid; β-Hydroxy-alanine	$HO \cdot CH_2 \cdot CH(NH_2) \cdot COOH$	105·1	monocl. prisms from H_2O	246 d.
189	D-Serine		COOH | $HC \cdot NH_2$ | CH_2OH	105·1	hexagonal tablets	228 d.
190	L-Serine		COOH | $H_2N \cdot CH$ | CH_2OH	105·1	hexagonal plates or prisms	223–8 d.
191	Spermidine	α-(γ-Amino-propylamino)-δ-aminobutane; 1,8-Diamino-4-azaoctane	$H_2N \cdot (CH_2)_3 \cdot NH \cdot (CH_2)_4 \cdot NH_2$	145·2; Trihydro-chloride, 254·6		Trihydro-chloride, 2
192	Spermine	α,δ-Bis(γ-amino-propylamino)-butane; 1,12-Diamino-4,9-diazadodecane	$NH \cdot (CH_2)_3 \cdot NH_2$ | $(CH_2)_4$ | $NH \cdot (CH_2)_3 \cdot NH_2$	202·3; Tetra-hydro-chloride, 348·2	wh. deliq. needles	55–60, B.p. 150^5; Tetrahyd chloride, 310–11 d.
193	Succinamide	Butanediamide	$H_2N \cdot CO \cdot (CH_2)_2 \cdot CO \cdot NH_2$	116·1	col. needles from H_2O	265–7
194	L-*N*-Succinyl-α-amino-ε-ketopimelic acid	2-(3-Carboxy-propionamido)-6-oxoheptane-dioic acid	$HOOC \cdot CO \cdot (CH_2)_3 \cdot CH \cdot COOH$ | $HOOC \cdot CH_2 \cdot CH_2 \cdot CO \cdot NH$	289·2	Li salt, wh. amorph. hygr. solid, pptd. from H_2O with EtOH/acet.	
195	*N*-Succinyl-α,ε-diamino-pimelic acid	2-Amino-6-(3-carboxy-propionamido)-heptanedioic acid	$HOOC \cdot CH(NH_2) \cdot (CH_2)_3 \cdot CH \cdot COOH$ | $HOOC \cdot CH_2 \cdot CH_2 \cdot CO \cdot NH$	290·3	solid	

]D	pK_a at 25°	*Solubility*	*Preparation*	*Estimation*	*General remarks*
	1. 2·21 2. 10·20	4·81^{20} H_2O; sl. s. EtOH; i. eth.	*J.B.C.* **21**, 563 (1915) *J.C.S.* **1931**, 1894 Greenstein & Winitz, vol. 3, p. 2750 *J.A.C.S.* **76**, 3213 (1954) ^{14}C. *J. org. Chem.* **15**, 1261 (1950)	*J.B.C.* **200**, 803 (1953) *See also* General methods	Hydrochloride, col. needles from H_2O/EtOH, M.p. 168–70 (168–74). *p*-Tosylsarcosine, M.p. 150–2.
	1. 2·19 2. 9·21	5·0^{25}, 19·21^{75} H_2O; 0·074^{25} 75% EtOH; 0·00067^{25} EtOH; i. eth.	*Org. Synth.* Coll. **3**, 774 (1955) *J.A.C.S.* **69**, 2738 (1947) *Arch. B.B.* **83**, 1 (1959)	Block & Bolling, p. 269 *Meth. biochem. Anal.* **6**, 63 (1958), **7**, 111 (1959) *J.B.C.* **207**, 709 (1954) *See also* General methods	Acetyl-DL-serine, M.p. 132. *N*-DNP-DL-serine, M.p. 186–8 d. Phenylthiohydantoin, M.p. 176–8.
5·1^{25} (c = 2 in HCl) 7·5^{25} (c = 2 in O)		*ca.* 25^{20} H_2O; i. EtOH, eth.	*J.B.C.* **194**, 455 (1952)		
5·1^{25} (c = 2 in HCl) ·5^{25} (c = 2 in O)		25^{20} H_2O	*Biochem. Preps.* **1**, 9 (1949)		Serious losses occur during acid hydrolysis of protein. Destroyed by hot dil. alkali. Racemized in aq. soln., pH 9. *N*-DNP-L-serine, M.p. 173.
		s. H_2O	SYN. *J.A.C.S.* **74**, 1836 (1952) *J. org. Chem.* **21**, 1374 (1956) ^{14}C. *J. org. Chem.* **25**, 1055 (1960) ISOL. *Naturwissenschaften* **46**, 495 (1959)	*Meth. Enzymol.* **6**, 615 (1963) *J.B.C.* **238**, 2098 (1963) *Chem. pharm. Bull., Tokyo* **11**, 148 (1963)	REVIEW. *Ann. Rev. Biochem.* **30**, 579 (1961). Trichloroaurate, M.p. 220–2. Picrate, M.p. 210–12. Phosphate much more soluble in H_2O than spermine phosphate.
		s. H_2O, EtOH, *n*-butanol; i. eth., benz.	SYN. *J.A.C.S.* **70**, 2666 (1948) ^{14}C. *J. org. Chem.* **25**, 1055 (1960) ISOL. *B.J.* **18**, 1263 (1924)	*Meth. Enzymol.* **6**, 615 (1963) *Chem. pharm. Bull., Tokyo* **11**, 148 (1963)	REVIEW. *Ann. Rev. Biochem.* **30**, 579 (1961). Strong base, absorbs CO_2 from air. Tetrachloroaurate +$4H_2O$, M.p. 225 d. Picrate, M.p. 248–50. Picrolonate, M.p. 288–9 d. Spermine phosphate, $C_{10}H_{26}N_4 \cdot 2H_3PO_4 \cdot 6H_2O$, M. wt. 506·4, col. cryst., solubility 0·037^{20}, 1·0^{100} H_2O, s. dil. acids and alkalis, PREP. *B.J.* **18**, 1263 (1924).
		0·45^{15}, 11·0^{100} H_2O; i. EtOH, eth.	*J.C.S.* **105**, 2698 (1914) *Acta chem. scand.* **17**, 1196 (1963)	*Analyt. Chem.* **31**, 1735 (1959)	
		s. H_2O	*J.B.C.* **236**, 1429 (1961)	*J.B.C.* **236**, 1429 (1961)	Free acid has not been isolated. 2,4-Dinitrophenylhydrazone, M.p. 137–43 d. NH_4 salt of 2,4-dinitrophenylhydrazone, M.p. 162–5 d.
2^{18} (c = 1·96 N-HCl)	1. 2·17 2. 3·21 3. 4·50	s. H_2O	*J.B.C.* **234**, 2955 (1959) ^{14}C. *J.B.C.* **236**, 3296 (1961)	*J.B.C.* **234**, 2955 (1959)	NH_4 salt, cryst. solid, s. H_2O.

No.	Name	Synonyms	Formula	M. wt.	Physical form	M.p.
196	Taurine	2-Amino-ethanesulphonic acid	$H_2N \cdot CH_2 \cdot CH_2 \cdot SO_3H$	125·2	tetragonal needles	320 d. (310–29)
197	Thiol-histidine	2-Thiol-β-imidazole-α-amino-propionic acid; 2-Mercapto-histidine	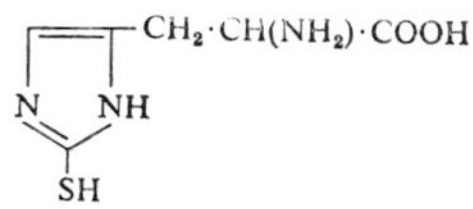	187·2	L- and DL-, straw-coloured plates of irregular shape	DL-, 300 d. (> 320)
198	DL-Threonine	α-Amino-β-hydroxy-*n*-butyric acid	$CH_3 \cdot CH(OH) \cdot CH(NH_2) \cdot COOH$	119·1; Hydrate, 128·1	orthorh. cryst. +½H_2O	Hydrate, decomp. 235
199	D-Threonine		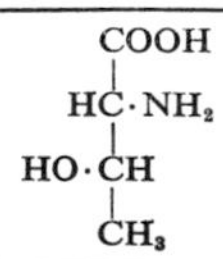	119·1		Decomp. 251–2
200	L-Threonine		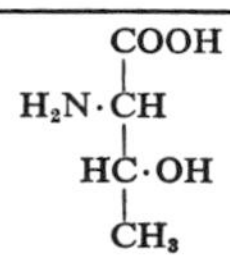	119·1; Hydrate, 128·1	orthorh. cryst. +½H_2O	Decomp. 253
201	DL-*allo*-Threonine		$CH_3 \cdot CH(OH) \cdot CH(NH_2) \cdot COOH$	119·1		244–5 (260 d.)
202	L-*allo*-Threonine		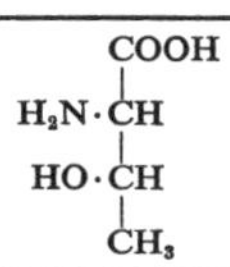	119·1		
203	L-Thyroxine	3,5,3′,5′-Tetra-iodothyronine; T_4	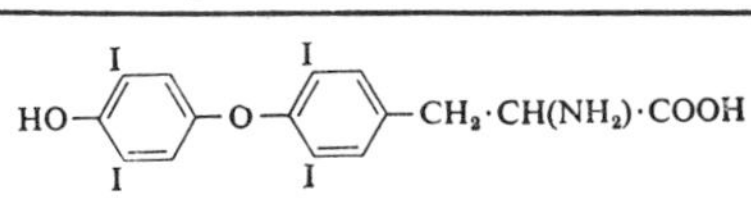	776·9; Na salt, 798·9, Hydrate, 888·9	wh. needles	236 d.

]D	pK_a at 25°	*Solubility*	*Preparation*	*Estimation*	*General remarks*
	1. −0·3 (SO_3H) 2. 9·06 (NH_2)	3·93^{0}, 10·48^{25}, 45·76^{100} H_2O; 0·0032^{17} EtOH; i. eth.	*Org. Synth.* Coll. **2**, 563 (1943) *J. org. Chem.* **16**, 1495 (1951) *Bull. Soc. chim. Fr.* **1955**, 945	*J.B.C.* **228**, 433 (1957) *Arch. B.B.* **91**, 219 (1960) *B.J.* **80**, 616 (1961) *See also* General methods	Stable to boiling acids. Hg salt used for isolation and identification. Diethyltaurine, M.p. 150.
10^{20} (c = 2 in HCl) $_{5461}$ −9·5 = 2·01 in HCl)	1. 1·84 (COOH) 2. 8·47 (NH_2) 3. 11·4 (SH)	s. H_2O, mineral acids	SYN. DL-, *J.C.S.* **1937**, 1166 L-, *J.C.S.* **1930**, 2586 *Helv. chim. Acta* **38**, 22 (1955) Greenstein & Winitz, vol. 3, p. 2671		DL-Thiolhistidine dihydrochloride, M.p. 204–6 d., v.s. H_2O.
	1. 2·09 2. 9·10	20^{25}, *ca.* 55^{80} H_2O; 0·0054^{25} EtOH; 0·07 95% EtOH; i. $CHCl_3$	*J.B.C.* **119**, 109 (1937) *J.A.C.S.* **71**, 1101 (1949) *Org. Synth.* Coll. **3**, 813 (1955)	Block & Bolling, p. 261 *J.B.C.* **138**, 91 (1941) *J.B.C.* **142**, 461 (1942) *B.J.* **40**, 632 (1946) *Analyt. Chem.* **24**, 1627 (1952) *See also* General methods	*N*-Benzoyl-DL-threonine, M.p. 143–4. *N*-Chloroacetyl-DL-threonine, M.p. 124. *N*-DNP-DL-threonine, M.p. 177–8. Phenylthiohydantoin, M.p. 194 d.
5·0^{25} (c = 1–2 N-HCl) 3·5^{25} (c = 1–2 H_2O)		i. $CHCl_3$, eth.	*J.B.C.* **119**, 109 (1937) Greenstein & Winitz, vol. 3, p. 2238		*N*-Benzoyl-D-threonine, M.p. 147–8.
5·0^{25} (c = 1–2 N-HCl) 3·5^{25} (c = 1–2 H_2O)		s. H_2O; i. EtOH, eth., $CHCl_3$	*J.B.C.* **119**, 109 (1937) Greenstein & Winitz, vol. 3, p. 2238	*J.B.C.* **160**, 35 (1945) *J.B.C.* **161**, 705 (1945)	Rapidly destroyed by hot dil. alkali and slowly destroyed by acid at high temperatures; serious losses occur during protein hydrolysis. *N*-Benzoyl-L-threonine, M.p. 147–8. *N*-DNP-L-threonine, M.p. 145.
	1. 2·11 2. 9·10	13·9^{25}, *ca.* 31·0^{80} H_2O; 0·3^{25} 95% EtOH	*J.B.C.* **119**, 109 (1937) *J.B.C.* **178**, 709 (1949) *J.C.S.* **1962**, 1116	*See* DL-threonine and General methods	*N*-Benzoyl-DL-*allo*threonine, M.p. 175–6.
·0^{25} (c = 1–2 H_2O) ·7^{25} (c = 1–2 N-HCl)		s. H_2O; v. sl. s. EtOH	Greenstein & Winitz, vol. 3, p. 2238		*N*-DNP-L-*allo*threonine, M.p. 152. D-*allo*Threonine has similar properties, but optical rotations have opposite sign, to those of L-*allo*threonine.
to −5·7 (in OH/EtOH, (c = 5 in l/95% EtOH,	1. 2·2 (COOH) 2. 6·45 (OH) 3. 10·1 (NH_2)	v. sl. s. H_2O; s. alkali; i. EtOH, eth.	*J.C.S.* **1949**, 3424 *J. org. Chem.* **26**, 1977 (1961) *Ber.* **96**, 1 (1963) *C.r. hebd. Séanc. Acad. Sci., Paris* **256**, 3898 (1963) ^{131}I and ^{14}C. *Biochem. Preps.* **10**, 171, 176 (1963) *Meth. Enzymol.* **4**, 856 (1957)	Dorfman (ed.), *Methods in Hormone Research*, vol. 1, p. 351, Academic Press (1962) Gray and Bacharach (eds.), *Hormones in Blood*, p. 93, Academic Press (1961) *Meth. Enzymol.* **4**, 856 (1957) *Meth. biochem. Anal.* **12**, 143 (1964)	Unstable in light, losing iodine. Deiodination occurs during protein hydrolysis. Strongly adsorbed to glass from dil. solns., *B.B.A.* **41**, 252 (1960). Forms insoluble chelates with Mg^{++}, Mn^{++} and other divalent ions. Spectrum, λ_{max} 295 mμ ϵ 4160 in 0·04N-HCl, λ_{max} (ϵ) 227 mμ (48 560) and 325 mμ (6210) in dil. NaOH. Na salt +5H_2O, wh. cryst. sl. s. H_2O.

1. Amino Acids, Amines, Amides, Peptides, and their Derivatives

No.	Name	Synonyms	Formula	M. wt.	Physical form	M.p.
204	3,5,3′-Triiodo-L-thyronine	T_3	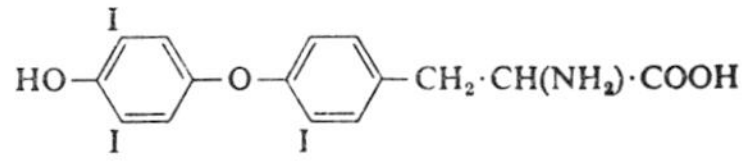	651·0	cryst.	233–4 d.
205	Trimethyl-amine		$(CH_3)_3N$	59·1; Hydro-chloride, 95·6	col. gas. Hydro-chloride, cryst. from EtOH	−124, B.p. 3·5; Hydro-chloride, 271–5 d.
206	Trimethyl-amine oxide		$(CH_3)_3NO$	75·1; Hydrate, 111·4	deliq. moncl. needles+$2H_2O$	96; Anhyd. sublimes 180
207	Tryptamine	3-(2-Amino-ethyl)-indole	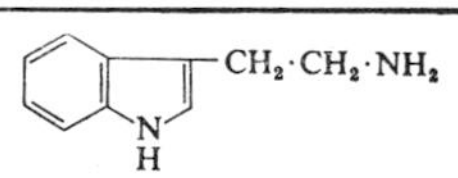	160·2; Hydro-chloride, 196·7	cryst. from EtOH/benz.	116–18
208	DL-Tryptophan	α-Amino-3-indole-propionic acid	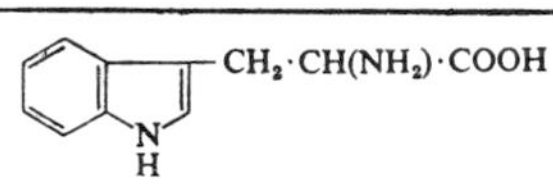	204·2	col. hexagonal plates	283–5
209	D-Tryptophan			204·2		281–2
210	L-Tryptophan			204·2	col. hexagonal leaflets	281–2 (289
211	Tyramine	*p*-(2-Amino-ethyl)-phenol	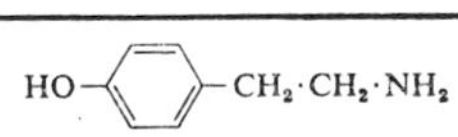	137·2; Hydro-chloride, 173·6	needles or leaflets from benz.	166, B.p. 205

D	pK_a at 25°	*Solubility*	*Preparation*	*Estimation*	*General remarks*
23·6[24] (c = 5 in HCl/EtOH, 1:2)	1. 2·2 (COOH) 2. 8·40 (OH) 3. 10·1 (NH_2)	s. alkalis; v. sl. s. H_2O	*C.r. hebd. Séanc. Acad. Sci., Paris* **234**, 997, 1228 (1952) *B.J.* **53**, 645 (1953) *Ber.* **96**, 1 (1963) ^{131}I. *Meth. Enzymol.* **4**, 856 (1957)	*See* L-thyroxine	Unstable in light, losing iodine. Deiodination occurs on heating in strong acid or, less so, in alkali. Adsorbed to glass from dil. solns. Spectrum, λ_{max} 295 mμ ϵ 4090 in 0·04N-HCl, λ_{max} (ϵ) 224 mμ (49 200) and 320 mμ (4660) in dil. NaOH. Hydrochloride, needles, M.p. 202–3.
	9·91[20], 9·69[30], 9·48[40]	v.s. H_2O, EtOH; s. eth. Hydrochloride, s. H_2O, EtOH, $CHCl_3$; i. eth.	*Org. Synth.* Coll. **1**, 514, 517 (1932)	Conway, *Micro-diffusion Analysis and Volumetric Error*, p. 195, Crosby, Lockwood & Son, London (1962) *Analytica chim. Acta* **24**, 397 (1961) *Nature, Lond.* **197**, 290 (1963) *B.J.* **46**, 578 (1950)	Picrate, M.p. 216.
	4·65[20]	s. H_2O, MeOH, EtOH, hot $CHCl_3$; i. eth.	SYN. *J.C.S.* **75**, 792, 1004 (1899) ISOL. *J.B.C.* **81**, 267 (1929)	*B.Z.* **273**, 243 (1934) *B.J.* **60**, 424 (1955)	On heating decomp. to dimethylamine and formaldehyde. Hydrochloride, darkens 185, decomp. 204–26, s. H_2O, hot MeOH. Aurichloride, hygr., M.p. 256–8. Picrate, M.p. 187–202.
	10·2	v.s. EtOH, acet.; sl. s. H_2O, eth.	*Ber.* **85**, 324 (1952) *J. org. Chem.* **23**, 146 (1958) *J.A.C.S.* **82**, 2386 (1960)	*Meth. med. Res.* **9**, 169, 175 (1961) *J. Pharmac. exp. Ther.* **126**, 217 (1959), **127**, 175 (1959) *Analyt. Chem.* **32**, 666 (1960)	Monohydrochloride, col. prisms from EtOH/eth., M.p. 252–3, v.s. H_2O. Picrate, M.p. 242–3, i. H_2O.
	1. 2·43 2. 9·44	0·25[30] H_2O; sl. s. EtOH	*J.A.C.S.* **77**, 1257 (1955) ^{14}C. *Biochem. Preps.* **6**, 90 (1958)	Block & Bolling, p. 117 *Analyt. Chem.* **20**, 30 (1948) *J.B.C.* **235**, 999 (1960) *See also* General methods	Spectrum, λ_{max} (ϵ) 218 mμ (33 500) 278 mμ (5550) 287·5 mμ (4550) in 0·1N-HCl, little change with pH. Benzoyl-DL-tryptophan, M.p. 188–91. Acetyl-DL-tryptophan, M.p. 205. Picrate, M.p. 186 d. Phenylthiohydantoin, M.p. 177.
·8[25] (c = 1–2 -HCl) 3·7[25] (c = 1–2 H_2O)			*J.B.C.* **180**, 473 (1949)		
·8[25] (c = 1–2 -HCl) 3·7[25] (c = 1–2 H_2O)		1·14[25], 2·80[75] H_2O; s. hot pyr.; sl. s. EtOH; i. $CHCl_3$, eth.	*Org. Synth.* Coll. **2**, 612 (1943) *J.B.C.* **180**, 473 (1949)	*J.B.C.* **160**, 35 (1945) *Helv. chim. Acta* **35**, 777 (1952) *Arch. B.B.* **67**, 387 (1957)	Unstable to mineral acids in the presence of carbohydrates, $CuSO_4$, $Fe_2(SO_4)_3$, aldehydes. Stable to 5N-NaOH at 125° provided that carbohydrate is absent. Hydrolysis conditions for estimation, *B.J.* **62**, 3P (1956). Benzoyl-L-tryptophan, M.p. 104–5. *N*-DNP-L-tryptophan, M.p. 221.
	1. 9·3 2. 10·4	1·05[15] H_2O; 10 EtOH; s. benz.; sl. s. eth., $CHCl_3$, hot xylene	*Helv. chim. Acta* **8**, 758 (1925) *Ber.* **90**, 1251 (1957)	*J.B.C.* **196**, 227 (1952) *Meth. med. Res.* **9**, 169 (1961) *J. Pharmac. exp. Ther.* **140**, 229 (1963) *Z.P.C.* **337**, 229 (1964)	Hydrochloride, cryst. from conc. HCl, M.p. 268, v.s. H_2O. Picrate, M.p. 206. *N*-Chloroacetyltyramine, M.p. 109.

No.	Name	Synonyms	Formula	M. wt.	Physical form	M.p.
212	DL-Tyrosine	β-(p-Hydroxyphenyl)alanine	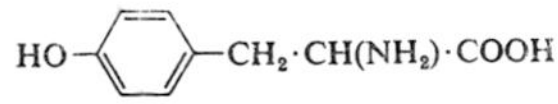	181·2	plates or needles	316 d.
213	D-Tyrosine			181·2	wh. needles	310–14 d.
214	L-Tyrosine			181·2	silky needles from H_2O	342–4 d. (295 d.)
215	Urea	Carbamide	$O{=}C(NH_2)_2$	60·1	col. tetragonal cryst. or needles	132·7
216	Urocanic acid	β-4(5)-Imidazolyl-acrylic acid; Urocaninic acid	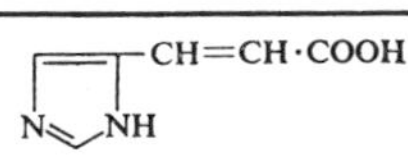	138·1; Hydrate, 174·1	*trans*-, wh. needles or prisms+$2H_2O$ from H_2O	*trans*-, 225 d. (218–31 *cis*-, 175–9
217	DL-Valine	α-Amino*iso*-valeric acid	$(CH_3)_2CH\cdot CH(NH_2)\cdot COOH$	117·1	monocl. leaflets from EtOH	298 d. (280 sea tube)

	pK_a *at 25°*	*Solubility*	*Preparation*	*Estimation*	*General remarks*
	At I = 0·16, 1. 2·20 (COOH) 2. 9·11 (NH_2) 3. 10·13 (OH)	0·035^{25}, 0·084^{50} H_2O; v. sl. s. EtOH; i. eth.	*J.C.S.* 1949, S 185	Block & Bolling, p. 112 *J.B.C.* **173,** 627 (1948) *J.B.C.* **196,** 227 (1952) *B.J.* **66,** 607 (1957) *See also* General methods	Spectrum, λ_{max} (ϵ) 223 mμ (8200) and 274·5 mμ (1340) in 0·1N-HCl, 240 mμ (11 050) and 293·5 mμ (2330) in 0·1N-NaOH, spectrum affected by ionization of OH gp. in alk. soln., *Adv. Protein Chem.* **7,** 319 (1952). *N*-Acetyl-DL-tyrosine+ $1H_2O$, M.p. 94–95. *O,N*-BisDNP-DL-tyrosine, M.p. 84 (191–3).
0^{25} (c = 2 in Cl)		0·045^{25}, 0·105^{50} H_2O	*Biochem. Preps.* **1,** 71 (1949)		*N*-Acetyl-D-tyrosine, M.p. 153–4.
0^{25} (c = 2 in Cl)		0·045^{25}, 0·244^{75} H_2O; 0·01^{17} 95% EtOH; s. alkalis; i. eth., acet.	*Org. Synth.* Coll. **2,** 612 (1943) *J.B.C.* **180,** 473 (1949) *J.B.C.* **194,** 455 (1952)	*B.J.* **41,** vii (1947) *J.B.C.* **161,** 705 (1945)	Pure L-tyrosine is stable to 5N-H_2SO_4 or 5N-NaOH for up to 30 hr at 100° but heating with acid in the presence of carbohydrate leads to destruction. There is up to 18% loss of tyrosine after hydrolysis of protein with NaOH. Acetyl-L-tyrosine, M.p. 153–4. *O*-DNP-L-tyrosine, wh. needles+ $1H_2O$, M.p. 202 d. *O,N*-BisDNP-L-tyrosine, M.p. 178. Phenylthiohydantoin, M.p. 216.
		78^{5}, 119·3^{25} H_2O; 15·8^{20} EtOH; s. conc. HCl; sl. s. eth.; i. $CHCl_3$		Conway, *Micro-diffusion Analysis and Volumetric Error*, pp. 162, 175, Crosby, Lockwood & Son, London (1962) Bergmeyer, *Methods of Enzymatic Analysis*, p. 401, Academic Press (1963) *Am. J. med. Technol.* **27,** 255 (1961) *Analyt. Chem.* **36,** 2145 (1964) *Analyt. Chem.* **25,** 662 (1953) *Clinica chim. Acta* **4,** 701 (1959) *Clin. Chem.* **7,** 488 (1961) *J.B.C.* **157,** 507 (1945) *J.B.C.* **167,** 535 (1947)	Nitrate, prisms, M.p. 152 d., s. hot H_2O. *N,N'*-Diacetylurea, M.p. 152–3. *N,N'*-Dibenzoylurea, M.p. 218–22 d. Solns. of urea develop a significant concentration of reactive cyanate ions on standing, *J.B.C.* **235,** 3177 (1960). Use fresh solns. or decompose cyanate by acidification before use. Traces of metals may be removed by treating a conc. soln. with a mixed anion-cation exchange resin.
	trans-, 1. 3·5 2. 5·8 *cis*-, 1. 3·0 2. 6·7	0·1^{0}, 0·6^{37}, 6·0^{100} H_2O; s. HCl, NaOH	*J.B.C.* **201,** 775 (1953) *Biochem. Preps.* **4,** 50 (1955) *J. pharm. Soc. Japan* **76,** 325 (1956); *C.A.* **50,** 13880 *b* (1956) ^{14}C. *J.B.C.* **234,** 3182 (1959)	*J.B.C.* **201,** 775 (1953) *J.B.C.* **202,** 351 (1953) *J.B.C.* **205,** 459 (1953) *Br. med. J.* **1,** 27 (1962) *J. clin. Invest.* **41,** 1472 (1962)	The *cis*-form is the less stable isomer, syntheses give mainly the *trans*-form. Slowly loses H_2O at room temp. Spectrum, *trans*-, λ_{max} 267 mμ at pH 2, 264 mμ at pH 5, 277 mμ (ϵ 18 800) at pH 7·2–11, see *J.B.C.* **201,** 775 (1953); *cis*-, λ_{max} 269 mμ at pH 2, 263 mμ at pH 5, 282 mμ at pH 10·7. Na salt and hydrochloride, v.s. H_2O. Picrate, M.p., *trans*-, 225; *cis*-, 204.
	1. 2·29 2. 9·74	7·04^{25}, 12·61^{75} H_2O; 0·015^{25} EtOH; 0·5^{25} 75% EtOH; i. eth.	*Org. Synth.* Coll. **3,** 848 (1955) *Can. J. Res.* **24B,** 301 (1946)	*See* General methods	Sublimes. Cu and Ag salts, sp. s. H_2O. Formyl-DL-valine, M.p. 140–5. Acetyl-DL-valine, M.p. 148. *N*-DNP-DL-valine, M.p. 183. Phenylthiohydantoin, M.p. 206.

No.	Name	Synonyms	Formula	M. wt.	Physical form	M.p.
218	D-Valine			117·1	leaflets from EtOH	293 d.
219	L-Valine			117·1	hexagonal leaflets from EtOH; prisms from H_2O	315 d.
220	Vasopressin	Pitressin; Anti-diuretic hormone	CyS → Tyr → Phe → Gln → Asn → CyS H_2N—Gly ← Arg ← Pro In hogs, Lys replaces Arg (lysine vasopressin)	1084	wh. amorph. powder	

	pK_a *at 25°*	*Solubility*	*Preparation*	*Estimation*	*General remarks*
·3[25] (c = 1–2 -HCl) 3[25] (c = 1–2 O)		5·3[20] H_2O; 0·45[25] 80% EtOH; v. sl. s. EtOH	*J.B.C.* **194**, 455 (1952)		Formyl-D-valine, M.p. 156.
·3[25] (c = 1–2 -HCl) ·3[25] (c = 1–2 O)		8·85[25], 10·24[65] H_2O; v. sl. s. EtOH; i. eth.	*J.B.C.* **194**, 455 (1952)	*J.B.C.* **160**, 35 (1945) *J.B.C.* **161**, 705 (1945)	Copper salt, $(C_5H_{10}O_2N)_2Cu$. Formyl-L-valine, M.p. 156. Acetyl-L-valine, M.p. 160. *N*-DNP-L-valine, M.p. 132.
e ressin, 8[22] (c = 0·5 acetic acid)	Isoelectric point, arginine vasopressin, 10·9	s. H_2O; i. acet.	ISOL. *J.B.C.* **222**, 951 (1956) *J.B.C.* **233**, 116 (1958) SYN. *J.A.C.S.* **80**, 3355 (1958) *J.A.C.S.* **82**, 3195 (1960)	Dorfman (ed.), *Methods in Hormone Research*, vol. 2, p. 495, Academic Press (1962) Gray and Bacharach (eds.), *Hormones in Blood*, p. 165, Academic Press (1961)	Principal actions, antidiuretic, raises blood pressure. Stable in acid, unstable in alkaline solns. Activity destroyed by thioglycollate. Pure arginine vasopressin contains *ca.* 400 units/mg, lysine vasopressin *ca.* 250 units/mg.

2. Carboxylic Acids, Alcohols, Aldehydes, and Ketones

Revised by R. A. COOPER (*Department of Biochemistry, University of Leicester*)

Carboxylic acids and aldehydes containing seven or more carbon atoms are included in the Lipids section (Table 11).

pK_a *Values*

Most of the values quoted are taken from G. Kortüm, W. Vogel, and K. Andrussow, *Disssociation Constants of Organic Acids in Aqueous Solution*, Butterworth (1961).

Metal chelating properties

Metal chelating properties of carboxylic acids are included in Table 17B.

2. Carboxylic Acids, Alcohols, Aldehydes, and Ketones

No.	*Name*	*Synonyms*	*Formula*	*M. wt.*	*Physical form*	*M.p.*
1	Acetaldehyde	Ethanal	$CH_3 \cdot CHO$	44·1	col. fuming inflammable liq., s.g. $0{\cdot}788_4^{16}$	−122
2	Acetic acid	Ethanoic acid	$CH_3 \cdot COOH$	60·1	col. liq., s.g. $1{\cdot}049_4^{20}$	16·6
3	—, NH_4 salt		$CH_3 \cdot COO \cdot NH_4$	77·1	v. hygr. wh. cryst.	114
4	—, Na salt		$CH_3 \cdot COO \cdot Na$	82·0	hygr. whitish grey powder	324
5	—, —, hydrate		$CH_3 \cdot COO \cdot Na \cdot 3H_2O$	136·1	efflor. col. monocl. prisms	58
6	—, K salt		$CH_3 \cdot COO \cdot K$	98·1	v. hygr. wh. powder	292
7	Acetic anhydride	Ethanoic anhydride	$CH_3 \cdot CO \cdot O \cdot CO \cdot CH_3$	102·1	strong smelling combustible liq., s.g. $1{\cdot}082_4^{20}$	−73
8	Acetoacetic acid	3-Oxobutanoic acid; Acetone carboxylic acid	$CH_3 \cdot CO \cdot CH_2 \cdot COOH$	102·1	col. syrup or col. cryst.	36–37

$[\alpha]^t_D$	pK_a at 25°	*Solubility*	*Preparation*	*Estimation*	*General remarks*
		∞ H_2O, EtOH, eth., benz.		*J.B.C.* **138**, 535 (1941) *B.J.* **29**, 1937 (1935)	Redistilled acetaldehyde keeps indefinitely in 2M-aq. soln. at −20°. Dilute solns. keep in cold at least a week. Polymerizes readily at room temp. 2,4-Dinitrophenylhydrazone, M.p. 167, spectrum (in $CHCl_3$) λ_{max} 354 mμ ε 22 200 (neutral), λ_{max} 430 mμ ε 22 500 (alkaline). Semicarbazone, λ_{max} 224 mμ, *J. Lab. clin. Med.* **35**, 983 (1950).
2	4·76	∞ H_2O, EtOH, eth.; s. most organic solvents; i. CS_2		*J.B.C.* **211**, 737 (1954) *J.B.C.* **210**, 539 (1954) *J.B.C.* **215**, 263 (1955) *J.B.C.* **177**, 571 (1949) *Meth. biochem. Anal.* **8**, 1 (1960) *Analyt. Chem.* **33**, 146 (1961) *See also* Volatile fatty acids	
).		148^{4} H_2O, decomp. hot H_2O; s. EtOH			Aq. soln. slightly acid.
		119^{0}, 170^{100} H_2O; 2·1 EtOH			
		$76{\cdot}2^{0}$, $138{\cdot}5^{50}$ H_2O; 2·1 EtOH; s. eth.			Loses water of cryst. at 120°. Aq. soln. alkaline (pH about 9).
		253^{30}, 492^{62} H_2O; 33 EtOH; i. eth.			Aq. soln. slightly alkaline (pH about 8).
40		13·6 cold H_2O d.; ∞ EtOH d.; ∞ eth.; s. $CHCl_3$, benz.		*J.B.C.* **159**, 21 (1945) *J.C.S.* **1958**, 2262 *J.C.S.* **1961**, 2305 After hydrolysis as acetic acid	Half-life of 50 min at 0° and 4·5 min at 25° in H_2O.
0 d.	3·62	∞ H_2O; s. EtOH, eth.	*B.J.* **37**, 230 (1943) *B.J.* **39**, 408 (1945) *J.A.C.S.* **74**, 5536 (1952)	*B.J.* **29**, 2082 (1935) *B.J.* **39**, 408 (1945) *J.B.C.* **190**, 339 (1951) *J.B.C.* **196**, 89 (1952) *B.J.* **58**, 699 (1954) *Z.P.C.* **286**, 145 (1960) *See also* acetone	Unstable to heat. Cryst. stable when dry but melt when exposed to air. Spectrum, see Li salt.

No.	*Name*	*Synonyms*	*Formula*	*M. wt.*	*Physical form*	*M.p.*
9	Acetoacetic acid, Li salt		$CH_3\cdot CO\cdot CH_2\cdot COO\cdot Li$	108·0	non-hygr. cryst. from MeOH-eth.	180–90 d.
10	Acetoacetic acid, Et ester	Ethyl 3-oxo-butanoate; Acetoacetic ester	$CH_3\cdot CO\cdot CH_2\cdot CO\cdot OC_2H_5$	130·1	col. liq., s.g. $1{\cdot}025_4^{20}$	< -80
11	DL-α-Aceto-α-hydroxy-butyric acid	2-Hydroxy-2-ethyl-3-oxo-butanoic acid	$CH_3\cdot CH_2\cdot C(OH)\cdot COOH$ | $CO\cdot CH_3$	146·1		
12	(±)-Acetoin	3-Hydroxy-2-butanone; Acetylmethyl-carbinol	$CH_3\cdot CO\cdot CH(OH)\cdot CH_3$	88·1	liq., s.g. $0{\cdot}997_4^{17}$	−72
13	(±)-α-Aceto-lactic acid	2-Hydroxy-2-methyl-3-oxobutanoic acid	$CH_3\cdot C(OH)\cdot COOH$ | $CO\cdot CH_3$	132·1		
14	Acetone	2-Propanone; Dimethyl ketone	$CH_3\cdot CO\cdot CH_3$	58·1	col. inflammable liq., s.g. $0{\cdot}792_4^{20}$	−95
15	Acetopyruvic acid	2,4-Dioxo-pentanoic acid	$CH_3\cdot CO\cdot CH_2\cdot CO\cdot COOH$	130·1	prisms from benz.	101
16	—, Et ester		$CH_3\cdot CO\cdot CH_2\cdot CO\cdot CO\cdot OC_2H_5$	158·2	liq.	18
17	Aconitic acid, *cis-*	1,2,3-Propene-tricarboxylic acid	$HOOC\cdot CH_2\cdot C\cdot COOH$ ‖ $HC\cdot COOH$	174·1	col. needles	130

$[\alpha]^t_D$	pK_a at 25°	*Solubility*	*Preparation*	*Estimation*	*General remarks*
		s. H_2O, MeOH	*Analyt. Biochem.* 3, 75 (1962)	*Analyt. Biochem.* 3, 75 (1962)	Stable several weeks *in vacuo* at 0–4°. Neutral solns. stable 2–3 weeks at −15°. λ_{max} 273 mμ ε 50 (in H_2O), λ_{max} 267 mμ ε 148 (in 0·1M-NaOH), λ_{max} 247 mμ ε 73 (in 0·1M-HCl).
		$14{\cdot}3^{16{\cdot}5}$ H_2O; s. EtOH, eth., benz., $CHCl_3$	*Org. Synth.* Coll. **1**, 235 (1941)		Semicarbazone, needles from eth., M.p. 129 d. Phenylhydrazone, needles, unstable in air, M.p. 50.
		s. H_2O	*B.B.A.* **31**, 583 (1959) *J.B.C.* **235**, 2316 (1960)	*J. Bact.* **80**, 18 (1960) *J.B.C.* **236**, 2486 (1961)	Obtained only in soln. as the Na salt. Prep. by hydrolysis of ethyl α-acetoxy-α-acetobutyrate, B.p. $87\text{–}88^5$, semicarbazone M.p. 124. The EtOH and acetate produced during the saponification do not interfere with the assay of aceto-hydroxybutyrate isomeroreductase. α-Aceto-α-hydroxybutyric osazone, cryst. from dioxane, M.p. 167–8.
		v.s. H_2O, EtOH; i. eth.	*J.B.C.* **191**, 401 (1951)	*J.B.C.* **161**, 495 (1945) *B.B.A.* **8**, 18 (1952) *Arch. B.* **9**, 229 (1946)	Forms dimer, M.p. 95. Dimer → monomer in aq. soln. (−)-Acetoin, $[\alpha]_D$ −82 approx., PREP. *J.B.C.* **191**, 401 (1951), semicarbazone, M.p. 193–4 (slow heating).
		s. H_2O	*Arch. B.* **17**, 81 (1948) *Meth. Enzymol.* 3, 277 (1957)	*J.B.C.* **195**, 715 (1952) *J.B.C.* **209**, 313 (1954) *Analyt. Biochem.* **4**, 159 (1962)	Obtained only in soln. as Na salt. Natural form is dextrorotatory.
		∞ H_2O, EtOH, eth., most organic solvents		*J.B.C.* **154**, 177 (1944) *J.B.C.* **136**, 25 (1940) *B.J.* **51**, 218 (1952) *J.B.C.* **176**, 501 (1948) *Arch. B.B.* **85**, 226 (1959)	2,4-Dinitrophenylhydrazone, yel. needles from 95% EtOH, M.p. 125–6, spectrum in $CHCl_3$, λ_{max} 364 mμ ε 22 400 (neutral), λ_{max} 431 mμ ε 20 000 and 530 mμ (alkaline). Semicarbazone, spectrum in aq. soln., λ_{max} 224 mμ ε 11 000.
	1. 2·61 2. 7·85 (enol)	s. H_2O, EtOH, eth., acet., $CHCl_3$, benz.; i. pet. eth.	*J.B.C.* **175**, 573 (1948)	*J.B.C.* **175**, 573 (1948)	Stable over long periods as di-sodium salt. Possesses strong u.v. absorption due to keto-enol tautomerism, see *J.B.C.* **175**, 573 (1948), λ_{max} 285 mμ ε 3030 (pH 1·5), λ_{max} 295 mμ ε 18 400 (pH 12·1).
29 7			*Org. Synth.* Coll. **1**, 233 (1941)		Absorbs in u.v. due to enolization, λ_{max} 290 mμ. Care should be taken in storing compound since spontaneous decomposition, accompanied by gas evolution, may shatter the container.
			B.J. **38**, 426 (1944)	*Analyt. Chem.* **24**, 1064 (1952) *B.J.* **52**, 527 (1952) *B.J.* **38**, 426 (1944)	Stable at least three months at room temp. Stability in soln., see *B.J.* **38**, 426 (1944)

2. Carboxylic Acids, Alcohols, Aldehydes, and Ketones

No.	Name	Synonyms	Formula	M. wt.	Physical form	M.p.
18	Aconitic acid, *trans-*		$HOOC\cdot CH_2\cdot C\cdot COOH$ ‖ $HOOC\cdot CH$	174·1	needles or leaflets from H_2O	190–210 d.
19	—, anhydride		$HOOC\cdot CH_2\cdot C\cdot CO$ ‖ $\rangle O$ $HC\cdot CO$	156·1	needles	77
20	Acrylic acid	Propenoic acid; Vinylformic acid	$CH_2:CH\cdot COOH$	72·1	col. liq., acrid odour, s.g. $1{\cdot}062_4^{16}$	12–13
21	Adipic acid	Hexanedioic acid	$HOOC\cdot(CH_2)_4\cdot COOH$	146·1	col. monocl. prisms from hot HNO_3	153
22	Benzoic acid	Benzene-carboxylic acid	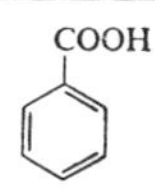	122·1	monocl. leaflets or needles	122
23	—, Na salt		$C_6H_5\cdot COO\cdot Na$	144·1	wh. amorph. powder	
24	—, K salt		$C_6H_5\cdot COO\cdot K\cdot 3H_2O$	Hydrate, 214·3	wh. cryst. powder	
25	2,3-Butanediol	2,3-Butylene glycol	$CH_3\cdot CH(OH)\cdot CH(OH)\cdot CH_3$	90·1	col. liq., s.g. $1{\cdot}003_4^{20}$	
26	Butyr-aldehyde	Butanal	$CH_3\cdot CH_2\cdot CH_2\cdot CHO$	72·1	col. liq., s.g. $0{\cdot}817_4^{20}$	−99
27	*n*-Butyric acid	Butanoic acid	$CH_3\cdot CH_2\cdot CH_2\cdot COOH$	88·1	col. liq., unpleasant odour, s.g. $0{\cdot}959_4^{20}$	−8, F.p. −
28	—, Na salt		$C_4H_7O_2\cdot Na$	110·1	cryst.	
29	—, Ca salt		$(C_4H_7O_2)_2\cdot Ca\cdot H_2O$	Hydrate, 232·3	leaflets or prisms	
30	*iso*Butyric acid	2-Methyl-propanoic acid	CH_3 $\rangle CH\cdot COOH$ CH_3	88·1	liq., pungent odour, s.g. $0{\cdot}949_4^{20}$	−47
31	—, Na salt		$C_4H_7O_2\cdot Na$	110·1	cryst.	

p.	$[\alpha]^t_D$	pK_a at 25°	*Solubility*	*Preparation*	*Estimation*	*General remarks*
		1. 2·80 2. 4·46	18^{13} H_2O; 50^{12} 88% EtOH; sl. s. eth.	*Org. Synth.* Coll. **2**, 12 (1943)	*Analyt. Chem.* **24**, 1064 (1952) *B.J.* **52**, 527 (1952)	
				Ber. **61**, 2521 (1928)		Salts usually prepared by neutralization of the anhydride.
, 56^{25}		4·25	∞ H_2O, EtOH, eth.	*Org. Synth.* Coll. **3**, 33 (1955)	*Analyt. Chem.* **24**, 1511 (1952)	Polymerizes readily in the presence of oxygen. Stabilized by addition of hydroquinone. λ_{max} below 210 mμ, λ_{max} and ϵ vary with concentration.
100		1. 4·43 2. 5·41	$1{\cdot}5^{15}$ H_2O; v.s. EtOH; $0{\cdot}6^{15}$ eth.; s. HNO_3; i. benz.	*Org. Synth.* Coll. **1**, 18 (1941)		
		4·20	$0{\cdot}18^{4}$, $0{\cdot}29^{20}$, $6{\cdot}8^{95}$ H_2O; $47{\cdot}1^{15}$, 66^{78} EtOH; 40^{15} eth.; 22 $CHCl_3$		*B.J.* **48**, 216 (1951) *Analyt. Chem.* **25**, 1490 (1953)	Starts to sublime at 100°. Spectrum, λ_{max} (ϵ) 230 mμ (11 600) and 273 mμ (970) in H_2O; for the anion, λ_{max} (ϵ) 224 mμ (8700) and 268 mμ (560) in H_2O.
			$62{\cdot}8^{0}$, 66^{20}, $74{\cdot}2^{100}$ H_2O; $0{\cdot}81^{15}$, $1{\cdot}64^{25}$ $8{\cdot}3^{78}$ EtOH			Aq. soln. slightly alkaline (pH about 8).
			52^{25}, 112^{100} H_2O; s. EtOH			Loses H_2O at 110°. Soluble in anhyd. EtOH.
			∞ H_2O, eth.; s. EtOH		*B.B.A.* **8**, 18 (1952)	
			3·7 H_2O; ∞ EtOH, eth.		*Org. Analysis* **1**, 243 (1953)	2,4-Dinitrophenylhydrazone, cryst. from EtOH, M.p. 114, spectrum in $CHCl_3$, λ_{max} 358 mμ ϵ 21 000 (neutral), λ_{max} 426 mμ ϵ 20 400 (alkaline).
		4·82	∞ H_2O, EtOH, eth.		*Meth. biochem. Anal.* **8**, 1 (1960) *Analyt. Chem.* **33**, 146 (1961) *See also* Volatile fatty acids	Volatile in steam.
			s. H_2O; sl. s. EtOH			
			Anhyd. salt, $20{\cdot}3^{0}$, $18{\cdot}2^{20}$ $15{\cdot}0^{65}$, $14{\cdot}9^{75}$, $15{\cdot}85^{100}$ H_2O			Solubility in H_2O reaches a minimum at 75°.
		4·86	20^{20} H_2O; ∞ EtOH, eth.		*Meth. biochem. Anal.* **8**, 1 (1960) *Analyt. Chem.* **33**, 146 (1961) *See also* Volatile fatty acids	Completely miscible with H_2O above 24°. Salts are more soluble in H_2O than are those of *n*-butyric acid.
			s. H_2O; sl. s. EtOH			

2. Carboxylic Acids, Alcohols, Aldehydes, and Ketones

No.	*Name*	*Synonyms*	*Formula*	*M. wt.*	*Physical form*	*M.p.*
32	*iso*Butyric acid, Ca salt		$(C_4H_7O_2)_2\cdot Ca\cdot 5H_2O$	Hydrate, 304·4	prisms + $5H_2O$ from cold H_2O	
33	Caproic acid	Hexanoic acid	$CH_3\cdot(CH_2)_4\cdot COOH$	116·2	col. oily liq., s.g. $0{\cdot}927^{20}_{4}$	−3·9
34	*iso*Caproic acid	4-Methyl-pentanoic acid	$(CH_3)_2{>}CH\cdot CH_2\cdot CH_2\cdot COOH$	116·2	col. oily liq., s.g. $0{\cdot}925^{20}_{4}$	−34
35	β-Carboxy-β-hydroxy-*iso*caproic acid	2-*iso*Propyl-malic acid	$(CH_3)_2{>}CH\cdot C(OH)(CH_2\cdot COOH)\cdot COOH$	176·2	wh. cryst. from Et acetate-ligroin	166–7
36	Catechol	1,2-Benzene diol; Pyrocatechol	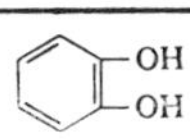	110·1	col. monocl. leaflets from benz.	105
37	Chorismic acid		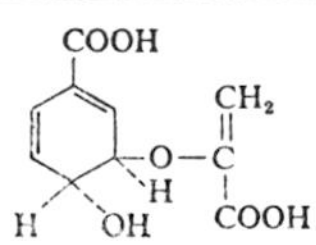	226·2; Hydrate, 244·2	monocl. prisms	146 d.
38	Cinnamic acid, *trans*-	*trans*-Benzene-propenoic acid	$C_6H_5\cdot CH{:}CH\cdot COOH$	148·2	col. monocl. cryst.	133
39	DL-Citra-malic acid	2-Methylmalic acid	$HOOC\cdot C(OH)(CH_3)\cdot CH_2\cdot COOH$	148·1	wh. cryst. from Et acetate	117
40	(+)-Citra-malic acid	*d*-Citramalic acid	$HOOC\cdot C(OH)(CH_3)\cdot CH_2\cdot COOH$	148·1	wh. cryst. from Et acetate-ligroin	109–13
41	Citric acid	2-Hydroxy-1,2,3-propane-tricarboxylic acid	$CH_2\cdot COOH$ / $C(OH)\cdot COOH$ / $CH_2\cdot COOH$	192·1	monocl. cryst.	153
42	—, mono-hydrate		$C_6H_8O_7\cdot H_2O$	210·1	orthorhombic cryst.	Softens melts c
43	—, NH_4 salt		$C_6H_5O_7\cdot(NH_4)_3$	243·2	deliq. wh. cryst.	Decom
44	—, Na salt		$C_6H_5O_7\cdot Na_3\cdot 2H_2O$	Hydrate, 294·1	wh. cryst., granules or powder	

p.	$[\alpha]^t_D$	pK_a at 25°	*Solubility*	*Preparation*	*Estimation*	*General remarks*
			Anhyd. salt, 20·1^{0}, 23·1^{25}, 28·7^{62}, 27·0^{80}, 26·1^{100} H_2O			Solubility in H_2O reaches a maximum at 62·5°. From hot aq. soln. crystallizes as $Ca(C_4H_7O_2)_2\cdot H_2O$. Transition point 62·5°.
5		4·87	0·97^{20}, 1·17^{60} H_2O; s. EtOH, eth.		*Meth. biochem. Anal.* **8**, 1 (1960) *See also* Volatile fatty acids	
·7		4·84	sl. s. H_2O; s. EtOH, eth.		*Meth. biochem. Anal.* **8**, 1 (1960) *See also* Volatile fatty acids	
	−4·0^{24} ±1·0 (c = 1 in MeOH)		s. Et acetate, H_2O; v. sl. s. ligroin	*Biochemistry* **2**, 1 (1963) *Biochemistry* **1**, 1157 (1962) *J. org. Chem.* **23**, 835 (1958)	*Biochemistry* **2**, 1 (1963)	The synthetic material has M.p. 146 and is only one-eighth as active as the naturally occurring compd. when assayed biologically
–5			45·1^{20} H_2O; v.s. EtOH; s. eth., benz.		*Meth. biochem. Anal.* **1**, 27 (1954) *B.J.* **55**, 146 (1953)	
	−295 (in H_2O)	1 and 2. *ca.* 3	v.s. H_2O, Et acetate, eth.; i. pet. eth.	*B.J.* **90**, 256 (1964)	*B.J.* **90**, 248 (1964)	Labile, store dry at −15°. Isomeric with prephenic acid. Spectrum, λ_{max} 272 mμ ε 2630 in H_2O. Ba salt, wh. labile powder, v.s. H_2O.
		4·44	0·1^{20}, 0·59^{98} H_2O; v.s. eth.; 23^{20} EtOH; 5·9^{15} $CHCl_3$			λ_{max} 274 mμ (in EtOH). Volatile in steam.
		1. 3·5 2. 5·3	s. H_2O, Et acetate; v. sl. s. eth.	*Biochem. Preps.* **9**, 25 (1962) *J. prakt. Chem.* **46**, 285 (1892)	*B.B.A.* **56**, 545 (1962)	Dicyclohexylamine salt, M.p. 159–64 d.
	+23·2^{24} (c = 4·4 in H_2O)		s. H_2O, Et acetate; v. sl. s. eth.	*Biochem. Preps.* **9**, 21 (1962)		The absolute configuration of (+)-citramalic acid is not known. (−)-Citramalic acid has been isolated in small amounts from apples, see *B.B.A.* **14**, 36 (1954).
mp.		1. 3·13 2. 4·76 3. 6·40	146^{20}, 525^{100} H_2O; 62^{25} EtOH; 2·25^{15} eth. (*See* General remarks)		*B.J.* **45**, 377 (1949) *J.B.C.* **175**, 745 (1948) *Analyt. Chem.* **23**, 467 (1951) *B.J.* **60**, 647 (1955) *J.B.C.* **175**, 849 (1948)	The solubilities are calculated in terms of the anhyd. compound although below 35·8° the monohydrate is the stable form.
			as for anhyd. citric acid			Loses H_2O at 70–75° or by standing over conc. H_2SO_4 in a desiccator.
			v.s. cold H_2O; i. EtOH, eth.			Decomposes in hot H_2O.
			72^{25}, 167^{100} H_2O; i. EtOH			Loses H_2O at 150°. Aq. soln. slightly alkaline. Pentahydrate also formed, deliq. wh. rh. cryst.

2. Carboxylic Acids, Alcohols, Aldehydes, and Ketones

No.	Name	Synonyms	Formula	M. wt.	Physical form	M.p.
45	Citric acid, K salt		$C_6H_5O_7 \cdot K_3 \cdot H_2O$	Hydrate, 324·4	wh. cryst. granules or powder	
46	(±)-*iso*Citric acid	1-Hydroxy-1,2,3-propane-tricarboxylic acid	HOOC·CH(OH)·CH(COOH)·CH₂·COOH → $HOOC \cdot CH(OH) \cdot CH(COOH) \cdot CH_2 \cdot COOH$	192·1	prisms	*ca.* 125
47	—, lactone		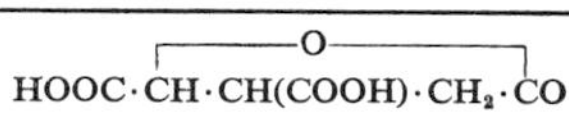	174·1	wh. cryst.	160–3
48	(+)-*iso*Citric acid	*threo*-D$_S$-*iso*-Citric acid; *d*-*iso*Citric acid	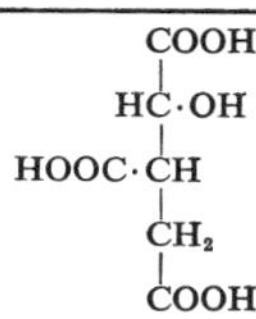	192·1		
49	—, KH_2 salt		$C_6H_5O_7 \cdot KH_2$	230·2	orthorhombic needles or prisms from H_2O	179–86 d.
50	—, lactone	*l*-*iso*Citric lactone	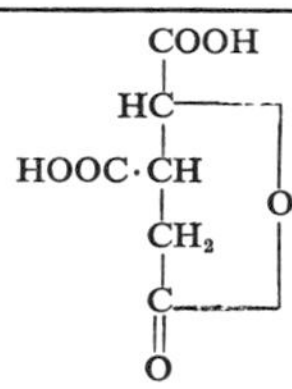	174·1	col. needles from EtOH-toluene (2:1)	156–7
51	—, —, dimethyl ester		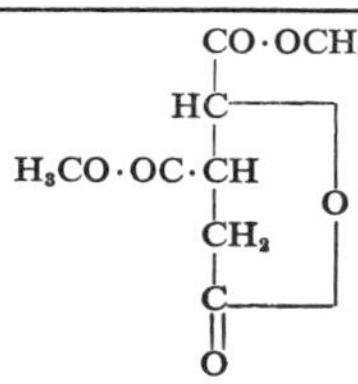	202·2	col. cryst. from H_2O	106
52	Crotonic acid, *trans*-	*trans*-2-Butenoic acid; *trans*-β-Methyl-acrylic acid	$CH_3 \cdot CH{:}CH \cdot COOH$	86·1	col. monocl. needles from H_2O	72
53	5-Dehydro-quinic acid	1,3,4-Trihydroxy-5-oxocyclo-hexanecarboxylic acid	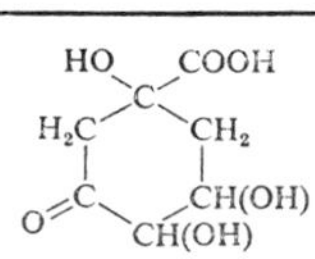	190·2	needles from acet.-$CHCl_3$	139–40, r solidifies 154–6, remelts 195–200

M.p.	$[\alpha]^t_D$	pK_a at 25°	*Solubility*	*Preparation*	*Estimation*	*General remarks*
			167^{15}, $199 \cdot 7^{31}$ H_2O; v. sl. s. EtOH			Loses H_2O at 180°. Aq. soln. slightly alkaline (pH about 8·5).
			v. sl. s. H_2O, EtOH, eth.	*J.B.C.* **174**, 133 (1948)		
				Biochem. Preps. 3, 52 (1953)		Stable if dry.
	dextro-rotatory	1. 3·29 2. 4·71 3. 6·40		*Biochem. Preps.* 3, 44 (1953)	*J.B.C.* **174**, 133 (1948) *B.J.* **45**, 578 (1949) *Analyt. Chem.* 23, 467 (1951) *Arch. B.B.* **31**, 460 (1951)	For discussion on nomenclature of *iso*citric acids, see *J.B.C.* **237**, 1739 (1962). The acid yields a laevo-rotatory lactone. $[\alpha]_D$ in NH_4 molybdate solns., see *B.J.* **45**, 578 (1949).
	$+20 \cdot 4^{25}$ (c = 2·3 in H_2O)		$3 \cdot 5^{0}$, 50^{100} H_2O; 0·4 50% EtOH	*Biochem. Preps.* 7, 72 (1960)		Stable at 115° for 24 hr if dry at start. 48% of a 2% soln. converted to lactone on boiling in H_2O; this is apparent equilibrium attained after 3 hr. Decomposes sharply at 179–86°, depending on rate of heating, and *iso*citric lactone is the major product.
	laevo-rotatory	1. 2·26 2. 4·49		*Biochem. Preps.* 3, 50 (1953)		Stable in desiccator. Used to prepare standard solns. of *iso*citric acid.
–8^{5}	−63 to -65^{20} (in MeOH)			*Biochem. Preps.* 3, 44 (1953)		Stable in dark at R.T. for several years.
		4·70	$8 \cdot 3^{15}$ H_2O; s. EtOH, acet.; sl. s. ligroin			*iso*-Crotonic acid (*cis*-β-methylacrylic acid), needles from pet. eth., M.p. 15·5, B.p. 169, s. H_2O. $+H_2O+$light → crotonic acid.
	$-82 \cdot 4^{28}$ (c = 0·71 in anhyd. EtOH) $-44 \cdot 0^{20}$ (c = 0·45 in MeOH)		v.s. H_2O, MeOH, EtOH, acet., dioxane, acetic acid; sl. s. Et acetate	*Meth. Enzymol.* 6, 498 (1963) *J.C.S.* **1961**, 1854	*J.B.C.* 223, 907 (1956) *J.A.C.S.* **75**, 5572 (1953)	Reduces Fehling's soln. and Tollen's reagent at R.T. Extremely unstable in alkaline solns. Moderate stability pH 1–5. λ_{max} 269 mμ ε 43·8.

2. Carboxylic Acids, Alcohols, Aldehydes, and Ketones

No.	*Name*	*Synonyms*	*Formula*	*M. wt.*	*Physical form*	*M.p.*
54	5-Dehydro-shikimic acid		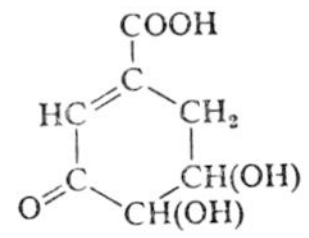	172·1; Hydrate, 190·2	wh. needles from Et acetate; $+1H_2O$ from $EtOH/H_2O$, loses H_2O at 85–90°	146–7, re-solidifies 161–8, remelts 201–2 (subl.)
55	Diacetyl	2,3-Butane-dione; Dimethyl-glyoxal	$CH_3\cdot CO\cdot CO\cdot CH_3$	86·1	greenish-yel. liq., s.g. $0{\cdot}990^{15}_{15}$	
56	Dihydroxy-acetone	1,3-Dihydroxy-propanone	$HO\cdot CH_2\cdot CO\cdot CH_2\cdot OH$	90·1	cryst. as dimer $(C_3H_6O_3)_2$, fairly hygr.	*ca.* 80
57	Dihydroxy-fumaric acid	Formerly thought to be dihydroxy-maleic acid	$HO\cdot C\cdot COOH$ $\Vert$ $HOOC\cdot C\cdot OH$	148·1; Hydrate, 184·1	plates$+2H_2O$	Anhyd., decomp. 155
58	α,β-Dihydroxy-β-methylvaleric acid	2,3-Dihydroxy-3-methylpentanoic acid; α,β-Dihydroxy-β-ethylbutyric acid	CH_3 $CH_3\cdot CH_2\cdot C(OH)\cdot CH(OH)\cdot COOH$	148·2	col. oil	
59	α,β-Dihydroxy-*iso*valeric acid	2,3-Dihydroxy-3-methylbutanoic acid; α,β-Dihydroxy-β-methylbutyric acid	CH_3 $>C(OH)\cdot CH(OH)\cdot COOH$ CH_3	134·1	col. syrup	
60	Ethanol	Ethyl alcohol	$CH_3\cdot CH_2\cdot OH$	46·1	hygr. col. liq., s.g. anhyd. $0{\cdot}798^{15\cdot5}_{15\cdot5}$, s.g. 95% $0{\cdot}816^{15\cdot5}_{15\cdot5}$	$-117{\cdot}3$
61	Ethylene glycol	1,2-Ethanediol; Glycol	$HO\cdot CH_2\cdot CH_2\cdot OH$	62·1	v. hygr. syrupy liq., s.g. $1{\cdot}115^{20}_{4}$	-12

p.	$[\alpha]_D^t$	pK_a at 25°	*Solubility*	*Preparation*	*Estimation*	*General remarks*
	−57·5[28] (c = 1·065 in EtOH) −54·1[20] (c = 1·0 hydrate in EtOH)	3·2	v.s. H_2O; s. MeOH, EtOH, acet.; sl. s. acetic acid; i. eth., $CHCl_3$	*Meth. Enzymol.* 6, 498 (1963) *J.A.C.S.* 75, 5567 (1953)	*J.A.C.S.* 75, 5567 (1953) *J.B.C.* 223, 907 (1956)	Aq. solns. moderately stable if neutral or weakly acidic. Stable 6 hr at pH 7·5–8·0. Destroyed in 1 hr at pH 10–10·5. Reduces Fehling's soln. and Tollen's reagent rapidly. Spectrum, λ_{max} 234 mμ ε 12 100 (in EtOH), λ_{max} 235 mμ ε 11 600 (0·1N-HCl), λ_{max} 234 mμ ε 11 900 (Na salt, pH 7·5 in H_2O). 2,4-Dinitrophenylosazone, red prisms from pyr.-MeOH-pentane, M.p. 250–6 d. Phenylosazone, leaflets from dioxane-eth.-hexane, M.p. 197–9, or needles from eth., M.p. 225–7 d. Methyl ester, needles from EtOH-eth., M.p. 124–6.
			25[15] H_2O; ∞ EtOH, eth.		*J.B.C.* 161, 495 (1945) *Arch. B.* 9, 229 (1946) *B.B.A.* 8, 18 (1952)	Forms trimers. Mono-2,4-dinitrophenylhydrazone, cryst. from EtOH, M.p. 178, PREP. *Analyt. Chem.* 29, 1305 (1957).
			s. H_2O, hot EtOH; v. sl. s. cold EtOH, eth.		*J.B.C.* 198, 127 (1952) *J.B.C.* 212, 847 (1955) *J.B.C.* 203, 153 (1953)	1,3-Diacetate, M.p. 48. 1,3-Dibenzoate, M.p. 120·5. *iso*-Propylidene deriv., M.p. 170. *p*-Nitrophenylhydrazone, M.p. 160. 2,4-Dinitrophenylhydrazone, M.p. 277–8 d.
		1·14	s. EtOH, MeOH; sl. s. H_2O, eth.	*Biochem. Preps.* 3, 56 (1953)	*Z.P.C.* 160, 196 (1926) *Meth. Enzymol.* 3, 249 (1957)	Crystals lose H_2O *in vacuo*. Anhyd. form more stable. Aq. soln. forms glycolaldehyde at R.T. Configuration, see *J.A.C.S.* 75, 6312 (1953). Absorption due to dienol group, λ_{max} 292 mμ ε 9100 (in H_2O), λ_{max} 308 mμ ε 7900 (in eth.).
	+3[23] (c = 2·3 in H_2O containing 1 eq. of $Ca(OH)_2$) −15[23] (c = 2·3 in dil. HCl, pH 1)		s. H_2O, EtOH, eth.	*J.A.C.S.* 76, 1085 (1954)	*J.B.C.* 235, 1425 (1960)	Synthetic prep. is one or both of the stereoisomeric DL-dihydroxy acids; resolution via quinine salt gives a compound identical with the naturally occurring compound. Quinine salt, M.p. 203 d., $[\alpha]_D^{23}$ −144 (c = 1 in MeOH). Biological activity only demonstrable at pH values below 6·0. Na salt can be heated for 5 min at 15 psi pressure.
	−12·5[23] (c = 2 in 0·1N-HCl) +9·5[23] (c = 2 in H_2O, pH 5·5–6·5)		s. H_2O, EtOH	*J.A.C.S.* 76, 1085 (1954)	*J.B.C.* 235, 1425 (1960)	DL-compound prepared and resolved via quinine salt to give a compound identical with the naturally occurring material. Quinine salt, M.p. 208–9 d., $[\alpha]_D^{23}$ −142 (c = 1 in MeOH). Biological activity only demonstrable at pH values below 6·0. Na salt can be heated for 5 min at 15 psi pressure.
			∞ H_2O, most organic solvents		*Acta pharmac. tox.* 10, 223 (1954) *J. Lab. clin. Med.* 33, 241 (1948) *Meth. biochem. Anal.* 7, 217 (1959) *Acta chem. scand.* 5, 1105 (1951)	
			∞ H_2O, EtOH, acet.; 7·9 eth.; sl. s. $CHCl_3$		*Glycols*, p. 328, Reinhold (1952)	For general reference see *Glycols*, eds. Curme and Johnston, A.C.S. Monograph Series No. 114, Reinhold (1952).

2. Carboxylic Acids, Alcohols, Aldehydes, and Ketones

No.	Name	Synonyms	Formula	M. wt.	Physical form	M.p.
62	Formaldehyde	Methanal	H·CHO	30·0	col. gas	−92
63	—, polymer	Paraform-aldehyde; Polyoxy-methylene	$(H{\cdot}CHO)_x$	$(30{\cdot}0)_x$	cryst. powder	121–3
64	Formic acid	Methanoic acid	H·COOH	46·0	col. liq., s.g. $1{\cdot}220_4^{20}$	8·4
65	—, NH_4 salt		$H{\cdot}COO{\cdot}NH_4$	63·1	deliq. cryst. or granules	116
66	—, Na salt		H·COO·Na	68·0	deliq. wh. cryst.	253
67	—, K salt		H·COO·K	84·1	deliq. col. rhombs or granules	167
68	Fumaric acid	*trans*-Butenedioic acid	HOOC·CH ‖ CH·COOH	116·1	col. monocl. needles or prisms	300–2 (sealed tube)
69	—, Na salt		$C_4H_2O_4{\cdot}Na_2$	160·0	cryst.	
70	Glutaric acid	Pentanedioic acid	$HOOC{\cdot}CH_2{\cdot}CH_2{\cdot}CH_2{\cdot}COOH$	132·1	monocl. prisms or needles	97·5
71	DL-Glycer-aldehyde	2,3-Dihydroxy-propanal	$HO{\cdot}CH_2{\cdot}CH(OH){\cdot}CHO$	90·1	needles or prisms from MeOH; crystallizes as dimer	Monom 69–70; Dimer, 132–42

ɔ.	$[\alpha]^t_D$	pK_a at 25°	*Solubility*	*Preparation*	*Estimation*	*General remarks*
21			s. H_2O, EtOH, eth.	*J.B.C.* **207**, 709 (1954) *J.B.C.* **201**, 161 (1953)	*J.B.C.* **158**, 107 (1945) *B.J.* **55**, 416 (1953) *Meth. biochem. Anal.* **6**, 63 (1958)	'Formalin' is 40% aq. soln. Dilute solns. stable for 1 week at 2°. Dimedon complex, M.p. 189. Bisulphite compound, $HOCH_2 \cdot O \cdot SO_2Na$, cryst.+ $1H_2O$ from H_2O, s. MeOH, sl. s. EtOH. 2,4-Dinitrophenylhydrazone, M.p. 165, spectrum (in $CHCl_3$) λ_{max} 344 mμ ε 19 000 (neutral), λ_{max} 430 mμ ε 15 000 (alkaline).
			0·24 H_2O; i. EtOH, eth.			Gives formaldehyde on heating or on dissolving in hot H_2O.
8		3·75	∞ H_2O, EtOH, eth.		*Meth. biochem. Anal.* **8**, 1 (1960) *J.B.C.* **156**, 303 (1944) *Analyt. Chem.* **20**, 267 (1948) *B.J.* **40**, 100 (1946) *Analyt. Biochem.* **4**, 116 (1962) *J.B.C.* **229**, 321 (1957) *See also* Volatile fatty acids	
			102^{0}, 531^{80} H_2O; s. EtOH			
			44^{0}, 97^{20}, 160^{100} H_2O; sl. s. EtOH; i. eth.			Aq. soln. neutral.
			331^{18}, 657^{90} H_2O; s. EtOH; i. eth.			Aq. soln. neutral.
nes		1. 3·02 2. 4·38	$0{\cdot}7^{25}$, $9{\cdot}8^{100}$ H_2O; $5{\cdot}75^{30}$, $4{\cdot}76^{78}$ EtOH; $0{\cdot}72^{25}$ eth.; v. sl. s. $CHCl_3$, CCl_4, acet.; i. benz.	*Org. Synth.* Coll. **2**, 302 (1943)	*B.J.* **50**, 349 (1952) *Z.P.C.* **236**, 43 (1935) *B.J.* **54**, 78 (1953) *B.J.* **34**, 1041 (1940) *Arch. B.* **24**, 110 (1949)	
			$22{\cdot}8^{25}$ H_2O			
		1. 4·34 2. 5·41	64^{20} H_2O; v.s. EtOH, eth.; s. benz., $CHCl_3$	*Org. Synth.* Coll. **1**, 289 (1941) *Org. Synth.* Coll. **4**, 496 (1963)		Recrystallize from benz.
			3^{18} H_2O; v. sl. s. EtOH, eth.; i. benz.	*Org. Synth.* Coll. **2**, 305 (1943) *J. org. Chem.* **14**, 1103 (1949)	*J.B.C.* **192**, 583 (1951) *J.B.C.* **212**, 847 (1955) *Nature, Lond.* **176**, 362 (1955)	Depolymerizes in soln. In solid state dimer is usual. M.p. depends on rate of heating. Diethyl acetal, B.p. $120–1^{8}$. Phenylosazone, M.p. 132. 2,4-Dinitrophenylhydrazone, M.p. 167. *p*-Bromophenylhydrazone, M.p. 168.

No.	Name	Synonyms	Formula	M. wt.	Physical form	M.p.
72	D-Glycer-aldehyde		CHO | HC·OH | CH_2·OH	90·1	syrup	
73	L-Glycer-aldehyde		CHO | HO·CH | CH_2·OH	90·1	syrup	
74	DL-Glyceric acid	2,3-Dihydroxy-propanoic acid	HO·CH_2·CH(OH)·COOH	106·1	syrup	
75	—, Ca salt		$(C_3H_5O_4)_2$·Ca·$2H_2O$	Hydrate, 286·3; Anhyd., 250·2	microscopic tablets or prisms	137–8 d. (dihydrat
76	D-Glyceric acid		COOH | HC·OH | CH_2OH	106·1	syrup	
77	—, Ca salt		$(C_3H_5O_4)_2$·Ca·$2H_2O$	Hydrate, 286·3; Anhyd., 250·2	prisms	142–3
78	L-Glyceric acid		COOH | HO·CH | CH_2OH	106·1	syrup	
79	—, Ca salt		$(C_3H_5O_4)_2$·Ca·$2H_2O$	Hydrate, 286·3; Anhyd., 250·2	monocl. prisms	137
80	Glycerol	1,2,3-Propane-triol; Glycerine	HO·CH_2·CH(OH)·CH_2·OH	92·1	rh. cryst. or col. liq.	18, solid at *ca.* 0
81	Glycol-aldehyde	Hydroxy-ethanal; Glycollic aldehyde	HO·CH_2·CHO	60·1	col. plates	97
82	Glycollic acid	Hydroxy-ethanoic acid; Hydroxyacetic acid	HO·CH_2·COOH	76·1	leaflets from eth.; needles from H_2O; somewhat hygr.	80

.p.	$[\alpha]_D^t$	pK_a *at 25°*	*Solubility*	*Preparation*	*Estimation*	*General remarks*
	+14 (in H_2O)			*J.B.C.* **128**, 463 (1939) *J.A.C.S.* **61**, 2607 (1939)	As DL-glyceraldehyde	Polymerizes rapidly. Optical rotation falls rapidly to a value of about +7 but fully active D-glyceraldehyde can be regenerated. Readily isomerizes to dihydroxyacetone on treatment with alkali. Dimethylacetal, B.p. 124–7^{14}, $[\alpha]_D^{15}$ +21·2 (c = 18 in H_2O). *iso*Propylidene deriv., B.p. 27^{2}, $[\alpha]_D^{21}$ +64·9 (in benz.). 2,4-Dinitrophenylhydrazone, M.p. 155–6. Methylphenylhydrazone, M.p. 108–10, $[\alpha]_D^{19}$ −20·5 (in pyr.). Dibenzoate, M.p. 80, $[\alpha]_D$ −35·6. Dimedon deriv., M.p. 198, $[\alpha]^{20}$ +198 (in EtOH).
	−14 (in H_2O)			*J.A.C.S.* **61**, 761 (1939) *Can. J. Chem.* **33**, 1216 (1955)	As DL-glyceraldehyde	Polymerizes rapidly. Optical rotation falls rapidly to a value of about −7 but fully active L-glyceraldehyde can be regenerated. Dimethylacetal, B.p. 126–9^{18}, $[\alpha]_D^{26}$ −20·9 (c = 19·2 in H_2O). *iso*Propylidene deriv., B.p. 38^{8}, $[\alpha]_D^{22}$ −67·9 (in benz.). 2,4-Dinitrophenylhydrazone, M.p. 147–8. Dimedon deriv., M.p. 198–200, $[\alpha]_D^{21}$ −198 (in EtOH).
		At I = 0·2, 3·52^{20}	∞ H_2O, EtOH; v.s. acet.; i. eth.	*Ber.* **54**, 465 (1921) ^{14}C. *J.C.S.* **1963**, 2563	*J.B.C.* **207**, 709 (1954) *J.B.C.* **234**, 469 (1959)	Polymerizes on long standing.
			3·85^{20} anhyd. H_2O; i. EtOH, eth.		*Analyt. Biochem.* **4**, 159 (1962)	Loses H_2O at 130°.
	laevo-rotatory			*J.A.C.S.* **61**, 2607 (1939) *Arch. B.* **3**, 105 (1943–4)		Salts are dextrorotatory. Methyl ester, B.p. 114–16^{8}, $[\alpha]_D^{26}$ +4·7 (pure substance). *p*-Phenylphenacyl deriv., M.p. 145–6.
	+14·5^{20} (anhyd. in H_2O)					Optical rotation values from +12·9 to +15·5 (in H_2O) have been reported.
	dextro-rotatory			See *J.A.C.S.* **61**, 2607 (1939)		Salts are laevorotatory. Methyl ester, B.p. 119–20^{14}, $[\alpha]_D^{15}$ −4·8 (pure substance).
	−14·6^{20} (anhyd. in H_2O)		9·32^{20} anhyd. H_2O			Optical rotation values from −11·6 to −15·2 (in H_2O) have been reported.
d.			∞ H_2O, EtOH; 0·2 eth.; i. $CHCl_3$, CS_2, benz., pet. eth.		*J.B.C.* **133**, 491 (1940) *B.J.* **59**, 353 (1955) *B.J.* **62**, 107 (1956) *Glycerol*, p. 167, Reinhold (1953)	For general reference see *Glycerol*, eds. Milner and Dalton, A.C.S. Monograph Series No. 117, Reinhold (1953).
			v.s. H_2O, hot EtOH; sl. s. eth.	*Biochem. Preps.* **4**, 56 (1955)	*J.B.C.* **180**, 1297 (1949) *Analyt. Chem.* **27**, 1348 (1955) *B.J.* **68**, 84 (1958)	Fresh aq. solns. contain dimeric form which becomes monomeric on standing for 24 hr. 2,4-Dinitrophenylhydrazone, M.p. 155–6. Phenylosazone, M.p. 169–70.
		3·83	s. H_2O, EtOH, eth.		*Ind. Engng. Chem. analyt. Edn.* **15**, 762 (1943) *Mikrochemie* **36/37**, 863 (1951)	

2. Carboxylic Acids, Alcohols, Aldehydes, and Ketones

No.	Name	Synonyms	Formula	M. wt.	Physical form	M.p.
83	Glyoxal	Ethanedial; Diformyl	CHO·CHO	58·0	yel. prisms	15
84	Glyoxylic acid	Oxoethanoic acid; Glyoxalic acid	$CHO \cdot COOH \cdot H_2O$	Hydrate, 92·1; Anhyd., 74·0	syrup or hygr. prisms	98
85	—, Na salt		$CHO \cdot COO \cdot Na \cdot H_2O$	Hydrate, 114·0	cryst.	
86	—, Et ester		$CHO \cdot CO \cdot OC_2H_5$	102·1	liq.	
87	Homogentisic acid	2,5-Dihydroxy-phenylacetic acid	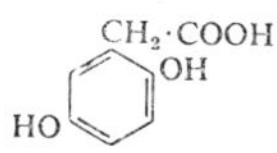	168·2; Hydrate, 186·2	leaflets from EtOH-$CHCl_3$, prisms+$1H_2O$ from H_2O	149–52
88	—, lactone	2-Oxo-5-hydroxy-coumaran	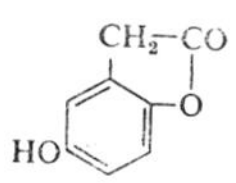	150·1	wh. cryst.	188–9
89	*p*-Hydroxy-benzoic acid	4-Hydroxy-benzoic acid	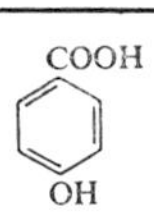	138·1; Hydrate, 156·1	col. monocl. cryst.+$1H_2O$ from aq. EtOH	212–13
90	DL-β-Hydroxy-butyric acid	DL-3-Hydroxy-butanoic acid	$CH_3 \cdot CH(OH) \cdot CH_2 \cdot COOH$	104·1	col. hygr. syrup	
91	D(−)-β-Hydroxy-butyric acid		$CH_3 \cdot CH(OH) \cdot CH_2 \cdot COOH$	104·1	col. syrupy hygr. liq.	
92	L(+)-β-Hydroxy-butyric acid		$CH_3 \cdot CH(OH) \cdot CH_2 \cdot COOH$	104·1	col. syrupy hygr. liq.	
93	DL-β-Hydroxy-*iso*butyric acid	2-Hydroxy-methylpropanoic acid	$CH_3 \cdot CH(CH_2OH) \cdot COOH$	104·1		

p.	$[\alpha]_D^t$	pK_a at 25°	*Solubility*	*Preparation*	*Estimation*	*General remarks*
			v.s. H_2O; s. EtOH, eth.	*Acta chem. scand.* **10**, 306 (1956)	*Analyt. Chem.* **26**, 449 (1954) *Analyt. Chem.* **27**, 1348 (1955)	Polymerizes rapidly on standing or in the presence of a trace of H_2O. Monomer obtained by distilling polyglyoxal. Bisphenylhydrazone, cryst. from benz., M.p. 170.
		3·32	v.s. H_2O; sl. s. EtOH, eth.	*J.B.C.* **191**, 707 (1951) *J.B.C.* **201**, 707 (1953) *J.B.C.* **229**, 305 (1957)	*J.B.C.* **210**, 269 (1954) *J.B.C.* **147**, 415 (1943) *Analyt. Biochem.* **4**, 143 (1962) *Analyt. Chem.* **31**, 250 (1959) *Arch. B.B.* **85**, 226 (1959) *See also* α-Oxo acids	The degree of hydration of glyoxylic acid is questionable. Anhyd. glyoxylic acid, PREP. *C.A.* **30**, 434 (1936). Hemihydrate, M.p. 70–75, *Arch. Pharm., Berl.* **262**, 240 (1924). 2,4-Dinitrophenylhydrazone, cryst. from H_2O, M.p. 202. Semicarbazone, λ_{max} 252 mμ ε 12 400 (in H_2O).
			s. H_2O	*Biochem. Preps.* **4**, 60 (1955)		Stable in neutral or slightly acid aq. soln.
)				*J.A.C.S.* **63**, 3338 (1941)		Phenylhydrazone, M.p. 131. Alcoholate, B.p. 137.
		4·40	85^{25} H_2O; s. EtOH, eth.; i. $CHCl_3$, benz.	*Biochem. Preps.* **4**, 6 (1955)	*B.J.* **41**, 431 (1947) *B.J.* **50**, 274 (1952)	Readily forms lactone. Neutral or acid aq. soln. stable, but rapidly decomposed by alkali. Spectrum, λ_{max} 290 mμ ε 3430 (in 0·03M-phosphate, pH 6·8). Oxidized to benzoquinone acetic acid, λ_{max} 250 mμ ε 10 790.
			0·075 H_2O	*Biochem. Preps.* **4**, 6 (1955)		Stable in air, and in acid or neutral aq. soln. Decomposed by alkali. λ_{max} 288 mμ (in H_2O).
		1. 4·58 2. 9·31	$0{\cdot}8^{15}$, $2{\cdot}6^{75}$ H_2O; $39{\cdot}3^{15}$ EtOH; $9{\cdot}4^{17}$ eth.; $0{\cdot}01^{11}$ benz.; i. CS_2	*J. org. Chem.* **12**, 85 (1947) *J.A.C.S.* **67**, 2089 (1945)		Spectrum, λ_{max} 207·5 mμ ε 13 400 and λ_{max} 255 mμ ε 13 900 (in 0·1N-HCl), λ_{max} 245 mμ ε 11 900 (pH 8, first anion), λ_{max} 280 mμ ε 16 300 (in N-NaOH, second anion). Propyl ester, cryst. from eth., M.p. 95.
[12]		At I = 0·2, 4·39	v.s. H_2O, EtOH, eth.; i. benz.		*J.B.C.* **154**, 177 (1944) *See also* Acetone	
	$-25{\cdot}3^{15}$ (c = 6·1 in H_2O)	4·41	v.s. H_2O, EtOH, eth.; i. benz.	*Biochem. Preps.* **9**, 63 (1962) *B.J.* **84**, 11 (1962)	As for DL-β-hydroxybutyric acid	It has been reported that the syrup will crystallize after standing for several months, to give v. hygr. cryst., M.p. 45–48, see *J.C.S.* **81**, 1402 (1902). Na salt, M. wt. 126·1 (anhyd.), $[\alpha]_D^{18}$ −14·4 (c = 8·5 in H_2O).
	$+25{\cdot}2^{15}$ (c = 6·0 in H_2O)		v.s. H_2O, EtOH, eth.	*Biochem. Preps.* **9**, 63 (1962)	As for DL-β-hydroxybutyric acid	Addition of a crystal of D(−)-β-hydroxybutyric acid causes syrup to crystallize immediately. Similarly, L(+)-β-hydroxybutyric acid crystal causes crystallization of D(−)-β-hydroxybutyric acid, see *J.C.S.* **81**, 1402 (1902). Na salt, M. wt. 126·1 (anhyd.), $[\alpha]_D^{17}$ +14·2 (c = 8·4 in H_2O).
				Meth. Enzymol. **6**, 549 (1963)	*J.B.C.* **224**, 1 (1957)	Dry Na salt (cryst. from EtOH) stable on storage. Phenylurethane, M.p. 122.

2. Carboxylic Acids, Alcohols, Aldehydes, and Ketones

No.	*Name*	*Synonyms*	*Formula*	*M. wt.*	*Physical form*	*M.p.*
94	α-Hydroxy-β-carboxy-*iso*caproic acid	3-*iso*Propylmalic acid	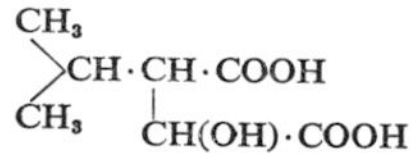	176·2	needles from Et acetate-$CHCl_3$	146–7
95	β-Hydroxy-β-methyl-glutaric acid	3-Hydroxy-3-methyl-glutaric acid	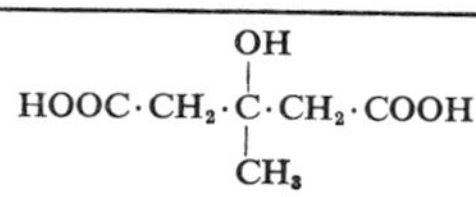	162·2	col. flakes from eth.-pet. eth.	108–9
96	β-Hydroxy-β-methyl-glutaric anhydride	3-Hydroxy-3-methyl-pentanedioic anhydride	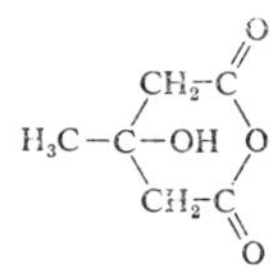	144·1	needles from benz.	102–3
97	DL-*p*-Hydroxy-phenyllactic acid		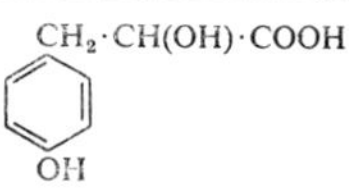	182·2; Hydrate, 200·2	needles+ $1H_2O$ from H_2O	Anhyd., 144
98	L-*p*-Hydroxy-phenyllactic acid		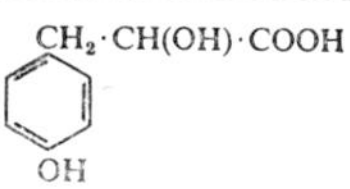	182·2; Hydrate, 191·2	needles+ $\frac{1}{2}H_2O$ from H_2O	169–70
99	*p*-Hydroxy-phenylpyruvic acid		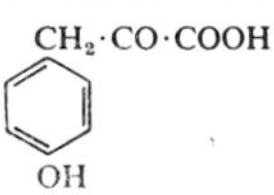	180·2	hexagonal plates from H_2O	220 d.
100	β-Hydroxy-propionic acid	3-Hydroxy-propanoic acid; Hydracrylic acid	$HO\cdot CH_2\cdot CH_2\cdot COOH$	90·1	syrup	
101	Hydroxy-pyruvic acid	2-Oxo-3-hydroxy-propanoic acid	$HO\cdot CH_2\cdot CO\cdot COOH$	Hydrate, 122·1; Anhyd., 104·1	wh. non-hygr. cryst.+ $1H_2O$ from acet.-pet. eth.	81–82 vigorous decomp.
102	—, Li salt		$HO\cdot CH_2\cdot C(OH)_2\cdot COO\cdot Li$	128·0 (hydrated form)	col. cryst. from H_2O	
103	Itaconic acid	Methylene-butanedioic acid	$CH_2{:}C(COOH)\cdot CH_2\cdot COOH$	130·1	wh. rhombs	164–5

p.	$[\alpha]^t_D$	pK_a at 25°	*Solubility*	*Preparation*	*Estimation*	*General remarks*
	$-5{\cdot}2^{24}$ (c = 1·5 in H_2O)		s. H_2O, Et acetate	*Biochemistry* **2**, 1053 (1963) *Biochemistry* **1**, 1157 (1962)	*Biochemistry* **2**, 1053 (1963)	Two racemates, M.p. 119 and 122 isolated from the synthetic material. The racemate with M.p. 119 is identical with the naturally occurring material. The configuration of the natural compound is *threo*-D_S.
			s. H_2O, eth.	*Biochem. Preps.* **6**, 25 (1958)		Stable when stored dry. Bis-*p*-toluide of methyl ester, M.p. 144. Bisanilide of methyl ester, M.p. 132. Synthesis of derivatives, *Ann.* **631**, 61 (1960). Chromatography and detection, *J. Chromat.* **4**, 458 (1960).
			s. H_2O d.	*B.Z.* **329**, 476 (1958)	*J.B.C.* **159**, 21 (1945)	Acetylated anhydride readily formed by refluxing acid with acetic anhydride and traces of acetyl chloride, transparent prisms, M.p. 85.
			s. H_2O, EtOH; sl. s. eth.	*J.A.C.S.* **73**, 4972 (1951)	*J. clin. Invest.* **20**, 199 (1941)	Loses H_2O at 100° but not over H_2SO_4.
	$-19{\cdot}6$ (c = 1·3 in H_2O)		s. H_2O, EtOH		As for DL-*p*-hydroxyphenyl-lactic acid	Loses H_2O at 100°.
			s. EtOH, eth., Et acetate; sl. s. H_2O, benz.	*Chem. Rev.* **41**, 585 (1947) *J.B.C.* **197**, 309 (1952) *Org. Synth.* **43**, 49 (1963)	*Z.P.C.* **286**, 19 (1950) *B.J.* **26**, 917 (1932) *B.J.* **41**, 449 (1947) *B.J.* **41**, 511 (1947) *Meth. biochem. Anal.* **5**, 107 (1957)	Decomposes in hot aq. solns. in the presence of air. Rapidly oxidized in alkaline soln., forming *p*-hydroxybenzaldehyde. Phenylhydrazone, M.p. 161–2. 2,4-Dinitrophenylhydrazone, M.p. 178.
mp.		3·73	v.s. H_2O; s. EtOH; ∞ eth.	*Meth. Enzymol.* **6**, 549 (1963)		Conc. solns. develop impurities on storage. Can be regenerated from propiolactone and purified via the cryst. Ca–Zn salt.
			s. H_2O, eth., acet.	*Biochem. Preps.* **9**, 86 (1962) *J.B.C.* **164**, 417 (1946)	*J.B.C.* **214**, 409 (1955) *B.J.* **68**, 84 (1958) *Analyt. Biochem.* **4**, 159 (1962)	Decomposes in alkaline soln. at pH 11·6, best kept in slightly acid aq. soln. The free acid exists in the oxo form in the solid state and in aq. soln. Water of crystallization cannot readily be removed. 2,4-Dinitrophenylhydrazone, cryst. from Et acetate–light pet. (3:1), M.p. 160–1 d.
			s. H_2O	*Biochem. Preps.* **9**, 86 (1962)	*B.J.* **68**, 84 (1958)	Exists in a hydrated diol form in the solid state, but probably in the oxo form in aq. soln. The solid is stable for many months at 4°. Less stable in aq. soln., particularly in the presence of alkali.
nes		1. 3·82 2. 5·55	$5{\cdot}9^{10}$, $8{\cdot}3^{20}$ H_2O; 20^{15} 88% EtOH; v. sl. s. eth., benz., $CHCl_3$, CS_2, pet. eth.	*Org. Synth.* Coll. **2**, 368 (1943) *Meth. Enzymol.* **3**, 437 (1957)	*Meth. Enzymol.* **3**, 437 (1957) *J.B.C.* **226**, 689 (1957)	Phenacyl ester, M.p. 78–79. Dibenzylamide, M.p. 106. Benzylammonium salt, M.p. 132–3. *p*-Bromophenacyl ester, M.p. 117.

No.	Name	Synonyms	Formula	M. wt.	Physical form	M.p.
104	DL-Lactic acid	2-Hydroxy-propanoic acid; Ordinary lactic acid	$CH_3\cdot CH(OH)\cdot COOH$	90·1	hygr. syrupy liq., s.g. $1{\cdot}249^{15}_{4}$	18
105	—, Li salt		$CH_3\cdot CH(OH)\cdot COO\cdot Li$	96·0	non-hygr. wh. cryst. from H_2O-EtOH	
106	—, Na salt		$CH_3\cdot CH(OH)\cdot COO\cdot Na$	112·1	v. hygr. col. or yel. liq., s.g. $1{\cdot}38^{20}_{4}$	17
107	—, Ca salt		$(CH_3\cdot CH(OH)\cdot COO)_2\cdot Ca\cdot 5H_2O$	Hydrate, 308·3	efflor. wh. powder	
108	—, Zn salt		$(CH_3\cdot CH(OH)\cdot COO)_2\cdot Zn\cdot 3H_2O$	Hydrate, 297·6	deliq. wh. rh. cryst.	
109	D-(−)-Lactic acid	Formerly known as *l*-lactic acid	$CH_3\cdot CH(OH)\cdot COOH$	90·1	v. hygr. prism. plates	28
110	—, Li salt		$CH_3\cdot CH(OH)\cdot COO\cdot Li\cdot \frac{1}{2}H_2O$	Hydrate, 105·0	plates	
111	—, Zn salt		$(CH_3\cdot CH(OH)\cdot COO)_2\cdot Zn\cdot 2H_2O$	Hydrate, 279·5	needles	
112	L-(+)-Lactic acid	Sarcolactic acid, formerly known as *d*-lactic acid	$CH_3\cdot CH(OH)\cdot COOH$	90·1	sl. hygr. cryst. from eth.-isopropyl ether (1:1)	51–52
113	—, Zn salt		$(CH_3\cdot CHOH\cdot COO)_2\cdot Zn\cdot 2H_2O$	Hydrate, 279·5	needles from EtOH-H_2O	
114	Maleic acid	*cis*-Butenedioic acid; Toxilic acid	$HC\cdot COOH$ ‖ $HC\cdot COOH$	116·1	wh. prisms	130–1
115	—, Na salt		$C_4H_2O_4\cdot Na_2\cdot \frac{1}{2}H_2O$	Hydrate, 169·0	wh. powder	
116	DL-Malic acid	2-Hydroxy-butanedioic acid; Hydroxysuccinic acid	$HOOC\cdot CH(OH)\cdot CH_2\cdot COOH$	134·1	col. cryst.	131
117	D-Malic acid		$HOOC\cdot CH(OH)\cdot CH_2\cdot COOH$	134·1	cryst.	98–99

….	$[\alpha]^t_D$	pK_a at 25°	*Solubility*	*Preparation*	*Estimation*	*General remarks*
…^{15}		3·86	∞ H_2O, EtOH, eth.; i. $CHCl_3$		*J.B.C.* **138**, 535 (1941) *B.J.* **55**, 289 (1953) *B.J.* **58**, 154 (1954)	Polymerizes. Can be regenerated by diluting with H_2O and boiling. Soln. (1 mg/ml, prep. from Li lactate) in 0·2N-H_2SO_4 will keep indefinitely at 2–4°.
			s. H_2O	*Meth. Enzymol.* 3, 245 (1957)		Material of choice for lactate standard soln. Aq. soln. about neutral.
			v.s. H_2O, EtOH; i. eth.			Aq. soln. neutral.
			$3{\cdot}1^{0}$, $7{\cdot}9^{80}$ H_2O; 3·0 90% EtOH; i. eth.			Loses H_2O at 120°. Aq. soln. slightly acid (pH about 6·5).
			$1{\cdot}67^{15}$, $16{\cdot}7^{100}$ H_2O; v. sl. s. EtOH			
	$-2{\cdot}26^{15}$ (c = 1·24 in H_2O)		∞ H_2O, EtOH, eth.	*Biochem. Preps.* 3, 61 (1953)	As for DL-lactic acid	On heating on a water bath forms anhydride.
	$+13{\cdot}3^{10}$ (c = 0·96 anhyd. in H_2O)		s. H_2O; v. sl. s. EtOH	*J. Ass. off. agric. Chem.* **20**, 130 (1937)		
	$+8{\cdot}0^{15}$ (c = 2·5 anhyd. in H_2O)		Anhyd. $5{\cdot}0^{15}$, $9{\cdot}0^{33}$ H_2O	*Biochem. Preps.* 3, 61 (1953)		Separate from inactive form by recrystallizing at 35°. Tends to form supersaturated soln.
	$+2{\cdot}67^{15}$ (c = 2·51 in H_2O)		∞ H_2O, EtOH, eth.	*Biochem. Preps.* 3, 61 (1953) *Biochem. Preps.* 8, 75 (1961)	*B.J.* **86**, 22 (1963) As for DL-lactic acid	On heating on a water bath forms anhydride. Specific rotation decreases markedly on increasing concentration, see *Biochem. Preps.* 8, 75 (1961).
	$-8{\cdot}0^{15}$ (c = 2·5 anhyd. in H_2O)		Anhyd. $5{\cdot}0^{15}$, $9{\cdot}0^{33}$ H_2O; 0·1 hot EtOH	*Biochem. Preps.* 3, 61 (1953)		Separate from inactive form by recrystallizing at 35°. Very readily forms supersaturated soln. Specific rotation is of opposite sign to free acid and decreases markedly on increasing concentration.
		1. 1·97 2. 6·24	$78{\cdot}8^{25}$, $392^{97\cdot5}$ H_2O; $69{\cdot}9^{30}$ EtOH; 8^{25} eth.; s. acet., gl. acetic; v. sl. s. benz.		*J.B.C.* **192**, 231 (1951)	λ_{max} 210 mμ, ε 32 000.
			$96{\cdot}1^{25}$ H_2O			Water of crystallization somewhat variable.
		1. 3·40 2. 5·26	144^{26}, 411^{79} H_2O; v.s. EtOH; sl. s. eth.		*J.B.C.* **212**, 787 (1955) *J.B.C.* **180**, 1225 (1949)	
	$+3{\cdot}07^{20}$ (c = 4 in H_2O) $+2{\cdot}92$ (c = 30 in MeOH)		v.s. H_2O, MeOH, EtOH, acet.	*J.B.C.* 59, 7 (1924) *J.C.S.* **1923**, 1090	As for DL-malic acid	Optical rotation in aq. soln. depends markedly upon concentration and temperature. With increasing concentration the rotation decreases and more concentrated solns. are laevorotatory.

No.	*Name*	*Synonyms*	*Formula*	*M. wt.*	*Physical form*	*M.p.*
118	L-Malic acid	*l*-Hydroxy-butanedioic acid; Ordinary malic acid	$HOOC\cdot CH(OH)\cdot CH_2\cdot COOH$	134·1	col. needles	100
119	Malonic acid	Propanedioic acid	$HOOC\cdot CH_2\cdot COOH$	104·1	col. cryst.	135
120	Malonic semialdehyde	3-Oxopropanoic acid; Formylacetic acid	$CHO\cdot CH_2\cdot COOH$	88·1		
121	Mesaconic acid	Methylfumaric acid	$HOOC\cdot C\cdot CH_3$ ‖ $HC\cdot COOH$	130·1	col. needles from H_2O or EtOH	202–4
122	Methanol	Methyl alcohol; Wood alcohol; Carbinol	$CH_3\cdot OH$	32·0	hygr. col. liq., s.g. $0{\cdot}792^{20}_{4}$	−97·8
123	*cis*-β-Methyl-glutaconic acid	*cis*-3-Methyl-glutaconic acid	$HOOC\cdot CH{:}C(CH_3)\cdot CH_2\cdot COOH$	144·1	lustrous plates	150
124	Methyl-glutaconic anhydride	6-Hydroxy-4-methyl-α-pyrone	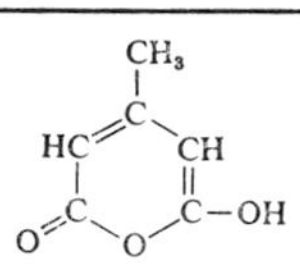	126·1	needles from benz.	90
125	Methylglyoxal	2-Oxopropanal; Pyruvic aldehyde	$CH_3\cdot CO\cdot CHO$	72·1	yel. liq., pungent odour	
126	Methyl-malonic acid	2-Methyl-propanedioic acid; *iso*Succinic acid	$HOOC\cdot CH(CH_3)\cdot COOH$	118·1	col. needles	132
127	DL-Methyl-malonic semialdehyde	2-Methyl-3-oxopropanoic acid	$HOOC\cdot CH(CH_3)\cdot CHO$	102·1		

p.	$[\alpha]_D^t$	pK_a at 25°	*Solubility*	*Preparation*	*Estimation*	*General remarks*
	−2·3[20] (c = 9·17 in H_2O) −5·7 (c = 3·73 in acet.)	1. 3·40 2. 5·13	v.s. H_2O, EtOH; 6·0 eth.		*B.J.* **50**, 349 (1952) *J.B.C.* **174**, 979 (1948) As for DL-malic acid.	Optical rotation in aq. soln. depends markedly upon concentration and temperature. With increasing concentration the rotation decreases and concentrated solns. (greater than 34 g per 100 ml H_2O at 20°) are dextrorotatory. Optical rotation enhanced by presence of molybdate, see *B.J.* **37**, 334 (1943).
		1. 2·85 2. 5·70	61·1[0], 73·5[20], 92·6[50], H_2O; 57[20] EtOH; 5·7[15] eth.		*Acta chem. scand.* **12**, 1437 (1958)	At 10^{-2} M, powerful inhibitor of certain enzymes, e.g. succinate dehydrogenase, fumarate hydratase, lactate and malate dehydrogenases.
			s. H_2O	*Meth. Enzymol.* **6**, 549 (1963)	*Meth. Enzymol.* **6**, 549 (1963)	Solns. of the aldehyde in phosphate buffer pH 6·0 are not stable on prolonged storage. 10–20% lost in 24 hr at 0° and 50% in 24 hr at R.T. The 2,4-dinitrophenylhydrazone is unstable but can be prepared at 0°, M.p. 136.
		1. 3·09 2. 4·75	2·7[18], 118[100] H_2O; 24·1[17] 90% EtOH; s. eth.; v. sl. s. benz., pet. eth., $CHCl_3$	*Org. Synth.* Coll. **2**, 382 (1943)	*J.B.C.* **234**, 320 (1959)	
7			∞ H_2O, EtOH, most organic solvents		*Am. J. clin. Path.* **25**, 1071 (1955)	
			s. H_2O, benz.	*J.A.C.S.* **75**, 2377 (1953) *J.A.C.S.* **77**, 4125 (1955)		Identity of *cis*- and *trans*-isomers uncertain until prep. and characterization of pure *trans*-isomer, *J.C.S.* **1960**, 2886. *trans*-Methylglutaconic acid, M.p. 140. Compound M.p. 115, initially identified as *trans*-isomer, shown to be a mixture of *cis*- and *trans*-isomers.
5			s. H_2O	*J.C.S.* **1912**, 856 *J.A.C.S.* **75**, 2377 (1953)		*Cis*- and *trans*-acids give same hydroxy anhydride which can be recrystallized from H_2O. Titrates as a monobasic acid, i.e. forms salts. Requires heating for some hr with excess alkali to form the di-alkali salt. Gives an intense purple colour with $FeCl_3$.
			s. H_2O, EtOH, eth.		*J.B.C.* **196**, 853 (1952) *B.J.* **57**, 227 (1954) *Z.P.C.* **160**, 116 (1926) *J.B.C.* **212**, 847 (1955)	Liq. at R.T. is dimeric, and rapidly polymerizes to a glassy mass. This at 50° gives either the dimeric liq. or a monomeric gas. Bis-2,4-dinitrophenylhydrazone, M.p. 299–300. *p*-Nitrophenylhydrazone, M.p. 217. Bis-*p*-nitrophenylhydrazone, M.p. 302–4.
		1. 3·07 2. 5·76	44·3[0], 66[20] H_2O; v.s. EtOH, eth.	*J.A.C.S.* **80**, 4949 (1958)	*J. Lab. clin. Med.* **66**, 667 (1965) *Analyt. Biochem.* **18**, 10 (1967)	Crystallizes from H_2O as hydrate. Gives propionic acid on heating at 150°. Does not inhibit respiration as does malonic acid. PREP. of diethyl ester, *Org. Synth.* Coll. **2**, 279 (1943).
			s. H_2O	*Biochem. Preps.* **7**, 69 (1960)	*J.B.C.* **224**, 1 (1957) *J.B.C.* **225**, 511 (1957)	Soln. stable for 3 weeks at −18° at pH 6·4. 50% loss in this time at pH 8·5. The 2,4-dinitrophenylhydrazone is less stable than the free acid and decomposes to give propionaldehyde 2,4-dinitrophenylhydrazone.

2. Carboxylic Acids, Alcohols, Aldehydes, and Ketones

No.	*Name*	*Synonyms*	*Formula*	*M. wt.*	*Physical form*	*M.p.*
128	DL-Mevalonic acid	3,5-Dihydroxy-3-methylvaleric acid	CH_3 | $HO{\cdot}CH_2{\cdot}CH_2{\cdot}C(OH){\cdot}CH_2{\cdot}COOH$	148·2	oil	
129	DL-Mevalonic acid lactone	**DL-β-Hydroxy-β-methylvalero-lactone; DL-3-Hydroxy-3-methylpentano-5-lactone**	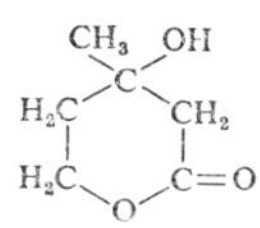	130·1	hygr. cryst. from acet.-eth. (at −69°)	27–28
130	*cis-cis*-Muconic acid	*cis-cis*-2,4-Hexadienedioic acid	CH—COOH ‖ CH | CH ‖ CH—COOH	142·1	prisms or rhombs from EtOH	194–5 (rapid heating)
131	Oxalic acid	Ethanedioic acid	$HOOC{\cdot}COOH{\cdot}2H_2O$	Hydrate, 126·1; Anhyd., 90·0	col. cryst.	101; Anhyd., 189
132	Oxaloacetic acid, keto form	2-Oxobutanedioic acid	$HOOC{\cdot}CO{\cdot}CH_2{\cdot}COOH$	132·1		
133	—, *cis*-enol	Hydroxymaleic acid	HOOC—C·OH ‖ HOOC—CH	132·1	cryst.	151–2
134	—, *trans*-enol	Hydroxy-fumaric acid	HOOC—C·OH ‖ H—C—COOH	132·1	cryst.	184
135	Oxalosuccinic acid		HOOC·CO·CH·COOH | $CH_2{\cdot}COOH$	190·1		

·	$[\alpha]^t_D$	pK_a *at 25°*	*Solubility*	*Preparation*	*Estimation*	*General remarks*
		4·3	v.s. H_2O; s. $CHCl_3$	*J.A.C.S.* 79, 2316 (1957)	*J. Bact.* **72**, 519 (1956)	No distinction between acid and lactone in biological systems. The preparation yields an equilibrium mixture of the acid and its δ-lactone. Natural isomer is (+); (−)-isomer biologically inactive, *Z.P.C.* 313, 291 (1958). Isolated via *N,N'*-dibenzylethylenediammonium bis-(3,5-dihydroxy-3-methylpentanoate), cryst. from MeOH-eth., M.p. 124–5. Synthetic material resolved via its (+)-α-phenyl-1-naphthalenemethylamide, M.p.151–2, *J.A.C.S.* **79**, 3294 (1957). Diphenylmethylamide, cryst. from benz., M.p. 97–98. REVIEW. *Adv. Enzymol.* **23**, 471 (1961).
·1			v.s. H_2O; s. $CHCl_3$	*B.J.* 69, 146 (1958) *J.A.C.S.* **79**, 2316 (1957)	*J. Bact.* **72**, 519 (1956)	Decomposed by NaOH to give the Na salt. Rotation of natural isomer, (+) for acid, (−) for lactone, *Helv. chim. Acta* **43**, **1508** (1960).
			s. hot H_2O; sl. s. eth.	*J.C.S.* **1950**, 2228	*B.J.* **51**, 339 (1952) See also *J.B.C.* **210**, 821 (1954)	Recrystallize from EtOH. Free acid is rapidly converted to the *cis-trans*-isomer by boiling H_2O, but not by boiling EtOH or MeOH, nor by alkali at R.T. or for short periods at 100°, nor by daylight. Spectrum, λ_{max} 257 mμ ε 17 300 (at pH 7·0). Methyl ester, M.p. 73–74. *cis-trans-* and *trans-trans*-Muconic acids, see *J.C.S.* **1950**, 2228, 2235.
imes		1. 1·27 2. 4·29	9·5^{15}, 120^{90} H_2O; 23·7^{15} EtOH; 16·9 eth.; i. $CHCl_3$, benz.		*Meth. Enzymol.* **3**, 271 (1957), **5**, 637 (1962)	Chelates metals. Inhibits lactate dehydrogenase from heart and succinate dehydrogenase competitively.
		1. 2·55 2. 4·37			*Meth. biochem. Anal.* **5**, 107 (1957) *B.J.* **39**, 408 (1945) *J.B.C.* **147**, 415 (1943) *B.Z.* **328**, 245 (1956) *B.B.A.* **10**, 623 (1953)	Known only in soln. or as derivatives. In aq. soln. at pH 6·0 ϵ_{260} = 850, corresponding to 9% of enol form, *J.C.S.* **1958**, 3673; at neutral pH enol content 15–16%, *J.C.S.* **1961**, 5043; see also *J.B.C.* **212**, 787 (1955). 2,4-Dinitrophenylhydrazone, cryst. from H_2O, M.p. 218.
		1. 2·15^{20} 2. 4·06^{20}	s. H_2O, EtOH, acet., Et acetate; sl. s. eth.; i. benz., $CHCl_3$	*B.J.* **35**, 595 (1941) *Biochem. Preps.* **3**, 59 (1953) *J.C.S.* **1952**, 3315		λ_{max} 260 mμ ε 8800 (in eth.). Thought to be completely enolized in eth. On chelation with transition metal ions max. absorption of enolate is shifted to a higher wavelength and ε is increased 2–3 fold. At pH 13 in aq. soln. complete enolization to give trianion which is stable; enolate ion, ϵ_{260} 3200.
		1. 2·56^{17}	s. H_2O, EtOH, eth.; i. $CHCl_3$, benz.	*J.C.S.* **1952**, 3315 *B.J.* **59**, 194 (1955) *J.A.C.S.* **72**, 4704 (1950)		The identification of compounds M.p. 152 and 184 as *cis-* and *trans*-isomers is questioned, *B.Z.* **328**, 245 (1956), since their i.r. spectra are identical. It is proposed that a compound of variable decomp. point 144–72 is the *trans*-enol form, *J.C.S.* **1961**, 5043.
				J.B.C. **174**, 115 (1948)	*J.B.C.* **174**, 115 (1948)	Very unstable. Acid keeps in neutral soln. at 0° for a few hr. Store as Ba salt.

No.	*Name*	*Synonyms*	*Formula*	*M. wt.*	*Physical form*	*M.p.*
136	Oxalosuccinic acid, triethyl ester		$C_2H_5O\cdot OC\cdot CO\cdot CH(CH_2\cdot CO\cdot OC_2H_5)\cdot CO\cdot OC_2H_5$	274·3	yel. oil	
137	α-Oxo acids		$R\cdot CO\cdot COOH$			
138	α-Oxoadipic acid	2-Oxohexane-dioic acid	$HOOC\cdot (CH_2)_3\cdot CO\cdot COOH$	160·1	light orange cryst. from acet.-eth.	124
139	β-Oxoadipic acid	3-Oxohexane-dioic acid	$HOOC\cdot CH_2\cdot CH_2\cdot CO\cdot CH_2\cdot COOH$	160·1	plates from acet.-$CHCl_3$	124–5
140	α-Oxobutyric acid	2-Oxobutanoic acid	$CH_3\cdot CH_2\cdot CO\cdot COOH$	102·1	hygr. plates	30–32
141	α-Oxocaproic acid	α-Ketocaproic acid	$CH_3\cdot (CH_2)_3\cdot CO\cdot COOH$	130·1	liq.	7
142	α-Oxo*iso*-caproic acid	'Ketoleucine'	$(CH_3)_2CH\cdot CH_2\cdot CO\cdot COOH$	130·1	liq.	−2
143	α-Oxoglutaric acid	α-Ketoglutaric acid	$HOOC\cdot CH_2\cdot CH_2\cdot CO\cdot COOH$	146·1	cryst. from acet.-benz.	110–12
144	D-α-Oxo-β-methylvaleric acid	'Ketoisoleucine'	$CH_3\cdot CH_2\cdot CH(CH_3)\cdot CO\cdot COOH$	130·1		38–40

.	$[\alpha]^t_D$	pK_a *at 25°*	*Solubility*	*Preparation*	*Estimation*	*General remarks*
–5[12]				*Org. Synth.* **Coll.** 3, 510 (1955)		
				Chem. Rev. **41**, 585 (1947) *J.B.C.* **197**, 309 (1952)	*J.B.C.* **147**, 415 (1943) *J.B.C.* **197**, 309 (1952) *J.B.C.* **218**, 897 (1956) *J.B.C.* **210**, 617 (1954) *J.B.C.* **208**, 23 (1954) *Org. Analysis* **1**, 243 (1953) *Meth. biochem. Anal.* **5**, 107 (1957)	Methods given are for total α-oxo acids but are particularly useful where only one α-oxo acid of known constitution is present. Separations of oxo acids may be achieved by chromatographic methods, see, for example, *B.J.* **53**, 340 (1953) and this book, p. 515.
			s. H_2O	*Ber.* **88**, 316 (1955) *J.B.C.* **176**, 1395 (1948)	*See* α-Oxo acids	2,4-Dinitrophenylhydrazone, cryst. from H_2O, M.p. 208. Phenylhydrazone, cryst. from H_2O–EtOH, M.p. 141–2. 2,4-Dinitrophenylhydrazone of diethyl-2-oxoadipic acid, yel. needles, M.p. 58–59.
				J.C.S. **1950**, 2223	*J. Bact.* **66**, 404 (1953)	
			v.s. H_2O, EtOH; sl. s. eth.	*J.B.C.* **164**, 417 (1946) *J.B.C.* **197**, 309 (1952) *Chem. Rev.* **41**, 585 (1947)	*J.B.C.* **184**, 117 (1950) *See also* α-Oxo acids	2,4-Dinitrophenylhydrazone, cryst. from H_2O, M.p. 198.
20				*See* α-Oxo acids	*See* α-Oxo acids	2,4-Dinitrophenylhydrazone, cryst. from H_2O, M.p. 153.
15				*Biochem. Preps.* **3**, 66 (1953) *See also* α-Oxo acids	*J.B.C.* **197**, 309 (1952) *See also* α-Oxo acids	Decomposes slowly at 0°. Cryst. Na salt (M. wt. 152·1) stable at R.T. 2,4-Dinitrophenylhydrazone, cryst. from H_2O, M.p. 162, spectrum in 1·25N-NaOH, λ_{max} 435 mμ ε 17 700.
		1. 2·47 2. 4·68	v.s. H_2O, EtOH; sl. s. eth.	*Org. Synth.* **Coll.** 3, 510 (1955)	*Meth. biochem. Anal.* **5**, 107 (1957) *J.B.C.* **147**, 415 (1943) *J.B.C.* **187**, 173 (1950) *B.J.* **47**, 605 (1950) *B.J.* **55**, 530 (1953) *Manometric Techniques*, 4th ed., p. 210, Burgess (1964) *Arch. B.B.* **85**, 226 (1959) *See also* α-Oxo acids	Can be recrystallized from acet. or gl. acetic by adding benz. 2,4-Dinitrophenylhydrazone, cryst. from H_2O, M.p. 220, spectrum, λ_{max} 420 mμ ε 15 400 (in 1·25N-NaOH). Semicarbazone, λ_{max} 247–8 mμ ε 10 000 (in aq. soln.).
		2·3		*J.B.C.* **190**, 269 (1951) *Chem. Rev.* **41**, 585 (1947)	*J.B.C.* **190**, 269 (1951) *J.A.C.S.* **74**, 4253 (1952) *See also* α-Oxo acids	2,4-Dinitrophenylhydrazone, M.p 176, $[\alpha]^{26}_D$ +16·7 (c = 2 in EtOH). Na salt (M. wt. = 152·1), $[\alpha]^{26}_D$ +32·6 (c = 1 in H_2O). L-α-oxo-β-methylvaleric acid ('Keto*allo*-isoleucine') exactly as D-isomer except that the optical rotations have the opposite sign.

2. Carboxylic Acids, Alcohols, Aldehydes, and Ketones

No.	Name	Synonyms	Formula	M. wt.	Physical form	M.p.
145	α-Oxovaleric acid	α-Ketovaleric acid	$CH_3 \cdot CH_2 \cdot CH_2 \cdot CO \cdot COOH$	116·1	liq.	6–7
146	α-Oxo*iso*-valeric acid	'Ketovaline'	CH_3 >$CH \cdot CO \cdot COOH$ CH_3	116·1	cryst.	31
147	Phenol	Carbolic acid	$C_6H_5 \cdot OH$	94·1	col. rh. needles	41
148	Phenylacetic acid	α-Toluic acid	$C_6H_5 \cdot CH_2 \cdot COOH$	136·2	col. leaflets	76–77
149	L-Phenyllactic acid	L-α-Hydroxyhydrocinnamic acid	$C_6H_5 \cdot CH_2 \cdot CH(OH) \cdot COOH$	166·2	needles	124
150	Phenylpyruvic acid	α-Oxohydrocinnamic acid	$C_6H_5 \cdot CH_2 \cdot CO \cdot COOH$	164·2	plates from $CHCl_3$	157 d.
151	—, Na salt		$C_6H_5 \cdot CH_2 \cdot CO \cdot COO \cdot Na \cdot H_2O$	Hydrate, 204·2	cryst.	
152	Pimelic acid	Heptanedioic acid	$HOOC \cdot (CH_2)_5 \cdot COOH$	160·2	monocl. prisms from H_2O	105·7
153	Prephenic acid	1-Carboxy-4-hydroxy-2,5-cyclohexadiene-1-pyruvic acid	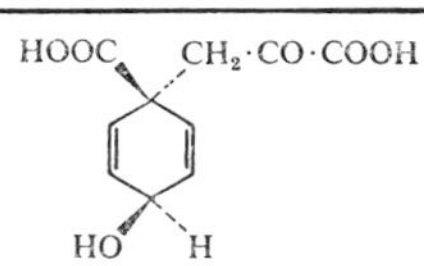	226·2		
154	—, Ba salt		$C_{10}H_8O_6 \cdot Ba \cdot H_2O$	379·5	wh. cryst.	
155	1,2-Propanediol	Propylene glycol	$CH_2OH \cdot CH(OH) \cdot CH_3$	76·1	col. liq., s.g. $1{\cdot}040_4^{20}$	
156	Propionaldehyde	Propanal	$CH_3 \cdot CH_2 \cdot CHO$	58·1	col. liq., s.g. $0{\cdot}807_4^{20}$	−81
157	Propionic acid	Propanoic acid	$CH_3 \cdot CH_2 \cdot COOH$	74·1	col. liq., s.g. $0{\cdot}993_4^{20}$	−21

p.	$[\alpha]^t_D$	pK_a at 25°	*Solubility*	*Preparation*	*Estimation*	*General remarks*
9			s. eth., $CHCl_3$, benz.; sl. s. H_2O	*Chem. Rev.* **41**, 585 (1947)	*J.B.C.* **184**, 117 (1950) *See also* α-Oxo acids	Phenylhydrazone, M.p. 101–2. 2,4-Dinitrophenylhydrazone, cryst. from H_2O, M.p. 167.
0			s. H_2O, EtOH, eth.	*J.B.C.* **197**, 309 (1952) *Chem. Rev.* **41**, 585 (1947)	*J.B.C.* **197**, 309 (1952) *J.B.C.* **205**, 475 (1953) *See also* α-Oxo acids	2,4-Dinitrophenylhydrazone, cryst. from H_2O, M.p. 196.
2		10·00	$6{\cdot}7^{16}$, ∞^{66} H_2O; ∞ EtOH; v.s. eth.; s. $CHCl_3$, CS_2		*Meth. biochem. Anal.* **1**, 27 (1954)	Spectrum, λ_{max} (ε) 210·5 mμ (6200) and 270 mμ (1450) in H_2O; phenate anion, 235 mμ (9400) and 287 mμ (2600) in H_2O.
		4·31	$1{\cdot}6^{20}$ H_2O; 186 EtOH; 151 $CHCl_3$; v.s. eth.	*J.A.C.S.* **83**, 4262 (1961) *Org. Synth.* Coll. **1**, 427 (1941)	*Analyt. Chem.* **26**, 1432 (1954) *Analyt. Biochem.* **4**, 423 (1962) *J. Antibiot., Tokyo* Ser. **B9**, 18 (1956)	In aq. soln. forms a complex with its Na salt. *N*-Phenylacetylmonoethanolamine, M.p. 94. *N*-(Phenylacetyl)chlorourethan, M.p. 117. *N*-Phenylacetylacrylamide, M.p. 134.
	$-21{\cdot}4^{24}$ (c = 1 in H_2O)		s. hot H_2O, EtOH, eth.	*J.B.C.* **18**, 29 (1914)	*P.S.E.B.M.* **75**, 83 (1950) *J.B.C.* **181**, 273 (1949)	
			v. sl. $s.^{100}$ H_2O; v.s. EtOH, eth.	*Org. Synth.* Coll. **2**, 519 (1943) *J.B.C.* **197**, 309 (1952)	*P.S.E.B.M.* **81**, 715 (1952) *B.J.* **31**, 266 (1937) *J.B.C.* **147**, 415 (1943) *B.J.* **90**, 248 (1964) *Meth. biochem. Anal.* **5**, 107 (1957)	Oxidizes in air. Spectrum, λ_{max} 320 mμ ε 17 500 (in 0·7N-NaOH). Phenylhydrazone, M.p. 162–3. 2,4-Dinitrophenylhydrazone, cryst. from H_2O or EtOH, M.p. 192–4, or cryst. from Et acetate-pet. eth., M.p. 162–4. Two forms are interconvertible, see *J. org. Chem.* **17**, 1534 (1952).
			s. H_2O; i. EtOH			Stable in air. H_2O remains at 100°.
		1. $4{\cdot}50^{18}$ 2. $5{\cdot}43^{18}$	$2{\cdot}5^{13}$, 5^{20} H_2O; v.s. EtOH, eth.; i. cold benz.	*Org. Synth.* Coll. **2**, 531 (1943)		
			s. H_2O	*Arch. B.B.* **64**, 51 (1956) *Can. J. Biochem.* **42**, 583 (1964) *Angew. Chem.* **74**, 423 (1962); *Int. ed.* **1**, 367 (1962)	*Arch. B.B.* **64**, 51 (1956) *Can. J. Biochem.* **42**, 583 (1964)	Decomp. by acid to phenylpyruvic acid and CO_2. Half-life at 0°, 1 hr in 0·1M-HCl, 7 hr at pH 4, no detectable loss at pH 6·8. More stable to alkali, but on heating forms *p*-hydroxyphenyllactic acid.
			s. H_2O; i. EtOH			In presence of excess $Ba(OH)_2$ cryst. as v. hygr. needles of $(C_{10}H_9O_6)_2{\cdot}Ba{\cdot}H_2O$.
			∞ H_2O, EtOH; s. eth.			
9			20^{20} H_2O; ∞ EtOH, eth.		*Analyt. Chem.* **26**, 1035 (1954) *Org. Analysis* **1**, 243 (1953)	2,4-Dinitrophenylhydrazone, M.p. 155, spectrum in $CHCl_3$, λ_{max} 356 mμ ε 22 500 (neutral), λ_{max} 438 mμ ε 22 500 (alkaline).
		4·87	∞ H_2O, EtOH, eth., $CHCl_3$		*Meth. biochem. Anal.* **8**, 1 (1960) *Analyt. Chem.* **33**, 146 (1961) *See also* Volatile fatty acids	

2. Carboxylic Acids, Alcohols, Aldehydes, and Ketones

No.	*Name*	*Synonyms*	*Formula*	*M. wt.*	*Physical form*	*M.p.*
158	Propionic acid, Na salt		$CH_3\cdot CH_2\cdot COO\cdot Na$	96·1	col. cryst. or powder	
159	—, K salt		$CH_3\cdot CH_2\cdot COO\cdot K\cdot H_2O$	Hydrate, 130·2	wh. hygr. cryst.	
160	—, Ca salt		$(CH_3\cdot CH_2\cdot COO)_2\cdot Ca\cdot H_2O$	Hydrate, 204·2	col. tablets	
161	—, anhydride	Propanoic anhydride	$CH_3\cdot CH_2\cdot CO\cdot O\cdot CO\cdot CH_2\cdot CH_3$	130·2	col. liq., s.g. 1·010$^{20}_{4}$	−45
162	Protocatechuic acid	3,4-Dihydroxy-benzene-carboxylic acid	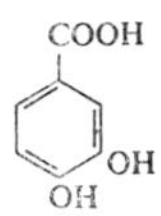	154·1; Hydrate, 172·1	monocl. needles $+1H_2O$ from H_2O	202–4
163	Pyruvic acid	2-Oxopropanoic acid	$CH_3\cdot CO\cdot COOH$	88·1	col. liq. s.g. 1·267$^{20}_{4}$	13·6
164	—, Li salt		$CH_3\cdot C(OH)_2\cdot COO\cdot Li$	112·0	cryst.	
165	—, Na salt		$CH_3\cdot CO\cdot COO\cdot Na$	110·0	plates from acet. $-H_2O$	
166	—, K salt		$CH_3\cdot CO\cdot COO\cdot K$	126·2	needles from EtOH–H_2O	
167	*l*-Quinic acid	1,3,4,5-Tetra-hydroxycyclo-hexanecarboxylic acid	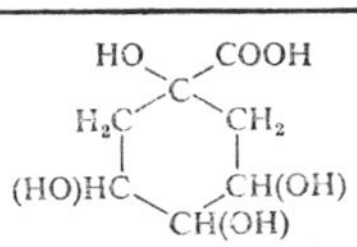	192·2	col. monocl. cryst. from H_2O	173–4
168	Shikimic acid	3,4,5-Trihydroxy-1-cyclohexene-carboxylic acid	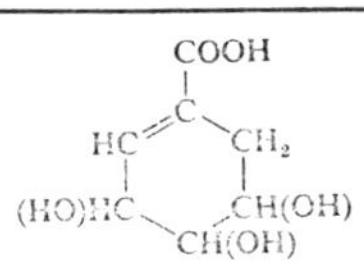	174·2	cryst. from H_2O or gl. acetic	190
169	Succinic acid	Butanedioic acid	$HOOC\cdot CH_2\cdot CH_2\cdot COOH$	118·1	col. monocl. prisms	184

p.	$[\alpha]_D^t$	pK_a at 25°	*Solubility*	*Preparation*	*Estimation*	*General remarks*
			100^{25}, 150^{100} H_2O; 4 EtOH			Aq. soln. neutral or slightly alkaline.
			207^{16}, 360^{100} H_2O; 22^{13} 95% EtOH			Loses H_2O at 120°.
			49^{0}, 56^{100} H_2O; i. EtOH			Solubility in H_2O reaches a minimum at 55°.
			s. H_2O d., EtOH d.; ∞ eth.		*Analyt. Chem.* **23**, 1717 (1951) *J.B.C.* **159**, 21 (1945)	
		4·48	$1{\cdot}8^{14}$, 27^{80} H_2O; v.s. EtOH; s. eth.	*Org. Synth.* Coll. **3**, 745 (1955)	*J.B.C.* **230**, 625 (1958) See *J.B.C.* **219**, 781 (1956)	Oxidizes in air. Diacetyl deriv., M.p. 157–8.
^{760} d., ^{20}		2·49	∞ H_2O, EtOH, eth.	*Org. Synth.* Coll. **1**, 475 (1941)	*Meth. biochem. Anal.* **5**, 107 (1957) *J.B.C.* **147**, 415 (1943) *Manometric Techniques*, 4th ed., Burgess, p. 210 (1964) *J.B.C.* **184**, 117 (1950) *J.B.C.* **161**, 559 (1945) *B.Z.* **279**, 174 (1935) *Arch. B.B.* **85**, 225 (1959) *See also* α-Oxo acids	Polymerizes and decomposes on standing unless pure and kept in air-tight container. Phenylhydrazone, M.p. 192. 2,4-Dinitrophenylhydrazone, cryst. from H_2O, M.p. 216, spectrum in alkali λ_{max} 445 mμ ε 20 400. Semicarbazone, spectrum in aq. soln. λ_{max} 246 mμ ε 10 200.
			s. H_2O	*J.B.C.* **94**, 717 (1932)		In the solid state the compound is consistent with the formula given and not $CH_3{\cdot}CO{\cdot}COOLi{\cdot}H_2O$, *B.J.* **68**, 81 (1958).
			s. H_2O; v. sl. s. EtOH	*Biochem. Preps.* **2**, 22 (1952)		
			s. H_2O	*J.B.C.* **193**, 721 (1951)		
	$-44{\cdot}0^{20}$ (in H_2O)		40^{9} H_2O; s. EtOH; v. sl. s. eth.	*Cont. Boyce Thompson Inst. Pl. Res.* **19**, 341 (1958) *J.C.S.* **1961**, 1854	*J.B.C.* **230**, 1043 (1958) *Bull. agric. chem. Soc. Japan* **22**, 205 (1958); *C.A.* **52**, 20911*h* (1958)	Forms γ-lactone (quinide) on heating to 200–50°.
	$-183{\cdot}8^{18}$ (c=4 in H_2O)	4·21	18 H_2O; $2{\cdot}25^{23}$ EtOH; $0{\cdot}015^{28}$ eth.; i. $CHCl_3$, benz.	*J.B.C.* **220**, 477 (1956) *J.A.C.S.* **81**, 2909 (1959)	*J. Bact.* **66**, 129 (1953) *Arch. B.B.* **70**, 377 (1957) *J.B.C.* **230**, 1043 (1958) *J.B.C.* **223**, 907 (1956)	λ_{max} 213 mμ ε 8900. Methyl ester, M.p. 113–14. REVIEW. *Chem. Rev.* **65**, 435 (1965).
		1. 4·21 2. 5·64	$6{\cdot}8^{20}$, 121^{100} H_2O; $7{\cdot}5^{21\cdot5}$ EtOH; 0·3 eth.; s. MeOH, acet.; i. benz., $CHCl_3$, CCl_4		*B.J.* **34**, 442 (1940) *J.B.C.* **195**, 75 (1952)	

2. Carboxylic Acids, Alcohols, Aldehydes, and Ketones

No.	*Name*	*Synonyms*	*Formula*	*M. wt.*	*Physical form*	*M.p.*
170	Succinic acid, Na salt		$C_4H_4O_4 \cdot Na_2 \cdot 6H_2O$	Hydrate, 270·1	granules or cryst. powder	
171	—, K salt		$C_4H_4O_4 \cdot K_2 \cdot 3H_2O$	Hydrate, 248·3	hygr. wh. cryst. powder	
172	—, anhydride	Butanedioic anhydride	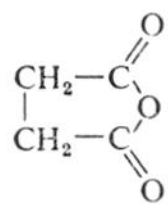	100·1	col. needles from EtOH	120
173	Succinic semialdehyde	4-Oxobutanoic acid; Formylpropionic acid	$HOOC \cdot CH_2 \cdot CH_2 \cdot CHO$	102·1	visc. col. liq.	
174	(±)-Tartaric acid	2,3-Dihydroxy-butanedioic acid; Racemic acid; Paratartaric acid	$HOOC \cdot CH(OH) \cdot CH(OH) \cdot COOH \cdot H_2O$	Hydrate, 168·1; Anhyd., 150·1	triclinic cryst. from H_2O, slightly efflor.	203–4
175	—, NH_4 salt		$C_4H_4O_6 \cdot (NH_4)_2$	184·2	prisms or wh. granules	
176	—, acid Na salt		$C_4H_4O_6 \cdot NaH \cdot H_2O$	Hydrate, 190·1	wh. monocl. cryst.	
177	—, acid K salt		$C_4H_4O_6 \cdot KH$	188·2	col. monocl. cryst.	
178	(+)-Tartaric acid	Ordinary tartaric acid; L-*threo*-Dihydroxy-succinic acid	COOH HC·OH HO·CH COOH	150·1	prisms	167–70
179	—, NH_4 salt		$C_4H_4O_6 \cdot (NH_4)_2$	184·2	wh. cryst.	
180	—, acid Na salt		$C_4H_4O_6 \cdot NaH \cdot H_2O$	Hydrate, 190·1	wh. cryst.	
181	—, acid K salt	Argol; Tartar; Cream of tartar	$C_4H_4O_6 \cdot KH$	188·2	cryst. or wh. powder	
182	—, K salt	Soluble tartar	$C_4H_4O_6 \cdot K_2 \cdot \frac{1}{2}H_2O$	Hydrate, 235·3	col. monocl. cryst.	
183	—, KNa salt	Rochelle salt; Seignette salt	$C_4H_4O_6 \cdot KNa \cdot 4H_2O$	Hydrate, 282·2	rh. cryst. or powder	70–80
184	(−)-Tartaric acid	D-*threo*-Dihydroxy-succinic acid	COOH HO·CH HC·OH COOH	150·1	cryst.	167–70
185	*meso*-Tartaric acid	*i*-Tartaric acid; *erythro*-Dihydroxy-succinic acid	COOH HC·OH HC·OH ·H_2O COOH	Hydrate, 168·1; Anhyd., 150·1	plates	Anhyd., 140

p.	$[\alpha]^t_D$	pK_a at 25°	*Solubility*	*Preparation*	*Estimation*	*General remarks*
			21·45^{0}, 86·6^{75} H_2O; v. sl. s. EtOH			Stable in air. Loses all H_2O at 120°. Aq. soln. neutral or slightly alkaline.
			v.s. H_2O			Aq. soln. practically neutral.
			s. EtOH d.; v. sl. s. H_2O d., eth.		*Analyt. Chem.* 27, 1464 (1955) *J.B.C.* 159, 21 (1945)	Half-life in H_2O of 4·3 min at 25°.
–6^{14}			s. H_2O	*Meth. Enzymol.* 5, 765 (1962) ^{14}C. *Acta biol. med. germ.* 11, 712 (1963)	*Acta biol. med. germ.* 11, 712 (1963) *Meth. Enzymol.* 5, 765 (1962)	Solns. at 2° and pH 6 or lower stable for more than 3 months. Tends to polymerize. *p*-Nitrophenylhydrazone, M.p. 177–8. 2,4-Dinitrophenylhydrazone, cryst. from H_2O or 95% EtOH, M.p. 202–3, unstable in alkaline soln., λ_{max} 420 mμ (in alkali).
		1. 3·04 2. 4·37	9·23^{0}, 20·6^{20}, 184·9^{100} H_2O; 2·1 EtOH; 1·1 eth.	*Org. Synth.* Coll. 1, 497 (1941)	*Moderne Methoden der Pflanzenanalyse*, vol. 2, p. 509, Springer-Verlag, Berlin (1955) *Analyt. Biochem.* 4, 143 (1962)	Loses H_2O at 100°. Anhyd. form obtained by crystallizing from H_2O above 73° or from EtOH or by drying monohydrate at 100°.
			6·3^{15} H_2O; sl. s. EtOH			
			8·9^{19} H_2O; i. EtOH			Loses H_2O at 100°. Decomposes without melting at 219°. Aq. soln. acid.
			0·42^{25} H_2O; i. EtOH			Aq. soln. acid.
	+11·98^{20} (c = 20 in H_2O) +0·47 (in MeOH)	1. 2·89 2. 4·16	139·5^{20}, 343^{100} H_2O; 20·4^{15} EtOH; 0·4 eth.; s. MeOH, acet.; i. $CHCl_3$			
	+34·6^{15} (in H_2O)		5·9 H_2O; sl. s. EtOH			Crystals slowly evolve NH_3.
	+21·8^{19} (in H_2O)		6·7^{18}, 50^{100} H_2O; v. sl. s. EtOH			Loses H_2O at 100°. Decomposes without melting at 234°.
			0·37^{20}, 6·1^{100} H_2O; i. EtOH; s. dil. acids and alkalis			
			150^{14}, 278^{100} H_2O; v. sl. s. EtOH			Aq. solns. pH 7–8.
			26^{0}, 66^{26} H_2O; v. sl. s. EtOH			Aq. soln. pH 7–8. Loses $3H_2O$ at 100°, becomes anhyd. at 130–40°.
	−11·98^{20} (c = 20 in H_2O)	1. 2·89 2. 4·16	v.s. H_2O; s. EtOH, MeOH, acet.			Properties of (−)-tartaric acid and salts are exactly the same as those of (+)-tartaric acid except that the optical rotations have the opposite sign.
		1. 3·22 2. 4·82	125^{15} H_2O; s. EtOH; sl. s. eth.	*Org. Synth.* Coll. 1, 497 (1941)		

No.	*Name*	*Synonyms*	*Formula*	*M.wt.*	*Physical form*	*M.p.*
186	Tartronic semialdehyde	2-Hydroxy-3-oxopropanoic acid	$HOOC{\cdot}CH(OH){\cdot}CHO$	104·1		
187	*n*-Valeric acid	Pentanoic acid	$CH_3{\cdot}(CH_2)_3{\cdot}COOH$	102·1	col. liq., s.g. $0{\cdot}942^{20}_{4}$	−59, F.p. −34·5
188	*iso*Valeric acid	3-Methyl-butanoic acid; *iso*Valerianic acid	CH_3 $\rangle CH{\cdot}CH_2{\cdot}COOH$ CH_3	102·1	col. liq., s.g. $0{\cdot}937^{15}_{4}$	−37·6, F.p. −29·3
189	—, Na salt	Sometimes called sodium valerate	$C_5H_9O_2{\cdot}Na$	124·1	hygr. col. cryst. or lumps	*ca.* 140
190	—, Ca salt	Calcium *iso*valerianate	$(C_5H_9O_2)_2{\cdot}Ca{\cdot}3H_2O$	Hydrate, 296·4	cryst. powder	
191	Vinylacetic acid	3-Butenoic acid; Propylene-3-carboxylic acid	$CH_2{:}CH{\cdot}CH_2{\cdot}COOH$	86·1	liq.	−39
192	Volatile fatty acids					

·p.	$[\alpha]^t_D$	pK_a *at 25°*	*Solubility*	*Preparation*	*Estimation*	*General remarks*
			s. H_2O, EtOH	*J. Biochem., Tokyo* **47,** 741 (1960) *B.J.* **81,** 273 (1961)	*J. Biochem., Tokyo* **47,** 741 (1960) *Analyt. Biochem.* **4,** 159 (1962)	Forms a bis derivative with 2,4-dinitrophenylhydrazine. *p*-Nitrophenylhydrazone, M.p. 236 d. Phenylosazone, M.p. 210 d. Can distinguish between tartronic semialdehyde and its isomer, hydroxypyruvate, by estimation given in *Analyt. Biochem.* **4,** 159 (1962), see also *B.J.* **78,** 69 (1961).
6·3		4·84	$3{\cdot}7^{16}$ H_2O; ∞ EtOH, eth.		*Meth. biochem. Anal.* **8,** 1 (1960) *Analyt. Chem.* **33,** 146 (1961) *See also* Volatile fatty acids	
6·7		4·78	$4{\cdot}2^{20}$ H_2O; ∞ EtOH, eth.; s. $CHCl_3$		*Meth. biochem. Anal.* **8,** 1 (1960) *Analyt. Chem.* **33,** 146 (1961) *See also* Volatile fatty acids	Salts more soluble than those of *n*-valeric acid.
			s. H_2O, EtOH			
			Anhyd. salt, 26^0, $21{\cdot}8^{20}$, $22{\cdot}0^{40}$, $16{\cdot}55^{100}$ H_2O			From hot aq. soln. crystallizes as $(C_5H_9O_2)_2{\cdot}Ca{\cdot}H_2O$. Transition point 45·5°.
, 70^{12}		4·35	s. H_2O; ∞ EtOH, eth.	*Org. Synth.* Coll. **3,** 851 (1955)		Contact with alkali causes isomerization to crotonic acid.
					B.J. **50,** 679 (1952) *B.J.* **58,** 670 (1954) *Meth. biochem. Anal.* **8,** 1 (1960) *Analyt. Chem.* **33,** 146 (1961) Hilditch & Williams, *Chemical composition of natural fats,* 4th ed., p. 678, Chapman & Hall (1964) *J.B.C.* **123,** 161 (1938) *J.B.C.* **169,** 403 (1947) *B.J.* **60,** 683 (1955) *Arch. B.B.* **23,** 347 (1949)	The methods in the first five references give estimates of individual fatty acids in mixtures. The methods in the last four references are for the estimation of total volatile fatty acids, and are especially useful when it is known that only one fatty acid is present.

3. Phosphate Esters excluding Nucleotides and Coenzymes

Revised by J. L. PEEL (*Agricultural Research Council Food Research Institute, Norwich*)

In this section the term 'hydrolysis' refers to the release of phosphorus as inorganic phosphate, unless otherwise indicated. The proportion of phosphate released is expressed as a percentage of the *total* phosphorus in the molecule.

The abbreviation 'Bergmeyer' refers to *Methods of Enzymatic Analysis*, ed. H. U. Bergmeyer, Academic Press (1963).

In a few cases where methods of estimation are not available, references have been given which contain information indicating a possible method of estimation.

Additional data on intermediates in purine and terpene synthesis, including data on compounds not included in this Table, are given in the following respective reviews:

J. M. Buchanan and S. C. Hartman, *Adv. Enzymol.* **21**, 199 (1959).
G. Popjak and J. W. Cornforth, *Adv. Enzymol.* **22**, 281 (1960).

Information on the separation of phosphate esters by chromatography and ionophoresis is given in the following:

H. E. Wade and D. M. Morgan, *B.J.* **60**, 264 (1955).
S. Aranoff, *Techniques of Radiobiochemistry*, p. 194, Iowa State University Press, Ames, Iowa (1956).
R. S. Bandurski and B. Axelrod, *J.B.C.* **193**, 405 (1951).
D. C. Mortimer, *Can. J. Chem.* **30**, 653 (1952).
W. W. Wells, T. Katagi, R. Bentley, and C. C. Sweeley, *B.B.A.* **82**, 408 (1964).

3. Phosphate Esters excluding Nucleotides and Coenzymes

No.	*Name*	*Synonyms*	*Formula*
1	*N*-Acetylglucosamine-1-phosphate		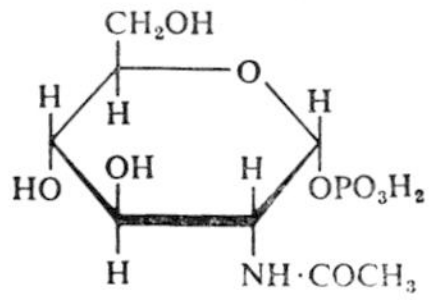 **(α-isomer)**
2	*N*-Acetylglucosamine-6-phosphate		**cf. *N*-Acetylglucosamine-1-phosphate**
3	Acetyl phosphate		$CH_3CO\cdot O\cdot PO_3H_2$
	—, Li_2 salt		$C_2H_3O_5PLi_2$
4	2-Aminoethanol-1-phosphate	Phosphorylethanolamine, Ethanolamine phosphoric acid	$H_2N\cdot CH_2\cdot CH_2\cdot O\cdot PO_3H_2$
	—, Ba salt —, acid Ba salt		$C_2H_6NO_4PBa\cdot 3H_2O$ $C_2H_7NO_4PBa_{0.5}\cdot 2{\cdot}5H_2O$
5	5-Amino-4-imidazole-carboxamide ribotide	5-Amino-1-β-D-ribosyl-4-imidazolecarboxamide-5′-phosphate, 5-Amino-4-imidazole-carboxamide ribonucleotide, AICAR, ACP	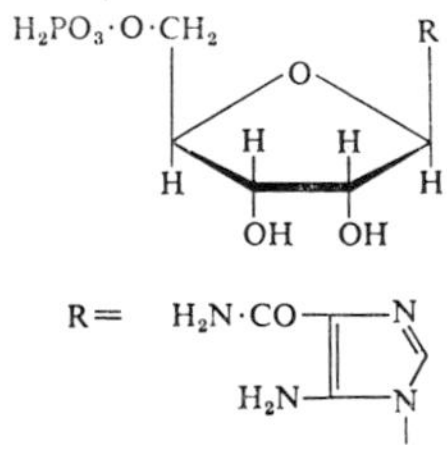
	—, Ba salt		$C_9H_{13}N_4O_8PBa$
6	5-Aminoimidazole ribotide	5-Amino-1-ribosyl-imidazole-5′-phosphate, 5-Aminoimidazole ribonucleotide, AIR	**cf. 5-Amino-4-imidazolecarboxamide ribotide** R= 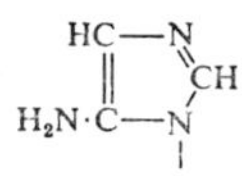
7	Arginine phosphate	Phosphoarginine	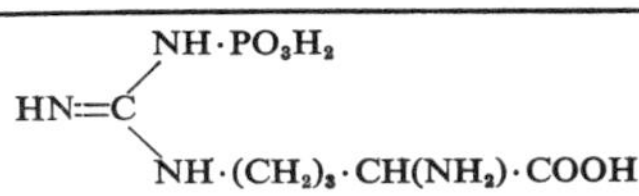
8	β-L-Aspartyl phosphate	BAP	$HOOC\cdot CH(NH_2)\cdot CH_2\cdot CO\cdot O\cdot PO_3H_2$
9	Carbamyl phosphate		$H_2N\cdot CO\cdot O\cdot PO_3H_2$
	—, Na_2 salt —, Li_2 salt —, $(NH_4)_2$ salt		$CH_2NO_5PNa_2$ $CH_2NO_5PLi_2$ $CH_2NO_5P(NH_4)_2$
10	Choline phosphate	Phosphorylcholine, Choline phosphoric acid	$(CH_3)_3N^+\cdot CH_2\cdot CH_2\cdot O\cdot PO_3H^-$
	—, Ba salt chloride —, Ca salt chloride		$C_5H_{13}NO_4PClBa$ $C_5H_{13}NO_4PClCa\cdot 4H_2O$

M. wt.	Preparation	Estimation	General remarks
01·2	SYN. *B.B.A.* **20,** 33 (1956)	*B.B.A.* **20,** 33 (1956)	41% hydrolysis in 2 hr at 37° in N-H_2SO_4. $[\alpha]_D$+107 for Ca salt (0·13M).
1·2	SYN. *B.J.* **84,** 185 (1962) *J.B.C.* **230,** 497 (1958) *J.A.C.S.* **78,** 1393 (1956)	*B.B.A.* **20,** 33 (1956)	60% hydrolysis in 3 min at 100° in 0·2N-alkali. $[\alpha]^{25}_D$ +29·5 (equilibrium value, c = 8 in 0·5M-Na acetate, final pH 3·0).
0·0 1·9	SYN. *J.B.C.* **185,** 549 (1950) *J.C.S.* **1955,** 732 *Meth. Enzymol.* **3,** 228 (1957) (also ^{32}P)	*J.B.C.* **159,** 21 (1945) *J.B.C.* **153,** 571 (1944) *J.B.C.* **162,** 421 (1946)	Unstable in solution, especially in acid and alkali. 20% hydrolysis in 30 min at room temp. at pH 7; 45% in 10 min in 0·5N-HCl. Solutions stable at −35°. Hydrolysis in acid accelerated by molybdate and behaves as inorg. P in Fiske & Subbarow method.
·1 ·5 ·8	SYN. ^{14}C. *J. org. Chem.* **26,** 1658 (1961) *B.J.* **31,** 1459 (1937) *Can. J. Chem.* **34,** 436 (1956) ISOL. *B.J.* **30,** 197 (1936)	*J.B.C.* **183,** 545 (1950) *P.S.E.B.M.* **87,** 643 (1954)	M.p. 244. pK_2 5·84. V. stable to acid and alkali, 5% hydrolysis in 5 hr at 100° in N-HCl. Ba, Ca salts cryst. ex aq. ethanol.
·2 5	ENZYME SYN. *J.B.C.* **228,** 201 (1957) SYN. *J.B.C.* **237,** 485 (1962)	*J.B.C.* **234,** 1791 (1959)	Glycosidic bond more stable than that of purine nucleotides, e.g. < 5% hydrolysis in 90 min at 100° in 0·2N-H_2SO_4. $\epsilon = 12{\cdot}6\times10^3$ at 269 mμ at pH 7, $9{\cdot}4\times10^3$ at pH 1. pK_a 6·3.
2	ENZYME SYN. *J.B.C.* **224,** 1005 (1957) ISOL. *J.B.C.* **212,** 647 (1955)	*J.B.C.* **224,** 1005 (1957)	Unstable. Obtained as Ba salt, 35–60% pure.
2	ISOL. *B.J.* **62,** 358 (1956) SYN., ISOL. and ENZYME SYN. *B.J.* **92,** 429 (1964)	*B.J.* **63,** 153 (1956)	Isolated as carbonate. 100% hydrolysis in 1 min at 100° in 0·1N-HCl. pK_1 2·0, pK_2 4·5, pK_3 9·40, pK_4 11·2. Cryst. ex aq. ethanol. M.p. 175–80 (free acid), 180 (Li_2 salt).
	SYN. *J.B.C.* **213,** 27 (1955)	*J.B.C.* **213,** 27 (1955)	Somewhat less stable than acetyl phosphate. V. unstable below pH 4·5 and above pH 13.
	SYN. *Biochem. Preps.* **7,** 23 (1960) ($(NH_4)_2$ and Na_2 salts) *Meth. Enzymol.* **3,** 653 (1957) (Li_2 salt) *J.A.C.S.* **77,** 819 (1955) (Li_2 salt)	*Biochem. Preps.* **7,** 23 (1960) *Meth. Enzymol.* **3,** 653 (1957)	100% hydrolysis of Li_2 salt in 2 min at 100° in water, in 10 min at room temp. in 0·1N-alkali. 50% hydrolysis in 2 hr at 30° in H_2O; pH has little effect in range 1·5–9. Anhydrous salts stable several weeks over desiccant in cold. Soln. of Li_2 salt stable frozen. $(NH_4)_2$ and Na_2 salts cryst. ex 32% ethanol at −23°. % purity of salts obtained: $(NH_4)_2$, 100; Na_2, 95·5–97·5; Li_2, 86.
	SYN. *Biochem. Preps.* **2,** 96 (1956) ^{32}P. *J.A.C.S.* **66,** 512 (1944)	*B.J.* **60,** 325 (1955)	15% hydrolysis in 5 hr at 100° in N-HCl, 100% in 4 hr refluxing with sat. $Ba(OH)_2$. Ba salt cryst. ex aq. ethanol.

3. Phosphate Esters excluding Nucleotides and Coenzymes

No.	*Name*	*Synonyms*	*Formula*
11	Creatine phosphate	Phosphocreatine	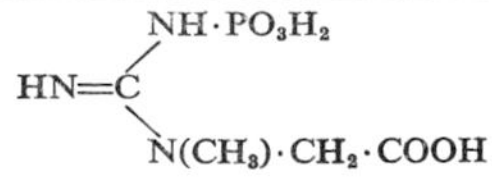
	—, Na_2 salts		$C_4H_8N_3O_5PNa_2 \cdot 4H_2O$, needles Usually $C_4H_8N_3O_5PNa_2 \cdot 6H_2O$, hex. platelets
12	3-Deoxy-D-arabino-heptulosonic acid-7-phosphate	2-Keto-3-deoxyheptonic acid-7-phosphate, KDHP, DAHP, DHP	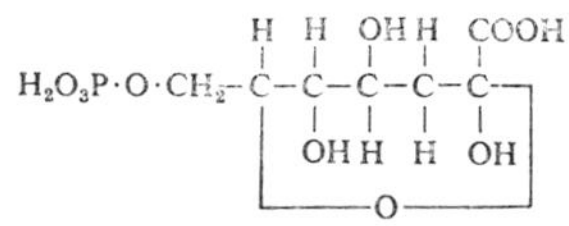
	—, Ba salts		$C_7H_{10}O_{10}PBa_{1.5} \cdot 2H_2O$ $C_7H_{10}O_{10}PBa_{1.5} \cdot 4H_2O$
13	2-Deoxyribose-1-phosphate		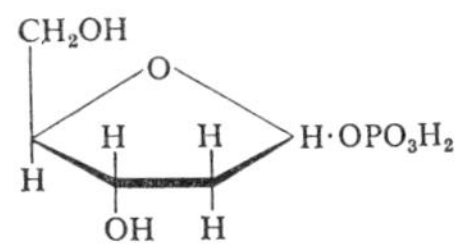
	—, $(NH_4)_2$ salt —, *bis*(Cyclohexyl-ammonium) salt		$C_5H_9O_7P(NH_4)_2$ $C_5H_{11}O_7P \cdot (C_6H_{13}N)_2$
14	Deoxyribose-5-phosphate		cf. Deoxyribose-1-phosphate
	—, Ba salt		$C_5H_9O_7PBa \cdot 2H_2O$
15	Dihydroxyacetone phosphate	DHAP	$HOCH_2 \cdot CO \cdot CH_2 \cdot O \cdot PO_3H_2$
16	Dimethylallyl pyrophosphate	3-Methylbut-2-enyl-1-pyrophosphate	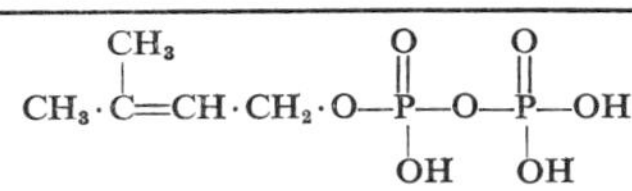
17	D-Erythrose-4-phosphate		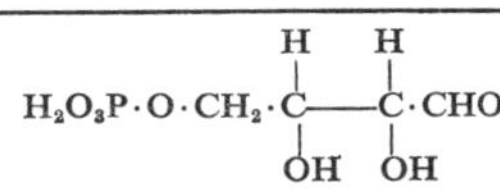
18	D-Erythritol-4-phosphate		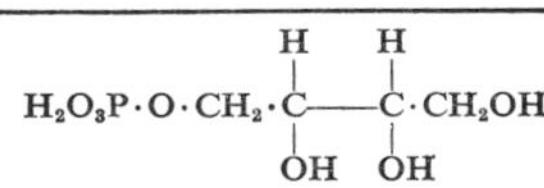
	—, *bis*(Cyclohexyl-ammonium) salt		$C_4H_{11}O_7P \cdot (C_6H_{13}N)_2$
19	Farnesyl pyrophosphate	*trans-trans*-2,6,10-Dodecatriene-3,7,11-trimethyl-1-pyrophosphate	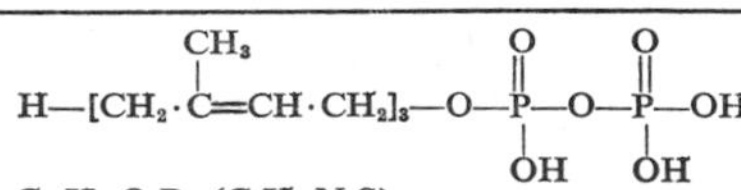
	—, *bis*(*S*-Benzyliso-thiuronium) salt		$C_{15}H_{28}O_7P_2 \cdot (C_8H_{10}N_2S)_2$

M. wt.	*Preparation*	*Estimation*	*General remarks*
211·1	SYN. *B.J.* **43**, 190 (1948) *Biochem. Preps.* **5**, 9 (1957)	*J.B.C.* **209**, 191 (1954) Bergmeyer, pp. 568, 610 *Aust. J. exp. Biol. med. Sci.* **28**, 647 (1950) *B.J.* **51**, 606 (1952)	100% hydrolysis in 1 min at 100° in N-HCl. 50% hydrolysis in 4 min at 25° in 0·5N-HCl. Hydrolysis accelerated by molybdate and behaves as inorg. **P** in Fiske & Subbarow method. Hydrolysis very slow at pH 7·8. Na_2 salt cryst. ex aq. ethanol; solid salts stable but hexahydrate gives tetrahydrate under vacuum with desiccant. pK_1 2·7, pK_2 4·58.
327·1 363·2			
288·1	*J.B.C.* **238**, 3170 (1963)	*J.B.C.* **234**, 716 (1959)	$[\alpha]_D^{25}$ +15·7 (c = 3·82 K salt in H_2O) +42 (c = 1·47 free acid in H_2O). Barium tetrahydrate gives dihydrate at 100° *in vacuo.*
527·2 563·2			
214·1	ISOL. *J.B.C.* **184**, 449 (1950) *Meth. Enzymol.* **3**, 183 (1957)		50% hydrolysis in 10–15 min at 23° and pH 4. Isolated as Ba salt. Cryst. cyclohexylammonium salt.
48·2 12·5			
14·1	ENZYME SYN. *J.B.C.* **215**, 389 (1955) ISOL. *J.B.C.* **198**, 885 (1952) *Biochem. Preps.* **9**, 35 (1962) *J.B.C.* **235**, 1292 (1960) (Ba salt)	*Biochem. Preps.* **9**, 35 (1962)	45% hydrolysis in 7 min at 100° in N-HCl. Ba salt obtained 87–96% pure; freely s. in water; stable at room temp.
85·5			
70·1	SYN. *Biochem. Preps.* **7**, 45 (1960) *J.A.C.S.* **78**, 1659 (1956) *Ber.* **67**, 869 (1934) ENZYME SYN. *B.Z.* **271**, 89 (1934)	*Arch. B.B.* **74**, 306 (1958) Bergmeyer, p. 246 *J. Bact.* **42**, 665 (1941)	100% hydrolysis in 20 min at room temp. in N-alkali. 50% in 8 min at 100° in N-HCl. pK_1 1·77, pK_2 6·45. Conveniently prepared as needed by treatment of cyclohexylammonium dihydroxyacetone phosphate dimethyl ketal (stable) with Dowex 50(H^+)—see ref. 1.
6·1	SYN. *Ber.* **94**, 174 (1961)	*J.B.C.* **235**, 326 (1960) *J. Lipid Res.* **1**, 286 (1960)	Stable to alkali, unstable below pH 5·2. Instantaneous release of all P as pyrophosphate at pH 2. Intermediate in cholesterol biosynthesis.
0·1	SYN. *J.A.C.S.* **77**, 5967 (1955) *Meth. Enzymol.* **9**, 35 (1966)	*Arch. B.B.* **74**, 306 (1958) Bergmeyer, p. 205	50% hydrolysis in 20 min at 100° in N-H_2SO_4. $[\alpha]_D$ 0 (c = 1 in H_2O).
2·1	SYN. *J.A.C.S.* **78**, 3720 (1956)	*J.B.C.* **236**, 2581 (1961)	Cryst. biscyclohexylammonium salt, fine needles, M.p. 183–6, softening above 177. $[\alpha]_D^{25}$ − 2·3 (c = 3 biscyclohexylammonium salt in H_2O) +2·6 (c = 1·5 free acid in H_2O).
0·5			
2·3	SYN. *J.B.C.* **237**, 56 (1962) (Li salt; also ^2H & ^3H labelled) *Ann.* **654**, 180 (1962) (*S*-Benzylisothiuronium salt)	As for Dimethylallyl pyrophosphate	Hydrolysis as for dimethylallyl pyrophosphate. Li salt obtained with about 85% *trans-trans* form; poorly s. in H_2O. Cryst. *S*-benzylisothiuronium salt, M.p. 142–3. Intermediate in cholesterol biosynthesis.
·8			

3. Phosphate Esters excluding Nucleotides and Coenzymes

No.	*Name*	*Synonyms*	*Formula*
20	Formylglycinamide ribotide	2-Formamido-*N*-ribosylacetamide-5′-phosphate, Formylglycinamide ribonucleotide, FGAR	cf. Glycinamide ribotide, R = $H \cdot CO \cdot NH \cdot CH_2 \cdot CO \cdot NH$—
21	D-Fructose-1,6-diphosphate	Hexose diphosphate, Harden-Young ester, HDP, FDP	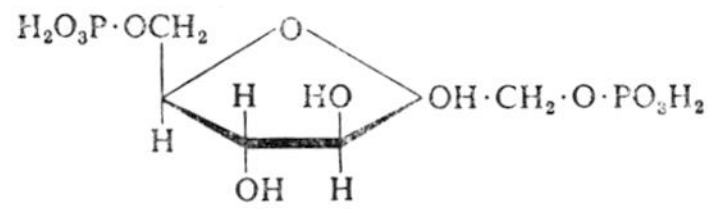
	—, Ba_2 salt		$C_6H_{10}O_{12}P_2Ba_2 \cdot H_2O$
	—, Ca_2 salt		$C_6H_{10}O_{12}P_2Ca_2 \cdot H_2O$
	—, Acid strychnine salt		$C_6H_{14}O_{12}P_2 \cdot (C_{21}H_{22}N_2O_2)_2 \cdot 2H_2O$
	—, *tris*(Cyclohexylammonium) salt		$C_6H_{14}O_{12}P_2 \cdot (C_6H_{13}N)_3$
	—, Na_3 salt		$C_6H_{11}O_{12}P_2Na_3$
22	D-Fructose-1-phosphate		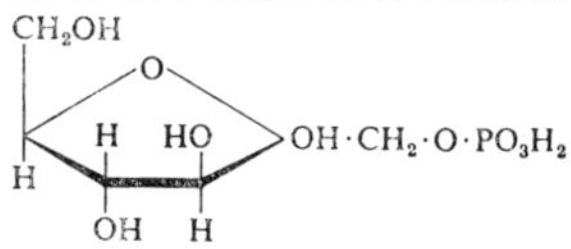
	—, Ba salt		$C_6H_{11}O_9PBa$
	—, *bis*(Cyclohexylammonium) salt		$C_6H_{13}O_9P \cdot (C_6H_{13}N)_2$
23	D-Fructose-6-phosphate	Neuberg ester	cf. Fructose-1-phosphate
	—, Ba salt		$C_6H_{11}O_9PBa$
	—, Ca salt		$C_6H_{11}O_9PCa$
24	α-D-Galactose-1-phosphate		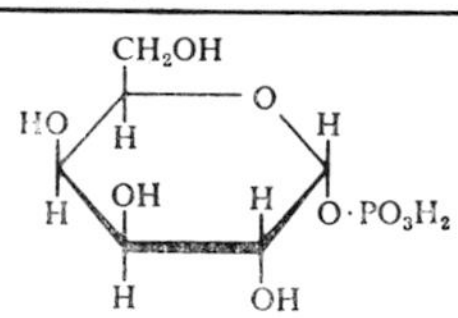
	—, Ba salt		$C_6H_{11}O_9PBa \cdot 3H_2O$
	—, K_2 salt		$C_6H_{11}O_9PK_2 \cdot 2H_2O$
25	D-Galactose-6-phosphate		cf. Galactose-1-phosphate
26	Geranyl pyrophosphate	*trans*-2,6-Octadiene-3,7-dimethyl-1-pyrophosphate	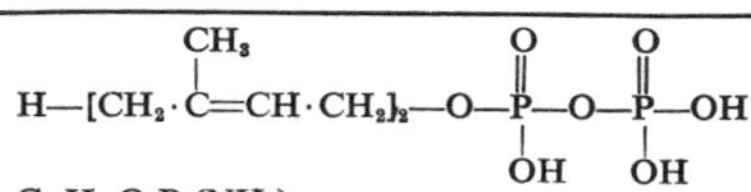
	—, $(NH_4)_3$ salt		$C_{10}H_{17}O_7P_2(NH_4)_3$
	—, *bis*(*S*-Benzylisothiuronium) salt		$C_{10}H_{20}O_7P_2 \cdot (C_8H_{10}N_2S)_2$
27	D-Gluconic acid-6-phosphate	6-Phosphogluconic acid	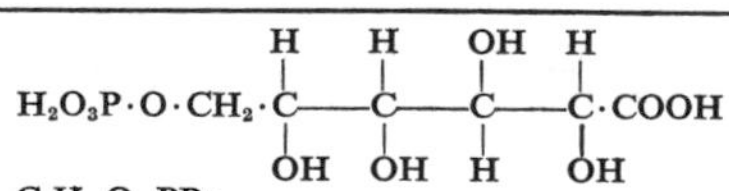
	—, Ba salt		$C_6H_{11}O_{10}PBa$
	—, *tris*(Cyclohexylammonium) salt		$C_6H_{13}O_{10}P \cdot (C_6H_{13}N)_3$
28	D-Glucosamine-6-phosphate		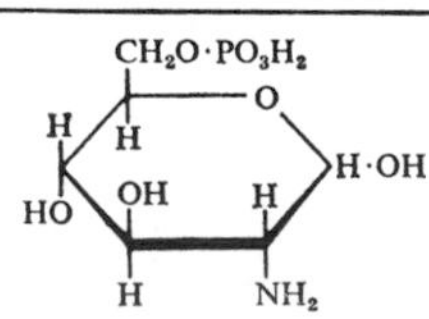

M. wt.	*Preparation*	*Estimation*	*General remarks*
14·2	ENZYME SYN. *J.B.C.* **221,** 1057 (1956) SYN. *J.B.C.* **221,** 1071 (1956)	*J.B.C.* **221,** 555 (1956)	Hydrolysis similar to glycinamide ribotide. p*K* 6·40.
0·1 28·8 34·3 45·0 37·7 06·1	ISOL. *J.A.C.S.* **64,** 2722 (1942) (Ba salt) PURIFICATION. *Arch. B.* **3,** 33 (1944) *Biochem. Preps.* **2,** 52 (1952) *Meth. Enzymol.* **3,** 240 (1957) *B.Z.* **161,** 240 (1925)	*J.B.C.* **208,** 55 (1954) *B.J.* **53,** 157 (1953) *Arch. B.B.* **74,** 326 (1958) Bergmeyer, pp. 160, 246	26·5% hydrolysis in 7 min at 100° in N-HCl. Na_3 salt v. hygr.; neutral soln. stable at −15°. Neutral Ba_2, Ca_2 salts, sp. s. in H_2O, 1 in 170; acid Ba, Ca salts, s. in H_2O, 1 in 2. Cryst. cyclohexylammonium salt, s. in H_2O. Dry salts generally stable at room temp. but Ba salt often decomposes on storage. $[\alpha]_D^{17}$ +4·04 to +4·15 (free acid). pK_1 1·48, pK_2 6·1. Mg salt is stable and soluble in water (30% soln.) and is often preferable for subsequent preparations—see refs. 3 and 4.
0·1 5·5 3·2	SYN. *Biochem. Preps.* **7,** 58 (1960) *J.B.C.* **201,** 645 (1953) *Meth. Enzymol.* **3,** 169 (1957)	*Meth. Enzymol.* **3,** 171 (1957)	100% hydrolysis in 30 min at 100° in N-HCl, 50% in 2·8 min. Naturally occurring laevorotatory isomer separated from fructose-6-phosphate by fractionation of brucine salt. Cryst. cyclohexylammonium salt. $[\alpha]_D^{20}$ −52·5 (free acid), $[\alpha]_D^{26}$ −304 (Ba salt).
·1 ·5 ·2	SYN. *Arch. B.* **3,** 33 (1944) *Meth. Enzymol.* **3,** 167 (1957)	*B.J.* **53,** 157 (1953) *B.B.A.* **11,** 416 (1953) *Arch. B.B.* **74,** 306 (1958) Bergmeyer, p. 134 *Meth. Enzymol.* **3,** 167 (1957)	50% hydrolysis in 70 min at 100° in N-HCl. pK_1 0·97, pK_2 6·11. $[\alpha]_D^{21}$ +2·5 (c = 3 in H_2O), $[\alpha]_D^{19}$ +3·58 (Ba salt).
1 ·5 ·4	SYN. *J.B.C.* **124,** 557 (1938) *B.J.* 33, 1087 (1939) *J.A.C.S.* **72,** 4824 (1950) *Biochem. Preps.* **4,** 1 (1955)	*Biochem. Preps.* **4,** 1 (1955)	50% hydrolysis in 2·1 min at 100° in N-HCl. $[\alpha]_D^{32}$ +100 (c = 1·57 K_2 salt in H_2O), $[\alpha]_D^{25}$ +96 (Ba salt in H_2O). pK_1 1·00, pK_2 6·17. Ba salt obtained 90–95% pure.
·1	SYN. *J.C.S.* **1951,** 980		$[\alpha]_D^{20}$ +36·5 (c = 0·6 in H_2O). $[\alpha]_D^{25}$ +24·5 (Ba salt).
·2 3 ·7	SYN. *Ber.* **94,** 174 (1961) *Ann.* **654,** 180 (1962) (*S*-Benzylisothiuronium salt)	As for Dimethylallyl pyrophosphate	Hydrolysis as for dimethylallyl pyrophosphate. Cryst. ammonium salt, M.p. 120. Cryst. *S*-benzylisothiuronium salt, M.p. 165–7.
1 5 7	SYN. *B.J.* **25,** 323 (1931) *J.B.C.* **192,** 175 (1951) *Meth. Enzymol.* **3,** 172 (1957)	*J.B.C.* **192,** 175 (1951) *Arch. B.B.* **74,** 306 (1958) Bergmeyer, p. 143	Ba salt obtained 95% pure. Cryst. cyclohexylammonium salt. At 70°, converted to lactone for which $[\alpha]_{5461}$ +17·4.
2	ENZYME SYN. *Biochem. Preps.* **9,** 44 (1962) *J.B.C.* **230,** 497 (1958) SYN. *J.A.C.S.* **78,** 1393 (1956)	Bergmeyer, p. 151	< 1% hydrolysis in 20 min at 100° in N-HCl. Decomp. 160–7. $[\alpha]_D^{25}$ +56·0 changing to equilibrium value +58·8 (c = 5 in H_2O). Readily s. H_2O; i. methanol, acet., eth. Unstable above pH 7. pK_2 6·08, pK_3 8·10. Barium diglucosamine 6-phosphate hydrobromide isolated.

3. Phosphate Esters excluding Nucleotides and Coenzymes

No.	*Name*	*Synonyms*	*Formula*
29	Glucose-1,6-diphosphate		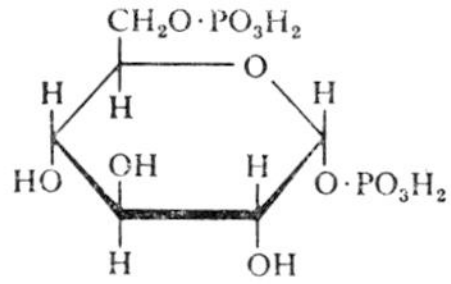 (α-isomer)
	—, Ba_2 salt		$C_6H_{10}O_{12}P_2Ba_2 \cdot H_2O$ (α-form)
30	α-D-Glucose-1-phosphate	Cori ester	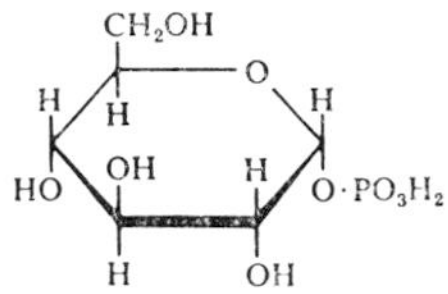
	—, Ba salt		$C_6H_{11}O_9PBa \cdot 3H_2O$
	—, K_2 salt		$C_6H_{11}O_9PK_2 \cdot 2H_2O$
	—, Na_2 salt		$C_6H_{11}O_9PNa_2 \cdot 4H_2O$
31	D-Glucose-6-phosphate	Robison ester	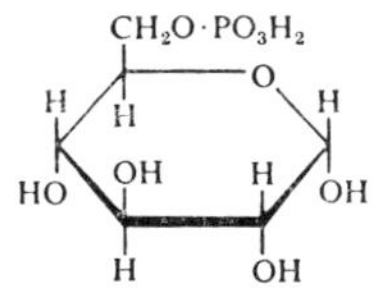 (α-isomer)
	—, Ba salt		$C_6H_{11}O_9PBa \cdot 7H_2O$
	—, Ca salt		$C_6H_{11}O_9PCa$
	—, K_2 salt		$C_6H_{11}O_9PK_2$
	—, Na_2 salt		$C_6H_{11}O_9PNa_2$
32	D-Glucuronic acid-1-phosphate		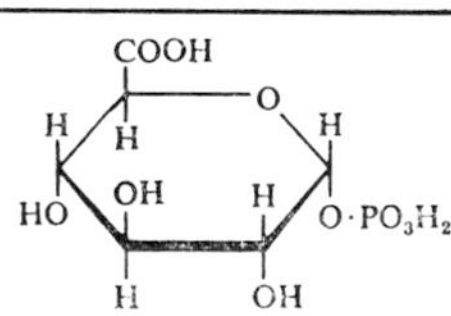 (α-isomer)
	—, K_3 salt		$C_6H_8O_{10}PK_3 \cdot 2H_2O$
33	D-Glyceraldehyde-3-phosphate	Phosphoglyceraldehyde	$CHO \cdot CHOH \cdot CH_2 \cdot O \cdot PO_3H_2$
	—, Ca salt		$C_3H_5O_6PCa \cdot 2H_2O$
34	D-Glyceric acid-1,3-diphosphate	1,3-Diphosphoglyceric acid	$CH_2(O \cdot PO_3H_2) \cdot CH(OH) \cdot CO \cdot O \cdot PO_3H_2$
35	D-Glyceric acid-2,3-diphosphate	2,3-Diphosphoglyceric acid	$CH_2(O \cdot PO_3H_2) \cdot CH(O \cdot PO_3H_2) \cdot COOH$
	—, $Ba_{1\cdot5}$ salt		$C_3H_5O_{10}P_2Ba_{1\cdot5} \cdot H_2O$
	—, $Ba_{2\cdot5}$ salt		$C_3H_3O_{10}P_2Ba_{2\cdot5} \cdot 1{\cdot}5H_2O$
36	D-(+)-Glyceric acid-2-phosphate	2-Phosphoglyceric acid	$CH_2OH \cdot CH(O \cdot PO_3H_2) \cdot COOH$
	—, Ba salt		$C_3H_5O_7PBa$
	—, Na_3 salt		$C_3H_4O_7PNa_3 \cdot 5H_2O$

M. wt.	*Preparation*	*Estimation*	*General remarks*
40·1 28·8	SYN. *J.B.C.* **180**, 1269 (1949)		Coenzyme of phosphoglucomutase. α-form, 9% hydrolysis in 2 hr at 30° in N-H_2SO_4; β-form, 31%. α-form, $[\alpha]_D^{28}$ +83 (c = 0·244 anhyd. Na salt in H_2O, pH 8·0); β-form, $[\alpha]_D^{26}$ − 19 (c = 0·373 anhyd. Na salt in H_2O, pH 8·0).
50·1 9·5 2·4 6·2	SYN. *B.J.* **59**, 203 (1955) *Biochem. Preps.* **1**, 33 (1949) ENZYME SYN. *J.A.C.S.* **66**, 560 (1944) *Biochem. Preps.* **4**, 63 (1955)	*B.J.* **53**, 157 (1953) *J.B.C.* **208**, 55 (1954) Bergmeyer p. 131	100% hydrolysis in 10 min at 100° in N-H_2SO_4. $[\alpha]_D^{25}$ +120 (c = 1 free acid in H_2O). K_2 salt cryst. ex aq. ethanol, $[\alpha]_D^{20}$ +78 (c = 4 in H_2O). Cryst. Na_2 salt. pK_1 1·11, pK_2 6·13.
0·1 1·6 8·2 5·3 4·1	SYN. *Biochem. Preps.* **2**, 39 (1952) ENZYME SYN. *Biochem. Preps.* **3**, 71 (1953) ^{32}P. *B.J.* **59**, 13 (1955)	*B.J.* **53**, 157 (1953) *J.B.C.* **208**, 55 (1954) *Arch. B.B.* **74**, 306 (1958) Bergmeyer, p. 134	50% hydrolysis in 21·7 hr at 100° in N-HCl. 60% hydrolysis in 3 min at 100° in N-KOH. pK_1 0·94, pK_2 6·11. $[\alpha]_D^{24}$ +21·2 (c = 1·3 K_2 salt in H_2O) +16·3 to 17·9 (Ba salt).
·1 ·4	SYN. *J.C.S.* **1952**, 1578 (α-form) *J.B.C.* **197**, 863 (1952) (β-form)		β-form: cryst. dibrucine salt, soly. 0·4 H_2O; cryst. dibenzylamine salt, $[\alpha]_D^{20}$ − 14 (c = 2·6 in H_2O). α-form: cryst. as K_3 salt ex aq. methanol, $[\alpha]_D^{20}$ +51 (c = 2·4 in H_2O), decomp. above 150°, sintering at 100°.
·1 ·2	ENZYME SYN. *J.B.C.* **212**, 811 (1955) *J.B.C.* **149**, 71 (1943) SYN. *J.A.C.S.* **77**, 3329 (1955) *Biochem. Preps.* **1**, 50 (1949) (DL-form)	*J. Bact.* **42**, 665 (1941) *Arch. B.B.* **74**, 306 (1958) Bergmeyer, p. 246 Bergmeyer, p. 241 (L-form)	50% hydrolysis in 8·1 min at 100° in N-HCl. Unstable in alkaline soln. $[\alpha]_D$ + 14 (c = 1 in H_2O). pK_1 1·42, pK_2 6·45. Ca salt unstable to storage. Dioxan addition compound and Ba or cyclohexylammonium salts of dimethyl or diethyl ketal derivatives stable to storage.
0	ISOL. *B.Z.* **301**, 135 (1939)	*B.Z.* **303**, 132 (1939) Bergmeyer, p. 234	50% hydrolysis in 27 min at 38° and pH 7·2. Generally v. unstable giving glyceric acid-3-phosphate. pK_1 7·5 pK_2 8·0.
0 0 4	SYN. *J.B.C.* **185**, 763 (1950) ISOL. *Biochem. Preps.* **6**, 12 (1958)	*J.B.C.* **226**, 777 (1957) Bergmeyer, p. 238	Extremely resistant to hydrolysis. Coenzyme of phosphoglyceric acid mutase.
	SYN. *Biochem. Preps.* **5**, 66 (1957) *J.A.C.S.* **76**, 3188 (1954) ISOL. *B.Z.* **276**, 239 (1935)	Bergmeyer, p. 224	$[\alpha]_D^{22}$ +3·6 (c = 2 Na_3 salt in H_2O) +12·9 (c = 1·8 free acid in N-HCl) +5 (c = 1 in neutral ammonium molybdate, calculated as free acid). Cryst. Na_3 salt ex aq. methanol.

3. Phosphate Esters excluding Nucleotides and Coenzymes

No.	Name	Synonyms	Formula
37	D-(−)-Glyceric acid-3-phosphate	3-Phosphoglyceric acid, Nilsson-Lohmann ester, PGA	$CH_2(O\cdot PO_3H_2)\cdot CH(OH)\cdot COOH$
	—, Ba salt		$C_3H_5O_7PBa\cdot 2H_2O$
	—, $Ca_{1\cdot 5}$ salt		$C_3H_4O_7PCa_{1\cdot 5}$
	—, Na_3 salt		$C_3H_4O_7PNa_3$
	—, *tris*(Cyclohexyl-ammonium) salt		$C_3H_7O_7P\cdot(C_6H_{13}N)_3\cdot 3H_2O$
38	L-Glycerol-1-phosphate	α-Glycerophosphoric acid	$CH_2OH\cdot CH(OH)\cdot CH_2\cdot O\cdot PO_3H_2$
	—, Ba salt		$C_3H_7O_6PBa$
	—, Na_2 salt		$C_3H_7O_6PNa_2\cdot H_2O$
	—, *bis*(Cyclohexyl-ammonium) salt		$C_3H_9O_6P\cdot(C_6H_{13}N)_2\cdot H_2O$
39	Glycerol-2-phosphate	β-Glycerophosphoric acid	$CH_2OH\cdot CH(O\cdot PO_3H_2)\cdot CH_2OH$
	—, Na_2 salt		$C_3H_7O_6PNa_2\cdot 5H_2O$
40	L-α-Glycerylphosphoryl-choline		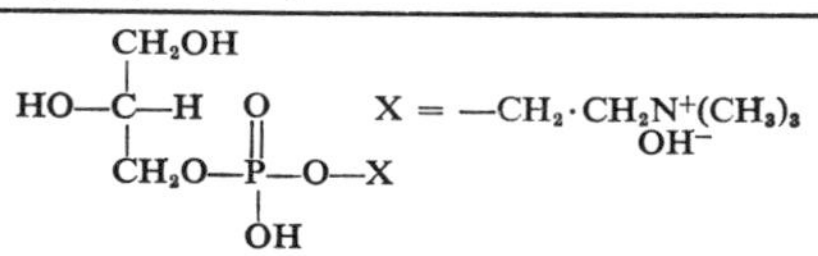
41	L-α-Glycerylphosphoryl-ethanolamine		cf. Glycerylphosphorylcholine $X = -CH_2\cdot CH_2NH_2$
	—, Monohydrate		$C_5H_{14}NO_6P\cdot H_2O$
42	Glycerylphosphorylinositol	1-(α-Glyceryl-phosphoryl)-L-*myo*-inositol, Glycerol inositol phosphate	cf. Glycerylphosphorylcholine 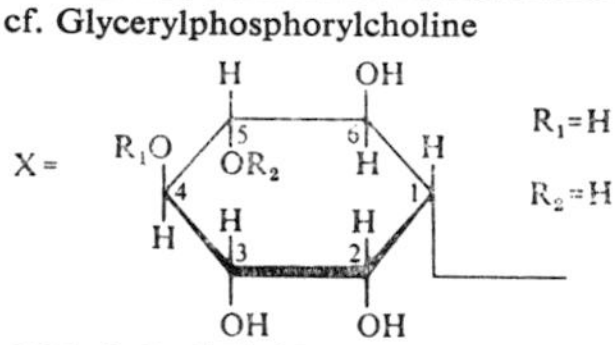
	—, Cyclohexylammonium salt		$C_9H_{19}O_{11}P\cdot C_6H_{13}N$
43	Glycerylphosphorylinositol monophosphate	1-(α-Glycerylphos-phoryl)-L-*myo*-inositol-4-phosphate, Glycerol inositol diphosphate	cf. Glycerylphosphorylinositol $R_1 = PO_3H_2$ $R_2 = H$
44	Glycerylphosphorylinositol diphosphate	1-(α-Glycerylphos-phoryl)-L-*myo*-inositol-4,5-diphosphate, Glycerol inositol triphosphate	cf. Glycerylphosphorylinositol $R_1 = PO_3H_2$ $R_2 = PO_3H_2$
45	Glycerylphosphorylserine		cf. Glycerylphosphorylcholine $X = -CH_2\cdot CHNH_2\cdot COOH$
	—, Monohydrate		$C_6H_{14}NO_8P\cdot H_2O$
46	Glycinamide ribotide	2-Amino-*N*-ribosyl-acetamide-5′-phosphate, Glycinamide ribo-nucleotide, GAR	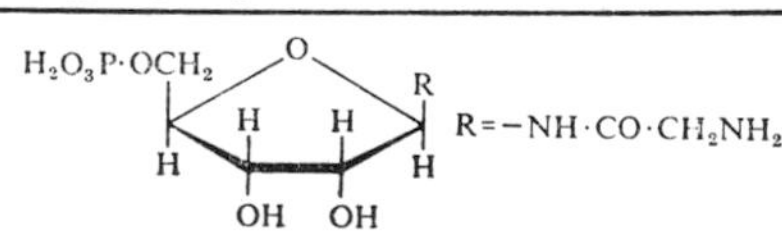
	—, Ca salt		$C_7H_{13}N_2O_8PCa\cdot\frac{1}{2}Ca(OH)_2$

. wt.	*Preparation*	*Estimation*	*General remarks*
6·1 7·4 3·2 2·0 7·6	SYN. *Arch. B.* **3**, 105 (1944) ISOL. *Arch. B.* **1**, 311 (1943) PURIFICATION. *J.B.C.* **226**, 777 (1957)	*B.Z.* **297**, 60 (1938) Bergmeyer, p. 224	50% hydrolysis in 35·7 hr at 100° in N-HCl, about 3 hr at 125°. $[\alpha]_D^{20}$ −13·85 (in H_2O) −745 (with ammonium molybdate). Cryst. Ba and cyclohexylammonium salts.
2·1 7·4 4·1 3·4	SYN. *Biochem. Preps.* **2**, 31 (1952)	*J.B.C.* **211**, 951 (1954) Bergmeyer, p. 215	2% hydrolysis in 180 min at 100° in N-HCl. Hydrolysed by heating at 160° in 10% H_2SO_4. $[\alpha]_D$ −1·45 (c = 10 Ba salt in 2N-HCl). pK_2 6·66.
2·1 ·1	SYN. *J.C.S.* **1914**, 1238	*Analyt. Biochem.* **6**, 54 (1963)	V. slow hydrolysis at 100° in N-HCl. pK_1 1·34, pK_2 6·55. Separation from glycerol-1-phosphate by gas chromatography, *B.B.A.* **82**, 408 (1964). Used as buffer and as substrate for assay of phosphomonoesterases, reaction followed by release of inorganic phosphate.
·2	SYN. *J.A.C.S.* **70**, 1394 (1948) *B.J.* **62**, 689 (1956) *Can. J. Biochem. Physiol.* **33**, 761 (1955) ISOL. *J.B.C.* **161**, 523 (1945) *Biochem. Preps.* **6**, 16 (1958) ENZYME SYN. *J.B.C.* **220**, 1 (1956)	*J.B.C.* **197**, 601 (1952) *J.B.C.* **212**, 887 (1955) *B.J.* **62**, 693 (1956)	Choline completely liberated in 15 min at 100° in N-HCl. M.p. 143, sinters 141. $[\alpha]_D^{23}$ −2·85 (c = 2·2 synthetic material in H_2O). V. hygr. cryst. $CdCl_2$ compound + $3H_2O$, M.p. 99.
2 2	SYN. *J.A.C.S.* **75**, 4510 (1953) ISOL. *B.J.* **50**, 449 (1952)	*J.B.C.* **212**, 887 (1955)	Ethanolamine completely liberated in 15 min at 100° in N-HCl. M.p. 86–87. $[\alpha]_D^{26}$ −2·9 (c = 7·6 synthetic material in H_2O). Cryst. monohydrate.
2 4	ISOL. *B.J.* **71**, 195 (1959) *J.A.C.S.* **81**, 2591 (1959) *J.B.C.* **236**, 1907 (1961) SYN. *J.C.S.* **1959**, 3547 (DL- compound)	*B.J.* **71**, 195 (1959)	Deacylation product of monophosphoinositides. Completely decomposed in 40 min at 100° in 0·5N-KOH giving glycerophosphate and inositol phosphate. $[\alpha]_D^{25}$ −18·7 (c = 2 free acid in water). Cryst. cyclohexylammonium salt, $[\alpha]_D^{25}$ −13·5 (c = 2 in water).
2	ISOL. *J.B.C.* **236**, 1907 (1961) *B.J.* **88**, 125 (1963)	*B.J.* **81**, 540 (1961) *J.B.C.* **236**, 1907 (1961)	Deacylation product of diphosphoinositide. $[\alpha]_D$ −5·5 (c = 1·5 in basic soln.) −4·8 (in acid soln.). Readily hydrolysed by 5N-HCl in 10 min at 100° forming inositol diphosphate, glycerophosphoric acid, glycerol, and inositol.
2	ISOL. *J.B.C.* **236**, 1907 (1961) *B.J.* **88**, 125 (1963)	*B.J.* **81**, 540 (1961) *J.B.C.* **236**, 1907 (1961)	Deacylation product of triphosphoinositide. $[\alpha]_D$ −3·3 (c = 7·5 in basic soln.) −1·1 (in acid soln.). Readily hydrolysed by 5N-HCl in 10 min at 100° forming inositol triphosphate and diphosphate, glycerophosphoric acid, glycerol, and inositol.
	SYN. *J.A.C.S.* **81**, 2167 (1959) ISOL. *B.J.* **71**, 195 (1959)	*J.B.C.* **212**, 887 (1955)	$[\alpha]_D^{24}$ +4·5 (c = 10 in N-HCl) −2·0 (c = 10 in H_2O). Cryst. monohydrate.
	ENZYME SYN. *J.B.C.* **221**, 1057 (1956) (Ba salt) ^{14}C. *J.B.C.* **221**, 1071 (1956) (Ca salt)	*J.B.C.* **229**, 613 (1957) *Adv. Enzymol.* **21**, 199 (1959)	25% hydrolysis in 60 min at 100° in N-HCl. Glycine and NH_3 liberated under same conditions. 1 μmole NH_3/mole ribotide released after 2 hr. pK_1 6·05, pK_2 8·15. Ba salt obtained 71% pure.

3. Phosphate Esters excluding Nucleotides and Coenzymes

No.	*Name*	*Synonyms*	*Formula*
47	Glycocyamine phosphate	Phosphoglycocyamine	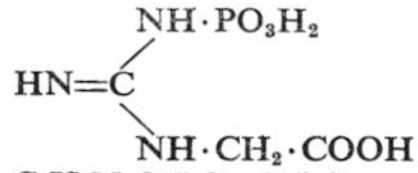
	—, Ca salt		$C_3H_6N_3O_5PCa \cdot 3H_2O$
48	Glycollic acid phosphate		$H_2O_3P \cdot O \cdot CH_2 \cdot COOH$
	—, Ba salt		$C_2H_3O_6PBa \cdot H_2O$
49	L-Histidinol phosphate		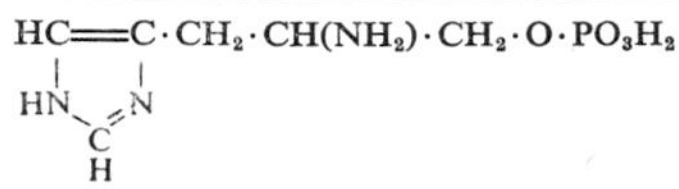
	—, Monohydrate		$C_6H_{12}N_3O_4P \cdot H_2O$
50	Homoserine phosphate	*O*-Phosphohomoserine	$H_2O_3P \cdot O \cdot CH_2 \cdot CH_2 \cdot CHNH_2 \cdot COOH$
51	Hydroxypyruvic acid-3-phosphate	Phosphohydroxypyruvic acid	$H_2O_3P \cdot O \cdot CH_2 \cdot CO \cdot COOH$
	—, $Ba_{1.5}$ salt		$C_3H_2O_7PBa_{1.5} \cdot 2H_2O$
52	*myo*-Inositol hexaphosphate	Phytic acid	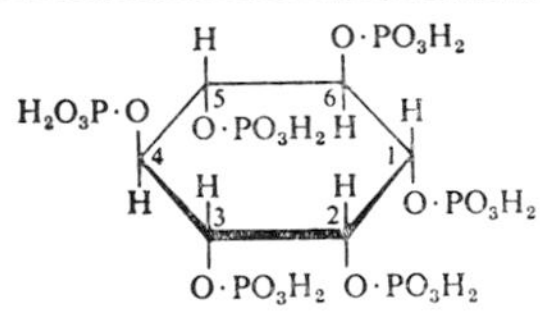
53	L-*myo*-Inositol-1-phosphate		cf. Inositol hexaphosphate
	—, *bis*(Cyclohexyl-ammonium) salt		$C_6H_{13}O_9P \cdot (C_6H_{13}N)_2$
54	*myo*-Inositol-2-phosphate		cf. Inositol hexaphosphate
	—, *bis*(Cyclohexyl-ammonium) salt		$C_6H_{13}O_9P \cdot (C_6H_{13}N)_2 \cdot 4H_2O$
55	Imidazole acetol phosphate	IAP	

/I. wt.	Preparation	Estimation	General remarks
97·1 39·2	SYN. *J.B.C.* **165**, 97 (1946) SYN. and ISOL. *Bull. Soc. Chim. biol.* **39**, 355 (1957)		100% hydrolysis in 2 min at 100° in N-HCl. More stable than creatine phosphate to Fiske & Subbarow reagents.
56·0)9·4	SYN. *Ber.* **68**, 243 (1935) ISOL. *Arch. B.B.* **33**, 484 (1951)	*J.B.C.* **236**, 1285 (1961)	7·8% hydrolysis in 2 hr at 100° in N-H_2SO_4. Cryst. Ba salt.
:1·2 9·2	ISOL. *J.B.C.* **212**, 687 (1955) SYN. *J.B.C.* **220**, 113 (1956)		Approx. 5% hydrolysis in 4 hr at 100° in N-NaOH or N-HCl. Approx. 20% hydrolysis at pH 4·5 and 100° in 4 hr. Obtained as stable monohydrate.
9·1	ENZYME SYN. *Arch. B.B.* **78**, 416 (1958) *J. Biochem., Tokyo* **43**, 283 (1956)	*Arch. B.B.* **78**, 416 (1958)	12·5% hydrolysis in 1 hr at 100° in 6N-HCl. 100% in 30 hr at 105° in 6N-HCl. Isolated as Ba salt, probable formula $C_4H_8NO_6PBa \cdot H_2O$.
4·0 3·1	SYN. *J.A.C.S.* **78**, 3718 (1956) (soln. and Ba salt) *Biochem. Preps.* **7**, 66 (1960) (soln.)	*J.A.C.S.* **78**, 3718 (1956)	50% hydrolysis in 20 min at 90° in N-HCl. 50% in 15 hr at room temp. in N-alkali.
)·0	ISOL. *C.r. hebd. Séanc. Acad. Sci., Paris* **168**, 1216 (1919)	*B.B.A.* **19**, 552 (1956) *B.J.* **92**, 42 (1964)	9·5% hydrolysis in 6 hr at 100° in N-H_2SO_4.
·1 ·5	ISOL. *B.J.* **75**, 501 (1960) *J.A.C.S.* **81**, 915 (1959) *Biochem. Preps.* **9**, 99 (1962) SYN. *J.C.S.* **1959**, 3547 (DL-form) *J.A.C.S.* **81**, 4745 (1959) (D-isomer)	*B.B.A.* **19**, 552 (1956)	Hydrolysis product of phosphatidylinositol. Phosphate migrates in hot dil. acid to give mixture of 1- and 2-phosphates. Cryst. cyclohexylammonium salt ex acet., M.p. 200–10 d., $[\alpha]^{25}_{5890}$ +3·4 (c = 3 in water at pH 9) −9·8 (free acid in water).
·1 5	ISOL. *J.A.C.S.* **81**, 4745 (1959) *J.C.S.* **1959**, 357 *Biochem. Preps.* **2**, 65 (1952)	*Biochem. Preps.* **2**, 65 (1952) *B.B.A.* **19**, 552 (1956)	Monophosphate product of enzymic hydrolysis of hexaphosphate. M.p. 195–7 d. Optically inactive. Stable to heating with strong alkali. Phosphate migrates in hot dil. acid to give mixture of 1- and 2-phosphates. Cryst. *mono-* and *bis*(cyclohexylammonium) salts, M.p. 211–13 and 203–5 respectively. For information on the di- and tri-phosphates of inositol, see *J.B.C.* **236**, 1902 (1961); *J. Lipid Res.* **1**, 255 (1960); *Adv. Carbohyd. Chem.* **14**, 135 (1959). For pentaphosphates, see *B.J.* **89**, 172 (1963).
1	ISOL. *J.B.C.* **212**, 687 (1955) ENZYME SYN. *J.B.C.* **220**, 113 (1956)	*J.B.C.* **220**, 113 (1956)	20% hydrolysis in 1 hr at 100° in 0·1N-HCl.

3. Phosphate Esters excluding Nucleotides and Coenzymes

No.	*Name*	*Synonyms*	*Formula*
56	D-*erythro*-Imidazole glycerol phosphate	IGP	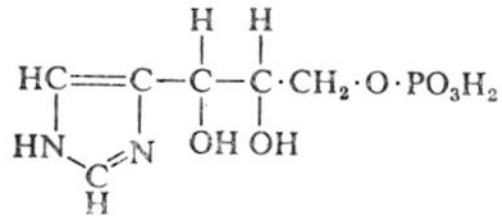
	—, Monohydrate		$C_6H_{11}N_2O_6P \cdot H_2O$
57	Indole-3-glycerol phosphate	InGP	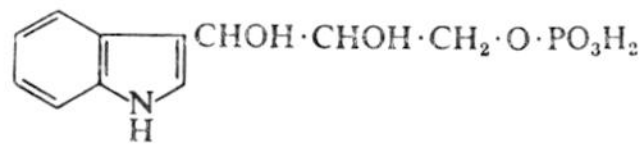
	—, Ba salt		$C_{11}H_{12}NO_6PBa \cdot 2H_2O$
58	Isopentenyl pyrophosphate	3-Methylbut-3-enyl-1-pyrophosphate	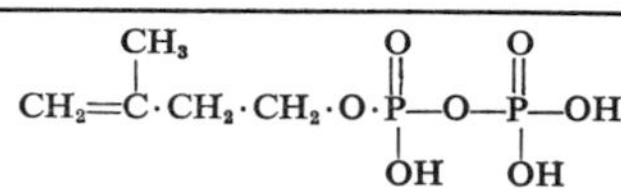
	—, Cyclohexylammonium salt		$C_5H_{12}O_7P_2 \cdot C_6H_{13}N$
59	2-Keto-3-deoxy-6-phosphogluconic acid	KDPG	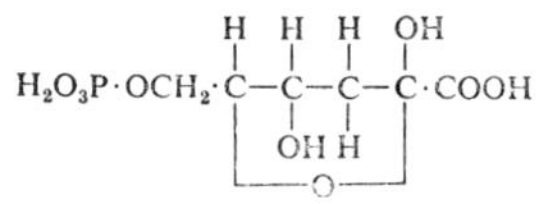
	—, Na_3 salt		$C_6H_8O_9PNa_3 \cdot 2H_2O$
60	Lactose-1-phosphate		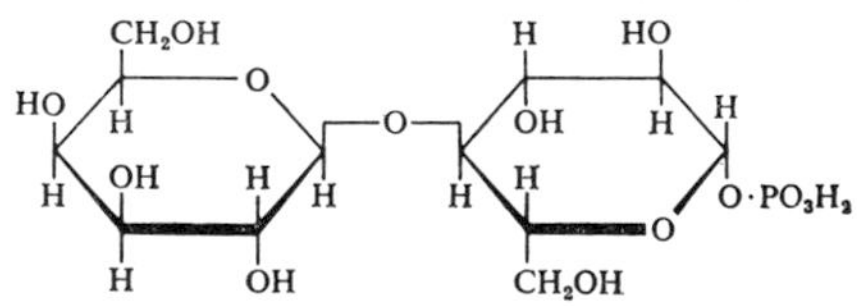 (β-ison
	—, Ba salt		$C_{12}H_{21}O_{14}PBa \cdot 5H_2O$
61	Lombricine	2-Amino-2-carboxyethyl 2-guanidoethyl hydrogen phosphate	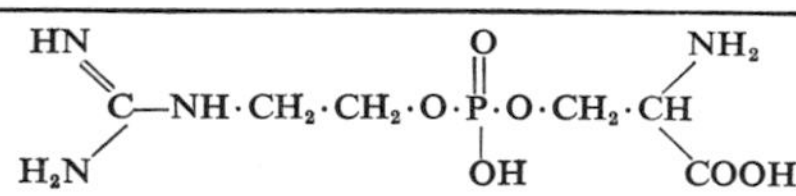
62	D-Mannose-1-phosphate		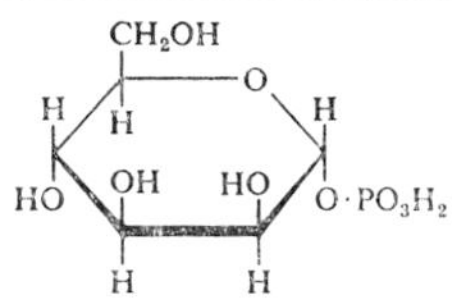 (α-isomer)
	—, Ba salt		$C_6H_{11}O_9PBa \cdot 2H_2O$
63	Mannose-6-phosphate		cf. Mannose-1-phosphate
	—, Ba salt		$C_6H_{11}O_9PBa \cdot 2H_2O$
64	Mevalonic acid-5-phosphate	Phosphomevalonic acid	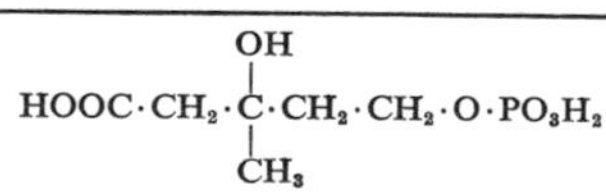
	—, *bis*(Cyclohexylammonium) salt		$C_6H_{13}O_7P \cdot (C_6H_{13}N)_2$
	—, *tris*(Cyclohexylammonium) salt		$C_6H_{13}O_7P \cdot (C_6H_{13}N)_3$

wt.	Preparation	Estimation	General remarks
·1 1	ISOL. and SYN. *J.B.C.* **228**, 131 (1957)	*J.B.C.* **228**, 131 (1957)	Hydrolysed overnight at 100° by 6N-HCl. Stable monohydrate. $[\alpha]_D^{20}$ −12·1 (c = 2·37 in H_2O, pH 7).
2 6	ISOL. *J.B.C.* **223**, 171 (1956)	*J.B.C.* **223**, 171 (1956)	Not hydrolysed by N-alkali at room temp. Indole released on heating with dil. alkali; labile to dilute acid at room temp.
1 3	SYN. *Biochemistry* **2**, 1254 (1963) *J.B.C.* **234**, 2605 (1959) (Cyclohexylammonium salt) *Angew. Chem.* **70**, 738 (1958) (Ba salt)	*J.B.C.* **234**, 2595 (1959)	Hydrolysis as for mevalonic acid-5-phosphate.
	ENZYME SYN. *J.B.C.* **210**, 617 (1954) *Meth. Enzymol.* **9**, 51 (1966)	*J.B.C.* **210**, 617 (1954)	62% hydrolysis in 60 min at 100° in N-HCl. $pK_1 < 2·5$, pK_2 3·12, pK_3 6·4.
	SYN. *J.A.C.S.* **74**, 4210 (1952) (α- and β-forms) ENZYME SYN. *Arch. B.B.* **69**, 85 (1957)		Complete hydrolysis in 7 min at 100° in N-H_2SO_4. Obtained as Ba salt. $[\alpha]_D^{23}$ calc. for free acid in H_2O, +99·5 (c — 0·4, α-form) +31·5 (c = 0·5, β-form). Identity of biosynthetic product disputed (see *J.B.C.* **237**, 1432 (1962)).
	SYN. *J.A.C.S.* **82**, 4983 (1960) ISOL. D-. *B.J.* **73**, 521 (1959) *B.J.* **75**, 179 (1960)	*B.J.* **83**, 14 (1962)	Occurs in earthworm both free and as *N*-phosphoryl-lombricine, a phosphagen (ISOL. *B.J.* **83**, 14 (1962); SYN. *Nature, Lond.* **188**, 1026 (1960)). Lombricine hydrolysed by 6N-HCl at 110° in 4 hr. pK_a *ca.* 2 and 8·9.
	SYN. *J.B.C.* **124**, 557 (1938) *Helv. chim. Acta* **36**, 1614 (1953)		$[\alpha]_D^{23}$ +33 (c = 3·19 in water calc. as anhyd. Ba salt).
	ENZYME SYN. *J.B.C.* **186**, 753 (1950) ISOL. *B.J.* **28**, 1844 (1934) SYN. *Helv. chim. Acta* **36**, 1614 (1953)	*J.B.C.* **186**, 753 (1950)	$[\alpha]_D^{22}$ +13·3 (c = 1·66 free acid in 0·1N-HCl). Phenylhydrazone, M.p. 144–5. Cryst. brucine salt.
	SYN. *Biochemistry* **2**, 1254 (1963) *Ber.* **94**, 1595 (1961) (Cyclohexylammonium salts of DL-form) ENZYME SYN. *B.J.* **75**, 417 (1960) (Ba salt)	*J.B.C.* **234**, 2595 (1959)	Natural compound laevorotatory. Stable for 7 min at 100° in N-HCl or N-KOH; 9% hydrolysis in 60 min in N-HCl. pK_1 1·7, pK_2 4·6, pK_3 6·9. Cryst. *bis*- and *tris*(cyclohexylammonium) salts, M.p. 145–7 and 152–4 respectively.

3. Phosphate Esters excluding Nucleotides and Coenzymes

No.	*Name*	*Synonyms*	*Formula*
65	Mevalonic acid-5-pyrophosphate	Diphosphomevalonic acid, Pyrophosphomevalonic acid	cf. Mevalonic acid-5-phosphate
66	D-(+)-Pantetheine-4′-phosphate	Phosphopantetheine	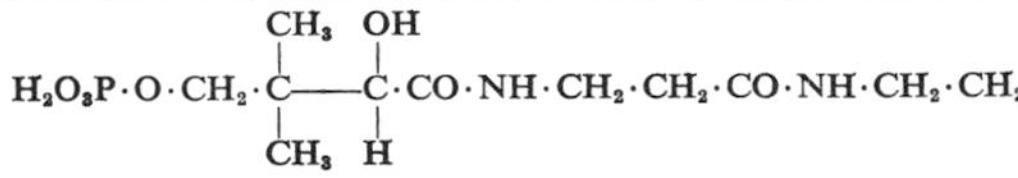
67	Pantothenic acid-4-phosphate		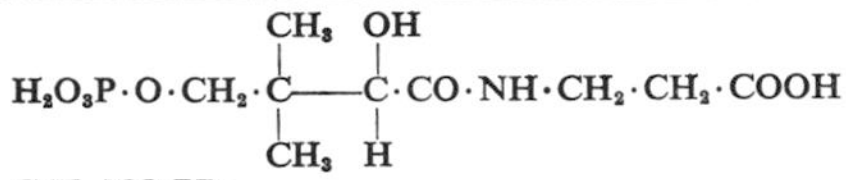
	—, $Ba_{1.5}$ salt		$C_9H_{15}NO_8PBa_{1.5}$
68	Phosphoenolpyruvic acid	Phosphopyruvic acid, PEP	$CH_2{=}C(O\cdot PO_3H_2)\cdot COOH$
	—, Na_3 salt		$C_3H_2O_6PNa_3\cdot 2H_2O$
	—, AgBa salt		$C_3H_2O_6PAgBa\cdot 2H_2O$
	—, Cyclohexylammonium salt		$C_3H_5O_6P\cdot C_6H_{13}N$
69	Phosphoribosyl pyrophosphate	α-D-Ribofuranose-1-pyrophosphate-5-phosphate, PRPP	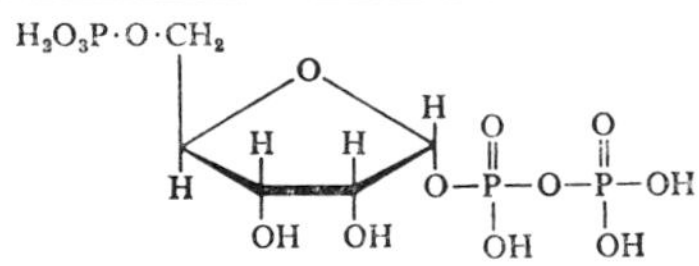
	—, Li_5 salt		$C_5H_8O_{14}P_3Li_5\cdot 5H_2O$
70	D-Ribitol-5-phosphate	L-Ribitol-1-phosphate	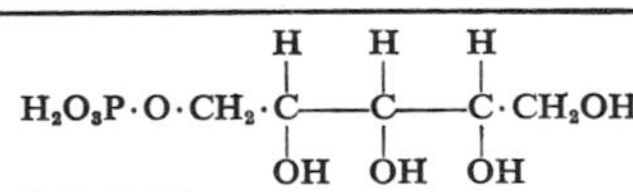
	—, Ba salt		$C_5H_{11}O_8PBa$
71	Ribose-1,5-diphosphate	α-D-Ribofuranose-1,5-diphosphate	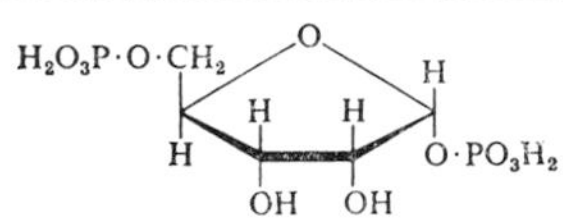
	—, *tetrakis*(Cyclohexylammonium) salt		$C_5H_{12}O_{11}P_2\cdot(C_6H_{13}N)_4\cdot 4H_2O$
72	Ribose-1-phosphate	α-D-Ribofuranose-1-phosphate	cf. Ribose-1,5-diphosphate
	—, Ba salt		$C_5H_9O_8PBa\cdot H_2O$
	—, *bis*(Cyclohexylammonium) salt		$C_5H_{11}O_8P\cdot(C_6H_{13}N)_2$
73	D-Ribose-5-phosphate		cf. Ribose-1,5-diphosphate
	—, Ba salt		$C_5H_9O_8PBa\cdot 5H_2O$
74	D-Ribulose-1,5-diphosphate		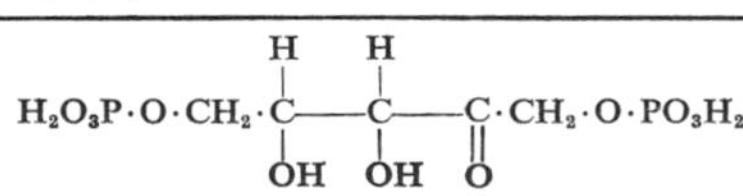
	—, Ba_2 salt		$C_5H_8O_{11}P_2Ba_2$

. wt.	*Preparation*	*Estimation*	*General remarks*
3·1	ENZYME SYN. *J. Lipid Res.* **2**, 235 (1961) *Arch. B.B.* **83**, 259 (1959)	*J.B.C.* **234**, 2595 (1959)	50% hydrolysis in 10 min at 100° in N-HCl. Stable for 10 min at 100° in N-KOH.
3·3	*J.C.S.* **1953**, 1610	*J.B.C.* **234**, 379 (1959)	Obtained as Ba salt, $[\alpha]_D^{18}$ +10·8 (c = 4·2 in water).
·2 ·2	SYN. *J.C.S.* 1951, 246	*J.B.C.* **234**, 379 (1959)	56% hydrolysis in 160 min at 100° in 2N-HCl. Stable for 2 hr at 100° in 0·05N-KOH. Ba salt, s. H_2O.
·0 ·0 ·3 ·2	SYN. *B.B.A.* **78**, 732 (1963) *Biochem. Preps.* **11**, 101 (1966) *J.B.C.* **190**, 21 (1951) *J.B.C.* **180**, 145 (1949) ENZYME SYN. *B.Z.* **273**, 60 (1934)	*B.Z.* **273**, 60 (1934) Bergmeyer, p. 224	50% hydrolysis in 8·3 min at 100° in N-HCl. AgBa salt light sensitive, 92% pure. Cryst. AgBa, Na_3, *mono*- and *tris*(cyclohexylammonium) salts; *mono*cyclohexylammonium salt stable 2 years at 4°.
1 8	ENZYME SYN. *J.B.C.* **215**, 389 (1955) *J.B.C.* **228**, 201 (1957) *Biochem. Preps.* **8**, 110 (1961) SYN. *J.A.C.S.* **80**, 1999 (1958)	*J.B.C.* **215**, 389 (1955)	Complete loss of pyrophosphate group as inorg. pyrophosphate in 20 min at 65° and pH 3·0, 50% at pH 6·7. Stable in neutral soln. at −15° for at least 3 months. pK_1 5·9, pK_2 6·7.
1 4	SYN. *J.C.S.* **1956**, 4583 *J.B.C.* **233**, 1049 (1958)		Chromatographic behaviour given in *J.C.S.* **1956**, 4583.
	ENZYME SYN. *Arch. B.B.* **46**, 186 (1953) SYN. *J.A.C.S.* **80**, 1999 (1958)	*Arch. B.B.* **46**, 186 (1953)	50% hydrolysis in 5 min under conditions of Fiske and Subbarow estimation. Coenzyme of phosphoribomutase. Cryst. *tetrakis*(cyclohexylammonium) salt, M.p. 171–2 d., $[\alpha]_D^{22}$ +20·8 (c = 0·43 in H_2O).
	ENZYME SYN. *J.B.C.* **167**, 477 (1947) *J.B.C.* **193**, 497 (1951) SYN. *J.A.C.S.* **79**, 441 (1957)	*J.B.C.* **162**, 421 (1946)	Rapid hydrolysis in strong acid, with slight acceleration by molybdate. 50% hydrolysis in 3·5 hr at 20° in 0·01N-HCl. β-furanose and pyranose forms more stable under these conditions. Behaves as inorg. P in Fiske and Subbarow method where hydrolysis complete in 2·5 min. Cryst. *bis*(cyclohexylammonium) salt, $[\alpha]_D^{20}$ +40·3 (c = 2·37 in H_2O).
	ISOL. *Arch. B.B.* **34**, 209 (1951) *J.A.C.S.* **75**, 1153 (1953) *J.A.C.S.* **76**, 5523 (1954) SYN. ^{32}P. *B.J.* **58**, 503 (1954)	*J.B.C.* **167**, 369 (1947) *Arch. B.B.* **74**, 306 (1958) Bergmeyer, p. 175	59% hydrolysis in 2 hr at 100° in N-HCl. $[\alpha]_D^{20}$ +22·8 (in 0·02N-HCl) +16·54 (c = 3·35 Ba salt in 0·226N-HCl).
	ENZYME SYN. *J.A.C.S.* **76**, 5572 (1954) *J.B.C.* **218**, 785 (1956) *Biochem. Preps.* **6**, 83 (1958) *J.B.C.* **223**, 993 (1956)	*J.B.C.* **218**, 785 (1956) *Arch. B.B.* **69**, 300 (1957) Bergmeyer, p. 188	50% hydrolysis in 20 min at 100° in N-H_2SO_4. Dry Ba salt obtained 60–80% pure, unstable even in cold.

3. Phosphate Esters excluding Nucleotides and Coenzymes

No.	*Name*	*Synonyms*	*Formula*
75	D-Ribulose-5-phosphate		cf. Ribulose-1,5-diphosphate
76	D-Sedoheptulose-1,7-diphosphate		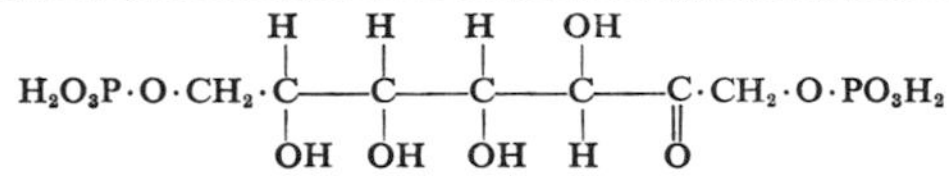
77	D-Sedoheptulose-7-phosphate		cf. Sedoheptulose-1,7-diphosphate
78	Serine phosphate	*O*-Phosphoserine	$H_2O_3P \cdot O \cdot CH_2 \cdot CH(NH_2) \cdot COOH$
	—, Ba salt		$C_3H_6NO_6PBa \cdot 3H_2O$
79	Serine ethanolamine phosphodiester		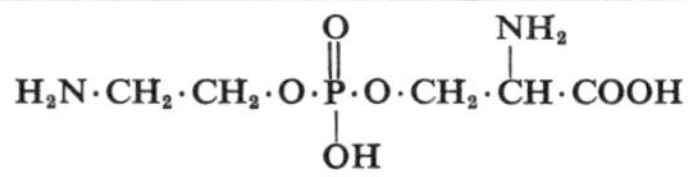
80	Shikimic acid-5-phosphate		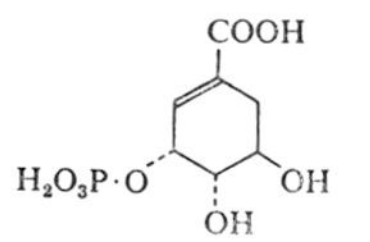
	—, K salt		$C_7H_{10}O_8PK \cdot H_2O$
	—, $Ba_{1 \cdot 5}$ salt		$C_7H_8O_8PBa_{1 \cdot 5} \cdot 2 \cdot 5H_2O$
81	Sucrose-6′-phosphate		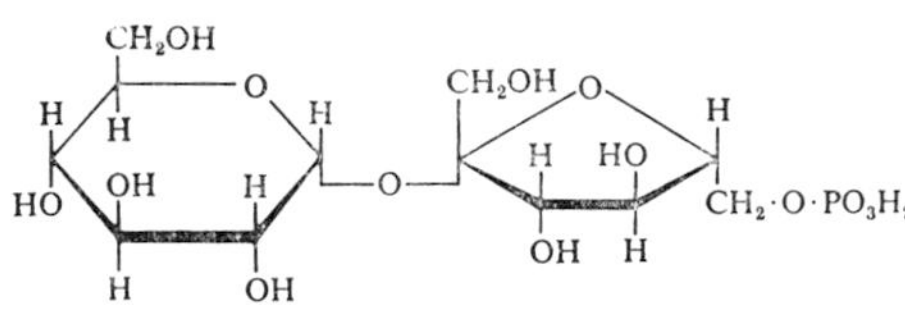
82	Taurocyamine phosphate	Phosphotaurocyamine	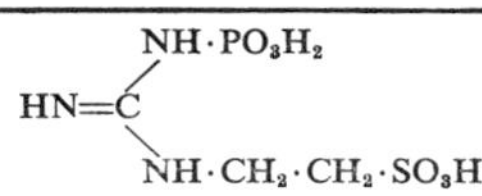
83	Trehalose phosphate (α,α)		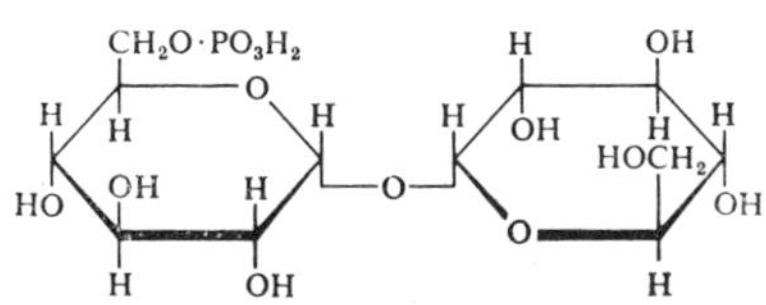
84	D-Xylulose-5-phosphate		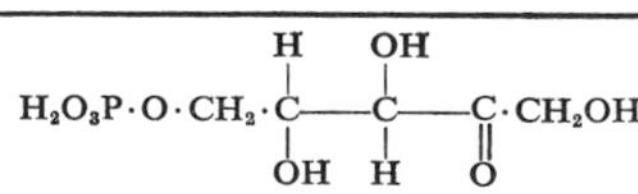

M. wt.	*Preparation*	*Estimation*	*General remarks*
30·1	ENZYME SYN. *Meth. Enzymol.* **9**, 41, 46 (1966) *Arch. B.B.* **74**, 295 (1958) *J.B.C.* **236**, 2975 (1961)	*Arch. B.B.* **74**, 306 (1958) Bergmeyer, p. 186 *J.B.C.* **196**, 135 (1952)	50% hydrolysis in 40 min at 100° in N-H_2SO_4. $[\alpha]_D^{20}$ −40. Ba salt obtained about 90% pure.
70·1	ENZYME SYN. *J.B.C.* **218**, 745 (1956) *Arch. B.B.* **74**, 326 (1958) *Arch. B.B.* **99**, 401 (1962)	*Arch. B.B.* **74**, 326 (1958) Bergmeyer, pp. 111, 113 *J.B.C.* **218**, 745 (1956)	50% hydrolysis in 30 min at 100° in N-H_2SO_4, 70% in 3 hr. Ba salt obtained 75% pure.
0·2	ENZYME SYN. *J.B.C.* **205**, 661 (1953) *Biochem. Preps.* **12**, 1 (1968)	*J.B.C.* **205**, 661 (1953) *Arch. B.B.* **74**, 306 (1958) Bergmeyer, p. 107	10–15% hydrolysis in 1 hr at 100° in N-H_2SO_4. Ba salt obtained 72% pure.
5·1 4·5	SYN. *B.J.* 35, 461 (1941) *Biochem. Preps.* **6**, 75 (1958) *J.B.C.* **234**, 113 (1959) ^{3}H. *J.C.S.* 1963, 289		61% hydrolysis in 24 hr at 100° in N-HCl, 51% in 0·5N-NaOH. Cryst. ex aq. ethanol, M.p. 165–6 d. pK_a 2·65, 5·91, 9·99.
·1	L-, DL-. *J.A.C.S.* **78**, 2408 (1956) L-, D-, DL-. *J.A.C.S.* **82**, 4983 (1960) L-. *J.B.C.* **211**, 1 (1954) *J.B.C.* **236**, 1028 (1961) D-. *B.J.* **75**, 179 (1960)		V. hygroscopic. Slow hydrolysis in N-HCl at 100°; complete < 48 hr in 6N-HCl at 105°. Gradually destroyed in 0·1N-NH_4OH at 105°, completely in 0·5M-$Ba(OH)_2$ at 100° in 1 hr. pK_a 2, 8·8, 10·0. L-isomer found in birds and fish, D- in earthworms.
·1 2 2	ISOL. *J.A.C.S.* **78**, 2894 (1956)	*J.A.C.S.* 78, 2894 (1956) *B.J.* **89**, 229 (1963)	25–30% hydrolysis in 30 min at 120° in 0·1N-HCl. $[\alpha]_D^{29}$ −107·6 (c = 1·02 K salt in water). 3-Enol-pyruvylshikimate-5-phosphate, ENZYME SYN. *J.B.C.* **239**, 1142 (1964).
3	ENZYME SYN. *J.B.C.* **235**, 3347 (1960) *J.B.C.* **214**, 157 (1955) SYN. *B.Z.* **23**, 515 (1910)	*J.B.C.* **214**, 157 (1955)	25% hydrolysis in 60 min at 100° in N-H_2SO_4. Stable in hot alkali. In 0·9N-HCl at 37°, release of reducing power is slower than with sucrose. Isolated as Ca salt. Product of chemical synthesis is mixture of isomers.
2	ISOL. *B.J.* **68**, 447 (1958) SYN. and ISOL. *Bull. Soc. Chim. biol.* 39, 355 (1957)		50% hydrolysed in N-HCl at 37° in 70 min. Stable in N-NaOH at 37° for 60 min. Isolated as Ba salt (ref. 1). Synthesized and isolated as ammonium salt (ref. 2).
3	ENZYME SYN. *B.J.* **22**, 1277 (1928) *B.J.* **24**, 119 (1930) *J.A.C.S.* **75**, 5445 (1953) *B.B.A.* **86**, 390 (1964)		10% hydrolysis in 8 hr at 100° in N-H_2SO_4. $[\alpha]_{5461}^{20}$ +185 (free acid in water) +132 (Ba salt in water). Cryst. Ba salt ex 20–25% aq. ethanol, sp. s. H_2O. Cryst. brucine salt.
	ENZYME SYN. *J.B.C.* **223**, 993 (1956) *Meth. Enzymol.* **9**, 41 (1966)	*Arch. B.B.* **74**, 306 (1958) Bergmeyer, p. 201	55% hydrolysis in 10 min at 100° in N-H_2SO_4. Obtained as Ba salt about 70% pure.

4. Sulphate Esters

By A. B. ROY (*Department of Physical Biochemistry, Australian National University, Canberra*)

Macromolecular sulphate compounds (chondroitin sulphates, dermatan sulphate, heparan sulphate, keratan sulphate) are included in Table 19, Macromolecules; heparin in Table 16, Drugs; and sulphate esters used as artificial substrates for sulphatase assay in Table 18, Artificial substrates and biochemical reagents.

4. Sulphate Esters

No.	*Name*	*Synonyms*	*Formula*	*M. w*
1	*N*-Acetyl-D-galactosamine-6-sulphate, K salt		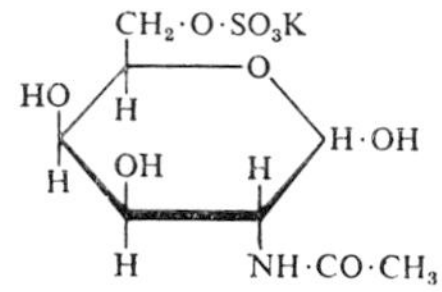	339·3
2	*N*-Acetyl-D-glucosamine-6-sulphate, K salt		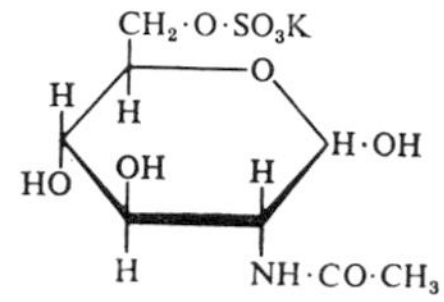	339·3
3	Adenosine-3′-phosphate-5′-sulphatophosphate	Phosphoadenosine-phosphosulphate, PAPS, active sulphate	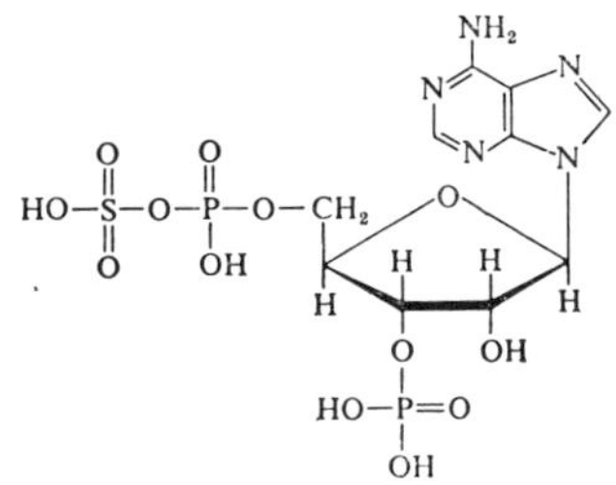	507·
4	Adenosine-5′-sulphatophosphate	Adenosine-phosphosulphate, APS	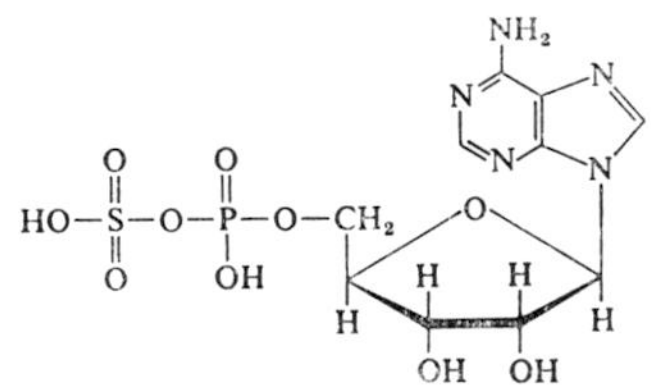	427
5	Androstenolone sulphate, K salt	Dehydro*iso*androsterone sulphate, dehydro*epi*androsterone sulphate, DHAS	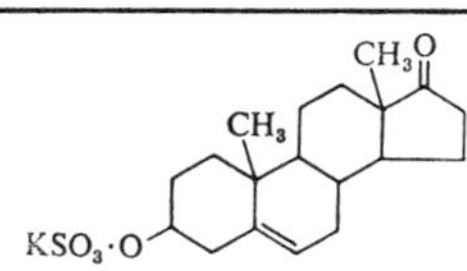	406
6	Cholesteryl sulphate, K salt		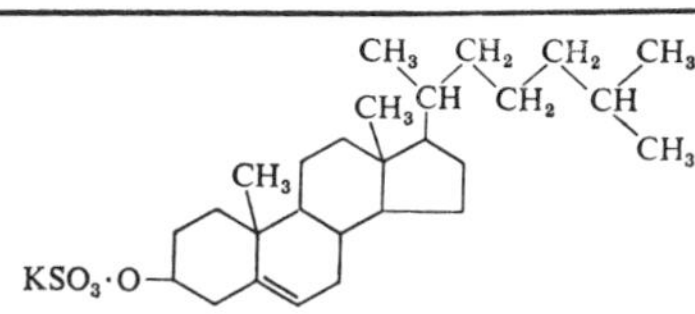	50
7	Choline-*O*-sulphate	Choline sulphate ester	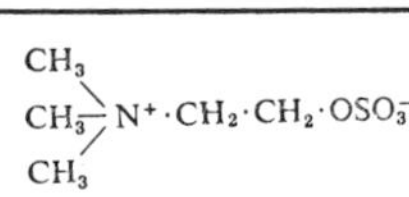	1
8	Glucose-3-sulphate, K salt		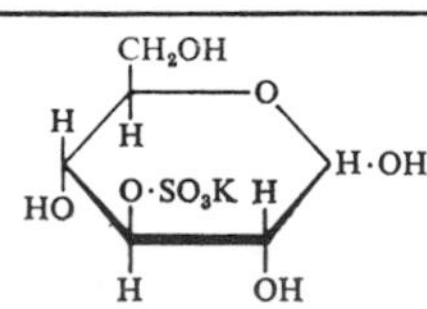	2

eparation	Estimation	General remarks
J. 75, 478 (1960) J. 83, 455 (1962) B.B.A. 58, 1 (1962)		
. 75, 478 (1960) . 83, 455 (1962)		
. Biochem. Preps. 10, 3 (1963) .S. 1959, 1731 ure, Lond. 193, 1180 (1962) .. J.B.C. 229, 837 (1957) C. 233, 472 (1958) J.B.C. 236, 1822 (1961)	J.B.C. 229, 837 (1957) J.B.C. 229, 1081 (1957)	Sulphate quantitatively liberated by 0·1N-HCl at 37° for 30 min. Relatively alkali-stable.
J.C.S. 1957, 1067 C.S. 81, 878 (1959) J.B.C. 236, 1822 (1961)	J.B.C. 233, 681, 686 (1958)	
62, 41 (1956)		Decomposes in boiling neutral solution to i-androstanolone. Rapidly hydrolysed in acid (*B.J.* 62, 41 (1956)).
.S. 63, 1259 (1941) . 1957, 3889		Decomposes in boiling neutral solution to i-cholesterol. Rapidly hydrolysed in acid. Very insoluble in water, ethanol, and non-polar solvents. Soluble in dimethylformamide.
37, 54 (1904)		
1945, 119 , 310 (1954)		Considerably less acid-stable than glucose-6-sulphate; partially decomposes on standing overnight at 0° in 3% trichloroacetic acid, under which conditions the 6-sulphate is stable.

4. Sulphate Esters

No.	*Name*	*Synonyms*	*Formula*	*M. w*
9	Glucose-6-sulphate, K salt		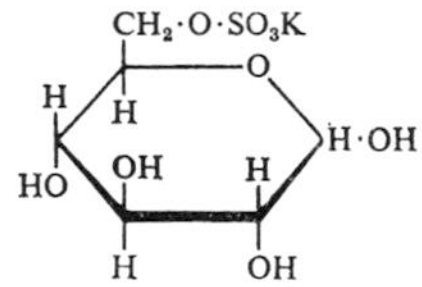	298·3
10	Indoxyl sulphate, K salt	Indican	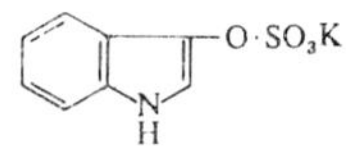	251·3
11	Oestrone sulphate, K salt		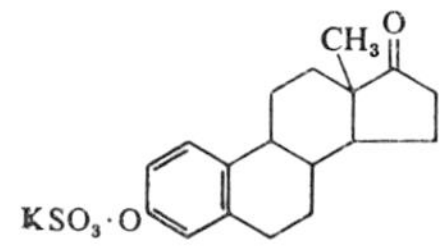	388·5
12	Pregnenolone sulphate, K salt		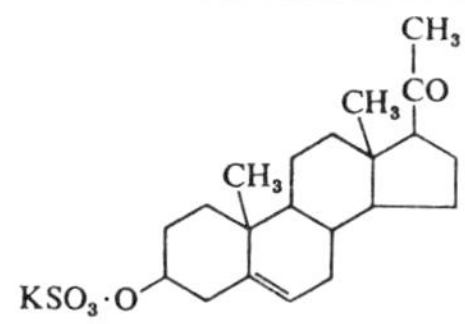	434·
13	Tyrosine-*O*-sulphate, mono-K salt		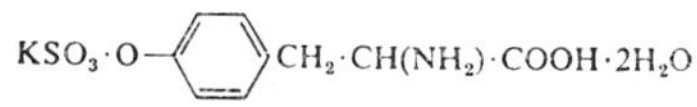	335·
14	Sinigrin, K salt	Potassium myronate	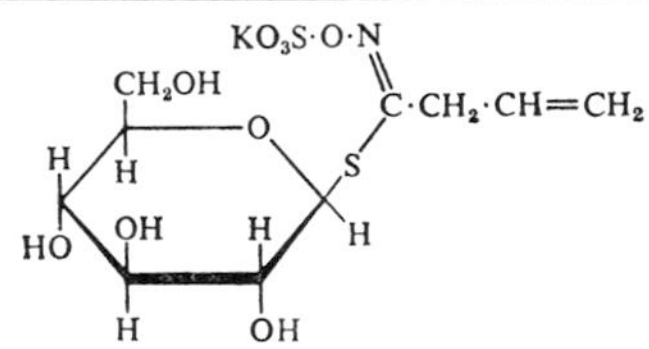	397

eparation	*Estimation*	*General remarks*
J. **75,** 478 (1960) *J.* **83,** 455 (1962) *ture, Lond.* **183,** 109 (1959)		
. **62,** 546 (1956)		
.S. **1957,** 3889 *J.B.C.* **235,** 973 (1960)		Pure compound apparently difficult to obtain. Pyridine salt crystallizes with $CHCl_3$ of crystallization (*J.C.S.* **1957,** 3889). Readily solvolysed in $CHCl_3$-dioxane.
62, 41 (1956) *Biochemistry* **2,** 648 (1963)		Decomposes in boiling neutral solution to i-preganolone. Rapidly hydrolysed in acid.
71, 10 (1959) *B.J.* **79,** 209 (1961)		
. biochem. Anal. **4,** 229 (1957)		Older texts give incorrect formula—see *J.A.C.S.* **78,** 4172 (1956).

5. Constituents of DNA and Related Compounds

Revised by MARY R. LUNT (*Department of Biochemistry, University of Oxford*)

Nomenclature

It is important to note that there are two different conventions of numbering pyrimidine compounds. In the newer system used in *Chemical Abstracts*, uracil for example is 2,4-dihydroxypyrimidine.

However, in Beilstein the older convention (uracil = 2,6-dihydroxypyrimidine) is employed; this system is in line with purine ring numbering. This older system, also used by Michelson (1963), has been used here since it occurs in almost all biochemical literature. Confusion can arise because original papers may use either system without specifying which. Thus 1-methylcytosine in *J.C.S.* **1962,** 1348, is the same compound as 3-methylcytosine in *J.A.C.S.* **85,** 4024 (1963); cytosine may be 6-amino-2-hydroxypyrimidine (older system) or 4-amino-2-hydroxypyrimidine (new system). A full discussion of pyrimidine nomenclature can be found in Brown (1962). The system of numbering used here is as follows:

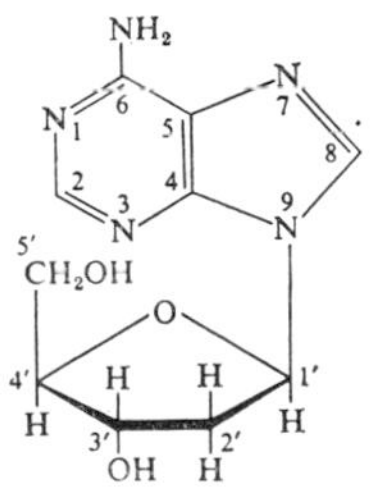

Adenine deoxyriboside

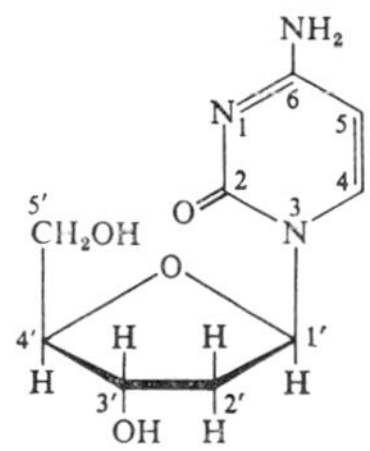

Cytosine deoxyriboside

Abbreviations and symbols for nucleic acids, polynucleotides and their constituents are given in *B.J.* **120,** 449 (1970); *J.B.C.*, **245,** 5171 (1970); *Eur. J. Biochem.* **15,** 203 (1970).

General references

Methods of analysis

1. E. Volkin and W. E. Cohn, *Meth. biochem. Anal.* **1,** 287 (1954).
2. J. M. Webb and H. B. Levy, *Meth. biochem. Anal.* **6,** 1 (1958) (purine-bound deoxyribose).
3. H. K. Miller, *Meth. biochem. Anal.* **6,** 31 (1958) (microbiological assay of nucleic acids and their derivatives).
4. L. Grossman and K. Moldave, eds., *Methods in Enzymology*, vol. 12, Nucleic Acids, part A, Academic Press, London and New York (1967). Series editors, S. P. Colowick and N. O. Kaplan.

Chromatographic separation, etc.

The Nucleic Acids, eds. Chargaff and Davidson, Academic Press, New York (1955).

R. Markham in *Modern Methods of Plant Analysis*, eds. Peach and Tracey, vol. 4, Springer, Berlin (1956).

L. Josefsson, *B.B.A.* **72,** 133 (1963) (semi-quantitative determination of nucleic acid derivatives—thin-layer chromatography).

Chemistry of components

A. M. Michelson, *The Chemistry of Nucleosides and Nucleotides*, Academic Press, London and New York (1963).

5. Constituents of DNA and Related Compounds

D. J. Brown, *The Pyrimidines*, Interscience, New York and London (1962).
P. A. Levene and L. W. Bass, *Nucleic Acids*, Chemical Catalog Co., New York (1931).

pK_a *values*

The values given are taken from K. Burton (pp. 169–79) and from D. D. Perrin, *Dissociation Constants of Organic Bases in Aqueous Solution*, Butterworth (1965).

No.	*Name*	*Synonyms*	*Structure*	*M. wt.*	pK_a
1	Adenine	6-Aminopurine	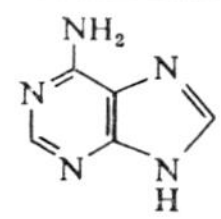	135·1	1 4·1 9·8
2	Adenine deoxyriboside	Deoxyadenosine, 9-β-D-2′-Deoxyribofuranosidoadenine	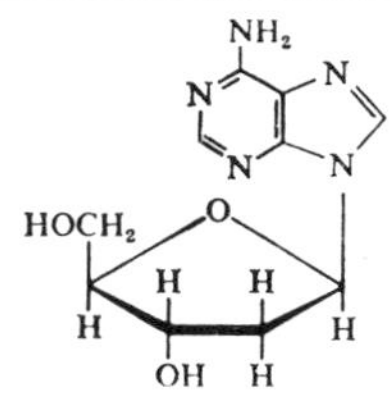	251·2	
3	Adenine deoxyribose-3′-phosphate	Deoxyadenosine-3′-phosphate, 3′-Deoxyadenylic acid	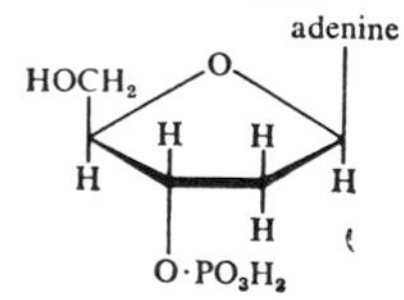	331·2	4·4 6·4
4	Adenine deoxyribose-5′-phosphate	Deoxyadenosine-5′-phosphate, 5′-Deoxyadenylic acid	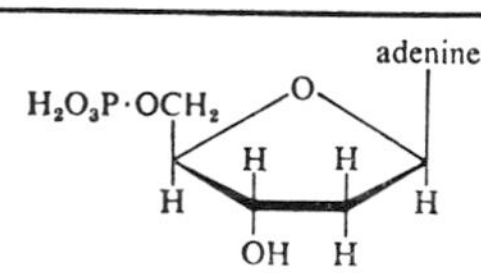	331·2	4·4 6·4
5	Adenine deoxyribose-3′,5′-diphosphate	Deoxyadenosine-3′,5′-diphosphate	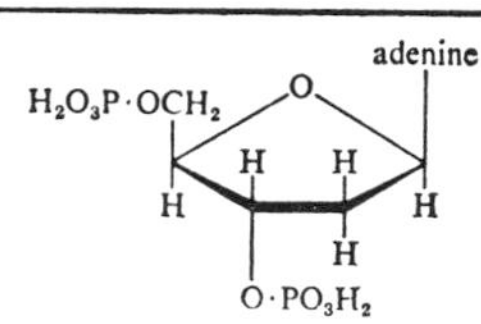	411·2	
6	Adenine deoxyribose-5′-triphosphate	Deoxyadenosine-5′-triphosphate	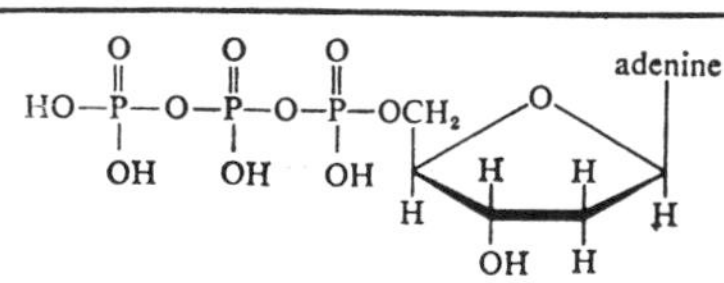	491·3	
	—, Na_4 salt		$C_{10}H_{12}N_5O_{12}P_3Na_4$	579·1	
7	Cytosine	6-Amino-2-hydroxypyrimidine	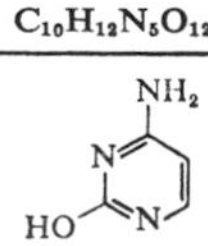	111·1; Hydrate, 129·1	4·4 12·

hysical rm	*M.p.*	*Solubility*	*Preparation*	*Estimation*	*General remarks*
eedles+ H_2O	sublimes 220	$0{\cdot}09^{25}$, $2{\cdot}5^{100}$ H_2O; sl. s. EtOH; i. eth., $CHCl_3$	ISOL. Levene and Bass, p. 114 SYN. 8-^{14}C. *Biochem. Preps.* **5**, 62 (1957)	*Meth. biochem. Anal.* **3**, 97 (1956) *Meth. biochem. Anal.* **6**, 79 (1958) *Arch. B.* **25**, 347 (1950)	Released from DNA by hydrolysis with dilute acid.
n. cryst.+ $_2$O	Hydrate, sinters 168–9, melts 186–9	s. H_2O	ISOL. *Z.P.C.* **224**, 244 (1934) *B.J.* **35**, 855 (1941) *J.C.S.* **1952**, 2721 SYN. *J.A.C.S.* **81**, 3967 (1959) *Ber.* **93**, 140 (1960)		Obtained by enzymic hydrolysis of DNA. Readily hydrolysed by dilute acids. Hydrate loses water of cryst. at 80° *in vacuo*.
			ISOL. *J.A.C.S.* **80**, 2546 (1958) SYN. *J.C.S.* **1955**, 808		Calcium salt ($3H_2O$), white amorphous solid. Easily hydrolysed by dilute mineral acids. Released quantitatively from DNA by use of phosphodiesterases of *Micrococcus pyogenes* and calf spleen (*J.B.C.* **236**, 864 (1961)). Diesterase of *Lactobacillus acidophilus* releases 3′-phosphates from deoxyoligonucleotides (*J.B.C.* **238**, 2789 (1963)).
edles			ISOL. *Biochem. Preps.* **5**, 49 (1957) *J.A.C.S.* **73**, 1533 (1951) *J.B.C.* **204**, 847 (1953) SYN. *J.C.S.* **1955**, 808 ^{32}P. *J.A.C.S.* **83**, 159 (1961)		Monocalcium salt ($2H_2O$), white amorphous solid, $[\alpha]_D^{19}$ −26 (c = 0·38 in H_2O). Easily hydrolysed by dilute mineral acids. Released from heated DNA by *E. coli* diesterase (*J.B.C.* **235**, 1479 (1960)) or by pancreatic DNA-ase followed by venom diesterase.
					Obtained by enzymic degradation of DNA (*J.B.C.* **235**, 1150 (1960)). Easily hydrolysed by dilute mineral acids.
			ENZ. SYN. *B.B.A.* **39**, 82 (1960) *Biochem. Preps.* **9**, 120 (1962) *J.B.C.* **233**, 263 (1958) *B.J.* **86**, 562 (1963) SYN. *Can. J. Chem.* **42**, 599 (1964) *J.A.C.S.* **80**, 1141 (1958)		
es+	320–5 d. (anhyd.); Hydrate, 312 d.	$0{\cdot}77^{25}$ H_2O; sl. s. EtOH; i. eth.	ISOL. *Ber.* **27**, 2215 (1894) SYN. *J.A.C.S.* **52**, 1152 (1930) Levene and Bass, p. 71 *J.B.C.* **177**, 357 (1949)	*Arch. B.* **26**, 209 (1950) *J.B.C.* **181**, 713 (1949)	Obtained from acid hydrolysates of DNA. Water of cryst. lost at 100°. Cryst. picrate, decomp. 300–5.

5. Constituents of DNA and Related Compounds

No.	Name	Synonyms	Structure	M. wt.	pK_a
8	Cytosine deoxyriboside	Deoxycytidine, 3-β-D-2′-Deoxyribofuranosidocytosine	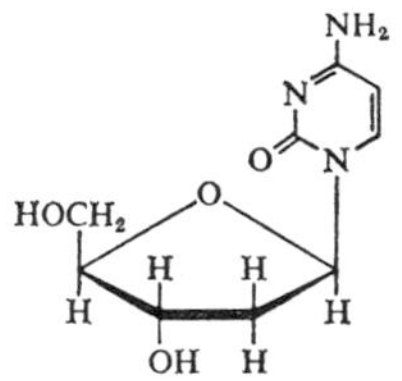	227·2	4·2
9	Cytosine deoxyribose-3′-phosphate	Deoxycytidine-3′-phosphate, 3′-Deoxycytidylic acid	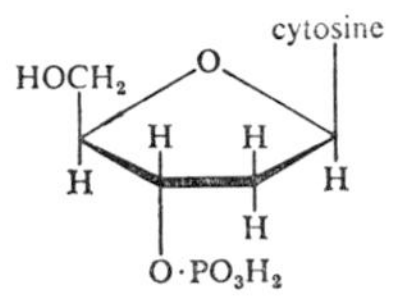	307·2	
10	Cytosine deoxyribose-5′-phosphate	Deoxycytidine-5′-phosphate, 5′-Deoxycytidylic acid	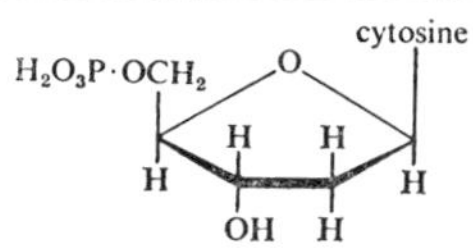	307·2	4·4
11	Cytosine deoxyribose-3′,5′-diphosphate	Deoxycytidine-3′,5′-diphosphate	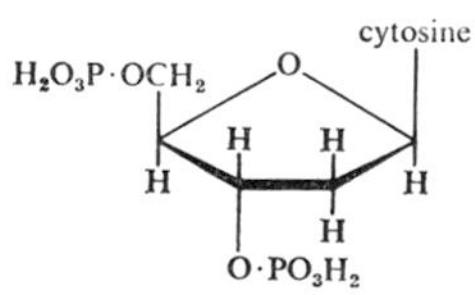	387·2	
12	Cytosine deoxyribose-5′-triphosphate	Deoxycytidine-5′-triphosphate	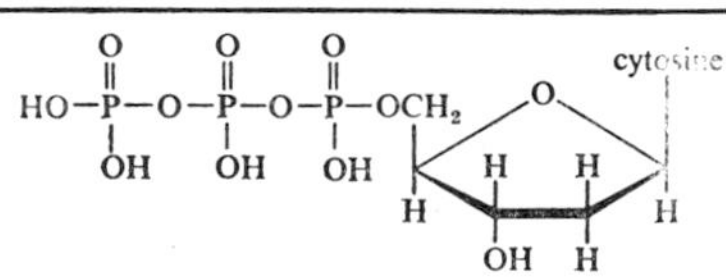	467·2	
	—, Na_4 salt		$C_9H_{12}N_3O_{13}P_3Na_4 \cdot H_2O$	573·1	
13	5-(α-Glucosidomethyl)-cytosine deoxyriboside	5-(α-Glucosidomethyl)-deoxycytidine, α-Glucosylhydroxymethyldeoxycytidine, Hydroxymethyl-deoxycytidine-α-glucoside	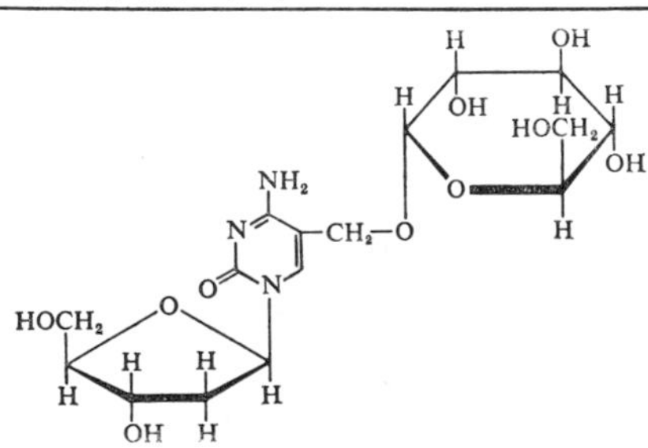	419·4	
14	5-(β-Glucosidomethyl)-cytosine deoxyriboside	5-(β-Glucosidomethyl)-deoxycytidine, β-Glucosylhydroxymethyldeoxycytidine, Hydroxymethyl-deoxycytidine-β-glucoside	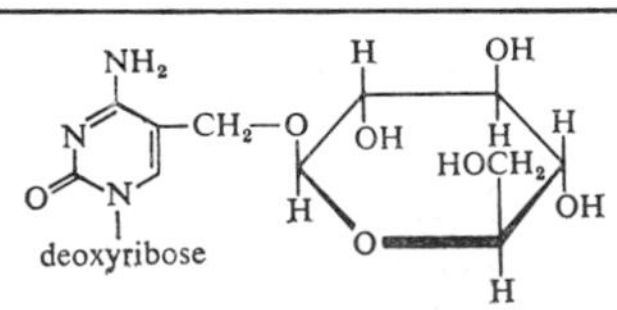	419·4	

ysical m	M.p.	Solubility	Preparation	Estimation	General remarks
isms om eOH/ ier	199–201; Hydro-chloride, 161–4 d.	s. H_2O	ISOL. *J.C.S.* **1950**, 1990 *J.C.S.* **1952**, 2721 SYN. *J.A.C.S.* **83**, 4066 (1961)		Isolated from enzymic hydrolysates of DNA. Picrate, needles, M.p. 192–8 d. Appearance of picrate, *J.B.C.* **178**, 43 (1951).
edles	196–7 d.		ISOL. *J.A.C.S.* **80**, 2546 (1958) SYN. *J.C.S.* **1954**, 34 *J.A.C.S.* **83**, 159 (1961)		Released quantitatively from DNA by use of phosphodiesterase of *Micrococcus pyogenes* and calf spleen (*J.B.C.* **236**, 864 (1961)). Diesterase from *Lacto-bacillus acidophilus* releases 3′-phosphates from deoxyoligonucleotides (*J.B.C.* **238**, 2789 (1963)).
dles	183–4		ISOL. *Biochem. Preps.* **5**, 49 (1957) *J.A.C.S.* **73**, 1533 (1951) *J.B.C.* **204**, 847 (1953) SYN. *J.C.S.* **1954**, 34 ^{32}P. *J.A.C.S.* **83**, 159 (1961) *Biochem. Preps.* **9**, 9 (1962)		Released from heated DNA by *E. coli* phosphodiesterase (*J.B.C.* **235**, 1479 (1960)) or quantitatively by pancreatic DNA-ase followed by venom diesterase.
			ISOL. *B.B.A.* **26**, 596 (1957) *B.J.* **75**, 17 (1960) SYN. *J.A.C.S.* **83**, 159 (1961) *J.C.S.* **1953**, 947		Tetrabrucine salt (23 H_2O), sinters 180, M.p. 185. Obtained from DNA by acid hydrolysis or diphenylamine degradation.
			ENZ. SYN. *B.B.A.* **39**, 82 (1960) *Biochem. Preps.* **9**, 120 (1962) *J.B.C.* **233**, 263 (1958) *B.J.* **86**, 562 (1963) SYN. *Can. J. Chem.* **42**, 599 (1964) *J.A.C.S.* **80**, 1141 (1958)		
			ISOL. *J.B.C.* **235**, 3254 (1960) *B.J.* **92**, 27 (1964)		Isolated from enzymic hydrolysates of DNA of T2 bacteriophage, or via diphenylamine degradation; obtained mixed with (β-glucosidomethyl)deoxy-cytidine from enzymic hydrolysates of T4 DNA. Glucose released by acid hydrolysis (1 N-HCl or H_2SO_4 at 100°/1 hr) or by glucosidase of *Sacch. italicus.*
			ISOL. *J.B.C.* **235**, 3254 (1960)		Obtained mixed with (α-glucosido-methyl)deoxycytidine from enzymic hydrolysates of T4 DNA. Glucose released by acid hydrolysis (1N-HCl or H_2SO_4) or by almond β-glucosidase.

5. Constituents of DNA and Related Compounds

No.	*Name*	*Synonyms*	*Structure*	*M. wt.*	pK_a
15	5-(α-Gentiobiosido-methyl)-cytosine deoxyriboside	5-(α-Gentiobiosido-methyl)-deoxycytidine, α-Gentiobiosylhydroxy-methyldeoxycytidine, Hydroxymethyl-deoxycytidine-α-gentiobioside, Diglucosylhydroxy-methyldeoxycytidine	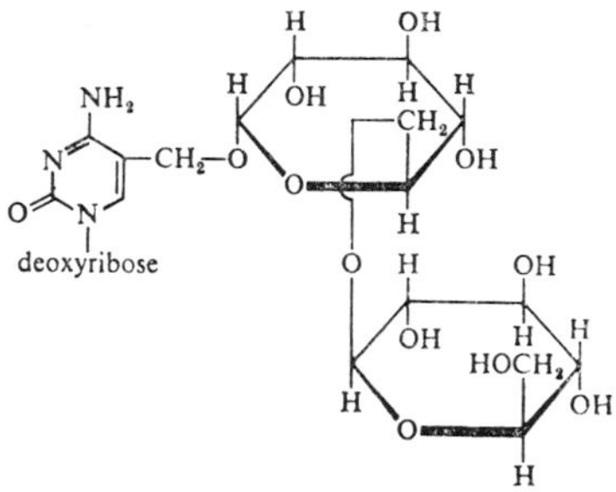	581·5	
16	5-(α-Glucosido-methyl)-cytosine deoxyribose-5′-phosphate	α-Glucosyl-5-hydroxy-methyldeoxycytidine-5′-phosphate, 5-Hydroxymethyl-deoxycytidine-5′-phosphate-α-glucoside	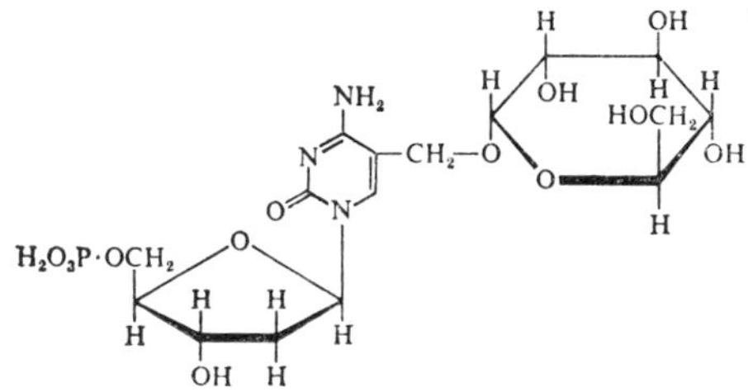	499·4	
17	5-(β-Glucosido-methyl)-cytosine deoxyribose-5′-phosphate	β-Glucosyl-5-hydroxy-methyldeoxycytidine-5′-phosphate	Cf. above and 5-(β-glucosidomethyl)-cytosine deoxyriboside	499·4	
18	5-(α-Gentiobiosido-methyl)-cytosine deoxyribose-5′-phosphate	Diglucosyl-5-hydroxy-methyldeoxycytidine-5′-phosphate	See 5-(α-gentiobiosidomethyl)-cytosine deoxyriboside	661·5	
19	Guanine	2-Amino-6-hydroxy-purine	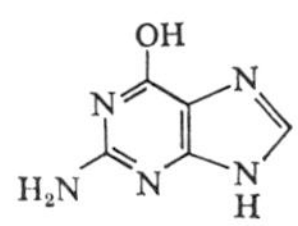	151·1	3·3 9·2 12·
20	Guanine deoxy-riboside	Deoxyguanosine, 9-β-D-2′-Deoxyribo-furanosidoguanine	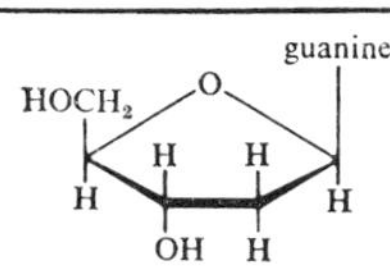	267·2	
21	Guanine deoxyribose-3′-phosphate	Deoxyguanosine-3′-phosphate, 3′-Deoxyguanylic acid	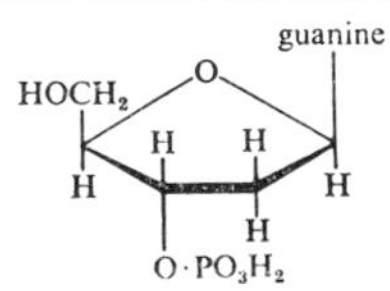	347·2	
22	Guanine deoxyribose-5′-phosphate	Deoxyguanosine-5′-phosphate, 5′-Deoxyguanylic acid	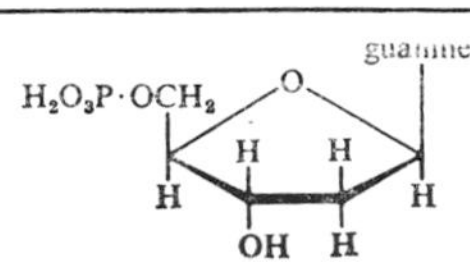	347·2	2· 6· 9·

…hysical …rm	*M.p.*	*Solubility*	*Preparation*	*Estimation*	*General remarks*
			ISOL. *J.B.C.* **234**, 364 (1959) *J.B.C.* **235**, 3254 (1960)		Isolated from enzymic hydrolysates of DNA of bacteriophages T2 and T6. Total glucose released by acid hydrolysis (1 N-HCl or H_2SO_4/100°/1 hr); 50% glucose released by almond β-glucosidase, and remaining 50% by subsequent treatment with α-glucosidase of *Sacch. italicus.*
			ISOL. *J.B.C.* **235**, 1134, 2688, 3254 (1960)		Obtained from DNA of T2 phage by hydrolysis with *E. coli* phosphodiesterase, or non-quantitatively with pancreatic DNA-ase and venom diesterase. Nitrous acid gives α-glucosyl derivative of 5-hydroxymethyldeoxyuridine (*J.B.C.* **237**, 1266 (1962)). Distinguish from non-glucosylated deriv. by spectra at pH 4·3. (*Science* **120**, 551 (1954)). Glucose released by acid hydrolysis (1 N-HCl or H_2SO_4 at 100°/1 hr). Chromatographic separation from gentiobiosyl and non-glucosylated deriv. in *J.B.C.* **235**, 1134 (1960); **236**, 1487 (1961).
			ISOL. *J.B.C.* **235**, 1134, 3254 (1960)		Obtained (as mixture with α-glucosido compound) from enzymic hydrolysates of T4 phage DNA. See above.
			ISOL. *J.B.C.* **235**, 1134, 3254 (1960) *J.B.C.* **237**, 1266 (1962)		Isolated from enzymic hydrolysates of DNA of T6 phage; small amount in T2 DNA. See above.
…rph. …der or …ets …n dil. …OH		s. acids and alkali; v. sl. s. EtOH; i. H_2O (0·004^{40}), organic acids	ISOL. *J.B.C.* **53**, 441 (1922) SYN. *J.B.C.* **153**, 203 (1944)	*Meth. biochem. Anal.* **6**, 79 (1958)	Released from DNA by hydrolysis with cold dilute acid. Forms cryst. salts with many acids and bases, and double salts with many metal salts. Hydrochloride, cryst.+ H_2O.
…les+ …	Darkens 250, Decomp. 300–1	s. H_2O	ISOL. *J.C.S.* **1952**, 2721 *J.C.S.* **1950**, 1990 *J.B.C.* **184**, 449 (1950) SYN. *Ber.* **93**, 140 (1960)		Obtained by enzymic hydrolysis of DNA. Water of cryst. lost at 135° at 1 mm for 20 hr. Easily hydrolysed by dilute mineral acids.
			ISOL. *J.A.C.S.* **80**, 2546 (1958) SYN. *J.C.S.* **1955**, 808		Monobarium salt ($2H_2O$), white amorphous powder, $[\alpha]_D^{19\cdot5}$ −8·5 (c = 0·412 in H_2O). Readily hydrolysed by dilute mineral acids. Released quantitatively from DNA using diesterases of *Micrococcus pyogenes* and calf spleen (*J.B.C.* **236**, 864 (1961)). Diesterase from *Lb. acidophilus* releases 3′-phosphates from deoxyoligonucleotides (*J.B.C.* **238**, 2789 (1963)).
			ISOL. *Biochem. Preps.* **5**, 49 (1957) *J.A.C.S.* **73**, 1533 (1951) *J.B.C.* **204**, 847 (1953) SYN. *J.C.S.* **1955**, 808		Monobarium salt ($4H_2O$), $[\alpha]_D^{19\cdot5}$ −18·6 (c = 0·366 in H_2O). Easily hydrolysed by dilute mineral acids. Obtained by hydrolysis of heated DNA by *E. coli* phosphodiesterase (*J.B.C.* **235**, 1479 (1960)), or by pancreatic DNA-ase followed by venom diesterase.

5. Constituents of DNA and Related Compounds

No.	*Name*	*Synonyms*	*Structure*	*M. wt.*	pK_a
23	Guanine deoxyribose-3′,5′-diphosphate	Deoxyguanosine-3′,5′-diphosphate	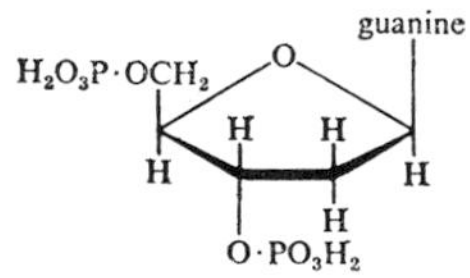	427·1	
24	Guanine deoxyribose-5′-triphosphate	Deoxyguanosine-5′-triphosphate	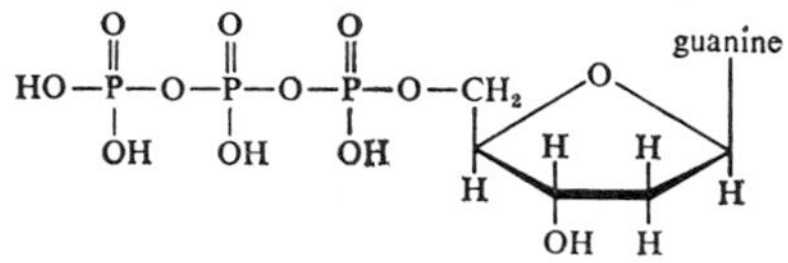	507·2	
	—, Na_4 salt		$C_{10}H_{12}N_5O_{13}P_3Na_4 \cdot 3H_2O$	649·2	
25	5-Hydroxymethyl-cytosine	6-Amino-2-hydroxy-5-hydroxymethyl-pyrimidine	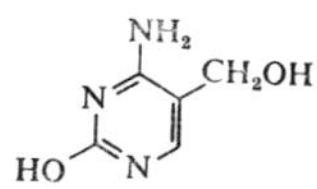	141·1	
26	5-Hydroxymethyl-cytosine deoxyriboside	5-Hydroxymethyl-deoxycytidine	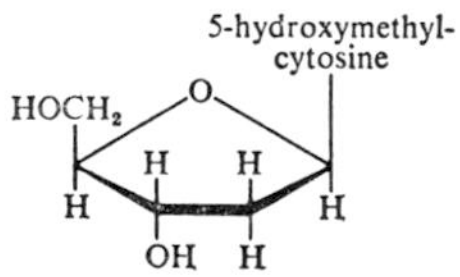	257·2	
27	5-Hydroxymethyl-cytosine deoxyribose-3′-phosphate	5-Hydroxymethyl-deoxycytidine-3′-phosphate	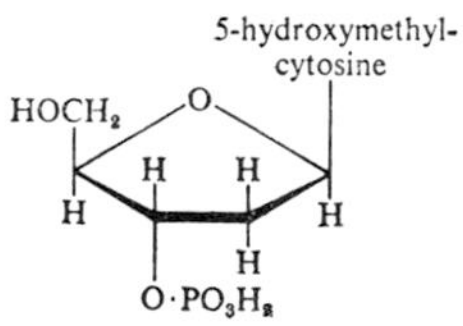	337·2	
28	5-Hydroxymethyl-cytosine deoxyribose-5′-phosphate	5-Hydroxymethyl-deoxycytidine-5′-phosphate	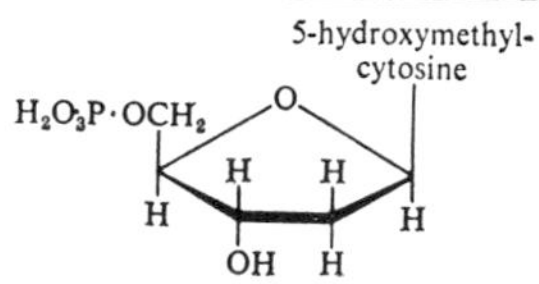	337·2	
29	5-Hydroxymethyl-cytosine deoxyribose-3′,5′-diphosphate	5-Hydroxymethyl-deoxycytidine-3′,5′-diphosphate	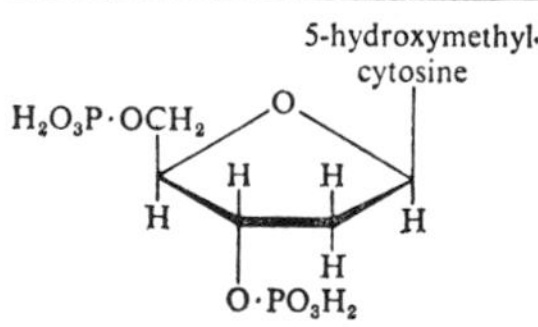	417·2	
30	5-Hydroxy-methyluracil	2,6-Dihydroxy-5-hydroxymethyl-pyrimidine	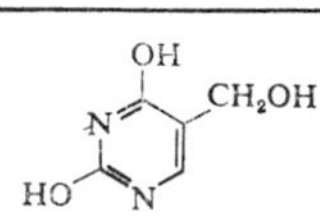	142·1	

hysical rm	*M.p.*	*Solubility*	*Preparation*	*Estimation*	*General remarks*
					Obtained by enzymic hydrolysis of DNA (*J.B.C.* **235**, 1150 (1960)).
			ENZ. SYN. *B.B.A.* **39**, 82 (1960) *Biochem. Preps.* **9**, 120 (1962) *J.B.C.* **233**, 263 (1958) *B.J.* **86**, 562 (1963) SYN. *Can. J. Chem.* **42**, 599 (1964) *J.A.C.S.* **80**, 1141 (1958)		
cryst. H_2O	Decomp. above 200	sl. s. H_2O	ISOL. *B.J.* **55**, 774 (1953) SYN. *J.A.C.S.* **77**, 752 (1955)		Isolated from acid (88% HCOOH or 6N-HCl) hydrolysates of DNA of T-even bacteriophages of *E. coli*. Destroyed if DNA heated with 72% $HClO_4$. Cryst. picrate (*J.B.C.* **226**, 631 (1957)).
			ISOL. *J.B.C.* **228**, 621 (1957)		Isolated from acid hydrolysates (10% $HClO_4$/100°/1 hr) of DNA of T-even bacteriophages of *E. coli*. Cryst. picrate (*J.B.C.* 226, 631 (1957)).
			ISOL. *B.J.* **92**, 27 (1964)		Isolated from T2 bacteriophage DNA degraded with diphenylamine and calf spleen diesterase.
d. es		*ca.* 4·5 µmole/ml at 0° and pH 3·0	ISOL. *J.B.C.* **235**, 1134, 2688, 3254 (1960) *J. exp. Med.* **106**, 233 (1957)		Distinguish from glucosylated derivative by spectra at pH 4·3 (*Science* **120**, 551 (1954)). Obtained from DNA of T2 and T6 phages by hydrolysis with *E. coli* phosphodiesterase, or non-quantitatively with pancreatic DNA-ase followed by venom diesterase. Corresponding di- and triphosphates have been synthesized (*J.B.C.* 235, 2688 (1960)).
			ISOL. *J.B.C.* **206**, 735 (1954) *B.J.* **92**, 27 (1964)		Obtained by acid hydrolysis or diphenylamine degradation of T2 DNA.
	260–300 d.		ISOL. *J. molec. Biol.* 5, 248 (1962) SYN. *J.A.C.S.* **81**, 2521 (1959) *J.A.C.S.* **82**, 991 (1960)		Isolated from formic acid hydrolysates of DNA of bacteriophage SP 8 of *B. subtilis*. Destroyed by heating with 12N-$HClO_4$ 100°. Action of hot acids discussed in *Nucleic Acids*, vol. 1, p. 86; see also *J.A.C.S.* **81**, 2521 (1959); **82**, 991 (1960).

5. Constituents of DNA and Related Compounds

No.	*Name*	*Synonyms*	*Structure*	*M. wt.*	pK_a
31	5-Hydroxymethyl-uracil deoxyriboside	5-Hydroxymethyl-deoxyuridine	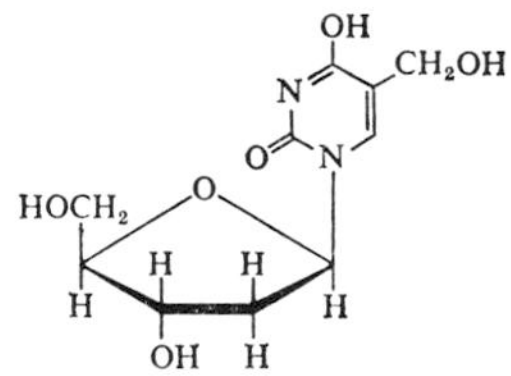	258·2	
32	5-Hydroxymethyl-uracil deoxyribose-5′-phosphate	5-Hydroxymethyl-deoxyuridine-5′-phosphate, 5-Hydroxymethyl-deoxyuridylic acid	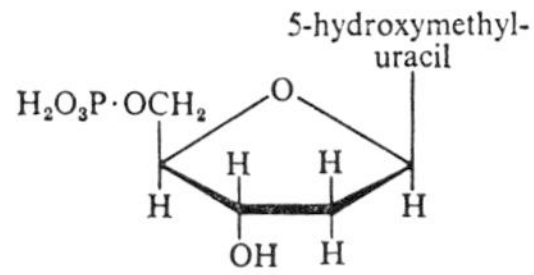	338·2	
33	6-Methylaminopurine		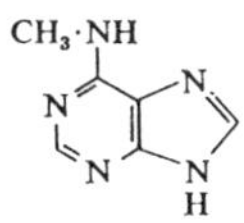	149·2	4·8 9·6
34	6-Methylaminopurine deoxyriboside		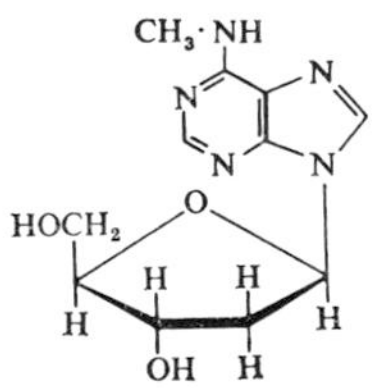	265·3	
35	5-Methylcytosine	6-Amino-2-hydroxy-5-methylpyrimidine	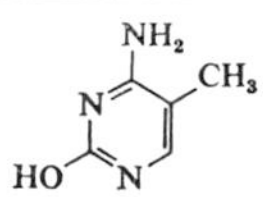	125·1	4·6 12·
36	5-Methylcytosine deoxyriboside	5-Methyldeoxycytidine, 3-β-D-2′-Deoxyribo-furanosido-5-methyl-cytosine	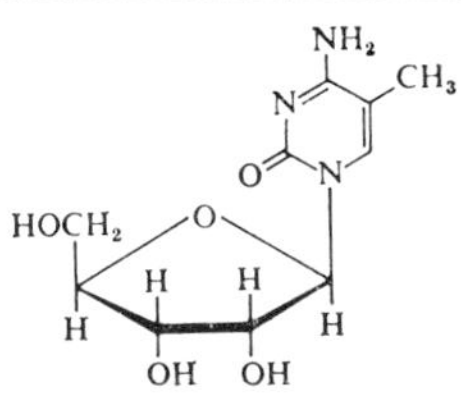	241·2	~ ~
	—, hydrochloride		$C_{10}H_{16}N_3O_4Cl \cdot H_2O$	295·7	
37	5-Methylcytosine deoxyribose-5′-phosphate	5-Methyldeoxy-cytidylic acid	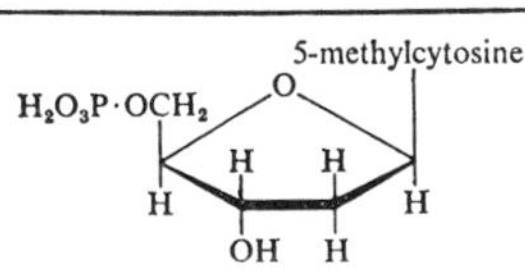	321·2	4·
38	5-Methylcytosine deoxyribose-3′,5′-diphosphate	5-Methyldeoxycytidine-3′,5′-diphosphate	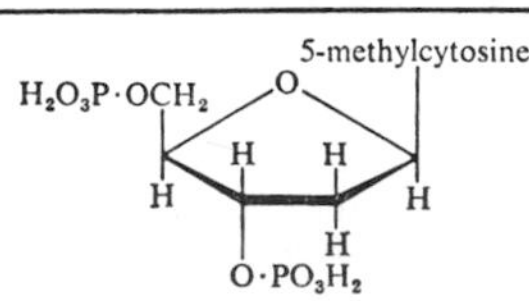	401·2	

hysical orm	M.p.	Solubility	Preparation	Estimation	General remarks
ryst. rom tOH/ tAc	176–9		SYN. *J.A.C.S.* **81**, 2521 (1959)		Occurs in DNA of phage SP 8 of *B. subtilis* (*J. molec. Biol.* **5**, 248 (1962)). Obtained by action of HNO_2 on 5-hydroxymethyldeoxycytidine (*J.B.C.* **228**, 621 (1957)).
			ISOL. *J. molec. Biol.* **5**, 248 (1962) *J.B.C.* **237**, 1266 (1962)		Isolated from enzymic hydrolysate of DNA of *B. subtilis* bacteriophage SP 8.
	312–14 d.	$0{\cdot}12^{20}$, $2{\cdot}0^{100}$ H_2O	ISOL. *B.J.* **68**, 627 (1958) SYN. *J.A.C.S.* **74**, 411 (1952)	*Meth. biochem. Anal.* **6**, 79 (1958)	Isolated from acid hydrolysates of DNA of *E. coli* 15 T^- grown in low conc. of thymine. Small amounts in DNA of certain bacteria and bacterial viruses. Formed quantitatively by action of 0·1N-NaOH/100°/18 hr on 1-methyladenine (*J.C.S.* **1960**, 539).
			ISOL. *B.J.* **68**, 627 (1958)		Isolated from enzymic hydrolysates of DNA of *E. coli* 15 T^- grown in low conc. of thymine. Hydrolysed by mineral acids. Has been synthesized enzymically. Corresponding nucleotide obtained after treatment of 1-methyladenylic acid with 0·1N-NaOH/100°/18 hr (*J.C.S.* **1960**, 539).
sms+ O	270	$4{\cdot}5^{25}$ H_2O	ISOL. *B.J.* **48**, 581 (1951) SYN. *J.B.C.* **177**, 357 (1949) Levene and Bass, p. 73 *J.A.C.S.* **81**, 178 (1959)	*B.J.* **48**, 581 (1951)	Isolated from acid hydrolysates of wheat germ DNA. Hydrochloride, sinters 280, M.p. 299–301 d. Picrate, M.p. 288–90.
r. dles t+)		s. H_2O	ISOL. *J.C.S.* **1951**, 2864 SYN. *J.A.C.S.* **81**, 178 (1959)		Isolated from wheat germ DNA. Hydrochloride loses H_2O at 100° *in vacuo*/48 hr. Anhyd. hydrochloride, M.p. 154–5 d. Picrate, needles, M.p. 175–7 d., also reported to darken above 170 to dark brown solid at 230. Appearance of picrate (*J.B.C.* **226**, 631 (1957)).
			ISOL. *J.A.C.S.* **73**, 1539 (1951) *J.B.C.* **204**, 847 (1953)		Obtained by hydrolysis of wheat germ DNA with pancreatic DNA-ase and venom diesterase.
			ISOL. *B.B.A.* **39**, 68 (1960) *B.B.A.* **55**, 953 (1962)		Isolated from acid hydrolysed or diphenylamine degraded wheat germ DNA. Smaller amounts from other DNAs.

5. Constituents of DNA and Related Compounds

No.	Name	Synonyms	Structure	M. wt.	pK_a
39	Thymine	5-Methyluracil, 2,6-Dihydroxy-5-methylpyrimidine	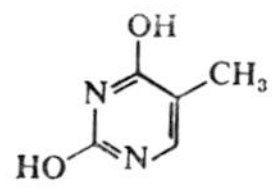	126·1	~0 9·9 > 13
40	Thymine deoxyriboside	Thymidine, 3-β-D-2′-Deoxyribofuranosido-thymine	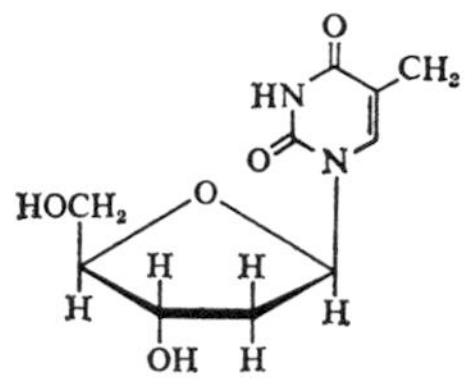	242·2	9·8 > 1
41	Thymine deoxyribose-3′-phosphate	Thymidine-3′-phosphate, 3′-Thymidylic acid	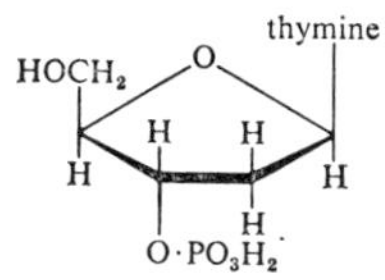	322·2	
42	Thymine deoxyribose-5′-phosphate	Thymidine-5′-phosphate, 5′-Thymidylic acid	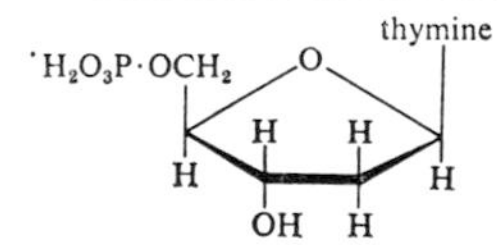	322·2	~1 6·5 10·
	—, Ba salt		$C_{10}H_{13}N_2O_8PBa$	457·5	
43	Thymine deoxyribose-3′,5′-diphosphate	Thymidine-3′,5′-diphosphate	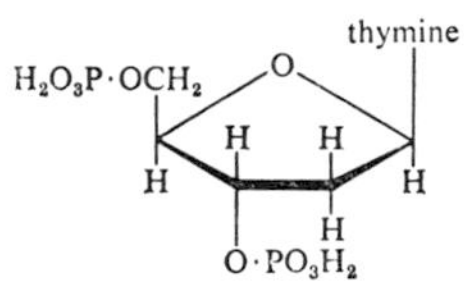	402·2	
44	Thymine deoxyribose-5′-triphosphate	Thymidine-5′-triphosphate	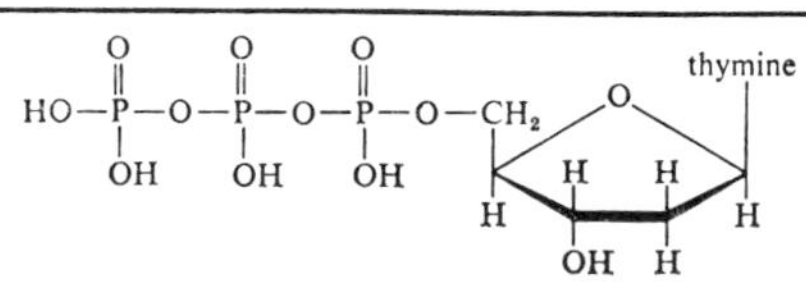	482·2	
	—, Na_4 salt		$C_{10}H_{13}N_2O_{14}P_3Na_4 \cdot 2H_2O$	606·2	
45	Uracil	2,6-Dihydroxy-pyrimidine	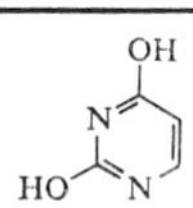	112·1	~ 9· >

Physical form	M.p.	Solubility	Preparation	Estimation	General remarks
plates or needles	318–21 d.	0·404[25] H_2O; s. hot H_2O; sl. s. EtOH; v. sl. s. eth.	SYN. *Am. chem. J.* **42**, 353 (1909) *J.A.C.S.* **68**, 912 (1946) Levene and Bass, p. 67	*J.B.C.* **197**, 227 (1952) *J. Bact.* **84**, 17 (1962)	
platelets	186–7		ISOL. *J.C.S.* **1950**, 1990 *J.C.S.* **1952**, 2721 *B.J.* 35, 855 (1941) *Helv. chim. Acta* **32**, 979 (1949) SYN. *J.C.S.* **1958**, 3035	*Arch. B.B.* 73, 180 (1958)	Isolated from enzymic hydrolysates of DNA. Formed on catalytic reduction of 5-hydroxymethyldeoxyuridine, or reduction/deamination of 5-hydroxymethyldeoxycytidine.
			ISOL. *J.A.C.S.* **80**, 2546 (1958) SYN. *J.C.S.* **1953**, **951** *J.A.C.S.* **83**, 159 (1961)		Monobarium salt ($2H_2O$), colourless needles, $[\alpha]_D^{20}$ +7·3 (c = 1·5 in H_2O). Dibrucine salt ($7H_2O$), colourless needles, soften 172, M.p. 178. Released quantitatively from DNA by phosphodiesterases of *Micrococcus pyogenes* and calf spleen (*J.B.C.* **236**, 864 (1961)).
eedles	softens 140, melts 175		ISOL. *Biochem. Preps.* 5, 49 (1957) *J.A.C.S.* 73, 1533 (1951) *J.B.C.* **204**, 847 (1953) SYN. *J.C.S.* **1953**, **951** [32]P. *J.A.C.S.* **83**, 159 (1961)		Monobarium salt, $[\alpha]_D^{17}$ −3·0. Dibrucine salt, needles, soften 140, M.p. *ca.* 175. Obtained from heated DNA by hydrolysis with *E. coli* diesterase (*J.B.C.* **235**, 1479 (1960)), or pancreatic DNA-ase and venom diesterase.
			ISOL. *J.C.S.* **1953**, **947** *B.J.* **75**, 17 (1960) SYN. *J.C.S.* **1953**, **947**		Tetrabrucine salt (18 H_2O), softens 176, M.p. 182–4. Obtained from DNA by acid hydrolysis or diphenylamine degradation.
			ENZ. SYN. *B.B.A.* **39**, 82 (1960) *Biochem. Preps.* **9**, 120 (1962) *J.B.C.* **233**, 263 (1958) *B.J.* **86**, 562 (1963) SYN. *Can. J. Chem.* **42**, 599 (1964) *J.A.C.S.* **80**, 1141 (1958)		
.. pow- r or sters of edles	335 d.	0·36[25] H_2O; s. alkalis; v. sl. s. EtOH; i. eth.	ISOL. *Z.P.C.* **31**, 162 (1900) *Z.P.C.* **39**, 4 (1903) SYN. *Am. chem. J.* **40**, 547 (1908) *J.A.C.S.* **48**, 2379 (1926) Levene and Bass, p. 62	*J.B.C.* **181**, 713 (1949)	Isolated from acid hydrolysates of DNA of bacteriophage PBS 2 of *B. subtilis* (*B.B.R.C.* **10**, 289 (1963)); small amount in wheat germ DNA (*J.C.S.* **1951**, **2864**). May occur, probably as artefact, in acid hydrolysates of other DNAs (*Nature, Lond.* **166**, 557 (1950); *J.C.S.* **1952**, **2721**).

5. Constituents of DNA and Related Compounds

No.	*Name*	*Synonyms*	*Structure*	*M. wt.*	pK_a
46	Uracil deoxy-riboside	3-β-D-2′-Deoxy-ribofuranosidouracil, Deoxyuridine	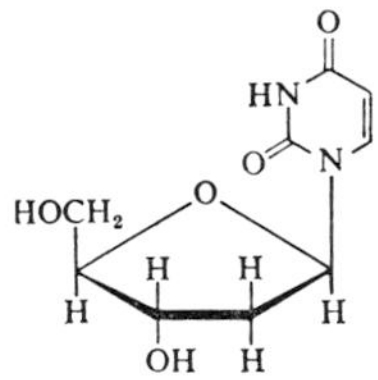	228·2	9·3
47	Uracil deoxyribose-5′-phosphate	Deoxyuridine-5′-phosphate, Deoxy-uridylic acid	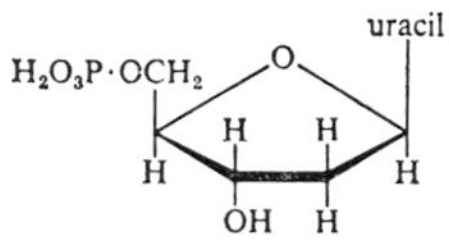	308·2	

Physical form	M.p.	Solubility	Preparation	Estimation	General remarks
needles	167	s. MeOH, H_2O	ISOL. *Nature, Lond.* **166,** 557 (1950) *J.C.S.* **1952,** 2721 SYN. *J.C.S.* **1958,** 3035		Occurs in DNA of phage PBS 2 of *B. subtilis* (*B.B.R.C.* **10,** 289 (1963)); may occur, probably as artefact, in enzymic hydrolysates of other DNAs (*Nature, Lond.* **166,** 557 (1950); *J.C.S.* **1952,** 2721). Formed by action of HNO_2 on deoxycytidine.
			ISOL. *B.B.R.C.* **10,** 289 (1963)		Isolated from enzymic hydrolysates of DNA of *B. subtilis* phage PBS 2; also found, probably as artefact, in enzymic hydrolysates of other DNAs (*Nature, Lond.* **166,** 557 (1950); *J.C.S.* **1952,** 2721). Formed by action of HNO_2 on deoxycytidine-5′-phosphate.

6. Constituents of RNA and Related Compounds

Revised by R. H. SYMONS (*Department of Biochemistry, University of Adelaide*)

Methods for the estimation of nucleic acid constituents depend, in the main, on separating the individual components, followed by the estimation of each by u.v. spectrophotometry. The determination of nucleic acids in biological materials has been comprehensively reviewed by H. N. Munro and A. Fleck (*Meth. biochem. Anal.* **14**, 113 (1966)), whilst methods for the separation of the individual components by paper electrophoresis, paper chromatography, and column chromatography are well covered by the following:

1. *The Nucleic Acids*, eds. E. Chargaff and J. N. Davidson, vol. 1, Academic Press, New York (1955).
2. R. Markham in *Modern Methods*, p. 246. (See below for full reference.)
3. *Meth. Enzymol.* **3,** 715, 724, 743 (1957); **12,** part A (1967).

Specific references are also given in the following section for the estimation of many of the compounds listed. In general, however, details for the separation and estimation of a compound can usually be obtained from the references given for the isolation and synthesis of each compound.

Four references have been abbreviated for the sake of simplicity. These are:

1. P. A. Levene and L. W. Bass, *Nucleic Acids*, Chemical Catalog Co., New York (1931). Abbreviated as 'Levene and Bass'.
2. *Manometric Techniques: Manometric Techniques*, eds. W. W. Umbreit, R. H. Burris, and J. V. Stauffer, Burgess, Minneapolis, Minn., 3rd edition (1957).
3. *Modern Methods: Modern Methods of Plant Analysis*, eds. K. Paech and M. V. Tracey, vol. 4, Springer-Verlag, Berlin (1955).
4. Bergmeyer: *Methods of Enzymatic Analysis*, ed. H. U. Bergmeyer, Academic Press, London and New York (1963).

Further details on many of the compounds listed can be obtained from:

1. A. M. Michelson, *The Chemistry of Nucleosides and Nucleotides*, Academic Press, New York (1963).
2. R. K. Robins in *Heterocyclic Compounds*, ed. R. C. Elderfield, vol. 8, p. 162, John Wiley & Sons, Inc., New York (1967).

Nomenclature

The system of numbering purine and pyrimidine rings is as described on page 129.

6. Constituents of RNA and Related Compounds

No.	Name	Synonyms	Structure	M. wt.	Approximate pK_a	Physical form
1	Adenine	6-Amino-purine	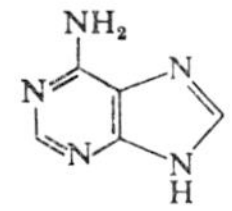	135·1; Hydrate, 189·2	< 1 4·1 9·8	needles+ $3H_2O$
	—, sulphate		$(C_5H_5N_5)_2 \cdot H_2SO_4 \cdot 2H_2O$	404·4		
2	Adenosine	Adenine riboside, 9-β-D-Ribo-furanosido-adenine	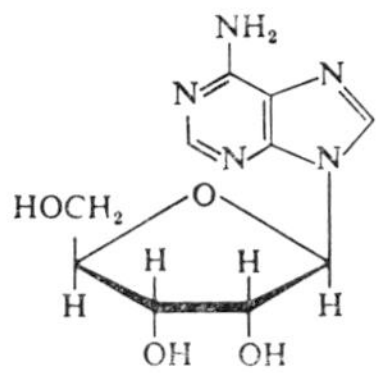	267·2; Hydrate, 294·3	3·6 12·5	col. needles $+1\frac{1}{2}H_2O$
3	Adenosine-2′,3′-cyclic phosphate	2′,3′-Cyclic AMP	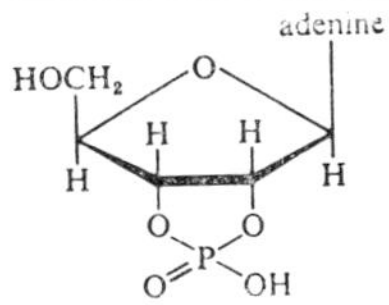	329·2		
4	Adenosine-3′,5′-cyclic phosphate	3′,5′-Cyclic AMP	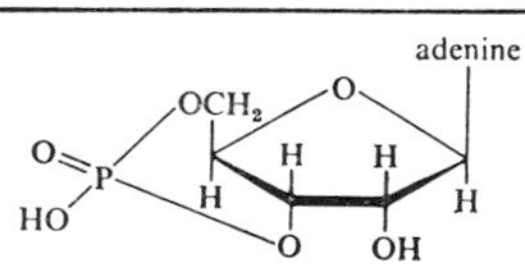	329·2		cryst. from 50% EtOH, pH 2·0
5	Adenosine-5′-diphosphate	ADP	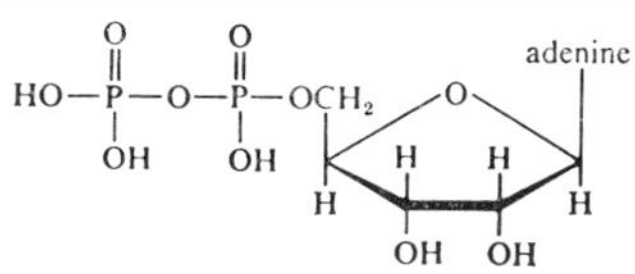	427·2	< 1 3·9 6·1–6·7	
	—, Ba_3 salt		$Ba_3 \cdot (ADP)_2 \cdot 8H_2O$	1404·6		
	—, Na salt		$NaH_2 \cdot ADP \cdot 2H_2O$	485·2		
6	Adenosine-2′-phosphate	2′-AMP, Adenylic acid a	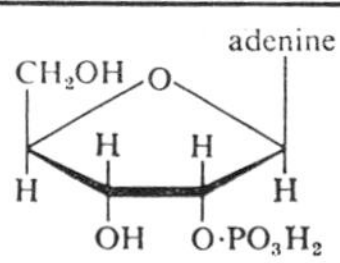	347·2; Hydrate, 374·3	< 1 3·8 6·2	cryst. $+1\frac{1}{2}H_2O$
7	Adenosine-3′-phosphate	3′-AMP, Yeast adenylic acid, Adenylic acid b	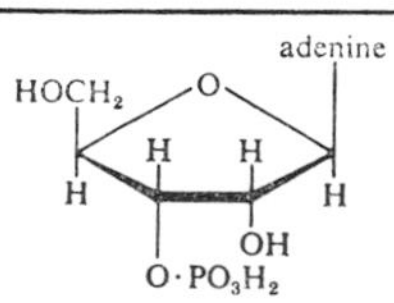	347·2; Hydrate, 365·2	< 1 3·7 5·9	cryst. $+H_2O$

.p.	Solubility	Preparation	Estimation	General remarks
ublimes 20	$0{\cdot}09^{25}$, $2{\cdot}5^{100}$ H_2O; sl. s. EtOH; i. eth., $CHCl_3$	ISOL. Levene and Bass, p. 110 8-^{14}C. *Biochem. Preps.* **5**, 62 (1957)	*Meth. biochem. Anal.* **3**, 97 (1956) *Arch. B.* **25**, 347 (1950) *Modern Methods*, p. 246 *Analyt. Biochem.* **5**, 64 (1963) *Analyt. Biochem.* **1**, 249 (1960)	Deaminated by nitrous acid to form hypoxanthine.
	0·7 H_2O; sl. s. EtOH			
4–5	s. H_2O; v. sl. s. EtOH	ISOL. *Ber.* **74**, 694 (1941) Levene and Bass, p. 163 *J.B.C.* **237**, 2283 (1962) *J.A.C.S.* **73**, 1650 (1951)	*J.B.C.* **167**, 445 (1947) *Arch. B.* **25**, 347 (1950)	Water of cryst. lost at 100° *in vacuo*. Readily hydrolysed in dil. mineral acids to adenine and D-ribose. Deaminated to inosine by nitrous acid.
		ISOL. *B.J.* **52**, 552 (1952) *J.C.S.* **1952**, 52 *Biochem. Preps.* **10**, 131, 139 (1963) *Meth. Enzymol.* **6**, 645 (1963) *J.A.C.S.* **80**, 6204 (1958) *J.C.S.* **1959**, 3655	*Meth. Enzymol.* **3**, 805 (1957) *Modern Methods*, p. 246	Produced as an intermediate during the hydrolysis of RNA by alkali. Readily converted to a mixture of 2′- and 3′-phosphates by dilute acid and alkali at room temp.
	s. H_2O	ISOL. *J.B.C.* **232**, 1065, 1077 (1958) *J.B.C.* **224**, 463 (1957) *J.A.C.S.* **79**, 3608 (1957) SYN. *J.A.C.S.* **79**, 3607 (1957) *J.A.C.S.* **81**, 6198 (1959) *J.A.C.S.* **83**, 698 (1961) *J. org. Chem.* **31**, 3247 (1966)	*Analyt. Biochem.* **13**, 71 (1965)	Stimulates the conversion of inactive glycogen phosphorylase into the active form in liver and the production of hormones by the adrenal cortex. Cyclic nucleotide more acid stable than the non-cyclic monophosphates. In N-HCl at 100°, the time for 50% liberation of adenine is 30 min for the cyclic phosphate and 2–4 min for adenosine 2′-, 3′-, or 5′-phosphate. 0·2 M-$Ba(OH)_2$ at 100° for 30 min completely hydrolyses cyclic phosphate to give a mixture of the adenosine 3′- and 5′-phosphates in the ratio 5:1.
		ISOL. *Biochem. Preps.* **1**, 1 (1949) *Manometric Techniques*, p. 290 SYN. *J.A.C.S.* **83**, 649 (1961) *B.B.A.* **91**, 1 (1964) *Ber.* **95**, 1664 (1962) *Ber.* **98**, 1045 (1965) ^{32}P. *Biochem. Preps.* **7**, 5 (1955) *J. Biochem., Tokyo* **47**, 207 (1960)	*Meth. biochem. Anal.* **1**, 341 (1954) *Manometric Techniques*, p. 276 *Meth. Enzymol.* **10**, 474 (1967)	In N-HCl at 100° the terminal phosphate group is liberated in 10 min. Hydrolysis for 60 min gives adenine, ribose-5-phosphate, ribose, and inorg. P. Reported number of H_2O molecules in salts variable.
		ISOL. Levene and Bass, p. 218 *Biochem. Preps.* **5**, 40 (1957) SYN. *Meth. Enzymol.* **3**, 811 (1957) ^{32}P. *J.C.S.* **1954**, 3396	*The Nucleic Acids*, vol. 1, pp. 211 and 243 (1955) *Modern Methods*, p. 246	Produced, with 3′-isomer, by the alkaline hydrolysis of RNA (0·3N-KOH, 37°, 16 hr). Completely hydrolysed to adenine, ribose-5-phosphate, ribose, and inorg. P by N-HCl at 100° for 1 hr.
d.		ISOL. Levene and Bass, p. 218 *Biochem. Preps.* **5**, 44 (1957) ^{32}P. *J.C.S.* **1954**, 3396	*The Nucleic Acids*, vol. 1, pp. 211 and 243 (1955) *J.B.C.* **201**, 535 (1953) *Modern Methods*, p. 246	Produced, with 2′-isomer, by the alkaline hydrolysis of RNA (0·3N-KOH, 37°, 16 hr). Acid hydrolysis as for adenosine-2′-phosphate. Quantitative yield of furfural when distilled from 20% HCl for 3 hr (cf. adenosine-5′-phosphate).

6. Constituents of RNA and Related Compounds

No.	Name	Synonyms	Structure	M. wt.	Approximate pK_a	Physical form
8	Adenosine-5′-phosphate	5′-AMP, Muscle adenylic acid	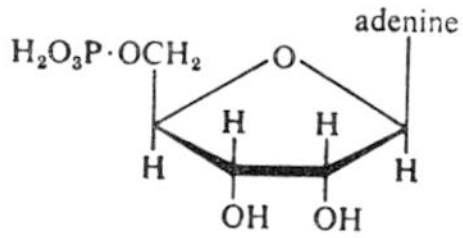	347·2; Hydrate, 383·3	< 1 3·7 6·2–6·4	cryst. $+2H_2$ from aq. acetone
9	Adenosine-3′,5′-pyrophosphate		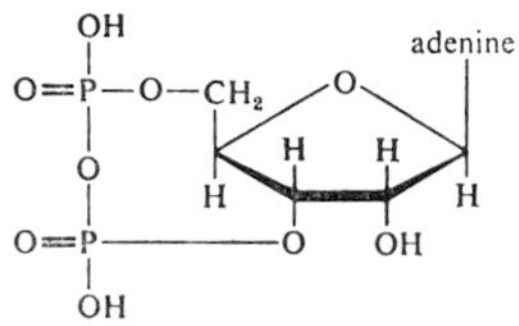	409·2		
10	Adenosine-5′-triphosphate	ATP	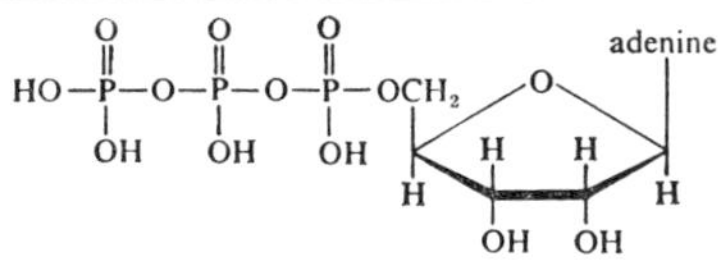	507·2	< 1 4·0 6·0–6·9	
	—, Ba salt		$BaH_2 \cdot ATP$	642·5		
	—, Ba_2 salt		$Ba_2 \cdot ATP \cdot 4H_2O$	850·0		
	—, Na_2 salt		$Na_2H_2 \cdot ATP \cdot 3H_2O$	605·2		
	—, K_2 salt		$K_2H_2 \cdot ATP$	583·3		
11	Cytidine	3-β-D-Ribofuranosido-cytosine, Cytosine riboside	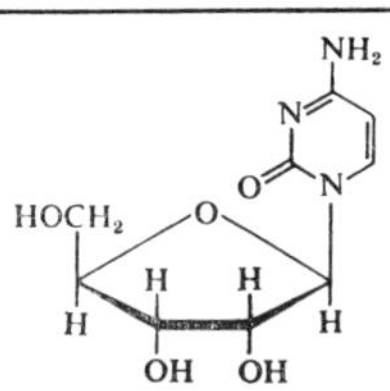	243·2	4·1 ~ 12·3	needles fr 90% EtO
	—, sulphate		$(C_9H_{13}N_3O_5)_2 \cdot H_2SO_4$	584·5		
	—, hydrochloride		$C_9H_{13}N_3O_5 \cdot HCl$	279·7		
12	Cytidine-2′,3′-cyclic phosphate	2′,3′-Cyclic CMP	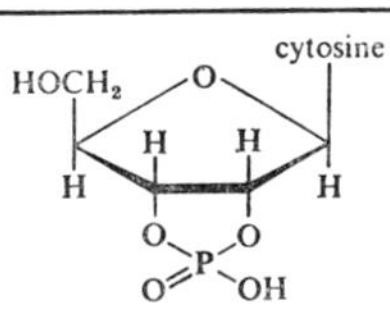	305·2		

M.p.	Solubility	Preparation	Estimation	General remarks
196–200	s. hot H_2O	SYN. *Meth. Enzymol.* **6**, 645 (1963) *Z. Naturf.* **17B**, 291 (1962) ^{32}P. *Biochem. Preps.* **9**, 5 (1962) *B.J.* **58**, 503 (1954) *Proc. natn. Acad. Sci. U.S.A.* **50**, 905 (1963) *B.B.R.C.* **24**, 872 (1966)	*J.B.C.* 167, 445 (1947) *Meth. biochem. Anal.* **1**, 341 (1954) *The Nucleic Acids*, vol. 1, pp. 211 and 243 (1955) Bergmeyer, p. 573 *Meth. Enzymol.* **10**, 474 (1967)	Only traces of furfural given when distilled from 20% HCl (cf. adenosine-3′-phosphate). Acid hydrolysis as for adenosine-2′-phosphate.
		ISOL. *J.B.C.* **235**, PC 36 (1960) *Biochemistry* **1**, 474 (1962) SYN. *B.B.A.* **68**, 136 (1963)		Isolated in the free state from a red alga, *Porphyra perforata*. No secondary phosphate dissociation between pH 6 and 7. Hydrolysed completely to adenosine-3′,5′-diphosphate by 0·2N-$Ba(OH)_2$ at 100° for 15 min but relatively stable in 1N-KOH at 80° for 45 min.
		ISOL. *Biochem. Preps.* **1**, 5 (1949) *Arch. B.B.* **62**, 253 (1956) SYN. *J.A.C.S.* **83**, 649 (1961) *Biochem. Preps.* **8**, 1 (1961) *B.B.A.* **91**, 1 (1964) *Can. J. Chem.* **42**, 599 (1964) ^{32}P. *Biochem. Preps.* **9**, 120 (1962) *B.J.* **55**, 434 (1953) *B.B.R.C.* **9**, 556 (1962) *Proc. natn. Acad. Sci. U.S.A.* **50**, 905 (1963) *B.B.A.* **47**, 389 (1961) *Biochem. Preps.* **7**, 5 (1960) *J. Biochem., Tokyo* **47**, 207 (1960) *J.A.C.S.* **87**, 2265 (1965) *Meth. Enzymol.* **10**, 702, 773 (1967)	*Meth. biochem. Anal.* **1**, 341 (1954) *Arch. B.B.* **52**, 33 (1954) *Modern Methods*, p. 305 Bergmeyer, p. 539 *Analyt. Biochem.* **14**, 261; **17**, 456 (1966) *Meth. Enzymol.* **10**, 474 (1967)	66% phosphorus liberated as inorg. P in 10 min at 100° in N-HCl. Neutral Na and K salts stable for months in soln. at −15°, for about 1 week at 0°, stable for several hours at 0° in 7% trichloroacetic acid. In alkaline soln. decomposes to inorg. pyrophosphate and adenosine-5′-phosphate even at 0°. Dibarium salt, i. H_2O; monobarium salt, s. H_2O, although it tends to form a gum. Water of crystallization in salts variable.
2–15	s. H_2O; sl. s. EtOH	ISOL. Levene and Bass, p. 164 *J.C.S.* **1950**, 2084 *J.B.C.* **237**, 2283 (1962)	*Modern Methods*, p. 246	
d.				
		ISOL. *B.J.* **52**, 552 (1952) *J.C.S.* **1952**, 52 SYN. *Biochem. Preps.* **12**, 107 (1968) *J. Biochem., Tokyo* **47**, 398 (1960) *J.A.C.S.* **80**, 6204 (1958) *Meth. Enzymol.* **6**, 645 (1963) *J.C.S.* **1959**, 3655 *B.J.* **74**, 230 (1960)	*Meth. Enzymol.* **3**, 805 (1957)	Produced as an intermediate in the hydrolysis of RNA by pancreatic ribonuclease and by dilute alkali. Readily converted to the 3′-phosphate by pancreatic ribonuclease and to a mixture of 2′- and 3′-phosphates by dilute acid and alkali.

6. Constituents of RNA and Related Compounds

No.	Name	Synonyms	Structure	M. wt.	Approximate pK_a	Physical form
13	Cytidine-5′-diphosphate	CDP	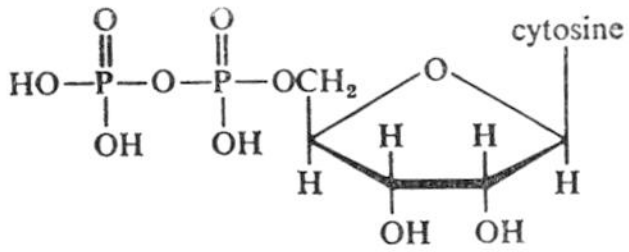	403·2	< 1 4·6 6·4	
	—, Na_3 salt		$Na_3 \cdot CDP \cdot 4H_2O$	541·2		
14	Cytidine-2′-phosphate	2′-Cytidylic acid, 2′-CMP	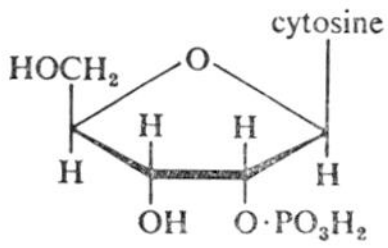	323·2	< 1 {4·3 {4·4 6·2	
	—, NH_4 salt		$NH_4 \cdot CMP \cdot H_2O$	358·2		
15	Cytidine-3′-phosphate	3′-Cytidylic acid, 3′-CMP	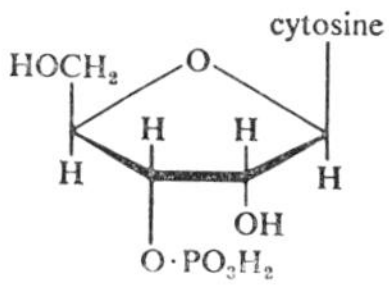	323·2	< 1 {4·2 {4·3 6·0	
16	Cytidine-5′-phosphate	5′-Cytidylic acid, 5′-CMP	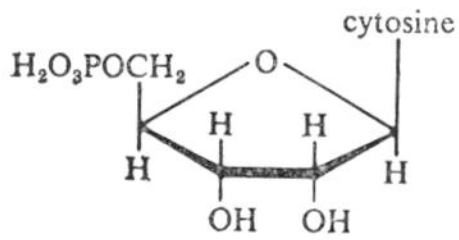	323·2	< 1 4·5 6·3	plates from aq. EtOH
17	Cytidine-5′-triphosphate	CTP	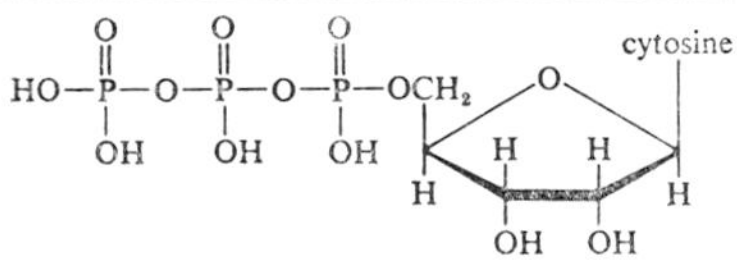	483·2	< 1 4·8 6·6	
	—, Na_2 salt		$Na_2H_2 \cdot CTP \cdot 4H_2O$	599·2		
18	Cytosine	6-Amino-2-hydroxy-pyrimidine	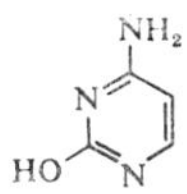	111·1; Hydrate, 129·1	4·4 12·2	plates + H
19	2,8-Dihydroxy-purine		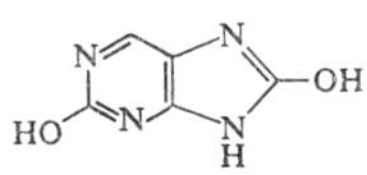	152·1	< 1 7·4 > 12	
20	N^6-Dimethyl-adenine	6-Dimethyl-aminopurine	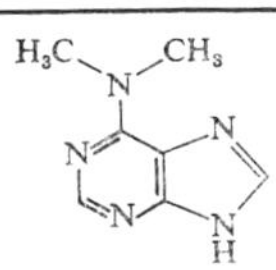	163·2	< 1 3·9 10·5	
21	N^2-Dimethyl-guanine	2-Dimethyl-amino-6-hydroxy-purine	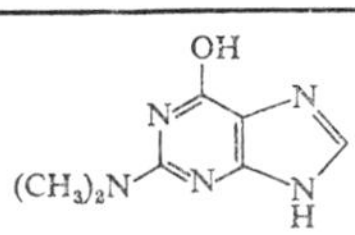	179·2		

M.p.	Solubility	Preparation	Estimation	General remarks
		ISOL. *Arch. B.B.* 35, 465 (1952) *J.B.C.* **209**, 23, 41 (1954) SYN. *J.A.C.S.* **83**, 649 (1961)		50% of total phosphorus released as inorg. P in 15 min at 100° in N-H_2SO_4.
38–40 d.	sl. s. H_2O	ISOL. *J.B.C.* **196**, 807 (1952) *J.B.C.* **203**, 319 (1953) *J.A.C.S.* **72**, 2606 (1950) *Biochem. Preps.* **5**, 40 (1957) SYN. *J.C.S.* **1949**, 2476	*J.B.C.* **196**, 807 (1952) *The Nucleic Acids*, vol. 1, p. 211 (1955) *Modern Methods*, p. 246	Only about 5% breakdown to nucleoside in N-HCl at 100° for 1 hr. Some deamination to uridylic acid in N-NaOH at 37° for 16 hr.
33–4 d.	s. H_2O	ISOL. *J.B.C.* **196**, 807 (1952) *J.B.C.* **203**, 319 (1953) *J.A.C.S.* **72**, 2606 (1950) *Biochem. Preps.* **5**, 40 (1957) SYN. *J.C.S.* **1949**, 2476 *J.A.C.S.* **86**, 4188 (1964)	*J.B.C.* **196**, 807 (1952) *The Nucleic Acids*, vol. 1, p. 211 (1955) *Modern Methods*, p. 246	Only about 5% breakdown to nucleoside in N-HCl at 100° for 1 hr. Some deamination to uridylic acid in N-NaOH at 37° for 16 hr.
33 d.		ISOL. *Arch. B.B.* 35, 465 (1952) SYN. *Meth. Enzymol.* **6**, 645 (1963) ^{32}P. *Biochem. Preps.* **9**, 5 (1962) *J.A.C.S.* **81**, 4118 (1959) *Proc. natn. Acad. Sci. U.S.A.* **50**, 905 (1963) *B.B.R.C.* **24**, 872 (1966)	*The Nucleic Acids*, vol. 1, p. 211 (1955) *Modern Methods*, p. 246	
		ISOL. *J.B.C.* **209**, 23, 41 (1954) SYN. *Biochem. Preps.* **9**, 120 (1962) *J.A.C.S.* **80**, 1141 (1958) *B.B.A.* **91**, 1 (1964) *Can. J. Chem.* **42**, 599 (1964) ^{32}P. *Biochem. Preps.* **9**, 120 (1962) *J.A.C.S.* **81**, 4118 (1959) *Proc. natn. Acad. Sci. U.S.A.* **50**, 905 (1963) *J.A.C.S.* **87**, 2265 (1965)		66% of total phosphorus liberated as inorg. P in 15 min at 100° in N-H_2SO_4.
0–5 d. hyd.)	$0{\cdot}77^{25}$ H_2O; sl. s. EtOH; i. eth.	ISOL. Levene and Bass, p. 57 *B.J.* **31**, 486 (1937) SYN. *J.B.C.* 177, 357 (1949) Levene and Bass, p. 71	*J.B.C.* **181**, 713 (1949) *Modern Methods*, p. 246 *Analyt. Biochem.* **1**, 249 (1960)	Water of cryst. lost at 100°. Gives red colour when dissolved in soln. of Na hypochlorite to which a drop of NH_4OH is added.
350	$0{\cdot}004^{20}$, $0{\cdot}04^{100}$ H_2O	ISOL. *J.B.C.* **229**, 641 (1957) *B.B.A.* **72**, 106 (1963) SYN. *J.C.S.* **1954**, 2060		Formed from purine in rat liver during the conversion of purine to uric acid by one of two possible pathways (see also 8-hydroxypurine). Fluoresces light blue under u.v. light. 5% loss after 1 hr at 100° in N-H_2SO_4 or 10N-NaOH.
1–3)	$0{\cdot}83^{20}$, $6{\cdot}7^{100}$ H_2O	ISOL. *B.J.* **70**, 642 (1958) *Nature, Lond.* **181**, 254 (1958) *B.B.A.* **34**, 286 (1959) SYN. *J.C.S.* **1954**, 2060	*B.J.* 70, 642 (1958)	Occurs in small amounts in both ribosomal and transfer RNA from many sources. A constituent of the antibiotic puromycin.
		ISOL. *B.J.* **72**, 294 (1959) *B.B.A.* **34**, 286 (1959) SYN. *J.A.C.S.* **78**, 217 (1956)	*B.J.* **72**, 294 (1959)	Present in small amounts in ribosomal and transfer RNA. Fluoresces under u.v. light at pH 1 and at 3–8 times this intensity at pH 13 and 11 resp. Fluorescence negligible at pH 7 (*Analyt. Biochem.* **3**, 49, 1962).

6. Constituents of RNA and Related Compounds

No.	Name	Synonyms	Structure	M. wt.	Approximate pK_a	Physical form
22	7,9-Dimethyl-guanine	Herbipoline	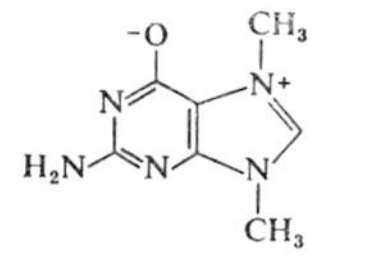 (site of charges indefinite)	179·2		
23	3,5-Diribosyl-uracil	Uracil-3,5-diriboside	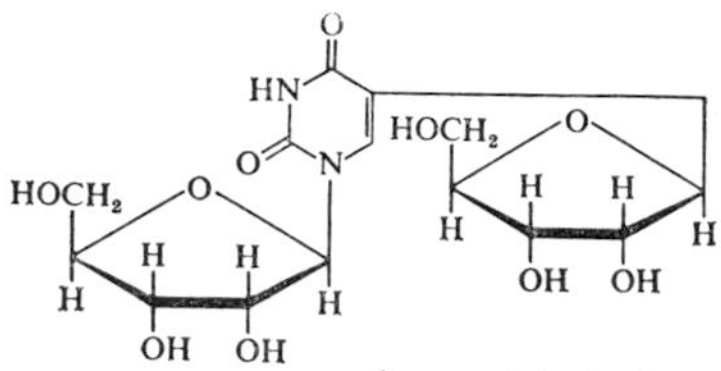 (presumed structure)	376·3		
24	Guanine	2-Amino-6-hydroxy-purine	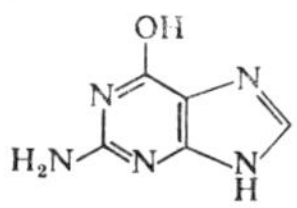	151·1	3·3 9·2 12·3	amorph. powder or tablets from dil. NH_4OH
25	*iso*Guanine	2-Hydroxy-6-amino-purine	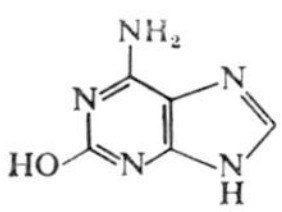	151·1; Hydrate, 178·1	4·5 9·0	cryst.+ $1\frac{1}{2}H_2O$
	—, sulphate		$(C_5H_5N_5O)_2 \cdot H_2SO_4$	418·3		cryst.+H_2C
26	Guanine-1-ribosyl-2′-(3′-)phos-phate	*neo*Guanylic acid, 1-Ribosyl-guanine-2′-(3′-)phos-phate	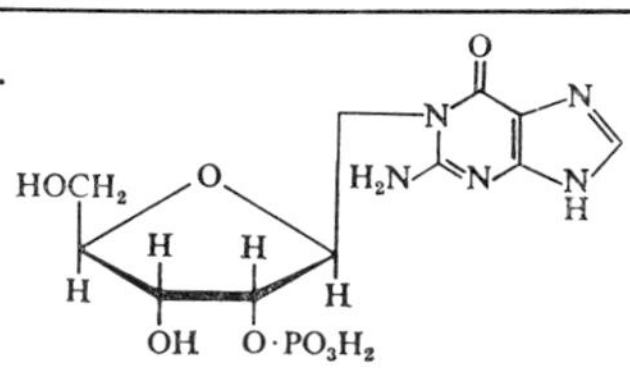	363·2	< 0 3·1 9·9 12·5	
27	Guanosine	9-β-D-Ribo-furanosido-guanine, Vernine	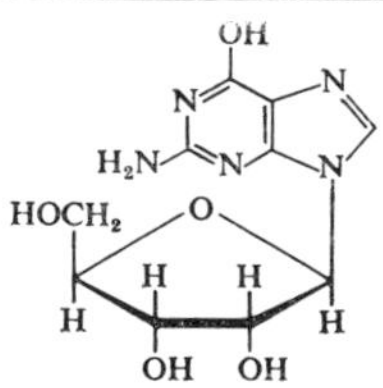	283·2; Hydrate, 319·3	1·6 9·2 12·3	needles+ $2H_2O$
28	Guanosine-2′,3′-cyclic phosphate	2′,3′-Cyclic GMP	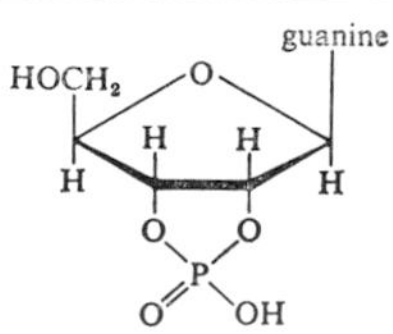	345·2		

M.p.	Solubility	Preparation	Estimation	General remarks
10–12		ISOL. *Z.P.C.* **309**, 286 (1957) *Z.P.C.* **318**, 281 (1960) SYN. *Ber.* **93**, 1206 (1960) *J.A.C.S.* **84**, 1914 (1962) *Ann.* **647**, 167 (1961)		Isolated from the sponge *Geodia gigas*.
		ISOL. *B.B.A.* **55**, 798 (1962) *B.B.A.* **61**, 799 (1962) *Fed. Proc.* **23**, 532 (1964)		May be involved in metabolism of 5-ribosyluracil. Present in commercial uridine. See *Progr. Nucleic Acid Res.* **5**, 399 (1966).
0 d.	s. acids and alkalis; v. sl. s. EtOH; i. H_2O (0·004^{40}), organic acids	ISOL. *J.B.C.* **53**, 441 (1922) Levene and Bass, p. 110 SYN. Levene and Bass, p. 118 *J.B.C.* **153**, 203 (1944) 2-^{14}C. *J.A.C.S.* **74**, 2432 (1952) 8-^{14}C. *Biochem. Preps.* **5**, 62 (1957)	*Modern Methods*, p. 246 *Analyt. Biochem.* **1**, 249 (1960) *Analyt. Biochem.* **3**, 49 (1962)	Forms cryst. salts with many acids and bases. Hydrochloride, cryst.+H_2O. Gives marked blue fluorescence at pH 1 and 11 with u.v. light but very little at pH 7 (*Analyt. Biochem.* **3**, 49, 1962). Deaminated by nitrous acid to produce xanthine.
	0·006^{25}, 0·025^{100} H_2O	ISOL. *J.A.C.S.* **61**, 350 (1939) SYN. *J.A.C.S.* **70**, 3109 (1948) *J.C.S.* **1949**, 2490 *J.B.C.* **185**, 439 (1950) *J.C.S.* **1954**, 2060 *J.A.C.S.* **81**, 2442 (1959)		Found as nucleoside (crotonoside) in croton bean (ref. 1). Water of cryst. of sulphate not lost at 130° *in vacuo* for 3 hr. Not deaminated by nitrous acid. Gives negligible fluorescence with u.v. light at pH 1, 7, 11, and 13 (*Analyt. Biochem.* **3**, 49, 1962).
	s. H_2O	ISOL. *B.B.A.* **68**, 284 (1963)		Hydrolysis in 6N-HCl at 100° for 1 hr gives guanine, ribose, and inorg. P. 0·1N-NaOH at 37° for 24 hr has no effect. Found in preparations of brewer's yeast RNA. Structure as 1-ribosyl derivative based on spectral resemblance to 1-methylguanine.
d.	0·08^{18}, 3·0^{100} H_2O; s. dil. mineral acids and alkalis, hot glacial acetic acid; i. eth., EtOH, $CHCl_3$, benz.	ISOL. Levene and Bass, p. 163 *Ber.* **74**, 694 (1941) *J.B.C.* **237**, 2283 (1963) SYN. *J.C.S.* **1958**, 1593	*J.B.C.* **167**, 429 (1947) *Modern Methods*, p. 246 Bergmeyer, p. 505	Easily hydrolysed in dil. mineral acids to guanine and D-ribose. Gives blue fluorescence at pH 1 with u.v. light but not in alkali. Deaminated to xanthosine by nitrous acid.
		ISOL. *B.J.* **52**, 552 (1952) *J.C.S.* **1952**, 52 SYN. *J.A.C.S.* **80**, 6204 (1958) *J.C.S.* **1959**, 3655 *Biochem. Preps.* **10**, 139 (1963) *Meth. Enzymol.* **3**, 805 (1957); **6**, 645 (1963)	*Meth. Enzymol.* **3**, 805 (1957)	Produced as an intermediate in the hydrolysis of RNA by Takadiastase T_1 ribonuclease and by alkali. Readily converted to the 3′-phosphate by T_1 and plant leaf ribonuclease and to a mixture of 2′- and 3′-phosphates by dil. acid and alkali. Not attacked by pancreatic ribonuclease.

6. Constituents of RNA and Related Compounds

No.	Name	Synonyms	Structure	M. wt.	Approximate pK_a	Physical form
29	Guanosine-5′-diphosphate	5′-GDP	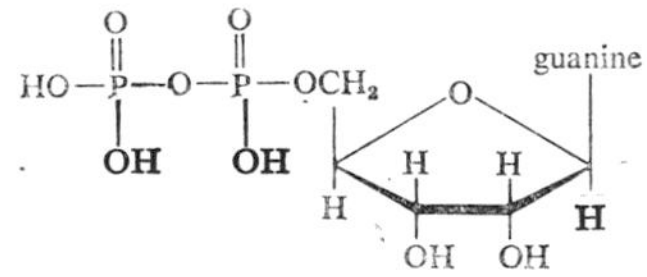	443·2	< 1 2·9 6·3 9·6	
	—, Na salt		$NaH_2\cdot GDP\cdot 2H_2O$	501·2		
30	Guanosine-2′-phosphate	2′-Guanylic acid, 2′-GMP	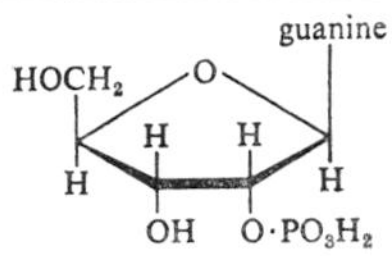	363·2	0·7 2·3 5·9 9·4	
31	Guanosine-3′-phosphate	3′-Guanylic acid, 3′-GMP	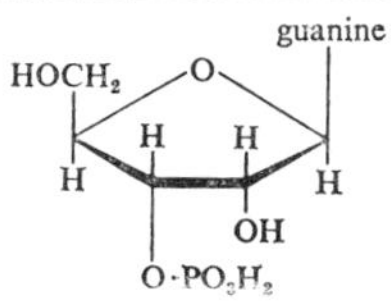	363·2	0·7 2·3 5·9 9·4	
32	Guanosine-5′-phosphate	5′-Guanylic acid, 5′-GMP	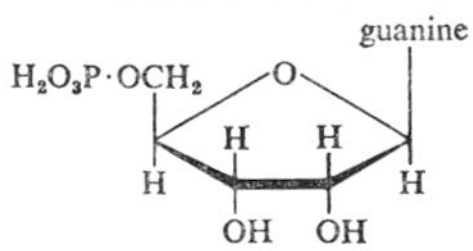	363·2; Hydrate, 372·2	< 1 2·4 6·1 9·4	cryst.+ $\frac{1}{2}H_2O$
	—, Na_2 salt		$Na_2\cdot GMP\cdot H_2O$	425·2		
33	Guanosine-5′-triphosphate	GTP	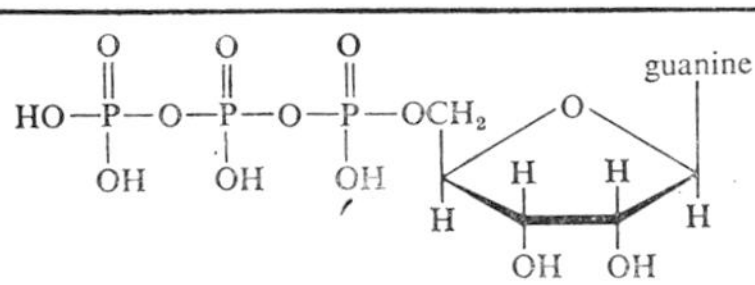	523·2	< 1 3·3 6·3 9·3	
	—, Na_2 salt		$Na_2H_2\cdot GTP\cdot 2H_2O$	603·2		
34	Hypoxanthine	6-Hydroxy-purine	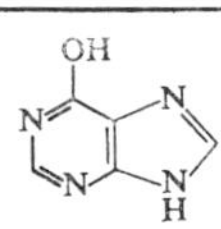	136·1	2·0 8·9 12·1	needles
	—, HCl		$C_5H_4N_4O\cdot HCl\cdot H_2O$	190·6		
35	Inosine	Hypoxanthine riboside, 9-β-D-Ribo-furanosido-hypoxanthine	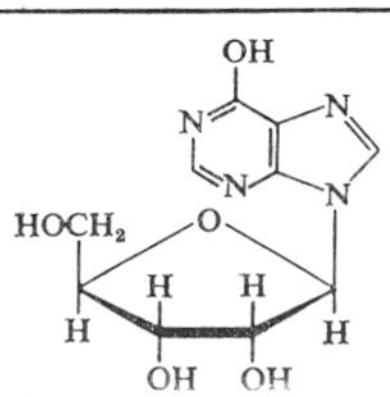	268·2; Hydrate, 304·3	1·2 8·9 12·5	anhyd. needles from 80% EtOH; dihydrate, plates from water

ɅI.p.	Solubility	Preparation	Estimation	General remarks
		ISOL. *J.B.C.* **209**, 23, 41 (1954) *J.B.C.* **218**, 521 (1956) SYN. *J.A.C.S.* **83**, 649 (1961) *Meth. Enzymol.* **6**, 645 (1963) *Ber.* **98**, 1045 (1965) *B.B.A.* **91**, 1 (1964)	*J.B.C.* **218**, 505 (1956) *Molec. Pharmacol.* **1**, 178 (1965)	50% of total phosphorus liberated as inorg. P in 15 min at 100° in N-H_2SO_4; after 1 hr converted to guanine, ribose-5-phosphate, ribose, and inorg. P.
92 d.	s. H_2O	ISOL. Levene and Bass, p. 224 *J.A.C.S.* **72**, 1471 (1950) *B.J.* **52**, 552 (1952) *Biochem. Preps.* **5**, 40 (1957) SYN. *J.C.S.* **1949**, 2476	*B.J.* **52**, 552 (1952) *Modern Methods*, p. 246	Produced, with 3′-isomer, by the alkaline hydrolysis of RNA (0·3N-KOH, 37°, 16 hr). Hydrolysed to guanine, ribose, and inorg. P by N-HCl at 100° for 1 hr. pK_a values are for a mixture of the 2′- and 3′-isomers.
92 d.	s. H_2O	ISOL. Levene and Bass, p. 224 *J.A.C.S.* **72**, 1471 (1950) *B.J.* **52**, 552 (1952) *Biochem. Preps.* **5**, 40 (1957) *J.A.C.S.* **86**, 4188 (1964)	*B.J.* **52**, 552 (1952) *Modern Methods*, p. 246	As for 2′-isomer. One of the products of the action of Takadiastase T_1 ribonuclease on RNA. pK_a values are for a mixture of the 2′- and 3′-isomers.
0–200 d.		ISOL. *J.B.C.* **209**, 23, 41 (1954) SYN. *J.A.C.S.* **79**, 3747 (1957) *Z. Naturf.* **17B**, 291 (1962) *Meth. Enzymol.* **6**, 645 (1963) ^{32}P. *Biochem. Preps.* **9**, 5 (1962) *Proc. natn. Acad. Sci. U.S.A.* **50**, 905 (1963) *B.B.R.C.* **24**, 872 (1966)		Acid hydrolysis as for guanosine-2′-phosphate.
		ISOL. *Acta chem. scand.* **7**, 1307 (1953) *J.B.C.* **209**, 23, 41 (1954) *J.B.C.* **218**, 521 (1956) SYN. *J.A.C.S.* **79**, 3752 (1957) *J.A.C.S.* **80**, 1141 (1958) *Biochem. Preps.* **9**, 120 (1962) *Can. J. Chem.* **42**, 599 (1964) *B.B.A.* **91**, 1 (1964) ^{32}P. *Proc. natn. Acad. Sci. U.S.A.* **50**, 905 (1963) *J.A.C.S.* **87**, 2265 (1965)	*J.B.C.* **209**, 41 (1954) *Molec. Pharmacol.* **1**, 178 (1965)	66% of total phosphorus liberated as inorg. P in 15 min at 100° in N-H_2SO_4; after 1 hr converted into guanine, ribose-5-phosphate, ribose and inorg. P.
d.	$0{\cdot}07^{19}$, $1{\cdot}4^{100}$ H_2O; s. dil. acids and alkalis	SYN. *J.A.C.S.* **74**, 411 (1952) *Ber.* **30**, 2226 (1897) *Z.P.C.* **10**, 258 (1886) *J.B.C.* **185**, 439 (1950) Levene and Bass, p. 121	*Meth. biochem. Anal.* **3**, 97 (1956) *J.B.C.* **167**, 429 (1947) *Manometric Techniques*, p. 212 Bergmeyer, p. 495	Formed during catabolism of adenine. Less than 5% decomposition after 1 hr at 100° in N-H_2SO_4 or 10N-NaOH. Formed from adenine by deamination with nitrous acid.
d. yd.), yd.)	$1{\cdot}6^{20}$ H_2O; v. sl. s. EtOH	ISOL. *Ber.* **42**, 336 (1909) *Ber.* **43**, 3161 (1910) Levene and Bass, p. 172 *B.B.R.C.* **13**, 394 (1963) SYN. *J.B.C.* **111**, 313 (1935) *J.C.S.* **1936**, 765 *J.B.C.* **167**, 477 (1947)	*J.B.C.* 167, 429, 477 (1947) Bergmeyer, p. 502	Not a usual component of nucleic acids but may arise during isolation of components. Recently isolated in small amounts from yeast soluble RNA. Readily hydrolysed in dil. mineral acids to hypoxanthine and D-ribose. Produced by deamination of adenosine by nitrous acid.

6. Constituents of RNA and Related Compounds

No.	Name	Synonyms	Structure	M. wt.	Approximate pK_a	Physical form
36	Inosine-5′-phosphate	5′-IMP, 5′-Inosinic acid, Hypoxanthine ribosyl-5′-phosphate	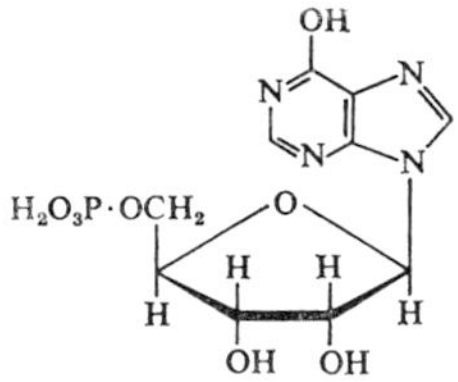	348·2	(? 1·2) 1·5 6·0 8·9	syrup or glass
	—, Ba salt		Ba·IMP·7½H_2O	618·7		
37	2-Methoxy-adenosine	Spongosine	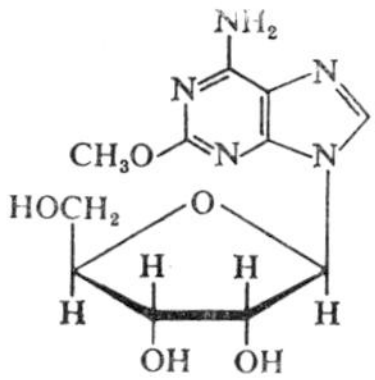	297·3		
38	1-Methyl-adenine	1-Methyl-6-aminopurine	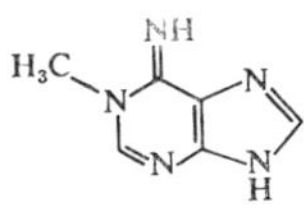	149·2	7·2 11·0	
39	2-Methyl-adenine	2-Methyl-6-aminopurine	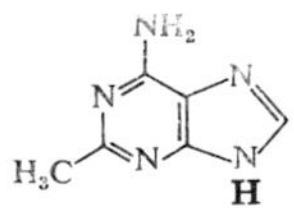	149·2		
40	*N*[6]-Methyl-adenine	6-Methyl-aminopurine	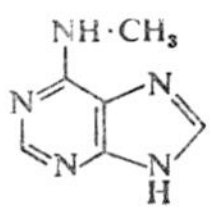	149·2	< 1 4·2 10·0	
41	1-Methyl-adenosine		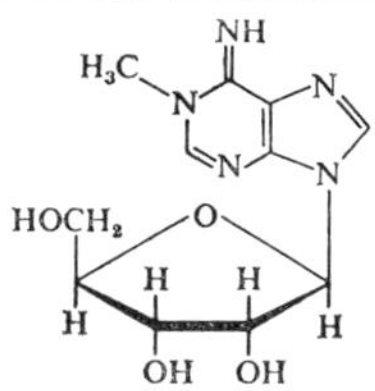	281·3		fine needles from aq. acet.
42	2′-*O*-Methyl-adenosine		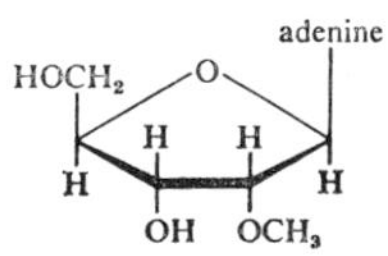	281·3		
43	*N*[6]-Methyl-adenosine	6-Methyl-aminopurine riboside	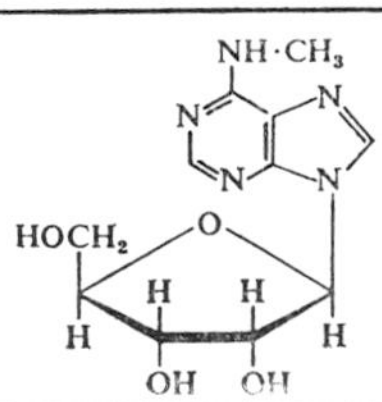	281·3		hygr. solid

p.	Solubility	Preparation	Estimation	General remarks
	s. H_2O, formic acid; v. sl. s. EtOH, eth.	ISOL. Levene and Bass, p. 229 *B.J.* **36**, 729 (1942) *Manometric Techniques*, p. 292 SYN. ^{14}C. *J.B.C.* **190**, 611 (1951) *Meth. Enzymol.* **6**, 645 (1963) *Biochem. Preps.* **9**, 5 (1962) ^{32}P. *B.J.* **58**, 503 (1954) *Proc. natn. Acad. Sci. U.S.A.* **50**, 905 (1963) *B.B.R.C.* **24**, 872 (1966)		Prepared from meat extract. Hydrolysed by dil. acids to hypoxanthine, ribose-5-phosphate, D-ribose, and inorg. P.
–3		ISOL. *J. org. Chem.* **21**, 226 (1956) SYN. *J. org. Chem.* **22**, 1575 (1957) *J.A.C.S.* **80**, 3738 (1958)		Isolated from a sponge, *Cryptotheca crypta*.
-8 phate); -9 d.		ISOL. *Naturwissenschaften* **48**, 74 (1961) *B.J.* **86**, 14P (1963) SYN. *J.C.S.* **1960**, 539 *J.A.C.S.* **85**, 193 (1963)		Present in small amounts in soluble RNA from mammalian and plant sources. Absent from RNA of *E. coli*. Converted to N^6-methyladenine (6-methylaminopurine) by heating in 0·1N-KOH at 100° for 1 hr but stable to 0·1N-KOH at 20° for 18 hr (*J.C.S.* **1960**, 539).
		ISOL. *B.J.* **70**, 642 (1958) *Nature, Lond.* **181**, 254 (1958) SYN. *J.A.C.S.* **74**, 1563 (1952) 8-^{14}C. *Biochem. Preps.* **5**, 62 (1957)		Present in small amounts in RNA from microbial, plant, and animal sources.
–14)	$0{\cdot}12^{20}$, $2{\cdot}0^{100}$ H_2O	ISOL. *J.B.C.* **230**, 717 (1958) *B.J.* **68**, 627 (1958) *B.J.* **70**, 642 (1958) *Nature, Lond.* **181**, 254 (1958) *B.B.A.* **46**, 198 (1961) SYN. *J.A.C.S.* **74**, 411 (1952)	*B.J.* **70**, 642 (1958)	Present in small amounts in DNA and in both ribosomal and soluble RNA from *E. coli* but probably absent from pig liver and yeast RNA (*B.B.A.* **46**, 198, 1961). Formed from 1-methyladenine by heating in 0·1N-KOH at 100° for 1 hr.
17 d.		ISOL. *B.B.A.* **68**, 278 (1963) SYN. *J.C.S.* **1960**, 539 *J.A.C.S.* **85**, 193 (1963)		Present in small amounts in soluble RNA from mammalian and plant sources. Absent from RNA of *E. coli*. Converted to N^6-methyladenosine (6-methylaminopurine riboside) by 0·25N-NaOH at 100° for 75 min. Hydrolysed to 1-methyladenine and D-ribose by 0·5N-HCl at 100° for 45 min.
		ISOL. *B.B.A.* **68**, 278 (1963) *B.B.R.C.* **12**, 429 (1963) *Biochemistry* **3**, 876 (1964) SYN. *J.A.C.S.* **87**, 1145 (1965)	*B.B.R.C.* **12**, 429 (1963)	Present in small amounts in RNA from animal, plant, and microbial sources.
0, fies nelts		SYN. *J.A.C.S.* **80**, 699 (1958) *Chem. pharm. Bull., Tokyo* **9**, 173 (1961) *J.A.C.S.* 85, 193 (1963)		Occurrence as for N^6-methyladenine. Formed from 1-methyladenosine by 0·25N-NaOH at 100° for 75 min.

6. Constituents of RNA and Related Compounds

No.	Name	Synonyms	Structure	M. wt.	Approximate pK_a	Physical form
44	1-Methyl-adenosine 2′-(3′-) phosphate	1-Methyl-adenylic acid	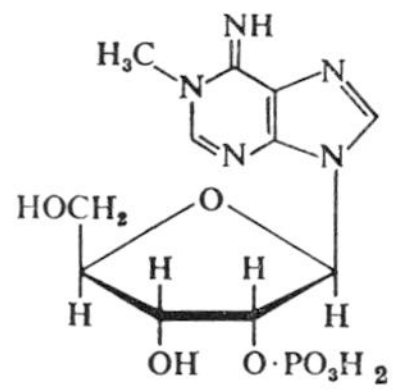	361·2		
45	1-Methyl-cytidine		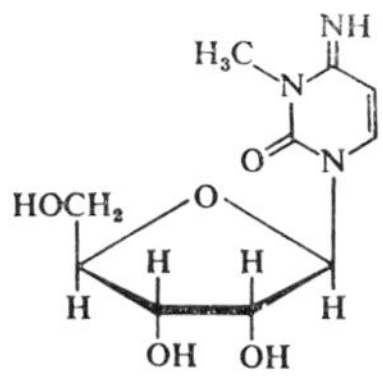	257·2		needles (metho-sulphate)
46	2′-*O*-Methyl-cytidine		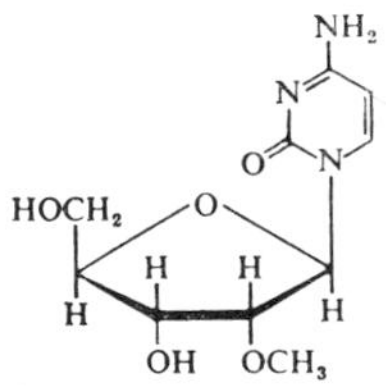	257·2		
47	5-Methyl-cytidine		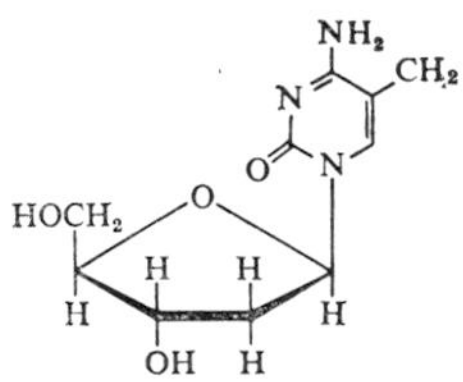	257·2		
48	5-Methyl-cytosine	6-Amino-2-hydroxy-5-methyl-pyrimidine	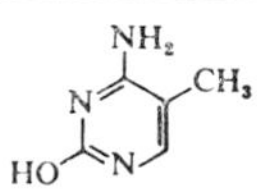	125·1; Hydrate, 143·1	4·6 12·4	prisms + H_2O
49	1-Methyl-guanine	1-Methyl-2-amino-6-hydroxy-purine	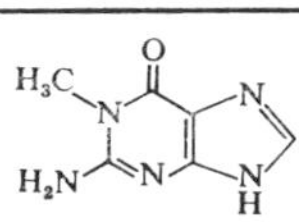	165·2	<1 3·2 10·4	
50	N^2-Methyl-guanine	2-Methyl-amino-6-hydroxy-purine	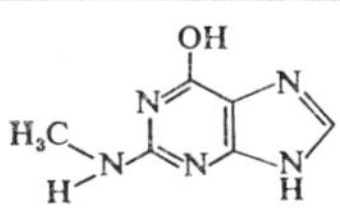	165·2		
51	7-Methyl-guanine		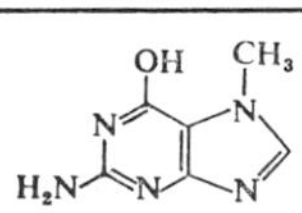	165·2	<1 3·5 9·4	

M.p.	Solubility	Preparation	Estimation	General remarks
		ISOL. *B.J.* **86**, 14P (1963)		Occurrence as for 1-methyladenine. Converted to N^6-methyl derivative by 0·1N-KOH at 20° for 18 hr. Extensively destroyed when RNA heated in N-HCl at 100° for 1 hr but high yield from RNA in N-$HClO_4$ at 28° for 18 hr.
3–4 etho- lphate)		ISOL. *B.B.R.C.* **12**, 361 (1963)		Isolated as a minor component of yeast soluble RNA.
		ISOL. *Nature, Lond.* **186**, 238 (1960) *B.B.A.* **68**, 278 (1963) *B.B.R.C.* **12**, 429 (1963) *Biochemistry* **3**, 876 (1964)	*B.B.R.C.* **12**, 429 (1963)	Present in small amounts in RNA from several animal, plant, and microbial sources.
		ISOL. *J.A.C.S.* **72**, 2811 (1950) *B.B.A.* **29**, 444 (1958) *B.B.A.* **34**, 286 (1959) *B.B.A.* **38**, 176 (1960) SYN. *J.A.C.S.* **81**, 178 (1959)		Present up to 6% (molar) of total bases in DNA and in smaller amounts in ribosomal and soluble RNA from many sources. Deaminated by nitrous acid to thymine riboside.
, rs 301 d.	$0{\cdot}45^{25}$ H_2O	ISOL. *J.A.C.S.* **73**, 1539 (1951) *B.J.* **48**, 584 (1951) *B.B.A.* **38**, 176 (1960) SYN. *J.A.C.S.* **81**, 178 (1959) *J.B.C.* **177**, 357 (1949) Levene and Bass, p. 73	*B.J.* **48**, 584 (1951) *Analyt. Biochem.* **1**, 249 (1960)	Occurrence as for 5-methylcytidine. Deaminated by nitrous acid to thymine.
		ISOL. *B.J.* **72**, 294 (1959) *B.B.A.* **34**, 286 (1959) SYN. *J. org. Chem.* **27**, 2478 (1962) *Ber.* **46**, 3839 (1913)	*B.J.* **72**, 294 (1959)	Present in small amounts in ribosomal and soluble RNA and in urine of normal human subjects.
		ISOL. *B.B.A.* **34**, 286 (1959) *B.J.* **72**, 294 (1959) SYN. *J.A.C.S.* **82**, 3773 (1960)	*B.J.* **72**, 294 (1959)	Present in small amounts in ribosomal and soluble RNA and in urine of normal human subjects. Stable in 0·1N-KOH at 37° for 18 hr. Gives blue fluorescence under u.v. light at pH 1 and at 2 and 7 times this intensity at pH 13 and 11 respectively. Fluorescence negligible at pH 7 (*Analyt. Biochem.* 3, 49, 1962).
		ISOL. *J.B.C.* **224**, 407 (1957) *B.J.* **83**, 114 (1962) *Cancer Res.* **22**, 469 (1962) *B.J.* **86**, 14P (1963) SYN. *J.B.C.* **228**, 475 (1957) *J.A.C.S.* **85**, 193 (1963)		Present in small amounts in urine of normal human subjects and in soluble RNA.

6. Constituents of RNA and Related Compounds

No.	Name	Synonyms	Structure	M. wt.	Approximate pK_a	Physical form
52	1-Methyl-guanosine		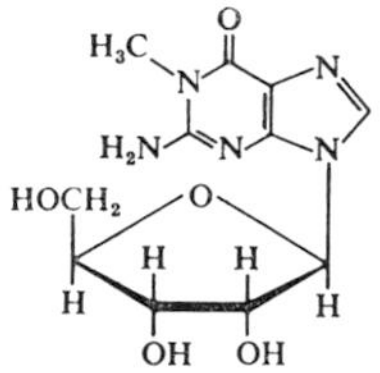	297·3		
53	2′-*O*-Methyl-guanosine		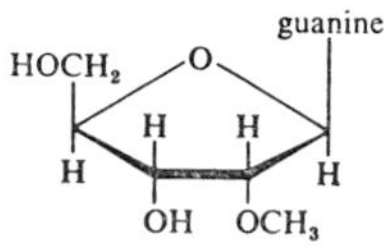	297·3		
54	7-Methyl-guanosine		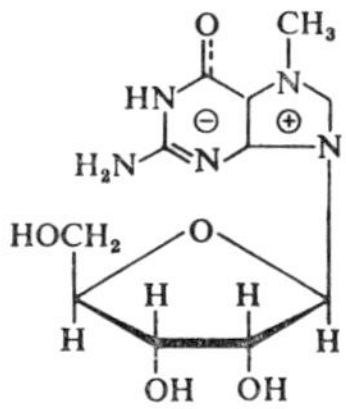	297·3	7·0	
55	7-Methyl-8-hydroxy-guanine		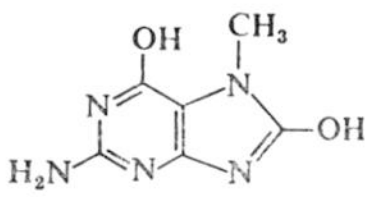	181·2	0·1 8·6 11·4	
56	1-Methyl-hypoxanthine	1-Methyl-6-hydroxy-purine	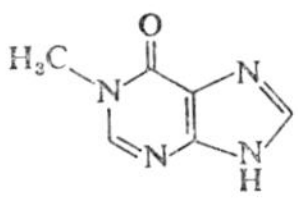	150·2	$\sim$2 9·1 (8·8) $\sim$13	
57	1-Methyl-inosine	1-Methyl-hypo-xanthine riboside	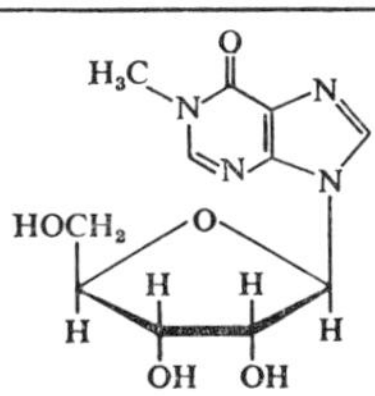	282·3		
58	1-Methyl-uridine		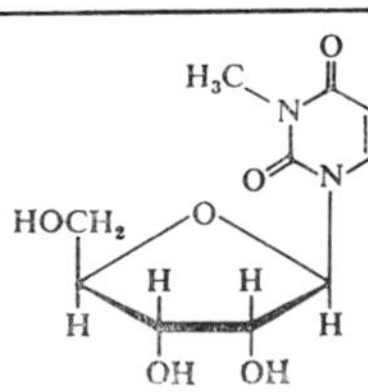	258·2		

.p.	Solubility	Preparation	Estimation	General remarks
)5–7		SYN. *Ber.* **80**, 401 (1949)		Present in small amounts in ribosomal and soluble RNA. Stable in 0·1N-KOH at 37° for 18 hr.
		ISOL. *B.B.A.* **68**, 278 (1963) *B.B.R.C.* **12**, 429 (1963) *Biochemistry* **3**, 876 (1964)	*B.B.R.C.* **12**, 429 (1963)	Present in small amounts in RNA of several animal, plant and microbial sources.
9–61		SYN. *J.A.C.S.* **85**, 193 (1963)		Present in small amounts in soluble RNA. Hydrolysed to 7-methylguanine and D-ribose by heating at 100° for 1 hr in water, methanol, or 2N-H_2SO_4.
		ISOL. *J.B.C.* **224**, 407, 423 (1957) *Am. J. Med.* **28**, 726 (1960) *Cancer Res.* **22**, 469 (1962)	*J.B.C.* **224**, 407, 423 (1957)	Present in small amounts in urine of normal human subjects. Increased level in patients with leukaemia.
300		ISOL. *J.B.C.* **224**, 407, 423 (1957) *Am. J. Med.* **28**, 726 (1960) *Cancer Res.* **22**, 469 (1962) SYN. *J. agric. Chem. Soc. Japan* **35**, 280 (1961) *J. org. Chem.* **27**, 990, 2478 (1962)		Isolated from human urine. Increased level in patients with leukaemia.
-12		ISOL. *B.B.R.C.* **13**, 394 (1963) SYN. *J.A.C.S.* **85**, 193 (1963) *J. org. Chem.* **26**, 4761 (1961)		Isolated in small quantities from yeast soluble RNA.
-20		ISOL. *B.B.R.C.* **12**, 361 (1963) SYN. *J.B.C.* **104**, 385 (1934) *B.B.A.* **22**, 247 (1956)		Isolated as a minor component from yeast soluble RNA.

6. Constituents of RNA and Related Compounds

No.	*Name*	*Synonyms*	*Structure*	*M. wt.*	*Approximate* pK_a	*Physical form*
59	2′-*O*-Methyl-uridine		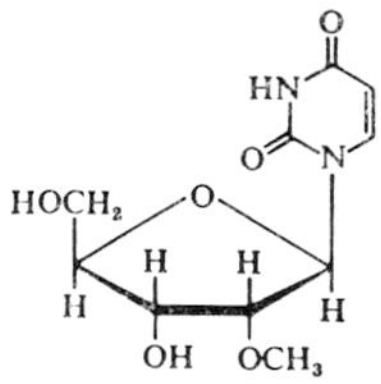	258·2		
60	Orotic acid	Uracil-4-carboxylic acid	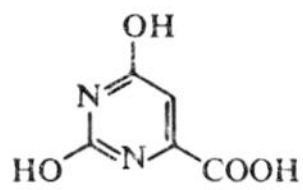	156·1; Hydrate, 174·1	~2·8 9·4 > 13·0	cryst.+ H_2O
61	Orotidine	Orotic acid riboside, 3-β-D-Ribo-furanosido-orotic acid	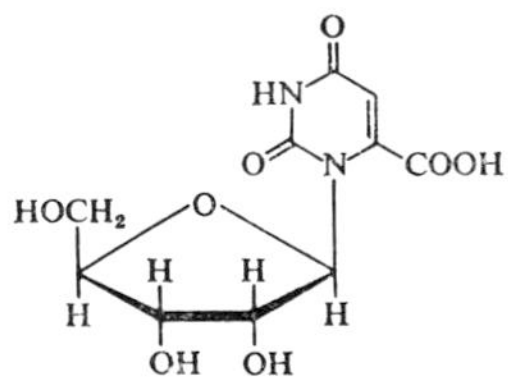	288·2		
	—, cyclo-hexylamine salt		$C_{10}H_{12}N_2O_8 \cdot C_6H_{13}N$	387·4		
62	Orotidine-5′-phosphate		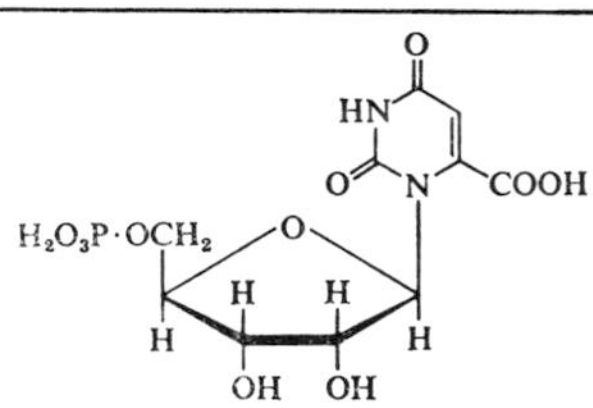	368·2		
63	Purine		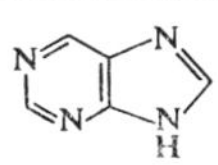	120·1	2·4 8·9	
64	5-Ribosyl-uracil	Pseudouridine C, 5-β-D-Ribo-syluracil	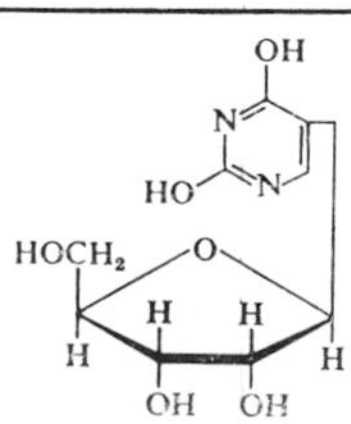	244·2	9·6 > 13	

M.p.	Solubility	Preparation	Estimation	General remarks
		ISOL. *B.B.A.* **68**, 278 (1963) *B.B.R.C.* **12**, 429 (1963) *Biochemistry* **3**, 876 (1964)	*B.B.R.C.* **12**, 429 (1963)	Present in small amounts in RNA from several animal, plant, and microbial sources.
45 d., eating arted at 0; with ow heat- g	$0{\cdot}18^{18}$ H_2O	ISOL. *J.B.C.* **172**, 525 (1948) SYN. *J.A.C.S.* **69**, 674, 1382 (1947) *J.A.C.S.* **53**, 1989 (1931) 4,7-^{14}C. *J.B.C.* **215**, 389 (1955) 6-^{14}C. *J.A.C.S.* **72**, 4704 (1950) *Ann.* **619**, 63 (1958) *Bull. Soc. chim. Fr.* **1959**, 1798	*J. pharm. Soc. Japan*, **81**, 1655 (1961) Bergmeyer, p. 508	Found in animal milk. Accumulates in large quantities during growth of mutants of Neurospora which require uridine, cytidine, or uracil. Ribotide is precursor in pyrimidine nucleotide biosynthesis.
400	s. H_2O, EtOH and aq. EtOH	ISOL. *J.B.C.* **215**, 403 (1955) SYN. *Tetrahedron Lett.* **1963**, 533		Hydrolyses readily in dilute mineral acids. Isolated in relatively large amounts from urine of tumour-bearing patients who have received 6-azauridine-5′-phosphate therapy.
3–4				
		ISOL. *J.A.C.S.* **76**, 2844 (1954) SYN. *J.B.C.* **215**, 403 (1955) *J.A.C.S.* **85**, 1118 (1963) ^{32}P. *Biochem. Preps.* **9**, 5 (1962)	*J.A.C.S.* **76**, 2844 (1954)	An intermediate in the biosynthesis of uridylic and cytidylic acids.
–13	v. s. H_2O, hot EtOH; sl. s. acet.; i. eth., $CHCl_3$	SYN. *J.C.S.* **1954**, 2060 *J.A.C.S.* **76**, 5633, 6073 (1954) *Angew. Chem.* **71**, 524 (1959) *Ber.* **95**, 54 (1962)		10% decomposition in N-H_2SO_4 after 1 hr at 100°. Stable in 10N-NaOH after 1 hr at 100°. Gives blue fluorescence under u.v. light at pH 11 and 13 with negligible fluorescence below pH 7 (*Analyt. Biochem.* **3**, 49, 1962). Occurrence as nucleoside, nebularine, in mushroom *Agaricus nebularis* (ISOL. *J. Antibiot., Tokyo*, Ser. A **14**, 94, 1961; SYN. *J.B.C.* **204**, 1019, 1953).
–4		ISOL. *B.B.A.* **34**, 286 (1959) *Science* **130**, 862 (1959) *J. molec. Biol.* **2**, 113 (1960) *J.B.C.* **235**, 1488 (1960) *Am. J. Med.* **28**, 726 (1960) *Biochem. Preps.* **10**, 135 (1963) SYN. *J.A.C.S.* **83**, 3920 (1961)	*J. Lab. clin. Med.* **59**, 620 (1962)	Occurs as the nucleotide in appreciable amounts in microsomal and soluble RNA from many sources. Urine of patients with leukaemia, polycythaemia, or gout provides a good source of 5-ribosyluridine. See *Progr. in Nucleic Acid Research* **5**, 349, 399 (1966)

6. Constituents of RNA and Related Compounds

No.	Name	Synonyms	Structure	M. wt.	Approximate pK_a	Physical form
65	Thymine	5-Methyl-uracil	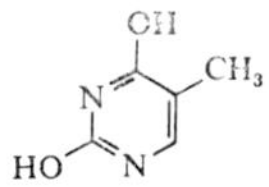	126·1	~0 9·9 > 13·0	plates or needles
66	Uracil	2,6-Dihydroxy-pyrimidine	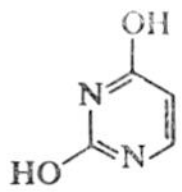	112·1	~0·5 9·5 > 13·0	wh. powder or clusters of needles
67	Uric acid	2,6,8-Tri-hydroxy-purine	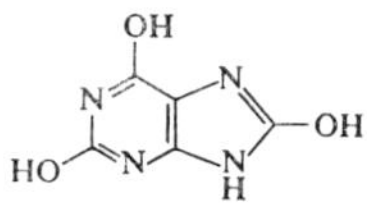	168·1	5·4 11·3	wh. cryst.
68	Uric acid-3-riboside	3-Ribosyluric acid, 3-β-D-Ribofuranosido-uric acid	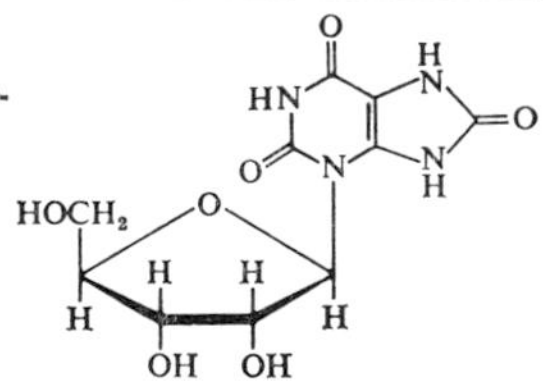	300·2; Hydrate 327·2	6·0 10·9	col. cryst.+ 1·5 H_2O from H_2O
69	Uridine	Uracil ribo-side, 3-β-D-Ribofuranosido-uracil	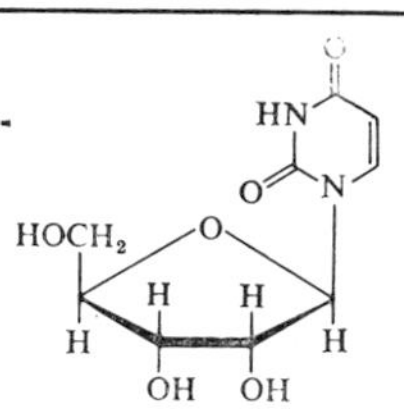	244·2	9·2 12·3	needles from aq. EtOH
70	Uridine-2′,3′-cyclic phosphate	2′,3′-Cyclic UMP	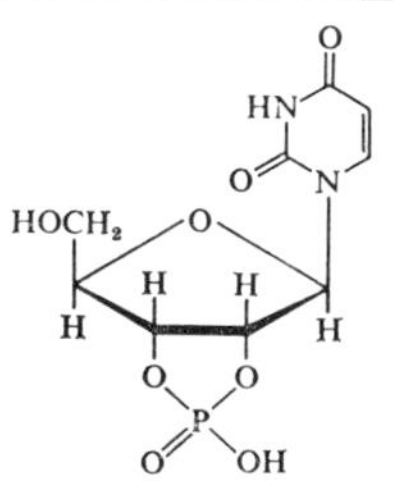	306·2		
71	Uridine-5′-diphosphate	5′-UDP	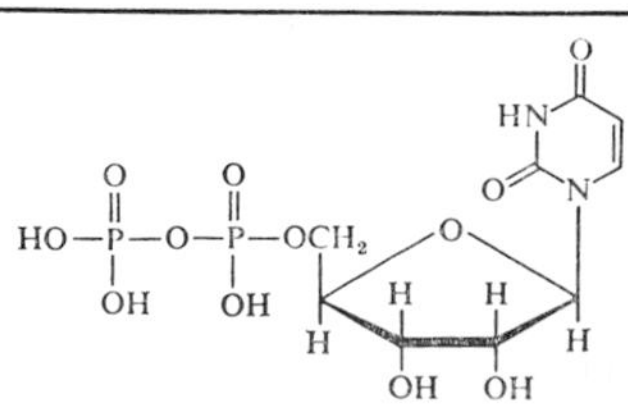	404·2	< 1 6·5 9·4	
	—, Na_2 salt		$Na_2H\cdot UDP\cdot 3H_2O$	502·2		

M.p.	Solubility	Preparation	Estimation	General remarks
18–21 d.	0·4[25] H_2O; s. hot H_2O; sl. s. EtOH; v. sl. s. eth.	ISOL. Levene and Bass, p. 57 *B.J.* **70**, 642 (1958) *Nature, Lond.* **181**, 254 (1958) *B.B.A.* **61**, 141 (1962) SYN. Levene and Bass, p. 67 2-^{14}C. *J.A.C.S.* **74**, 2432 (1952)	*Arch. B.* **26**, 209 (1950) *J.B.C.* **197**, 227 (1952) *Modern Methods*, p. 246 *Analyt. Biochem.* **1**, 249 (1960)	Not limited to DNA but found in small amounts in soluble RNA from many sources. Riboside also isolated (*B.J.* **70**, 642, 1958).
35 d.	0·36[25] H_2O; s. alkalis; v. sl. s. EtOH; i. eth.	ISOL. Levene and Bass, p. 57 SYN. *J.A.C.S.* **48**, 2379 (1926) Levene and Bass, p. 62 2-^{14}C. *J.A.C.S.* **74**, 2432 (1952)	*J.B.C.* **181**, 713 (1949) *Modern Methods*, p. 246 *Analyt. Biochem.* **1**, 249 (1960)	
without elting	0·002[20], 0·05[100] H_2O; s. alkalis, glycerol; i. EtOH, eth., H_2SO_4	ISOL. Levene and Bass, p. 111 SYN. Levene and Bass, p. 92 *Ber.* **93**, 2810 (1960)	*Standard Methods in Clinical Chemistry*, p. 123, Academic Press (1953) *J.B.C.* **218**, 497 (1956) *Meth. biochem. Anal.* **3**, 97 (1956) *Meth. biochem. Anal.* **6**, 79 (1958) *Analyt. Biochem.* **4**, 24 (1962)	Chief end-product of nitrogen metabolism of birds and reptiles. Present in urine of all carnivorous animals.
350		ISOL. *J.C.S.* **1961**, 963 *Diss. Abstr.* **23**, 54 (1962) SYN. *B.B.A.* **62**, 185 (1962)		Isolated from beef blood where it accounts for most of the uric acid present. Absent from blood of humans, sheep, pigs, horses and a number of other animals. The corresponding 5′-nucleotide also exists in beef blood but in very small amounts. 66% hydrolysed to uric acid after 1 hr at 100° in N-HCl. About 50% loss of absorption at 297 mμ after 140 hr in 0·1 N-NaOH at 25°. Corresponding 3-ribosyluric acid 5′-phosphate isolated (*J.C.S.* **1963**, 899).
3·5–6	s. H_2O; sp. s. EtOH	ISOL. Levene and Bass, p. 165 *J.C.S.* **1950**, 2084 *J.B.C.* **237**, 2283 (1962) SYN. *J. org. Chem.* **25**, 2143 (1960)	*Modern Methods*, p. 246	Formed from cytidine by deamination with nitrous acid.
		ISOL. *B.J.* **52**, 552 (1952) SYN. *Chemy Ind.* **1955**, 143 *J.A.C.S.* **80**, 6204 (1958) *J.C.S.* **1959**, 3655 *Meth. Enzymol.* **3**, 805 (1957); **6**, 645 (1963) *J. Biochem., Tokyo* **47**, 398 (1960) *Biochem. Preps.* **10**, 139 (1963)	*Meth. Enzymol.* 3, 805 (1957)	Produced as an intermediate in the hydrolysis of RNA by pancreatic ribonuclease and dilute alkali. Readily converted to a mixture of 2′- and 3′-phosphates by dilute acid and alkali, and to 3′-phosphate by pancreatic ribonuclease.
		ISOL. *J.B.C.* **209**, 23, 41 (1954) SYN. *J.A.C.S.* **76**, 5056 (1954) *J.A.C.S.* **81**, 3032 (1959) *J.A.C.S.* **83**, 649 (1961) *B.B.A.* **91**, 1 (1964) *Ber.* **98**, 1045 (1965) ^{32}P. *J.A.C.S.* **81**, 3032 (1959)		50% of total phosphorus liberated as inorg. P in 15 min at 100° in N-H_2SO_4.

No.	Name	Synonyms	Structure	M. wt.	Approximate pK_a	Physical form
72	Uridine-2′-phosphate	2′-UMP, 2′-Uridylic acid	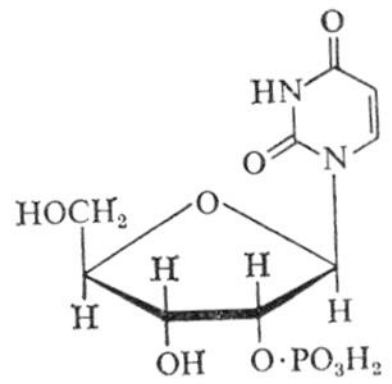	324·2	1·0 5·9 9·4 (Equilibr. mixture of 2′- and 3′-)	wh. amorph. powder
	—, Ba salt		Ba·UMP	459·5		
73	Uridine-3′-phosphate	3′-UMP, 3′-Uridylic acid	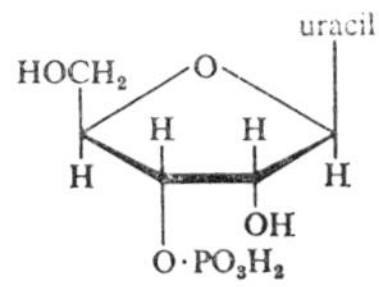	324·2; Hydrate 351·2	1·0 5·9 9·4 (Equilibr. mixture of 2′- and 3′-)	powder + $1\frac{1}{2}$ H_2O
74	Uridine-5′-phosphate	5′-UMP, 5′-Uridylic acid	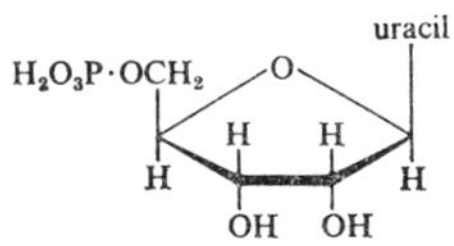	324·2	~1 6·4 9·5	
	—, Ba salt		Ba·UMP·H_2O	477·5		
	—, Na_2 salt		Na_2·UMP·2H_2O	404·2		
75	Uridine-5′-triphosphate	UTP	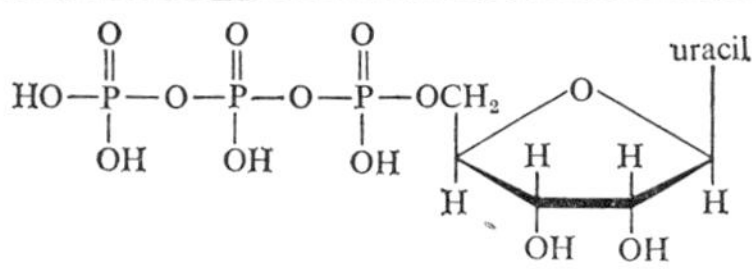	484·2	~1 6·6 9·5	
	—, Ba_3 salt		Ba_3·$(UTP)_2$·4H_2O	1446·5		
	—, Na_3 salt		Na_3·UTP·2H_2O	586·2		
76	Xanthine	2,6-Dihydroxy-purine	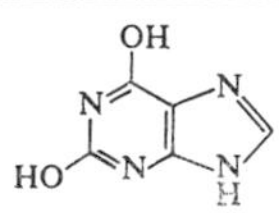	152·1	~0·8 7·4 11·1	plates

M.p.	*Solubility*	*Preparation*	*Estimation*	*General remarks*
	v.s. H_2O	ISOL. Levene and Bass, p. 220 *J.B.C.* **203**, 319 (1953) *Biochem. Preps.* **5**, 40 (1957) SYN. *J.C.S.* **1947**, 338		40·7% of total phosphorus liberated as inorg. P in 30 hr at 100° in 0·1N-H_2SO_4. 5% decomposition in N-HCl at 100° for 1 hr. Slightly more alkali labile than 5′-isomer; however stable in 0·3N-KOH at 37° for 16 hr and liberated from RNA, together with 3′-isomer, under these conditions. pK_a values are for a mixture of 2′- and 3′-isomers.
02 d.	s. H_2O	ISOL. Levene and Bass, p. 220 *J.B.C.* **203**, 319 (1953) *Biochem. Preps.* **5**, 40 (1957) SYN. *J.C.S.* **1949**, 2476		Hydrolysis in 10% H_2SO_4 gives uracil. 5% decomposition in N-HCl at 100° for 1 hr. 81% of total phosphorus liberated as inorg. P in 30 hr at 100° in 0·1 N-H_2SO_4. Stable in 0·3 N-KOH at 37° for 16 hr and liberated, together with 2′-isomer, from RNA under these conditions. pK_a values are for mixture of 2′- and 3′-phosphates.
98·5		ISOL. *J.B.C.* **203**, 319 (1953) SYN. *J.A.C.S.* **77**, 1871 (1955) *J.C.S.* **1958**, 1957 *Biochem. Preps.* **8**, 130 (1961) *Z. Naturf.* **17B**, 291 (1962) *Meth. Enzymol.* **6**, 645 (1963) ^{32}P. *J.A.C.S.* **81**, 3032 (1959) *B.B.A.* **47**, 186 (1961) *B.B.A.* **61**, 29 (1962) *Biochem. Preps.* **9**, 5 (1962) *Proc. natn. Acad. Sci. U.S.A.* **50**, 905 (1963) *B.B.R.C.* **24**, 872 (1966)	*J.B.C.* **209**, 41 (1954)	
		ISOL. *J.A.C.S.* **75**, 5449 (1953) *J.B.C.* **209**, 23, 41 (1954) SYN. *J.A.C.S.* **76**, 5056 (1954) *J.A.C.S.* **80**, 1141 (1958) *Chem. pharm. Bull., Tokyo,* **10**, 220 (1962) ^{32}P. *Biochem. Preps.* **9**, 120 (1962) *Proc. natn. Acad. Sci. U.S.A.* **50**, 905 (1963) *J.A.C.S.*, **87**, 2265 (1965) ^{14}C and ^{32}P. *B.B.A.* **61**, 29 (1962)	*J.B.C.* **209**, 41 (1954)	66% of total phosphorus liberated as inorg. P in 15 min at 100° in N-H_2SO_4.
	$0{\cdot}05^{20}$, $0{\cdot}2^{100}$ H_2O; sl. s. EtOH; s. alkalis; i. organic solvents	SYN. *J.C.S.* **1933**, 662 Levene and Bass, p. 123 *J.B.C.* **185**, 439 (1950) 2-^{14}C. *J.B.C.* **233**, 138 (1958)	*Meth. biochem. Anal.* **3**, 97 (1956) *Manometric Techniques*, p. 212 Bergmeyer, p. 495	Less than 10% decomposition after 1 hr at 100° in N-H_2SO_4 or 10 N-NaOH. Formed from guanine by deamination with nitrous acid. Riboside; ISOL. *J.C.S.* **1933**, 662; SYN. *J.C.S.* **1949**, 232.

7. Spectral Data and p*K* Values for Purines, Pyrimidines, Nucleosides, and Nucleotides

By K. BURTON (*Department of Biochemistry, University of Newcastle upon Tyne*)

Spectral Data

* An asterisk against the compound means that the extinction coefficients are compromise values between independent measurements. Otherwise the first reference given is usually the source of the absolute values. Independent sources are rarely in serious disagreement; in the absence of special comment or the listing of separate values (*a*) and (*b*), the data usually agree to within 3 per cent.

Some references are cited by name only. Fuller references are:

1. Beaven *et al.* in *The Nucleic Acids*, eds. E. Chargaff and J. N. Davidson, vol. 1 (1955).
2. Volkin and Cohn in *Meth. biochem. Anal.* **1**, 287 (1954).
3. Deutsch, unpublished and thesis data cited by Calbiochem. Inc., Los Angeles 63, California (1962).

p*K Values*

Values of 0–2 usually represent primary phosphate groups, 3–5 amino groups, and 6–7 secondary phosphate groups. Enolic hydroxyl groups titrate between pH 5 and 14 depending on the compound. p*K* values are not always listed for all the titratable groups of each compound. In particular the sugar dissociations (p*K* *ca.* 13) have not been listed because no exhaustive study has been made and accurate p*K* values are not available. Ionization of the sugar groups has relatively small effects on the spectra unless there is a free hydroxyl group at position 2 of the sugar (*J.A.C.S.* **75**, 4315 (1953)).

The reference to Cohn is in *The Nucleic Acids*, eds. E. Chargaff and J. N. Davidson, vol. 1, pp. 217, 227 (1955). His table also gives references to many other p*K* measurements for nucleic acid components.

7. Spectral Data and p*K* Values for Purines, Pyrimidines, Nucleosides, and Nucleotides

No.	*Name*	p*H*	λ_{max} (mμ)	ϵ_{max} $\times 10^{-3}$	ϵ_{260} $\times 10^{-3}$	$(\epsilon_{260}-\epsilon_{290})$ $\times 10^{-3}$	λ_{min}	ϵ_{min} $\times 10^{-3}$	250/260	280/260	290/260
1	Adenine	1–3	262·5	13·15	13·0	12·5	229	2·55	0·76	0·375	0·035
		6–8	260·5	13·35	13·3	13·2	226	2·55	0·76	0·125	0·005
		0·01N-NaOH	269	12·3	10·45	10·2	237	3·35	0·57	0·60	0·025
2	Adenosine (Adenine riboside)	1–2	257	14·6	14·3	13·9	230	3·5	0·84	0·215	0·03
		7–12	259·5	14·9	14·9	14·9	227	2·25	0·78	0·144	0·002
3	Adenine deoxyriboside	2	258	14·1	..	..	..	..	0·83	0·24	..
4	Adenosine-2′- or 3′-phosphate*	2	257	15·0	14·5	14·0	229	3·2	0·85	0·23	0·038
		7–12	259	15·3	15·3	15·2	..	..	0·80	0·15	0·009
5	Adenosine-5′-phosphate* (AMP)	2	257	15·0	14·5	14·0	230	3·5	0·84	0·22	0·038
		7–12	259	15·3	15·3	15·2	227	2·6	0·79	0·15	0·009
6	Adenine deoxyribose-5′-phosphate*	2	258	14·8	14·5	..	..	..	0·82	0·23	..
		7–12	..	..	15·3	15·2	..	..	0·80	0·14	0·007
7	Adenosine-5′-diphosphate (ADP)	2	257	15·0	14·5	..	..	..	0·85	0·21	..
		7–12	259	15·4	15·4	..	..	..	0·78	0·16	..
8	Adenosine-5′-triphosphate (ATP)	2	257	14·7	14·3	13·9	230	3·5	0·85	0·22	0·027
		7–11	259	15·4	15·4	15·3	227	2·5	0·80	0·15	0·003
	Other Adenine derivatives										
9	Dimethyladenines										
10	6-Dimethylaminopurine	1	277	15·6	..	..	235	..	0·52	1·35	..
		7	275	17·8	..	..	..	..	..	..	..
		13	281	17·8	..	..	245	..	0·51	2·6	..
11	Riboside of 10	1	268	18·5	..	..	235	4·5	0·57	0·94	..
		13	276	13·2	..	..	235	..	0·39	1·65	..
12	1-Methyladenine	4	259	11·7	..	..	228	..	..	0·23	..
		9	271	11·7	..	..	~244	..	..	~0·9	..
		13	270	14·4	..	..	239	..	..	0·84	..
13	Riboside of 12	1	256·5	13·6	..	..	231	2·3	..	..	..
		7	257	14·6	..	..	..	..	..	..	..
		11	257	14·6	..	..	223	3·2	..	..	..
14	2-Methyladenine	1	265	12·9	..	..	230	3·3	0·78	0·57	..
		13	271	9·2	..	..	240	3·7	0·63	0·84	..
15	3-Methyladenine	2	274	15·9	..	..	235	..	..	1·26	..
		13	273	12·8	..	..	244	..	..	1·48	..
16	7-Methyladenine	1	272	..	..	..	..	..	..	..	..
		11	271	..	..	..	..	..	..	..	..
17	9-Methyladenine	1	261	..	..	..	..	..	..	..	..
		11	262	..	..	..	..	..	..	..	..
18	6-Methylaminopurine	1	267	15·1	..	..	230	2·7	0·66	0·74	..
		7	266	16·2	..	..	..	..	..	..	..
		13	273	15·7	..	..	240	3·6	0·53	1·23	..
19	Riboside of 18	2	262	18·3	..	..	232	2·5	..	0·43	..
		13	266	16·5	..	..	~232	..	0·61	0·66	..

References and comments	p*K* Base	p*K* Phosphate	*References*
Beaven *et al.*	< 1 4·1 9·8		As spectra.
Beaven *et al.*	3·63		*J.B.C.* **193**, 425 (1951). $\mu = 0{\cdot}15$.
Deutsch			
Deutsch Beaven *et al.* *J.B.C.* **209**, 285 (1954)	3·81 (2′) 3·74 (3′)	6·17 (2′) 5·92 (3′)	*J.A.C.S.* **75**, 5268 (1953). $\mu = 0{\cdot}00$.
Arch. B.B. **62**, 253 (1956) Beaven *et al.*	3·74	6·2–6·4	*J.B.C.* **193**, 425 (1951). *J. phys. Chem.* **60**, 180 (1956). $\mu = 0{\cdot}2$. Apparent p*K* of phosphate depends on cation.
Deutsch *J.B.C.* **208**, 445 (1954) *J.A.C.S.* **73**, 1533 (1951) Ratio of ϵ_{260} at pH 2 to ϵ_{260} at pH 7 taken to be as for 5	4·4	6·4	*J.B.C.* **204**, 847 (1953).
rch. B.B. **62**, 253 (1956) ϵ_{260} pH 7 taken to be as for ATP	3·95	6·1–6·7	*J.B.C.* **193**, 425 (1951). *J. phys. Chem.* **60**, 180 (1956). $\mu = 0{\cdot}2$. Apparent p*K* of phosphate depends on cation.
rch. B.B. **62**, 253 (1956)	4·00	6·0–6·95	*J.B.C.* **193**, 425 (1951). *J. phys. Chem.* **60**, 180 (1956). $\mu = 0{\cdot}2$. Apparent p*K* of phosphate depends on cation.
.C.S. **1944**, 318; **1960**, 539 *m. chem. Soc. Abstr.* **146**, p. 39A, No. 79 (1964)			
.C.S. **1954**, 2071 *.J.* **70**, 642 (1958)	3·87 10·5		*J.C.S.* **1954**, 2071.
.C.S. **1954**, 2071 *.J.* **70**, 642 (1958)			
C.S. **1960**, 539 *C.S.* **1954**, 2071 *.J.* **70**, 642 (1958)	7·2 11·0		As spectra.
A.C.S. **85**, 193 (1963) ata for deoxyriboside are higher			
C.S. **1944**, 318 *C.S.* **1954**, 2071 *J.* **70**, 642 (1958)			
C.S. **1960**, 539 *C.S.* **1954**, 2071 *J.* **70**, 642 (1958)			
ba Symposium on Chemistry and Biology of Purines)57)			
ba Symposium on Chemistry and Biology of Purines)57)			
. **68**, 627 (1958); **70**, 642 (1958) *.S.* **1954**, 2071	4·78 9·56		*J.C.S.* **1954**, 2071.
. **68**, 627 (1958); **70**, 642 (1958) *.S.* **1954**, 2071 *.C.S.* **85**, 193 (1963) *.S.* **1960**, 539			

7. Spectral Data and p*K* Values for Purines, Pyrimidines, Nucleosides, and Nucleotides

No.	*Name*	p*H*	λ_{max} (mμ)	ϵ_{max} $\times 10^{-3}$	ϵ_{260} $\times 10^{-3}$	$(\epsilon_{280}-\epsilon_{300})$ $\times 10^{-3}$	$(\epsilon_{270}-\epsilon_{300})$ $\times 10^{-3}$	λ_{min}	250/260	280/260	290/260
20	Cytosine	1–3	276	10·0	6·0	8·95	8·65	238	0·48	1·53	0·78
			210	9·7	..	..	..	..	..	..	..
		7–10	267	6·13	5·55	3·55	6·00	247	0·78	0·58	0·08
		14	282	7·86	2·35	6·35	3·6	250	0·595	3·28	2·6
21	Cytidine (Cytosine riboside)	1–2	280	13·4	6·4	10·5	8·0	241	0·45	2·10	1·58
		7–12	271	9·1	7·55	6·9	8·9	250	0·86	0·94	0·34
22	Cytosine deoxyriboside	1–2	280	13·2	6·15	9·1	7·6	241	0·42	2·14	1·61
		7–12	271	9·0	7·35	7·0	8·8	250	0·83	0·965	0·305
23	Cytidine-2′-phosphate	1–2·5	278	12·75	6·9	10·4	..	240	0·48	1·83	1·22
		6–12	270	8·89	7·75	..	8·8	252	0·90	0·86	0·26
24	Cytidine-3′-phosphate*	1–2·5	279	13·2	6·6	10·6	..	240	0·45	2·00	1·43
		6–12	271	9·2	7·6	..	9·1	251	0·86	0·93	0·30
25	Cytidine-5′-phosphate	1–2·5	280	13·2	6·3	..	..	241	0·45	2·10	1·55
		6–12	271	9·1	7·4	..	9·0	250	0·84	0·99	0·33
26	Cytosine deoxyribose-5′-phosphate*	1–2·5	280	13·2	6·3	..	..	241	0·46	2·12	1·55
		6–12	..	..	7·4	7·2	9·0	250	0·82	0·99	0·30
27	Cytidine-5′-diphosphate (CDP)	1–2·5	280	12·8	6·2	..	..	..	0·46	2·07	..
		6–12	271	9·1	7·4	..	..	..	0·83	0·98	..
28	Cytidine-5′-triphosphate (CTP)	2	280	12·8	6·0	9·7	..	..	0·45	2·12	1·67
		7–11	271	9·0	7·4	7·1	8·9	..	0·84	0·97	0·41
29	Cytosine deoxyribose-3′,5′-diphosphate	2	280	12·9	6·2	..	..	241	0·46	2·05	1·48
		7–11	271–2	..	6·9	..	..	251	0·84	0·99	0·32
	Other Cytosine derivatives										
30	5-Hydroxymethylcytosine	1	279·5	9·7	4·89	..	..	..	..	..	..
		7·4	269·5	5·71	4·89	..	..	..	..	..	..
		0·1N-NaOH	283·5	7·59	2·44	..	..	..	..	..	..
31	5-Hydroxymethylcytosine deoxyribose-5′-phosphate	2	284	12·5	..	..	..	..	..	2·75	..
		6–12	..	..	6·09	..	..	..	..	1·22	..
32	5-Hydroxymethylcytosine deoxyribose-3′,5′-diphosphate	2	283	10·7	..	..	..	..	..	2·36	..
							$(\epsilon_{280}-\epsilon_{250})$ $\times 10^{-3}$				
33	5-Methylcytosine	1	283·5	9·79	3·6	5·51	8·08	242	0·41	2·66	2·42
			210·5	12·0	..	..	..	..	..	..	..
		7	273·5	6·23	4·45	4·09	1·74	251	0·81	1·20	0·55
			210·5	14·2	..	..	..	..	..	..	..
		14	289·5	8·05	1·7	1·01	4·92	253	0·85	3·75	4·75
34	5-Methylcytidine	7	278	8·7	..	..	..	..	..	..	..
35	5-Methylcytosine deoxyriboside	1–2	286	12·2	3·2	..	..	245	0·43	3·0	3·20
		6–12	277	8·81	6·0	..	..	255	1·0	1·5	0·98
		14	279	8·8	5·3	..	..	..	0·96	1·66	1·1
36	5-Methylcytosine deoxyribose-5′-phosphate	1–2·5	287	12·0	3·4	7·6	10·6	..	0·36	3·15	3·4
		6–13	278	8·7	5·45	7·16	3·31	..	0·96	1·52	1·02
						$(\epsilon_{260}-\epsilon_{300})$ $\times 10^{-3}$	λ_{min}	ϵ_{min} $\times 10^{-3}$			
37	Guanine	1–2	275·5	7·35	8·0	6·9	267	7·15	1·37	0·84	0·495
			248·5	11·4	..	..	..	..	..	..	..
		7	275·5	8·15	7·2	6·3	262	7·05	1·42	1·04	0·54
			246	10·7	..	..	..	..	..	..	..
		11	273·5	8·0	6·4	5·5	255	6·05	0·985	1·135	0·585
			246	6·3	..	..	..	..	..	..	..
		N-NaOH	274	9·9	7·3	6·6	240	5·15	0·805	1·24	0·605

References and comments	p*K* *Base*	p*K* *Phosphate*	*References*
Beaven *et al.*	4·45 12·2		*B.B.A.* **9**, 199 (1952).
.*B.A.* **9**, 369 (1952) olkin and Cohn .*B.C.* **178**, 431 (1949)	4·11		*J.A.C.S.* **75**, 4315 (1953). $\mu = 0{\cdot}05$.
.*B.A.* **9**, 369 (1952) *cta chem. scand.* **4**, 1047 (1950)	4·25		*J.A.C.S.* **75**, 4315 (1953). $\mu = 0{\cdot}05$.
.*B.C.* **196**, 807 (1952) .*C.S.* **1953**, 489 ohn, cited by Beaven *et al.*	(*a*) 4·30 (*b*) 4·44	6·19	(*a*) *J.A.C.S.* **75**, 4315 (1953). $\mu = 0{\cdot}05$. (*b*) *J.A.C.S.* **75**, 5268 (1953). $\mu = 0{\cdot}00$.
.*B.C.* **196**, 807 (1952) .*C.S.* **1953**, 489 ohn, cited by Beaven *et al.*	(*a*) 4·16 (*b*) 4·31	6·04	(*a*) *J.A.C.S.* **75**, 4315 (1953). $\mu = 0{\cdot}05$. (*b*) *J.A.C.S.* **75**, 5268 (1953). $\mu = 0{\cdot}00$.
rch. B.B. **62**, 253 (1956) ohn, cited by Beaven *et al.*	4·5	6·3	As spectra. In 0·1M-NaCl.
eutsch; *B.B.A.* **26**, 596 (1957) ohn, cited by Beaven *et al.* *B.C.* **208**, 445 (1954)	(*a*) 4·44	(*b*) 6·6	(*a*) *J.A.C.S.* **75**, 4315 (1953). $\mu = 0{\cdot}05$. (*b*) *J.B.C.* **204**, 847 (1953).
rch. B.B. **62**, 253 (1956) $_{60}$, pH 7 taken to be as for CMP	4·6	6·4	As spectra. In 0·1M-NaCl.
rch. B.B. **62**, 253 (1956) $_{60}$, pH 7 taken to be as for CMP	4·8	6·6	As spectra. In 0·1M-NaCl.
B.A. **26**, 596 (1957) *C.S.* **1953**, 947 ohn, cited by Beaven *et al.*			
J. **55**, 774 (1953)			
B.C. **237**, 1266 (1962) *exp. Med.* **106**, 233 (1957). Glucosylated derivatives ve same spectrum at pH 2 (*J.B.C.* **237**, 1266 (1962)) t differ at pH 4·3 (*Science* **120**, 557 (1954)).			
.C. **206**, 735 (1954) $_{max}$ low.			
aven *et al.*	4·6 12·4		*B.B.A.* **9**, 199 (1952).
.*C.S.* **74**, 668 (1952)			
.*C.S.* **81**, 178 (1959) .*S.* **1951**, 2864	~4·5 ~13		Beaven *et al.*
.*C.* **208**, 445 (1956) nn, cited by Beaven *et al.*	4·4		Cohn.
ven *et al.*	3·3 9·2 12·3		*J.C.S.* **1954**, 2060.

7. Spectral Data and p*K* Values for Purines, Pyrimidines, Nucleosides, and Nucleotides

No.	*Name*	p*H*	λ_{max} (mμ)	ϵ_{max} $\times 10^{-3}$	ϵ_{260} $\times 10^{-3}$	$(\epsilon_{260}-\epsilon_{300})$ $\times 10^{-3}$	λ_{min}	ϵ_{min} $\times 10^{-3}$	250/260	280/260	290/260
38	Guanosine	1	256·5	12·2	11·75	9·75	228	2·4	0·94	0·695	0·50
		7	252·5	13·65	11·7	11·4	223	2·8	1·15	0·67	0·275
		11	258–266	11·3	11·3	11·3	231	4·1	0·89	0·61	0·13
39	Guanine deoxyriboside	1	255	12·1	11·3	9·7	..	..	1·02	0·70	..
		7	..	..	11·75	11·6	230	2·2	0·99	0·61	..
40	Guanosine phosphate* (mixture of 2′- and 3′-isomers). N.B. Data not very consistent.	1	257	12·5	12·3	10·2	..	..	0·9	0·68	0·48
		2	256	13·0	12·0	10·5	..	..	..	..	..
		7	253	13·7	11·8	11·5	..	..	1·15	0·68	0·285
		12	..	..	..	..	..	..	0·89	0·60	0·11
41	Guanosine phosphate (largely 3′-isomer)	0·2N-HCl	257	12·2	11·8	9·8	..	..	0·94	0·69	0·50
		7	252	13·4	11·4	11·0	..	..	1·17	0·70	0·30
		10·8	257	11·25	11·2	11·1	..	..	0·92	0·64	0·15
42	Guanosine-5′-phosphate (GMP)	1	256	12·2	11·6	..	..	..	0·96	0·67	..
		7	252	13·7	11·7	..	..	..	1·16	0·66	..
		11	258	11·6	11·5	..	..	..	0·90	0·61	..
43	Guanine deoxyribose 5′-phosphate	2	..	..	11·7	..	..	..	1·03	0·70	0·46
		4·3–7	..	..	12·8	12·4	..	..	1·13	0·67	0·27
44	Guanosine-5′-diphosphate (GDP)	1	256	12·3	11·8	..	..	..	0·95	0·67	..
		7	253	13·7	11·8	..	..	..	1·15	0·66	..
		11	257	11·7	11·7	..	..	..	0·91	0·61	..
45	Guanosine-5′-triphosphate (GTP)	1	256	12·4	11·8	8·6	..	..	0·96	0·67	0·49
		7	253	13·7	11·7	11·4	..	..	1·17	0·66	0·27
		11	257	11·9	11·8	11·6	..	..	0·92	0·59	0·11
	Other Guanine derivatives										
46	Neoguanylic acid (? 5′-phosphorylribosyl 1-guanine)	6N-HCl	250	..	..	..	225	..	1·25	0·56	..
		1	248	..	..	..	223	..	1·28	0·73	..
		5·5	248	..	..	..	224	..	1·34	0·85	..
			270	..	..	..	..	..	..	..	..
		11·1	248	..	..	..	236	..	1·06	0·89	..
			270	..	..	..	..	..	..	..	..
		11·9	270	..	..	..	240	..	1·00	0·91	..
		13	274	..	..	..	243	..	0·93	1·12	..
47	1-Methylguanine	1	250	10·8	..	..	227	4·2	1·25	0·80	..
			271	7·6	..	..	267	7·4	..	..	..
		7	248	10·7	..	..	227	4·5	..	..	..
			272	8·5	..	..	262	8·0	..	..	..
		13	278	9·3	..	..	240	5·2	0·83	1·17	..
48	3-Methylguanine	1	265	..	..	..	..	..	0·80	0·35	..
		13	274	..	..	..	..	..	0·93	1·12	..
49	7-Methylguanine	1	249	11·0	..	..	227	4·7	..	0·79	..
			272	7·3	..	..	268	7·3	..	..	..
		7	282	7·4	..	..	260	3·9	..	1·8	..
			247	5·9	..	..	236	5·5	..	..	..
		12	280·5	7·3	..	..	257	..	..	1·9	..
		13	280	7·7	..	..	257	4·0	..	..	..
50	Riboside of 49	2	258	10·0	..	..	229	2·2	..	..	..
		7	258	8·5	..	..	238	4·6	..	..	..
			281	7·4	..	..	271	6·9	..	..	..
		9·2	283	8·1	..	..	259	5·5	..	..	..
			242	4·5	..	..	..	..	..	..	..
51	2-Methylamino-6-hydroxypurine	1	250	12·3	..	..	272	6·6	1·23	0·65	..
			280	6·9	..	..	233	..	..	..	..
		11	245	8·0	..	..	263	6·1	..	..	..
		13	278	..	..	..	260	..	1·0	1·3	..
52	2-Dimethylamino-6-hydroxypurine	1	258	14·5	..	..	235	6·9	0·92	0·36	..
		11	245	9·2	..	..	265	7·1	..	..	..
			277	8·0	..	..	..	..	..	..	..
		13	283	..	..	..	265	..	1·6	1·5	..

?eferences and comments	p*K* Base	p*K* Phosphate	References
̇eaven *et al.* *ırch. B.B.* **62**, 253 (1956) 'olkin & Cohn *.B.C.* **175**, 315 (1948)	1·6 9·2 12·3		Cohn.
.B.C. **175**, 315 (1948) *'cta chem. scand.* **4**, 1047 (1950)			
'ohn, cited by Beaven *et al.* *B.C.* **209**, 285 (1954) urton (unpublished)	2·3 9·36	0·7 5·9	Cohn.
eaven *et al.*			
rch. B.B. **62**, 253 (1956) $_{50}$ pH 7 taken to be as for mixed 2′ and 3′-phosphates	2·4 9·4	6·1	As spectra. In 0·1M-NaCl.
B.C. **208**, 445 (1954) *B.A.* **26**, 596 (1957)	2·9 9·7	6·4	*J.B.C.* **204**, 847 (1953).
ch. B.B. **62**, 253 (1956) $_{0}$ pH 7 taken to be as for mixed 2′ and 3′-phosphates	2·9 9·6	6·3	As spectra. In 0·1M-NaCl.
ch. B.B. **62**, 253 (1956) $_{0}$ pH 7 taken to be as for mixed 2′ and 3′-phosphates	3·3 9·3	6·5	As spectra. In 0·1M-NaCl.
B.A. **68**, 284 (1963) tefact produced by action of acid on RNA *B.A.* **91**, 332 (1964)]	0 3·1 9·9 12·5		As spectra.
.A. **68**, 284 (1963) *.S.* **1962**, 5281			
.A. **68**, 284 (1963)			
.S. **1961**, 3923; **1962**, 5281 re data in *J.A.C.S.* **85**, 193 (1963)			
S. **1962**, 5281 *ıre, Lond.* **192**, 1081 (1961)	7·0		As spectra.
C.S. **78**, 217 (1956) *A.* **68**, 284 (1963)			
.S. **78**, 217 (1956) *A.* **68**, 284 (1963)			

7. Spectral Data and p*K* Values for Purines, Pyrimidines, Nucleosides, and Nucleotides

No.	*Name*	p*H*	λ_{max} (mμ)	ϵ_{max} $\times 10^{-3}$	ϵ_{260} $\times 10^{-3}$	$(\epsilon_{260}-\epsilon_{290})$ $\times 10^{-3}$	λ_{min}	ϵ_{min} $\times 10^{-3}$	250/260	280/260	290/260
53	Hypoxanthine	1·2 N-HCl	248	10·8	7·35	7·35	215	1·7	1·45	0·04	0·000
		4–7	249·5	10·7	7·9	7·82	221	2·55	1·32	0·092	0·010
		11	258·5	11·05	10·95	10·9	232	3·75	0·84	0·124	0·007
		N-NaOH	262·5	11·45	11·3	11·2	233	3·5	0·705	0·19	0·007
54	Inosine (Hypoxanthine riboside)	2 N-HCl	251	10·9	9·0	9·0	..	..	1·21	0·11	0·000
		3–6	248·5	12·25	7·1	6·9	223	3·4	1·68	0·25	0·025
		11·2	253	13·1	11·7	11·6	224	2·5	1·05	0·18	0·008
55	Hypoxanthine deoxyriboside	1	249	11·3	..	..	..	..	..	..	..
		2	249	13·2	..	..	..	..	1·63	0·23	..
56	Inosine-5′-phosphate (IMP)	2	249	11·7	7·5	..	..	..	1·59	0·22	..
		7	248	12·3	..	..	..	..	1·63	0·23	..
		11	254	12·3	11·4	..	223	..	1·09	0·20	..
57	Methylhypoxanthines										
58	Orotic acid	1–2	205	10·9	4·2	..	240	0·9	0·55	1·80	1·55
			280	7·52	..	..	..	..	..	..	..
		4–7·2	207	11·6	4·5	..	..	..	0·57	1·71	1·38
			278·5	7·68	..	..	..	..	..	..	..
		12–13	286	5·98	3·35	..	243	3·4	0·79	1·73	1·73
		14	289	5·35	2·4	..	..	..	0·81	2·00	2·23
59	Orotidine	2	267	9·57	..	..	234	2·6	0·65	0·79	..
		12	267	7·6	..	..	245	5·7	0·82	0·72	..
60	Thymine	1–7	264·5	7·89	7·4	6·74	233	1·9	0·67	0·53	0·09
			207	9·5	..	..	..	..	..	..	..
		12–13	291	5·44	3·7	..	244	2·2	0·65	1·31	1·41
61	Thymine deoxyriboside (Thymidine)	1–7	267	9·65	8·75	6·5	235	2·2	0·65	0·72	0·235
		12–13	267	7·38	6·65	5·4	240	4·6	0·75	0·67	0·16
62	Thymine riboside	7	(*a*) 267	9·8	..	..	..	..	..	..	..
			(*b*) 268	10·8	..	..	..	..	..	..	..
63	Thymidine-3′-phosphate	2	..	..	..	..	..	..	..	0·69	..
64	Thymidine 5′-phosphate	1–7	267	9·9	9·0	7·1	..	..	0·65	0·72	0·23
			207	9·5	..	..	..	..	..	..	..
		12	..	..	6·9	5·7	..	..	0·74	0·67	0·17
65	Thymidine 3′,5′-phosphate	1–7	267	9·9	9·0	7·1	233	~2·0	0·65	0·70	0·20
		12	266	..	..	..	244	..	0·74	0·64	..
66	Uracil	6 N-HCl	260	7·80	7·80	7·41	229	1·5	0·795	0·30	0·05
		2–7	259·5	8·20	8·2	8·12	227	1·8	0·84	0·175	0·01
		14	284	6·15	4·1	..	241	2·1	0·71	1·40	1·27
67	Uridine (Uracil riboside)	1–7	262	10·1	9·95	9·92	231	2·0	0·74	0·35	0·03
		11–12	262	7·45	7·35	7·35	237	4·5	0·83	0·29	0·02
68	Uracil deoxyriboside	1–7	262	10·2	10·1	..	231	2·2	0·72	0·375	..
		11–12	262	7·63	7·55	..	242	5·3	0·81	0·31	..
69	Uridine mixed 2′- and 3′-phosphates	1–7	262	10·0	9·9	9·6	230	1·95	0·79(2′)	0·30	0·03
			..	..	..	..	..	..	0·74(3′)	0·33	0·03
		12	261	7·29	7·29	7·1	242	5·37	0·85(2′)	0·25	0·02
			..	..	..	..	..	..	0·83(3′)	0·25	0·02
70	Uridine-5′-phosphate (UMP)	2–7	262	10·0	9·9	9·6	..	..	0·73	0·39	0·03
		11	261	7·8	7·7	7·6	..	..	0·83	0·31	0·02
		12	..	..	7·3	7·1	..	..	0·82	0·33	0·02
71	Uridine-5′-diphosphate (UDP)	2–7	262	10·0	9·9	..	..	..	0·73	0·39	..
		11	261	7·9	7·8	..	..	..	0·80	0·32	..
72	Uridine-5′-triphosphate (UTP)	2–7	262	10·0	9·9	9·5	..	..	0·75	0·38	0·04
		11	261	8·1	8·0	7·9	..	..	0·81	0·31	0·02

References and comments	p*K* Base	p*K* Phosphate	*References*
Beaven *et al.*	1·98 8·94 12·10		*J.C.S.* **1954**, 2060.
Beaven *et al.*	1·2 8·9		Cohn. *J.B.C.* **70**, 243 (1926).
Acta chem. scand. **4**, 1047 (1950) Deutsch			
.B.C. **196**, 513 (1952))eutsch	8·9	1·54 6.04	*J.B.C.* **70**, 243 (1926). Base should also have p*K* ~ 1·2 by analogy with inosine.
Ciba Symposium on Chemistry and Biology of Purines 1957)			
.B.A. **9**, 199 (1952)	~ 2·8 9·45 > 13·0		*B.B.A.* **9**, 199 (1952).
)ata of Drell quoted by California Foundation for iochemical Research. Cf. *Proc. natn. Acad. Sci. U.S.A.* 7, 396 (1951)			
eaven *et al.*	~ 0 9·9 > 13		Beaven *et al.* *B.B.A.* **9**, 199 (1952).
.B.A. **9**, 369 (1952); cf. *J.B.C.* **175**, 315 (1948) *A.C.S.* **75**, 2506 (1953) *cta chem. scand.* **4**, 1047 (1950)	9·8		As spectra.
) *Acta chem. scand.* **9**, 1275 (1955)) *J.A.C.S.* **74**, 668 (1952)			
C.S. **1953**, 951			
.J. **75**, 17 (1960) *B.A.* **26**, 596 (1957) olkin & Cohn	10·0	1·6 6·5	*J.B.C.* **204**, 847 (1953).
J. **75**, 17 (1960) *B.A.* **26**, 596 (1957) eutsch			
eaven *et al.*	~ 0·5 9·5 > 13		*J.A.C.S.* **77**, 691 (1955). Beaven *et al.*
B.A. **9**, 369 (1952) *B.C.* **178**, 431 (1949) lkin & Cohn	9·25		As spectra.
B.A. **9**, 369 (1952) *ta chem. scand.* **9**, 1275 (1955)	9·3		As spectra.
lkin & Cohn *.C.* **178**, 431 (1949); **209**, 285 (1954)	9·43	1·02 5·88	Cohn.
lkin & Cohn *ch. B.B.* **62**, 253 (1956) *.C.* **209**, 41 (1954)	9·5	6·4	*Arch. B.B.* **62**, 253 (1956). In 0·1M-NaCl.
ch. B.B. **62**, 253 (1956)	9·4	6·5	*Arch. B.B.* **62**, 253 (1956). In 0·1M-NaCl.
ch. B.B. **62**, 253 (1956)	9·5	6·6	*Arch. B.B.* **62**, 253 (1956). In 0·1M-NaCl.

7. Spectral Data and p*K* Values for Purines, Pyrimidines, Nucleosides, and Nucleotides

No.	*Name*	p*H*	λ_{max} (mμ)	ϵ_{max} $\times 10^{-3}$	ϵ_{260} $\times 10^{-3}$	$(\epsilon_{260}-\epsilon_{290})$ $\times 10^{-3}$	λ_{min}	ϵ_{min} $\times 10^{-3}$	250/260	280/260	290/260
	Other uracil derivatives										
73	Pseudouridine (3-ribosyl-uracil)	1–7	262	7·9	7·7	..	232	2·0	0·74	0·42	0·07
		12	287	7·96	3·4	..	245	1·7	0·62	2·1	2·2
74	Pseudouridine-3′-phosphate	2	263	8·4	8·3	..	233	2·3	0·74	0·42	0·07
		12	286	8·4	3·7	..	246	2·1	0·66	2·09	2·18
75	5-Hydroxymethyluracil	1–7	261	7·5	..	..	231	..	0·75	0·36	..
		12	285	..	..	..	245	..	..	..	..
76	5-Hydroxymethyluracil deoxyribose-5′-phosphate	acid	264	..	..	..	234	..	0·70	0·57	..
		alkali	264	..	..	..	246	..	..	..	..
77	Gentiobiosyl deriv. of 76	2	264	10·2	..	..	..	..	0·69	0·56	..
78	Xanthine	6 N-HCl	260	9·15	9·15	9·10	242	5·2	0·765	0·15	0·005
			230·5	6·35	..	..	..	..	..	..	..
		2–6	267	10·25	8·85	8·23	240	2·7	0·565	0·61	0·07
		10	277·5	9·3	5·2	0·41	257	5·0	1·29	1·71	0·92
			240·5	8·9	..	..	..	..	..	..	..
		N-NaOH	284	9·4	3·75	..	257	3·6	1·11	2·39	2·27
79	Xanthosine (Xanthine riboside)	2	263	8·95	8·7	8·4	248	6·4	0·75	0·28	0·03
			235	8·4	..	..	217	3·9	..	..	..
		7	277	..	7·9	..	..	..	1·29	1·10	0·58
			248	..	..	..	..	..	..	..	..
		8–11	278	8·9	7·65	..	264	7·0	1·30	1·13	0·61
			248·5	10·2	..	..	222	2·8	..	..	..
80	Xanthosine-5′-phosphate	7	278	..	..	..	..	..	..	..	..
			248	..	..	..	..	..	..	..	..
81	Methylxanthines										
82	Uric acid	2·5	285	..	..	..	..	..	..	..	..
		8	292	..	..	..	..	..	..	..	..
		9·4	292	..	..	..	260	..	1·57	2·45	3·43
			~239	..	..	..	..	..	..	..	..
		12–14	294	..	..	..	..	..	..	..	..
83	3-Ribosyluric acid	1	288	12·4	..	..	256	2·9	1·25	3·4	4·1
			233	6·8	..	..	220	5·7	..	..	..
		7	298	17·7	..	..	257	2·3	..	..	..
		7·4	..	..	..	..	..	..	1·17	3·6	6·3
		13	..	..	..	..	..	..	1·0	4·8	8·4
		14	297	16·5	..	..	254	1·6	..	..	..
84	Methyluric acids										

References and comments	pK Base	pK Phosphate	References
3.B.A. 32, 393 (1959) .A.C.S. 83, 3920 (1961) Biochem. Preps. 10, 135 (1963) $_{300}/\epsilon_{260}$ = 1·22 at pH 12	9·2		B.B.A. 32, 393 (1959).
.B.C. 227, 907 (1957)	9·6		As spectra.
3.B.A. 32, 393 (1959) . molec. Biol. 5, 248 (1962) $_{max}$, pH 12/ϵ_{max}, pH 7 = 0·87 $_{max}/\epsilon_{min}$ = 4·15 at pH 1–7			
. molec. Biol. 5, 248 (1962) $_{max}/\epsilon_{min}$ = 3·5 in acid			
.B.C. 237, 1266 (1962)			
eaven et al.	~0·8 7·44 11·12		J.C.S. 1954, 2060. Beaven et al.
eaven et al. olkin & Cohn A.C.S. 77, 4685 (1955)	~0 5·5 ~13		Beaven et al. J.A.C.S. 76, 1119 (1954). μ = 0·05.
A.C.S. 77, 4685 (1955) as for xanthosine			
A.C.S. 76, 1119 (1954); 77, 691 (1955) C.S. 1962, 5281			
B.C. 238, 3348 (1962) A.C.S. 77, 691 (1955)	(a) 5·40 5·54 (b) 5·75 10·3		(a) Helv. chim. Acta 23, 245 (1940) (titration). (b) J.A.C.S. 77, 691 (1955) (spectral).
C.S. 1961, 963 B.C. 238, 3348 (1962)	6·0 10·9		As spectra.
C.S. 1939, 1369; 1961, 963 A.C.S. 77, 691 (1955)			

8. Nucleotide Derivatives of Amino Acids, Carbohydrates, and Phospholipid Components

Compiled from information supplied by N. L. BLUMSOM (*Department of Organic Chemistry, University of Newcastle upon Tyne*), R. M. C. DAWSON (*A.R.C. Institute of Animal Physiology, Babraham, Cambridge*), R. E. MONRO (*M.R.C. Laboratory of Molecular Biology, Cambridge*), R. H. SYMONS (*Waite Agricultural Research Station, Adelaide*), *and* R. K. WOLFENDEN (*Department of Chemistry, Princeton University*)

Nomenclature

The trivial names of these compounds, for example uridine diphosphate glucose or UDP-glucose, are in common use. Two systems of formal nomenclature are sometimes employed; in these systems UDP-glucose is called uridine 5′-(α-D-glucopyranosyl pyrophosphate) or P^1-uridine-5′ P^2-α-D-glucopyranose-1 pyrophosphate. Other compounds are named analogously.

U.V. spectra

These compounds generally have exactly the same spectrum as that of the free nucleotide moiety of the molecule. When the sugar, amino acid, etc., moiety also absorbs in the u.v. its spectrum is superimposed on the nucleotide spectrum.

Preparation

General methods of synthesis of these nucleotide derivatives are discussed and described in: A. M. Michelson, *The Chemistry of Nucleosides and Nucleotides*, Academic Press (1963); *J.A.C.S.* **83**, 659 (1961); *Tetrahedron* **19**, 1207 (1963); *Biochemistry* **1**, 1171 (1961); *Bull. Soc. Chim. biol.* **45**, 1353 (1963); *B.B.A.* **91**, 1 (1964); *Meth. Enzymol.* **8**, 136, 142 (1966).

Estimation

The nucleoside diphosphate sugars (choline, etc.), in particular, are usually estimated by separating them from other cell constituents by ion-exchange chromatography, paper electrophoresis and paper chromatography, and then estimating the nucleotide portion by u.v. spectrophotometry and the sugar (choline, etc.) by appropriate colorimetric methods after hydrolysis.

Biochemical properties are discussed in the following articles:

Nucleotide-sugars: *Adv. Enzymol.* **26**, 35 (1964).
Adv. Carbohyd. Chem. **18**, 309 (1963).

Nucleotides in phospholipid synthesis:

Fed. Proc. **20**, 934 (1961).
G. B. Ansell and J. N. Hawthorne, *Phospholipids*, Elsevier (1964).

Amino acyl-nucleotides and protein synthesis:

Prog. Nucl. Acid Res. **2**, 289 (1963).
P. D. Boyer, H. Lardy, and K. Myrbäck (eds.), *The Enzymes*, vol. 6, p. 401, 2nd ed., Academic Press (1963).
H. Neurath (ed.) *The Proteins*, vol. 1, p. 190, 2nd ed., Academic Press (1963).

8. Nucleotide Derivatives of Amino Acids, Carbohydrates, and Phospholipid Components

No.	*Name*	*Synonyms*	*Formula*	*M. wt.*
1	Adenosine 5′-diphosphate D-glucose	ADPG	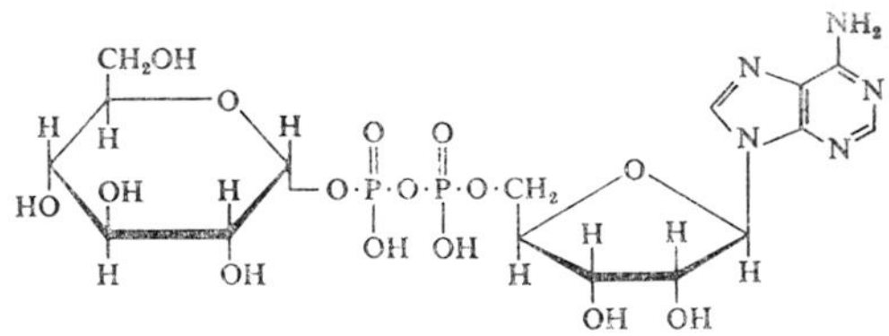	589·3
2	Amino acyl-adenosine compounds		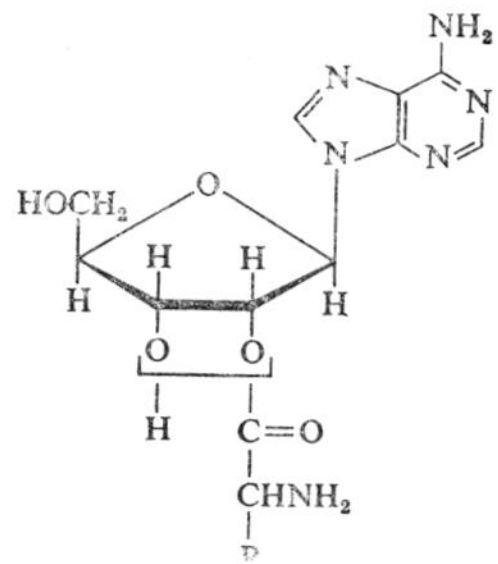 R = amino acid side chain Position of amino acyl group *see* General remarks	249·2+M. wt of *amino acid* OR 323·2+R
3	Amino acyl-adenylates	Adenyl-5′-yl-amino acids; Amino acyl-AMP	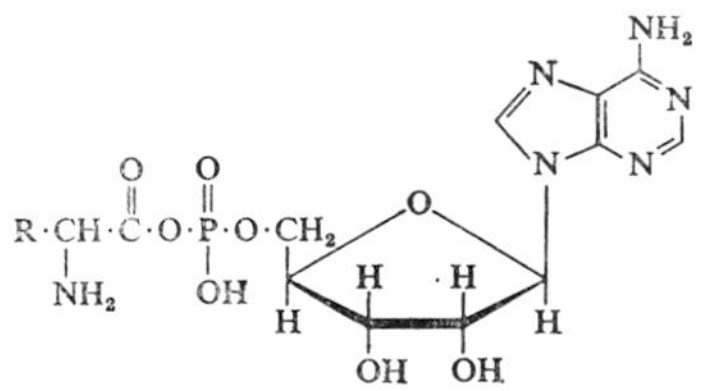 R = amino acid side chain	329·2+M. wt of *amino acid* OR 403·2+R
4	Amino acyl-soluble RNA	Amino acyl-s-RNA; Amino acyl-transfer RNA	Soluble-RNA with an amino acyl group esterified with the 2′- or 3′-hydroxyl group of the terminal adenosine residue. The amino acyl group is in tautomeric equilibrium between the 2′- and 3′-positions. Each isomer has a half-life of 0·1 sec or less at neutral pH.	
5	Cytidine 5′-diphosphate choline	CDP-choline	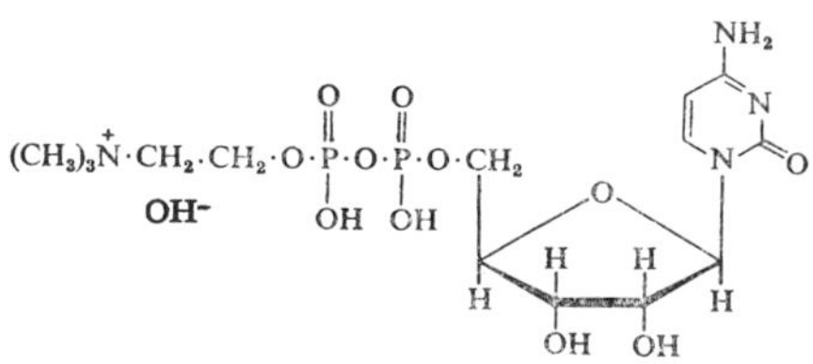	506·3
6	Cytidine 5′-diphosphate diglyceride	CDP-diglyceride	$H_2C·O·CO·R$ $R'·CO·O·CH$ $H_2C·O—CDP$ R, R′ = fatty acid chains CDP = cytidine diphosphate residue, cf. CDP-choline	531·3+R+

·eparation	*Estimation*	*General remarks*
·L. *Z. Naturforsch.* **17B**, 8 (1962) ·*ch B.B.* **106**, 371 (1964) N. *J.B.C.* **237**, 3577 (1962) *B.A.* **91**, 1 (1964)	*J.B.C.* **237**, 3577 (1962)	s. H_2O; i. MeOH, acet., eth. Completely hydrolysed to ADP and D-glucose by 0·01N-HCl at 100° in 15 min. Mild alkaline hydrolysis yields AMP and glucose 1,2-cyclic phosphate. Synthesized enzymically from ADP and α-D-glucose 1-phosphate.
N. *Dokl. (Proc.) Acad. Sci., S.S.R., Chem. Sect.* **128**, 1 (1959) ·*r.* **93**, 1816 (1960) *4.C.S.* **85**, 1997 (1963) ·L. *Biochemistry* **3**, 329 (1964) ·*ochemistry* **4**, 1442 (1965)	*Biochemistry* **3**, 329 (1964)	Amino acid group migrates v. rapidly between 2′- and 3′-hydroxyl groups of adenosine, so that substance obtained is an equilibrium mixture of these two isomers. Wh. amorphous solid, s. H_2O. Spectrum identical with that of adenosine. Rapidly hydrolysed in acid or alkali, most stable at pH 2–4. Half-life at pH 7 and 37°, about 30 min. Store cold and dry. Reacts with hydroxylamine forming amino acylhydroxamic acid. Not oxidized by periodate.
·EMICAL. *J.B.C.* **234**, 841 ·59) ·*chem. Preps.* **8**, 11, 17 ·61) ·*th. Enzymol.* **6**, 751 (1963) ·*3.A.* **80**, 242 (1964) ·ZYMIC. *J.A.C.S.* **80**, 2335 ·58) ·*c. natn. Acad. Sci. U.S.A.* 757 (1958)	*J.B.C.* **234**, 841 (1959) *Meth. Enzymol.* **6**, 751 (1963)	s. H_2O. Spectrum identical with that of adenylic acid. V. unstable compds., most stable between pH 2 and 5, but v. rapidly hydrolysed in acid or alkali. Half-life at pH 7·2 and 37°, about 5 min. (β-alanyl-AMP, about 1 hr). Slow spontaneous conversion to 2′- or 3′-amino acyl esters of adenosine occurs during storage. React with hydroxylamine to form amino acylhydroxamic acid. Powerful non-enzymic amino acylating agents, react with NH_3, amino acids, proteins, nucleotides, RNA. Oxidized by periodate. Carbobenzyloxy derivs. much more stable at neutral pH.
·*th. Enzymol.* **6**, 757 (1963) ·*c. natn. Acad. Sci. U.S.A.* 497, 941 (1961) ·*nolec. Biol.* **4**, 347 (1962) ·*chemistry* **1**, 580 (1962)	*Meth. Enzymol.* **6**, 757 (1963) *See also under* soluble-RNA	Amino acyl-s-RNA's are obtained by the reaction between amino acids, ATP and s-RNA catalysed by the amino acid activating enzymes. Individual compds. may be prepared by using a single amino acid, together with, where possible, the appropriate purified activating enzyme and the appropriate purified s-RNA. Compds. are rapidly hydrolysed to the amino acid and s-RNA above pH 6, rate increases with pH, *Biochemistry* 3, 1090 (1963). Half-life at pH 7 and 37°, 10–60 min. Hydrolysis complete in 30 min at 37° and pH 9–10; this treatment used to remove amino acyl groups from s-RNA preparations. Compds. with basic amino acids generally more labile than others. Store at −20° and pH 5 either in soln. or lyophilized.
.*C.S.* **77**, 250 (1955) ·*.C.* **222**, 185 (1956) *l. Soc. Chim. biol.* **45**, 3 (1963)	*B.B.A.* **40**, 425 (1960) *J.B.C.* **235**, 37 (1960) *B.J.* **78**, 209 (1961)	Wh. hygr. powder, s. H_2O. N-H_2SO_4 at 100° for 18 min causes 50% hydrolysis to CMP and phosphorylcholine; 7·5% of total P released as P_i after 40 min. Absorption spectrum 245–300 mμ identical to CMP, 280/260 = 2·17.
.*C.* **235**, 1303 (1960) ·*chem. Preps.* **10**, 47 (1963)		Free acid, s. $CHCl_3$; K salt, clear aq. dispersion. Dipalmitoyl deriv. (di-NH_4 salt), M.p. 171–2. K salt stable at 0° as dry solid or in aq. dispersion. Free acid unstable in $CHCl_3$ soln. at R.T.

8. Nucleotide Derivatives of Amino Acids, Carbohydrates, and Phospholipid Components

No.	*Name*	*Synonyms*	*Formula*	*M. wt.*
7	Cytidine 5′-diphosphate ethanolamine	CDP-ethanolamine	$H_2N \cdot CH_2 \cdot CH_2 \cdot O$—CDP CDP = cytidine diphosphate residue, cf. CDP-choline	446·3
8	Cytidine 5′-diphosphate D-glucose	CDPG	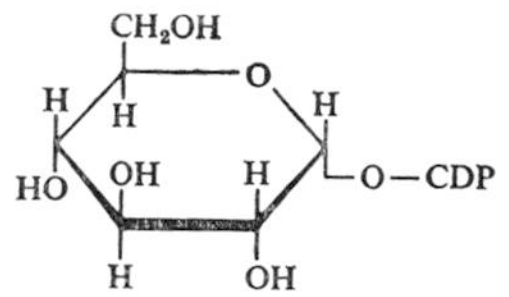 **CDP = cytidine diphosphate** residue, cf. CDP-choline	565·3
9	Cytidine 5′-diphosphate glycerol	CDP-glycerol	CH_2OH HOCH CH_2—O—CDP CDP = cytidine diphosphate residue, cf. CDP-choline	477·2
10	Cytidine 5′-diphosphate ribitol	CDP-ribitol	CH_2OH HCOH HCOH HCOH CH_2—O—CDP CDP = cytidine diphosphate residue, cf. CDP-choline	537·3
11	Cytidine 5′-monophosphate *N*-acetylneuraminic acid	C-5′-PNAN; CMP-sialic acid	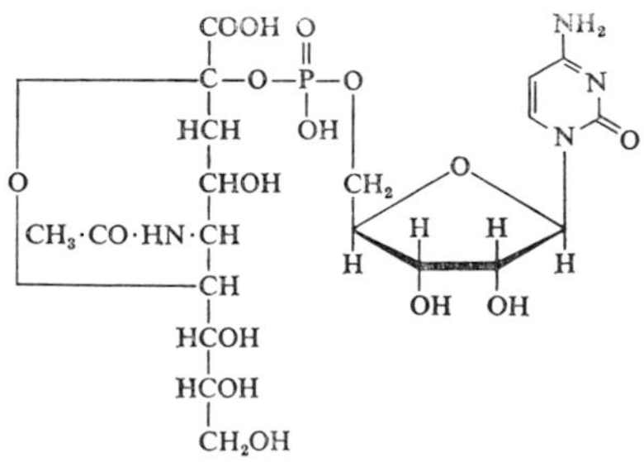	614·5
12	Guanosine 5′-diphosphate L-fucose	GDP-fucose	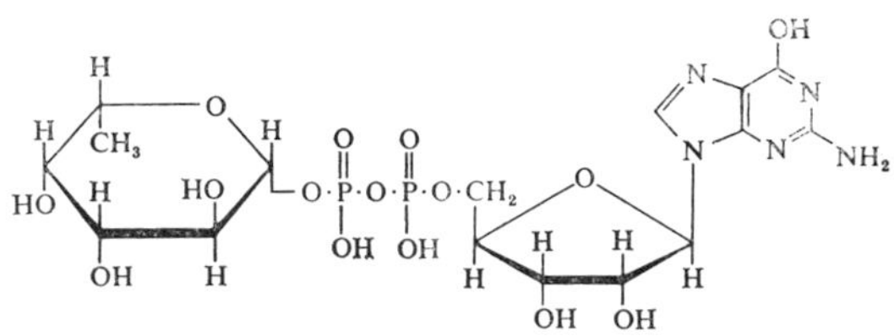	589·3
13	Guanosine 5′-diphosphate D-glucose	GDPG	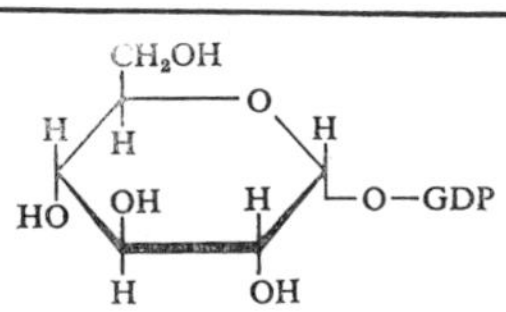 **GDP = guanosine** diphosphate residue, cf. GDP-fucose	605·3
14	Guanosine 5′-diphosphate D-mannose	GDPM	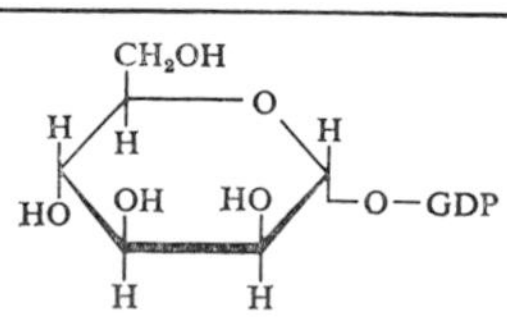 GDP = guanosine diphosphate residue, cf. GDP-fucose	605·3

reparation	Estimation	General remarks
B.C. **222**, 185 (1956) *ull. Soc. Chim. biol.* **45**, 353 (1963)	*J.B.C.* **233**, 462 (1959) *J.B.C.* **235**, 2109 (1960)	Absorption spectrum: pH 2: λ_{max} 278–80 mμ, λ_{min} 242 mμ. pH 13: λ_{max} 270 mμ, λ_{min} 251–3 mμ.
B.R.C. **7**, 1 (1962) *trahedron* **19**, 1207 (1963)		Prepared by enzyme isolated from *Salmonella paratyphi* A. Hydrolysis in 0·01N-HCl for 10 min at 100° gives cytidine 5′-diphosphate and D-glucose.
L. *B.J.* **64**, 599 (1956) *.S.* **1956**, 4186 N. *J.C.S.* **1958**, 3107 *.C.S.* **83**, 659 (1961)	*B.J.* **64**, 599 (1956)	Labile in acid and alkali. Hydrolysis in N-HCl at 100° for 30 min gives cytidine 5′-phosphate and a mixture of α- and β-glycerophosphates. Conc. NH_3 at 100° for 1 hr gives partial hydrolysis to cytidine 5′-phosphate and 1,2-cyclic phosphate of glycerol. Glycerol phosphate moiety has L-α-configuration.
L. *B.J.* **64**, 599 (1956) *.S.* **1956**, 4583 . *J.C.S.* **1959**, 2192	*B.J.* **64**, 599 (1956)	Functions in the synthesis of cell wall materials (teichoic acids) in Gram-positive organisms. Very labile in both acid and alkali. 19% hydrolysis at pH 2 after 18 hr at 20°. Complete hydrolysis to cytidine 5′-phosphate and ribitol 4,5-cyclic phosphate in 8M-NH_4OH at 100° in 30 min. Ribitol phosphate moiety has D-configuration.
. *J.A.C.S.* **81**, 5513 (1959) . *Proc. natn. Acad. Sci. .A.* **48**, 437 (1962) *C.* **237**, 3527 (1962)	*J.B.C.* **237**, 3527 (1962) *J.B.C.* **234**, 1971 (1959)	s. H_2O; i. MeOH, acet., eth. In dry state decomp. at −16°, 5–10% per day, to CMP and *N*-acetylneuraminic acid. 0·01N-HCl at 23° for 5 min yields 83% hydrolysis. Absorption spectrum as for CMP λ_{max} 272 mμ (pH 12), 280 mμ (pH 2).
. *J.A.C.S.* **80**, 3481 (1958) *hebd. Séanc. Acad. Sci.*, *s* **246**, 2820 (1958) *J.B.C.* **235**, 2196 (1960)	*J.B.C.* **235**, 2196 (1960) *J.B.C.* **236**, 2389 (1961)	s. H_2O; i. MeOH, acet., eth. Completely hydrolysed to GDP and L-fucose by 0·01N-HCl at 100° for 10 min. Formed by $NADPH_2$ dependent reduction of GDP-mannose by enzyme from *Aerobacter aerogenes*.
B.J. **75**, 428 (1960) *.* **237**, 1260 (1962) *J.C.S.* **1961**, 2574 *.* **237**, 1260 (1962) *4.* **91**, 1 (1964)		Completely hydrolysed to GDP and D-glucose by 0·01N-HCl at 100° in 15 min; after 3 hr the products are GMP, P_i and D-glucose.
J.B.C. **206**, 779 (1954) *emistry* **1**, 474 (1962) . *Enzymol.* **6**, 777 (1963); 5 (1966) *Arch. B.B.* **55**, 592 (1955) *.S.* **83**, 659 (1961)	*J.B.C.* **236**, 2389 (1961)	s. H_2O; i. MeOH, acet., eth. Completely hydrolysed to GDP and D-mannose by 0·01N-HCl in 10 min at 100°. Formed enzymically from GTP and α-D-mannose-1-phosphate.

8. Nucleotide Derivatives of Amino Acids, Carbohydrates, and Phospholipid Components

No.	*Name*	*Synonyms*	*Formula*	*M. wt.*
15	Soluble-RNA	s-RNA; Transfer-RNA; t-RNA; Acceptor-RNA	Polyribonucleotides containing 70–80 nucleotide residues. There is at least one species of s-RNA of characteristic base sequence corresponding to each of the protein-bound amino acids.	24 000–30 000
16	Thymidine 5′-diphosphate D-glucose	TDPG	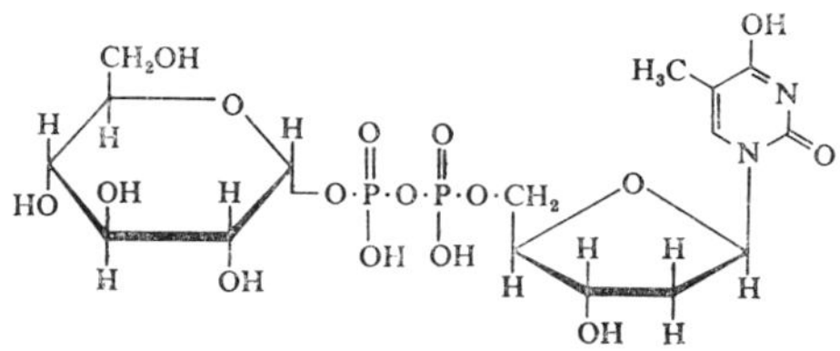	564·4
17	Thymidine 5′-diphosphate L-rhamnose	TDP-rhamnose	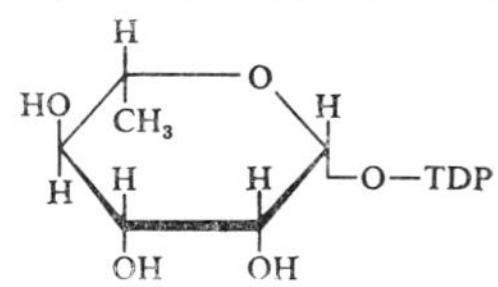 **TDP = thymidine diphosphate residue, cf. TDP-glucose**	548·4
18	Uridine 5′-diphosphate *N*-acetyl-galactosamine	UDPAGal	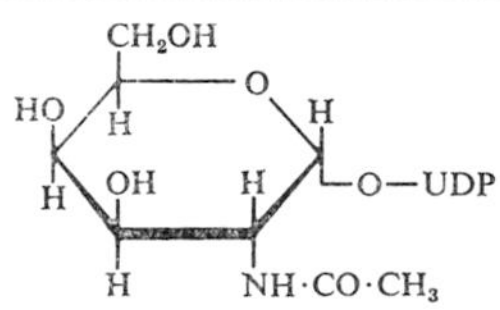 **UDP = uridine diphosphate residue, cf. UDP-glucose**	607·4
19	Uridine 5′-diphosphate *N*-acetyl-glucosamine	UDPAG	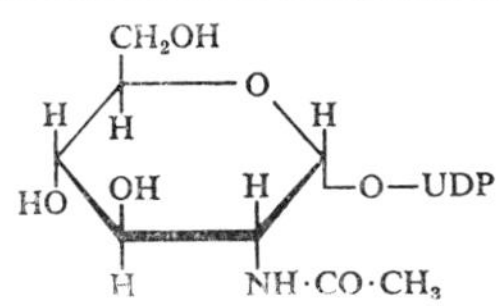 **UDP = uridine diphosphate residue, cf. UDP-glucose**	607·4
20	Uridine 5′-diphosphate L-arabinose	UDP-arabinose	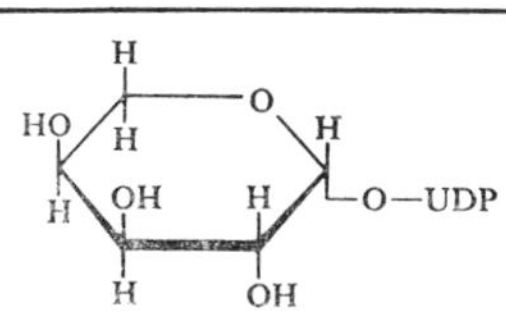 **UDP = uridine diphosphate residue, cf. UDP-glucose**	536·3
21	Uridine 5′-diphosphate D-galactose	UDPGal	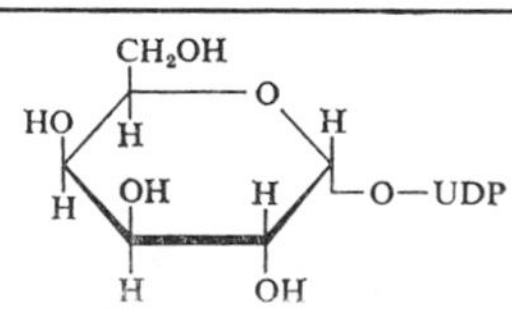 **UDP = uridine diphosphate residue, cf. UDP-glucose**	566·4

·paration	Estimation	General remarks
·g. *nucl. Acid Res.* **2**, 259 63) ·th. *Enzymol.* **12A** 588 et seq. 67) ·ST. *B.B.A.* **43**, 1 (1960) ·.C. **236**, 200 (1961) ·.R.C. **10**, 186 (1963) ·OLI. *J.B.C.* **236**, 1741 51) ·*olec. Biol.* **4**, 347 (1962) ·ER. *J.B.C.* **235**, 2370 (1960) ·.R.C. **8**, 1 (1962)	*Prog. nucl. Acid Res.* **2**, 259 (1963) *J.B.C.* **236**, 200 (1961) *J.B.C.* **236**, 1726, 1741 (1961) *J. molec. Biol.* **4**, 347 (1962) *B.B.A.* **80**, 574 (1964) *Meth. Enzymol.* **12B**, 166, 169, 173 (1968)	Store at −20° either in soln. or lyophilized. s. H_2O. Spectrum like RNA; 1 mg/ml gives OD_{260} of 22–24. Hydrolysed by alkali. Separation of s-RNA's corresponding to individual amino acids—*Prog. nucl. Acid Res.* **2**, 259 (1963); *J.B.C.* **237**, 796 (1962); *B.B.A.* **80**, 169 (1963); *Biochemistry* **3**, 1406 (1964); *Meth. Enzymol.* **12**, 638 et seq. (1967); *Biochemistry* **6**, 3043 (1967).
. *J.B.C.* **236**, 1780 (1961) *C.* **236**, 1791 (1961) *C.* **237**, 3014 (1962)	*J.B.C.* **237**, 3014 (1962)	s. H_2O; i. MeOH, acet., eth. Completely hydrolysed to TDP and D-glucose by 0·01N-HCl at 100° in 10 min. Synthesized from TTP and α-D-glucose 1-phosphate by enzyme from *Streptococcus faecalis* or *Pseudomonas aeruginosa*.
. *B.B.A.* **44**, 478 (1960) **81**, 114 (1961) *J.B.C.* **236**, 1780 (1961) *C.* **236**, 1795 (1961)	*J.B.C.* **236**, 1795 (1961) *J.B.C.* **237**, 3014 (1962)	s. H_2O; i. MeOH, acet., eth. Completely hydrolysed to TDP and L-rhamnose by 0·01N-HCl at 100° in 10 min.
B.B.A. **72**, 112 (1963) ·*hemistry* **3**, 402 (1964) ·*h. Enzymol.* **8**, 147 (1966)		Hydrolysed to *N*-acetylgalactosamine and UDP at pH 2 for 15 min at 100°. $[\alpha]_D^{25}$ +81·7 (c = 0·8 Li salt in H_2O).
B.B.A. **46**, 595 (1961) ·*h. Enzymol.* **6**, 777 (1963); ·7 (1966) ·*h. biochem. Anal.* **10**, 1962) *J.A.C.S.* **83**, 659 (1961)	*J.B.C.* **203**, 1055 (1953)	$[\alpha]_D^{25}$ +54·6 (c = 1·0 anhyd. Li salt in H_2O). Hydrolysed to UDP and *N*-acetylglucosamine by 0·01N-HCl at 100° in 15 min. N-acid at 100° for 30 min causes hydrolysis to UMP, P_i and *N*-acetylglucosamine.
J.B.C. **223**, 977 (1956) *Arch. B.B.* **69**, 602 (1957) ·. **235**, 910 (1960) ·. *Enzymol.* **6**, 782 (1963)	*J.B.C.* **223**, 977 (1956)	s. H_2O; i. MeOH, acet., eth. Completely hydrolysed to UDP and L-arabinose in 15 min at 100° by 0·01N-HCl. Enzymic synthesis occurs from UTP and β-L-arabinopyranose 1-phosphate; also formed by enzymic epimerization of UDP-xylose.
Arch. B.B. **33**, 186) ·. **223**, 977 (1956) *J.A.C.S.* **83**, 659 (1961) ·*t. Biochem.* **2**, 281 (1961) . *biochem. Anal.* **10**, 107)		s. H_2O, MeOH; i. acet. $[\alpha]_D^{25}$ +42·9 (c = 1·0 anhyd. Li salt in H_2O). Completely hydrolysed to UDP and D-galactose by 0·01N-HCl at 100° in 10 min.

8. Nucleotide Derivatives of Amino Acids, Carbohydrates, and Phospholipid Components

No.	*Name*	*Synonyms*	*Formula*	*M. wt.*
22	Uridine 5′-diphosphate D-galacturonic acid	UDP-galact-uronic acid	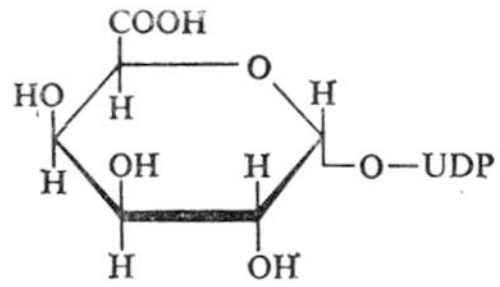 **UDP** = **uridine diphosphate** residue, cf. UDP-glucose	580·3
23	Uridine 5′-diphosphate α-D-glucose	UDP-glucose; UDPG	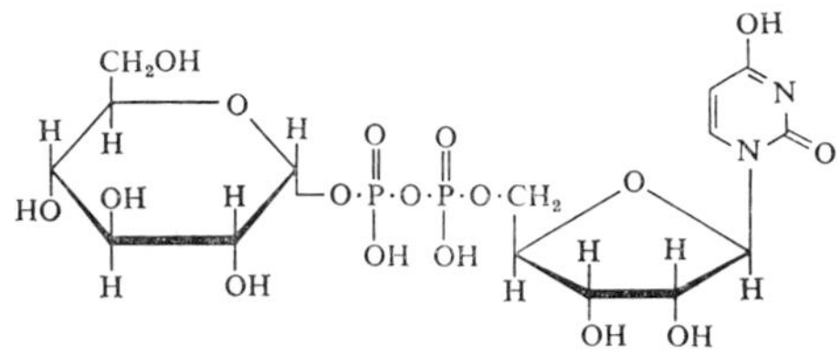	566·4
24	Uridine 5′-diphosphate D-glucuronic acid	UDP-glucuronic acid	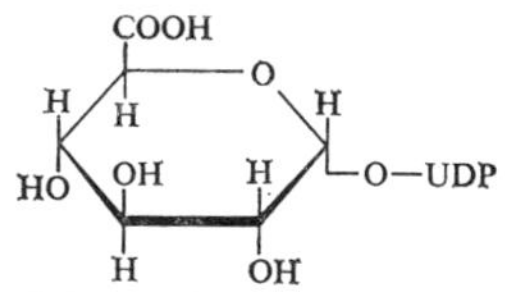 **UDP** = **uridine diphosphate** residue, cf. UDP-glucose	580·3
25	Uridine 5′-diphosphate L-rhamnose	UDP-rhamnose	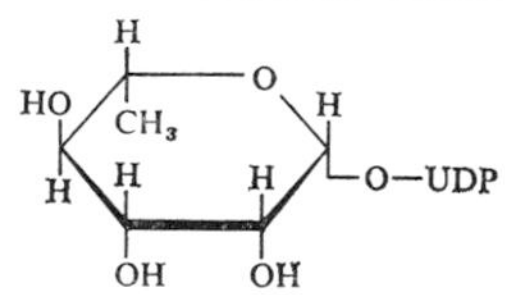 **UDP** = **uridine diphosphate** residue, cf. UDP-glucose	550·3
26	Uridine 5′-diphosphate D-xylose	UDP-xylose	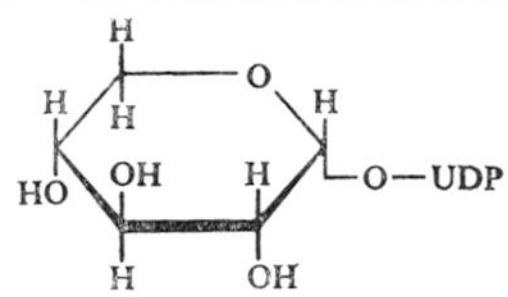 **UDP** = **uridine diphosphate** residue, cf. UDP-glucose	536·3

eparation	*Estimation*	*General remarks*
ɔL. *B.B.A.* 53, 589 (1961) N. *Arch. B.B.* 78, 401 (1958) *3.C.* **235**, 910 (1960)		Completely hydrolysed by 0·01N-HCl at 100° in 10 min to UDP and D-galacturonic acid. 0·1N-HCl at 100° for 90 min or N-HCl at 100° for 15 min yield UMP, P_i and D-galacturonic acid.
L. *B.J.* **51**, 426 (1952) *.C.* **223**, 977 (1956) *B.A.* **26**, 146 (1957) *th. biochem. Anal.* **10**, 107 62) *th. Enzymol.* **6**, 777 (1963) *. J.C.S.* **1956**, 3459 *.C.S.* **83**, 659 (1961) *chem. Preps.* **8**, 125 (1961)	*Meth. biochem. Anal.* **10**, 107 (1962) *Meth. Enzymol.* **2**, 676 (1955); **3**, 968, 974 (1957)	s. H_2O, MeOH; i. acet., eth. Ba salt, v. s. H_2O. Completely hydrolysed to UDP and D-glucose by 0·01N-HCl at 100° in 10 min. Hydrolysis with N-HCl at 100° for 15 min yields UMP, P_i and glucose. Mild alkaline treatment, e.g. 2 min at 100° at pH 8·5 or 30 min at 0° in conc. NH_3, forms UMP and glucose 1,2-cyclic phosphate.
. B.J. **59**, 279 (1955) *.C.S.* **79**, 2342 (1957) *.C.* **228**, 357 (1957) *Biochem., Tokyo* **51**, 277 62) *. Arch. B.B.* **78**, 401 (1958) *.C.S.* **83**, 659 (1961) *chemistry* **1**, 1171 (1962)		s. H_2O; i. MeOH, acet. $[\alpha]_D^{25}$ +54·5 (c = 1·0 anhyd. Li salt in H_2O). pK_a (COOH) 4·4. Solid decomp. slowly at room temp. Hydrolysis with 0·01N-acid at 100° for 15 min forms mainly UDP and glucuronic acid but also small amounts of UMP and glucuronic acid 1-phosphate. N-acid at 100° for 15 min forms UMP, P_i and glucuronic acid.
. B.B.A. **33**, 276 (1959) *.R.C.* **8**, 204 (1962) *Arch. B.B.* **103**, 276 3)		Present in *Streptococcus* and tobacco and mung bean leaves. 0·01N-HCl for 15 min at 100° causes complete hydrolysis to UDP and L-rhamnose. 0·1N-HCl at 100° for 90 min forms UMP, P_i and L-rhamnose.
. J.B.C. **223**, 977 (1956) *h. Enzymol.* **6**, 782 (1963)		Completely hydrolysed to UDP and D-xylose by 0·01N-HCl at 100° in 10 min. Formed enzymically from UTP and α-D-xylose 1-phosphate.

9. Vitamins and Coenzymes

Revised by J. G. MORRIS *and* E. R. REDFEARN† (*Department of Biochemistry, University of Leicester*)

General bibliography

W. H. Sebrell and R. S. Harris (eds.), *The Vitamins*, Academic Press. The first edition, in 3 volumes, was published in 1954. The second edition, in 7 volumes, is in course of publication; vols. 1, 6 and 7 were published in 1967, vol. 2 in 1968.

P. D. Boyer, H. Lardy, and K. Myrbäck (eds.), *The Enzymes*, 2nd ed., vols. 2 and 3, Academic Press (1960).

A. F. Wagner and K. Folkers, *Vitamins and Coenzymes*, Interscience (1964).

M. Florkin and E. H. Stotz (eds.), *Comprehensive Biochemistry*, vols. 5 (ascorbic acid), 9 (vitamins A, E, and K and quinones), and 11 (B group vitamins), Elsevier (1963).

Vitamins and Hormones. Academic Press, a review serial published annually; vol. 1 (1943), vol. 26 (1968).

D. W. Hutchinson, *Nucleotides and Coenzymes*, Methuen (1964).

Methods of assay

Detailed procedures for the assay of vitamins and coenzymes are given in:

M. Freed (ed.) for the Association of Official Vitamin Chemists, *Methods of Vitamin Assay*, 3rd ed., Interscience (1966).

P. György and W. N. Pearson (eds.), *The Vitamins*, vols. 6 and 7, Academic Press (1967). This is an extensively revised new edition of P. György (ed.), *Vitamin Methods*, 2 volumes, Academic Press (1950–1).

S. P. Colowick and N. O. Kaplan (eds.), *Methods in Enzymology*, Academic Press, vols. 2 (1955) and 6 (1963).

Nomenclature

Rules (or tentative rules) for nomenclature of vitamins and coenzymes are given in: *B.B.A.* **107,** 1, 5, 11 (1965); *J.B.C.* **241,** 2987, 2989, 2991, 2992 (1966); *B.J.* **102,** 15, 17, 19, 20 (1967). *B.J.* **119,** 1 (1970); *J.B.C.* **245,** 4229 (1970) (vitamin B_6 and related compounds).

International Union of Biochemistry, *Enzyme Nomenclature*, Elsevier (1965) (nicotinamide nucleotide coenzymes).

† Professor Redfearn died on 6 March 1968.

9. Vitamins and Coenzymes

No.	Name	Synonyms	Formula	M. wt.	Physical properties
1	**Acetyl coenzyme A**	Acetyl-CoA; Acetyl-S-CoA	Cf. Coenzyme A, —SH replaced by $—S\cdot CO\cdot CH_3$	809·6	wh. powder
2	**Acyl coenzyme A compounds (General methods and properties)**	*S*-Acyl coenzyme A; Acyl-CoA; Acyl-S-CoA	Cf. Coenzyme A, —SH replaced by $—S\text{-}CO\cdot R$	749·5+ M. wt. of *acid* OR 794·5+ R	
3	**Adeninyl-cobamide coenzyme**	α-(Adeninyl)-5′-deoxyadenosyl-cobamide; AC coenzyme	As Coenzyme B_{12}, but with 5,6-dimethylbenzimidazole replaced by adenine	1568·6	orange oil
4	***p*-Amino-benzoic acid**	pAB; pABA	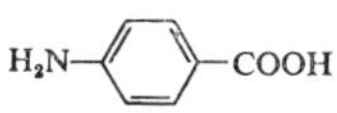	137·1	wh. monocl. cryst., yellows air and light; M.p. 187; pK_a 1. 2·38 2. 4·89
5	**Ascorbic acid**	L-Ascorbic acid; Vitamin C	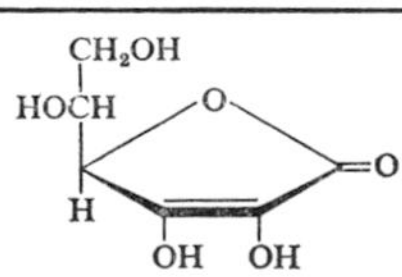	176·1	wh. cryst.; M.p. 192 d.; pK_a 1. 4·19 2. 11·57; E'_0 +0·058 v (1st stage, pH [α]$^{20}_{D}$ +23 (c = in H_2O)

olubility	Absorption spectrum	Preparation	Estimation	General remarks
H_2O	λ_{max} 260 mμ ε 16 400 ϵ_{232} 8700 $\Delta\epsilon_{232}$ on hydrolysis 4500	*Meth. Enzymol.* **3**, 931 (1957) *J.A.C.S.* **74**, 3205 (1952) *Biochem. Preps.* **5**, 27 (1957) *See also* Acyl-CoA compds.	*Meth. Enzymol.* 3, 935, 938 (1957) Bergmeyer, *Methods of Enzymatic Analysis*, p. 419, Academic Press (1963) *B.B.R.C.* **10**, 333 (1963)	Stability, see Acyl-CoA compds. Can be heated to 100° for 15 min at pH 3·5 to 5 without decomp.
H_2O	Absorption maxima usually about 260 mμ, due to adenine in CoA, and about 232 mμ, due to thioester bond. Hydrolysis of thioester bond causes decrease in absorption at 232 mμ, $\Delta\epsilon_{232}$ approx. 4500	*Meth. Enzymol.* **3**, 931 (1957) *Meth. Enzymol.* **6**, 538, 540, 544 (1963) With most acids, methods based upon one of the following are applicable: *J.A.C.S.* **75**, 2520 (1953) *Angew. Chem.* **65**, 186 (1953) *Ann.* **581**, 1 (1953), **588**, 15 (1954) *B.Z.* 335, 540 (1962) *J.A.C.S.* **74**, 3205 (1952)	*Meth. Enzymol.* **3**, 931 (1957) Bergmeyer, *Methods of Enzymatic Analysis*, pp. 419–53, Academic Press (1963) *J.B.C.* **161**, 415 (1945)	Methods and properties in this entry apply to the majority of acyl-CoA compds. Exceptions to these generalizations and some commonly used acyl-CoA compds. are dealt with in individual entries, see Acetyl-CoA, Crotonyl-CoA, Fatty acyl-CoA, β-Hydroxyacyl-CoA, Lactoyl-CoA, Malonyl-CoA, β-Oxoacyl-CoA, Succinyl-CoA. For some enzymic reactions *S*-acyl derivs. of *N*-acetyl- or *N*-succinyl- or *N*-capryloyl-cysteamine or of pantetheine can be used in place of CoA derivs. Methods of preparation and estimation and properties are similar to the corresponding CoA derivs. *Stability*. Dry solids may be stored at 0° in desiccator over long periods. Generally stable in neutral and moderately acid soln. even at elevated temp., hydrolysed in strong acid and v. rapidly in alkaline soln. Instability in alkali increases as pK_a of acid decreases. React quantitatively with neutral NH_2OH forming acyl-hydroxamic acid.
I_2O, EtOH, nol; i. acet., , dioxane	In H_2O: λ_{max} 263 303 375 ε 45 300 21 600 9030 λ_{max} 458 mμ ε 8750	*J.B.C.* **235**, 181 (1960)	*J.B.C.* **236**, 2347, PC 1 (1961) *Biochem. Preps.* **10**, 28 (1963)	Dry cryst. stable in dark, decomp. in light. Aq. soln. rapidly decomp. by u.v. or visible light. Most stable at pH 6–7; dil. neutral solns. stable many months at −10°. V. unstable in acid soln.; 50% loss in 3 days at pH 2 and −10°, completely destroyed in 1 hr at 0° on Dowex-50 (H^+) column. With alk. cyanide forms dicyano-adeninylcobamide.
⁵, ·⁰⁰ H_2O; EtOH; h.; s. MeOH, Cl_3, gl. acetic; , benz.; t. eth.	In H_2O: λ_{max} 266 mμ ε 15 000 *Analyt. Chem.* **20**, 919 (1948)		*Vitamin Methods*, vol. 1, pp. 256, 327 (1950) *The Vitamins*, 1st ed., vol. 3, p. 19 (1954) *J.B.C.* **148**, 281 (1943) *J.B.C.* **153**, 193 (1944) *J.B.C.* **128**, 537 (1939)	Competitively counteracts sulphonamide bacteriostasis. Readily absorbed by man after oral dosage and excreted as *p*-aminohippurate, some as glucuronate.
H_2O; OH; i. eth., Cl_3, benz., eth.	In H_2O or neutral soln.: λ_{max} 265 mμ ε 7000 In acid: λ_{max} 245 mμ ε 7500 *J.C.S.* **1933**, 1270	ISOL. *B.J.* **22**, 1387 (1928) *B.J.* **27**, 279 (1933) *J.B.C.* **97**, 325 (1932) *Ind. Engng Chem.* **42**, 387 (1950)	*Meth. biochem. Anal.* **1**, 115 (1954) *Moderne Methoden der Pflanzenanalyse*, eds. Paech and Tracey, vol. 2, p. 95, Springer-Verlag (1955) *Methods of Vitamin Assay*, 3rd ed., p. 287 (1966)	Stable in dry state. pH of aq. soln. about 3, acts as a monobasic acid. Aq. solns. (especially alkaline) unstable, most stable at pH 5–6. Oxidation catalysed by Cu, Fe. Reduces Fehling's solution in the cold.

No.	Name	Synonyms	Formula	M. wt.	Physical properties
6	Benz-imidazolyl-cobamide coenzyme	α-(Benz-imidazolyl)-5′-deoxadenosyl-cobamide; BC coenzyme	As Coenzyme B_{12}, but with 5,6-dimethylbenzimidazole replaced by benzimidazole	1551·6	small red or yellow cryst.+ variable H_2O
7	Biocytin	ε-*N*-Biotinoyl-L-lysine	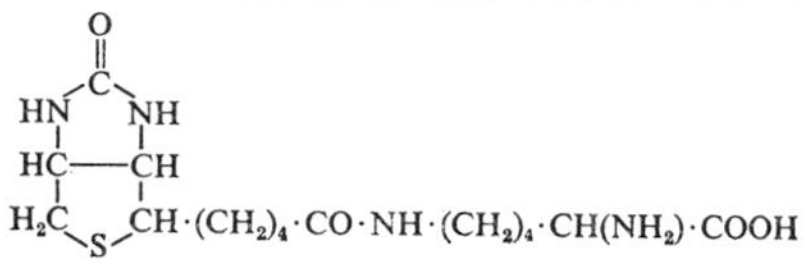	372·5	cryst.; M.p. 245–52 d. *J.A.C.S.* **74,** 19 (1952); $[\alpha]_D^{25}$ +53 (c = 1·05 in 0·1N-NaOH)
8	Biotin	*d*-Biotin; Coenzyme R; Vitamin H;	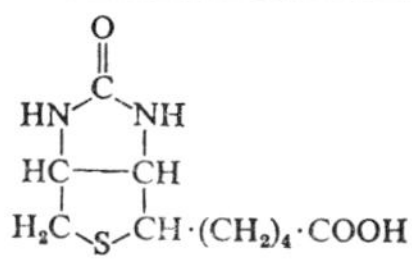	244·3	wh. needles; M.p. 232–3; $[\alpha]_D^{22}$ +92 (c = 0·3 in 0·1N-NaOH)
9	Coenzyme A	CoA; CoA·SH	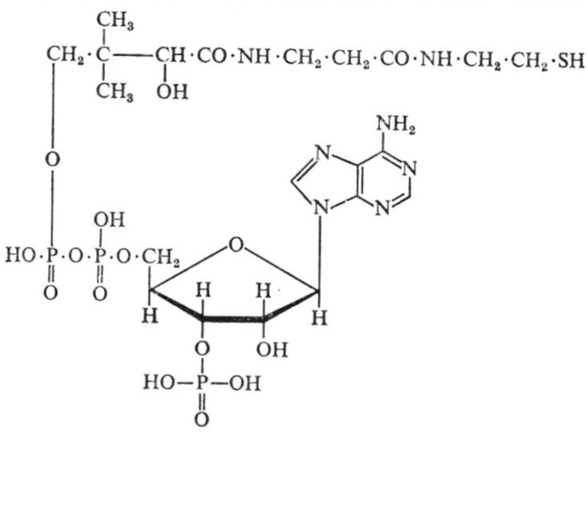	767·6	hygr. powder
10	Coenzyme B_{12}	α-(5,6-Dimethyl-benzimidazolyl)-cobamide coenzyme; 5′-Deoxyadenosyl-cobalamin; α-(5,6-Dimethyl-benzimidazolyl)-5′-deoxyadenosyl-cobamide; DMBC coenzyme	Cf. Cyanocobalamin, —CN group replaced by 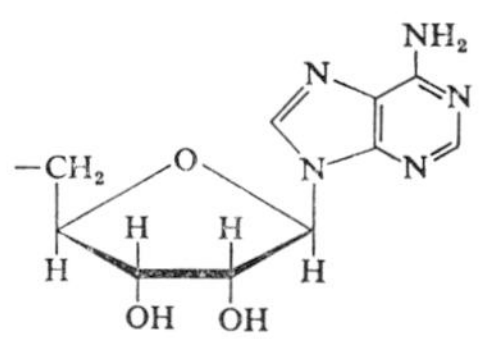	1579·6	flattened, diamond-shap red crystals; from H_2O or acet. contains 8–9% H_2O.

lubility	Absorption spectrum	Preparation	Estimation	General remarks
19^{22} H_2O; EtOH, phenol; acet., eth., oxane	In H_2O: λ_{max} 261 340 375 ϵ 34 700 12 300 10 200 λ_{max} 519 mμ ϵ 7650	*J.B.C.* **235**, 480 (1960)	*J.B.C.* **236**, 2347, PC1 (1961) *Biochem. Preps.* **10**, 28 (1963)	Stability similar to Coenzyme B_{12}.
H_2O, gl. etic; i. acet.	I.r. spectrum, *J.A.C.S.* **74**, 1999 (1952)	ISOL. *J.A.C.S.* **74**, 1996 (1952) SYN. *J.A.C.S.* **74**, 2002 (1952)	After acid hydrolysis to yield biotin *J.A.C.S.* **74**, 1996 (1952)	Complete hydrolysis requires 3N-H_2SO_4 at 120° for 1 hr. Combines with avidin.
2^{25} H_2O; in hot H_2O+ . alkali; 8^{25} EtOH; organic vents. salt, v.s. H_2O		SYN. *Comprehensive Biochemistry*, eds. Florkin and Stotz, vol. 11, p. 69, Elsevier (1963)	*The Vitamins*, 2nd ed., vol. 7, p. 303 (1967) *Methods of Vitamin Assay*, 3rd ed., p. 245 (1966) *J. Bact.* **69**, 67 (1955) *Analyt. Biochem.* **3**, 31 (1962)	Thermostable as solid. Stable at 100° in moderately acid or neutral aq. soln., less stable above pH 9. Inactivated by avidin (a glycoprotein). REVIEW. *Vitams Horm.* **18**, 1 (1960); **22**, 1 (1964).
H_2O; cet., eth.	pH 2·5–11·0: λ_{max} 257 mμ 16 840	SYN. *J.A.C.S.* **83**, 663 (1961) ISOL. *Meth. Enzymol.* **3**, 907 (1957)	*Meth. biochem. Anal.* **2**, 189 (1955) *Meth. Enzymol.* **3**, 913 (1957)	Store solid at 0° over desiccant Purified material often contains some mixed disulphides especially with glutathione. Pure coenzyme A contains 413 Lipmann units per mg. Solns. unstable above pH 7, relatively stable pH 2–6, store frozen.
^{24} H_2O; tOH, phenol; cet., eth., xane	In H_2O: λ_{max} 260 340 375 ϵ 34 700 12 300 10 900 λ_{max} 522 mμ ϵ 8000	*Biochem. Preps.* **10**, 27 (1963), **12**, 124 (1968) *Arch. B.B.* **92**, 381 (1961) *J.C.S.* **1963**, 4146 *J.B.C.* **236**, 2119 (1961)	*J.B.C.* **236**, 2347, PC1 (1961) *Biochem. Preps.* **10**, 28 (1963)	Dry cryst. stable for months at 0° in the dark; slowly decomp. by light at room temp. Aq. soln. rapidly decomp. by u.v. or visible light. In dark, solns. most stable at pH 6–7; dil. aq. solns. stable for months at −10°. Acid soln. turns yellow. Heating in acid or alkaline soln. causes slow inactivation. Reacts with alkaline cyanide to give dicyanocobalamin. REVIEW. *Ann. N.Y. Acad. Sci.* **112**, 547 (1964).

No.	Name	Synonyms	Formula	M. wt.	Physical properties
11	Crotonoyl coenzyme A	*trans*-Crotonyl-S-CoA	Cf. Coenzyme A, —SH replaced by —S·CO·CH=CH—CH_3	835·6	
12	Cyanocobalamin	Vitamin B_{12}; α-(5,6-Dimethylbenzimidazolyl)-cobamide cyanide	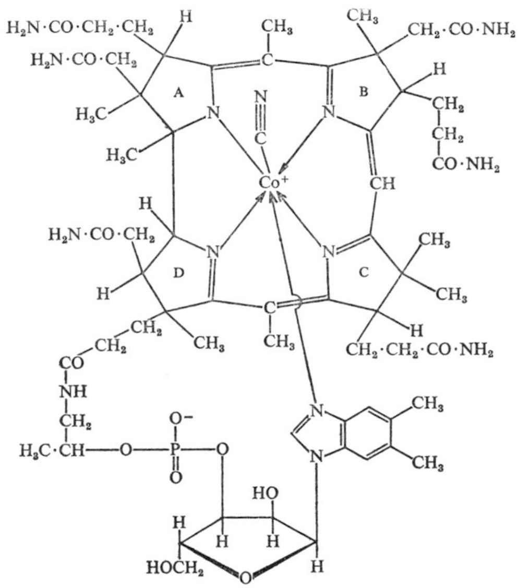	1355·4	cherry-red needles or prisms + variab[le] H_2O; M.p. > 320; Diamagnetic; $[\alpha]^{20}_{6438}$ −110 (c = 0·5 in H_2[O])
13	Dehydroascorbic acid	Dehydro-L-ascorbic acid; Oxidized vitamin C	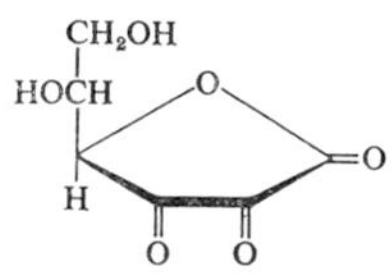	174·1	wh. needles; M.p. 225 d.; $[\alpha]^{20}_{D}$ +50 (c = 1 in H_2O) +56 (c = 1 in phthalate-HCl, pH 3·6)
14	7-Dehydrocholesterol	Provitamin D_3	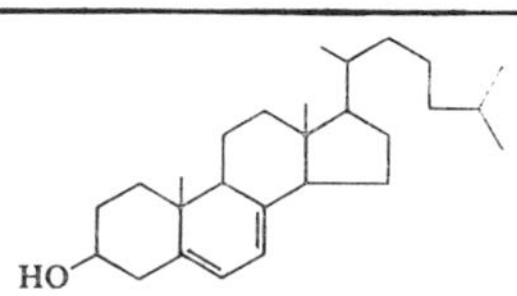	384·7; Hydrate, 402·7	plates + $1H_2O$ from MeOH-e[ther]; M.p. 149–50; $[\alpha]^{20}_{D}$ −124 (in $CHCl_3$)
15	Dihydronicotinamide adenine dinucleotide	Reduced nicotinamide adenine dinucleotide; $NADH_2$; $NADH+H^+$; Dihydrodiphosphopyridine nucleotide; DPNH	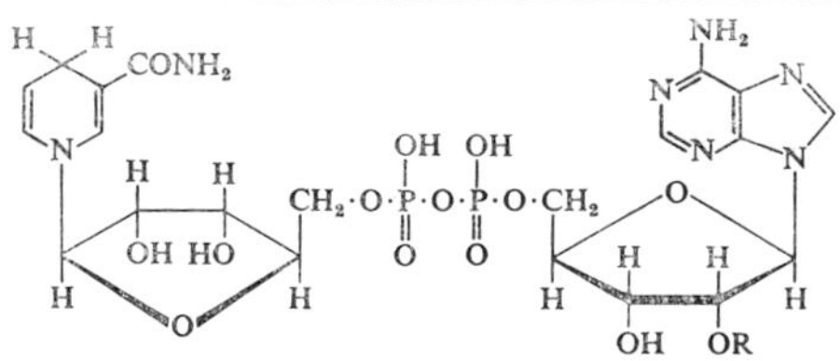 R (at 2′ of adenosine) = —H	665·5	
	—, Na_2 salt		$Na_2\cdot NADH_2$	709·5	
	—, Na_2 salt hydrate		$Na_2\cdot NADH_2\cdot 4H_2O$	781·5	

olubility	Absorption spectrum	Preparation	Estimation	General remarks
H_2O	λ_{max} (ε) 260 mμ (22 600) and 225 mμ (16 300). On hydrolysis of thio-ester bond $\Delta\epsilon_{225}$ 8400, $\Delta\epsilon_{263}$ 6400. See general remarks.	*Meth. Enzymol.* **1**, 560 (1955) *See also* Acyl-CoA compds.	*Meth. Enzymol.* **1**, 561 (1955) Bergmeyer, *Methods of Enzymatic Analysis*, p. 437, Academic Press (1963) *See also* Acyl-CoA compds.	Properties and methods apply to all α,β-unsaturated acyl-CoA compds. More stable in alkali than saturated acyl-CoA compds. Thioester absorption band is shifted to 263 mμ by α,β-double bond and is superimposed on adenine absorption at 260 mμ. Interference by adenine may be overcome by addition of AMP to reference cell or by use of *S*-crotonyl-*N*-acetylcysteamine, etc.
2 H_2O; alcohols, phatic acids, enols; pyridine	In H_2O: λ_{max} 278 361 550 mμ ε 15 600 27 700 8550	*Science* **107**, 396 (1948) *Proc. R. Soc.* **B136**, 592 (1949–50)	*Meth. biochem. Anal.* **1**, 81 (1954), **14**, 53 (1966) *Vitams Horm.* **13**, 101 (1955) *Analyt. Chem.* **24**, 1155 (1952) *Analyst* **81**, 435 (1956) *J. Protozool.* **3**, 101 (1956) *Br. J. Nutr.* **7**, 299 (1953) *The Vitamins*, 2nd ed., vol. 7, p. 277 (1967)	Commercial samples usually contain 10–12% H_2O, removable by heating under reduced pressure. Stable as solid. Aq. solns. photolabile giving hydroxocobalamin, prolonged exposure causes irreversible destruction. Solns. most stable at pH 4–6; may be kept for years in dark at room temperature in neutral or faintly acid soln. at conc. above 0·1 μg/ml. May be sterilized by autoclaving at 120°. In strongly acid and esp. alk. solns. slow hydrolysis of amide gps. occurs at room temperature. Vitamin B_{12} activity completely destroyed by heating in alk. soln. Reduced by thioglycollate but *not* by ascorbic acid. Reacts with alk. cyanide to form purple dicyanocobalamin. REVIEWS. E. Lester Smith, *Vitamin B_{12}*, 3rd ed., Methuen (1965); *Chem. Rev.* **63**, 573 (1963); *Adv. Enzymol.* **26**, 233 (1964).
ot H_2O, c organic ents; utral organic ents	No selective absorption in u.v.	*J.B.C.* **176**, 529 (1948) *J.C.S.* **1948**, 158	*Meth. biochem. Anal.* **1**, 115 (1954) *Methods of Vitamin Assay*, 3rd ed., p. 287 (1966)	Aq. solns. much less stable than ascorbic acid. pH of aq. soln. approx. neutral.
h., $CHCl_3$; MeOH; O	In EtOH: λ_{max} 262 271 282 ε .. 10 470 10 920 λ_{max} 293·5 mμ ε 6300	SYN. *Ann.* **520**, 98 (1935) L. F. and M. Fieser, *Steroids*, p. 153, Reinhold (1959)	*The Vitamins*, 1st ed., vol. 2, p. 201 (1954)	Oxidizes in air. Stable as paste containing 17% MeOH or when crystallized with cholesterol or as 3,5-dinitrobenzoate (M.p. 210–12). Digitonin complex insoluble. Forms vitamin D_3 on u.v. irradiation.
O))	At pH 7·5: λ_{max} 259 338 mμ ε 16 900 6220 λ_{min} 234 290 mμ ε 6600 1300	*Biochem. Preps.* **2**, 92 (1952) *Meth. Enzymol.* **3**, 885 887 (1957)	*Meth. Enzymol.* **3**, 890 (1957) *Meth. Enzymol.* **6**, 792 (1963)	Store solid at 0° in desiccator. Solid labile when moist. Inhibitor formed on exposure to moist air or on freezing and thawing soln., *B.B.A.* **54**, 210 (1961). Soln. decomposes slowly 0·7% per hour at 38° and pH 7 in maleate, rate faster in phosphate. Stable in alk. soln., 0·1N-NaOH at 100° for 10 min has no effect. Enzymically prep. $NADH_2$ destroyed at pH 4 or below at R.T. $NADH_2$ prep. by dithionite reduction, and so containing sulphite, is less stable and decomp. at pH 7. Stability and storage, see *J.B.C.* **236**, 2756 (1961).

No.	Name	Synonyms	Formula	M. wt.	Physical properties
16	Dihydro-nicotinamide adenine dinucleotide phosphate	Reduced nicotin-amide adenine dinucleotide phosphate; $NADPH_2$; $NADPH+H^+$; Dihydrotri-phosphopyridine nucleotide; TPNH	Cf. Dihydronicotinamide adenine dinucleotide, $R = -P(=O)(OH)OH$	745·4	
	—, Na_4 salt		$Na_4 \cdot NADPH_2$	833·4	
17	Dihydro-pteroyl-glutamic acid	7,8-Dihydro-pteroylglutamic acid; Dihydrofolic acid; DHFA	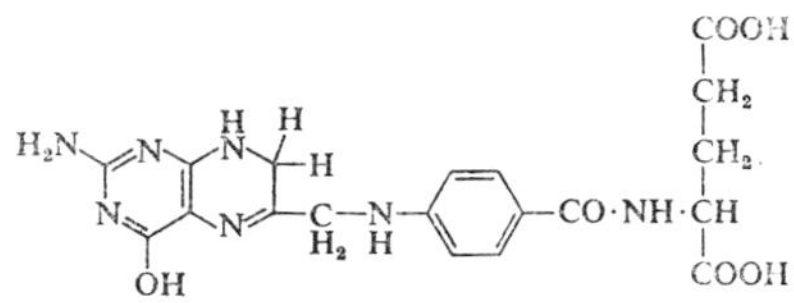	443·4	wh. needles+ $2\frac{1}{2}H_2O$ when dri at 25° over P_2O_5 become yellow o storage; NMR spectrum, *J.A.C.S.* **85**, 305 (1963)
18	Dolichol		$H(CH_2-C(CH_3)=CH-CH_2)_{19}-CH_2-CH(CH_3)-CH_2-CH_2OH$	1382·4	col. viscous liq. M.p. −10
19	Ergosterol	Provitamin D_2	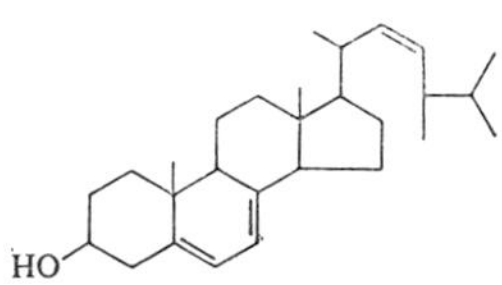	396·7; Hy-drate, 414·7	anhyd. needles from eth., M.p. 163; plates+$1H_2O$ from EtOH, M.p. 163; $[\alpha]_D$ −133 (c = 1·6 in $CHCl_3$)
20	Fatty acyl coenzyme A	Fatty acyl-CoA	Cf. Coenzyme A, —SH replaced by —S·CO·R where R·CO— = fatty acid radical	Butyryl, 837·6; Palmi-toyl, 1006·0	
21	Flavin adenine dinucleotide	FAD	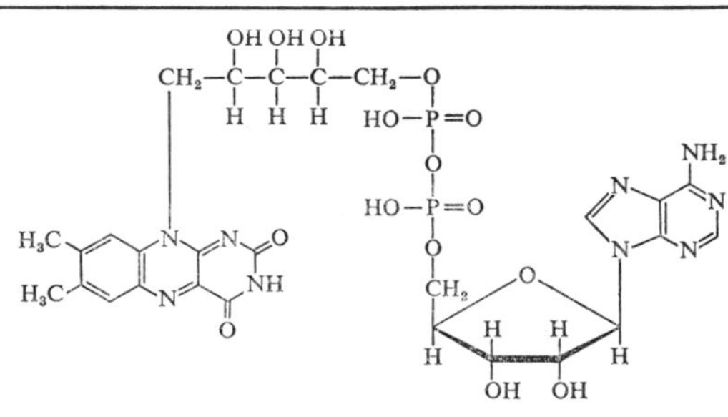	785·6	orange hygr powder; E_0' −0·219 v (p 30°)
	—, Na salt		NaH·FAD	807·6	

olubility	*Absorption spectrum*	*Preparation*	*Estimation*	*General remarks*
H_2O	At pH 7·5: λ_{max} 259 339 mμ ε 16 900 6200 λ_{min} 236 290 mμ ε 7600 1400	*Meth. Enzymol.* **3**, 887 (1957)	*Meth. Enzymol.* 3, 890 (1957) *Meth. Enzymol.* **6**, 792 (1963)	Keep solid at 0° in desiccator. Stability of solns. qualitatively similar to that of $NADH_2$, i.e. stable in alk., slow decomp. at neutral pH, v. unstable in acid but $NADPH_2$ is quantitatively somewhat less stable than $NADH_2$. See *J.B.C.* **236**, 2756 (1961).
H_2O				
	At pH 7·4 in 0·04M-tris-HCl-0·01M-mercapto-ethanol, λ_{max} 282 mμ, ε 28 000 (values of 19 000–22 000 also reported) *J.B.C.* **237**, 3794 (1962)	*Meth. Enzymol.* **6**, 801 (1963) *Nature, Lond.* **188**, 231 (1960) *J.A.C.S.* **69**, 250 (1947) *J.B.C.* **237**, 3794 (1962) *J.B.C.* **230**, 271 (1958)	*J.B.C.* **230**, 271 (1958) CHROMATOGRAPHY, *Meth. Enzymol.* **6**, 802 (1963)	Decomp. about 50% overnight at room temp. at pH 6. Mercaptoethanol protects. Unstable above pH 6. Stable at 0° for several days as suspension in 0·005N-HCl. Store *in vacuo* or in 0·005N-HCl at 0°. Material prep. by reduction with H_2 and PtO_2 in alkali liable to contain traces of tetrahydropteroyl-glutamic acid.
th., light pet.; s. EtOH; H_2O	*p*-Phenylazobenzoate: λ_{max} 324 mμ $E^{1\%}_{1\,cm}$ 171·4 *p*-Nitrobenzoate: λ_{max} 256 mμ $E^{1\%}_{1\,cm}$ 195	*Nature, Lond.* **186**, 470 (1960) *B.J.* **88**, 470 (1963)	*B.J.* **82**, 454 (1962)	
ot $CHCl_3$, z.; sl. s. OH, EtOH, , light pet.; $_2O$	In EtOH: λ_{max} 262 271 282 ε .. 11 090 11 500 λ_{max} 293·5 mμ ε 6450	*J.A.C.S.* **67**, 609 (1945) *Annls Chim. Phys.* [8] **15**, 313 (1908) *Analyst* **78**, 509 (1953)	*Analyst* **78**, 509, 514, 519, 524 (1953)	Oxidizes in air. Store *in vacuo*, cold and in the dark. Forms sp. s. digitonide. Forms Vitamin D_2 on u.v. irradiation.
. in H_2O eases with :asing chain :h of fatty . Long chain acid derivs. . from aq. by acid.	*See* Acyl-CoA compds. Palmitoyl-CoA, ϵ_{260} 16 400, ϵ_{232} 9400	Palmitoyl-CoA, *Biochem. Preps.* **7**, 80 (1960) *See also* Acyl-CoA compds.	Bergmeyer, *Methods of Enzymatic Analysis*, p. 433, Academic Press (1963) *J.B.C.* **204**, 329 (1953) *Meth. Enzymol.* **3**, 931 (1957)	Stability, see Acyl-CoA compds.
H_2O; r., phenol;)H, eth., , $CHCl_3$	In 0·1M-PO_4 buffer, pH 7: λ_{max} 263 375 450 mμ ε 38 000 9300 11 300 ϵ_{260} 37 000 Fluorescence max., 530 mμ Reduced form, ϵ_{450} 980	SYN. *J.C.S.* **1954**, 46 *J.B.C.* **223**, 569 (1956) *J.A.C.S.* **80**, 3756 (1958) ISOL. *Meth. Enzymol.* **3**, 950 (1957) *Biochem. Preps.* **7**, 51 (1960)	*J.B.C.* **223**, 559 (1956) *Meth. Enzymol.* **3**, 955, 960 (1957) *Meth. biochem. Anal.* **10**, 319 (1962)	Solid and neutral aq. solns. stable indefinitely at 0° in the dark. Cold dil. acids have no effect, but on heating hydrolysis to FMN occurs. In neutral soln. at 80° or higher and rapidly in alk. soln. hydrolysed to ribo-flavin-4′,5′-cyclic phosphate. In neutral soln. FAD less photo-labile than FMN or riboflavin, but v. photolabile in alk. soln. All solns. best kept dark. Reduced to colourless dihydro compound by dithionite, Na amalgam, Zn+acid or H_2+ catalyst; dihydro compd. v. readily autoxidizable.

No.	Name	Synonyms	Formula	M. wt.	Physical properties
22	Flavin mono-nucleotide	Riboflavin-5′-phosphate; FMN	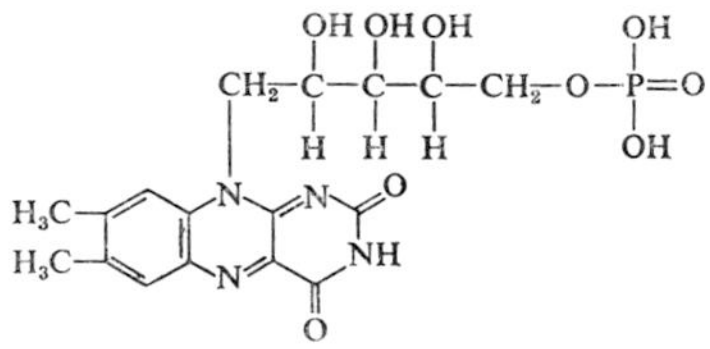	456·4	orange sl. hygr. powder; general 2–3 moles H_2O per mole FMN free acid and N salts; E_0' −0·219 v (pH 7, 30°)
	—, Na salt		NaH·FMN	478·3	hygr.
	—, Na salt hydrate		NaH·FMN·$2H_2O$	514·4	
23	N^5-Formyl-tetrahydro-pteroyl-glutamic acid	*dl*-form: Folinic acid SF; Leucovorin. *l*-form: Citrovorum factor	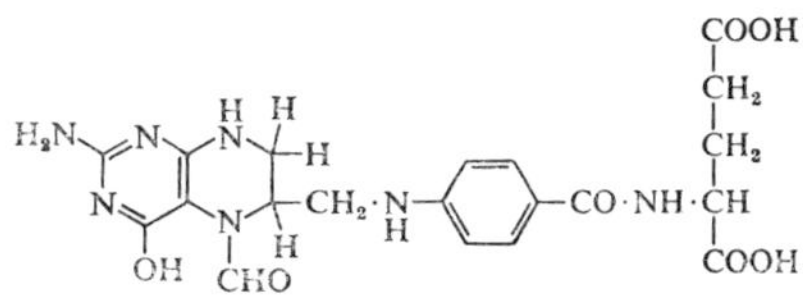	473·4; Hy-drate, 527·5	lt. cream cryst. $3H_2O$ from formate, pH 3· H_2O lost at 100 high vacuum fo 2 hr; M.p. 248 50 d.; pK_a 1. 3·1 2. 4·8 3. 10·4; $[\alpha]_D^{25}$ +16·8 (c = 3·5 anhyd in 5% NaHCO pH 8·36)
	—, Ca salt		$C_{20}H_{21}N_7O_7·Ca·5H_2O$	601·6	
24	N^{10}-Formyl-tetrahydro-pteroyl-glutamic acid	'Active formate'	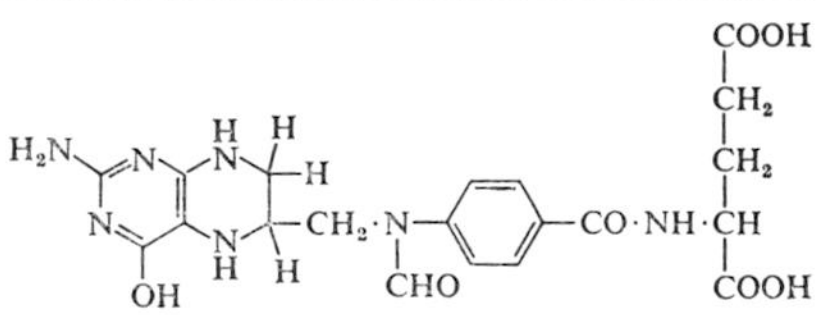	473·4	Has not been isolated as sol
25	Hydroxo-cobalamin	Aquocobalamin; Vitamin B_{12a}; Vitamin B_{12b}; α-(5,6-Dimethyl-benzimidazolyl)-hydroxocobamide	In alkaline soln., OH^- replaces CN in Cyanocobalamin. In acid soln., H_2O replaces CN in Cyanocobalamin	Hy-droxo, 1346·4; Aquo, 1347·4	dark red cryst recryst. from aq. acet.; $[\alpha]_{6438}^{20}$ −19·5 (c = 0·5 in H
26	β-Hydroxy-acyl coenzyme A	β-Hydroxyacyl-CoA	Cf. Coenzyme A, —SH replaced by —S·CO·CH_2·CHOH·R	β-Hydroxy-butyryl, 853·6; β-Hydroxy-β-methyl-glutaryl, 911·7	
27	Hydroxy-ethylthiamin pyro-phosphate	'Active acet-aldehyde'; α-Hydroxyethyl-2-thiamin pyrophosphate; 2-Hydroxyethyl-TPP; HETPP	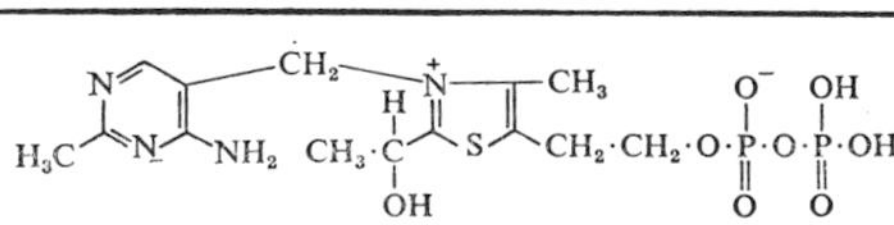	468·4	

ɔlubility	Absorption spectrum	Preparation	Estimation	General remarks
H_2O, gl. acetic, ·r., phenol; acet., eth., HCl_3 . H_2O	In 0·1M-PO_4 buffer, pH 7: λ_{max} 266 373 445 mμ ε 31 800 10 400 12 500 λ_{ref} 260 375 450 mμ ε 27 100 10 400 12 200 Fluorescence max., 530 mμ Reduced form, ϵ_{450} 870	SYN. *J.C.S.* **1950**, 3295 ISOL. *Meth. Enzymol.* **3**, 957 (1957)	*Meth. Enzymol.* **3**, 958 (1957) *Meth. biochem. Anal.* **10**, 319 (1962)	Most stable at about pH 6. Neutral solns. stable at 100°. In acid soln. phosphate ester bond hydrolysed, in alk. soln. ring–ribitol bond unstable. NH_4 salt v. unstable. Rapidly photolysed at all pHs, but esp. in alk. soln. Store in dark. Reduced to colourless dihydro compound by dithionite, Na amalgam, Zn+ acid or H_2+catalyst; dihydro compound v. readily autoxidizable.
H_2O ɪ$_2$O	At pH 13: λ_{max} 282 mμ ε 32 600	SYN. *J.A.C.S.* **73**, 3067 (1951) *J.A.C.S.* **74**, 3247 (1952) ISOL. *J.A.C.S.* **73**, 5510 (1951) *J.B.C.* **195**, 337 (1952)	*Meth. biochem. Anal.* **2**, 121 (1955) *J. Bact.* **71**, 433 (1956) *Meth. Enzymol.* **6**, 383 (1963) By conversion to N^5,N^{10}-methenyltetrahydropteroylglutamic acid (q.v.) with acid; see *J.A.C.S.* **73**, 3067 (1951) *J.A.C.S.* **74**, 3252 (1952)	Solid stable indefinitely in air. V. unstable in acid soln. due to cyclization of formyl group to N^5,N^{10}-methenyltetrahydropteroylglutamic acid. Stable in neutral or alk. soln.; *not* susceptible to oxidation by air. Naturally occurring form is *l*,L-compound, *J.A.C.S.* **74**, 4215 (1952), $[\alpha]_D$ −15·1 (c = 1·8 anhyd. Ca salt in H_2O).
ɪ$_2$O	At pH 7·5: λ_{max} 260 mμ ε 17 000 ϵ_{300} 8500 ϵ_{340} 2170 *B.J.* **74**, 71 (1960)	*Meth. Enzymol.* **6**, 814 (1963) *J.A.C.S.* **73**, 3067 (1951) *J.A.C.S.* **74**, 3247 (1952) *J.B.C.* **237**, 2903 (1962) *Analyt. Biochem.* **6**, 100 (1963)	*J.B.C.* **237**, 2915 (1962) *Meth. Enzymol.* **6**, 373, 375 (1963)	Rapidly oxidized in air, mercaptoethanol protects. In acid cyclizes to form N^5,N^{10}-methenyltetrahydropteroylglutamic acid. On heating in alk. isomerizes to N^5-formyltetrahydropteroylglutamic acid.
	In H_2O: λ_{max} 273 351 525 mμ ε 18 400 22 300 7560	*J.A.C.S.* **71**, 2952 (1949) *J.A.C.S.* **73**, 335, 337 (1951) *B.J.* **52**, 389 (1952) *Biochem. Preps.* **12**, 121 (1968)		Highly photolabile. Somewhat less stable than cyanocobalamin esp. in alk. soln. On treatment with alk. cyanide forms same purple dicyanide complex as does cyanocobalamin. Destroyed by ascorbic acid.
O	*See* Acyl-CoA compds.	β-Hydroxybutyryl-CoA, *Angew. Chem.* **65**, 186 (1953) β-Hydroxy-β-methylglutaryl-CoA, *B.Z.* **329**, 476 (1958) *See also* Acyl-CoA compds.	Bergmeyer, *Methods of Enzymatic Analysis*, pp. 441, 445, Academic Press (1963) *See also* Acyl-CoA compds.	Stability similar to most acyl-CoA compds., though somewhat more sensitive to alkali.
ɔ	In PO_4 buffer, pH 8: λ_{max} 229 269 mμ ε .. 7700 λ_{min} 248 mμ ε 4450 (lower than TPP, ϵ_{248} 5900). In PO_4 buffer, pH 5: λ_{max} 248 262 mμ. Isosbestic point (pH 5–8) 270·5 mμ *B.B.A.* **62**, 1 (1962)	*B.B.R.C.* **5**, 447 (1961) *B.Z.* **337**, 345 (1963)	*B.B.A.* **62**, 1 (1962)	Synthetic compd. is a racemic mixture of which only one isomer is enzymically active. Soln. relatively stable pH 3–8, most stable at pH 7. Decomp. in acid and esp. alk. soln.

No.	Name	Synonyms	Formula	M. wt.	Physical properties
28	Inositol	*meso*-Inositol; *myo*-Inositol; i-Inositol	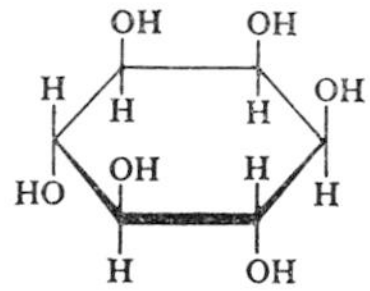	180·2; Hydrate, 216·2	wh. cryst.+$2H_2$ efflor.; hydrate becomes anhyd. 100°; M.p., Hydrate 225, Anhyd. 2
29	Lactoyl coenzyme A	Lactoyl-CoA; Lactyl-CoA	Cf. Coenzyme A, —SH replaced by —S·CO·CHOH·CH_3	839·6	
30	Lipoic acid	α-(+)-Lipoic acid; Thioctic acid; 6,8-Dithiooctanoic acid; 1,2-Dithiolane-3-valeric acid	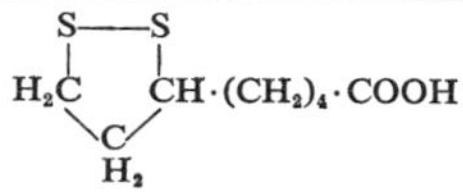	206·3	pale yel. platele M.p. 47·5; pK_a 4·7; $[\alpha]_D^{25}$ +96·7 (c = 1·88 in benz.); E_0' −0·325 v (pH 7, 25°); DL-, M.p. 61
31	Malonyl coenzyme A	Malonyl-CoA; Malonyl-S-CoA	Cf. Coenzyme A, —SH replaced by —S—CO·CH_2·COOH	853·6	
32	N^5,N^{10}-Methenyl-tetrahydro-pteroyl-glutamic acid	'Active formate'; 5,10-Methylidyne-tetrahydropteroyl-glutamic acid; N^5,N^{10}-Anhydro-formyltetrahydro-folic acid; Anhydro-leucovorin; Isoleucovorin	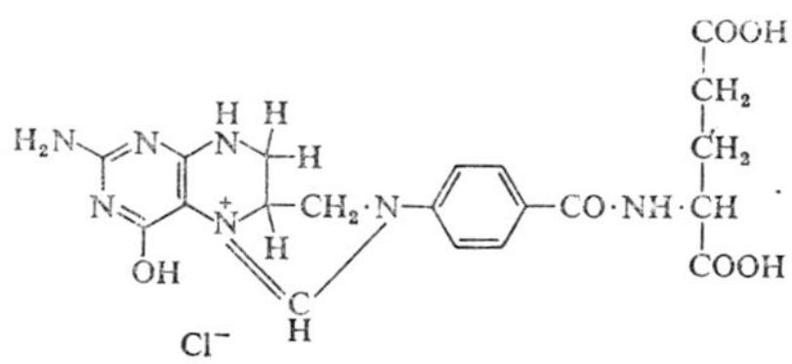	Chloride, 491·9; Internal salt, 455·4	several cryst. forms, *J.A.C.S.* **74**, 3252 (1952) yel. cryst. from HCl, pH < 1·3, chloride (iso-leucovorin chloride), M.p. 250–1 d.; recryst. of chloride at pH gives hair-like needles of inte salt (anhydro-leucovorin A), M.p. 250–7 d.
33	Methyl-cobalamin	Methyl B_{12}; α-(5,6-Dimethyl-benzimidazolyl)-methylcobamide	CH_3 replacing CN group in Cyanocobalamin	1344·4	deep red needl
34	N^5,N^{10}-Methylene-tetrahydro-pteroyl-glutamic acid	'Active form-aldehyde'	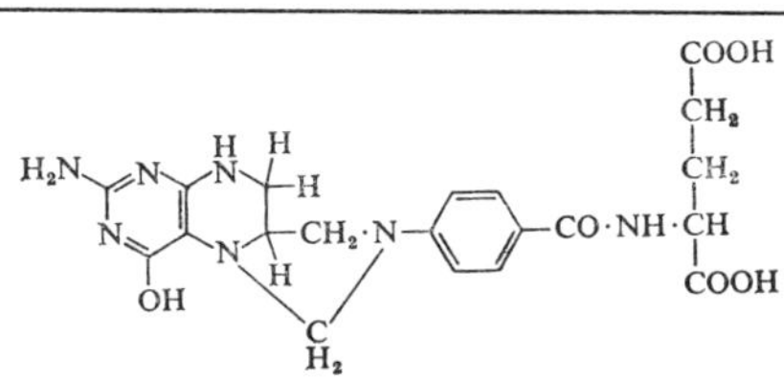	457·4	Not isolated a solid
35	N^5-Methyl-tetrahydro-pteroyl-glutamic acid	Prefolic A	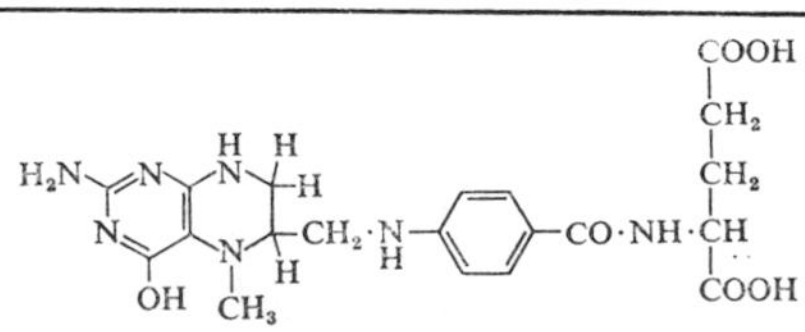	459·5	Na salt, wh. amorph. powd

Solubility	Absorption spectrum	Preparation	Estimation	General remarks
4[25] H_2O; 1. s. EtOH; . other organic olvents		ISOL. *J.B.C.* **139**, 29 (1941) SYN. *J.A.C.S.* **70**, 2931 (1948) *Helv. chim. Acta* **33**, 1597 (1950)	*Meth. biochem. Anal.* **7**, 115 (1959) *B.J.* **65**, 24 (1957) *B.J.* **67**, 523 (1957) *Fed. Proc.* **16**, 209 (1957) *J.B.C.* **225**, 575 (1957)	Hexaacetate, M.p. 216.
. H_2O	*See* Acyl-CoA compds.	*Meth. Enzymol.* **6**, 544 (1963)	*See* Acyl-CoA compds.	Cannot be prepared by usual methods for synthesis of acyl thioesters. Stability, see Acyl-CoA compds.
. H_2O; .s. benz., tOH, MeOH; . s. pet. eth.; e cryst. from et. eth. or yclohexane	In MeOH: λ_{max} 330 mμ ε 150	*Science* **114**, 93 (1951) *J.A.C.S.* **77**, 416, 5144 (1955) *J.A.C.S.* **76**, 1828 (1954)	*Meth. biochem. Anal.* **3**, 23 (1956) *Meth. Enzymol.* **3**, 941 (1957)	Reduced by borohydride to dihydrolipoic acid, $[\alpha]_D^{20}$ −14·5 (c = 0·6 in benz.), *Meth. Enzymol.* 3, 944 (1957). REVIEW: *Vitams Horm.* **20**, 1 (1962).
H_2O	*See* Acyl-CoA compds. $\Delta\epsilon_{236}$ on hydrolysis 4900 (in 0·1M-PO_4 buffer, pH 7)	*Meth. Enzymol.* **6**, 540, 542, 545 (1963) *J.A.C.S.* **82**, 2972 (1962) *B.Z.* **335**, 540 (1962)	*Meth. Enzymol.* **6**, 543 (1963) *See also* Acyl-CoA compds.	General methods of preparation not applicable to malonyl-CoA, *J.B.C.* 235, 346 (1960). Stability, *see* Acyl-CoA compds.
H_2O	In 0·1N-HCl: λ_{max} 350 mμ ε 25 100 *J.B.C.* **239**, 106 (1964) *The Enzymes*, vol. 2, p. 185 (1960)	*Meth. Enzymol.* **6**, 806, 814 (1963) *J.A.C.S.* **73**, 5006 (1951) *J.A.C.S.* **74**, 3252 (1952)	*Meth. Enzymol.* **6**, 811, 815 (1963) *The Enzymes*, vol. 2, p. 185 (1960) *J.B.C.* **237**, 2903 (1962)	Solid and acid solns. stable in air. At pH 7 and above forms N^{10}-formyltetrahydropteroylglutamic acid; rate at pH 7 varies with buffer, maleate (half-life 40 min) > tris (9·4 min) > PO_4 (6 min) > pyrophosphate (4·8 min).
	λ_{max} 268 343 525 mμ ε 22 700 12 000 7600 *B.Z.* **336**, 299 (1962–3)	*B.Z.* **336**, 299 (1962–3) *J.B.C.* **238**, 3318 (1963) *J.C.S.* **1963**, 4146	*J.B.C.* **239**, 1944 (1964)	V. unstable to light forming hydroxocobalamin. Relatively insensitive to alkaline cyanide.
	At pH 7·0: λ_{max} 294 mμ ε 32 000 (also reported as 25 000) ϵ_{340} 1010 *J.A.C.S.* **82**, 4921 (1960)	*Meth. Enzymol.* **6**, 806 (1963) *J.A.C.S.* **82**, 4921 (1960) *J.B.C.* **238**, 1498 (1963)	*Meth. Enzymol.* **6**, 809 (1963)	Stable in air at pH 9·5 in the cold for several days. At neutral or acid pH dissociates into HCHO and tetrahydropteroylglutamic acid; at pH 7 dissociation essentially complete in 15 min. Stable in presence of excess HCHO and mercaptoethanol or ascorbic acid. Association constant (HCHO + tetrahydropteroylglutamic acid) at 22°: pH 4·3, $1{\cdot}3\times10^4$ M^{-1}; pH 7·2, $2{\cdot}1\times10^4$ M^{-1}. Enzymically active form is *d*,L-compound.
H_2O	At pH 7·0: λ_{max} 290 mμ ε 32 000 λ_{min} 245 mμ In 0·1N-HCl: λ_{max} 269 292 mμ	*Biochem. Preps.* **10**, 103 (1963) *B.J.* **105**, 633 (1967)	*J.B.C.* **237**, 1298 (1962) *J.B.C.* **238**, 1746 (1963)	Decomp. slowly in air, to form N^5-methyldihydropteroylglutamic acid, λ_{max} 249 and 290 mμ. Decomp. accelerated by heavy metal ions.

9. Vitamins and Coenzymes

No.	*Name*	*Synonyms*	*Formula*	*M. wt.*	*Physical properties*
36	Nicotinamide	Nicotinic acid amide; Niacinamide	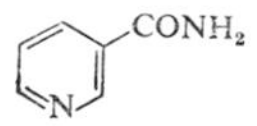	122·1	wh. needles; M.p. 128–31; recryst. from benz.; p*K* 1. 10·6 2. 13·5
37	Nicotinamide adenine dinucleotide	Diphospho-pyridine nucleotide; Coenzyme I; NAD; NAD^+; DPN; DPN^+; DPN_{ox}	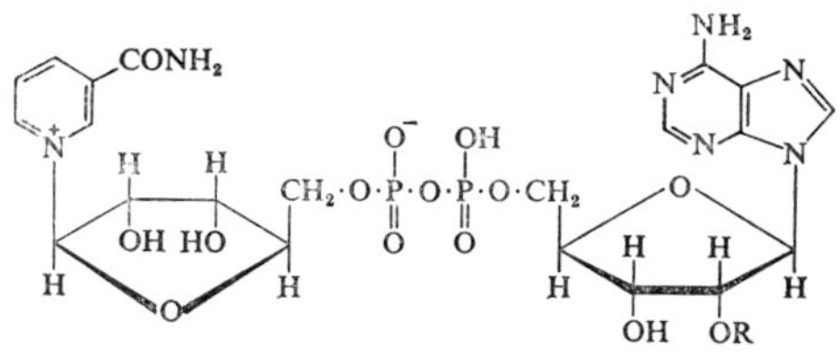 R (at 2′ of adenosine) = —H	663·4; Hy-drate + $4H_2O$, 735·5	wh. powder; v. hygr.; water content depends upon conditions of drying and storage; $[\alpha]_D^{23}$ −34·8 (c = 1 in H_2O); E_0' −0·318 v (pH 7, 30°)
38	Nicotinamide adenine dinucleotide phosphate	Triphospho-pyridine nucleotide; Coenzyme II; NADP; $NADP^+$; TPN; TPN^+; TPN_{ox}	Cf. Nicotinamide adenine dinucleotide, R = —P(OH)(OH)=O	743·4	wh. powder; v. hygr.; pK_a 1. 3·9 2. 6·1; E_0' −0·317 v (pH 7, 30°)
	—, sodium salt		$NaH_2\cdot$NADP	765·4	
39	Nicotinamide mono-nucleotide	Nicotinamide ribotide; NMN	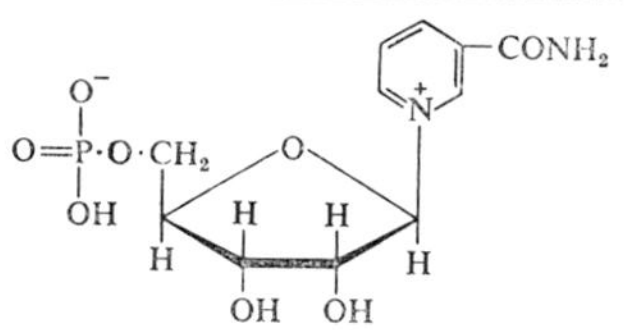	334·2	$[\alpha]_D$ −38·3 (c = 1 in H_2O)
40	Nicotinic acid	Niacin; Pyridine-3-carboxylic acid; Pellagra-preventive factor	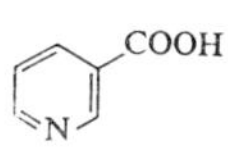	123·1	wh. needles; melts 236–7 then sublimes; pK_a 1. 4·82 2. 12·0
41	β-Oxoacyl coenzyme A	β-Ketoacyl coenzyme A; β-Oxoacyl-CoA	Cf. Coenzyme A, —SH replaced by $—S\cdot CO\cdot CH_2\cdot CO\cdot R$	Aceto-acetyl, 851·6; β-Oxo-oct-anoyl, 907·7	

Solubility	*Absorption spectrum*	*Preparation*	*Estimation*	*General remarks*
100 H_2O; 66 EtOH; s. acet., $CHCl_3$; sl. s. benz., eth.	In H_2O: λ_{max} 261·5 mμ; ε varies with pH; *J. phys. Colloid Chem.* **55**, 173 (1951)		*The Vitamins*, 2nd ed., vol. 7, p. 137 (1967) *B.J.* **44**, 343 (1949) *Naturwissenschaften* **44**, 617 (1957) *Acta chem. scand.* **15**, 823 (1961)	Stable as dry solid below 50°. In aq. soln. may be autoclaved at 120° for 20 min but is hydrolysed to nicotinic acid in acid and alkaline solution.
. H_2O	At pH 7·5: λ_{max} 259 mμ; ε 17 800; λ_{min} 230 mμ; ε 8000	ISOL. *Biochem. Preps.* **3**, 20 (1953) *Meth. Enzymol.* **3**, 876, 882 (1957) *J.B.C.* **239**, PC 3598 (1964) *Biochem. Preps.* **11**, 84 (1966) ^{14}C. *Biochem. Preps.* **11**, 89 (1966) SYN. *J.C.S.* **1957**, 3733	*Meth. Enzymol.* **3**, 890 (1957) *Meth. Enzymol.* **6**, 792 (1963)	Solid stable in desiccator at 0° or R.T. Neutral or sl. acid (pH between 3 and 7) soln. stable at 0° for at least 2 weeks. Solns. decomp. rapidly on heating. V. labile in alk. soln., decomp. accelerated by phosphate, maleate, and carbonate. Stability, see *J.B.C.* **236**, 2756 (1961). Destroyed by u.v. light. Purified as quinine salt. Reduced by hydrosulphite. Only β-form is enzymically active.
H_2O	At pH 7: λ_{max} 259 mμ; ε 18 000; λ_{min} 231 mμ; ε 8100	*Biochem. Preps.* **3**, 24 (1953) *Meth. Enzymol.* **3**, 879 (1957) *Biochem. Preps.* **11**, 87 (1966)	*Meth. Enzymol.* **3**, 890 (1957) *Meth. Enzymol.* **6**, 792 (1963)	Solid stable over desiccant at 0° or R.T. Soln. of free acid stable many weeks in cold. Stability generally similar to nicotinamide adenine dinucleotide but less stable in strong acid or dil. alk. See *J.B.C.* **236**, 2756 (1961).
H_2O; acet.	At pH 7·0: λ_{max} 266 mμ; ε 4600; λ_{min} 249 mμ; ε 3600	*Biochem. Preps.* **5**, 55 (1957) *Meth. Enzymol.* **3**, 900 (1957)	*Meth. Enzymol.* **3**, 899 (1957)	Resembles NAD in reaction with cyanide.
^{20}, v.s.^{100} O; EtOH, alkalis; s. benz., eth.	In H_2O: λ_{max} 261·5 mμ; ε varies with pH; *J. phys. Colloid Chem.* **53**, 414 (1949)	ISOL. *J.B.C.* **179**, 783 (1949) SYN. *J.A.C.S.* **63**, 2283 (1941)	*The Vitamins*, 2nd ed., vol. 7, p. 137 (1967) *B.J.* **44**, 343 (1949) *Naturwissenschaften* **44**, 617 (1957) *Acta chem. scand.* **15**, 823 (1961)	Very stable in air. Solid non-hygroscopic. Soln. in H_2O stable to autoclaving at 120° for 20 min. Stable in acid and alkaline solution.
I_2O	λ_{max} 260 mμ ε 16 000 and 303 mμ ε 22 000 (pH 8·8 in presence of 0·02M-$MgCl_2$). ϵ_{303} varies with pH and Mg^{++} conc., *J.B.C.* **205**, 575 (1953)	Acetoacetyl-CoA. *Meth. Enzymol.* **1**, 581 (1955) *Angew. Chem.* **65**, 186 (1953) β-Oxooctanoyl-CoA. *Analyt. Biochem.* **1**, 8 (1960) *Meth. Enzymol.* **6**, 546 (1963)	Bergmeyer, *Methods of Enzymatic Analysis*, p. 425, Academic Press (1963) *Meth. Enzymol.* **1**, 581 (1955) *See also* Acyl-CoA compds.	Stability, see Acyl-CoA compds. Reaction with neutral NH_2OH yields isoxazolones, *not* hydroxamic acids. Partially stabilized against alkaline hydrolysis by Mg^{++} ions.

No.	Name	Synonyms	Formula	M. wt.	Physical properties
42	Pantetheine	*Lactobacillus bulgaricus* factor; *N*-(Pantothenyl)-β-aminoethane-thiol	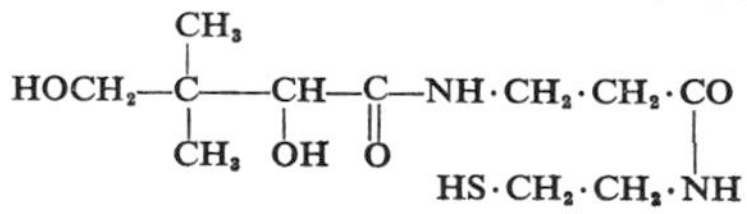	278·4	hygr. oil or resin
43	Pantothenic acid	D-(+)-*N*-(α,γ-Dihydroxy-β,β-dimethylbutyryl)-β-alanine	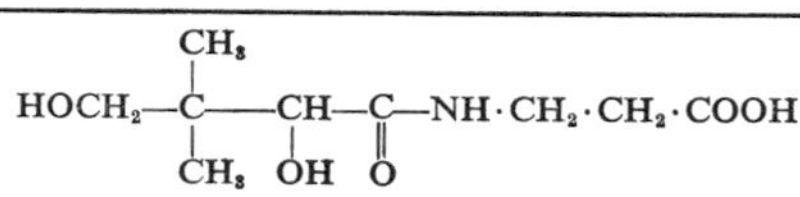	219·2	hygr. viscous oil; $[\alpha]_D^{25}$ +37·5 (in H_2O); pK_a 4·4
	—, Ca salt		$(C_9H_{16}NO_5)_2\cdot Ca$	476·5	wh. cryst.; moderately hygr. M.p. 196 d.; $[\alpha]_D^{25}$ +24·3 (c = 1·57 in H_2(
44	Plasto-quinone-45	Plastoquinone-9; Koflerquinone; Plastoquinone A; PQ-45; PQ_9; PQ-9	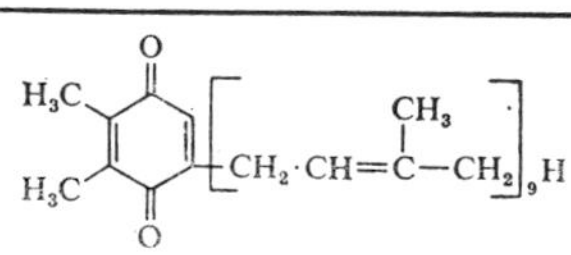	749·2	yellow cryst.; M.p. 48–49
45	Pteroic acid		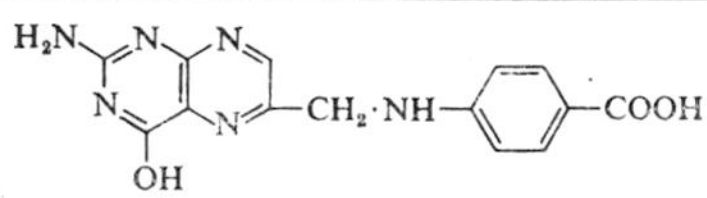	312·3	yel. cryst. powd
46	Pteroyl-glutamic acid	Folic acid; Vitamin B_c; Vitamin M; Liver *Lactobacillus casei* factor	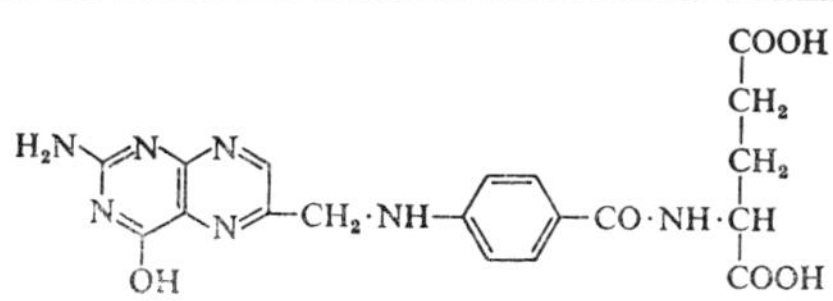	441·4; Hy-drate, 477·4	orange-yel. needles or plate-lets; samples dr below 140° con-tain 2 moles H_2 Decomp. 250; pK_a 8·2 (enolic OH); $[\alpha]_D^{20}$ +16 (c = 0·76 in 0·1N-NaOH)
47	Pyridoxal hydro-chloride		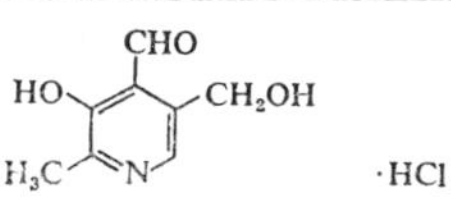	203·6	wh. rh. cryst.; M.p. 165 d.; pK_a 1. 4·23 (phenolic (2. 8·70 (pyridinium 3. 13·0
48	Pyridoxal phosphate	Pyridoxal-5′-phosphate; Codecarboxylase	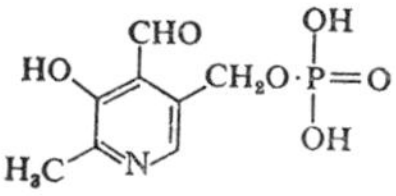	247·1; Hy-drate, 265·1	needles + $1H_2$(pK_a 1. < 2·5 (2. 4·14 (ph 3. 6·20 (4. 8·69 (pyridin

olubility	*Absorption spectrum*	*Preparation*	*Estimation*	*General remarks*
. H_2O, EtOH, th.		*Meth. Enzymol.* **3**, 918 (1957) *J.A.C.S.* **75**, 1694 (1953) *J.C.S.* **1952**, 800	*J. Bact.* **61**, 283 (1951) *Meth. Enzymol.* **3**, 923 (1957)	Readily oxidized to the disulphide, pantethine, $[\alpha]_D^{26}$ +16 (in H_2O). Store as pantethine and regenerate pantetheine by reduction with Na_2S or cysteine. *S*-Benzoylpantetheine, cryst., M.p. 116, $[\alpha]_D^{27}$ +31 (in H_2O), s. H_2O, full growth promoting activity, stable in neutral aq. soln. but hydrolyses rapidly in alk. to pantetheine and benzoate. REVIEW: *Adv. Enzymol.* **14**, 49 (1953).
s. H_2O, EtOH, . acetic; eth., acet.; benz., $CHCl_3$		SYN. *J.A.C.S.* **62**, 1785 (1940) *J.A.C.S.* **63**, 1237 (1941)	*The Vitamins*, 2nd ed., vol. 7, p. 209 (1967) *Methods of Vitamin Assay*, 3rd ed., p. 197 (1966)	Stable in neutral soln. Rapidly destroyed by acid, alk. or heat.
·5 H_2O; s. EtOH, et.				Reasonably stable to light and air. Soln. most stable at pH 5–7; not stable to autoclaving.
EtOH, eth., ht pet.; H_2O	In EtOH: Quinone: λ_{max} 255 mμ ϵ 15 200 Quinol: λ_{max} 290 mμ ϵ 3442	SYN. *Helv. chim. Acta* **42**, 2252 (1959) *J.A.C.S.* **81**, 5000 (1959) ISOL. *Pl. Physiol.* **34**, 546 (1959) *Helv. chim. Acta* **42**, 2252 (1959)	*Meth. biochem. Anal.* **11**, 279 (1963) *Phytochemistry* **1**, 147 (1962)	REVIEW: *Vitams Horm.* **24**, 291 et seq. (1966)
s. aq. NaOH, $_2CO_3$, HCO_3; il. acid	At pH 7·0: λ_{max} 280 350 mμ ϵ 27 800 7180 At pH 11·0: λ_{max} 256 275 365 mμ ϵ 25 800 24 000 8120 *J.A.C.S.* **69**, 2751 (1947)	*J.A.C.S.* **70**, 19, 23 (1948) *J.A.C.S.* **75**, 5893 (1953)	*J.A.C.S.* **70**, 19 (1948) *J.B.C.* **168**, 705 (1947) *J.B.C.* **205**, 361 (1953)	Growth factor activity only for *Streptococcus faecalis* and other Enterococci.
e acid: 0·001°, ^{100} H_2O; $_2O$ below 5; . gl. acetic; ost organic ents. salt, H_2O	At pH 7: λ_{max} 282 350 mμ ϵ 27 000 7000 At pH 13: λ_{max} 256 283 365 mμ ϵ 30 000 26 000 9800	ISOL. *J.A.C.S.* **70**, 3 (1948) SYN. *J.A.C.S.* **70**, 19, 23, 25, 27 (1948) *J.A.C.S.* **75**, 5893 (1953) *J.A.C.S.* **77**, 6365 (1955)	*J.B.C.* **205**, 361 (1953) *Meth. biochem. Anal.* **2**, 121 (1955) *Adv. Enzymol.* **21**, 390 (1959) *The Vitamins*, 2nd ed., vol. 7, p. 243 (1967)	Photolabile; inactivated by u.v. irradiation. Solid stable in dark. Alk. soln. reasonably stable in the dark. Destroyed by heat in acid or alk. soln. Naturally occurring forms may be polyglutamyl derivs. e.g. triglutamate = teropterin. REVIEW. *Adv. Enzymol.* **21**, 369 (1959); *Fortschr. Chem. org. NatStoffe* **21**, 183 (1963).
H_2O; 5% EtOH	At pH 7·0: λ_{max} 252 318 mμ ϵ .. 8200 In 0·1N-NaOH: λ_{max} 300 393 mμ ϵ 5800 1700 *J.A.C.S.* **76**, 169 (1954)	*J.B.C.* **154**, 315 (1944) *J.A.C.S.* **66**, 2088 (1944)	*Meth. biochem. Anal.* **12**, 183 (1964) *J.B.C.* **175**, 147 (1948) *J.B.C.* **176**, 1157 (1948)	Photolabile in soln. at neutral and particularly alk. pH. Solid and acid soln. relatively photostable. Neutral and acid solns. (up to 5N-H_2SO_4 or HCl) stable in heat, some destruction in hot strong alk. Forms Schiff bases with amines.
$_2O$; MeOH; s. EtOH; ICl_3, acet., .	In 0·05M-PO_4, pH 7·0: λ_{max} 330 388 mμ ϵ 2500 4900 In 0·1N-NaOH: λ_{max} 305 388 mμ ϵ 1100 6550 *J.A.C.S.* **76**, 169 (1954)	SYN. *J.A.C.S.* **73**, 3430 (1951) *Biochem. Preps.* **3**, 34 (1953) *Meth. Enzymol.* **3**, 965 (1957)	*Meth. biochem. Anal.* **12**, 183 (1964) *J.B.C.* **161**, 743 (1945) *Meth. Enzymol.* **3**, 963 (1957) *Analyt. Biochem.* **7**, 335 (1964)	Stable in aqueous soln. in the cold and dark, 2–3% decomposed in 3 weeks at 0°, only sl. greater decomp. at R.T. even in 1N-HCl or NaOH. Hydrolysed by 3 hr autoclaving at 126° in 0·055N-H_2SO_4. Photolabile as solid and in soln. particularly at alk. pH. Forms Schiff bases with amines. Normal coenzyme form of Vitamin B_6.

No.	Name	Synonyms	Formula	M. wt.	Physical properties
49	Pyridoxamine dihydrochloride		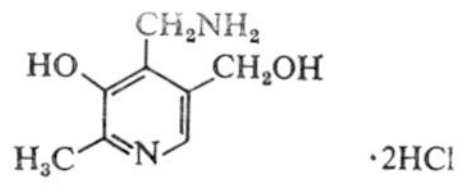	241·1	wh. deliq. platelets; M.p. 226–7 d.; pK_a 1. 3·54 2. 8·21 3. 10·63 (NH_2)
50	Pyridoxamine phosphate	Pyridoxamine-5′-phosphate	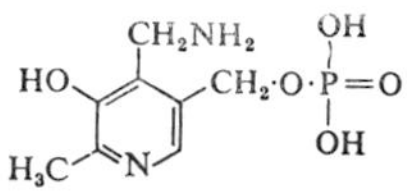	248·2; Hydrate, 284·2	wh. prism. cryst.+ $2H_2O$; anhyd. hygr. needles; pK_a 1. < 2·5 (PO 2. 3·69 (pheno 3. 5·76 (PO 4. 8·61 (pyridiniu 5. 10·92 (amin
51	Pyridoxol hydrochloride	Vitamin B_6 HCl; Pyridoxine HCl	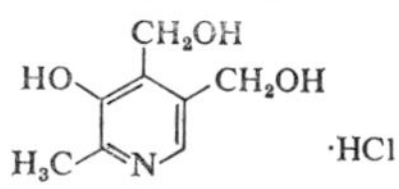	205·7	wh. platelets; M.p. 204–6 d.; pK_a 1. 5·00 2. 8·96
52	Riboflavin	Vitamin B_2; Lactoflavin	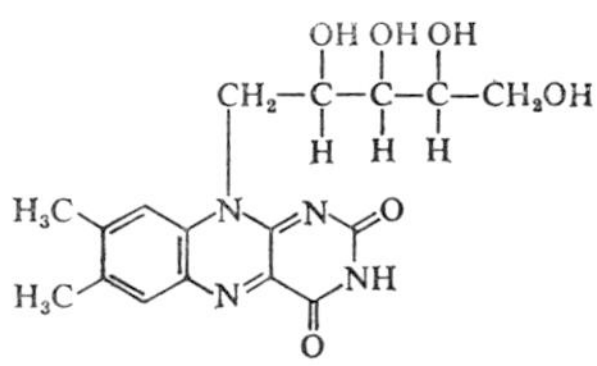	376·4	yel. cryst.; M.p. approx. 280 d.; $[\alpha]_D^{21}$ −117 (c = 0·5 in 0·1N-NaOH); E_0' −0·208 v (pH 7, 30°); pK_a 9·69
53	Succinyl coenzyme A	Succinyl-CoA; Succinyl-S-CoA	**Cf. Coenzyme A, —SH replaced by —S·CO·CH$_2$·CH$_2$·COOH**	867·6	
54	Tetrahydropteroylglutamic acid	5,6,7,8-Tetrahydropteroylglutamic acid; Tetrahydrofolic acid; THFA	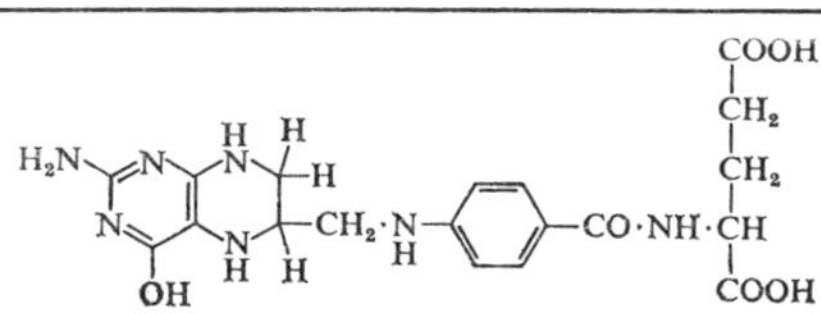	445·4; +2 Acetic acid, 565·4	as prepd. from acetic acid, fluff wh. powder+ $2CH_3\cdot COOH$; E_0' −0·19 v (fo DHFA/THFA)

Solubility	Absorption spectrum	Preparation	Estimation	General remarks
50 H_2O; 0·65 95% EtOH	At pH 7·0: λ_{max} 253 325 mμ; ε 4600 7700. In 0·1N-NaOH: λ_{max} 245 308 mμ; ε 5900 7300. *J.A.C.S.* 76, 169 (1954)	SYN. *J.A.C.S.* **66**, 2088 (1944)	*Meth. biochem. Anal.* **12**, 183 (1964); *J.B.C.* **176**, 1157 (1948); *Analyt. Biochem.* **2**, 463 (1961)	Photolabile in soln., particularly at alk. pH. Neutral, acid and alk. solns. stable to heat.
s. H_2O	At pH 7·2: λ_{max} 254 327 mμ; ε 5200 9400. At pH 10·0: λ_{max} 244 312 mμ; ε 7500 8300. *J.A.C.S.* **76**, 169 (1954)	SYN. *Helv. chim. Acta* **34**, 2199 (1951); *Biochem. Preps.* **3**, 29 (1953); *J.A.C.S.* **76**, 169 (1954)	*Meth. biochem. Anal.* **12**, 183 (1964); *J.B.C.* **182**, 557 (1950); *Biochem. Preps.* **3**, 29 (1953)	Aq. solns. stable in the dark. Negligible hydrolysis in dark at room temp. or below in 3 weeks in 1N-NaOH or HCl. Complete hydrolysis by 3 hr autoclaving at 126° in 0·055N-H_2SO_4. Photolabile in soln. particularly at alk. pH.
2 H_2O; ·1 EtOH; l. s. acet.; eth.	At pH 6·8: λ_{max} 254 324 mμ; ε 3700 7100. In 0·1N-NaOH: λ_{max} 245 308 mμ; ε 6500 7000. *J.A.C.S.* 76, 169 (1954)	SYN. *J.A.C.S.* **61**, 1245 (1939)	*Meth. biochem. Anal.* **12**, 183 (1964); *J.B.C.* **176**, 1157 (1948); TOTAL VITAMIN B_6. *J. gen. Microbiol.* **20**, 566 (1959)	Cryst. stable in light, but neutral and especially alk. solns. somewhat photolabile. Sterilized by autoclaving in soln. of pH 5 or below. REVIEWS: *Vitamin B_6*. *Vitams Horm.* **15**, 77 (1958); **22**, 361 et seq. (1964).
·01[25], 0·23[100] H_2O; ·0045 EtOH; s. dil. alk. with decomp., conc. HCl; gl. acetic, phenol; eth., $CHCl_3$, acet., benz.	In 0·1M-PO_4, pH 7: λ_{max} 266 373 445 mμ; ε 32 500 10 600 12 500; λ_{ref} 260 375 450 mμ; ε 27 700 10 600 12 200. Fluorescence max., 530 mμ. Reduced form, ϵ_{450} 780	SYN. *Helv. chim. Acta* **18**, 426 (1935); *Naturwissenschaften* **23**, 260 (1935); ISOL. *Ber.* **66**, 315 (1933)	*Meth. Enzymol.* 3, 960 (1957); *Meth. biochem. Anal.* **10**, 319 (1962); *The Vitamins*, 2nd ed., vol. 7, p. 99 (1967); *Methods of Vitamin* Assay, 3rd ed., p. 147 (1966)	Dry solid stable to diffuse light. Highly photolabile in soln. especially in alk. Neutral and acid aq. solns. stable in dark; may be sterilized by autoclaving. Rapidly destroyed in alk. soln. Stable to mild oxidizing agents. Reduced by dithionite, Na amalgam, Zn+acid or H_2+catalyst to colourless dihydro compd., which is v. readily autoxidizable.
H_2O	*See* Acyl-CoA compds. $\Delta\epsilon_{232}$ on hydrolysis 4500	*J.A.C.S.* 75, 2520 (1953); *Biochem. Preps.* **5**, 30 (1957); *See also* Acyl-CoA compds.	*See* Acyl-CoA compds.	Unstable at neutral pH at R.T. half-life 1–2 hr in bicarbonate buffer pH 7·5, slower decomp. in PO_4 buffer. Hydrolysis v. rapid if heated, complete hyrolysis in 1–2 min at 100°. Neutral soln. may be stored at −15° with negligible decomp. Stable at pH 1.
H_2O, acetic	In 0·01M-PO_4, pH 7·0: λ_{max} 298 mμ; ε 28 000 (lower values also reported). λ_{max} shifts to 282 mμ due to decomp. to dihydropteroylglutamic acid	*dl*,L-, *Biochem. Preps.* **7**, 89 (1960); *Meth. Enzymol.* **6**, 802 (1963); *l*,L-, *Meth. Enzymol.* **6**, 805 (1963)	*J.B.C.* **237**, 2903 (1962); *J.B.C.* **239**, 106 (1964); *Analyt. Biochem.* **2**, 558 (1961); *Analyt. Biochem.* **6**, 100 (1963)	Solid slowly oxidized in air, store in vacuum or inert atmosphere. In soln. rapidly oxidized to dihydropteroylglutamic acid, further decomp. occurs more slowly. Unstable in acid, most stable at pH 7·4. Stability affected by buffer; most stable in veronal, tris or triethanolamine, least stable in phosphate or maleate. Stabilized by ascorbate (34 mM) or, less well, by mercaptoethanol (10 mM). Solns. containing ascorbate stable months at −15°, hours at 0°, up to 15 min in tris buffer at 100°. See *J.B.C.* **239**, 106 (1964), *Analyt. Biochem.* **2**, 558 (1961). Enzymically active form is *l*,L-.

No.	Name	Synonyms	Formula	M. wt.	Physical properties
55	Thiamin chloride hydrochloride	Thiamin hydrochloride; Vitamin $B_1 \cdot HCl$; Aneurin·HCl	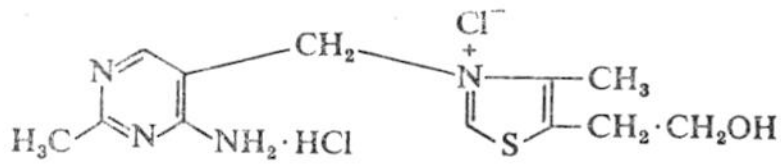	337·3; Hydrate, 355·3	monocl. plates; hygr., usually + $1H_2O$; yeast-like odour; M.p. 247–8 d.; pK_a 1. 4·8 2+3. 9·2
56	Thiamin monophosphate	Aneurin phosphate	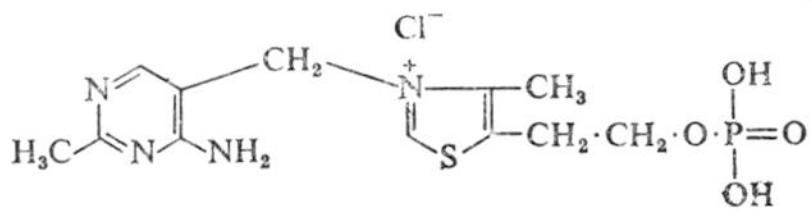	Chloride, 380·8; Hydrate, 398·8	cryst. of chloride + $1H_2O$; M.p. 200–2
57	Thiamin pyrophosphate	Diphosphothiamin; Cocarboxylase; TPP	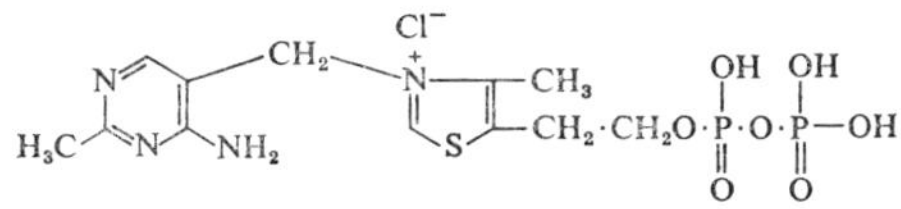	Free cation, 425·3; Chloride, 460·8; Hydrate, 478·8	Chloride, cryst. + $1H_2O$ from EtOH; M.p. 240–4 d.; pK_a 1. 5·0
58	α-Tocopherol	Vitamin E; 5,7,8-Trimethyltocol	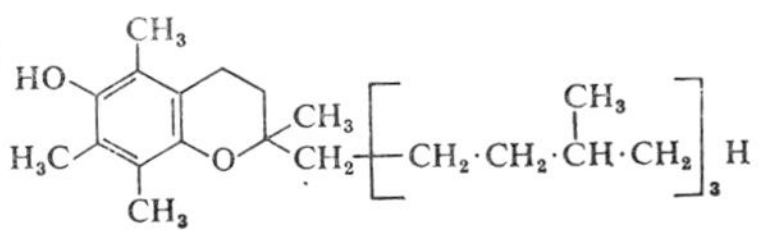	430·7	pale yellow oil; M.p. 2·5–3·5
59	β-Tocopherol	5,8-Dimethyltocol	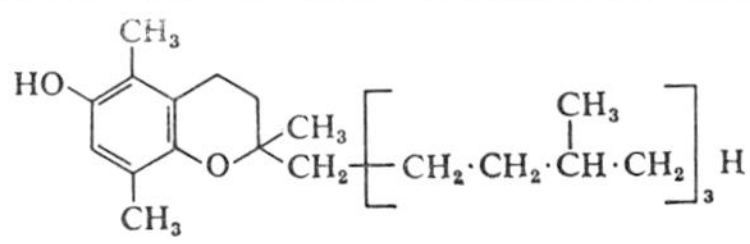	416·7	pale yellow oil
60	γ-Tocopherol	7,8-Dimethyltocol	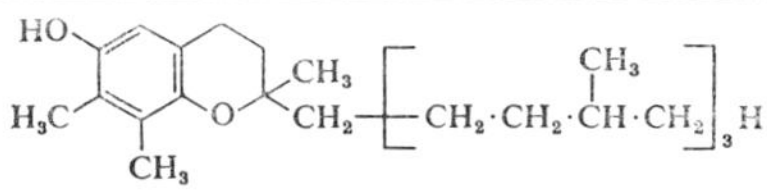	16·7	pale yellow oil; M.p. −3 to −2
61	δ-Tocopherol	8-Methyltocol	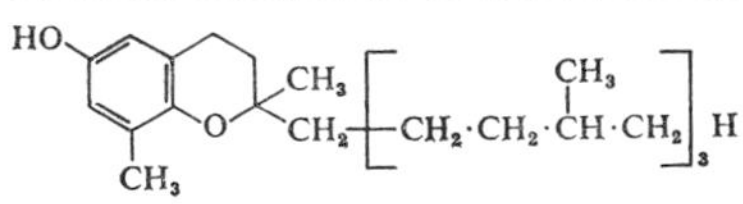	402·7	pale yellow oil
62	Ubichromenol-50	Ubichromenol-9; UC-50; SC	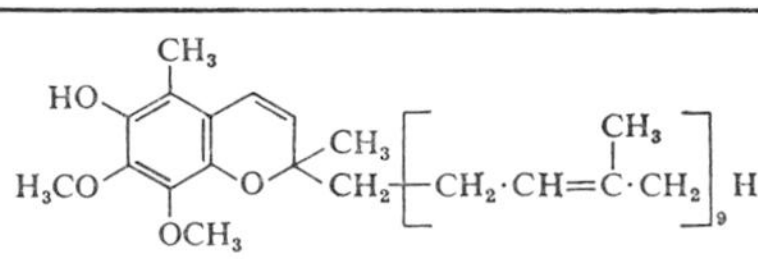	863·4	yellow cryst.; M.p. approx. 18

Solubility	Absorption spectrum	Preparation	Estimation	General remarks
00 H_2O; ·35 EtOH; . MeOH; . eth., benz., $CHCl_3$	In H_2O: At pH 7 and above: λ_{max} 235 267 mμ; ε 11 300 8300. At pH 5·5 and below: λ_{max} 247 mμ; ε 14 200	SYN. *J.A.C.S.* **59**, 1052 (1937) *J.C.S.* **1937**, 364	*Meth. biochem. Anal.* **6**, 191 (1958) *Meth. Enzymol.* **3**, 946 (1957) *The Vitamins*, 2nd ed., vol. 7, p. 53 (1967)	Commercial samples contain about 4% H_2O removable at 100°. Soln. at pH 3·5 stable at 120°. Solns. above pH 5 unstable, especially to heat. Unstable to reducing and oxidizing agents.
. H_2O		*J.A.C.S.* **64**, 2279 (1942) *Helv. chim. Acta* **29**, 711 (1946) *B.B.A.* **34**, 277 (1959) *B.B.R.C.* **1**, 63 (1959)		
. H_2O	In PO_4 buffer, pH 5·0: λ_{max} 245 261 mμ At pH 8: λ_{max} 231·5 266 mμ; λ_{min} 248 mμ Isosbestic point (pH 5–8): 272·5 mμ	*Helv. chim. Acta* **29**, 1901 (1946) *Helv. chim. Acta* **32**, 1478 (1949)	*B.B.A.* **14**, 52 (1954) *B.J.* **62**, 601 (1956) *Meth. Enzymol.* **3**, 946 (1957) *B.B.A.* **64**, 13 (1962) Bergmeyer, *Methods of Enzymatic Analysis*, p. 602, Academic Press (1963)	Solid stable when dry. Solns. somewhat less stable than thiamin chloride hydrochloride. REVIEW: *Ann. N.Y. Acad. Sci.* **98**, 383 et seq. (1962).
. acet., EtOH, $CHCl_3$, eth.; H_2O	In EtOH: λ_{max} 292 mμ; ε 32 600	ISOL. *J.B.C.* **113**, 319 (1936) *B.J.* **32**, 1953 (1938) *J.A.C.S.* **65**, 918 (1943) SYN. *Vitams Horm.* **20**, 389 (1962)	*Vitams Horm.* **20**, 407 (1962) *Meth. biochem. Anal.* **2**, 153 (1955) *The Vitamins*, 2nd ed., vol. 6, p. 261 (1967)	Slowly oxidized by air, rapidly in presence of alk., or on heating. Stable to heat and alk. in absence of oxygen. Sensitive to u.v. light. Active anti-oxidant. REVIEW: *Vitams Horm.* **18**, 49 (1960), **20**, 375 (1962). Acetate, M. wt. 472·7, yellow liq., much more stable to O_2 and light than α-tocopherol. Allophanate, M.p. 172–3. *p*-Nitrophenylurethane, M.p. 130–1.
acet., EtOH, $CHCl_3$, eth.; H_2O	In EtOH: λ_{max} 296 mμ; ε 37 200	ISOL. *J.B.C.* **113**, 319 (1936) *J.B.C.* **122**, 99 (1937–8) *B.J.* **32**, 1953 (1938) *J.A.C.S.* **65**, 918 (1943) SYN. *Vitams Horm.* **20**, 389 (1962)	*Vitams Horm.* **20**, 407 (1962) *Meth. biochem. Anal.* **2**, 153 (1955) *The Vitamins*, 2nd ed., vol. 6, p. 261 (1967)	Stability similar to α-tocopherol. Allophanate, M.p. 138–9.
acet., EtOH, HCl_3, eth.; H_2O	In EtOH: λ_{max} 298 mμ; ε 38 100	ISOL. *J.B.C.* **122**, 99 (1937–8) *J.A.C.S.* **65**, 918 (1943) SYN. *Vitams Horm.* **20**, 389 (1962)	*Vitams Horm.* **20**, 407 (1962) *Meth. biochem. Anal.* **2**, 153 (1955) *The Vitamins*, 2nd ed., vol. 6, p. 261 (1967)	Stability similar to α-tocopherol. Allophanate, M.p. 158–9. *p*-Nitrophenylurethane, M.p. 129–31.
acet., EtOH, HCl_3, eth.; H_2O	In EtOH: λ_{max} 298 mμ; ε 35 100	ISOL. *J.A.C.S.* **69**, 869 (1947) SYN. *Vitams Horm.* **20**, 389 (1962)	*Vitams Horm.* **20**, 407 (1962) *Meth. biochem. Anal.* **2**, 153 (1955) *The Vitamins*, 2nd ed., vol. 6, p. 261 (1967)	Stability similar to α-tocopherol. Most potent anti-oxidant of the group.
EtOH, eth., ht pet., clohexane; H_2O	In cyclohexane: λ_{max} 233 275 283; ε 18 700 8300 7900; λ_{max} 322 mμ; ε 3300	*Chemy Ind.* **1959**, 1019 *B.J.* **74**, 541 (1960)	*B.J.* **74**, 541 (1960) *B.J.* **76**, 563 (1960)	

9. Vitamins and Coenzymes

No.	Name	Synonyms	Formula	M. wt.	Physical properties
63	Ubiquinones	Coenzymes Q; Q275; SA	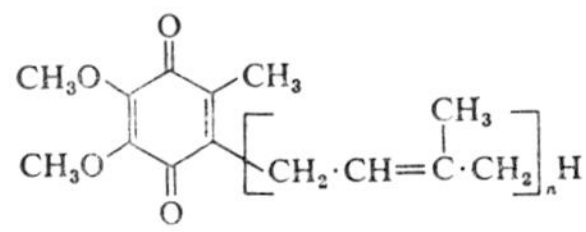		
64	Ubiquinone-30	Ubiquinone-6; Coenzyme Q_6; UQ-30; UQ_6; Q-6; CoQ_6	Cf. Ubiquinones, $n = 6$	590·9	orange oil; M.p. 18 (19–20)
65	Ubiquinone-35	Ubiquinone-7; Coenzyme Q_7; UQ-35; UQ_7; Q-7; CoQ_7	Cf. Ubiquinones, $n = 7$	659·0	orange cryst.; M.p. 30·5 (31–32)
66	Ubiquinone-40	Ubiquinone-8; Coenzyme Q_8; UQ-40; UQ_8; Q-8; CoQ_8	Cf. Ubiquinones, $n = 8$	727·1	orange cryst.; M.p. 37
67	Ubiquinone-45	Ubiquinone-9; Coenzyme Q_9; UQ-45; UQ_9; Q-9; CoQ_9	Cf. Ubiquinones, $n = 9$	795·3	orange cryst.; M.p. 45
68	Ubiquinone-50	Ubiquinone-10; Coenzyme Q_{10}; UQ-50; UQ_{10}; Q-10; CoQ_{10}	Cf. Ubiquinones, $n = 10$	863·4	orange cryst.; M.p. 50 (48–49)
69	Vitamin A_1 (all-*trans*)	Retinol; Axerophthol	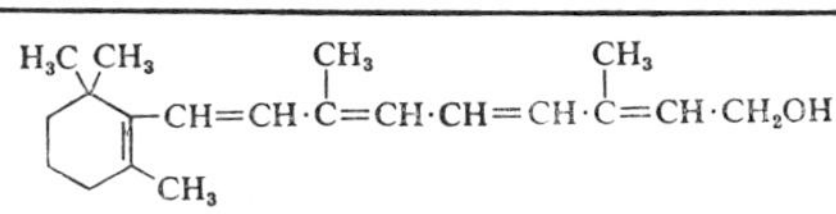	286·5	yellow prisms; M.p. 64
70	Vitamin A_1 acid (all-*trans*)	Retinoic acid	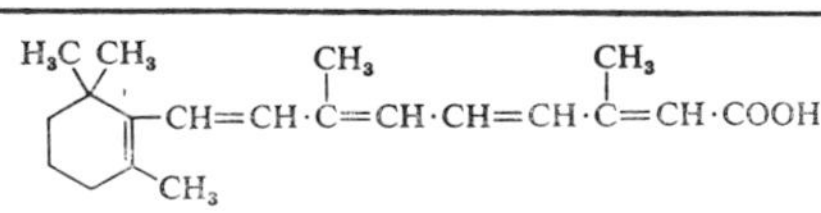	300·4	yel. needles; M.p. 179–80
71	Vitamin A_1 aldehyde (all-*trans*)	Retinal; Retinene; Retinaldehyde	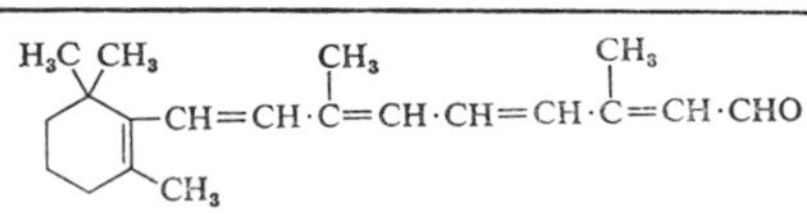	284·4	orange crystals; M.p. 61–62

Solubility	*Absorption spectrum*	*Preparation*	*Estimation*	*General remarks*
	All homologues in EtOH: Quinone, λ_{max} 275 405 mμ Quinol, λ_{max} 290 mμ	SYN. *J.A.C.S.* **80**, 4753 (1958) *J.A.C.S.* **81**, 5000 (1959) *Helv. chim. Acta* **42**, 2616 (1959) ISOL. *Meth. biochem. Anal.* **11**, 279 (1963) *Adv. Enzymol.* **25**, 275 (1963) *J.B.C.* **234**, 2169 (1959)	*Meth. biochem. Anal.* **11**, 279 (1963) *Adv. Enzymol.* **25**, 275 (1963) *B.J.* **76**, 61 (1960)	Slowly destroyed by oxygen, u.v. light or sunlight. Rapidly oxidized in alk., but stable to alk. in presence of pyrogallol to remove oxygen. Reduced by dithionite, borohydride or Zn+acid to quinol. Quinol slowly reoxidized by air. REVIEWS: *Quinones in Electron Transport*, CIBA Symposium, eds. Wolstenholme and O'Connor (1961); *Vitams Horm.* **19**, 1 (1961), **24**, 291 et seq. (1966); *Adv. Enzymol.* **25**, 275 (1963); *Prog. Chem. Fats* **7**, 267 (1964).
s. EtOH, eth., light pet., cyclohexane; . H_2O	In EtOH: Quinone, λ_{max} 275 mμ ϵ 14 870 Quinol, λ_{max} 290 mμ ϵ 4890	*J.C.S.* **1956**, 4094		
s. EtOH, eth., ight pet., cyclohexane; . H_2O	In EtOH: Quinone, λ_{max} 275 mμ ϵ 14 240 Quinol, λ_{max} 290 mμ ϵ 4120	*J.B.C.* **234**, 2169 (1959) *B.B.A.* **32**, 492 (1959)		
. EtOH, eth., ight pet., yclohexane; . H_2O	In EtOH: Quinone, λ_{max} 275 mμ ϵ 14 670 Quinol, λ_{max} 290 mμ ϵ 4280	*J.B.C.* **234**, 2169 (1959) *B.B.A.* **32**, 492 (1959)		
. EtOH, eth., ght pet., yclohexane; H_2O	In EtOH: Quinone, λ_{max} 275 mμ ϵ 14 440 Quinol, λ_{max} 290 mμ ϵ 4040	*J.B.C.* **234**, 2169 (1959) *B.B.A.* **32**, 492 (1959) SYN. *J.A.C.S.* **81**, 5000 (1959)		
EtOH, eth., ght pet., yclohexane; H_2O	In EtOH: Quinone, λ_{max} 275 mμ ϵ 14 020 Quinol, λ_{max} 290 mμ ϵ 3940	*Biochem. Preps.* **9**, 30 (1962) *J.B.C.* **234**, 2169 (1959) *Helv. chim. Acta* **41**, 2343 (1959) *B.B.A.* **32**, 73 (1959) *J.A.C.S.* **82**, 1647 (1960)		
EtOH, MeOH, HCl_3, eth., clohexane; H_2O	In EtOH: λ_{max} 325 mμ, ϵ 52 480 $SbCl_3$ complex in $CHCl_3$: λ_{max} 620 mμ $E^{1\%}_{1\,cm}$ 5070	ISOL. *The Vitamins*, 2nd ed., vol. 1, p. 1 (1967) SYN. *Vitams Horm.* **5**, 1 (1947) *Angew. Chem.* **72**, 948 (1960) *Vitams Horm.* **18**, 295 (1960)	*The Vitamins*, 2nd ed., vol. 6, p. 139 (1967) *Meth. biochem. Anal.* **4**, 43 (1957); **15**, 1 (1967) *Vitams Horm.* **18**, 315, 341 (1960)	Destroyed by u.v. light. Readily oxidized in air. Stabilize by dissolving in oil, by addition of anti-oxidant such as α-tocopherol or hydroquinone, or by conversion to acetate. Stable in alk., unstable in acid. REVIEW: *Vitams Horm.* **18**, 289 (1960); Moore, *Vitamin A*, Elsevier (1957).
EtOH, ICl_3, eth., clohexane; H_2O	In EtOH: λ_{max} 350 mμ, ϵ 45 200 $SbCl_3$ complex in $CHCl_3$: λ_{max} 574 mμ	SYN. *Recl Trav. chim. Pays-Bas Belg.* **65**, 338 (1946) *Vitams Horm.* **18**, 295 (1960)	*The Vitamins*, 2nd ed., vol. 6, p. 139 (1967) *Meth. biochem. Anal.* **4**, 43 (1957) *Vitams Horm.* **18**, 315 (1960)	
EtOH, MeOH, ICl_3, eth., lohexane; I_2O	In EtOH: λ_{max} 381 mμ, ϵ 43 400 $SbCl_3$ complex in $CHCl_3$: λ_{max} 664 mμ $E^{1\%}_{1\,cm}$ 3400	*B.J.* **42**, 516 (1948) SYN. *J.A.C.S.* **72**, 234 (1950) *J.A.C.S.* **77**, 4120 (1955)	*The Vitamins*, 2nd ed., vol. 6, p. 139 (1967) *Meth. biochem. Anal.* **4**, 43 (1957) *Vitams Horm.* **18**, 315 (1960)	Less stable than Vitamin A_1 alcohol. Oxime, M.p. 134–6.

9. Vitamins and Coenzymes

No.	Name	Synonyms	Formula	M. wt.	Physical properties
72	Vitamin A_2 (all-*trans*)	3-Dehydro-retinol	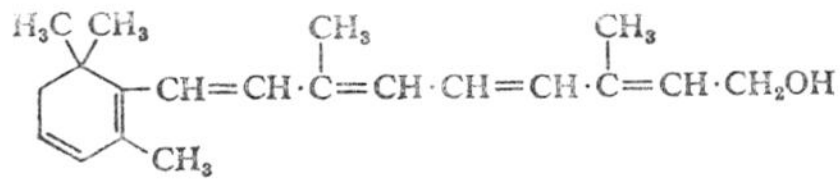	284·4	orange oil; M.p. 17–19
73	Vitamin A_2 aldehyde (all-*trans*)	3-Dehydroretinal; Retinene$_2$; Retinal$_2$; Retinaldehyde$_2$	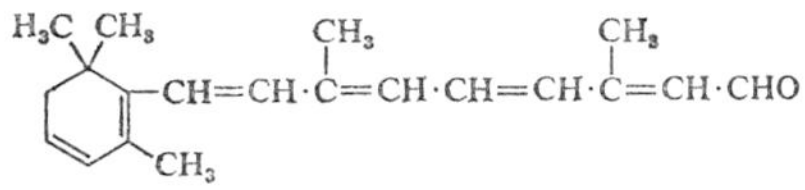	282·4	orange cryst.; M.p. 77–78
74	Vitamin D_2	Ergocalciferol; Calciferol	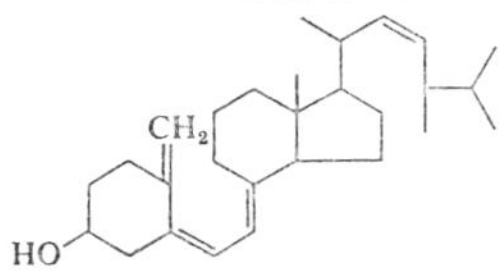	396·7	col. long prisms from acet.; needles from MeOH; M.p. 121; $[\alpha]_D$ +48·2 (c = 1·6 in $CHCl_3$)
75	Vitamin D_3	Cholecalciferol	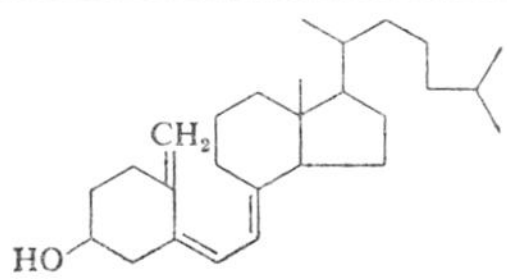	384·7	fine needles; M.p. 84–85; $[\alpha]_D$ +51·9 (c = 1·6 in $CHCl_3$)
76	Vitamin K_1	2-Methyl-3-phytyl-1,4-naphtho-quinone; Phylloquinone	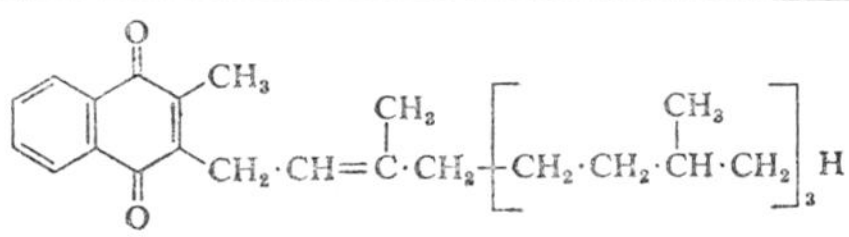	450·7	yel. viscous oil; M.p. −20
77	Vitamin $K_2(30)$	2-Methyl-3-difarnesyl-1,4-naphtho-quinone; Farnoquinone; Menaquinone-6; MK-6	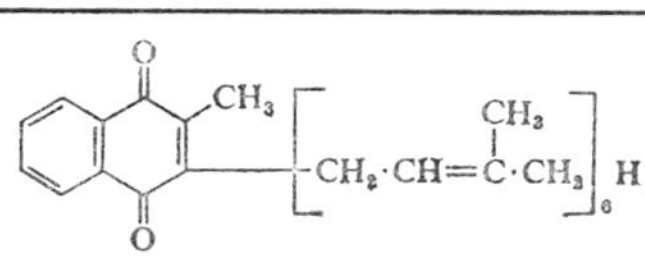	580·9	yel. cryst.; M.p. 50
78	Vitamin $K_2(35)$	2-Methyl-3-farnesyl-geranylgeranyl-1,4-naphtho-quinone; Menaquinone-7; MK-7	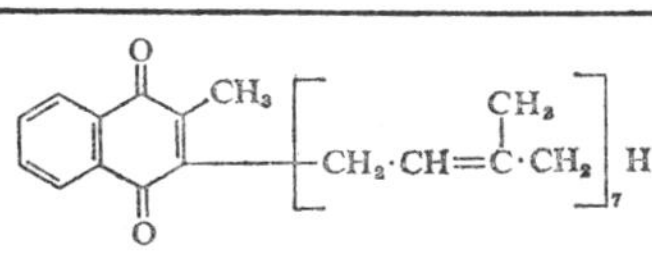	649·0	light yel. cryst. plates; M.p. 54

Solubility	*Absorption spectrum*	*Preparation*	*Estimation*	*General remarks*
s. EtOH, $CHCl_3$, eth., cyclohexane; i. H_2O	In EtOH: λ_{max} 287 352 mμ; ε 23 300 41 400 $SbCl_3$ complex in $CHCl_3$: λ_{max} 693 mμ; $E^{1\%}_{1\,cm}$ 4100	ISOL. *B.J.* **52**, 535 (1952) *J.C.S.* **1952**, 2657, **1955**, 2765 SYN. *Vitams Horm.* **18**, 295 (1960)	*The Vitamins*, 2nd ed., vol. 6, p. 139 (1967) *Meth. biochem. Anal.* **4**, 43 (1957); **15**, 1 (1967) *Vitams Horm.* **18**, 315 (1960)	Stability similar to Vitamin A_1. *p*-Phenylazobenzoate, M.p. 76–77.
s. EtOH, $CHCl_3$, eth., cyclohexane; i. H_2O	In EtOH: λ_{max} 397 mμ, ε 39 800 $SbCl_3$ complex in $CHCl_3$: λ_{max} 730–40 mμ falling to 705 mμ; $E^{1\%}_{1\,cm}$ 3720 at 705 mμ	ISOL. *B.J.* **52**, 535 (1952) SYN. *J.C.S.* **1952**, 2657 *Vitams Horm.* **18**, 295 (1960)	*The Vitamins*, 2nd ed., vol. 6, p. 139 (1967) *Meth. biochem. Anal.* **4**, 43 (1957) *Vitams Horm.* **18**, 315 (1960)	Oxime, M.p. 141–3.
28^{26} EtOH; 25^{26} acet.; s. eth.; i. H_2O	In EtOH or hexane: λ_{max} 265 mμ; ε 19 400	*Proc. R. Soc.* B **109**, 488 (1932) *B.J.* **49**, 45 (1951) *J.A.C.S.* **67**, 609 (1945)	*The Vitamins*, 2nd ed., vol. 6, p. 211 (1967) *J.B.C.* **148**, 245 (1943) *B.J.* **49**, 36, 45, 54, 232, 243 (1951) *A. Rev. Biochem.* **21**, 342 (1952) *Z. analyt. Chem.* **138**, 1 (1953)	Less stable than ergosterol. Sensitive to light under all conditions. Oxidized in air in a few days. Low temp. and inert atmosphere slow, but do not halt, decomp. May be stored for months in sealed evacuated amber glass ampoules in the cold. Stable in soln. in propylene glycol or corn oil or as esters of various nitrobenzoic acids, e.g. 3,5-dinitrobenzoate, M.p. 146–8. No ppt. with digitonin.
. EtOH, cet., $CHCl_3$; . H_2O	In hexane or EtOH: λ_{max} 265 mμ; ε 18 200	*Naturwissenschaften* **25**, 159 (1937) *Z.P.C.* **249**, 176 (1937) *J.A.C.S.* **67**, 609 (1945)	*See* Vitamin D_2 *B.J.* **49**, 232, 243 (1951) *The Vitamins*, 2nd ed., vol. 6, p. 211 (1967)	Somewhat more stable than vitamin D_2, much more stable than 7-dehydrocholesterol. Most favourable storage conditions same as vitamin D_2. 3,5-Dinitrobenzoate, M.p. 129.
. EtOH, cet., benz., ght pet., eth.; H_2O	In hexane: λ_{max} 243 249 260 269 325 mμ; ϵ_{249} 18 600	ISOL. *Helv. chim. Acta* **22**, 310, 945, 1464 (1939) SYN. *J.B.C.* **130**, 791 (1939) *J.A.C.S.* **61**, 2559 (1939) *J.A.C.S.* **76**, 4592 (1954)	*Vitams Horm.* **17**, 53 (1959) *Meth. biochem. Anal.* **11**, 279 (1963) *The Vitamins*, 2nd ed., vol. 6, p. 245 (1967)	Moderately stable to air and moisture, but rapidly decomp. in light. Unaffected by dil. acids but destroyed by alk. and by reducing agents. REVIEWS: *Vitams Horm.* **17**, 53 (1959); **24**, 291 et seq. (1966).
	In hexane: λ_{max} 243 249 260 269 325 mμ; ϵ_{249} 18 600	SYN. *Helv. chim. Acta* **41**, 786 (1958)	*Vitams Horm.* **17**, 53 (1959) *Meth. biochem. Anal.* **11**, 279 (1963) *The Vitamins*, 2nd ed., vol. 6, p. 245 (1967)	Stability similar to Vitamin K_1. Extremely sensitive to light.
ghtly less luble than K_1 the same ganic solvents	In hexane: λ_{max} 243 249 260 269 325 mμ; ϵ_{249} 18 900	ISOL. *J.B.C.* **131**, 327 (1939) *Proc. Soc. exp. Biol. Med.* **68**, 136 (1948) SYN. *Helv. chim. Acta* **41**, 786 (1958)	*Vitams Horm.* **17**, 53 (1959) *Meth. biochem. Anal.* **11**, 279 (1963) *The Vitamins*, 2nd ed., vol. 6, p. 245 (1967)	Stability similar to Vitamin K_1. Extremely sensitive to light.

10. Carbohydrates and Related Compounds

Revised by R. W. BAILEY (*Plant Chemistry Division, D.S.I.R., Palmerston North, New Zealand*)

Nomenclature

Rules of carbohydrate nomenclature are reported in *B.J.* **125,** 673 (1971); *Eur. J. Biochem.* **21,** 455 (1971); *B.B.A.* **244,** 223 (1971).

The configuration of a monosaccharide (designated by the letters D- and L-) is decided by the configuration of the highest numbered asymmetric carbon atom and is related to the configuration of glyceraldehyde, which is known. D-Glyceraldehyde has the same absolute configuration as D-serine and D-lactic acid.

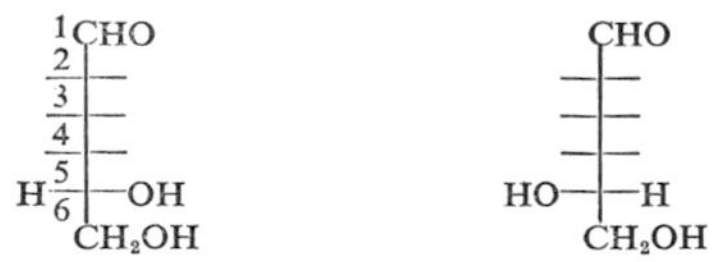

D-series L-series

Reference works

1. Tollens and Elsner, *Kurzes Handbuch der Kohlenhydrate*, J. A. Barth Verlag, Leipzig (1935).
2. W. W. Pigman and R. M. Goepp, Jr., *Chemistry of the Carbohydrates*, Academic Press (1948). W. Pigman, *The Carbohydrates*, Academic Press (1957).
3. E. H. Rodd (ed.), *Chemistry of Carbon Compounds*, vol. 1B, Elsevier (1952), vol. 5 (1962).
4. F. J. Bates *et al.*, *Polarimetry, Saccharimetry and the Sugars*, U.S. Department of Commerce, National Bureau of Standards, Washington, D.C. (1942).
5. *Beilstein's Handbuch der Organischen Chemie*, vol. 31, Springer, Berlin (1938).
6. R. L. Whistler and M. L. Wolfram, *Methods in Carbohydrate Chemistry*, vols. 1, 2, 3, 4, and 5, Academic Press (1962–5).

Analysis

The methods of analysis available for carbohydrates are often specific only for a class of carbohydrates, e.g. keto-sugars, heptoses, and generally not for single substances. Chromatographic methods are often used for separation of mixtures. The following reviews deal with some of these points.

Colorimetric analysis of mixtures: *Meth. biochem. Anal.* **2,** 313 (1955).
Paper chromatography: *Adv. Carbohyd. Chem.* **9,** 304 (1954).
Column chromatography: *Adv. Carbohyd. Chem.* **10,** 55 (1955).
Chromatography: *Meth. biochem. Anal.* **1,** 205 (1954).
F. J. Bates *et al.*, *Polarimetry, Saccharimetry and the Sugars*, National Bureau of Standards, Washington, D.C. (1942).

Abbreviations

The sign → is used to signify mutarotation.

Bates *et al.* refers to *Polarimetry, Saccharimetry and the Sugars*, by F. J. Bates *et al.*, National Bureau of Standards, Washington, D.C. (1942).

Meth. Carb. Chem. refers to R. L. Whistler and M. L. Wolfram, *Methods in Carbohydrate Chemistry*, Academic Press (1962–5).

TETROSES AND RELATED SUBSTANCES

No.	Name	Synonyms	Formula	M. wt.	Physical form
1	*meso*-Erythritol	Erythritol, *i*-erythritol, erythrol, phycitol, 1,2,3,4-tetrahydroxybutane	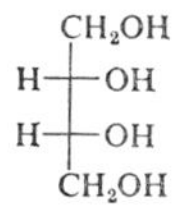	122·1	wh. prisms
2	D-Erythrose		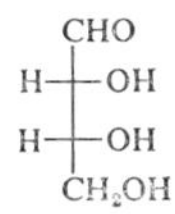	120·1	col. syrup
3	L-Erythrulose	Formerly known as *d*-erythrulose	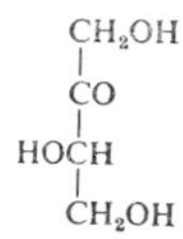	120·1	col. syrup
4	D-Threose		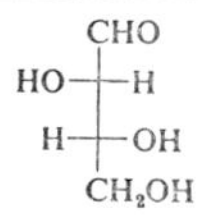	120·1	v. hygr. col. needles

PENTOSES AND RELATED SUBSTANCES

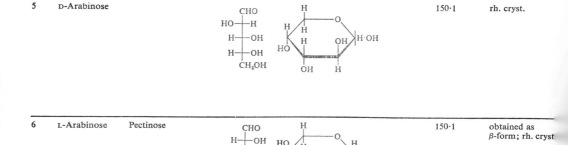

No.	Name	Synonyms	Formula	M. wt.	Physical form
5	D-Arabinose		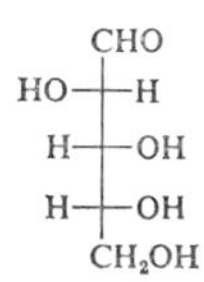 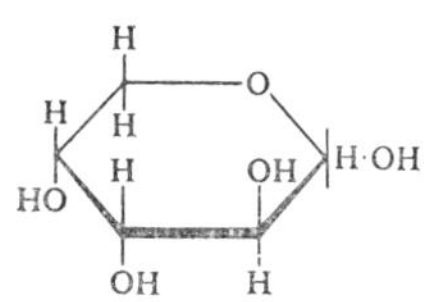	150·1	rh. cryst.
6	L-Arabinose	Pectinose	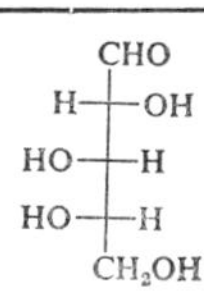 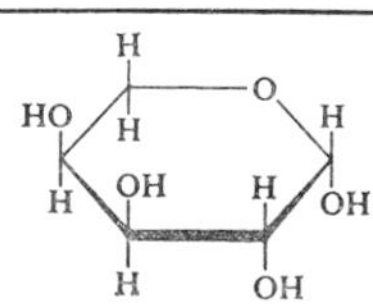 (β)	150·1	obtained as β-form; rh. cryst

M.p.	$[\alpha]^t_D$	Solubility	References	Derivatives	General remarks
26	Inactive	v.s. H_2O; s. hot EtOH; sl. s. cold EtOH, pyr.; i. eth.		Tetra-*O*-acetate, M.p. 85 Tetra-*O*-benzoate, M.p. 188–9 Di-*O*-*iso*propylidene deriv., M.p. 56 Di-*O*-benzylidene deriv., M.p. 201 d.	Non-reducing.
	$-1{\cdot}2 \rightarrow -18{\cdot}5^{14{\cdot}5}$ (c = 3·2 in H_2O)	s. H_2O, MeOH, EtOH	PREP. *J.C.S.* **1949**, 1358 *Can. J. Chem.* **33**, 1216 (1955) See also *J.A.C.S.* 73, 5524 (1951)	Benzylphenylhydrazone, M.p. 105; $[\alpha]_D$ −32 (in EtOH) Phenylosazone, M.p. 162–4 (identical with osazones of D-threose and D-erythrulose) Tri-*O*-acetate, M.p. 134	
	$+12^{20}$ (in H_2O)	s. H_2O	PREP. *J.B.C.* **201**, 161 (1953) *J.A.C.S.* **60**, 2507 (1938) *Helv. chim. Acta* **20**, 1468 (1937)	*o*-Nitrophenylhydrazone, M.p. 152–3; $[\alpha]^{18}_D$ +48 (in EtOH) Phenylosazone, M.p. 164 (identical with osazones of L-threose and L-erythrose) *p*-Bromophenylosazone, M.p. 194	Not fermented by yeasts.
26–32	$+29{\cdot}1 \rightarrow +19{\cdot}6^{22}$ (in H_2O)	s. H_2O, MeOH, EtOH; i. eth., pet. eth.	PREP. *Helv. chim. Acta* **19**, 1016 (1936) *J.A.C.S.* **65**, 1663 (1943)	Benzylphenylhydrazone, M.p. 194·5 Phenylosazone, M.p. 162–4 (identical with osazones of D-erythrose and D-erythrulose) Di-*O*-acetate, M.p. 140–2; $[\alpha]^{23}_D$ +83·5 → +34·5 (in $CHCl_3$) *O*-*iso*Propylidene deriv., M.p. 84; $[\alpha]^{22}_D$ −15·27 (in acet.)	
	GENERAL METHODS OF ESTIMATION OF PENTOSES		*Meth. biochem. Anal.* **2**, 313 (1955) *J.B.C.* **167**, 369 (1947) *J.B.C.* **194**, 261 (1952) *J.B.C.* **204**, 1011 (1953) *J.B.C.* **205**, 661 (1953) *J.B.C.* **201**, 71 (1953) *B.J.* **58**, 288 (1954)		
59–60	−104·5 (final, c = 1 in H_2O)	s. H_2O; v. sl. s. EtOH; i. eth.	PREP. *Org. Synth.* Coll. 3, 101 (1955) [*Org. Synth.* **20**, 14 (1940)] *J.A.C.S.* **72**, 4546 (1950)	Benzylphenylhydrazone, M.p. 177–8; $[\alpha]^{16}_D$ +14·4 Diphenylhydrazone, M.p. 206 2,4-Dinitrophenylhydrazone, 259 d. Phenylosazone, M.p. 163 (identical with osazones of D-ribose and D-ribulose) Tetra-*O*-acetate, M.p. 99–100; $[\alpha]^{23}_D$ −44·2 (in $CHCl_3$) Methyl ethers. See *Adv. Carbohyd. Chem.* **10**, 261 (1955)	Not fermented by yeasts.
50	$+190{\cdot}6 \rightarrow +104{\cdot}5$ (c = 4·3 in H_2O)	s. H_2O; v. sl. s. EtOH; i. eth.	PREP. *Org. Synth.* Coll. 1, 67 (1941) Bates *et al.*, p. 457	*p*-Nitrophenylhydrazone, M.p. 187–8; $[\alpha]^{21}_D$ +14·9 (in EtOH) Benzylphenylhydrazone, M.p. 174; $[\alpha]_D$ −14·8 → −11·5 (in MeOH) Diphenylhydrazone, M.p. 204 *p*-Toluenesulphonylhydrazone, M.p. 153–4; $[\alpha]_D$ +3 (in pyr.) 2,5-Dichlorophenylhydrazone, M.p. 170 Phenylosazone, M.p. 166 (identical with osazones of L-ribose and L-ribulose) Methyl ethers, see *Adv. Carbohyd. Chem.* **10**, 262 (1955)	Not fermented by yeasts.

10. Carbohydrates and Related Compounds

No.	Name	Synonyms	Formula	M. wt.	Physical form
7	D-Arabitol		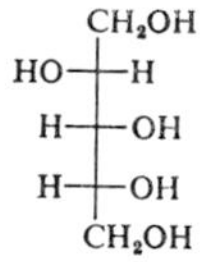	152·1	prisms
8	2-Deoxy-D-ribose	2-D-Ribodesose, thyminose, 2-deoxy-β-D-*erythro*pentose	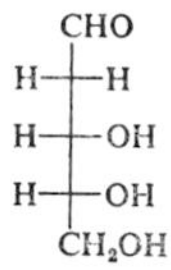 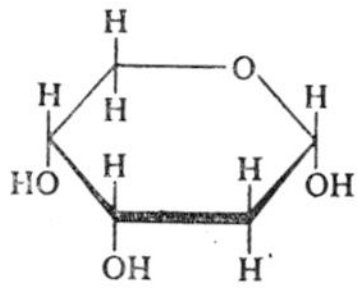 (α)	134·1	cryst. from *iso*propanol, slightly hygr.
9	L-Lyxonic acid		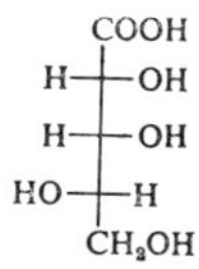	166·1	Cryst. as lyxono-γ-lactone
10	D-Lyxose		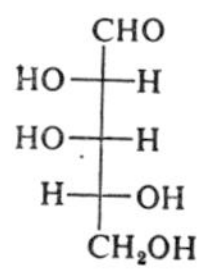 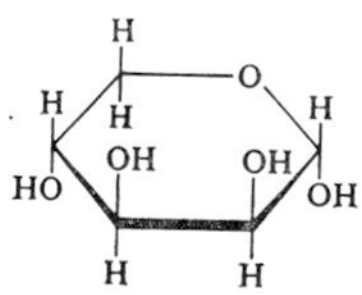 (α)	150·1	(α) hygr. monocl cryst. from EtOH (β) needles from EtOH
11	Ribitol	Adonitol	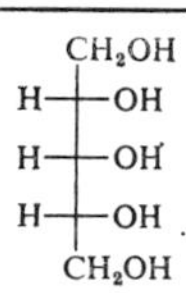	152·1	cryst.
12	D-Ribonic acid		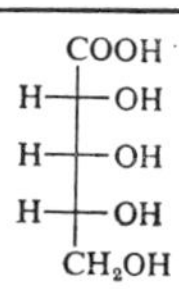	166·1	
13	D-Ribose		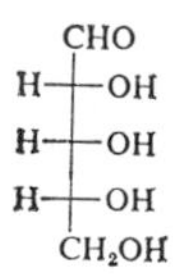 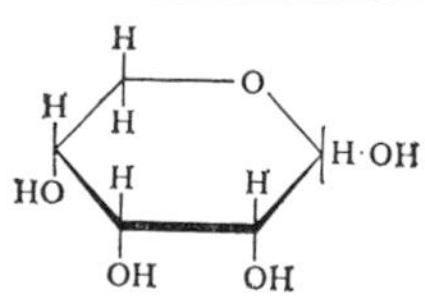 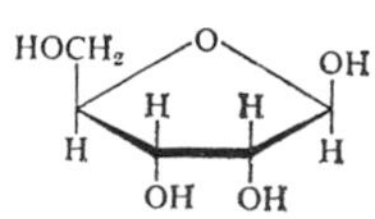 (β)	150·1	v. hygr. orthorh. cryst.

M.p.	$[\alpha]^t_D$	*Solubility*	*References*	*Derivatives*	*General remarks*
103	$+7{\cdot}82^{20}$ (in saturated borax soln.)	v.s. H_2O; s. 90% EtOH	PREP. *Ber.* **32,** 550 (1899)	Penta-*O*-acetate, M.p. 74–75; $[\alpha]^{20}_D$ +37·2 (in $CHCl_3$)	
87–90	-56^{25} (final, c = 1 in H_2O)	s. H_2O; v. sl. s. *iso*-propanol	REVIEW. *Adv. Carbohyd. Chem.* **8,** 45 (1953) *The Nucleic Acids*, eds. Chargaff and Davidson, vol. 1, p. 9, Academic Press, New York (1955) PREP. *Chemy Ind.* **1955,** 92 *Biochem. Preps.* **5,** 75 (1957) EST. *The Nucleic Acids*, eds. Chargaff and Davidson, vol. 1, p. 285	*p*-Nitrophenylhydrazone, M.p. 160; $[\alpha]^{14}_D$ −11·1 (in EtOH) Benzylphenylhydrazone, M.p. 128; $[\alpha]^{25}_D$ −17·5 (in pyr.) Anilide, M.p. 169–70	Gives Molisch test. Gives Dische test for deoxy sugars. Negative anthrone reaction.
05–7 actone)	-78^{24} (in H_2O)	s. H_2O	PREP. *J.B.C.* **235,** 2518 (1960)	Phenylhydrazide, M.p. 163; $[\alpha]^{24}_D$ +13·7 Hydrazide, M.p. 188; $[\alpha]^{14}_D$ −3·6 (in H_2O)	
) 106–7) 117–18	(α) $+5{\cdot}6 \rightarrow -13{\cdot}8^{20}$ (c = 4 in H_2O) (β) $-72{\cdot}6 \rightarrow -13{\cdot}8^{20}$ (c = 4 in H_2O)	s. H_2O; $2{\cdot}1^{17}$ EtOH	PREP. *J.A.C.S.* **72,** 4546 (1950) Bates *et al.*, p. 469	*p*-Bromophenylhydrazone, M.p. 156–7; $[\alpha]^{20}_D$ +34·5 → +10·0 (in pyr.) *p*-Nitrophenylhydrazone, M.p. 172; $[\alpha]_D$ +32·3 Benzylphenylhydrazone, M.p. 128 anhyd.; $[\alpha]_D$ +23 (in MeOH) *p*-Toluenesulphonylhydrazone, M.p. 141 Tetra-*O*-acetate, M.p. 93–94; $[\alpha]_D$ +25 (in $CHCl_3$) Methyl ethers. See *Adv. Carbohyd. Chem.* **10,** 266 (1955)	Not fermented by yeasts.
2	Inactive	s. H_2O, EtOH; i. eth.	PREP. *J.C.S.* **1949,** S44 *J.A.C.S.* **73,** 4691 (1951)	Di-*O*-benzylidene deriv., M.p. 164–5 Penta-*O*-acetate, M.p. 51	Non-reducing.
2–13	$-17{\cdot}3^{25}$ (c = 4 in MeOH)	s. H_2O, MeOH EtOH	PREP. *J.A.C.S.* **66,** 1217 (1944)	1,4-Lactone, M.p. 72–78; $[\alpha]_D$ +18·4 (in H_2O) Hydrazide, M.p. 150 Benzimidazole deriv., M.p. 190 d.; $[\alpha]^{25}_D$ +22·5 (in 1N-HCl) Preparation of salts. See *J.A.C.S.* **66,** 1217 (1944)	Unstable at room temp.
87	$-23{\cdot}1 \rightarrow +23{\cdot}7^{1}$ (c = 4 in H_2O) (mutarotation complex)	s. H_2O; v. sl. s. EtOH	REVIEW. *Adv. Carbohyd. Chem.* **6,** 135 (1951) *The Nucleic Acids*, eds. Chargaff and Davidson, vol. 1, p. 9 (1955) EST. *The Nucleic Acids*, eds. Chargaff and Davidson vol. 1, p. 285 (1955) *J.B.C.* **167,** 369 (1947) *J.B.C.* **194,** 261 (1952) *J.B.C.* **204,** 999 (1953) *J.B.C.* **205,** 661 (1953) PREP. Bates *et al.*, p. 476	*p*-Bromophenylhydrazone, M.p. 170; $[\alpha]^{23}_D$ +10·3 (in EtOH) Benzylphenylhydrazone, M.p. 127–8 *p*-Toluenesulphonylhydrazone, M.p. 164; $[\alpha]_D$ +23 → +14 (in pyr.) Diphenylhydrazone, M.p. 149–50 Phenylosazone, M.p. 163–4 (identical with osazones of D-arabinose and D-ribulose) Benzimidazole deriv. of ribonic acid (q.v.) Methyl ethers. See *Adv. Carbohyd. Chem.* **10,** 265 (1955)	Occurs in combination as the furanose form. Solutions probably contain a mixture of pyranose and furanose forms. Normal cryst. form is probably β-D-ribopyranose.

No.	Name	Synonyms	Formula	M. wt.	Physical form
14	D-Ribulose	Adonose, D-riboketose, D-arabulose, D-araboketose, D-*erythro*-pentulose	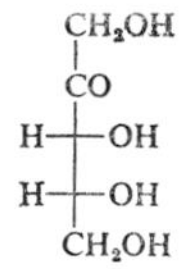	150·1	syrup
15	L-Ribulose	L-Riboketose, L-arabulose, L-araboketose, L-*erythro*-pentulose	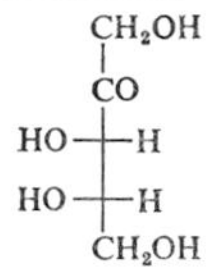	150·1	syrup
16	Xylitol		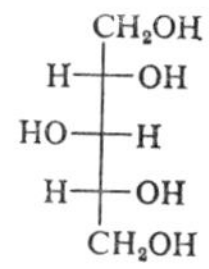	152·1	cryst. from EtOH
17	L-Xylonic acid		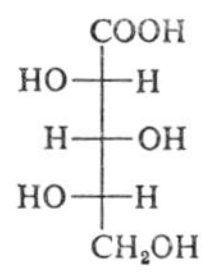	166·1	syrup, isol. as xylono-γ-lactone
18	D-Xylose	Wood sugar	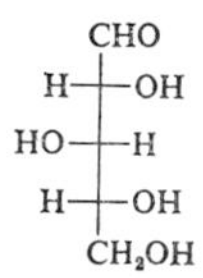 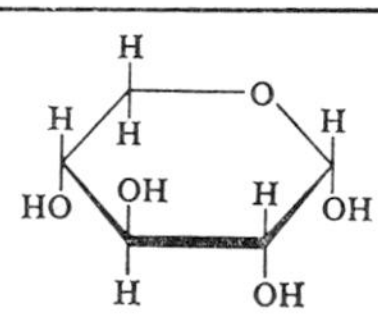 (α)	150·1	obtained as α-form; wh. needles
19	D-Xylulose	D-Xyloketose, D-lyxoketose, D-*threo*-pentulose	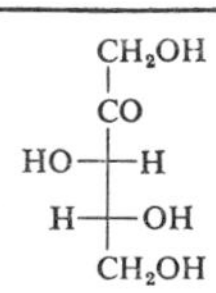	150·1	syrup
20	L-Xylulose	L-Xyloketose, L-lyxoketose, L-*threo*-pentulose. Formerly known as *d*-xylulose	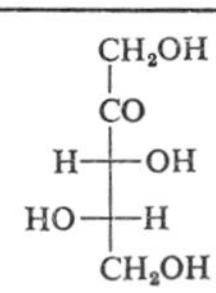	150·1	syrup

M.p.	$[\alpha]^t_D$	*Solubility*	*References*	*Derivatives*	*General remarks*
			PREP. *Helv. chim. Acta* **18**, 80 (1935) EST. *J.B.C.* **201**, 71 (1953) *J.B.C.* **194**, 261 (1952) *J.B.C.* **204**, 1011 (1953)	*o*-Nitrophenylhydrazone, M.p. 168–70; $[\alpha]_D^{20}$ −48·3 (in MeOH)	Gives Seliwanoff test. Reduces Fehling's soln. in the cold.
	$+16^{21}$ (c = 2 in H_2O)	s. H_2O	PREP. *Helv. chim. Acta* **17**, 996 (1934) EST. As for D-ribulose	*o*-Nitrophenylhydrazone, M.p. 168–9; $[\alpha]_D^{19}$ +47·5 (in MeOH) *p*-Nitrophenylhydrazone, M.p. 121–3; $[\alpha]_D^{21}$ −48·7 (in MeOH-pyr.) Di-*O*-*iso*propylidene deriv., M.p. 5; $[\alpha]_D^{27}$ +105·5 (in acet.)	Gives Seliwanoff test. Reduces Fehling's soln. in the cold.
93–94	inactive	s. H_2O, hot EtOH, MeOH	PREP. *Can. J. Chem.* **38**, 316 (1960)	Penta-*O*-acetate, M.p. 62 Dibenzylidene deriv., M.p. 175	Sweetest polyol known.
	γ-Lactone, $-91{\cdot}8^{24}$ (in H_2O)	s. H_2O	PREP. *J.B.C.* **235**, 2518 (1960) *Ann.* **403**, 252 (1914)	Brucine salt, M.p. 177–8; $[\alpha]_D$ +24·3 γ-Lactone, M.p. 99–103	
45–8	$+93{\cdot}6 \rightarrow +18{\cdot}8^{20}$ (c = 4 in H_2O)	v.s. H_2O; s. EtOH, gl. acetic; i. eth.	PREP. Bates *et al.*, p. 481 EST. *J.B.C.* **204**, 1011 (1953)	*m*-Nitrophenylhydrazone, M.p. 163 2,5-Dichlorophenylhydrazone, M.p. 136–7 *p*-Toluenesulphonylhydrazone, M.p. 149; $[\alpha]_D$ −36 (in pyr.) Phenylosazone, M.p. 163; $[\alpha]_D^{18}$ −38·7 (in EtOH) (identical with osazones of D-lyxose and D-xylulose) DL-Xylose phenylosazone, M.p. 210–15 Di-*O*-benzylidene dimethylacetal, M.p. 211; $[\alpha]_D^{20}$ −9 (in $CHCl_3$). On bromine oxidation in the presence of $CdCO_3$ forms cadmium bromide double salt of cadmium xylonate, $Cd(C_5H_9O_6)_2 \cdot CdBr_2 \cdot 2H_2O$; $[\alpha]_D^{20}$ +8·8 (in H_2O) Methyl ethers, see *Adv. Carbohyd. Chem.* **10**, 257 (1955)	Not fermented by yeasts.
	$-33{\cdot}2^{18}$ (in H_2O)	s. H_2O	PREP. *J.A.C.S.* **60**, 1201 (1938) *J.B.C.* **115**, 731 (1936) EST. *J.B.C.* **192**, 583 (1951) *J.A.C.S.* **76**, 5889 (1954) *B.J.* **63**, 542 (1956)	*p*-Bromophenylhydrazone, M.p. 129; $[\alpha]_D^{20}$ +23·7 → −31·2 (in pyr.) Phenylosazone, M.p. 163; $[\alpha]_D^{18}$ −38·7 (in EtOH) (identical with osazones of D-xylose and D-lyxose) DL-Xylose phenylosazone, M.p. 210–15 *O*-*iso*Propylidene deriv., M.p. 70–71; $[\alpha]_D^{25}$ +1·7 (in acet.)	Reduces Fehling's soln. in the cold. Gives Seliwanoff's test.
	$+33{\cdot}1^{20}$ (c = 2 in H_2O)	s. H_2O	PREP. *J.B.C.* **215**, 677 (1955) *Ber.* **68**, 18 (1935) EST. As for D-xylulose	*p*-Bromophenylhydrazone, M.p. 131; $[\alpha]_D^{20}$ −25·8 → +31·5 (in pyr.) Phenylosazone, M.p. 161–3 (identical with osazones of L-lyxose and L-xylose) DL-Xylose phenylosazone, M.p. 210–15	Reduces Fehling's soln. in the cold. Gives Seliwanoff's test.

No.	Name	Synonyms	Formula	M. wt.	Physical form
DEOXYHEXOSES					
21	2-Deoxy-D-glucose	D-2-Glucodesose	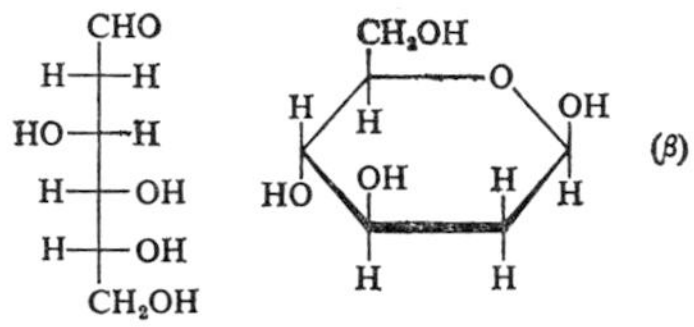	164·2	obtained as β-form; cryst.
22	6-Deoxy-D-glucose	D-Glucomethylose, D-*iso*rhamnose, D-*epi*rhamnose, *iso*rhodeose, chinovose	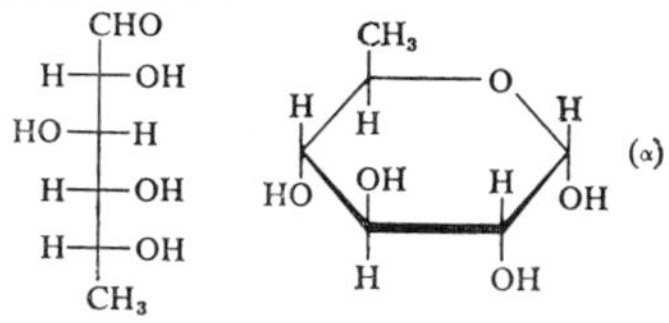	164·2	obtained as α-form; cryst. from Et acetate
23	Digitoxose	2,6-Dideoxy-*ribo*-hexose, 2,6-dideoxy-D-allose	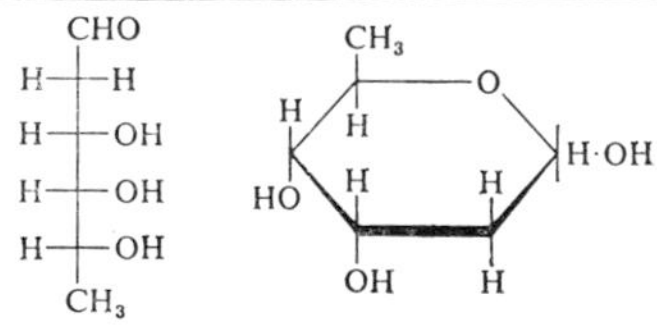	148·1	dense cryst.
24	D-Fucose	Rhodeose, D-galactomethylose, 6-deoxy-D-galactose	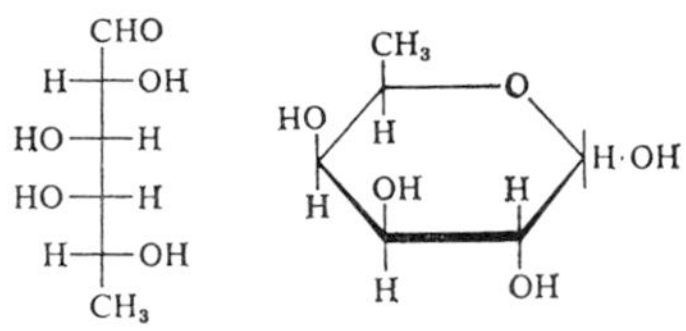	164·2	needles from EtOH
25	L-Fucose	L-Rhodeose, L-galactomethylose, 6-deoxy-L-galactose	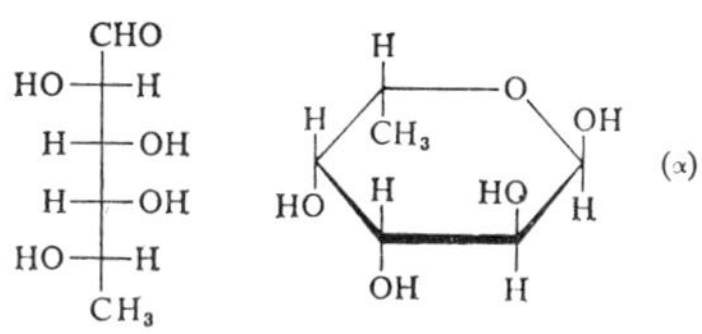	164·2	obtained as α-form; needles from EtOH
26	L-Rhamnose	L-Mannomethylose, 6-deoxy-L-mannose	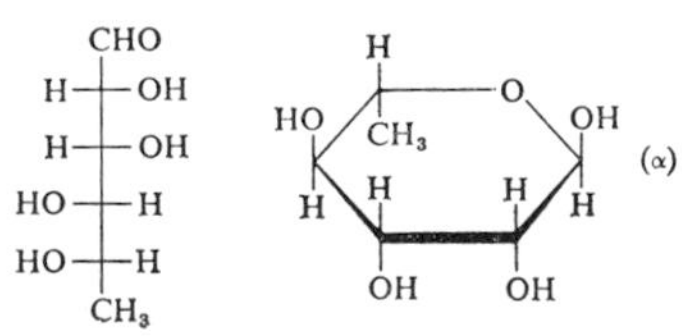	164·2; Hydrate 182·2	(α) col. monoc cryst.+ $1H_2O$ from H_2O (β) anhyd. needles from acet.

M.p.	$[\alpha]_D^t$	Solubility	References	Derivatives	General remarks
	GENERAL METHODS OF ESTIMATION OF METHYLPENTOSES		*J.B.C.* **175**, 595 (1948) *J.B.C.* **192**, 579 (1951) *Analyst* **80**, 268 (1955)		
48	+38·5 → +45·9[17·1] (c = 0·5 in H_2O)	s. H_2O, EtOH	PREP. *J.C.S.* **1949**, 2841 *J. Franklin Inst.* **253**, 277 (1952) EST. *P.S.E.B.M.* **89**, 579 (1955)	Methylphenylhydrazone, M.p. 157 Benzylphenylhydrazone, M.p. 158 α-Tetra-*O*-benzoate, M.p. 148; $[\alpha]_D^{16}$ +9 (in $C_2H_2Cl_4$) Dibenzylmercaptal, M.p. 154; $[\alpha]_D^{18}$ −40 (in EtOH)	α-form has been prepared.
40	+73·3 → +29·7[20] (c = 8 in H_2O)	s. H_2O EtOH	PREP. *Ber.* **62**, 373 (1929)	Phenylhydrazone, M.p. 184–5 Phenylosazone, M.p. 189–91; $[\alpha]_D$ −77 (in pyr.−EtOH, 2/3, v/v) (identical with osazone of D-rhamnose) *p*-Bromophenylosazone, M.p. 225 With HCl gives 5-methylfurfural	
8–10	+46 (in H_2O) +37 (in MeOH)	s. H_2O, EtOH, acetone; i. eth.	PREP. *Meth. Carb. Chem.* vol. 1, p. 204 (1962)	Phenylhydrazone, M.p. 204–9; $[\alpha]_D$ +215 (in pyr.) Oxime, M.p. 102	Sugar component of the glycosides digitoxin, gitoxin, and digoxin.
;	+153 → +76[20] (c = 4 in H_2O)	s. H_2O; sl. s. EtOH; i. eth.	PREP. See *J.C.S.* **1945**, 746	Methylphenylhydrazone, M.p. 181 Benzylphenylhydrazone, M.p. 178–9; $[\alpha]_D$ −14·9 (in MeOH) Diphenylhydrazone, M.p. 199 *p*-Bromophenylhydrazone, M.p. 184 *p*-Toluenesulphonylhydrazone, M.p. 175 With HCl gives 5-methylfurfural Methyl ethers, see *Adv. Carbohyd. Chem.* **10**, 268 (1955)	Not fermented by yeasts.
	−152·6 → −75·9[20] (c = 4 in H_2O)	s. H_2O; sl. s. EtOH	PREP. Bates *et al.*, p. 460 *J.A.C.S.* **61**, 1658 (1939)	Methylphenylhydrazone, M.p. 180 Benzylphenylhydrazone, M.p. 178; $[\alpha]_D$ +14·9 (in MeOH) Diphenylhydrazone, M.p. 198 *p*-Bromophenylhydrazone, M.p. 181–4 *p*-Toluenesulphonylhydrazone, M.p. 174; $[\alpha]_D$ −19 → −9 (in pyr.) With HCl gives 5-methylfurfural Methyl ethers, see *Adv. Carbohyd. Chem.* **10**, 269 (1955)	Not fermented by yeasts.
Iy- :, 94 23–6	(α) −8·6 → +8·2[20] (c = 4 hydrate in H_2O) (β) +38·4 → +8·9[20] (c = 4 in H_2O)	57[18], 109[40] H_2O; s. EtOH, MeOH; i. eth. benz.	PREP. *J.A.C.S.* **43**, 127 (1921) Bates *et al.*, p. 475	Phenylhydrazone, M.p. 159; $[\alpha]_D$ +57·1 → +44·3 (in H_2O) β-Naphthylhydrazone, M.p. 170 *p*-Nitrophenylhydrazone, M.p. 190–1; $[\alpha]_D$ −50·3 → −8·5 (in pyr.−EtOH, 1/1, v/v) 2,5-Dichlorophenylhydrazone, M.p. 171 Phenylosazone, M.p. 182; $[\alpha]_D^{20}$ +94 (in pyr.) β-Tetra-*O*-acetate, M.p. 98–99; $[\alpha]_D^{19}$ +14·1 (in $C_2H_2Cl_4$) Methyl ethers, see *Adv. Carbohyd. Chem.* **10**, 266 (1955)	Not fermented by yeasts.

No.	Name	Synonyms	Formula	M. wt.	Physical form

HEXOSES AND RELATED SUBSTANCES

No.	Name	Synonyms	Formula	M. wt.	Physical form
27	*N*-Acetyl-D-galactosamine	*N*-Acetylchondrosamine, 2-acetamido-2-deoxy-D-galactose	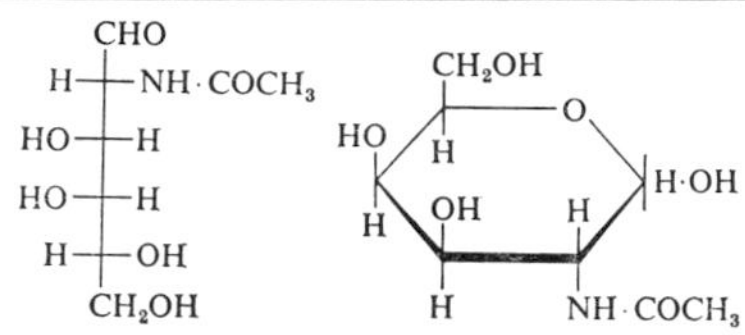	221·2	cryst.
28	*N*-Acetyl-D-glucosamine	2-Acetamido-2-deoxy-D-glucose	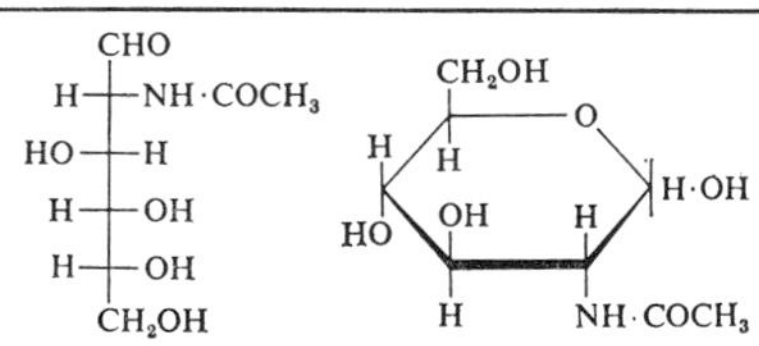	221·2	col. needles
29	*N*-Acetyl-D-mannosamine	2-Acetamido-2-deoxy-D-mannose	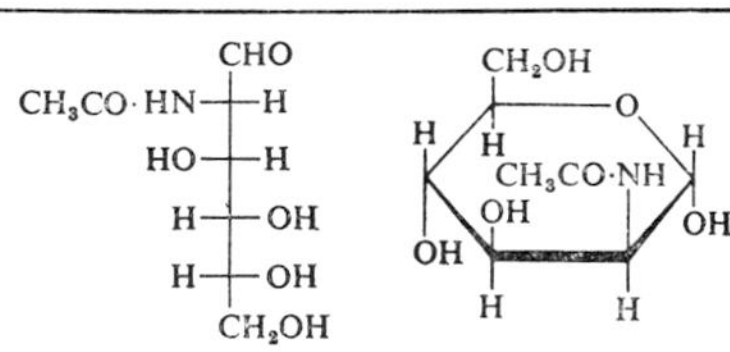	221·2; Hydrate, 239·2	large prisms+ $1H_2O$
30	*N*-Acetyl-neuraminic acid	Lactaminic acid, gynaminic acid, ovine sialic acid, 5-acetamido-3,5-dideoxy-D-*glycero*-D-*galacto*-nonulosonic acid	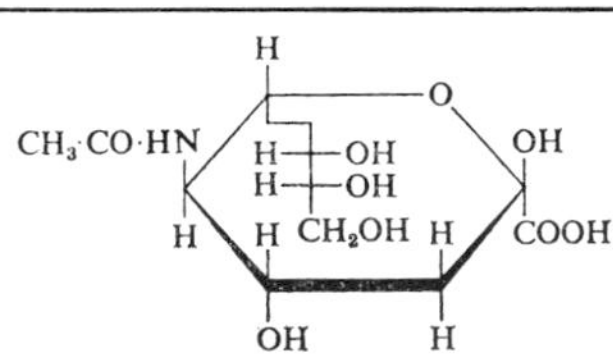	309·2	cryst.
31	Arbutin	Hydroquinone-β-D-glucoside, ursin	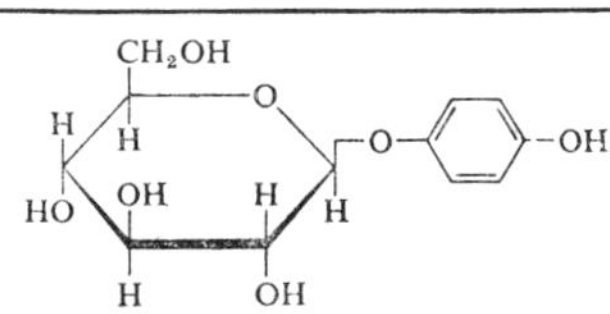	272·2; Hydrate, 290·2	long needles+ $1H_2O$
32	2,3-Diketo-L-gulonic acid		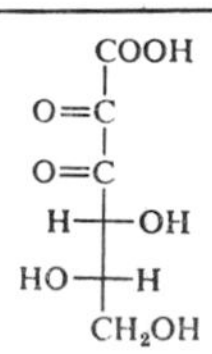	192·2	Ba, Ca salts amorphous

.p.	$[\alpha]_D^t$	Solubility	References	Derivatives	General remarks
	GENERAL METHODS OF ESTIMATION OF HEXOSES		*J.B.C.* **220**, 583 (1956) *B.J.* **58**, 288 (1954) *J. Physiol.* **132**, 289 (1956) *J.B.C.* **181**, 149 (1949) *J.B.C.* **195**, 19 (1952) KETOSES. *J.B.C.* **192**, 583 (1951) *P.S.E.B.M.* **74**, 117 (1950) *B.J.* **63**, 542 (1956) HEXURONIC ACIDS. *Analyt. Chem.* **28**, 1098 (1956)		
-3	$+86{\cdot}1^{27}$ (final, c = 1 in H_2O) $+131 \rightarrow +98_{5461}$ (c = 0·5 in H_2O)	s. H_2O	PREP. *J.A.C.S.* **76**, 301 (1954) EST. *J.B.C.* **217**, 959 (1955) *B.J.* **51**, 379 (1952)	Generally identified by Morgan–Elson reaction and by hydrolysis to galactosamine	Lower M.p.'s have been recorded. Form with M.p. 120–2 may be monohydrate.
	$+55{\cdot}6 \rightarrow +41{\cdot}3$ (c = 1 in H_2O)	s. H_2O	PREP. *J.A.C.S.* **76**, 301 (1954) *J.A.C.S.* **78**, 4722 (1956) EST. *J.B.C.* **217**, 959 (1955) *B.J.* **51**, 379 (1952)	Generally identified by Morgan–Elson reaction and by hydrolysis to glucosamine	
-9	$-9{\cdot}4 \rightarrow +9{\cdot}7^{20}$ (c = 10 in H_2O)	s. H_2O	PREP. *J.A.C.S.* **81**, 2403 (1959)	Generally identified by the Morgan–Elson reaction	
-7 d.	-32 ± 1^{22} (c = 2 in H_2O)	s. H_2O, MeOH; sl. s. EtOH; i. eth., acet., $CHCl_3$	PREP. *Biochem. Preps.* **7**, 1 (1960) *B.B.A.* **39**, 161 (1960)	Methyl glycoside, M.p. 200; $[\alpha]_D^{23}$ −55	One of the sialic acids which are *N*-acetyl, *N*-glycolyl or *N*-acetyl-*O*-acetylneuraminic acids.
	-64^{20} (c = 3 in H_2O)	s. H_2O, EtOH, eth.	PREP. *J.C.S.* **1923**, 717 *J.C.S.* **1930**, 2729	Penta-*O*-acetate, M.p. 146; $[\alpha]_D$ +28·8 (in acetone)	Non-reducing sugar. $FeCl_3$-blue.
	Ba salt $-6{\cdot}8^{22}$ (in 0·1N-HCl) Ca salt $-8{\cdot}3^{22}$ (in 0·1N-HCl)	s. H_2O	PREP. *B.J.* **39**, 1 (1945) *J.B.C.* **216**, 539 (1955)	2,4-Dinitrophenylhydrazone, M.p. 280	Free acid known only in solution.

No.	*Name*	*Synonyms*	*Formula*	*M. wt.*	*Physical form*
33	D-Fructose	Laevulose, fruit sugar	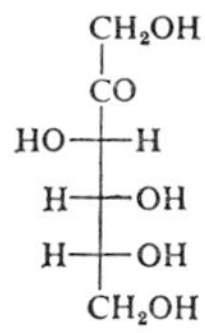 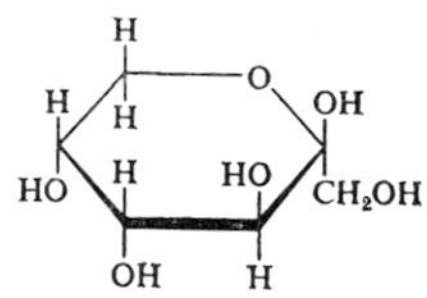	180·2	obtained as β-form; v. hygr. col. prisms or needles
34	D-Galactaric acid	Mucic acid, galacto-saccharic acid, tetrahydroxyadipic acid	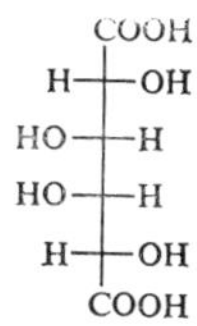	210·1	col. cryst. or wh. powder
35	Galactitol	Dulcitol, dulcite, melampyrin	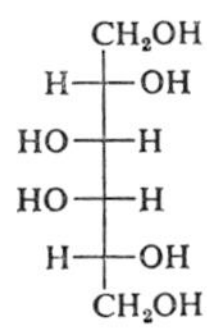	182·2	col. monocl. prisms
36	D-Galactonic acid	D-Lactonic acid	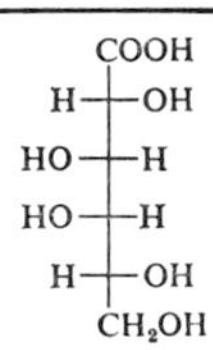	196·2	anhyd. needles from EtOH; $+\frac{1}{2}H_2O$ from aq. EtOH; $+2H_2O$ from H_2O
37	—, K salt		$C_6H_{11}O_7K.H_2O$	252·3	cryst.
38	—, Ca salt		$(C_6H_{11}O_7)_2Ca.5H_2O$	520·5	cryst.
39	D-Galactonic acid, γ-lactone	D-Galactono-1,4-lactone	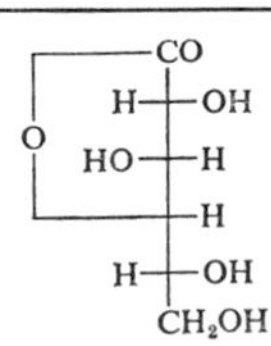	178·1; Hydrate, 196·2	needles $+1H_2$

M.p.	$[\alpha]^t_D$	*Solubility*	*References*	*Derivatives*	*General remarks*
02–4 d.	$-132{\cdot}2 \rightarrow -92{\cdot}4^{20}$ (c = 4 in H_2O)	375^{20}, 740^{55} H_2O; s. MeOH, EtOH, pyr., acet., gl. acetic	REVIEW. *Adv. Carbohyd. Chem.* 7, 53 (1952) EST. *J.B.C.* **127**, 601 (1939) *J.B.C.* **192**, 583 (1951) *P.S.E.B.M.* **74**, 117 (1950) *Scand. J. clin. Lab. Invest.* **7**, 305 (1955) *B.J.* **42**, 397 (1948)	Methylphenylosazone (not readily formed by glucose), M.p. 158–60; $[\alpha]_D$ +83·5 (in pyr.–EtOH) *o*-Nitrophenylhydrazone, M.p. 162 *p*-Nitrophenylhydrazone, M.p. 180–1 Phenylosazone, M.p. 204–5 (identical with osazones of D-glucose and D-mannose) 2,5-Dichlorophenylhydrazone, M.p. 154; $[\alpha]^{22}_D$ +5·3 (in pyr.) *β*-Penta-*O*-acetate, M.p. 108–9; $[\alpha]^{20}_D$ −120·9 (in $CHCl_3$) 2,3-4,5-Di-*O*-*iso*propylidene deriv., M.p. 97; $[\alpha]^{22}_D$ −32·9 (in H_2O) 1,2-4,5-Di-*O*-*iso*propylidene deriv., M.p. 119–20; $[\alpha]^{20}_D$ −161·3 (in H_2O) Methyl ethers, see *Adv. Carbohyd. Chem.* 7, 53 (1952)	Recrystallize from MeOH. Gives Seliwanoff's test. Cryst. sugar is thought to be pyranose, but in soln. appreciable amounts of the furanose and open chain forms are present. In combination only the furanose form is found.
55 25)	Inactive	$0{\cdot}33^{14}$ H_2O; s. alkalis; sp. s. eth., EtOH		Dimethyl ester, M.p. 205 Diethyl ester, M.p. 163–4 Diamide, M.p. 220 d. Dibenzimidazole deriv., M.p. 298	Recrystallize from H_2O. M.p. depends markedly on rate of heating. Reduces ammoniacal $AgNO_3$ but not Fehling's soln.
8–9	Inactive	$3{\cdot}0^{14}$ H_2O; sp. s. EtOH, eth.	REVIEW. *Adv. Carbohyd. Chem.* **4**, 211 (1949)	Hexa-*O*-acetate, M.p. 168–9	
hyd., ; O, –2; O, –20	$-13{\cdot}6^{20}$ (initial, in H_2O)	s. H_2O	PREP. *Bur. Stand. J. Res.* **11**, 649 (1933)	Amide, M.p. 176; $[\alpha]^{20}_D$ +31·8 (in H_2O) Phenylhydrazide, M.p. 203; $[\alpha]^{20}_D$ +10·4 (in H_2O) Et ester, pentaacetyl, M.p. 101–2	Dihydrate readily loses H_2O by air drying.
	$+3{\cdot}1^{20}$ (in H_2O)	s. H_2O	PREP. *J.A.C.S.* **61**, 340 (1939)		
	+2·9 (in H_2O)	s. H_2O	PREP. *Bur. Stand. J. Res.* **6**, 1145 (1931)		Loses part of H_2O at 100°. Rest is lost with decomp. at 140°.
yd., 5 -12); ate,	$-77{\cdot}4^{20}$ (anhyd. in H_2O)		PREP. *Bur. Stand. J. Res.* **11**, 649 (1933)		Salts generally prepared by neutralization of lactone.

No.	*Name*	*Synonyms*	*Formula*	*M. wt.*	*Physical form*
40	D-Galactosamine HCl	Chondrosamine HCl, 2-amino-2-deoxy-D-galactose HCl	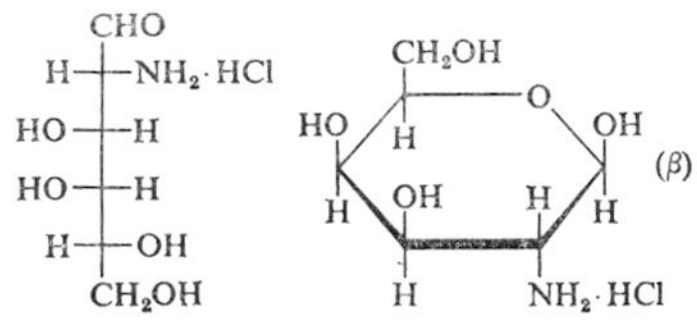	215·6; Free base, 179·2	(α) needles (β) cryst.
41	D-Galactose		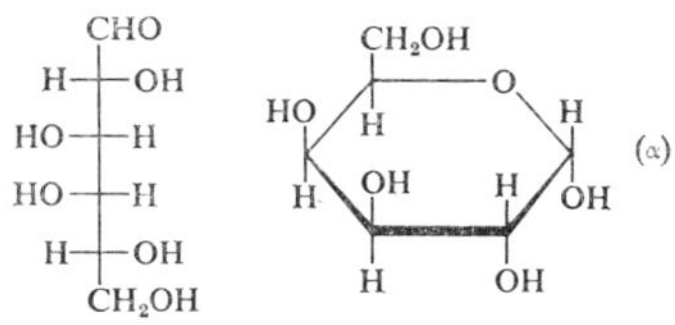	180·2; Hydrate, 198·2	(α) prisms or needles $+1H_2O$ from H_2O; anhyd. plates from EtOH
42	D-Galacturonic acid		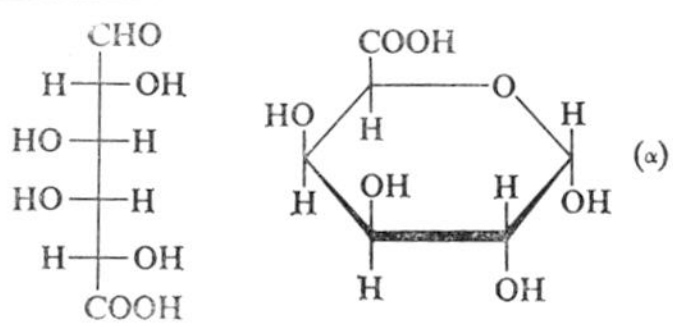	194·1; Hydrate, 212·2	(α) needles $+1H_2O$ (β) anhyd.
43	—, Na salt		$C_6H_9O_7Na$	216·1	obtained as β-form; cryst.
44	—, Ca salt		$(C_6H_9O_7)_2Ca.H_2O$	444·4	obtained as α-form; prisms
45	D-Glucaric acid	D-Glucosaccharic acid, saccharic acid	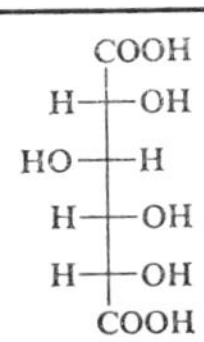	210·1	deliq. needles from EtOH
46	—, KH salt		$C_6H_8O_8.KH$	248·2	cryst.
47	D-Gluconic acid	Dextronic acid, maltonic acid, glycogenic acid	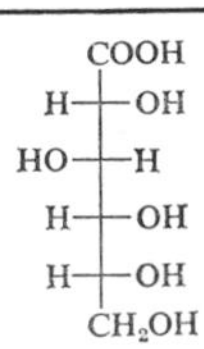	196·2	cryst.

M.p.	$[\alpha]^t_D$	*Solubility*	*References*	*Derivatives*	*General remarks*
α) 185 β) 187	(α) +121 → +95[20] (in H_2O) (β) +44·5 → +95[20] (in H_2O)	 (β) s. H_2O	REVIEW. Kent & Whitehouse, *Biochemistry of the Amino Sugars*, Butterworth (1955) *Adv. Carbohyd. Chem.* **7**, 247 (1952) PREP. *J.A.C.S.* **76**, 301 (1954) EST. *Analyt. Chem.* **28**, 1743 (1956) *B.J.* **61**, 586 (1955) *Meth. biochem. Anal.* **6**, 289 (1958)	*N*-2,4-Dinitrophenyl deriv., M.p. 184–6; $[\alpha]_D$ +84 (in 80% EtOH) *N*-2-Hydroxynaphthylidene deriv., M.p. 175–8; $[\alpha]_D$ +287 → +258 (in MeOH) α-Pentaacetate, M.p. 178; $[\alpha]^{20}_D$ +102 (in $CHCl_3$) β-Pentaacetate, M.p. 235 d.; $[\alpha]^{20}_D$ +7 (in $CHCl_3$) With phenylhydrazine forms D-galactosazone	Usually obtained as β-form. Reducing sugar. Gives ninhydrin reaction. Negative Molisch test.
·) Anhyd. 58; ydrate, 18–20	(α) +150·7 → +80·2[20] (c = 5 in H_2O) (β) +52·8 → +80·2[20] (c = 4 in H_2O)	10[0], 68[25] H_2O; v. sl. s. MeOH; 5·45[25] pyr.	PREP. Bates *et al.*, p. 462 EST. *Analyt. Chem.* **27**, 857 (1955)	α-Methylphenylhydrazone (+1H_2O), M.p. 190 *o*-Tolylhydrazone, M.p. 176 Phenylosazone, M.p. 196–7; $[\alpha]^{20}_D$ +0·80 → +0·34 (in pyr.–EtOH) (identical with osazones of D-talose and D-tagatose) Phenylosotriazole, M.p. 110–11 α-Penta-*O*-acetate, M.p. 96; $[\alpha]^{20}_D$ +106·7 (in $CHCl_3$); i. H_2O β-Penta-*O*-acetate, M.p. 142; $[\alpha]^{20}_D$ +25 (in $CHCl_3$); i. H_2O Yields galactaric acid (q.v.) on oxidation with HNO_3 Methyl ethers, see *Adv. Carbohyd. Chem.* **10**, 273 (1955)	Generally obtained as α-form
· Sinters, 0–11;)–60 d. 160 d.	(α) +107·0 → +51·9[20] (c = 4 hydrate in H_2O) (β) +31·1 → +56·7[20] (c = 4 anhyd. in H_2O)	(α) s. H_2O, hot EtOH; sp. s. cold EtOH; i. eth.	PREP. *Biochem. Preps.* **3**, 74 (1953) *J. Res. natn. Bur. Stand.* **33**, 389, 401 (1944) (β) *J. Res. natn. Bur. Stand.* **31**, 33 (1943) EST. *Analyt. Chem.* **28**, 1098 (1956)	Brucine salt, M.p. 180 d.; $[\alpha]^{20}_D$ −7·7 (in H_2O) Phenylhydrazone, M.p. 140–1 *p*-Bromophenylhydrazone, M.p. 150–1 Methyl ethers, see *Adv. Carbohyd. Chem.* **9**, 136 (1954)	Generally obtained as α-form or as mixture of α- and β-forms.
	+11·5 → +36·0[20] (c = 4 in H_2O)	s. H_2O; i. EtOH	PREP. *J. Res. natn. Bur. Stand.* **32**, 77 (1944)		
	+75·0 → +36·8[20] (c = 1·4 anhyd. in H_2O)	4·9[20], 10[100] H_2O; i. EtOH	PREP. *J. Res. natn. Bur. Stand.* **32**, 77 (1944)		
–6 d.	+6·86 → +20·6 (c = 2·8 in H_2O)	v.s. H_2O, EtOH	PREP. *Ber.* **58**, 2344 (1925) *Ber.* **70**, 2402 (1937)	1,4-Lactone, M.p. 133 3,6-Lactone, M.p. 144; $[\alpha]_D$ +37·9 → +22·5 (in H_2O) 1,4–3,6-Dilactone, M.p. 134 Diamide, M.p. 172–3 Diphenylhydrazide, M.p. 212 d. Dibenzimidazole deriv., M.p. 243	Crystals lactonize spontaneously to a mixture of lactones. Reduces ammoniacal $AgNO_3$ but not Fehling's soln. Dilactone and methyl esters of monolactones reduce Fehling's soln.
	+5·1[20] (c = 0·8 in H_2O)		PREP. *J.C.S.* **1944**, 65		
·6	−6·72[20] (in H_2O)	s. H_2O; i. EtOH, eth.	PREP. *J.A.C.S.* **55**, 2512 (1933)	1,4-Lactone, M.p. 133–5; $[\alpha]^{20}_D$ +68 (c = 5 in H_2O) 1,5-Lactone, M.p. 146; $[\alpha]^{25}_D$ +66·7 → +8·5 (c = 5 in H_2O) Amide, M.p. 144; $[\alpha]^{20}_D$ +31·2 (in H_2O) Phenylhydrazide, M.p. 200; $[\alpha]^{20}_D$ +12 (in H_2O)	

No.	Name	Synonyms	Formula	M. wt.	Physical form
48	D-Gluconic acid, Na salt		$C_6H_{11}O_7Na$	218·1	cryst.
49	—, Ca salt		$(C_6H_{11}O_7)_2Ca.H_2O$	448·4	wh. cryst.
50	D-Glucosamine	Chitosamine, 2-amino-2-deoxy-D-glucose	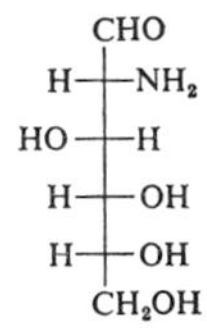 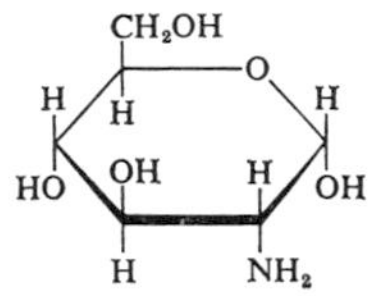 (α)	179·2	(α) wh. cryst. powder (β) wh. cryst. powder
51	—, hydrochloride		$C_6H_{13}O_5N.HCl$	215·6	(α) monocl. cryst.
52	D-Glucose	Dextrose, grape sugar	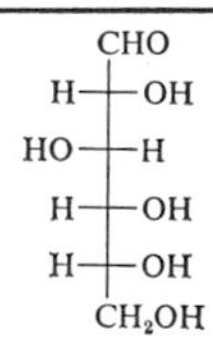 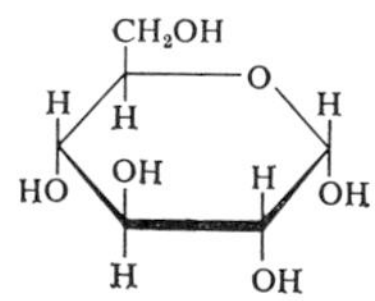 (α) 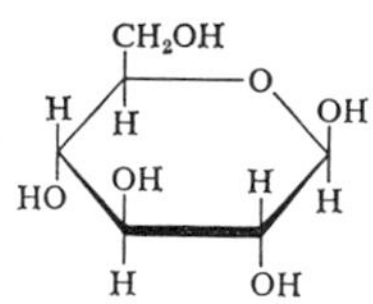 (β)	180·2; Hydrate, 198·2	(α) monocl. plates $+1H_2O$ from H_2O; anhyd. rh. crys from MeOH (β) cryst. from gl. acetic
53	D-Glucosone	D-*arabino*-Hexosone, 2-hydroxy-*arabino*-hexose	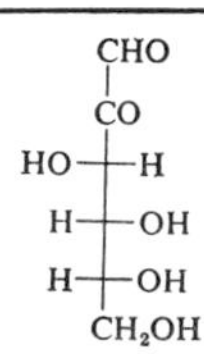	178·1	syrup
54	D-Glucuronic acid		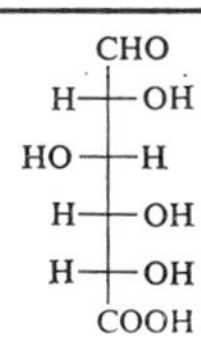 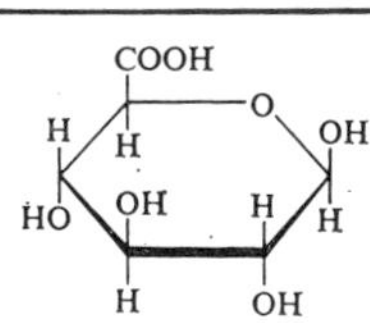 (β)	194·1	obtained as β-form; needles
55	—, Na salt		$C_6H_9O_7Na.H_2O$	234·1	col. cryst.
56	—, K salt		$C_6H_9O_7K.2H_2O$	268·3	col. cryst.

M.p.	$[\alpha]^{t}_{D}$	*Solubility*	*References*	*Derivatives*	*General remarks*
	$+11{\cdot}8^{20}$ (c = 20 in H_2O)	s. H_2O			
178	$+11{\cdot}03$ (in H_2O)	sl. s. H_2O; i. EtOH, eth.	PREP. *Mfg. Chem.* **16**, 239 (1945)		
(α) 88 (β) 120	(α) $+100 \rightarrow +47{\cdot}5^{20}$ (c = 1 in H_2O) (β) $+14 \rightarrow +47{\cdot}5^{20}$ (c = 1 in H_2O)	v.s. H_2O; s. hot MeOH; sl. s. EtOH; i. eth., $CHCl_3$	REVIEW. Kent & Whitehouse, *Biochemistry of the Amino Sugars*, Butterworth (1955) *Adv. Carbohyd. Chem.* **7**, 247 (1952) EST. *Analyt. Chem.* **28**, 1743 (1956) *Analyst* **76**, 88 (1951) *B.J.* **61**, 586 (1955) *Meth. biochem. Anal.* **6**, 289 (1958)	Diphenylhydrazone, M.p. 162 With phenylhydrazine forms D-glucosazone *N*-Benzoyl deriv., M.p. 204–6; $[\alpha]^{16}_{D}$ +31 (in H_2O) *N*-2,4-Dinitrophenyl deriv., M.p. 202–4; $[\alpha]_{D}$ +65 (in H_2O–EtOH) α-Penta-acetate, M.p. 139; $[\alpha]^{20}_{D}$ +92 (in $CHCl_3$) β-Penta-acetate, M.p. 187–9; $[\alpha]^{20}$ +1·2 (in $CHCl_3$)	Generally obtained as α-form. Reducing sugar. Gives ninhydrin reaction. Negative Molisch test. pK_a 7·80.
α) De- omp. a. 250	(α) $+100 \rightarrow +72{\cdot}5$ (c = 1 in H_2O) (β) $+25 \rightarrow +72{\cdot}5$ (c = 1 in H_2O)	sl. s. H_2O	PREP. *Org. Synth.* **Coll. 3**, 430 (1955)	α-Tetra-*O*-acetate of hydrochloride, M.p. 230; $[\alpha]_{D}$ +29·7 (in H_2O)	
) Hy- rate 83; nhyd., 46) 148–50	(α) $+112{\cdot}2 \rightarrow +52{\cdot}7^{20}$ (c = 3·9 anhyd. in H_2O) (β) $+18{\cdot}7 \rightarrow +52{\cdot}7^{20}$ (c = 3·9 in H_2O)	(α) Hydrate, $32{\cdot}3^{0}$, $82{\cdot}0^{25}$ H_2O; sl. s. EtOH; i. eth., acet. (β) 154^{15} H_2O; sl. s. EtOH; i. eth.	EST. *J. Physiol.* **130**, 456 (1956) *J. Physiol.* **132**, 289 (1956) *Analyst* **81**, 430 (1956) *J.B.C.* **195**, 19 (1952) *J.B.C.* **181**, 149 (1949)	α-Phenylhydrazone, M.p. 159–60; $[\alpha]^{20}_{D}$ −87 → −50 (in H_2O) β-Phenylhydrazone, M.p. 140–2; $[\alpha]^{20}_{D}$ −5 → −50 (in H_2O) 2,5-Dichlorophenylhydrazone, M.p. 160 Phenylosazone, M.p. 204–5 (identical with osazones of D-mannose and D-fructose) *p*-Nitrophenylhydrazone, M.p. 189–95 Phenylosotriazole, M.p. 195–6; $[\alpha]^{20}_{D}$ −81·6 (in pyr.) α-Penta-*O*-acetate, M.p. 114; $[\alpha]^{20}_{D}$ +101·6 (in $CHCl_3$) β-Penta-*O*-acetate, M.p. 135; $[\alpha]^{20}_{D}$ +3·8 (in $CHCl_3$) 1,2–5,6-Di-*O*-*iso*propylidene, M.p. 110–11; $[\alpha]^{20}_{D}$ −18·5 (in H_2O) Methyl ethers, see *Adv. Carbohyd. Chem.* **5**, 145 (1950)	Glucose of commerce is generally largely α-glucose·H_2O.
	$-10{\cdot}6 \rightarrow +7{\cdot}9^{15}$ (c = 8·5 in H_2O)	v.s. H_2O	REVIEW. *Adv. Carbohyd. Chem.* **11**, 43 (1956) PREP. *Helv. chim. Acta* **17**, 510 (1934)	Methylphenylhydrazone, M.p. 170; $[\alpha]_{D}$ −268 (in pyr.) Tri-*O*-*iso*propylidene deriv. of hydrate, M.p. 125; $[\alpha]^{15}_{D}$ −6·6 (in MeOH) Forms glucose phenylosazone in the cold with phenylhydrazine	Reduces Fehling's soln. in the cold. Blue colour with Benedict's uric acid reagent. The 2-keto group is probably stably hydrated.
5 d.	$+11{\cdot}7 \rightarrow +36{\cdot}3$ (in H_2O)	s. H_2O, EtOH	REVIEWS. *Adv. Carbohyd. Chem.* **8**, 251 (1953); **9**, 186 (1954) PREP. *Adv. Carbohyd. Chem.* **8**, 231 (1953)	*p*-Nitrophenylhydrazone, M.p. 224–5 2,4-Dinitrophenylhydrazone, M.p. 205 d. Cinchonine salt, M.p. 202–4; $[\alpha]^{20}_{D}$ +139·9 (in H_2O) Brucine salt +1H_2O, M.p. 156–7; $[\alpha]^{20}_{D}$ −15·1 (in H_2O) Methyl ethers, see *Adv. Carbohyd. Chem.* **9**, 133 (1954)	Unstable in aq. soln. forming lactone. Reduces Fehling's soln. Gives Bial's test.
	$-0{\cdot}6 \rightarrow +22{\cdot}5^{20}$ (in H_2O)	s. H_2O	PREP. *J.A.C.S.* **76**, 917 (1954)		H_2O remains *in vacuo* over $CaCl_2$.
		s. H_2O	PREP. *J.A.C.S.* **76**, 917 (1954)		Loses 1H_2O *in vacuo* over $CaCl_2$.

10. Carbohydrates and Related Compounds

No.	Name	Synonyms	Formula	M. wt.	Physical form
57	D-Glucuronic acid, lactone	D-Glucurono-lactone, D-glucurone	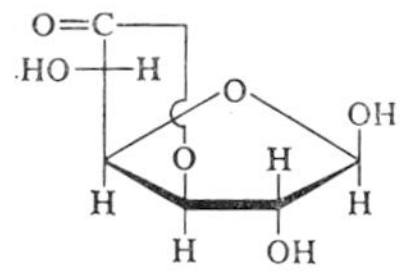 (β)	176·1	monocl. plates
58	L-Gulonic acid	Xylosecarboxylic acid	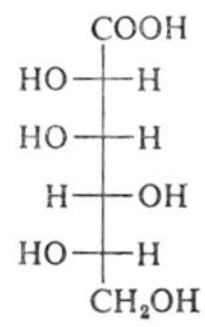	196·2; γ-lactone, 178·1	cryst. from EtOH as lactone
59	L-Gulose		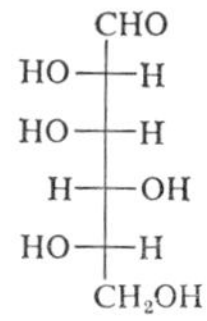 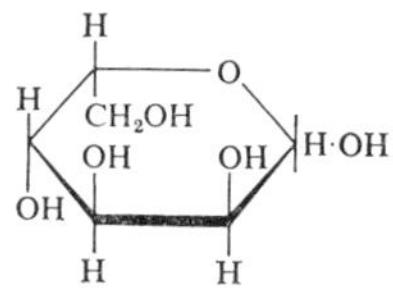	180·2; Hydrate, 198·2	syrup
60	L-Guluronic acid		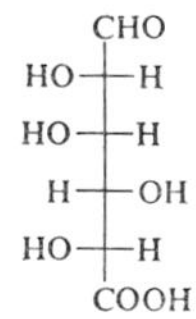 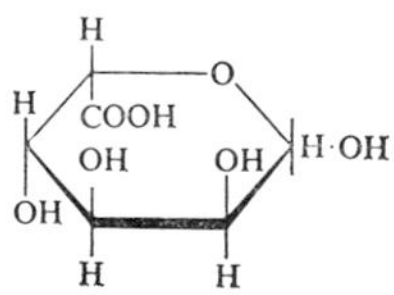	194·1	cryst. from EtOH as lactone
61	L-Iduronic acid		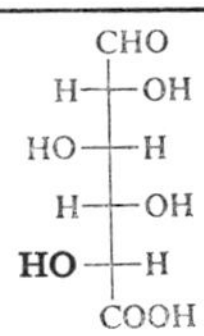 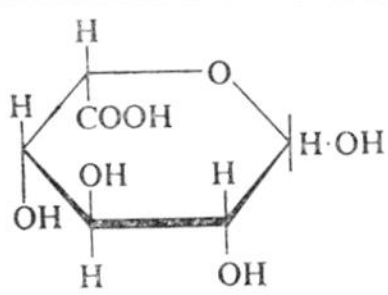	194·1	cryst.
62	2-Keto-D-gluconic acid	2-Oxo-D-gluconic acid, D-glucosonic acid, fructuronic acid	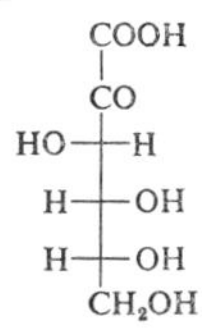	194·1	syrup or hygr. cryst.
63	2-Keto-D-gluconic acid, Ca salt		$(C_6H_9O_7)_2Ca.3\frac{1}{2}H_2O$	489·4	cryst.
64	5-Keto-D-gluconic acid	5-Oxo-D-gluconic acid, L-sorburonic acid	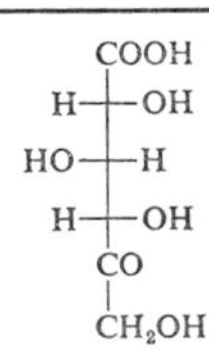	194·1	unstable; turns black and evolves gas
65	—, Ca salt		$(C_6H_9O_7)_2Ca.2\frac{1}{2}H_2O$	471·4	cryst.

M.p.	$[\alpha]^t_D$	Solubility	References	Derivatives	General remarks
180 d.	$+19{\cdot}2^{20}$ (in H_2O)			Oxime, M.p. 149–51; $[\alpha]_D$ $+14{\cdot}4$ (in H_2O)	
180 (186–8) (γ-lactone)	$+55^{20}$ (c = 1 in H_2O) Na salt, $+12{\cdot}7$ (c = 9 in H_2O)	s. H_2O	PREP. *B.J.* 56, 1 (1954) *J.A.C.S.* **74**, 5583 (1952)		
	$+20^{23}$ (in H_2O)	s. H_2O; sl. s. EtOH	PREP. *J.A.C.S.* **67**, 1713 (1945)	Benzylphenylhydrazone, M.p. 130–1; $[\alpha]_D$ $+29$ (in MeOH) α-L-Gulose · $CaCl_2$ · H_2O, M.p. 200–3; $[\alpha]^{24}_D$ $-18{\cdot}7 \rightarrow +11{\cdot}2$ (c = 5 in H_2O)	Reducing sugar.
141–2 (lactone)	$+81{\cdot}7^{22}$ (in H_2O)	s. H_2O	PREP. *Z.P.C.* **302**, 186 (1955)		
131–2	$+37 \rightarrow +33^{25}$ (c = 3 in H_2O)	s. H_2O, MeOH	PREP. *Meth. Carb. Chem.*, vol. 2, p. 32 (1962)		
	$-99{\cdot}62$ (K salt in HCl)		PREP. *J.A.C.S.* **66**, 243 (1944) *Ind. Engng Chem.* **32**, 1626 (1940) EST. *J.B.C.* **189**, 109 (1951) *J.B.C.* **215**, 353 (1955)	Et ester, M.p. 123–4; $[\alpha_D]$ $-66{\cdot}6$ (in H_2O) Me ester, M.p. 175–6; $[\alpha]^{20}_D$ $-76{\cdot}8$ (c = 2 in H_2O) Phenylhydrazone of Me ester, M.p. 163 Di-*O*-*iso*propylidene deriv. of Me ester, M.p. 52; $[\alpha]^{20}_D$ $-44{\cdot}7$ (in $CHCl_3$) Quinoxaline deriv., M.p. 199–200 d.; $[\alpha]^{20}_D$ $-87{\cdot}5$ (in N-NaOH)	
	$-70{\cdot}8^{20}$ (c = 2 in H_2O)	s. H_2O			
	$-14{\cdot}43^{20}$ (in H_2O)	s. H_2O	PREP. *J.A.C.S.* **55**, 3653 (1933) EST. *J.B.C.* **215**, 353 (1955) *Analyt. Chem.* **28**, 963 (1956)	*p*-Nitrophenylosazone, M.p. 206–10	Reduces Fehling's solution.
		i. H_2O			

10. Carbohydrates and Related Compounds

No.	Name	Synonyms	Formula	M. wt.	Physical form
66	2-Keto-L-gulonic acid	2-Oxo-L-gulonic acid	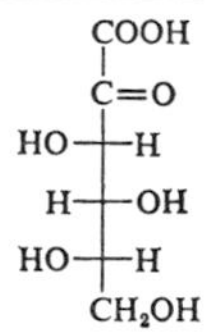	194·2	cryst.
67	D-Mannitol	D-Mannite	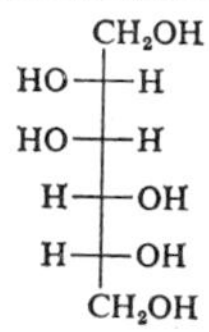	182·2	needles
68	D-Mannosamine HCl		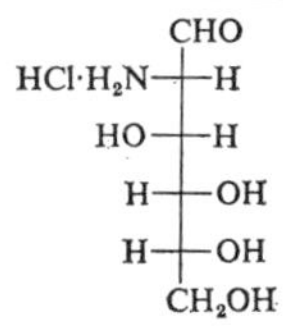 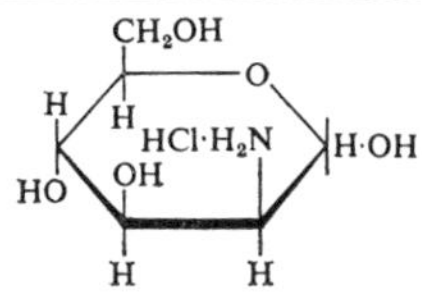	215·6; Free base, 179·2	cryst.
69	D-Mannose	Seminose, carubinose	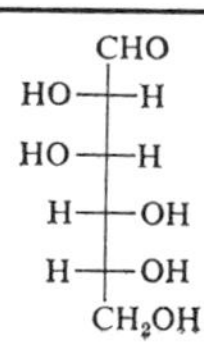 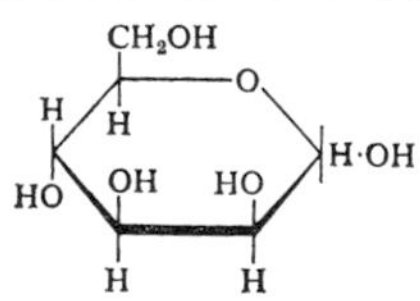	180·2	obtained as α- or β-form (α) cryst. mass (β) rh. needles
70	D-Mannuronic acid	Mannurone	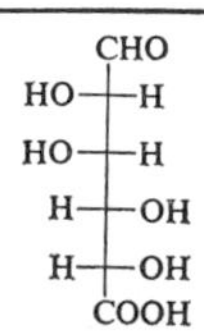 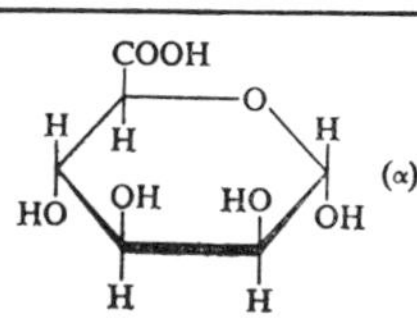	194·1	(α) v. hygr. micro-needles (β) micro-pillars
71	—, Na salt		$C_6H_9O_7Na$	216·1	wh. cryst. powder
72	—, K salt		$C_6H_9O_7K\cdot H_2O$	250·2	col. plates or prisms
73	α-Methyl-D-galacto-pyranoside	α-Methyl-galactoside	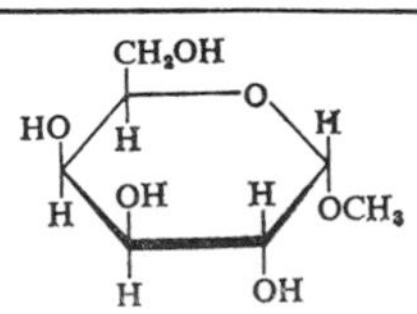	194·2; Hydrate, 212·2	needles+1H₂O

M.p.	$[\alpha]^t_D$	*Solubility*	*References*	*Derivatives*	*General remarks*
71	−48 (c = 1 in H_2O)	s. H_2O	PREP. *Helv. chim. Acta* **17**, 311 (1934)	Me ester, M.p. 155–7; $[\alpha]_D$ −25 (c = 1 in MeOH)	Rapidly reduces boiling Fehling's solution.
66	+28·6 (in borax soln.)	15·6[18] H_2O; s. hot EtOH; sl. s. pyr.; i. eth.	REVIEW. *Adv. Carbohyd. Chem.* **4**, 211 (1949) EST. *P.S.E.B.M.* **70**, 141 (1949)	Hexa-*O*-acetate, M.p. 126; $[\alpha]_D$ +25 (in $CHCl_3$)	
	−4·6[20] (c = 10 in 5% HCl)	s. H_2O, MeOH	PREP. *J.A.C.S.* **81**, 2403 (1959)	*N*-Acetyl deriv., M.p. 128–9; $[\alpha]^{20}_D$ −9·4 → +9·7 (c = 10 in H_2O)	Reducing.
) 133 132	(α) +29·3 → +14·2[20] (c = 4 in H_2O) (β) −17·0 → +14·2[20] (c = 4 in H_2O)	248[17] H_2O; sp. s. EtOH; i. eth.	PREP. Bates *et al.*, p. 471	D-Mannose·$CaCl_2$·$4H_2O$, M.p. 101–2; $[\alpha]^{20}_D$ −31·3 → +6·0 (in H_2O) Phenylhydrazone, M.p. 199–200; $[\alpha]^{20}_D$ +26·3 → +6·3 (9 hr) → +33·8 (in pyr.) Benzylphenylhydrazone, M.p. 170–1; $[\alpha]_D$ +29·8 (in MeOH) Phenylosazone, M.p. 204–5 (identical with osazones of D-glucose and D-fructose) α-Penta-*O*-acetate, M.p. 64; $[\alpha]^{20}_D$ +54·9 (in $CHCl_3$) β-Penta-*O*-acetate, M.p. 117–18; $[\alpha]^{20}_D$ −25·3 (in $CHCl_3$) Methyl ethers, see *Adv. Carbohyd. Chem.* **8**, 217 (1953) 2,3–5,6-Di-*O*-*iso*propylidene, M.p. 122; $[\alpha]^{16}_D$ +11·9 → +1·1 (in H_2O) (complex mutarotation); non-reducing	
Sinters ; kens –30 165–7	(α) +16·01[25] → −6·05 (in H_2O) (β) −47·9[25] → −23·94 (in H_2O)	(α) s. H_2O (β) s. H_2O	PREP. *J.B.C.* **100**, 397 (1933) *J.C.S.* **1935**, 517 *J.C.S.* **1944**, 587	Lactone, M.p. 143–4; $[\alpha]^{21}_D$ +50 → +94 (in H_2O) (β-form)	
	−6·6[20] (in H_2O)				
	−5·6[20] (in H_2O)				
–12 hyd.)	+196 (in H_2O, anhyd. form)	s. H_2O, MeOH	REVIEW. *Adv. Carbohyd. Chem.* **12**, 158 (1957)		Non-reducing sugar.

10. Carbohydrates and Related Compounds

No.	*Name*	*Synonyms*	*Formula*	*M. wt.*	*Physical form*
74	β-Methyl-D-galacto-pyranoside	β-Methyl-galactoside	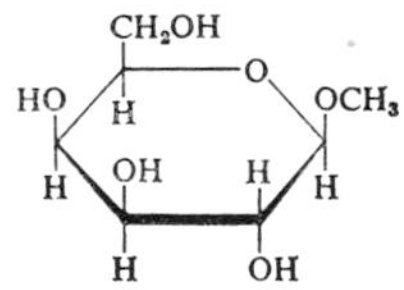	194·2	cryst.
75	α-Methyl-D-gluco-pyranoside	α-Methyl-glucoside	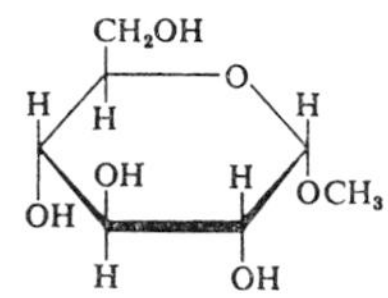	194·2	cryst. mass from EtOH
76	β-Methyl-D-gluco-pyranoside	β-Methyl-glucoside	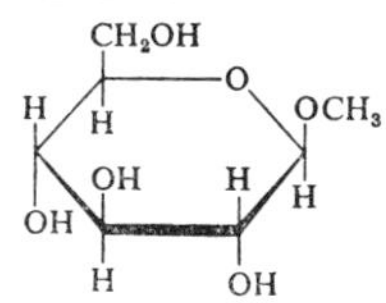	194·2	cryst. + $\frac{1}{2}H_2O$ from hot EtOH
77	Muramic acid	2-Amino-3-*O*-(1-carboxyethyl)-2-deoxy-D-glucose	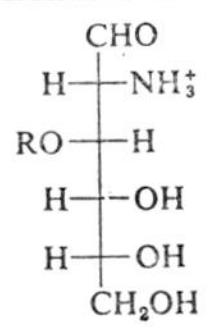 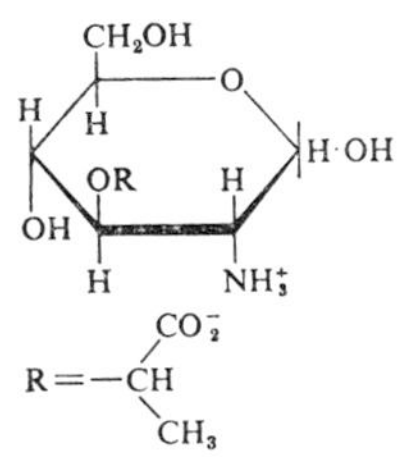	251·2; Hydrate, 269·2	cryst. + $1H_2O$ from aq. EtOH
78	Salicin	Saligenin-β-D-glucopyranoside	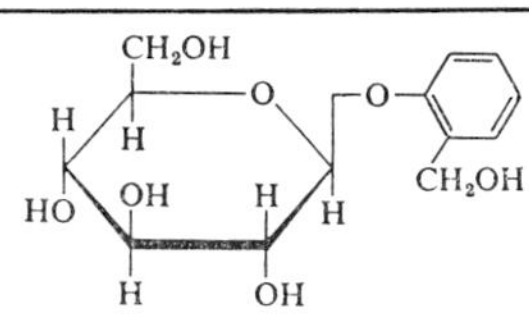	286·2	needles or prisms
79	Scyllitol	Scylloinositol, quercin	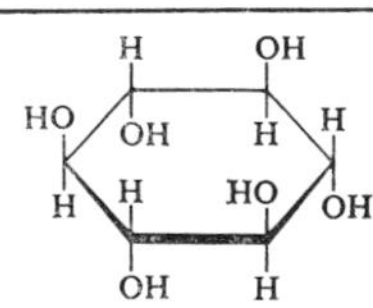	180·2; Hydrate, 234·2	prisms + $3H_2O$
80	D-Sorbitol	Sorbitol, D-glucitol	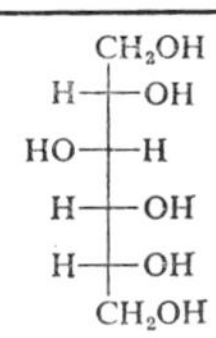	182·2; Hydrate, 200·2	needles + $1H_2O$

M.p.	$[\alpha]_D^t$	Solubility	References	Derivatives	General remarks
78–80	+0·61 (in H_2O)	s. H_2O, MeOH	REVIEW. *Adv. Carbohyd. Chem.* **12,** 158 (1957)		Non-reducing sugar.
55–6	+158[20] (c = 10 in H_2O)	s. H_2O, MeOH, hot EtOH	PREP. *Org. Synth.* **Coll. 1,** 364 (1958)		Non-reducing sugar.
0 (anhyd.)	−31 (c = 8 in H_2O, anhyd. form)	s. H_2O, MeOH	REVIEW. *Adv. Carbohyd. Chem.* **12,** 158 (1957)		Non-reducing sugar.
	+109±3[20] (c = 2 in H_2O)	s. H_2O	PREP. *B.J.* **71,** 333 (1959)	Generally identified by the Morgan–Elson reaction	Reducing sugar.
	−62[20] (c = 5 in H_2O)	s. H_2O, NaOH soln., gl. acetic, pyridine; v. sl. s. EtOH; i. $CHCl_3$, eth.	*J.C.S.* **89,** 814 (1906) *J.A.C.S.* **48,** 262 (1926)	Penta-*O*-acetate, M.p. 130; $[\alpha]_D^{25}$ −18·5 (in $CHCl_3$)	Non-reducing sugar. H_2SO_4-purple.
		v. sl. s. H_2O; i. EtOH, MeOH, $CHCl_3$, benz.	PREP. *J.C.S.* **109,** 2383 (1912) *J.B.C.* **68,** 399 (1926) DETECTION. *B.J.* **81,** 425 (1961)	Hexa-*O*-acetate, M.p. 290	Non-reducing sugar.
rate, ... yd.,	−2·0 (in H_2O) +6·5 (in borax) +30·9 (in NH_4 molybdate)	s. H_2O, hot EtOH; v. sl. s. cold EtOH; i. eth.	REVIEW. *Adv. Carbohyd. Chem.* **4,** 211 (1949) EST. *P.S.E.B.M.* **70,** 141 (1949)	Hexa-*O*-acetate, M.p. 101–2; $[\alpha]_D$ +10 (in $CHCl_3$); i. H_2O	

No.	Name	Synonyms	Formula	M. wt.	Physical form
81	L-Sorbose	L-Sorbinose, 2-oxo-L-*xylo*-hexose	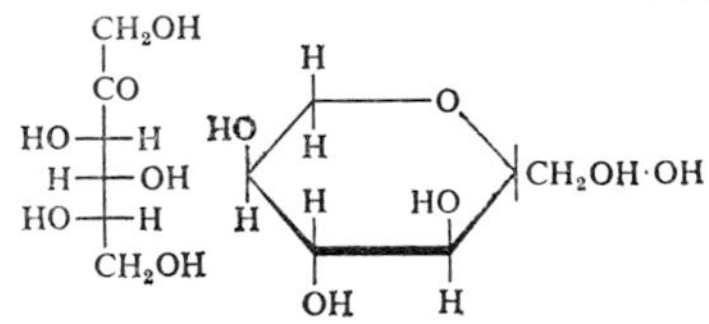	180·2	rh. cryst.
82	D-Tagatose	2-Oxo-D-*lyxo*-hexose	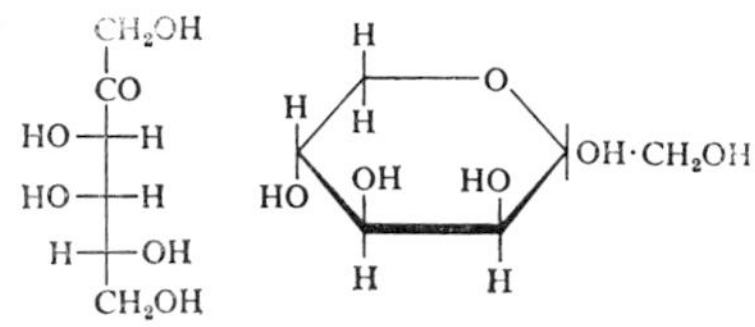	180·2	cryst.
83	D-Talose		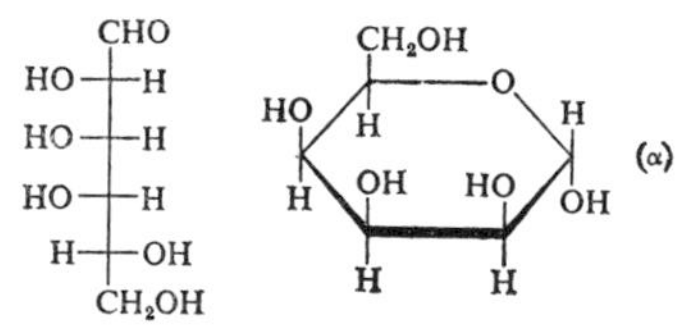	180·2	(α) cryst. from aq. MeOH; (β) cryst. from aq. EtOH

HEPTOSES AND RELATED SUBSTANCES

No.	Name	Synonyms	Formula	M. wt.	Physical form
84	D-α-Gluco-heptose	D-Gluco-D-*gulo*-heptose, D-*glycero*-D-*gulo*-heptose	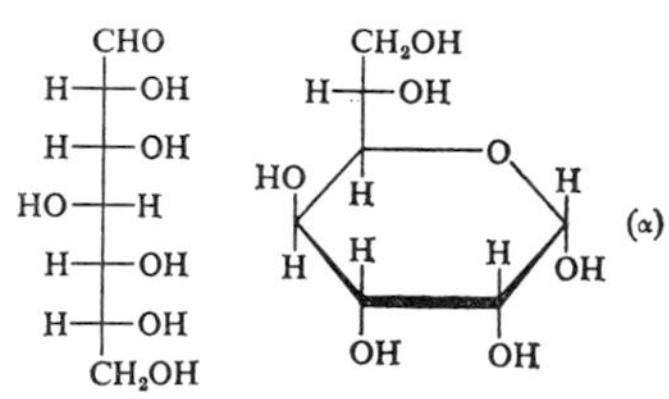	210·2	plates from H_2(
85	D-*manno*-Heptulose	D-*manno*-Keto-heptose	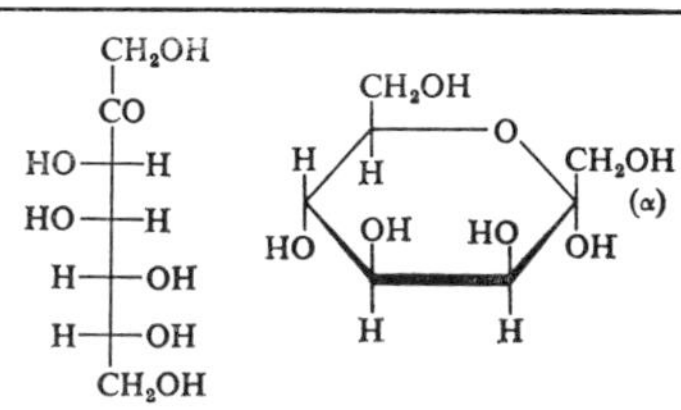	210·2	prisms from MeOH
86	Sedo-heptulosan	2,7-Anhydro-β-D-*altro*-heptulo-pyranose	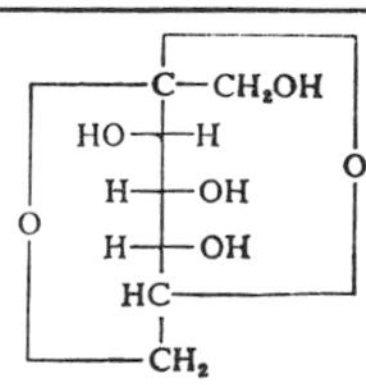	192·2; Hydrate, 210·2	col. prisms + 1H from 90% EtO anhyd. prisms from absolute MeOH

M.p.	$[\alpha]^t_D$	*Solubility*	*References*	*Derivatives*	*General remarks*
165	$-43{\cdot}7 \rightarrow -43{\cdot}4^{20}$ (c = 12 in H_2O) (mutarotation complex)	55^{17} H_2O; sp. s. hot EtOH, MeOH	REVIEW. *Adv. Carbohyd. Chem.* **7**, 99 (1952) PREP. Bates *et al.*, p. 479	2,5-Dichlorophenylhydrazone, M.p. 116–17; $[\alpha]^{22}_D$ $-32{\cdot}6$ (in EtOH) Phenylosazone, M.p. 168; $[\alpha]^{15}_D$ -13 (in pyr.–EtOH) (identical with osazones of L-gulose and L-idose) *p*-Bromophenylosazone, M.p. 181; dextrorotatory (in pyr.–EtOH) Phenylosotriazole, M.p. 158–9; $[\alpha]^{20}_D$ $-46{\cdot}7$ (in pyr.)	Not fermented by yeasts. Gives Seliwanoff's test.
134–5	$+2{\cdot}7 \rightarrow -4$ (in H_2O)	s. H_2O; sp. s. EtOH	REVIEW. *Adv. Carbohyd. Chem.* **7**, 99 (1952)	Phenylosazone, M.p. 196–7; $[\alpha]_D$ $+80 \rightarrow +34$ (in pyr.–EtOH) (identical with osazones of D-galactose and D-talose) *p*-Bromophenylosazone, M.p. 180–2 Phenylosotriazole, M.p. 110–11; $[\alpha]_D$ $-30{\cdot}6$ (in pyr.)	Gives Seliwanoff's test.
(α) 133–4 (β) 120–1	(α) $+68 \rightarrow +21^{20}$ (c = 4 in H_2O) (β) $+13 \rightarrow +21^{20}$ (c = 4 in H_2O)	s. H_2O	PREP. *J. Res. natn. Bur. Stand.* **19**, 189 (1937)	Methylphenylhydrazone, M.p. 154 (220)	Reducing.
	GENERAL METHODS OF ESTIMATION OF HEPTOSES		*J.B.C.* **204**, 983 (1953) *J.B.C.* **205**, 661 (1953)		
193	$-28{\cdot}7 \rightarrow -20{\cdot}2$ (c = 4 in H_2O)	9·5 H_2O; v. sl. s. EtOH	PREP. *J.C.S.* **1931**, 2864	β-Naphthylhydrazone, M.p. 182; $[\alpha]^{17}_D$ -13 (in pyr.) Phenylosazone, M.p. 194–5; $[\alpha]^{20}_D$ $-1 \rightarrow +35{\cdot}6$ (in pyr.–EtOH) α-Hexa-*O*-acetate, M.p. 164; $[\alpha]^{20}_D$ $+87$ (in $CHCl_3$); s. EtOH; i. H_2O β-Hexa-*O*-acetate, M.p. 135; $[\alpha]^{20}_D$ $+4{\cdot}8$ (in $CHCl_3$); s. EtOH; i. H_2O	Not fermented by yeasts.
152	$+29{\cdot}2$ (in H_2O)	s. H_2O; sp. s. EtOH	PREP. *J.A.C.S.* **61**, 1654 (1939)	*p*-Bromophenylhydrazone, M.p. 179 Phenylosazone, M.p. 200 α-Hexa-*O*-acetate, M.p. 110; $[\alpha]^{20}_D$ $+41{\cdot}5$ (in $CHCl_3$)	Not fermented by yeasts.
anhyd., 155–6; hydrate, 101–2	-146^{20} (c = 2 anhyd. in H_2O)	s. H_2O	PREP. *J.A.C.S.* **74**, 2200 (1952)	*O-iso*Propylidene deriv., M.p. 226–7; $[\alpha]^{20}_D$ -124 (in H_2O) Tetra-*O*-benzoate, M.p. 165–6; $[\alpha]^{20}_D$ -195 (in $CHCl_3$)	Non-reducing. Stable to alkali. Partially hydrolysed by acid to sedoheptulose (9% sedoheptulose at 20°). Anhyd. form stable in desiccator. Hydrate stable in air.

No.	Name	Synonyms	Formula	M. wt.	Physical form
87	Sedoheptulose	D-*altro*-Heptulose	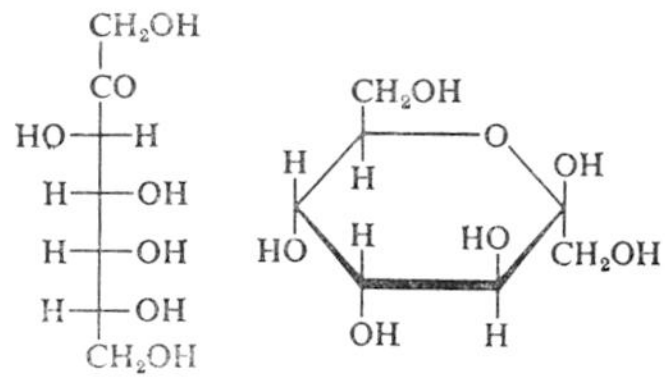 (β)	210·2	syrup

OLIGOSACCHARIDES

Reviews

1. *Adv. Carbohyd. Chem.* **17**, 121 (1962).
2. *Chromat. Rev.* **4**, 114 (1962).

DISACCHARIDES

88	Cellobiose	Cellose, 4-*O*-β-D-glucopyranosyl-D-glucopyranose	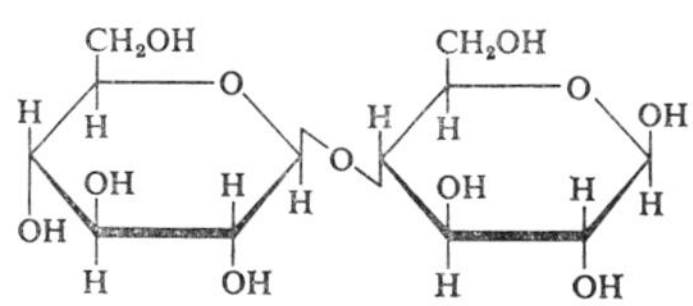 (β)	342·3	obtained as β-form; col. needles
89	Chondrosine	2-Amido-2-deoxy-3-*O*-(β-D-glucopyranosyluronic acid)-D-galactose	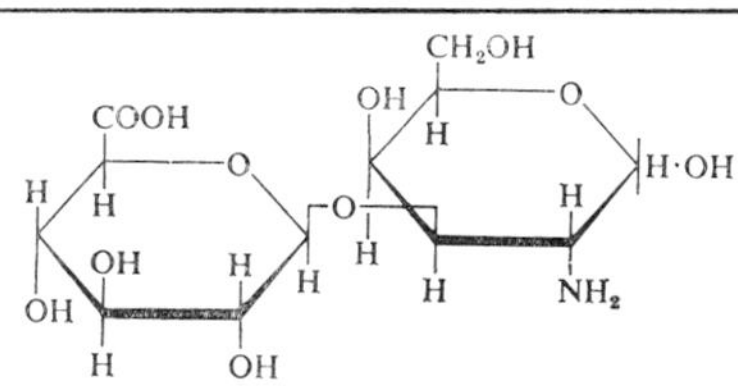	355·3	fine needles
90	*N,N'*-Diacetyl-chitobiose	Chitobiose, 2-acetamido-2-deoxy-4-*O*-(2-acetamido-2-deoxy-β-D-glucopyranosyl)-D-glucopyranose	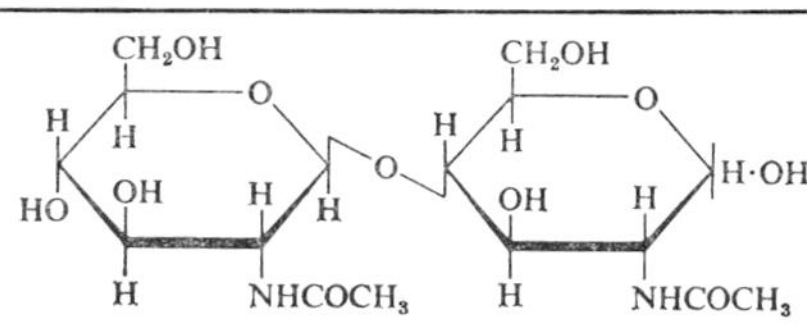	424·4	cryst. from aq. EtOH
91	Gentiobiose	Amygdalose, 6-*O*-β-D-glucopyranosyl-D-glucopyranose	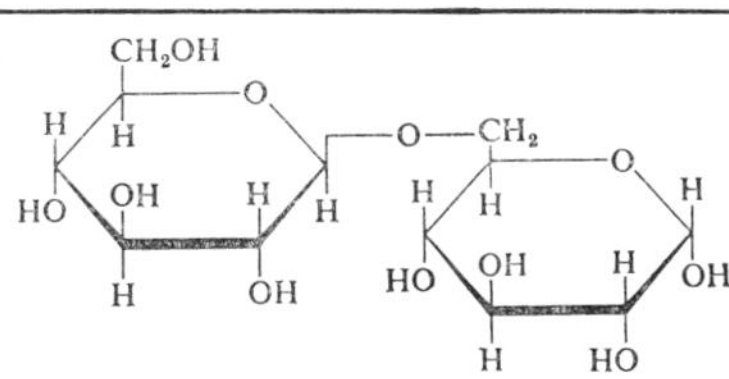 (α)	342·3	(α) cryst.+ 2MeOH from MeOH (β) cryst. from 90% EtOH
92	Hyalobiuronic acid	2-Amino-2-deoxy-3-*O*-(β-D-glucopyranosyluronic acid)-D-glucose	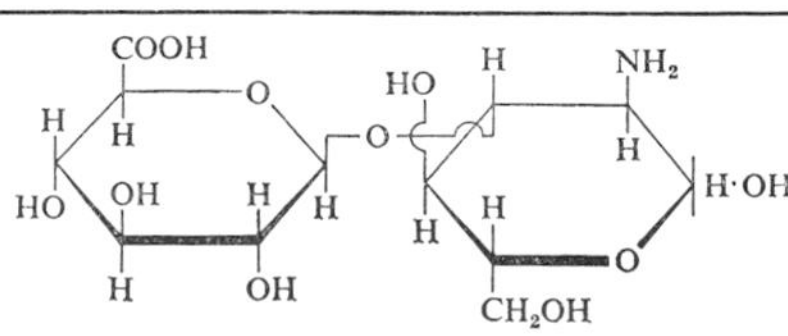	355·3; Hydrate, 373·3	crystalline+ $1H_2O$, lost over P_2O_5 at 80°

M.p.	$[\alpha]^t_D$	*Solubility*	*References*	*Derivatives*	*General remarks*
	+8·2 (in H_2O)	s. H_2O; sp. s. EtOH	PREP. *J.A.C.S.* 78, 4717 (1956)	Phenylosazone, M.p. 197 d. *p*-Bromophenylosazone, M.p. 227–8 d. Hexa-*O*-acetate, M.p. 98–100; $[\alpha]^{20}_D$ +59·0 (in $CHCl_3$) Forms sedoheptulosan (q.v.) on treatment with acid	Not fermented by yeasts.
	GENERAL METHOD OF ESTIMATION OF DISACCHARIDES		*B.J.* 58, 288 (1954)		
Darkens 180; decomp. 225	+14·2 → +34·6[20] (c = 8 in H_2O)	s. H_2O; i. EtOH, eth.	PREP. *Org. Synth.* Coll. 2, 122 (1943) Bates *et al.* p. 459	Phenylosazone, M.p. 208–10; $[\alpha]^{18}_D$ −6·5 (in pyr.–EtOH, 2/3,v/v) Phenylosotriazole, M.p. 164–5; $[\alpha]_D$ −50·8 *β*-Octa-*O*-acetate, M.p. 202; $[\alpha]^{20}_D$ −14·7 (in $CHCl_3$) *α*-Octa-*O*-acetate, M.p. 229; $[\alpha]^{20}_D$ +41·0 (in $CHCl_3$)	Reducing sugar. Not fermented by yeasts.
	+42[24] (c = 2 in H_2O) +40[24] (c = 1 in 0·05M-HCl)	s. in dil. acid	PREP. *J.A.C.S.* 74, 1491 (1952) *J.A.C.S.* 76, 5686 (1954)	Me ester HCl, M.p. 159–61; $[\alpha]^{23}_D$ +42 (in H_2O) Benzoate, M.p. 126–9; $[\alpha]_D$ +83[22] (in $CHCl_3$)	Reducing sugar.
245–7 and 260–7	+25 → +18 (c = 1 in H_2O)	s. H_2O	PREP. *J.A.C.S.* 77, 1296 (1955); 79, 5046 (1957) *J.C.S.* 1958, 2218	Alcohol, M.p. 102–5; $[\alpha]_D$ −11 (in H_2O)	Reducing sugar; acetyl-free sugar isol. but not characterized.
(*α*) 86 (+ 2MeOH) (*β*) 190–5	(*α*) +21·4 → +8·7[20] (c = 5 alcoholate in H_2O) [+31 → +9·6[20] (in H_2O)] (*β*) −11 → +9·6[20] (in H_2O)	s. H_2O, hot EtOH, hot MeOH	PREP. *Org. Synth.* Coll. 3, 428 (1955) Bates *et al.*, p. 463	Phenylosazone, reported M.p.'s vary between 163 and 180; values of Bates *et al.* M.p. 170–3; $[\alpha]^{20}_D$ −74·8 (in pyr.–EtOH) Phenylosotriazole alcoholate, M.p. 91–93; $[\alpha]_D$ −34 *β*-Octa-*O*-acetate, M.p. 196; $[\alpha]^{20}_D$ −5·3 (in $CHCl_3$) *α*-Octa-*O*-acetate, M.p. 188–9; $[\alpha]^{20}_D$ +52·4 (in $CHCl_3$)	Generally obtained as *β*-form. Reducing sugar. Not fermented by top yeasts.
190 d.	+22·5[23] (c = 1 in 1·0M-HCl) +34 → +30[24] (c = 1 in 0·1M-HCl)	s. dil. acid	PREP. *J.B.C.* 205, 205 (1953) *J.A.C.S.* 84, 3029, 3030 (1962)	*N*-Acetyl-, $[\alpha]_D$ + 31 to +32 (in H_2O) Me ester hepta-*O*-acetate, M.p. 120; $[\alpha]_D$ +27 (in $CHCl_3$)	Reducing sugar.

10. Carbohydrates and Related Compounds

No.	*Name*	*Synonyms*	*Formula*	*M. wt.*	*Physical form*
93	Isomaltose	Brachyose, 6-*O*-α-D-glucopyranosyl-D-glucose	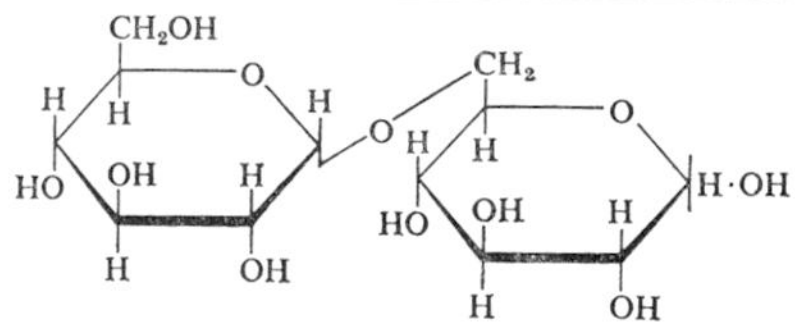	342·3	amorphous
94	Kojibiose	Sakebiose, 2-*O*-α-D-glucopyranosyl-D-glucose	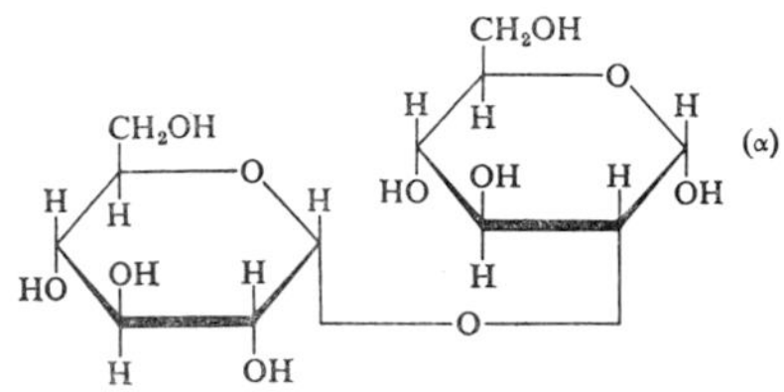	342·3	fine prisms from aq. MeOH, α-form
95	Lactose	Milk sugar, lactobiose, 4-*O*-β-D-galacto-pyranosyl-D-gluco-pyranose	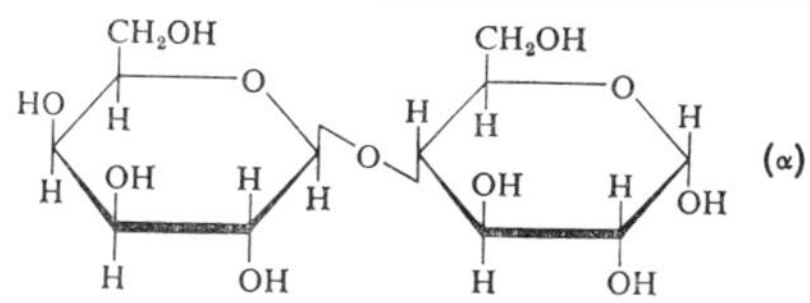	342·3; Hydrate, 360·3	(α) cryst. + $1H_2O$ (β) anhyd. Anhyd. forms (α and β) hygr.
96	Laminari-biose	3-*O*-β-D-Gluco-pyranosyl-D-glucose	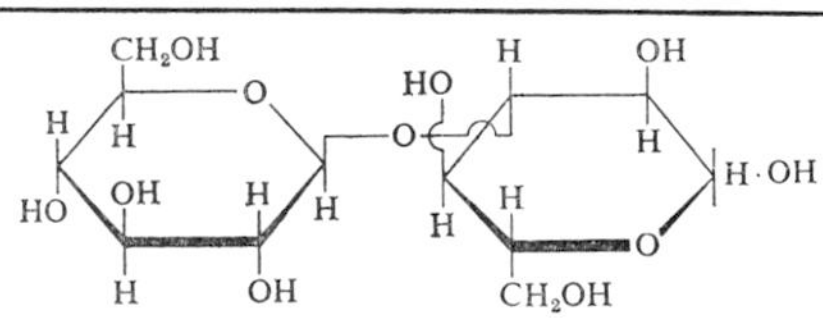	342·3	needles
97	Maltose	Malt sugar, malto-biose, 4-*O*-α-D-glucopyranosyl-D-glucopyranose	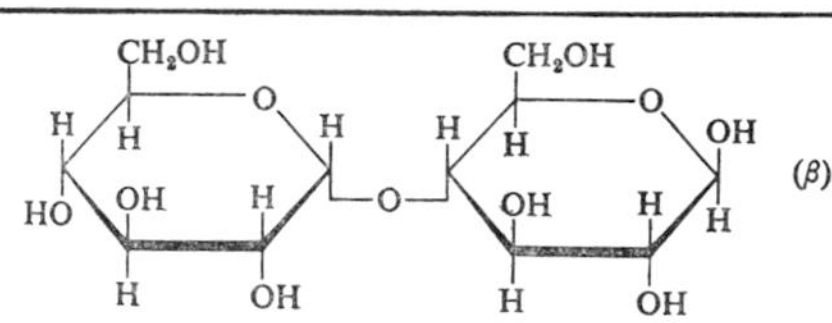	342·3; Hydrate, 360·3	obtained as β-form, fine needles + $1H_2O$
98	Melibiose	6-*O*-α-D-Galacto-pyranosyl-D-glucopyranose	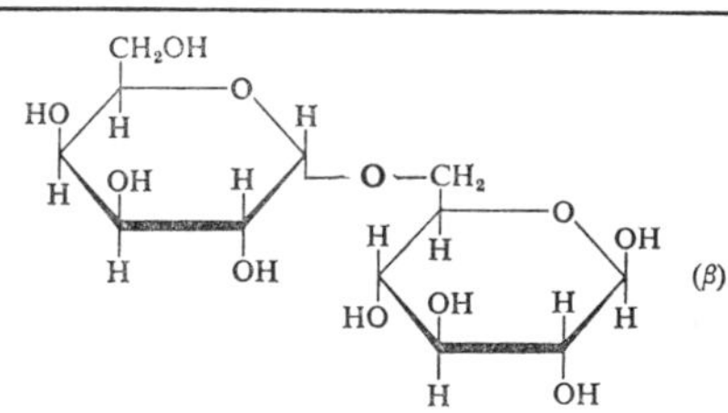	342·3; Hydrate, 378·3	obtained as β-form + $2H_2O$
99	Nigerose	3-*O*-α-D-Gluco-pyranosyl-D-glucose	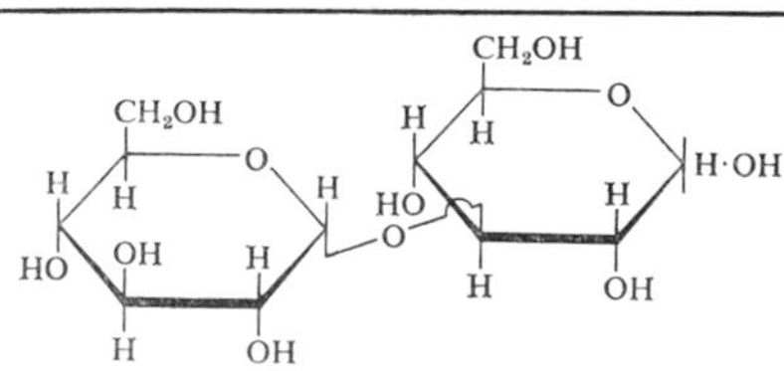	342·3	

M.p.	$[\alpha]_D^t$	*Solubility*	*References*	*Derivatives*	*General remarks*
	$+119 \rightarrow$ $+122^{25}$ (in H_2O)	s. H_2O, MeOH	PREP. *B.J.* **67**, 49 (1957) *J.A.C.S.* **75**, 5911 (1953) *J.B.C.* **196**, 265 (1952)	β-Octa-*O*-acetate, M.p. 144–5; $[\alpha]_D$ +96 to $+99^{25}$ (in $CHCl_3$) 1-Phenylflavazole, M.p. 234	Reducing sugar; not fermented by yeasts.
38	$+162 \rightarrow$ $+137^{18}$ (c = 2·1 in H_2O)	s. H_2O	PREP. *Nature, Lond.* **182**, 1303 (1958); **189**, 753 (1961); **191**, 278 (1961)	α-Octa-*O*-acetate, M.p. 166; $[\alpha]_D$ +152 (in $CHCl_3$) β-Octa-*O*-acetate, M.p. 118; $[\alpha]_D$ +112 (in $CHCl_3$) Alcohol, $[\alpha]_D$ +81 (in H_2O)	Reducing sugar.
Hyd- te, 202; hyd., 3 252	(α) $+85{\cdot}0 \rightarrow$ $+52{\cdot}6^{20}$ (c = 7·6 hydrate in H_2O) [$+89{\cdot}4 \rightarrow$ $+55{\cdot}4^{20}$ on anhyd. basis] (β) $+34{\cdot}9 \rightarrow$ $55{\cdot}4^{20}$ (c = 4 in H_2O)	$21{\cdot}6^{25}$, 139^{89} H_2O; sl. s. gl. acetic; i. MeOH, EtOH, eth.	REVIEW. *Adv. Carbohyd. Chem.* **16**, 159 (1961)	Benzylphenylhydrazone, M.p. 128; $[\alpha]_D^{20}$ −25·7 (in MeOH) Phenylosazone, M.p. 210–12; $[\alpha]_D^{20}$ $-25{\cdot}4 \rightarrow -7{\cdot}9$ (in MeOH) Phenylosotriazole, M.p. 180–1; $[\alpha]_D^{20}$ −43·6 α-Octa-*O*-acetate, M.p. 152; $[\alpha]_D^{20}$ +53·6 (in $CHCl_3$) β-Octa-*O*-acetate, M.p. 90; $[\alpha]_D^{20}$ −4·7 (in $CHCl_3$) Forms mucic acid on oxidation and hydrolysis with HNO_3	Generally obtained as α-lactose·H_2O. α-Lactose·H_2O loses H_2O at 130° and at 70° *in vacuo*. Reducing sugar. Fermented by lactose yeasts and lactose-adapted yeasts.
5–205	$+24 \rightarrow +19^{16}$ (c = 2 in H_2O)	s. H_2O, MeOH	PREP. *J.C.S.* **1952**, 1243 *J.C.S.* **1958**, 724, 729	α-Octa-*O*-acetate, M.p. 77–78; $[\alpha]_D$ +20 (in $CHCl_3$) β-Octa-*O*-acetate, M.p. 157–60; $[\alpha]_D$ −28 (in $CHCl_3$) Phenylosazone, M.p. 192–202; $[\alpha]_D$ −71 to −76 (in EtOH)	Reducing sugar.
drate, –3; yd., –5	$+111{\cdot}7 \rightarrow$ $+130{\cdot}4^{20}$ (c = 4 hydrate in H_2O)	108^{20} H_2O; v. sl. s. EtOH; i. eth.	PREP. Bates *et al.*, p. 470	β-Naphthylhydrazone, M.p. 176; $[\alpha]_D^{20}$ +10·6 (in MeOH) Phenylosazone, M.p. 206; $[\alpha]_D^{20}$ +82·6 (in pyr.–EtOH) α-Octa-*O*-acetate, M.p. 125; $[\alpha]_D^{20}$ +122·8 (in $CHCl_3$) β-Octa-*O*-acetate, M.p. 159–60; $[\alpha]_D^{20}$ +62·6 (in $CHCl_3$)	Reducing sugar. Fermented by yeasts in presence of glucose.
35 d.	$+111{\cdot}7 \rightarrow$ $+129{\cdot}5^{20}$ (c = 4 hydrate in H_2O)	s. H_2O; v. sl. s. EtOH	REVIEW. *Adv. Carbohyd. Chem.* **9**, 165 (1954) Bates *et al.*, p. 473	Phenylosazone, M.p. 178–9; $[\alpha]_D^{21}$ +43·2 (in pyr.) Phenylosotriazole, M.p. 153–4; $[\alpha]_D$ +61 (in EtOH) β-Octa-*O*-acetate, M.p. 177–8 d.; $[\alpha]_D^{20}$ +102·5 (in $CHCl_3$) On reduction yields melibiitol, M.p. 176–7; $[\alpha]_D$ +113 (in H_2O) Gives galactaric acid on oxidation and hydrolysis with HNO_3	Reducing sugar. Fermented by bottom yeasts but not by most top yeasts.
	+134 to +138 (c = 0·17 in H_2O)	s. H_2O	PREP. *J.C.S.* **1957**, 2448 *J.C.S* **1958**, 1342	β-Octa-*O*-acetate, M.p. 149–52; $[\alpha]_D$ +84 to +86 (in $CHCl_3$) Phenylosazone, M.p. 204–5	Reducing sugar.

No.	Name	Synonyms	Formula	M. wt.	Physical form
100	Sophorose	2-*O*-β-D-Gluco-pyranosyl-α-D-glucose	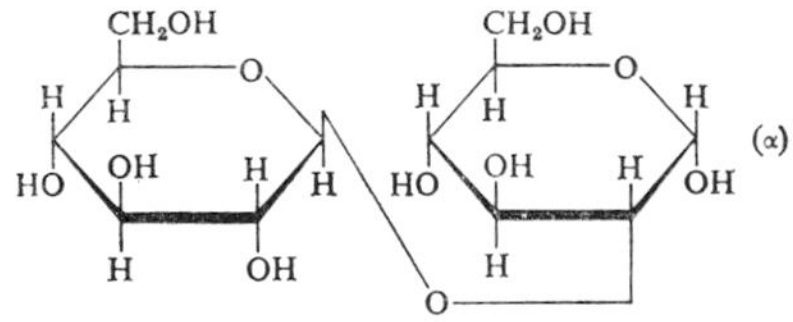	342·3; Hydrate, 360·3	long needles+ $1H_2O$
101	Sucrose	Cane sugar, saccharose, 1-*O*-α-D-glucopyranosyl-β-D-fructofuranoside	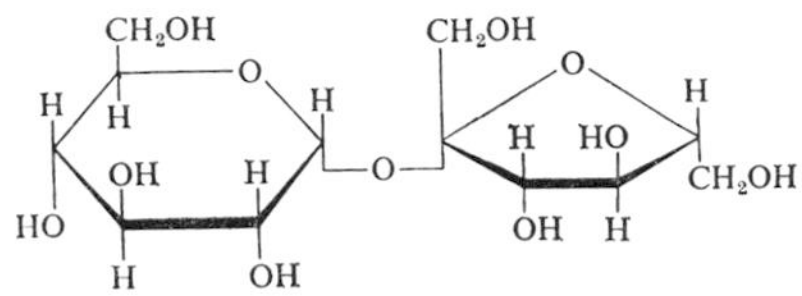	342·3	exists in A and B forms (A) cryst. from EtOH and most solvents (B) cryst. from MeOH
102	α,α-Trehalose	Mycose, 1-*O*-α-D-glucopyranosyl-α-D-glucopyranoside	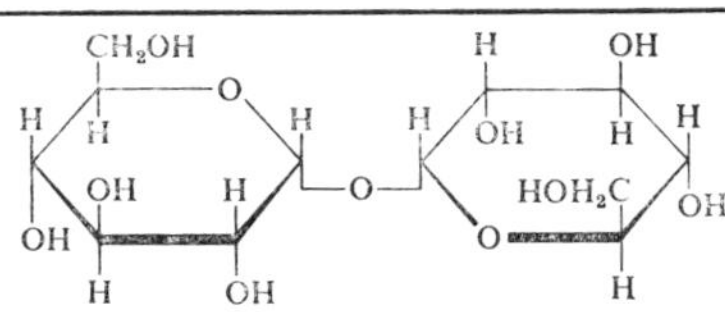	342·3; Hydrate, 378·3	cryst. $+2H_2O$
103	Turanose	3-*O*-α-D-Gluco-pyranosyl-β-D-fructose	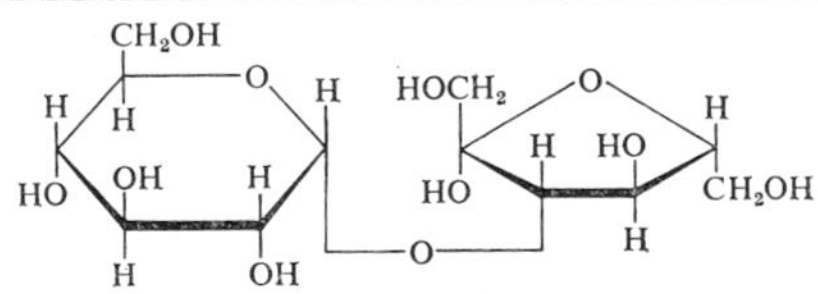	342·3	prisms
104	Xylobiose	4-*O*-β-D-Xylo-pyranosyl-β-D-xylose	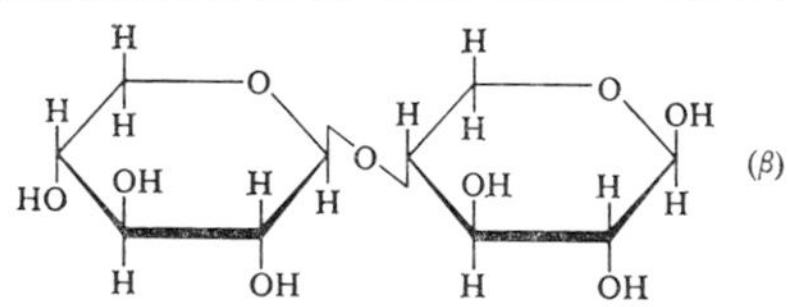	282·3	cryst.

TRI-, TETRA- AND PENTA-SACCHARIDES

No.	Name	Synonyms	Formula	M. wt.	Physical form
105	Cellotriose	4-β-Glucosyl-cellobiose	β-D-Glucosyl*p*-(1 → 4)-β-D-glucosyl*p*-(1 → 4)-D-glucose	504·4	
106	*Iso*kestose	1-Kestose, inulo-biosyl-α-glucoside, 1F-β-fructosyl-sucrose	β-D-Fructosyl*f*-(2 → 1)-β-D-fructosyl*f*-(2 → 1)-α-D-glucoside*p*	504·4	cryst.
107	*Iso*maltotriose	6-α-Glucosyl-*iso*maltose	α-D-Glucosyl*p*-(1 → 6)-α-D-glucosyl*p*-(1 → 6)-D-glucose	504·4	amorph.
108	Kestose	6-Kestose, 6F-β-fructosylsucrose	β-D-Fructosyl*f*-(2 → 6)-β-D-fructosyl*f*-(2 → 1)-α-D-glucoside*p*	504·4	fine needles
109	Laminaritriose	3-β-Glucosyl-laminaribiose	β-D-Glucosyl*p*-(1 → 3)-β-D-glucosyl*p*-(1 → 3)-D-glucose	504·4	amorph.
110	Maltotriose	4-α-Glucosyl-maltose, amylotriose	α-D-Glucosyl*p*-(1 → 4)-α-D-glucosyl*p*-(1 → 4)-D-glucose	504·4	amorph.

M.p.	$[\alpha]^t_D$	Solubility	References	Derivatives	General remarks
195–6 (Hydrate)	+19 to +22^{18} (c = 1·2 in H_2O)	s. H_2O	PREP. *J.C.S.* **1960**, 4213 *J. org. Chem.* **26**, 2892 (1961)	β-Octa-*O*-acetate, M.p. 191–4; $[\alpha]^{18}_D$ −3·2 (in $CHCl_3$) Nona-*O*-acetyl-sophoritol, M.p. 151–2; $[\alpha]^{20}_D$ −21 (c = 2·5 in $CHCl_3$)	Reducing sugar.
A) 188 B) 169–70	+66·53^{20} (c = 26 in H_2O)	180^{0}, 197^{15}, 487^{100} H_2O; sl. s. EtOH, MeOH; i. eth., benz., acet., $CHCl_3$		Octa-*O*-acetate, M.p. 69 (cryst. from EtOH); $[\alpha]^{20}_D$ +59·6 (in $CHCl_3$) An alkaline soln. of diazouracil turns blue-green only in the presence of sucrose or other oligosaccharides having sucrose as a component, e.g. raffinose (Raybin test)	Non-reducing. Fermented by yeasts.
7; nhyd., 03	+178·3 (c = 7 in H_2O)	s. H_2O, hot EtOH; i. eth.		Hexa-*O*-acetate, M.p. 93–96; $[\alpha]^{19}_D$ +159 (in $CHCl_3$) Octa-*O*-acetate, M.p. 98; $[\alpha]^{20}_D$ +162·3 (in $CHCl_3$)	Non-reducing. Fermented by most yeasts.
57 d.	+27·3 → +75·8^{22} (c = 4 in H_2O)	s. H_2O; sl. s. MeOH	REVIEW. *Adv. Carbohyd. Chem.* **2**, 1 (1946) PREP. *J.A.C.S.* **52**, 2522 (1930)	Phenylosazone, M.p. 200–5; $[\alpha]^{20}_D$ +24 → +33 (in pyr.–EtOH) Phenylosotriazole, M.p. 193–4; $[\alpha]^{20}_D$ +74 (in H_2O)	Reducing sugar, not fermented by yeasts.
5–90	−32 → −25^{25} (c = 1 in H_2O)	s. H_2O	PREP. *J.A.C.S.* **73**, 1389 (1951); **74**, 3609 (1952)	β-Hexa-*O*-acetate, M.p. 155–6; $[\alpha]_D$ −74 to −75 (in $CHCl_3$) Phenylosazone, M.p. 195–6; $[\alpha]_D$ −22·5 → −77 (in pyr.–EtOH)	Reducing sugar.
6–9 d.	+35 → +21·6^{20} (in H_2O)	s. H_2O; sl. s. MeOH; i. EtOH	PREP. *J.A.C.S.* **74**, 5331 (1952) *Tappi* **41**, 204 (1958)	α-Hendeca-*O*-acetate, M.p. 223–4; $[\alpha]^{20}_D$ +22·6 (in $CHCl_3$)	Reducing sugar; cellodextrins D.P. 4–7 also prepared.
)–200	+28 to +32^{20} (in H_2O)	s. H_2O	PREP. *Meth. Carb. Chem.*, vol. 1, pp. 360, 365 (1962)		Non-reducing sugar. −ve Raybin test.
	+136·7 to +142^{25} (in H_2O)	s. H_2O	PREP. *B.J.* **67**, 49 (1957) *J.A.C.S.* **75**, 5911 (1953)	Undeca-*O*-benzoate, M.p. 226–7; $[\alpha]_D$ +131 (in $CHCl_3$)	Reducing sugar; isomaltodextrins D.P. 4–6 also prepared.
;	+27 to +28^{20} (in H_2O)	s. H_2O	PREP. *Meth. Carb. Chem.*, vol. 1, p. 360 (1962)		Non-reducing sugar. −ve Raybin test.
	+2·4^{21} (in H_2O)	s. H_2O	PREP. *J.C.S.* **1958**, 724 *Chemy Ind.* **1957**, 1573	Hendeca-*O*-acetate, M.p. 121–2; $[\alpha]_D$ −37 (in $CHCl_3$)	Reducing sugar.
	+158 to +160^{25} (c = 2 in H_2O)	s. H_2O	PREP. *J.C.S.* **1953**, 1293 *J.B.C.* **205**, 75 (1953) *J.A.C.S.* **74**, 3612 (1952) *J.A.C.S.* **71**, 3357 (1949)	β-Hendeca-*O*-acetate, M.p. 134–6; $[\alpha]^{25}_D$+86 (in $CHCl_3$) Phenylflavazole, M.p. 248	Reducing sugar. Not fermented by maltose-fermenting baker's yeast. Maltodextrins D.P. 4–7 also prepared.

No.	Name	Synonyms	Formula	M. wt.	Physical form
111	Melezitose	3^{F}-α-Glucosyl-sucrose	α-D-Glucosyl*p*-(1 → 3)-β-D-fructosyl*f*-(2 → 1)α-D-glucoside*p*	504·4; Dihydrate, 540·4	rhombic crysts. $+2H_2O$
112	Neokestose	6^{G}-β-Fructosyl-sucrose	β-D-Fructosyl*f*-(2 → 6)-α-D-glucosyl*p*-(1 → 2)-β-D-fructoside*f*	504·4	amorph.
113	Panose	6-α-Glucosyl-maltose	α-D-Glucosyl*p*-(1 → 6)-α-D-glucosyl*p*-(1 → 4)-D-glucose	504·4	thin prisms
114	Raffinose	6^{G}-α-Galactosyl-sucrose	α-D-Galactosyl*p*-(1 → 6)-α-D-glucosyl*p*-(1 → 2)-β-D-fructoside*f*	504·4; Hydrate, 594·5	wh. prisms $+5H_2O$ from dil. EtOH
115	Stachyose	6^{Gal}-α-Galactosyl-raffinose, lupeose, β-galactan, manneotetrose	α-D-Galactosyl*p*-(1 → 6)-α-D-galactosyl*p*-(1 → 6)-α-D-glucosyl*p*-(1 → 2)-β-D-fructoside*f*	666·6; Tetra-hydrate, 738·7	fine cryst. $+4H_2O$
116	Verbascose	6^{Gal}-α-Galactosyl-stachyose	α-D-Galactosyl*p*-(1 → 6)-α-D-galactosyl*p*-(1 → 6)-α-D-galactosyl*p*-(1 → 6)-α-D-glucosyl*p*-(1 → 2)-β-D-fructoside*f*	828·8	fine needles

M.p.	$[\alpha]_D^t$	*Solubility*	*References*	*Derivatives*	*General remarks*
153–4	+88·2[20] (c = 4 in H_2O)	s. H_2O; i. aq. EtOH	REVIEW. *Adv. Carbohyd. Chem.* **2**, 2 (1946)	Hendeca-*O*-acetate, M.p. 117; $[\alpha]_D$ +104 (in $CHCl_3$)	Non-reducing sugar. Not fermented by top baker's yeast.
	+21 to +22[20] (in H_2O)	s. H_2O	PREP. *Meth. Carb. Chem.* vol. 1, p. 362 (1962)		Non-reducing sugar. +ve Raybin test.
221 d.	+162 → +154[25] (c = 0·76 in H_2O)	s. H_2O	PREP. *J.A.C.S.* **73**, 2547 (1951) EST. *Analyt. Chem.* **25**, 231 (1953)	Dodeca-*O*-acetate of panitol, M.p. 147–9; $[\alpha]_D^{27}$ +120 (in $CHCl_3$) Alcohol, $[\alpha]_D$ +133 (in H_2O)	Reducing sugar. Not fermented by yeasts.
78; anhyd., 118–20	+104·8[20] (hydrate in H_2O)	14·3[20] H_2O; 9·8 MeOH; v.s. pyr.; i. EtOH	REVIEW. *Adv. Carbohyd. Chem.* **9**, 167 (1954) PREP. Bates *et al.*, p. 475 EST. *Meth. biochem. Anal.* **1**, 308 (1954)	Hendeca-*O*-acetate, M.p. 99–100; $[\alpha]_D^{20}$ +92·2 (in EtOH) Identify by X-ray powder photograph [*J.A.C.S.* 75, 3664 (1953)]	Non-reducing, fermented by bottom yeasts.
101–5 (Tetrahydrate)	+131 to +132[25] (c = 9 in H_2O)	s. H_2O	REVIEW. *Adv. Carbohyd. Chem.* **9**, 149 (1954) PREP. *Chemy Ind.* **1961**, 475		Non-reducing sugar.
219–20	+170[20] (in H_2O)	s. H_2O	REVIEW. *Adv. Carbohyd. Chem.* **9**, 149 (1954)		Non-reducing sugar.

11. Lipids and Long-chain Fatty Acids

Revised by G. A. GARTON (*Rowett Research Institute, Aberdeen*)

Note. Compounds are arranged in alphabetical order except for simple fatty acid glycerides which are included under 'Glycerides'. Fat-soluble vitamins, carotenoids, steroid hormones, and fatty acids with less than 8 carbon atoms are dealt with in other sections.

General bibliography

1. A. W. Ralston, *Fatty Acids and their Derivatives*, Chapman and Hall, London, and Wiley, New York (1948).
2. H. J. Deuel, Jr., *The Lipids*, vol. 1, Interscience, New York and London (1951).
3. T. P. Hilditch and P. N. Williams, *The Chemical Constitution of Natural Fats*, 4th ed. revised, Chapman and Hall, London (1964).
4. J. A. Lovern, *The Chemistry of Lipids of Biochemical Significance*, 2nd ed. revised, Methuen, London, and Wiley, New York (1957).
5. K. S. Markley, *Fatty Acids*, 2nd ed., parts 1–3, Interscience, New York and London (1960–4).
6. D. J. Hanahan, *Lipide Chemistry*, Wiley, New York and London (1960).
7. *Progress in the Chemistry of Fats and Other Lipids*, Pergamon Press, Oxford. Published irregularly; vol. 1 (1952), vol. 10 (1967).
8. G. B. Ansell and J. N. Hawthorne, *Phospholipids: Chemistry, Metabolism and Function*, Elsevier (1964).

Nomenclature

Rules for the nomenclature of lipids are given in *Eur. J. Biochem.* **2**, 127 (1967); *B.J.* **105**, 897 (1967).

11. Lipids and Long-chain Fatty Acids

No.	Name	Synonyms	Formula	M. wt.	Physical form
1	Arachidic acid	*n*-Eicosanoic, eicosoic, eicosanic, acids	$CH_3\cdot(CH_2)_{18}\cdot COOH$	312·5	plates from EtOH
2	Arachidonic acid	5:6, 8:9, 11:12, 14:15-Eicosatetraenoic acid	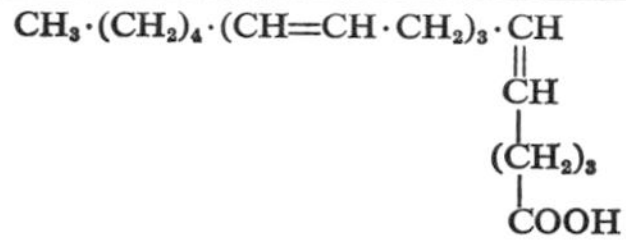	304·5	light amber oil; fishy odour
3	Azelaic acid	Nonanedioic, heptamethylene-1,7-dicarboxylic, lepargylic, acids	$HOOC\cdot(CH_2)_7\cdot COOH$	188·2	col. needles or leaflets
4	Behenic acid	*n*-Docosanoic acid	$CH_3\cdot(CH_2)_{20}\cdot COOH$	340·6	col. needles
5	Capric acid	*n*-Decanoic, decoic, acids	$CH_3\cdot(CH_2)_8\cdot COOH$	172·3	col. needles; rancid odour
6	Caprylic acid	*n*-Octanoic, octoic, acids	$CH_3\cdot(CH_2)_6\cdot COOH$	144·2	col. leaflets or col. liq. with rancid odour
7	Cardiolipin		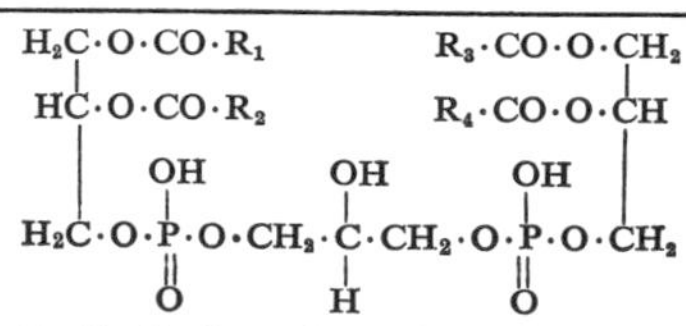 R_1, R_2, R_3, R_4 = fatty acid residues	508·3 $+R_1+R_2$ $+R_3+R_4$	yel. oil
8	Cephalin	Phosphatidylethanolamine, diacylglycerylphosphorylethanolamine, kephalin	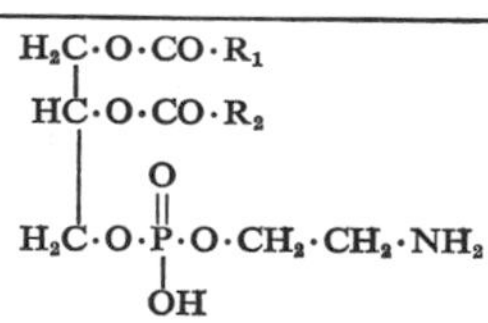 R_1, R_2 = fatty acid residues	269·2 $+R_1+R_2$	isolated as sticky wh. powder; synthesized as microscopic spherulites

M.p.	$[\alpha]^t_D$	*Solubility*	*Preparation*	*Estimation*	*General remarks*
75·4		0·45[20] EtOH; s. $CHCl_3$, benz., eth.	SYN. *Ber.* **64**, 2504 (1931) *J.B.C.* **59**, 905 (1924) ISOL. *J. Soc. Chem. Ind., Lond.* **44**, 219 (1925)	(*a*) *Meth. biochem. Anal.* **8**, 1 (1960) (*b*) T. P. Hilditch and P. N. Williams, *The Chemical Constitution of Natural Fats*, 4th ed., p. 678, Chapman and Hall (1964)	Found in vegetable and fish oils and in milk.
−49·5		i. H_2O; s. eth.	ISOL. *J.B.C.* **80**, 455 (1928) *B.J.* **34**, 879 (1940) *J.B.C.* **142**, 671 (1942)		Occurs only in animal fats. 'Essential' fatty acid produced *in vivo* from linoleic acid.
07 .p. 225·5[10], 86·5[100]		0·1[0], 0·212[22], 1·648[55] H_2O; s. eth.; v.s. EtOH	*J. Soc. Chem. Ind., Lond.* **44**, 43T (1925) *Org. Synth.* **Coll. 2**, 53 (1943)		Product of oxidative cleavage of oleic acid.
1		sp. s. H_2O, EtOH; sl. s. eth.; s. $CHCl_3$	*J.A.C.S.* **48**, 968 (1926) *J.B.C.* **59**, 905 (1924)	*See* arachidic acid	Occurs in peanut, rape seed, and mustard oils.
1·6 .p. 268–70		At 20°: 0·015 H_2O, 398 benz., 326 $CHCl_3$, 210 CCl_4, 510 MeOH, 407 acet., 567 gl. acetic, 289 Et acetate	SYN. *Ber.* **42**, 3613 (1909) *J.C.S.* **1931**, 2046	*B.J.* **50**, 679 (1952) *B.J.* **63**, 144 (1956) *See also* arachidic acid	Found in butter, coconut oil, and head of sperm whale.
5·7 .p. 237·5		At 20°: 0·068 H_2O; ∞ benz., $CHCl_3$, CCl_4, MeOH, acet., Et acetate	SYN. *Ann.* **161**, 175 (1872) *Ber.* **67B**, 218 (1934) *Oil Soap* **19**, 126 (1942)	*J.B.C.* **173**, 773 (1948) *B.J.* **50**, 679 (1952) *B.J.* **63**, 144 (1956) *See also* arachidic acid	Dissociation constant $1{\cdot}41\times10^{-5}$. Pb salt, i. H_2O. Cu and Zn salts, sp. s. H_2O.
	+5·8[25] (in EtOH)	i. H_2O; s. acet., $CHCl_3$, eth., EtOH	ISOL. *J.B.C.* **161**, 71 (1945) *B.J.* **70**, 409 (1958) *B.J.* **78**, 44 (1961)	*B.J.* **84**, 497 (1962) *B.B.A.* **84**, 109 (1964)	Free acid unstable. Na salt stored 18 months shows no loss of serological activity.
myristoyl- -, sinters , melts 5–7; istearoyl- -, sinters , melts 3–5; palmitoyl- -, sinters , melts 2·5–5·0	Dimyristoyl-L-α-, +6·0[26] (in $CHCl_3$); Distearoyl-L-α-, +6·0[24] (in $CHCl_3$–gl. acetic (9:1)); Dipalmitoyl-L-α-, +6·4[26] (in $CHCl_3$)	ISOL. i. acet.; s. MeOH, EtOH, $CHCl_3$, benz., wet eth., pet. eth. SYN. (saturated). i. acet., eth., pet. eth.; sl. s. EtOH, benz., CCl_4; s. $CHCl_3$, pyr.	ISOL. *J.B.C.* **146**, 35 (1942) *B.J.* **60**, 353 (1955) *Biochem. Preps.* **5**, 5 (1957) *B.J.* **80**, 557 (1961) SYN. *J.A.C.S.* **74**, 152 (1952)	*J.B.C.* **157**, 585 (1945) *J.B.C.* **192**, 465 (1951) *B.J.* **84**, 497 (1962) *J. Lipid Res.* **3**, 467 (1962)	Hygr.; isolated compound quickly becomes brown even *in vacuo*. Solubility data depend on absence of other lipids. Labile in N-alkali at 37°. Occurs naturally as α-isomer.

No.	Name	Synonyms	Formula	M. wt.	Physical form
9	Cerebrosides	Glyco-sphingosides	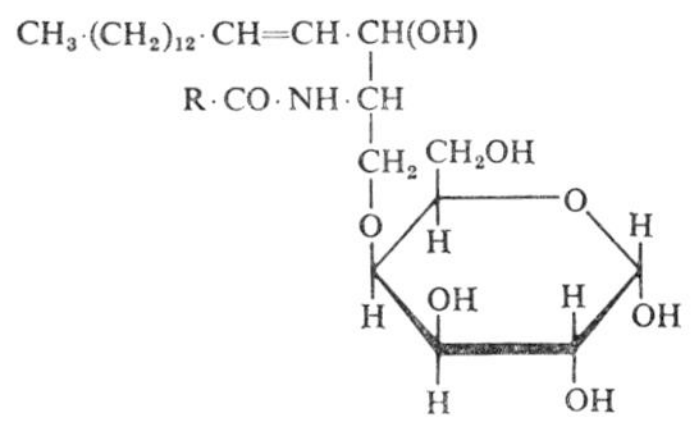 Contain sphingosine, a fatty acid and a sugar, usually galactose. R = fatty acid residue Cerasine: lignoceric acid Phrenosine: cerebronic acid Nervone: nervonic acid Oxynervone: α-hydroxynervonic acid	488·6 +R	wax-like wh. powders
10	Ceryl alcohol	1-Hexacosanol, cerotin	$CH_3\cdot(CH_2)_{24}\cdot CH_2OH$	382·7	rh. plates
11	Cetyl alcohol	1-Hexadecanol, ethal, palmityl alcohol	$CH_3\cdot(CH_2)_{15}\cdot OH$	242·5	leaflets from EtOH
12	Chaulmoogric acid	*d*-13-(2-Cyclo-pentenyl)-tridecanoic acid, hydnocarpyl-acetic acid	$CH{=}CH\cdot CH_2\cdot CH_2\cdot CH\cdot(CH_2)_{12}\cdot COOH$ (ring closed between first CH and CH)	280·4	leaflets from EtOH
13	Cholesterol	Cholesterin, Δ^5-cholestene-3β-ol	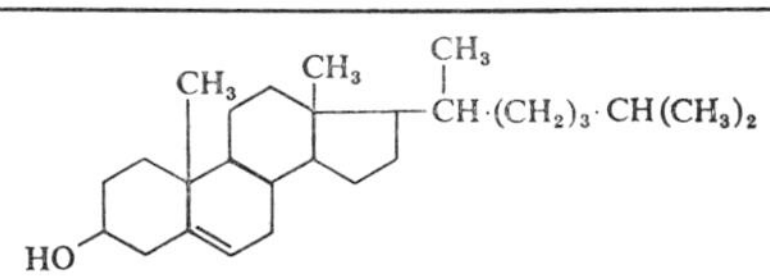	386·6; Hydrate, 404·6	monocl. leaflets $+H_2O$ from 95% EtOH; needles from anhyd. solvents
14	Cholesteryl esters (*a*) acetate		(*a*) $C_{27}H_{45}O\cdot OC\cdot CH_3$	(*a*) 428·7	(*a*) plates or needles from EtOH-eth.
	(*o*) oleate		(*o*) $C_{27}H_{45}O\cdot OC(CH_2)_7\cdot CH{=}CH\cdot(CH_2)_7CH_3$	(*o*) 651·1	(*o*) long thin needles
	(*p*) palmitate		(*p*) $C_{27}H_{45}O\cdot OC(CH_2)_{14}\cdot CH_3$	(*p*) 625·1	
	(*s*) stearate		(*s*) $C_{27}H_{45}O\cdot OC(CH_2)_{16}\cdot CH_3$	(*s*) 653·1	(*s*) wh. platelets
15	Coprosterol	Coprostanol, 5β-cholestan-3β-ol	As cholesterol with double bond saturated; isomeric with dihydrocholesterol, differing in spatial configuration of H atom at carbon atom number 5 (i.e. it is the C_5 epimer of cholestanol)	388·6	
16	Dicholesteryl ether		$C_{27}H_{45}\cdot O\cdot C_{27}H_{45}$	755·3	needles
	Diglycerides *see* glycerides				
17	Dihydro-cholesterol	Cholestanol, 5α-cholestan-3β-ol	As cholesterol with saturated double bond; isomeric with coprosterol, differing in spatial configuration at carbon atom number 5	388·6; Hydrate, 406·6	hex. plates from EtOH; $+H_2O$ from 95% EtOH

M.p.	$[\alpha]^t_D$	*Solubility*	*Preparation*	*Estimation*	*General remarks*
Phrenosine melts finally 212–15; Cerasine melts finally 185–7; Nervone melts finally 180	Diverse values reported which probably depend on purity. *See* H. Deuel, *The Lipids*, vol. 1, p. 485, Interscience, New York (1951)	i. H_2O, eth., pet. eth.; sl. s. EtOH; s. pyr., acet., gl. acetic, $CHCl_3$	ISOL. *Z.P.C.* **68**, 464 (1910) *Z.P.C.* **74**, 282 (1911) *Z.P.C.* **145**, 144 (1925) *B.J.* **8**, 110 (1914) *J.B.C.* **169**, 77 (1947) *J.B.C.* **219**, 977 (1956) *Biochem. Preps.* **7**, 31 (1960) *J. Lipid Res.* **2**, 228 (1961) Isol. of cerebroside containing only dihydrosphingosine *J. Neurochem.* **6**, 112 (1960)	*J.B.C.* **141**, 545 (1941) *Acta physiol. scand.* **18**, *Suppl.* 63 (1949) *J.B.C.* **219**, 977 (1956) *Meth. biochem. Anal.* **6**, 178 (1958)	Resistant to hydrolysis with boiling sat. $Ba(OH)_2$.
79–80		i. H_2O; s. EtOH, eth.	*Proc. R. Soc.* **A128**, 214 (1930)		Widely distributed in various waxes of plant and animal origin, usually esterified with fatty acids.
49·3 B.p. 190[15]		i. H_2O; s. EtOH, MeOH, eth., benz.	*J.C.S.* **1931**, 1732		Found in various marine oils.
;8·5	+62 (in $CHCl_3$)	i. H_2O; v. sl. s. EtOH; s. eth., $CHCl_3$	*J.A.C.S.* **51**, 1515 (1929) *J.A.C.S.* **59**, 963 (1937)		
48·5 anhyd.)	−31·1[15] (in eth.)	sp. s. H_2O, EtOH; s. eth., $CHCl_3$, benz., pet. eth., pyr., Et acetate, hot EtOH	*Z.P.C.* **192**, 77 (1930) *Z.P.C.* **241**, 81 (1936)	*Meth. biochem. Anal.* **10**, 263 (1962) R. P. Cook, *Cholesterol*, pp. 117, 481, Academic Press (1958) *J. Lipid Res.* **3**, 383 (1962)	Slowly oxidizes in air causing yellowing and changes in solubility and M.p. Shows birefringence. Dibromide, needles, M.p. 109–11, or 123–4.
ı) 115) *cis*, 44·5) 90·5) 82·5	(*a*) −47·4[20] (*o*) −23·4[20] (*p*) −25·1[20] (*s*) −24·3[20]	sp. s. EtOH; sl. s. acet.; s. hot EtOH, hot acet., eth., $CHCl_3$	*Recl Trav. chim. Pays-Bas Belg.* **25**, 334 (1906) *C. r. hebd. Séanc. Acad. Sci., Paris* **147**, 498 (1908) *B.Z.* **220**, 304 (1930) *J.B.C.* **212**, 141 (1955)	*See* cholesterol	Exhibit mesomorphism on heating and change to turbid liq. state before melting.
1	+28[25] (in $CHCl_3$)	s. eth., $CHCl_3$, benz.; sl. s. MeOH; i. H_2O	ISOL. AND STRUCTURE *Z.P.C.* **223**, 249 (1934); **225**, 197 (1934 *See also* Fieser and Fieser, *Steroids*, p. 27 Reinhold; Chapman and Hall (1959) ^{14}C. *J. Lipid Res.* **4**, 337 (1963)	R. P. Cook, *Cholesterol*, pp. 117, 481, Academic Press (1958)	Found in faeces; produced by action of intestinal micro-organisms on cholesterol. Acetate, M.p. 89. Benzoate, M.p. 125.
3 (205–9)	−40·8[20] (in CCl_4)	sp. s. EtOH, acet., eth.; s. $CHCl_3$, CCl_4, hot benz.	SYN. *J.B.C.* **72**, 1 (1927) ISOL. *J.B.C.* **159**, 603 (1945)		
2–3	+27·4[20] (in $CHCl_3$)	s. $CHCl_3$, eth.	*Org. Synth.* Coll. **2**, 191 (1943)		Forms insol. digitonin complex but does not give colour reactions of cholesterol which depend on double bond. Acetate, M.p. 111. Benzoate, M.p. 135.

No.	Name	Synonyms	Formula	M. wt.	Physical form
18	Dihydro-sphingosine	*erythro*-1,3-Dihydroxy-2-aminooctadecene	As sphingosine with saturated double bond	301·5	col. cryst. from pet. eth. and Et acetate
19	Elaeostearic acid (α or *cis*, and β or *trans*)	9:10, 11:12, 13:14-Octa-decatrienoic acid	$CH_3\cdot(CH_2)_3\cdot(CH{=}CH)_3\cdot(CH_2)_7\cdot COOH$	278·4	*cis*, leaflets or needles from EtOH; *trans*, plates or needles from EtOH
20	Erucic acid (*cis*-)	13-Docosenoic acid; *trans*-isomer, brassidic acid, *iso*erucic acid	$CH_3\cdot(CH_2)_7\cdot CH{=}CH\cdot(CH_2)_{11}\cdot COOH$	338·6	*cis*, col. needles from EtOH; *trans*, col. leaflets
	Galacto-glycerides	Galactosyl-glycerol lipids	(i) 2,3-diacyl ester of β-D-galactopyranosyl-1-glycerol 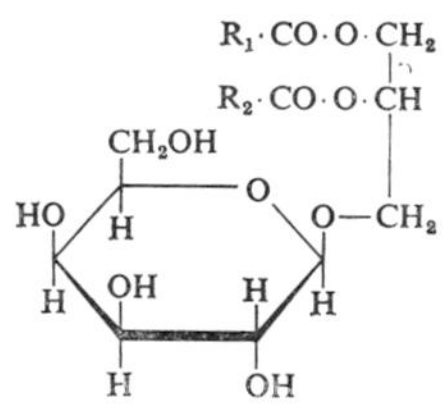 (ii) 2,3-diacyl ester of α-D-galactopyranosyl-1,6-β-D-galactopyranosyl-1-glycerol 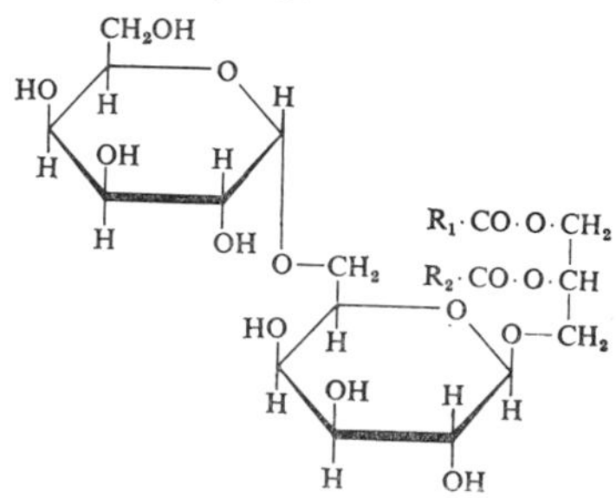 R_1, R_2 = fatty acid residues	Formula (i) 308·2 $+R_1+R_2$; (ii) 470·4 $+R_1+R_2$	Monogalactosyl-glycerol, cryst. from MeOH. Digalactosyl-glycerol, cryst. from EtOH–H_2O
22	Gangliosides		A group of acylsphingosyl oligosaccharides containing sialic acid. They have predominantly the common basic structure *N*-acylsphingosine-glucose-galactose-*N*-acetylgalactosamine-galactose to which one or more molecules of *N*-acetyl-neuraminic acid are bound, *J. Neurochem.* **10**, 613 (1963) Structure of monosialoganglioside, see *Ber.* **96**, 866 (1963)		

M.p.	$[\alpha]^t_D$	*Solubility*	*Preparation*	*Estimation*	*General remarks*
35–87		s. EtOH, eth.	ISOL. *J.B.C.* **170**, 269 (1947) *J. Neurochem.* **6**, 112 (1960) *J.B.C.* **236**, 1912 (1961) SYN. *J.A.C.S.* **80**, 2170 (1958)	*J. Lipid Res.* **1**, 40 (1959)	Occurs in cerebrosides of brain, spinal cord, and wheat flour. Tribenzoyl deriv., M.p. 142–4. Triacetyl deriv., M.p. 102–3. *N*-acetyl deriv., M.p. 122–4.
is α, 48–49 *rans* β, 1·5–71·8		*cis*, i. H_2O; s. EtOH, eth., CS_2, hot gl. acetic. *trans*, i. H_2O; sl. s. EtOH; s. hot gl. acetic, eth., CS_2	ISOL. *J.A.C.S.* **56**, 898 (1934)	*B.J.* **59**, 309 (1955) *Meth. biochem. Ana*. **8**, 1 (1960)	*cis*-Form is naturally occurring acid and is easily converted to *trans*-isomer by light, heat, catalysts such as I or S. α-Tetrabromide, M.p. 115.
is, 33·5 *ans*, 60		*cis*, s. EtOH, eth. *trans*, sl. s. H_2O, EtOH; s. eth.	*cis*, *J.A.C.S.* **48**, 968 (1926) *Org. Synth.* **Coll. 2**, 258 (1943) *trans*, *Bull. Soc. chim. Belg.* **44**, 467 (1935) *J.B.C.* **200**, 287 (1953)	*J.A.C.S.* **48**, 968 (1926) *Meth. biochem. Anal.* **8**, 1 (1960)	*cis*-Form isomerized by treatment with aq. sulphurous acid, 24 hr at 200°.
Iono-alactosyl-ycerol, 39–40; igalactosyl-ycerol, 32–4	Mono-galactosyl-glycerol, +3·77[27]; Digalactosyl-glycerol, +86·4[27]	(i) s. MeOH (ii) s. H_2O	ISOL. AND STRUCTURE *J.A.C.S.* **78**, 3735 (1956) *Acta chem. scand.* **12**, 1183, 1187 (1958) *J. Lipid Res.* **2**, 215, 223 (1961) *J. Sci. Fd Agric.* **12**, 34 (1961)	*B.B.A.* **44**, 49 (1960)	Found in lipids of green leaves, peas, wheat flour, algae. Fatty acids present include a high content of linoleic acid (wheat flour) and of linolenic acid (leaves).
		Form micellar aggregates in aqueous solution	ISOL. *Z.P.C.* **278**, 1 (1943) *J. Biochem., Tokyo* **43**, 63 (1956) *Z.P.C.* **307**, 266 (1957) *B.B.A.* **53**, 422 (1961) *Angew. Chem.* **73**, 580 (1961) *B.B.A.* **60**, 350 (1962) *Z.P.C.* **327**, 249 (1962)	*B.J.* **82**, 527 (1962) Sialic acid—see *Meth. biochem. Anal.* **8**, 199 (1960) *J. Lipid Res.* **3**, 269 (1962)	Complex lipids present in brain, spleen, and erythrocytes.

No.	Name	Synonyms	Formula	M. wt.	Physical form
	GLYCERIDES (fatty acid)		General formula CH_2OX_1 – $CHOX_2$ – CH_2OX_3		
	Monoglycerides				
23	α-Mono-olein	Glycerol-1-oleate	X_1 = —CO·$(CH_2)_7$·CH=CH·$(CH_2)_7$·CH_3 X_2 = H X_3 = H	356·5	
24	α-Mono-palmitin	Glycerol-1-palmitate	X_1 = —CO·$(CH_2)_{14}$·CH_3 X_2 = H X_3 = H	330·4	plates
25	β-Mono-palmitin	Glycerol-2-palmitate	X_1 = H X_2 = —CO·$(CH_2)_{14}$·CH_3 X_3 = H	330·4	wh. flakes
26	α-Mono-stearin	Glycerol-1-stearate	X_1 = —CO·$(CH_2)_{16}$·CH_3 X_2 = H X_3 = H	358·5	cryst. or waxy solid
27	β-Mono-stearin	Glycerol-2-stearate	X_1 = H X_2 = —CO·$(CH_2)_{16}$·CH_3 X_3 = H	358·5	cryst.
	Diglycerides				
28	D-α,β-Di-myristin	Glycerol-1,2-dimyristate	X_1 and X_2 = —CO·$(CH_2)_{12}$·CH_3 X_3 = H	512·8	plates
29	D-α,β-Di-palmitin	Glycerol-1,2-dipalmitate	X_1 and X_2 = —CO·$(CH_2)_{14}$·CH_3 X_3 = H	568·9	cryst.
30	α,γ-Di-palmitin	Glycerol-1,3-dipalmitate	X_1 and X_3 = —CO·$(CH_2)_{14}$·CH_3 X_2 = H	568·9	cryst. from EtOH
31	D-α,β-Distearin	Glycerol-1,2-distearate	X_1 and X_2 = —CO·$(CH_2)_{16}$·CH_3 X_3 = H	625·0	cryst. from ligroin
32	α,γ-Distearin	Glycerol-1,3-distearate	X_1 and X_3 = —CO·$(CH_2)_{16}$·CH_3 X_2 = H	625·0	rh. plates from $CHCl_3$
	Triglycerides				
33	Trilaurin	Glycerol tri-laurate, laurin	X_1, X_2, and X_3 = —CO·$(CH_2)_{10}$·CH_3	639·0	needles from EtOH
34	Trimyristin	Glycerol tri-myristate, myristin	X_1, X_2, and X_3 = —CO·$(CH_2)_{12}$·CH_3	723·1	plates from EtOH; needles from eth.
35	Triolein	Glycerol trioleate	X_1, X_2, and X_3 = —CO·$(CH_2)_7$·CH=CH·$(CH_2)_7$·CH_3	885·4	odourless oil
36	Tripalmitin	Glycerol tri-palmitate, palmitin	X_1, X_2, and X_3 = —CO·$(CH_2)_{14}$·CH_3	807·3	col. needles from eth.

M.p.	$[\alpha]^t_D$	Solubility	Preparation	Estimation	General remarks
35		i. H_2O; s. EtOH, $CHCl_3$, eth.	*Chem. ZentBl.* **1**, 2971 (1935)	*B.J.* **62**, 455 (1956) *J. Am. Oil Chem. Soc.* **37**, 7 (1960)	
71–72	−4·37 (in pyr.)	i. H_2O; s. EtOH; $2{\cdot}75^{25}$ eth.	*J.B.C.* **128**, 475 (1939)	*See* monoölein	Optical rotation falls on standing at room temp.
68·5		i. H_2O; s. EtOH	*J.A.C.S.* **56**, 1724 (1934)	*See* monoölein	In acid soln. tends to revert to α-form.
76–77	−3·58 (in pyr.)	disperses in H_2O; sl. s. EtOH; s. hot EtOH, hot eth., $CHCl_3$	*J.B.C.* **128**, 475 (1939)	*See* monoölein	Optical rotation falls on standing at room temp.
74·4		s. hot EtOH, hot eth.	*J.A.C.S.* **56**, 1724 (1934)	*See* monoölein	In acid soln. tends to revert to α-form.
58–59	−3·3 (in $CHCl_3$)	s. $CHCl_3$	*J.A.C.S.* **72**, 942 (1950)		Acyl group readily migrates to form 1,3-isomer.
8–69	−2·9 (in $CHCl_3$)	s. $CHCl_3$	ENZYME SYN. *J.A.C.S.* **76**, 1804 (1954) SYN. *J.A.C.S.* **63**, 3244 (1941) *J.A.C.S.* **72**, 942 (1950)		Acyl group readily migrates to form 1,3-isomer.
9·5		sl. s. EtOH; s. hot eth., $CHCl_3$, hot EtOH	*J.A.C.S.* **51**, 866 (1929)		
6–77	−2·8 (in $CHCl_3$)	sp. s. gl. acetic; s. eth., $CHCl_3$	*J.A.C.S.* **63**, 3244 (1941)		Acyl group readily migrates to form 1,3-isomer.
9·0		sl. s. EtOH; s. hot EtOH, hot eth., hot $CHCl_3$	*J.C.S.* **1937**, 1409		
, 14 prime, 34 43·9		i. H_2O; sl. s. EtOH; s. $CHCl_3$, eth., benz., hot EtOH	*J.A.C.S.* **51**, 866 (1929)	T. P. Hilditch and P. N. Williams, *The Chemical Constitution of Natural Fats*, 4th ed., p. 700, Chapman and Hall (1964) *Chem. Rev.* **29**, 333 (1941)	For nomenclature of polymorphic forms see *J.A.C.S.* **67**, 524 (1945).
32 prime, 44 55·5		i. H_2O; sp. s. ligroin, CS_2; s. eth., benz., $CHCl_3$, pet. eth., hot EtOH	ISOL. *Org. Synth.* **Coll. 1**, 538 (1941)	*See* trilaurin	*See* trilaurin.
−32 prime, −13 3·8 (5·5)		i. H_2O; sp. s. EtOH; s. eth., $CHCl_3$	*J.A.C.S.* **69**, 1445 (1947)	*See* trilaurin	*See* trilaurin.
44 prime, 55·5 65·5		i. H_2O; sp. s. EtOH; s. hot EtOH, eth., $CHCl_3$	*B.J.* **7**, 429 (1913) *J.C.S.* **1934**, 666 *J.A.C.S.* **70**, 1376 (1948)	*See* trilaurin	*See* trilaurin.

11. Lipids and Long-chain Fatty Acids

No.	Name	Synonyms	Formula	M. wt.	Physical form
37	Tristearin	Glycerol tristearate, stearin	X_1, X_2, and X_3 = $—CO·(CH_2)_{16}·CH_3$	891·5	cryst. from eth.
38	α-Glyceryl ethers	(*a*) alkoxyglycerides when the molecule contains one or two esterified fatty acids and contains no P; (*b*) alkoxyphospholipids or ether phospholipids, when one free glyceryl hydroxyl is esterified to phosphorylethanolamine (or phosphorylcholine)	$CH_2·O·R$ $CH·OH$ $CH_2·OH$ α-glyceryl ether $CH_2·O·R$ $CH·O·CO·R_1$ $CH_2·O·CO·R_2$ alkoxydiglyceride Glyceryl ether is called chimyl, batyl, or selechyl alcohol when R is $CH_3·(CH_2)_{15}—$, $CH_3·(CH_2)_{17}—$, and $CH_3·(CH_2)_7·CH{=}CH·(CH_2)_8—$ respectively. $CH_2·O·R$ $CH·O·CO·R_1$ $CH_2—O—P(OH)(=O)—O—CH_2·CH_2·NH_2$ 1-alkoxy-2-acyl-3-glycerylphosphorylethanolamine R = fatty alcohol residue; R_1, R_2 = fatty acid residues	α-glyceryl ether, 91·1+R; alkoxydiglyceride, 145·1+R+R_1+R_2; alkoxyphospholipid, 241·1+R+R_1 (when the base present is ethanolamine)	
39	Heptadecanoic acid	Margaric, daturic, heptadecylic, heptadecoic acids	$CH_3·(CH_2)_{15}·COOH$	270·4	col. plates
40	DL-2-Hydroxystearic acid	α-Hydroxystearic, 2-hydroxyoctadecanoic acids	$CH_3·(CH_2)_{15}·CH(OH)·COOH$	300·4	needles from $CHCl_3$
41	10-Hydroxystearic acid	Rosilic, 10-hydroxyoctadecanoic acid	$CH_3·(CH_2)_7·CH(OH)·(CH_2)_8·COOH$	300·4	hex. plates
42	Lanosterol	Lanosta-8,24-dien-3β-ol, ,4,14-trimethy esta-8,24	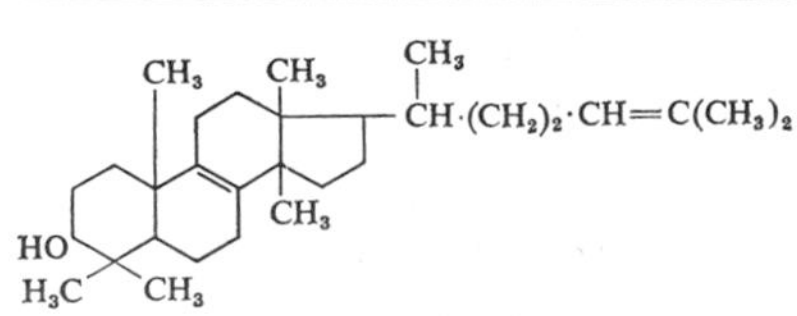	426·7	cryst.

M.p.	$[\alpha]^t_D$	Solubility	Preparation	Estimation	General remarks
, 54 prime, 64 , 73·1		i. H_2O; sp. s. EtOH; s. hot EtOH, hot pet. eth., hot eth., $CHCl_3$, benz.	*J.C.S.* **1934**, 666 *J.A.C.S.* **67**, 524 (1945)	*See* trilaurin	*See* trilaurin.
himyl lcohol, 0·5–61·5; atyl alcohol, 0–71. elechyl lcohol is quid)		(*a*) s. in fat solvents	ISOL. (*a*) *J.C.S.* **1933**, 165 *J.C.S.* **1934**, 1232 *Bull. Soc. chim. Fr.* **5**, 789 (1935) *J.A.C.S.* **63**, 2607 (1941) *J. Soc. Chem. Ind., Lond.* **67**, 193 (1948) *Clinica chim. Acta* **3**, 253 (1958) *J. Lipid Res.* **1**, 446 (1960) *J. Lipid Res.* **3**, 31, 39 (1962) (*b*) *B.J.* **88**, 56 (1963) *B.B.A.* **41**, 371 (1960) *J.B.C.* **236**, PC 59 (1961) SYN. AND STRUCTURE (*a*) *J.B.C.* **140**, 397 (1941) *J.B.C.* **170**, 337 (1947) *J.B.C.* **216**, 689 (1955) (*b*) *J.B.C.* **232**, 681 (1958)	*J.B.C.* **216**, 689 (1955) *J. Lipid Res.* **3**, 31 (1962)	Glyceryl ethers and alkoxy-diglycerides found in liver oils of Elasmobranch fishes, bone marrow, spleen, milk, and neonatal depot fat of calves. Alkoxyphospholipids found in brain, erythrocytes, egg yolk, and slugs.
·3		v.s. eth. At 20°: 0·00042 H_2O, 9·23 benz., 2·5 MeOH, 4·17 95% EtOH, 4·28 acet., 0·12 gl. acetic	ISOL. *B.J.* **61**, 453 (1955) SYN. *J.B.C.* **16**, 475 (1914)	*See* arachidic acid (*a*)	Traces found in many natural lipids, e.g. mutton fat, shark liver oil, butter-fat.
		i. H_2O; s. EtOH, eth.; v.s. hot benz.	ISOL. *J.C.S.* **1954**, 177 *B.B.A.* **45**, 402 (1960) *J.B.C.* **236**, 1912 (1961) SYN. *J.C.S.* **85**, 827 (1904)	*Aust. J. Chem.* **13**, 80 (1960)	Occurs in wool wax and wheat flour cerebrosides. Me ester, M.p. 66.
82 . $213–17^{4}$		i. H_2O; s. EtOH, eth.	SYN. *J.A.C.S.* **49**, 522 (1927) *J. org. Chem.* **18**, 686, 693 (1953) *Acta chem. scand.* **6**, 1157 (1952)	*B.J.* **78**, 333 (1961)	Present in faecal lipids. Me ester, M.p. 53–54.
	$+60^{25}$ (in $CHCl_3$)	i. H_2O; s. fat solvents	ISOL. AND STRUCTURE *Helv. chim. Acta* **27**, 472 (1944); **28**, 759 (1945); **29**, 204 (1946) *See also* Fieser and Fieser, *Steroids*, p. 364, Reinhold; Chapman and Hall (1959)	*See* coprosterol	Found in small amounts in many natural lipids, e.g. wool wax, yeast, latex. Intermediate in biosynthesis of cholesterol. Acetate, M.p. 130. Benzoate, M.p. 194.

No.	Name	Synonyms	Formula	M. wt.	Physical form
43	Lauric acid	*n*-Dodecanoic, dodecoic, acids	$CH_3\cdot(CH_2)_{10}\cdot COOH$	200·3	needles from EtOH
44	Lecithin	Diacylglyceryl-phosphoryl-choline, phosphatidyl-choline	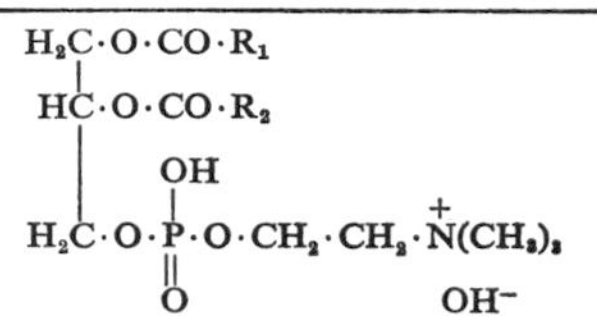 R_1, R_2 = saturated or unsaturated fatty acid residues. For doubly saturated *see* lecithin (hydro).	329·3 $+R_1+R_2$	waxy, plastic-like solid
45	Lecithin (hydro)	As for lecithin	As for lecithin R_1 and R_2 both saturated	329·3 $+R_1+R_2$	Dipalmitoyl, needles from di*iso*butyl ketone
46	Lignoceric acid	*n*-Tetracosanoic, tetracosoic, acids	$CH_3\cdot(CH_2)_{22}\cdot COOH$	368·6	fine wh. crystals
47	Lignoceryl-sphingosine	Ceramide group	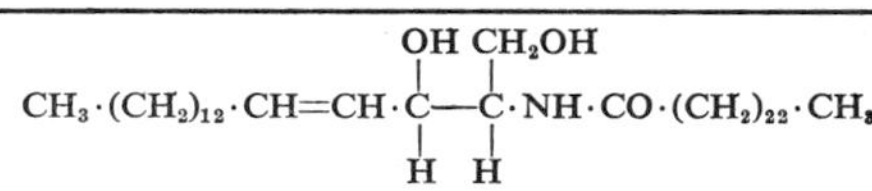	650·1	
48	Linoleic acid	9:10, 12:13-Octadecadienoic, linolic, acids	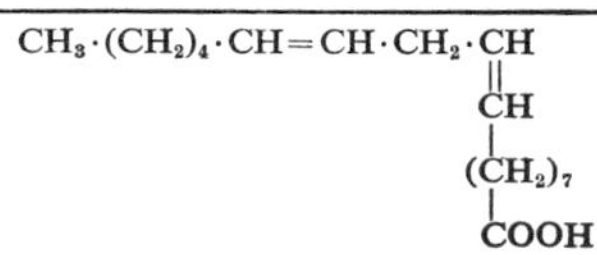	280·4	col. or yel. oil
49	Linolenic acid	9:10, 12:13, 15:16-Octadeca-trienoic acid	$CH_3\cdot(CH_2\cdot CH{=}CH)_3\cdot(CH_2)_7\cdot COOH$	278·4	α, β, γ } col. liquids
50	Lysolecithin (β)	Monoacyl-glycerylphos-phorylcholine	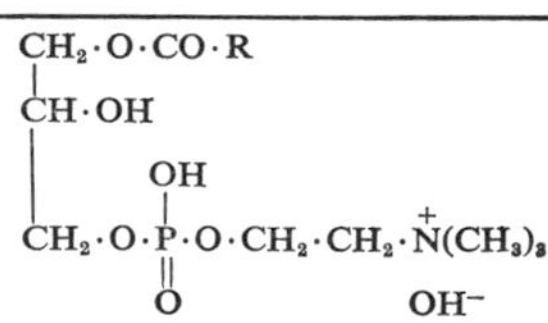 R = fatty acid residue	Mono-stearoyl, 541·7; Mono-palmitoyl, 513·7	cryst.; v. hygr.; monostearoyl, needles
51	9,10-Methylene-hexadecanoic acid		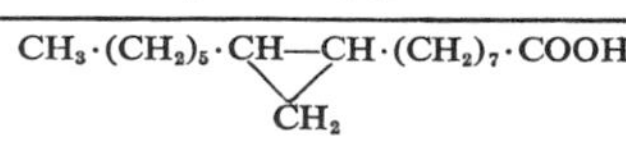	268·4	cryst.

.p.	$[\alpha]^t_D$	*Solubility*	*Preparation*	*Estimation*	*General remarks*
·2 .p. 225^{100}		At 20°: 0·0055 H_2O, 93·6 benz., 83 $CHCl_3$, 53 CCl_4, 120 MeOH, 105 EtOH, 60·5 acet., 297 gl. acetic, 52 Et acetate; v.s. eth.	ISOL. *J. Soc. Chem. Ind., Lond.* **49**, 138T (1930) *J.B.C.* **25**, 55 (1916) PURIFICATION *J.C.S.* **1936**, 283	*See* Arachidic acid *B.J.* **63**, 144 (1956)	Widely distributed in animal, vegetable, and marine fats and oils.
	Dipalmitole-oyl-L-α-, +6·6 ($CHCl_3$/ MeOH, 1:1)	i. acet., Me acetate; s. EtOH, eth., pet. eth., CS_2, $CHCl_3$, CCl_4, benz. Dipalmitoleoyl, i. pet. eth.	ISOL. *Can. J. Res.* **26B**, 777 (1948) *J.B.C.* **188**, 471 (1950) *Biochem. Preps.* **4**, 12 (1955) *B.J.* **60**, 353 (1955) *B.J.* **88**, 414 (1963) SYN. Dioleoyl, *J.A.C.S.* **78**, 232 (1956)	*Acta physiol. scand.* **18**, *Suppl.* 63 (1949) *J.B.C.* **169**, 137 (1947) *B.J.* **84**, 497 (1962)	Hygr.; turns brown in air. Solubility data depend on the absence of other lipids. Labile in N-alkali at 37°. Occurs naturally as α-isomer.
L. (from ng), ters 75–80, lts 237–8. N. Di- ristoyl- -, ters 90, lts 236–7; palmitoyl- -, ters 120, lts 235–6; tearoyl- -, ers 120, lts 230–2	ISOL. (from lung), +6·25 (in MeOH/ $CHCl_3$). SYN. Dimyristoyl-L-α-, $+7·0^{24}$ (in EtOH/ $CHCl_3$); Dipalmitoyl-L-α-, $+7·0^{25}$ (in $CHCl_3$); Distearoyl-L-α-, +6·1 (in MeOH/ $CHCl_3$)	i. eth.; sl. s. acet.; s. EtOH, gl. acetic $CHCl_3$	ISOL. *J.B.C.* **166**, 669 (1946) SYN. *J.A.C.S.* **74**, 158 (1952)	As lecithin	Labile in N-alkali at 37°.
2		s. eth., EtOH, acet., benz., gl. acetic, CS_2	*J.A.C.S.* **52**, 4536 (1930) *J.C.S.* **1936**, 283	*See* Arachidic acid	Found in vegetable and marine oils. Methyl ester, M.p. 57. Ag, Pb salts, M.p. 117.
95		s. eth., $CHCl_3$; sl. s. acet.	*J.B.C.* **24**, 69 (1916) *Z.P.C.* **209**, 112 (1932) *Z.P.C.* **222**, 39 (1933)		
to −8 , 230^{16}		i. H_2O; ∞ EtOH, eth.	*Org. Synth.* **Coll. 3**, 526 (1955) *Biochem. Preps.* **4**, 86 (1955)	*See* Arachidic acid *B.J.* **59**, 309 (1955) *J. Am. Oil Chem. Soc.* **30**, 182 (1953)	Takes up O_2 from the air forming hard glossy substance. Naturally occurring acid is the *cis, cis*-isomer. Found in vegetable oils, e.g. linseed. Precursor of arachidonic acid in animals.
−17 to 5		α-, i. H_2O; s. EtOH, eth.	*Org. Synth.* **Coll. 3**, 531 (1955)	*See* Arachidic acid *B.J.* **59**, 309 (1955)	Naturally occurring isomer is the α- or *cis, cis, cis*-form.
o- nitoyl, 6; o- oyl, 5–8·5	Mono-palmitoyl, $-2·2^{25}$; Mono-stearoyl, $-2·87^{25}$ (in MeOH/ $CHCl_3$)	Emulsifies in H_2O; i. eth.; sp. s. acet.; s. EtOH, gl. acetic, $CHCl_3$, pyr.	*J.B.C.* **129**, 619 (1939) *J.B.C.* **211**, 321 (1954) *J.B.C.* **206**, 431 (1954) *B.B.A.* **30**, 187 (1958)	*J.B.C.* **206**, 443 (1954) *J.B.C.* **206**, 647 (1954) *J. Lipid Res.* **3**, 1, 467 (1962)	Labile in N-KOH at 37°. Isolated enzymically with the fatty acid on the α-carbon atom of the glycerol.
Me , $140^{0·8}$		i. H_2O; s. fat solvents	ISOL. *C. r. hebd. Séanc. Acad. Sci., Paris*, **250**, 2653 (1960) SYN. *Annls Chim.* **7**, 638 (1962)		Present in lipids of some bacteria, e.g. *E. coli.* Amide, M.p. (ISOL.) 70–72, (SYN.) 79–81.

11. Lipids and Long-chain Fatty Acids

No.	Name	Synonyms	Formula	M. wt.	Physical form
	Monoglycerides, *see* Glycerides				
52	Mono-phospho-inositide	Phosphatidyl-inositol	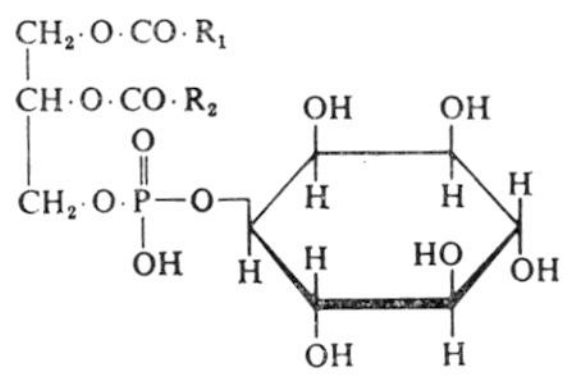 R_1, R_2 = fatty acid residues	388·2+ R_1+R_2	wh. amorph. solid; cryst. Na salt
53	Myristic acid	*n*-Tetradecanoic, tetradecoic acids	$CH_3\cdot(CH_2)_{12}\cdot COOH$	228·4	waxy leaflets
54	Nervonic acid	15:16-Tetra-cosenoic acid, selacholeic acid	$CH_3\cdot(CH_2)_7\cdot CH{=}CH\cdot(CH_2)_{13}\cdot COOH$	366·6	*cis*, wh. needles
55	Oleic acid	*cis*-9:10-Octa-decenoic acid; *trans*-isomer, elaidic acid	$CH_3\cdot(CH_2)_7\cdot CH{=}CH\cdot(CH_2)_7\cdot COOH$	282·5	*cis*, col. needles; *trans*, leaflets
56	Oleoyl alcohol	*cis*-9:10-Octa-decenol	$CH_3\cdot(CH_2)_7\cdot CH{=}CH\cdot(CH_2)_7\cdot CH_2OH$	268·5	liquid
57	Palmitaldehyde	Hexadecanal	$CH_3\cdot(CH_2)_{14}\cdot CHO$	240·4	
58	Palmitic acid	*n*-Hexadecanoic, hexadecoic, acids	$CH_3\cdot(CH_2)_{14}\cdot COOH$	256·4	waxy needles
59	Palmitoleic acid	9:10-Hexa-decenoic acid, zoomaric acid	$CH_3\cdot(CH_2)_5\cdot CH{=}CH\cdot(CH_2)_7\cdot COOH$	254·4	liquid
60	Pelargonic acid	*n*-Nonanoic, nonylic, acids	$CH_3\cdot(CH_2)_7\cdot COOH$	158·2	liquid

M.p.	$[\alpha]^t_D$	Solubility	Preparation	Estimation	General remarks
	Liver, $+5{\cdot}60^{25}$	s. H_2O, $CHCl_3$, benz.; sl. s. MeOH, eth., pet. eth.; i. 95% EtOH, acet., Et acetate	*C. r. hebd. Séanc. Acad. Sci., Paris*, **236**, 1104 (1953); **238**, 411 (1954) *J.B.C.* **206**, 27 (1954); **215**, 295 (1955); **220**, 537 (1956); **231**, 813 (1958) *B.J.* **81**, 535 (1961) Ansell & Hawthorne, *Phospholipids*, p. 96 (1964) SYN. *Chemy Ind.* **1959**, 1155	*B.J.* **84**, 497 (1962) *B.Z.* **339**, 327 (1964)	Ba salt insoluble in H_2O but soluble in $CHCl_3$/MeOH (3:1 v/v).
–53 p. 249^{100}		At 20°: 0·002 H_2O, 29·2 benz., 32·5 $CHCl_3$, 17·6 CCl_4, 17·3 MeOH, 23·9 EtOH, 15·9 acet., 10·2 gl. acetic, 15·3 Et acetate; sp. s. eth.	SYN. *Org. Synth.* **Coll. 1**, 379 (1941)	*See* Arachidic acid *B.J.* **63**, 144 (1956)	Widely distributed in natural oils and fats.
, 39 *ns*, 61		s. EtOH, $CHCl_3$, acet.	*Z.P.C.* **166**, 287 (1927) *J.A.C.S.* **52**, 4536 (1930)		Occurs in marine oils and brain lipids; naturally occurring is *cis*-form.
, α, 13·4 16·3 *ns*, 44·5		*cis, trans*, i. H_2O; s. EtOH, benz., $CHCl_3$, eth., MeOH, acet.	*J.A.C.S.* 56, 1563 (1934) *J.C.S.* **1939**, 974 *J.B.C.* **154**, 437 (1944) *cis*, *Biochem. Preps.* **2**, 100 (1952); **9**, 113 (1962) *trans*, *Biochem. Preps.* **3**, 118 (1953) *J.C.S.* **1953**, 2393	*Analyt. Chem.* **22**, 1261 (1950) *See also* Arachidic acid *B.J.* **59**, 309 (1954)	*Cis-trans* conversion catalysed by nitrogen oxides, sulphurous acid, S, P, and Se. The cryst. form melting at 13·4 changes slowly to the stable form melting at 16·3. Dibromo compounds: oleic, M.p. 28·5–9; elaidic, M.p. 29–30. Ca salt, M.p. 83–84. Na salt, M.p. 230–5.
. 209^{15}		s. EtOH, eth.	*Ind. Engng Chem.* **41**, 446 (1949)		Constituent of marine oils.
		i. H_2O; s. eth., acet., pet. eth., EtOH	*J.B.C.* **152**, 501 (1944)	*J.B.C.* **219**, 39 (1956) *J. Lipid Res.* 3, 21 (1962)	Polymerizes on keeping to trimeride, M.p. 73. Oxime M.p. 88. Semicarbazone, M.p. 107.
$211{\cdot}5^{10}$		i. H_2O; s. eth. At 20°: 7·3 benz., 15·1 $CHCl_3$, 5·8 CCl_4, 3·7 MeOH, 7·21 EtOH, 5·4 acet., 2·1 gl. acetic, 6·1 Et acetate	*Ber.* **21**, 2265 (1888) *Ber.* **24**, 936 (1891) *Org. Synth.* **Coll. 3**, 607 (1955) ^{14}C. *J.A.C.S.* **70**, 1376 (1948) PURIFICATION *J.C.S.* **1931**, 802	*See* Arachidic acid *B.J.* **63**, 144 (1956)	Widespread occurrence in plant and animal lipids. Ca salt, M.p. 153–6. Na salt, M.p. 270.
5 to 0·5		s. $CHCl_3$, eth.	*J. Soc. Chem. Ind., Lond.* **44**, 180T (1925)	*See* Arachidic acid	A major component of many vegetable and animal fats.
2·5 180^{100}, 0		At 20°: 0·026 H_2O; ∞ benz., hexane, acet., Et acetate, MeOH	*See* Azelaic acid *J.A.C.S.* **64**, 2239 (1942)	*See* Arachidic acid (*a*)	Product of oxidative cleavage of oleic acid.

11. Lipids and Long-chain Fatty Acids

No.	Name	Synonyms	Formula	M. wt.	Physical form
61	Pentadecanoic acid	Pentadecylic acid	$CH_3\cdot(CH_2)_{13}\cdot COOH$	242·4	cryst. waxy solid
62	Phosphatidic acid	Diacylglycerophosphoric acid	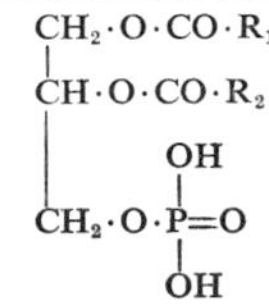 R_1, R_2 = fatty acid residues	226·1 $+R_1+R_2$. Di-myristoyl, 592·5; Di-palmitoyl, 648·6; Distearoyl, 704·6	ISOL. olive brown oil SYN. solids
63	Phosphatidyl-glycerol		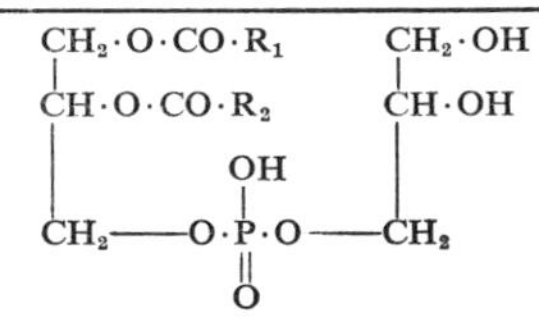 R_1, R_2 = fatty acid residues	300·1 $+R_1+R_2$	Distearoyl-L-α-, cryst. Dioleoyl-L-α-, oil
64	Phosphatidyl-serine	Diacylglyceryl-phosphorylserine	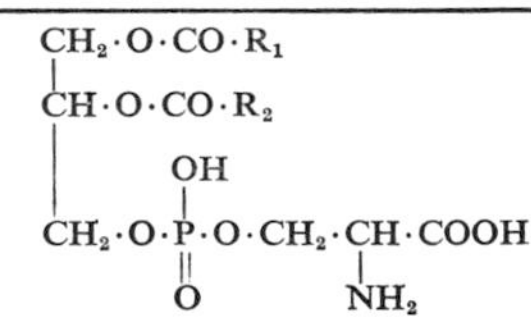 R_1, R_2 = fatty acid residues	313·2 $+R_1+R_2$	loose wh. or tan powder
65	Plasmalogens	Formerly called acetal phosphatides, phosphatidal-ethanolamine (-serine, -choline)	Consist of glycerylphosphoryl-ethanolamine (or -choline or -serine) with one esterified fatty acid and one aldehydogenic fatty acid residue in enol-ether linkage: example below refers to ethanolamine plasmalogen. (*a*) In tissues 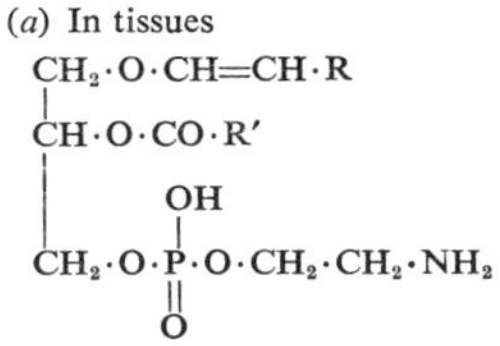	(*a*) 267·2 +R+R′	(*a*) not isolated i pure form
			(*b*) as isolated using alkali, i.e. lysoplasmalogen 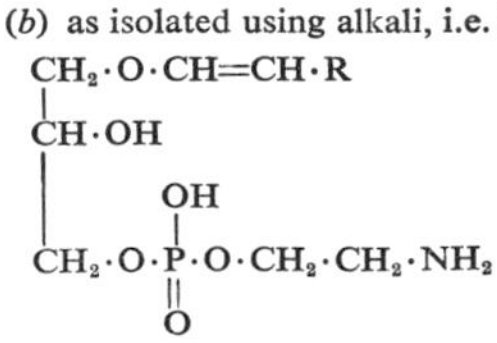 R′ = fatty acid residue R = fatty alcohol residue	(*b*) 240·2 +R	(*b*) cryst.
66	Ricinoleic acid	12-Hydroxy-*cis*-9:10-octadecenoic acid, ricinolic acid	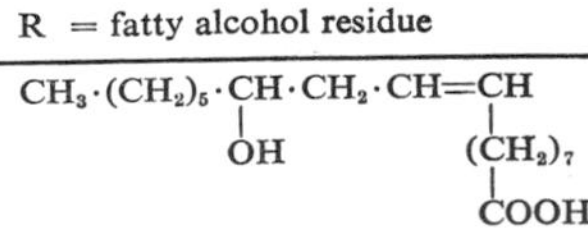	298·5	col. liquid or c

M.p.	$[\alpha]_D^t$	Solubility	Preparation	Estimation	General remarks
52·3 B.p. 202–5[10]		At 20°: 0·0012 H_2O, 36·2 benz., 16·4 MeOH, 19·5 95% EtOH, 13·8 acet., 8·8 gl. acetic, 15·4 Et acetate, 22·3 Bu acetate	ISOL. *B.J.* **61**, 453 (1955) SYN. *J.B.C.* **16**, 475 (1914) *Pharm. Archs* **10**, 88 (1939)	*See* Arachidic acid (*a*)	Traces found in many natural lipids, e.g. butter-fat, mutton fat, shark liver oil.
	Dimyristoyl-L-α-, +4·4[24] (in $CHCl_3$); Dipalmitoyl-L-α-, +4·0[26] (in $CHCl_3$); Distearoyl-L-α-, +3·8[26] (in $CHCl_3$)	ISOL. i. H_2O, EtOH; s. acet., eth., $CHCl_3$. SYN. i. H_2O; sl. s. EtOH; sp. s. acet.; s. $CHCl_3$, benz.	*Can. J. Biochem. Physiol.* **33**, 575 (1955) *B.B.A.* **41**, 45 (1960) SYN. *J.B.C.* **212**, 25 (1955)	*B.J.* **84**, 497 (1962)	On acid hydrolysis α-phosphatidic acid yields α- and β-glycerophosphoric acid. On alkaline hydrolysis no migration of the phosphoric acid.
Distearoyl- -α-, 65·5–67·0	Distearoyl-L-α-, +2·0[22] (in $CHCl_3$); Dioleoyl-L-α-, +2·0[21] (in $CHCl_3$)	Emulsifies in H_2O; s. EtOH, eth., $CHCl_3$, acet., benz., MeOH	ISOL. *B.B.A.* **27**, 189 (1958) *B.J.* **88**, 42P (1963) *B.B.A.* **84**, 35 (1964) SYN. *J.B.C.* **232**, 895 (1958) *B.J.* **102**, 205 (1967)	*B.J.* **84**, 497 (1962)	Found mainly in plants but traces in animal tissues.
istearoyl- α-, nters 120, elts 159–61	See *J.B.C.* **212**, 25 (1955)	ISOL. (Na, K salt) emulsifies in H_2O; i. EtOH, MeOH, acet.; s. $CHCl_3$, eth., pet. eth. SYN. s. $CHCl_3$ only	ISOL. *B.J.* **85**, 251 (1962) *B.B.A.* **30**, 41 (1958) *Nature, Lond.* **200**, 887 (1963) *B.B.A.* **135**, 624 (1967) SYN. *J.B.C.* **212**, 25 (1955) *J.C.S.* **1957**, 3086	*J.B.C.* **192**, 465 (1951) *J.B.C.* **157**, 585 (1945) *B.J.* **84**, 497 (1962) *J. Lipid. Res.* **3**, 467 (1962)	Salt only stable when stored in $CHCl_3$ at −72°. Free acid more stable. Labile in methanolic N-NaOH at 37°. Occurs in animal tissues as α-isomer. Isolated lipid usually contains serine-containing plasmalogen.
			80% pure: *B.J.* **70**, 409 (1958) *J.B.C.* **237**, 329 (1962) *J. Neurochem.* **10**, 941 (1963) *Acta chem. scand.* **17**, 634 (1963)	*J.B.C.* **219**, 39 (1956) *J.B.C.* **217**, 199 (1955) *B.B.A.* **38**, 340 (1960) *B.J.* **84**, 497 (1962) *Prog. Chem. Fats* **6**, 1 (1963) *J. Lipid Res.* **3**, 21, 378 (1962)	(*a*) Converted to (*b*) structure by incubation in methanolic N-NaOH at 37°.
muscle, –90	(*b*) muscle, −8·6[26] (c = 4 in $CHCl_3$:MeOH (1:1 v/v))	(*b*) i. H_2O; sl. s. EtOH, eth., pet. eth., acet., benz.; s. hot MeOH, hot EtOH, $CHCl_3$	(*b*) ISOL. ethanolamine, *J.B.C.* **225**, 859 (1957) choline, *B.J.* **75**, 251 (1960)	As above	(*b*) Stable in N-NaOH at 37°. Labile in acids at room temp. Many early preparations produced the cyclic acetal.
5·5 *ns*, 53)	+6·4[22] (in acet.)	i. H_2O; s. $CHCl_3$, acet., eth.	ISOL. *J.A.C.S.* **53**, 4130 (1931) *J.A.C.S.* **62**, 738 (1940) *Chemy Ind.* **1954**, 1197	*B.J.* **59**, 309 (1954) *Meth. biochem. Anal.* **8**, 1 (1960)	Occurs in castor oil as the triglyceride triricinolein. Absolute configuration, see *Chemy Ind.* **1958**, 1554.

No.	Name	Synonyms	Formula	M. wt.	Physical form
67	Sitosterols (α_1-, β-)		(α_1) 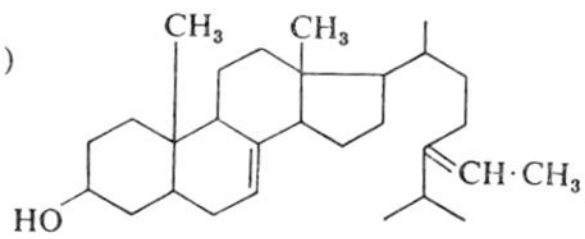	α_1, 412·7	α_1, needles from EtOH
		β-, 22-Dihydro-stigmasterol, Δ^5-Stigmastene-3β-ol	(β) 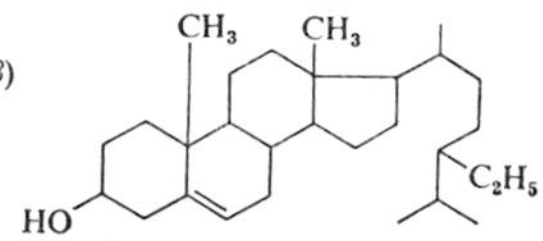	β, 414·7	β, needles from EtOH
68	Sphingomyelin		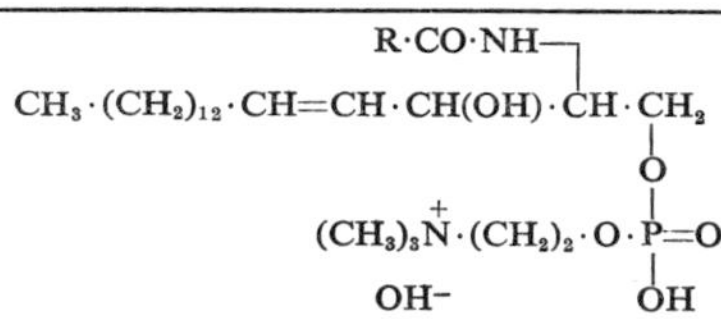 R = fatty acid residue	509·6 +R	wh. cryst. solid
69	Sphingosine	*trans*-D-*erythro*-1,3-Dihydroxy-2-amino-4:5-octadecene	$CH_3\cdot(CH_2)_{12}\cdot CH{=}CH\cdot CH(OH)CH(NH_2)CH_2OH$	299·5	needles from pet. eth.
	— sulphate		$C_{18}H_{37}NO_2\cdot H_2SO_4$	397·6	Sulphate, rosettes o needles from EtOH v. hygr.
70	Squalene	Spinacene	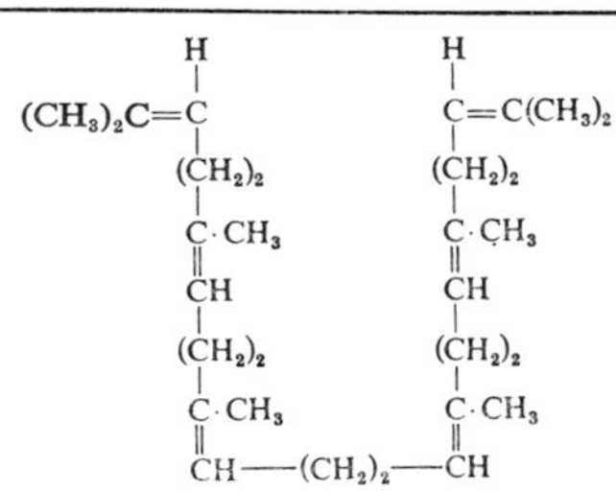	410·7	col. mobile oil
71	Stearaldehyde	Octadecanal	$CH_3\cdot(CH_2)_{16}\cdot CHO$	268·5	scales from eth.
72	Stearic acid	*n*-Octadecanoic, octadecoic, acids	$CH_3\cdot(CH_2)_{16}\cdot COOH$	284·4	leaflets from EtOH

Triglycerides, *see* Glycerides

M.p.	$[\alpha]_D^t$	Solubility	Preparation	Estimation	General remarks
α_1, 164–6	α_1, $-1{\cdot}7^{28}$ (in $CHCl_3$)	α_1, s. $CHCl_3$, eth.	α_1, *J.A.C.S.* **58**, 2446 (1936)		Occurs in wheat germ and soya-bean oils. Precipitated by digitonin. α_1-form: Acetate, M.p. 137. Benzoate, M.p. 172.
β, 136–8	β, $-37{\cdot}8^{25}$ (in $CHCl_3$)	β, s. $CHCl_3$	β, *Ber.* **64**, 2167 (1931) *J.A.C.S.* **66**, 489 (1944)		β-form: Acetate, M.p. 123–4. Benzoate, M.p. 145–6.
196–8 (209)	+6 to 7 (in $CHCl_3$/ MeOH)	i. eth., acet., H_2O; s. benz., $CHCl_3$, hot EtOH, hot Et acetate	ISOL. *J.B.C.* **166**, 677 (1946) *J.B.C.* **232**, 63 (1958) *Biochem. Preps.* **8**, 121 (1961) SYN. *J.A.C.S.* **81**, 4360 (1959) *J.A.C.S.* **84**, 1047 (1962)	*J.B.C.* **166**, 505 (1946) *B.J.* **56**, 621 (1954) *B.J.* **84**, 497 (1962) *J. Lipid Res.* **3**, 1, 467 (1962)	Stable on incubation in N-NaOH at 37°.
32·5–83 Sulphate, 40–50 149–52)	Free base, $+3^{25}$ (26 mg in 2 ml pyr.) Sulphate, $-13{\cdot}12^{20}$ (in $CHCl_3$)	i. H_2O; s. $CHCl_3$, EtOH, acet. MeOH. Sulphate, s. $CHCl_3$, hot EtOH containing H_2SO_4	*J.B.C.* **170**, 269 (1947) *J. Neurochem.* **1**, 18 (1956) *Biochem. Preps.* **9**, 127 (1962)	*J.B.C.* **178**, 29 (1949) *J. Neurochem.* **1**, 18 (1956) *J. Lipid Res.* **1**, 40 (1959)	Triacetyl deriv., M.p. 101–2
elow −20 .p. 213[1]		s. eth., $CHCl_3$; sp. s. EtOH, gl. acetic	ISOL. *J.C.S.* **1926**, 1631 *J.A.C.S.* **74**, 4321 (1952) SYN. *Helv. chim. Acta* **14**, 78 (1931); **36**, 130 (1953) ^{14}C. *J.A.C.S.* **74**, 5204 (1952)	*J. Ass. off. agric. Chem.* **28**, 282 (1945); **29**, 247 (1946) *J.A.C.S.* **74**, 4321 (1952)	Intermediate in cholesterol biosynthesis. Found in many tissues in traces, but in appreciable amount in some marine liver oils. Hexahydrochlorides, M.p. 108–10, 144–5.
3·5 (38), olymerizes ery rapidly M.p. nreliable		i. H_2O; s. EtOH, eth., pet. eth., acet.	*J.B.C.* **152**, 501 (1944)	*J.B.C.* **173**, 547 (1948) *J.B.C.* **219**, 39 (1956) *J. Lipid Res.* **3**, 21 (1962)	Polymerizes very rapidly on keeping.
·6 p. 213·0[5]		i. H_2O; s. eth. At 20°: 2·5 benz., 6·0 $CHCl_3$, 2·4 CCl_4, 0·1 MeOH, 2·25 EtOH, 1·54 acet., 0·12 gl. acetic, 0·5 Et acetate	*Ber.* **17**, 1627 (1884) *J. Soc. Chem. Ind., Lond.* **43**, 346T (1924) *J.A.C.S.* **62**, 230 (1940) PURIFICATION *J.C.S.*' **1931**, 802 *Biochem. Preps.* **7**, 84 (1960)	*See* Arachidic acid *B.J.* **63**, 144 (1956)	Widely distributed in natural oils and fats; notably high content in depot fats of ruminants. Ca salt, M.p. 150–4. Na salt, M.p. 260.

11. Lipids and Long-chain Fatty Acids

No.	Name	Synonyms	Formula	M. wt.	Physical form
73	Triphospho-inositide	1-Phosphatidyl-(inositol-4,5-diphosphate)	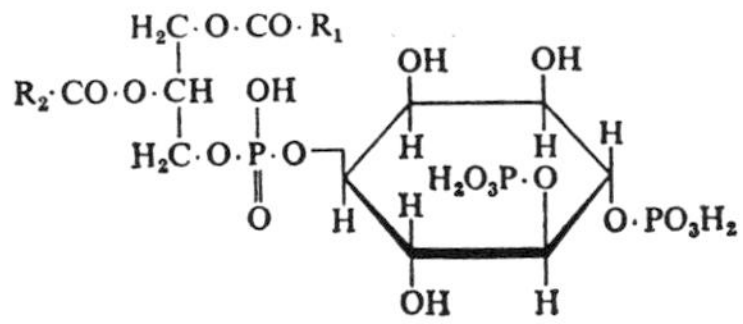 (Sodium salt, Na_4) R_1, R_2 = fatty acid residues	548·2+ R_1+R_2	Na salt, wh. amorph. solid
74	Tuberculo-stearic acid	10-Methylstearic acid, (—)-10-(D)-methylocta-decanoic acid	$CH_3\cdot(CH_2)_7\cdot CH(CH_3)\cdot(CH_2)_8\cdot COOH$	298·5	liquid
75	Vaccenic acid	*trans*-11:12-Octadecenoic acid	$CH_3\cdot(CH_2)_5\cdot CH{=}CH\cdot(CH_2)_9\cdot COOH$	282·4	cryst.

M.p.	$[\alpha]^t_D$	Solubility	Preparation	Estimation	General remarks
		Free lipid, s. H_2O, MeOH, EtOH, $CHCl_3$. Na salt, s. H_2O, wet $CHCl_3$; i. MeOH, acet., eth.	*B.J.* **81**, 535 (1961) *J.B.C.* **239**, 1369 (1964)	*B.J.* **81**, 540 (1961) *B.Z.* **339**, 327 (1964)	Sodium salt (Na_4) stable when stored in moist $CHCl_3$ at −18°, free acid slowly decomposes.
12·8–13·4 B.p. 175–8$^{0.7}$	−0·08[19]	i. H_2O; s. fat solvents	ISOL. *J.B.C.* **85**, 77 (1929) SYN. *J.A.C.S.* **70**, 298 (1948) *Ark. Kemi Miner. Geol.* **26A**, 1 (1948) *J.C.S.* **1951**, 1130	*See* Arachidic acid (*a*)	Found in human and bovine tubercle wax and in leprosy bacilli. Amide, M.p. 76·5–77. Tribromanilide, M.p. 93–94.
cis, 6·8 *trans*, 42·5		s. $CHCl_3$, acet.	*J.A.C.S.* **70**, 1102 (1948) *J.C.S.* **1950**, 3484	*J.B.C.* **169**, 227 (1947)	*trans*-Isomer present in butter, beef fat. *cis*-Isomer present in lipids of many bacteria.

RETENTION VOLUMES OF METHYL ESTERS OF THE LONG-CHAIN FATTY ACIDS RELATIVE TO METHYL PALMITATE

(From A. T. James, *Meth. biochem. Anal.* **8,** 1 (1960) with additions by J. H. Recourt, Unilever Research Laboratory, Vlaardingen, Holland)

		Stationary phase				
Acid (chemical or trivial name)	*Shorthand designation*	*Apiezon L at 197°*	*Apiezon M at 197°*	*Reoplex 400 at 197°*	*Polyethylene glycol adipate at 180°*	*Poly-diethylene glycol succinate at 203°*
n-Pentanoic	5:0	0·008	..	..	..	..
n-Hexanoic	6:0	0·013	..	..	..	..
4-Methylhexanoic	a.i.br. 7:0	0·017	..	..	..	..
n-Heptanoic	7:0	0·019	..	..	..	..
6-Methylheptanoic	a.i.br. 8:0	0·024	..	..	..	..
n-Octanoic	8:0	0·030	..	..	0·060	..
6-Methyloctanoic	a.i.br. 9:0	0·041	..	..	..	..
n-Nonanoic	9:0	0·047	..	..	0·082	..
8-Methylnonanoic	i.br. 10:0	0·061	..	..	..	..
n-Decanoic	10:0	0·073	0·069	0·179	0·134	..
8-Methyldecanoic	a.i.br. 11:0	0·10	..	..	..	..
n-Undecanoic	11:0	0·117	0·112	0·232	0·183	..
10-Methylundecanoic	i.br. 12:0	0·15	..	..	..	..
n-Dodecanoic	12:0	0·18	0·18	0·286	0·26	0·36
10-Methyldodecanoic	a.i.br. 13·0	0·242	..	..	..	..
Undefined branched tridecanoic	br. 13:0	..	0·203 0·234	..	..	..
n-Tridecanoic	13:0	0·250	0·267	0·388	0·362	..
n-Tetradecatrienoic	14:3	0·291	..	..	0·90	..
n-Tetradecadienoic	14:2	..	..	..	..	..
n-Tetradecenoic	14:1	0·39	0·38	0·634	0·615	..
Undefined branched tetradecanoic	br. 14:0	..	0·37	..	..	..
n-Tetradecanoic	14:0	0·42	0·416	0·555	0·51	0·60
Undefined branched pentadecanoic	br. 15:0	0·55	0·548	..	..	..
12-Methyltetradecanoic	a.i.br. 15:0	0·58	..	..	..	..
Undefined branched pentadecanoic	br. 15:0	..	0·52	..	..	..
n-Pentadecanoic	15:0	0·66	0·65	..	0·705	..
$\Delta^{6,9,12,15}$-Hexadecatetraenoic	$16:4^{6,9,12,15}$	..	0·74	1·97	..	..
$\Delta^{6,9,12}$-Hexadecatrienoic	$16:3^{6,9,12}$	..	0·77	1·59	..	..
$\Delta^{9,12}$-Hexadecadienoic	$16:2^{9,12}$	..	0·79	1·39	..	..
$\Delta^{6,9}$-Hexadecadienoic	$16:2^{6,9}$	..	0·86	1·28	..	..
Δ^{8}-Hexadecenoic	$16:1^{8}$	..	0·89	1·13	..	..
cis-Δ^{9}-Hexadecenoic	*cis*-$16:1^{9}$	0·90	0·89	1·13	1·15	1·17
trans-Δ^{9}-Hexadecenoic	*trans*-$16:1^{9}$	0·92	..	..	1·15	..
n-Hexadecanoic	16:0	1·0	1·0	1·0	1·0	1·0
Dihydrohydnocarpic	..	1·43*	..	..	1·66†	..
n-Heptadecenoic	17:1	1·31	..	..	1·62	..
14-Methylheptadecanoic	a.i.br. 17:0	1·38	..	..	..	..
n-Heptadecanoic	17:0	1·51	1·55	1·32	1·40	..
$\Delta^{6,9,12,15}$-Octadecatetraenoic	$18:4^{6,9,12,15}$	..	1·72	3·48	..	..
All-*cis*-$\Delta^{9,12,15}$-octadecatrienoic	*cis*-$18:3^{9,12,15}$	1·93	1·84	2·95	3·51	..

* column at 205°. † column at 175°.

		Stationary phase				
Acid (chemical or trivial name)	*Shorthand designation*	*Apiezon L at 197°*	*Apiezon M at 197°*	*Reoplex 400 at 197°*	*Polyethylene glycol adipate at 180°*	*Poly-diethylene glycol succinate at 203°*
All-*cis*-$\Delta^{6,9,12}$-octadecatrienoic	*cis*-18:$3^{6,9,12}$	1·76*	..	..	2·84†	..
cis-trans-trans-$\Delta^{9,11,13}$-Octadecatrienoic	*cis-trans-trans*-18:$3^{9,11,13}$	3·82	..	..	..	..
All-*trans*-$\Delta^{9,11,13}$-octadecatrienoic	*trans*-18:$3^{9,11,13}$	4·44	..	..	..	..
cis-cis-$\Delta^{9,12}$-Octadecadienoic	*cis*-18:$2^{9,12}$	1·9	1·81	2·38	2·69	2·40
cis-trans-$\Delta^{9,11}$-Octadecadienoic	*cis-trans*-18:$2^{9,11}$	2·56	..	..	..	..
trans-cis-$\Delta^{10,12}$-Octadecadienoic	*trans-cis*-18:$2^{10,12}$	2·56	..	..	..	..
All-*trans*-$\Delta^{9,11}$-octadecadienoic	*trans*-18:$2^{9,11}$	3·09	..	..	..	..
All-*trans*-$\Delta^{10,12}$-octadecadienoic	*trans*-18:$2^{10,12}$	3·09	..	..	..	..
$\Delta^{6,9}$-Octadecadienoic	18:$2^{6,9}$	..	1·81	2·56	..	..
cis-Δ^{9}-Octadecenoic	*cis*-18:1^{9}	2·03	2·08	2·02	2·21	1·93
trans-Δ^{9}-Octadecenoic	*trans*-18:1^{9}	2·12	..	..	2·21	..
cis-Δ^{6}-Octadecenoic	*cis*-18:1^{6}	2·09	..	..	2·22	..
cis-Δ^{4}-Octadecenoic	*cis*-18:1^{4}	2·12	..	..	2·23	..
trans-Δ^{4}-Octadecenoic	*trans*-18:1^{4}	2·22	..	..	..	..
n-Octadecanoic	18:0	2·36	2·39	1·79	1·97	1·66
Dihydrochaulmoogric	..	3·52*	..	..	3·18†	..
All-*cis*-$\Delta^{7,10,13}$-nonadecatrienoic	*cis*-19:$3^{7,10,13}$	2·62*	..	..	3·85†	..
All-*cis*-$\Delta^{10,13}$-nonadecadienoic	*cis*-19:$2^{10,13}$	2·92*	..	..	3·48†	..
n-Nonadecanoic	19:0	..	..	..	..	..
$\Delta^{5,8,11,14,17}$-Eicosapentaenoic	20:$5^{5,8,11,14,17}$	3·48	3·48	6·64	8·5	..
$\Delta^{8,11,14,17}$-Eicosatetraenoic	20:$4^{8,11,14,17}$	..	3·48	5·35	..	..
Arachidonic	20:$4^{5,8,11,14}$	3·48	3·48	5·28	6·56	..
Undefined eicosatrienoic	20:3	3·65	3·92	4·80	5·96	..
Undefined	20:2	..	4·5	3·88	..	..
	20:1	..	4·75	3·57	..	..
	20:0	5·8	5·83	3·15	3·87	..
	21:0	..	8·72	..	..	..
	22:$6^{4,7,10,13,16,19}$	7·15	7·15	13·5	18·2	..
	22:$5^{5,8,11,14,17}$	..	7·88	12·2	..	..
	22:1	10·9	..	..	8·15	..
	22:0	..	14·2	6·8	..	4·67
	26:0	..	..	..	..	13·8

* column at 205°. † column at 175°.

12. Steroids

Revised by V. H. T. JAMES (*St. Mary's Hospital, London*) *and* J. A. J. JEFFERY (*I.C.I. Ltd., Macclesfield*)

IN this section the spelling oestrogen is preferred to estrogen.

The following classified bibliography is given in order to assist in tracking down information on certain general aspects of the biochemistry of steroid compounds.

General Chemistry

L. F. Fieser and M. Fieser, *Steroids*, Reinhold, New York (1959).
W. Klyne, *Chemistry of the Steroids*, Methuen, London (1960).
E. Heftmann and E. Mossetig, *Biochemistry of Steroids*, Reinhold, New York (1960).

Nomenclature

J.A.C.S. **80,** 5577 (1960); *B.J.* **113,** 5 (1969); **127,** 613 (1972); *Eur. J. Biochem.* **10,** 1 (1969); **12,** 1 (1970).

Spectroscopic data

K. Dobriner, E. R. Katzenellenbogen, R. N. Jones, G. Roberts, and B. S. Gallagher, *Infra-red absorption spectra of Steroids. An Atlas*, vols. 1 and 2, Interscience, New York (1953 and 1958).
L. Dorfman, 'Ultraviolet absorption spectra', *Chem. Rev.* **53,** 47 (1953).
S. Bernstein and R. H. Lenhard, 'Absorption spectra of steroids in sulphuric acid', *J. org. Chem.* **18,** 1146 (1953); **19,** 1269 (1954).
H. Rosenkrantz, 'Analysis of steroids by infra-red spectrometry', *Meth. biochem. Anal.* **2,** 1 (1955).

Polarimetric data

J. P. Mathieu and A. Petit, *Pouvoir Rotatoire Naturel*, 1-*Stéroides*, Masson et Cie, Paris (1956).

Chromatography

I. E. Bush, *Chromatography of Steroids*, Pergamon Press, London (1961).
R. Neher, *Steroid Chromatography*, Elsevier, Amsterdam (1963).
R. Knuppen, 'Papierchromatographie phenolischer Steroide', *Z. Vitam. Horm. u. Fermentforsch.* **12,** 355 (1963).
H. H. Wotiz and S. J. Clark, *Gas Chromatography in the Analysis of Steroid Hormones*, Plenum Press, New York (1966).

Synthetic procedures and reactions

Comprehensive Biochemistry, eds. Florkin and Stotz, vol. 10, Elsevier, Amsterdam (1963).
C. Djerassi, *Steroid Reactions*, Holden–Day, San Francisco (1963).
Useful reviews appear almost each year in *Rep. Prog. Chem.*

Stereochemistry

D. H. R. Barton and R. C. Cookson, *Q. Rev. chem. Soc.* **10,** 44 (1956).
W. Klyne, *Progress in Stereochemistry*, vol. 1, p. 36, Butterworth, London (1954).

Metabolic transformations

L. T. Samuels and T. Uchikawa, 'Biosynthesis of adrenal steroids', *The Adrenal Cortex*, ed. Eisenstein, Churchill, London (1967).
R. I. Dorfman and F. Ungar, *Metabolism of Steroid Hormones*, Academic Press, New York (1965).
K. Fotherby, 'The biochemistry of progesterone', *Vitams Horm.* **22,** 153 (1964).
H. Breuer, 'The metabolism of the natural oestrogens', ibid. **20,** 285 (1962).
Ch. Tamm, 'Conversion of natural substances by microbial enzymes', *Angew. Chem. internat. ed.* **1,** 178 (1962).
Various aspects are reviewed annually in *Recent Prog. Horm. Res.*

Biological data

(*a*) *General*

I. E. Bush, 'Chemical and biological factors in the activity of adrenocortical steroids', *Pharmac. Rev.* **14,** 317 (1962).
R. I. Dorfman and R. A. Shipley, *Androgens: Biochemistry, Physiology and Clinical Significance*, Wiley, New York (1956).
N. Appelzweig, *Steroid Drugs*, McGraw-Hill, New York (1962).

(*b*) *Assay methods*

Methods in Hormone Research, ed. R. I. Dorfman, Academic Press, New York (1962).
J. B. Brown, 'The determination and significance of the natural estrogens', *Adv. clin. Chem.* **3,** 158 (1960).
M. F. Jayle, *Analyse des Stéroides Hormonaux*, Masson, Paris (1961).

(*c*) *Bile acids*

G. A. D. Haslewood, 'Bile salts, structure, distribution and possible biological significance as a species character', *Comparative Biochemistry*, eds. Florkin and Mason, vol. 3A, p. 205, Academic Press, New York (1962).

Miscellaneous methods

C. Djerassi, *Optical Rotary Dispersion*, McGraw-Hill, New York (1960).
W. Klyne, 'Optical rotatory dispersion and the study of organic structures', *Adv. org. Chem.* **1,** 239 (1960).

Reference standards and radioactive steroids

1. Small quantities of steroids are available from the Medical Research Council steroid reference collection. Requests should be made to Professor W. Klyne, Westfield College, Hampstead, London, N.W. 3.
2. Certain steroids labelled with radio-isotopes may be purchased from commercial sources: Radiochemical Centre, Amersham, Bucks; New England Nuclear Corp., Boston, Mass.; Centre d'Étude de l'Énergie Nucléaire, Mol-Donk, Belgium.

No.	*Name*	*Synonyms*	*Structure*	*M. wt.*	*Physical form*
1	Adrenosterone	Δ^4-Androstene-3,11,17-trione	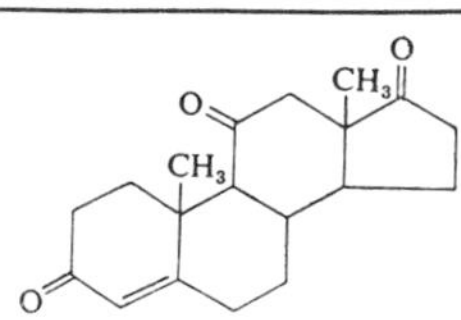	300·4	needles from EtO
2	Aetiocholanolone	3α-Hydroxy-5β-androstan-17-one	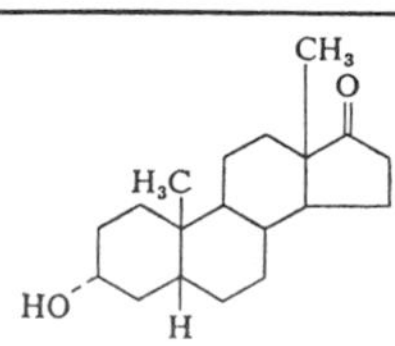	290·4	needles from hexa

Numbering of steroid carbon atoms

The carbon skeleton of a steroid is numbered according to the system given for cholestane below.

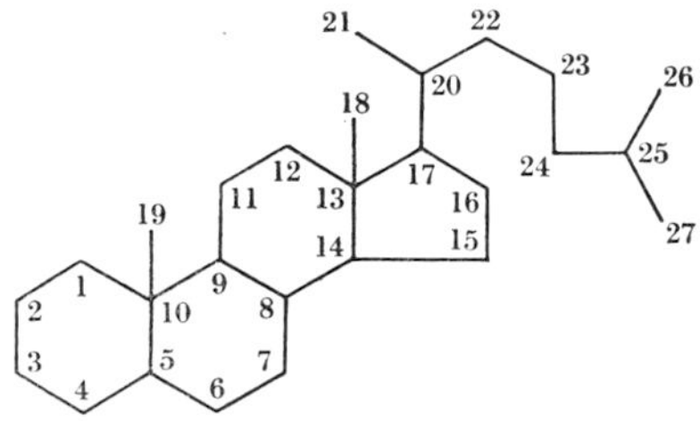

M.p.	$[\alpha]_D^t$	Solubility	References	General remarks
20–4	$+262 \pm 5^{20}$ (c = 1 in EtOH)	sl. s. H_2O; s. acet., eth., EtOH	ISOL. *Helv. chim. Acta* **19**, 223 (1936); **20**, 979 (1937)	E_{max} at 235 mμ. The compound is androgenic. The compound might possibly be formed from 17-hydroxycorticosterone during the isolation from adrenals. Sublimes *in vacuo*.
53	+109 (in EtOH)	i. H_2O; s. organic solvents	*Helv. chim. Acta* **17**, 1405 (1934) *B.J.* **66**, 196 (1957)	Occurs as conjugate in human urine. Metabolite of Δ^4-androstenedione and testosterone. Has some pyrogenic activity.

12. Steroids

No.	*Name*	*Synonyms*	*Structure*	*M. wt.*	*Physical form*
3	Aldosterone	Electrocortin; 11β,21-dihydroxy-3,20-diketo-Δ⁴-pregnen-18-al; 18-oxocorticosterone	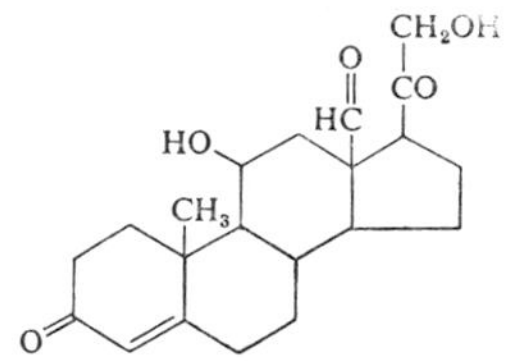	360·4	
4	Allopregnane-3α,11β,17α,21-tetrol-20-one	Kendall's compound C; 3α,11β,17α,21-tetrahydroxy-5α-pregnan-20-one	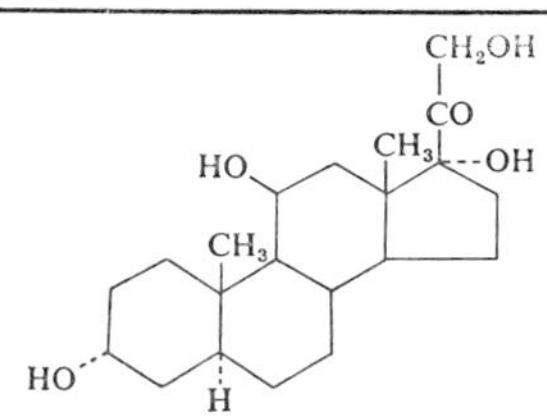	366·5	needles (from EtOH)
5	Androstanediol-17-one	Androstane-3α,11β-diol-17-one; 11-hydroxyandrosterone	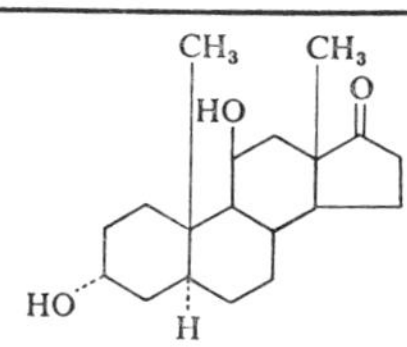	306·4	needles from acet.-ligroin
6	Androstanedione	Androstane-3,17-dione	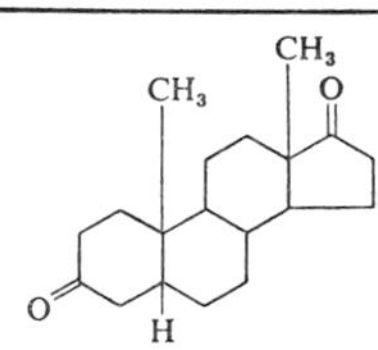	288·4	leaflets from acetone
7	Δ⁴-Androstenedione	Δ⁴-Androstene-3,17-dione	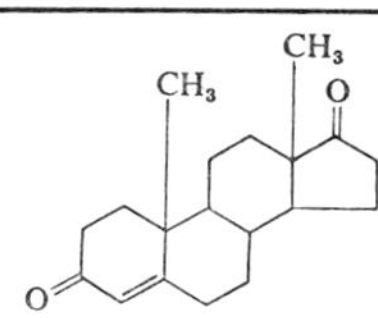	286·4	cryst. from hexane
8	Androsterone	Androstane-3α-ol-17-one	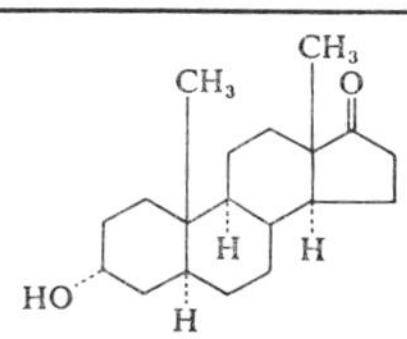	290·4	leaflets or prismatic needles from EtOH or acet.
9	*iso*Androsterone	Androstane-3β-ol-17-one; *epi*androsterone; *trans*androsterone	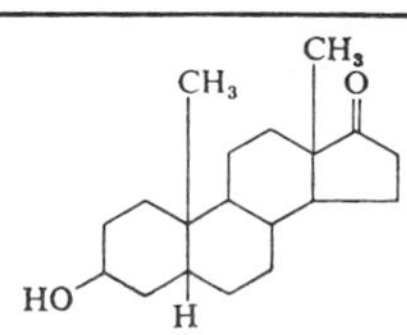	290·4	cryst. from EtOH

Bile acids: *see* chenodeoxycholic acid, cholic acid, deoxycholic acid, lithocholic acid

M.p.	$[\alpha]_D^t$	Solubility	References	General remarks
Anhyd., 164 Monohydrate, 108–12	+145[23] (c = 1 in acetone) anhyd., +152[23] (in acetone)	s. $CHCl_3$, acet.	ISOL. *Helv. chim. Acta* 37, 1163 (1954) *Experientia* 9, 333 (1953); **10**, 132 (1954)	Found in bovine adrenal gland and in human blood and urine. The form shown is in equilibrium with 11,18-semiacetal. Crystallizes with $1H_2O$ from acetone-water. The biology of this compound is reviewed in *Recent Prog. Horm. Res.* **15**, 311 (1959); *Br. med. Bull.* **18**, 164 (1962).
273–5 d.	+73 to +90[20] in EtOH	i. H_2O; s. EtOH, MeOH, $CHCl_3$	*J.B.C.* **114**, 613 (1936); **124**, 459 (1938) *Helv. chim. Acta* **41**, 1516 (1958)	Occurs in adrenal cortex. 3,21-Diacetate, M.p. 204–5 d., $[\alpha]_D^{20}$ +73·8.
197–200	+98·4±3·0[22] (c = 0·18 in EtOH)	s. acet.-eth. (1:4) or eth.-benz. (3:7), EtOH, $CHCl_3$, CCl_4	ISOL. *J.B.C.* **172**, 263 (1948) *J.B.C.* **161**, 235 (1943)	Occurs in normal human urine. Acetate, M.p. 240–2.
132–4	+112·5±2·5[31] (c = 0·2 in EtOH)	s. eth., benz., ligroin	ISOL. *Ber.* **68**, 2097 (1935) *J.B.C.* **172**, 263 (1948)	Found in normal male and female urine. Probably formed from precursors of adrenal and testicular origin. Metabolite of injected testosterone.
170–4	+196[23] (c = 0·13 in EtOH)	s. benz., EtOH, $CHCl_3$	ISOL. *J.B.C.* **172**, 263 (1948) *Helv. chim. Acta* **24**, 879 (1941); **19**, 1373 (1936)	E_{max} at 239 mμ. Found in adrenal vein blood, *Biochem. Soc. Symp.* **18**, 59 (1960). Androgenic potency one-eighth that of testosterone (Fieser and Fieser, p. 519).
183·5	+97[25] (c = 0·5 in EtOH)	i. H_2O; s. organic solvents	ISOL. *J.B.C.* **172**, 263 (1948) SYN. (partial) *Helv. chim. Acta* **17**, 1395 (1934)	Androgenic. Found in urine of normal human male and female. 0·1 mg = standard I.U. of androgenic activity [*J. Am. med. Ass.* **132**, 610 (1946)]. Metabolite of testosterone and Δ^4-androstenedione.
174·5	+82±9·8 (c = 0·12 in MeOH)	s. eth., benz., EtOH, MeOH	PREP. *Z.P.C.* **234**, 218 (1935)	Occurs in normal male and female urine. Weakly androgenic. 700 μg = 1 I.U. Probably derived from testicular and adrenal precursor(s).

12. Steroids

No.	Name	Synonyms	Structure	M. wt.	Physical form
10	Chenodeoxycholic acid	3α, 7α-Hydroxycholanic acid	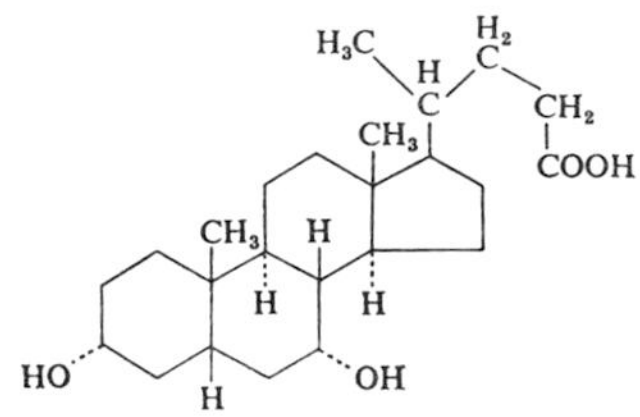	392·6	cryst. from Et acetate
11	Chlormadinone	17α-Acetoxy-6-chloropregna-4,6-diene-3,20-dione	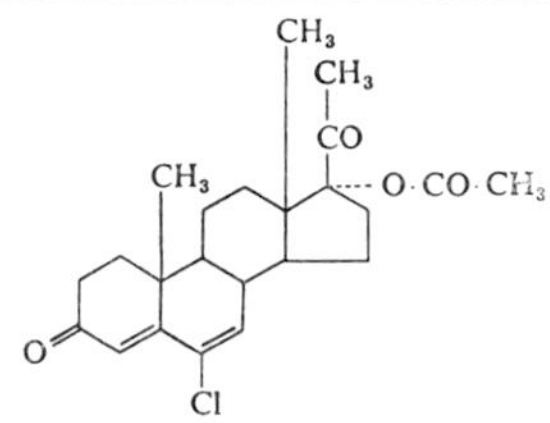	404·9	cryst.
12	Cholanic acid	Ursocholanic acid; 17(β)-(1-methyl-3-carboxypropyl)-etiocholane	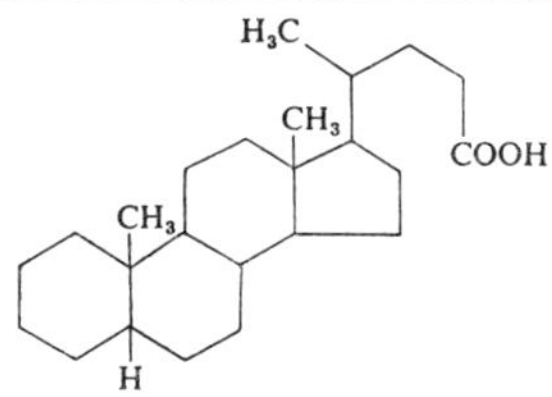	360·6	needles (from EtOH)
13	Cholic acid	3α,7α,12α-Trihydroxycholanic acid; cholalic acid	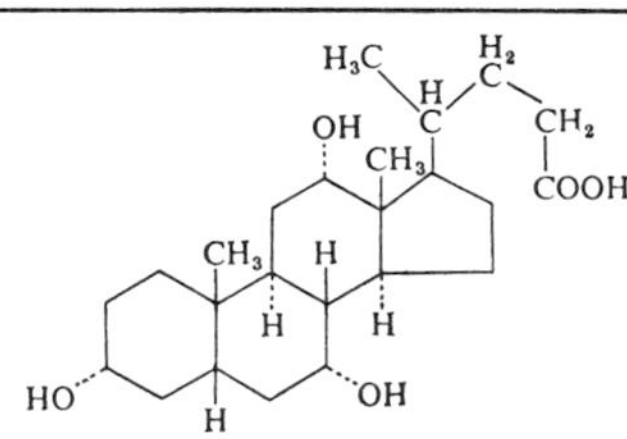	408·6 (anhyd.); Hydrate, 426·6	plates $+H_2O$ from H_2O; +EtOH from EtOH
14	Corticosterone	Δ^4-Pregnene-11β,21-diol-3,20-dione; 17β-(1-keto-2-hydroxyethyl)-Δ^4-androstene-3-one-11β-ol; 11,21-dihydroxyprogesterone; Compound B (Kendall)	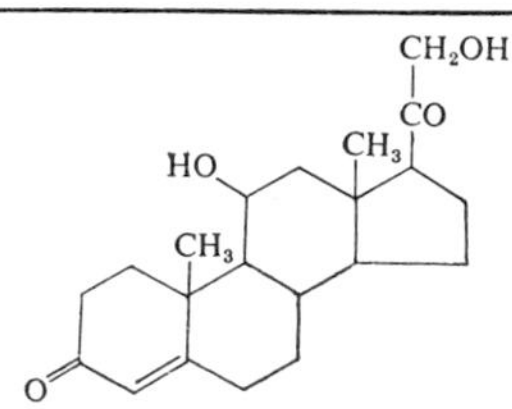	346·4	trigonal plates from acet.; needles +EtOH from EtOH
15	Cortisone	Δ^4-Pregnene-17α,21-diol-3,11,20-trione; 17-hydroxy-11-dehydrocorticosterone; 17-(1-keto-2-hydroxyethyl)-Δ^4-androstene-3,11-dione-17-ol; Compound E (Kendall)	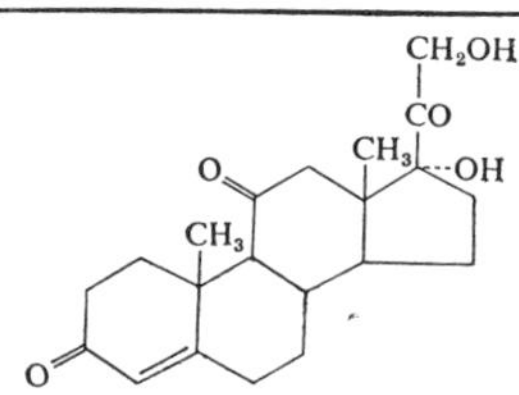	360·4	rh. cryst. from EtOH
16	Dehydro*epi*androsterone	Δ^5-Androstene-3β-ol-17-one; dehydro*iso*androsterone; *trans*-dehydroandrosterone; dehydroandrosterone	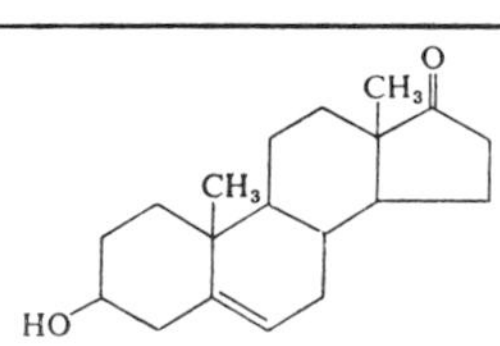	288·4	dimorphous cryst. forms from benz.-pet. eth.

M.p.	$[\alpha]^t_D$	Solubility	References	General remarks
140	+11 (c = 2 in EtOH)	v. sl. s. H_2O; s. MeOH, EtOH, acetic acid	ISOL. *Z.P.C.* **140**, 177, 186 (1924)	Found as glycine or taurine conjugate in bile of man, ox, guinea-pig, hen, and goose.
210–11	+8 in $CHCl_3$	i. H_2O; s. EtOH, $CHCl_3$		Absorption max. in EtOH 284–6 mμ, log ε 4·30. (N.B. shifts from 240 mμ (typical of isolated Δ^4-3-oxo group) to longer wavelength.)
164	$+21{\cdot}7^{20}$ in $CHCl_3$	i. H_2O; s. $CHCl_3$, EtOH, gl. acetic	*Z.P.C.* **191**, 69 (1930)	Ethyl ester, M.p. 93–94, $[\alpha]^{19}_D$ +21 in $CHCl_3$.
Anhyd., 196–8	$+37^{20}$ (c = 0·6 in EtOH)	$0{\cdot}028^{20}$ H_2O; 3·0 EtOH; sl. s. eth.; s. acetic acid, acet., $CHCl_3$, alkalis	ISOL. *Z.P.C.* **110**, 136 (1920) See also *Elsevier's Encyclopaedia of Organic Chemistry*, **14**, Series III (1940), p. 191	Found in bile of most animals chiefly as glycine or taurine conjugate. Not precipitated by digitonin. pK_a = 6·4. Can crystallize with 1 molecule of EtOH or H_2O removable only by prolonged heating. Soluble in conc. H_2SO_4, giving yel. soln. with green fluorescence.
182	$+223^{15}$ (c = 1·1 in EtOH)	i. H_2O; s. EtOH, organic solvents	ISOL. *J.B.C.* **114**, 613 (1936) SYN. (partial) *Helv. chim. Acta* **27**, 1287 (1944) EST. *J. clin. Endocr. Metab.* **21**, 1146 (1961)	E_{max} at 240 mμ. Active glucocorticoid, found in adrenal vein blood of man, *J. clin. Endocr. Metab.* 13, 1546 (1953); of monkey, *J. Endocr.* **9**, 94 (1953); and of rat, *J. Physiol.* **130**, 601 (1955). Reduces ammoniacal silver nitrate. With conc. H_2SO_4 gives orange red soln. with green fluorescence.
215	$+209^{25}$ (c = 1·2 in EtOH)	s. MeOH, EtOH, acet.; sl. s. eth., benz., $CHCl_3$; sp. s. H_2O (0·028)	ISOL. *J.B.C.* **114**, 613 (1936) SYN. *J.A.C.S.* **74**, 4223 (1952) EST. *J. clin. Endocr. Metab.* **12**, 519 (1952) *B.J.* **54**, 523 (1953)	E_{max} at 237 mμ, ε $1{\cdot}4\times10^4$. Glucocorticoid is found in normal human male urine, *J.B.C.* **183**, 365 (1950). Pharmacology of cortisone reviewed *Pharmac. Rev.* **8**, 1 (1956).
148 (needles) 152 (plates)	$+10{\cdot}4^{25}$ (c = 0·58 in EtOH)	s. benz., eth., EtOH; sl. s. $CHCl_3$, pet. eth.; sp. s. CCl_4	ISOL. *Z.P.C.* **229**, 192 (1934) PREP. *Z.P.C.* **237**, 57 (1935)	Found in human urine; of adrenal origin [*Recent Prog. Horm. Res.* **19**, 275 (1963)]. Androgenic. 200 μg = 1 I.U.

12. Steroids

No.	Name	Synonyms	Structure	M. wt.	Physical form
17	Dehydrocorticosterone	Δ^4-Pregnene-21-ol-3,11,20-trione; 11-dehydrocorticosterone; Compound A (Kendall)	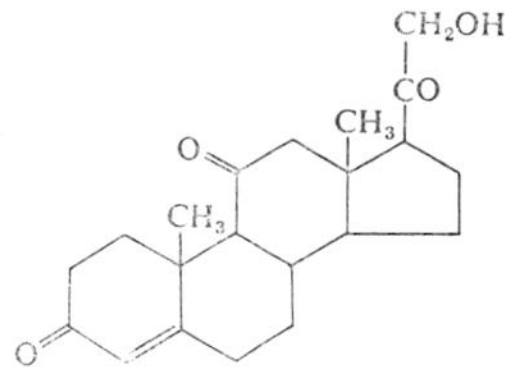	344·4	prisms from aq. acet.
18	Deoxycholic-acid	3α,12α-Dihydroxy-cholanic acid	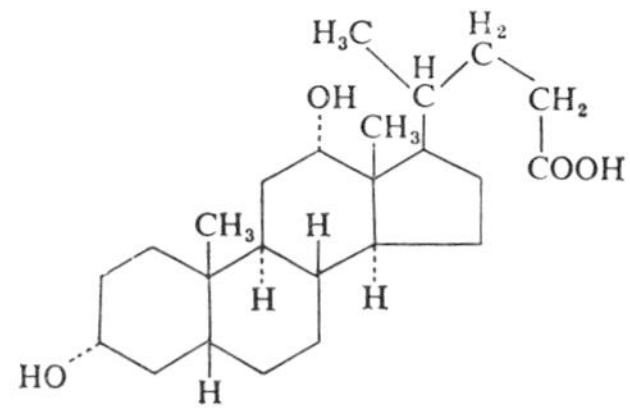	392·6	cryst. from EtOH or 60% aq. acetic
19	Deoxycorticosterone	Δ^4-Pregnene-21-ol-3,20-dione; 21-hydroxy-progesterone; 17α-(1-keto-2-hydroxyethyl)-Δ^4-androstene-3-one. DOCA = acetate	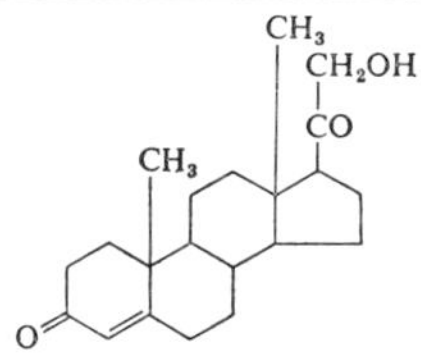	330·4	plates; cryst. from eth.
20	Digitonin	Digitin	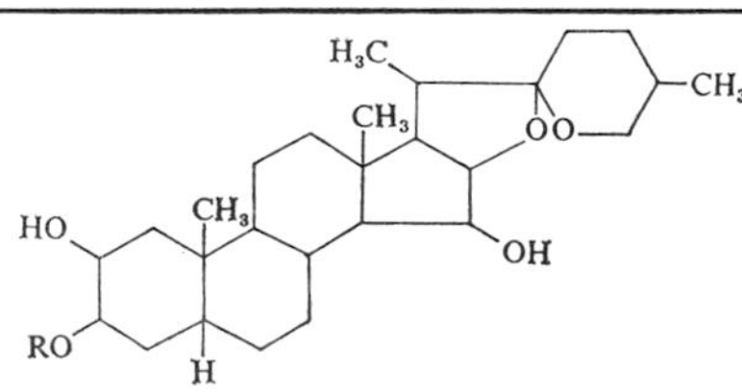 R=2 galactose+2 glucose+1 xylose	1229·3	wh. cryst.
21	Ethisterone	Anhydrohydroxy-progesterone; 17β-ethynyl-Δ^4-androsten-17α-ol-3-one; 17-ethynyl-testosterone; pregneninolone	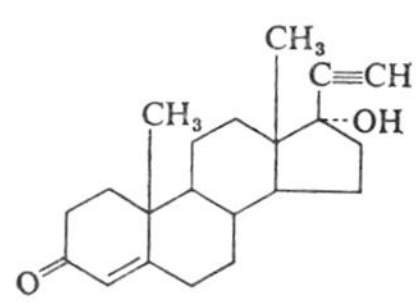	312·4	minute wh. cryst.
22	Ethynyloestradiol	19-Nor-17α-pregna-1,3,5(10)-triene-20-yne-3,17β-diol; 17α-ethynyloestra-1,3,5(10)-triene-3,17β-diol	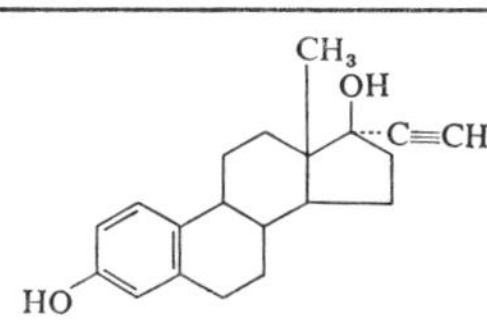	296·4	needles (from MeOH–H_2O)
23	9α-Fluorohydrocortisone	9α-Fluoro-11β,17α,21-trihydroxy-4-pregnene-3,20-dione; 9α-fluorocortisol	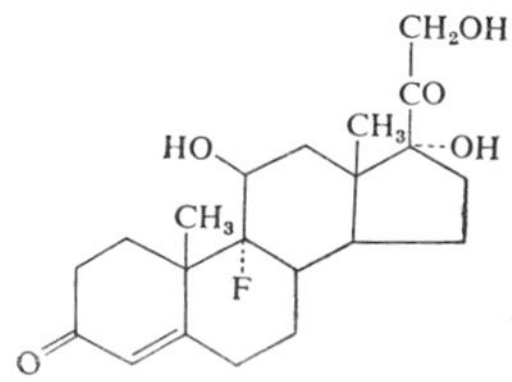	380·5	cryst.

M.p.	$[\alpha]_D^t$	Solubility	References	General remarks
177–80	$+258^{25}$ (in EtOH)	s. benz., pet. eth.	ISOL. *J.B.C.* **114**, 613 (1936) *Helv. chim. Acta* **21**, 1183 (1938)	Reduces ammoniacal silver nitrate. Acetate, M.p. 179–81; $[\alpha]_D^{18} = +233{\cdot}7$ (in dioxan).
172–6	+53 to 55 (c = 1 in EtOH)	0·02 H_2O; > 20 EtOH; v. sl. s. eth.; s. alkalis	ISOL. as for cholic acid *J.B.C.* **165**, 359 (1946) *B.J.* **23**, 1165 (1929)	Found in bile of man, ox, dog, sheep, goat, and rabbit. Not precipitated by digitonin. p*K* is approx. 6·6. Very stable coordination compounds, known as choleic acids, are formed with acids, esters, alcohols, ethers, phenols, hydrocarbons, and alkaloids. The choleic acid formed with stearic acid contains 8 molecules of deoxycholic acid to 1 of stearic acid.
141–2	$+178^{22}$ (c = 1 in EtOH)	s. EtOH, acet., eth.; sp. s. H_2O	PREP. *Helv. chim. Acta* **24**, 371 (1941); **20**, 1164 (1937) ISOL. *Helv. chim. Acta* **21**, 1197 (1938)	E_{max} at 240 mμ. Does not fluoresce with H_2SO_4 (cf. corticosterone and hydrocortisone). Pharmacologically used as the acetate for replacement therapy in adrenal insufficiency. Acetate, M. wt. 372·5, M.p. 154–60, $[\alpha]_D^{20}$ +168 to 176 (c = 1 in dioxan), sl. s. MeOH, EtOH, acet., eth., PREP. *Helv. chim. Acta* **23**, 136 (1940).
235–40	-54^{20} (c = 2·8 in MeOH)	s. H_2O; 1·8 EtOH; i. $CHCl_3$	*J. Am. Pharm. Ass.* **23**, 664 (1934)	Commonly obtained 80% pure. Forms equimolecular insoluble complex with free cholesterol. Also precipitates β-hydroxysteroids other than *epi*-C_{20} compounds and is used for this purpose as an analytical reagent. The aglycone is digitogenin, M. wt. 448·6; for preparation see *J.A.C.S.* **64**, 1843 (1942).
266–73	$+22{\cdot}5^{25}$ (c = 1 in dioxan)	i. H_2O; sl. s. EtOH, $CHCl_3$, acet.	*Ber.* **71**, 1024 (1938)	Absorption maximum at 241 mμ in EtOH. Orally active progestational agent. 10 mg = 1 I.U. Identification, *J. Pharm. Pharmac.* **1**, 130 (1949).
[illegible]46; [illegible]83	+1 to $+10^{20}$ (c = 1 in dioxan)	i. H_2O; s. MeOH, EtOH, $CHCl_3$, acet., dioxan, eth.	*Ber.* **71**, 1024 (1938) *Bull. Soc. chim. Fr.* **18**, 121 (1951)	Exists in two crystalline forms. 3-Benzoate, M.p. 202. 3-Acetate, M.p. 153, $[\alpha]_D^{20}$ +3 in $CHCl_3$. Absorption max. 248 mμ.
[illegible]61 d.	$+139^{23}$ (c = 0·55 in 95% EtOH)	sp. s. H_2O; s. MeOH, EtOH, $CHCl_3$, gl. acetic	*J.A.C.S.* **76**, 1455 (1954)	Absorption max. 239 mμ ε 17 600 in EtOH. Orally-active mineralocorticoid with some glucocorticoid effect, *J. clin. Endocr. Metab.* **17**, 280 (1957).

12. Steroids

No.	*Name*	*Synonyms*	*Structure*	*M. wt.*	*Physical form*
24	Hydrocortisone	Δ^4-Pregnene-11β,17α,21-triol-3,20-dione; Compound F (Kendall); cortisol; 17-hydroxycorticosterone	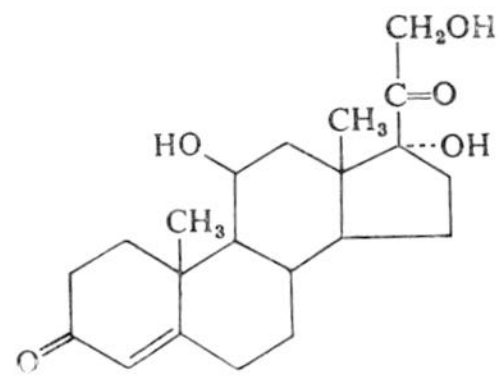	362·4	rectilinear cryst. from EtOH
25	Lithocholic acid	3α-Hydroxycholanic acid	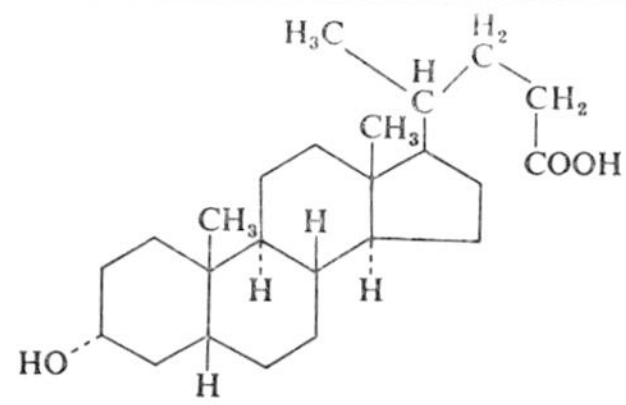	376·6	leaflets from EtOH; prisms from acetic acid
26	Megesterol acetate	17α-Acetoxy-6-methylpregna-4,6-diene-3,20-dione	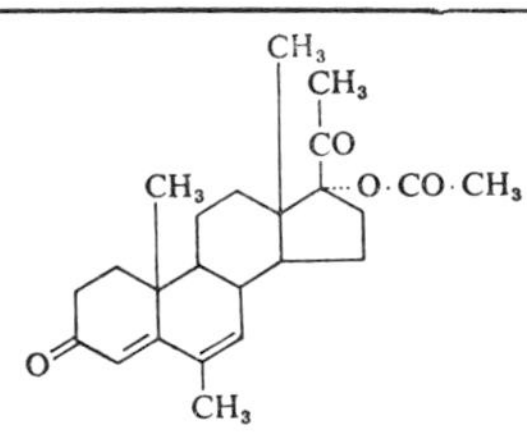	384·5	wh. cryst.
27	Methyltestosterone	17α-Methyltestosterone; 17α-methyl-Δ^4-androstene-3-one-17β-ol	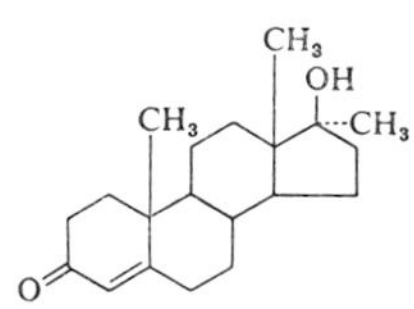	302·4	wh. cryst. powder
28	19-Norethisterone	17β-Hydroxy-19-nor-17α-pregn-4-ene-20-yne-3-one; 19-nor-17α-ethynyltestosterone	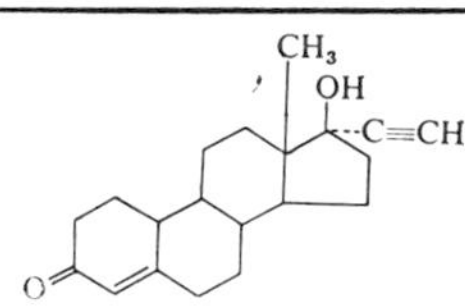	298·4; Acetate, 340·5	cryst.
29	Norethynodrel	17β-Hydroxy-19-nor-17α-pregn-5(10)-ene-20-yne-3-one	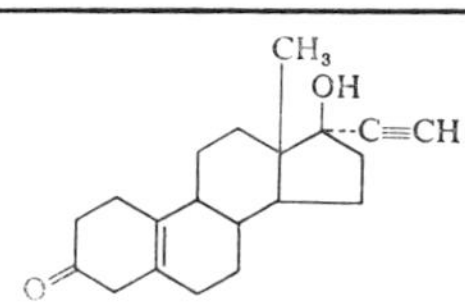	298·4	cryst.
30	Oestradiol-17β	Dihydroxyoestrin; 17β-oestradiol; dihydroxyoestratriene; 'α-oestradiol' in old trivial terminology; 1,3,5-oestratriene-3,17β-diol; dihydrotheelin	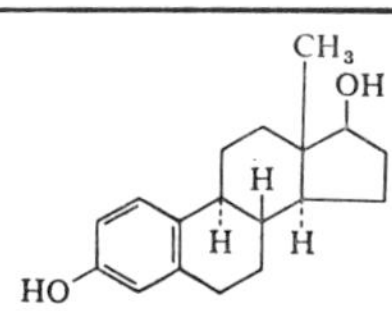	272·4	prisms
31	Oestradiol-17α	'β-Oestradiol' in old trivial nomenclature; 1,3,5-oestratriene-3,17α-diol	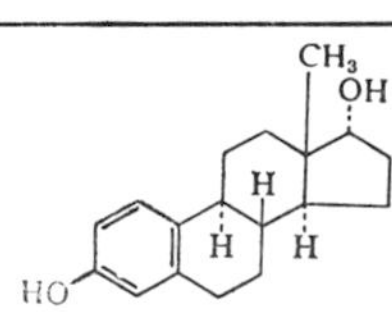	272·4; Hydrate, 281·4	needles from aq. EtOH with $\frac{1}{2}H_2O$

M.p.	$[\alpha]_D^t$	Solubility	References	General remarks
217–20	+167[22] (c = 1 in EtOH)	sl. s. H_2O; s. gl. acetic, dioxan, $CHCl_3$, MeOH	PREP. *J.B.C.* **124**, 459 (1938) *J.B.C.* **175**, 451 (1948)	Absorption maximum at 242 mμ, ε = 15 800. Found in adrenal vein blood and in human urine, *J.B.C.* **175**, 451 (1948); *Mem. Soc. Endocr.* **2**, 25 (1953). Green fluorescence in ethanolic H_2SO_4. Assay: *J. clin. Endocr. Metab.* **21**, 1146 (1961).
84–6	+32 (c = 1 in EtOH) (+23 to +34 given in various sources)	s. hot EtOH, Et acetate, $CHCl_3$, gl. acetic, hot NaOH, $NaHCO_3$; sp. s. eth.; i. H_2O, ligroin	ISOL. *Z.P.C.* **73**, 234 (1911) *Z.P.C.* **110**, 123 (1920)	Found in bile of man, ox, and rabbit as glycine or taurine conjugates.
18–20	+5 ($CHCl_3$)	i. H_2O; s. $CHCl_3$; 1·8 EtOH; 9·1 acet.; 22 benz.	*J. Reprod. Fert.* **5**, 331 (1963) *B.J.* **91**, 31P (1964)	Anti-ovulatory. U.v. max. 287·5 mμ in EtOH, log ε 4·40. I.r. max. 1738, 1716, 1256, 1244 cm^{-1} in CS_2, 1660, 1620, 1575 cm^{-1} in paraffin. Shift of absorption peak from 240 mμ (typical of isolated Δ^4-3-oxo group) to longer wavelength.
1–6	+69[25] to +75 (c = 1 in dioxan) +79[20] to +85 (c = 1 in EtOH)	i. H_2O; s. EtOH, acet., MeOH, benz.; sp. s. vegetable oils	PREP. *Recl Trav. chim. Pays-Bas Belg.* **56**, 137 (1937) *Helv. chim. Acta* **18**, 1487 (1935)	$E_{1\,cm.}^{1\%}$ 241 mμ = 495 to 530 (in EtOH). Androgenic. Administration to man does not raise the 17-ketosteroid output in urine. Therapeutically effective by mouth. Identification, *J. Pharm. Pharmac.* **1**, 130 (1949). Estimation, *J.B.C.* **201**, 279 (1953).
3–4; etate, 1–2	+31·7[20] in $CHCl_3$	i. H_2O; s. $CHCl_3$, Et acetate, EtOH	*J.A.C.S.* **76**, 4092 (1954) *Ann. N.Y. Acad. Sci.* **71**, 500 (1958)	Absorption max., u.v. in EtOH 240 mμ, log ε 4·38; i.r. in $CHCl_3$ 1668 cm^{-1} and free hydroxyl band. Acetate, u.v. 240 mμ, log ε 4·28; i.r. 1754, 1667, 1621 cm^{-1}.
)–70	+108 in $CHCl_3$	s. $CHCl_3$	*Recent Prog. Horm. Res.* **14**, 29 (1958)	I.r. max 3597, 3226, 1715 cm^{-1}.
–9	+76 to +83[25] (c = 1 in dioxan)	i. H_2O; s. aq. alkalis, EtOH, acet.	ISOL. *J.B.C.* **115**, 435 (1936) *J.B.C.* **133**, 569 (1940) *J.B.C.* **134**, 391 (1940) *B.J.* **34**, 1293 (1940) PREP. *Ber.* **74**, 1914 (1941)	E_{max} at 280 and 225 mμ. Obtained from sow's ovaries and pregnant mare's urine. The 3-benzoate is a U.S.P. preparation. Precipitated by digitonin. Found in human urine. The estimation is described in *J. Endocr.* **16**, 49 (1957).
lrate, –3	+53·8 (c = 0·7 in dioxan)	i. H_2O; v.s. EtOH; s. acet. and most organic solvents	ISOL. *J.B.C.* **118**, 789 (1937) *J.B.C.* **122**, 303 (1938) *J.B.C.* **141**, 709 (1941)	E_{max} at 280 mμ. Found in equine pregnancy urine. Not precipitated by digitonin in 80% EtOH. Benzoate, M. wt. 376·5, M.p. 191–6, $[\alpha]_D^{25}$ + 58 to 63 (c = 2 in dioxan), s. EtOH, acet., eth.

12. Steroids

No.	Name	Synonyms	Structure	M. wt.	Physical form
32	Oestriol	1,3,5-Oestratriene-3,16α,17β-triol; trihydroxyoestrin; estriol; theelol	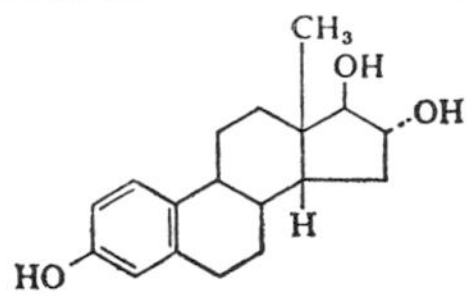	288·4	monocl. cryst.
33	Oestrone	1,3,5-Oestratriene-3-ol-17-one; theelin; folliculin (oestrin)	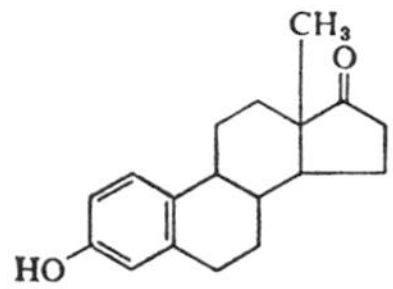	270·4	monocl. or orthorh cryst.
34	Prednisolone	11β,17α,21-trihydroxy-1,4-pregnadiene-3,20-dione	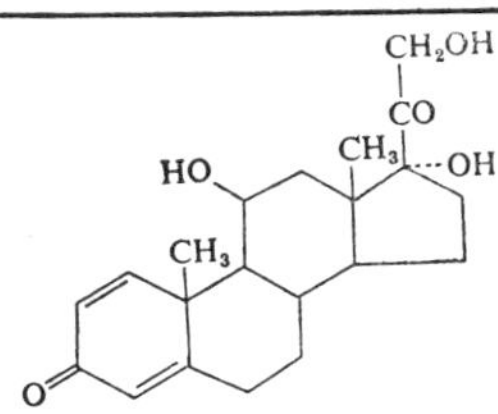	360·5	cryst.
35	Prednisone	17α,21-dihydroxy-1,4-pregnadiene-3,11,20-trione	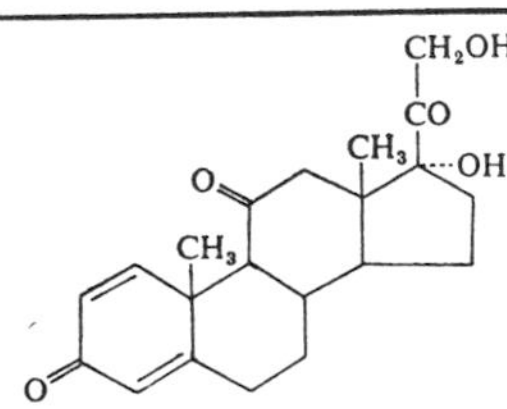	358·5	cryst. from acet.-hexane
36	Pregnanediol	Pregnane-3α,20α-diol; 5β-pregnane-3α,20α-diol	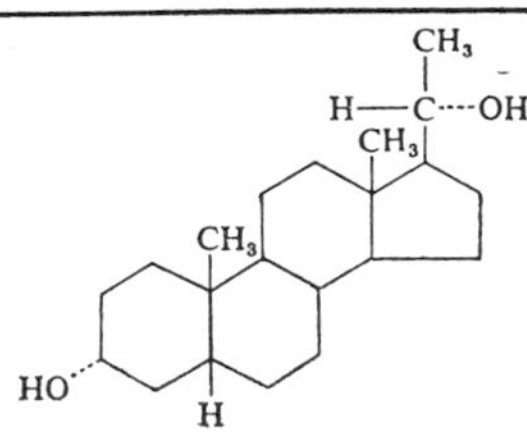	320·5	plates from EtOH acet.
37	*allo*Pregnane-dione	*allo*Pregnane-3,20-dione; 5α-pregnane-3,20-dione	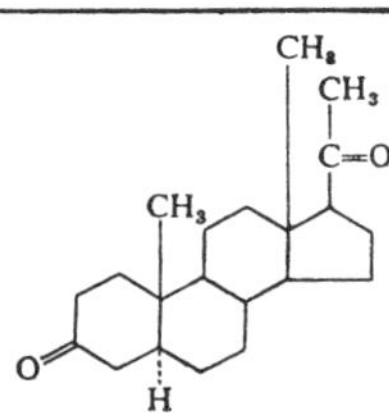	316·5	plates
38	3,20-Pregnane-dione		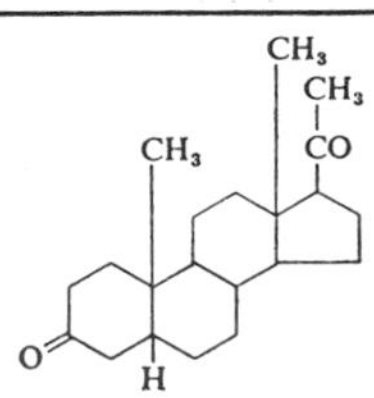	316·5	needles from EtOH-H_2O

M.p.	$[\alpha]_D^t$	Solubility	References	General remarks
282 normal monocl. form changes at 270–5)	$+58\pm5^{25}$ (c = 4 in dioxan)	sp. s. H_2O; s. EtOH, $CHCl_3$, eth., pyr., aq. alkali	ISOL. *B.J.* **24**, 435, 1021 (1930) *Nature, Lond.* **131**, 766 (1933) *J.B.C.* **91**, 641, 655 (1931)	E_{max} at 280 mμ. Precipitated by digitonin. Found in human urine. Estimation given in *J. Endocr.* **16**, 49 (1957).
258–62	+158 to +168 (c = 1 in dioxan)	4·0 EtOH; 2·0 acet.; 1·0 $CHCl_3$; s. aq. alkali; i. H_2O	ISOL. *Naturwissenschaften* **17**, 879 (1929) *Am. J. Physiol.* **90**, 329 (1929) *B.J.* **34**, 1293 (1940) SYN. *Experientia* **4**, 25 (1948)	Occurs in human urine and placenta. Used therapeutically (U.S.P.). Estimation given in *J. Endocr.* **16**, 49 (1957).
41	$+102^{25}$ (in dioxan)	v. sl. s. H_2O; 3·3 EtOH; 0·55 $CHCl_3$; 2 acet.	*Science* **121**, 176 (1955) *J.A.C.S.* **77**, 4781 (1955)	Absorption max. 242 mμ, ϵ 15 000 in MeOH.
1 d.	$+172^{25}$ (in dioxan)	sp. s. H_2O; 0·67 EtOH; 0·5 $CHCl_3$	*Science* **121**, 176 (1955) *J.A.C.S.* **77**, 4781 (1955)	Absorption max. 238 mμ, ϵ 15 000 in MeOH.
8	$+27{\cdot}4^{20}$ (c = 0·7 in EtOH)	sp. s. organic solvents	PREP. *J.B.C.* **143**, 716 (1942) *J.A.C.S.* **60**, 2931 (1938)	Found in pregnancy urine [*B.J.* **23**, 1090 (1929)]. Used in preparation of progesterone [*Ber.* **67**, 1893 (1934)]. Not precipitated by digitonin. Principal metabolite of progesterone—excretion is therefore index of progesterone production [*J. Endocr.* **12**, 209 (1955)].
–200	+127 (c = 2 in $CHCl_3$)	s. aq. acetone, EtOH, eth., benz., ligroin, CCl_4	PREP. *J.A.C.S.* **60**, 1559 (1938); **59**, 2297 (1937) *Ber.* **68**, 2096 (1935) *J.B.C.* **172**, 263 (1948)	Found in human urine [*J.B.C.* **172**, 263 (1948)] and in pregnant mare's urine [*J.A.C.S.* **59**, 2297 (1937)].
		i. H_2O; s. $CHCl_3$, EtOH, acet., gl. acetic	*J.A.C.S.* **59**, 1595 (1937) *Helv. chim. Acta* **24**, 356 (1941)	Found in pregnancy urine of mares.

No.	Name	Synonyms	Structure	M. wt.	Physical form
39	Pregnanolone	Pregnane-3α-ol-20-one	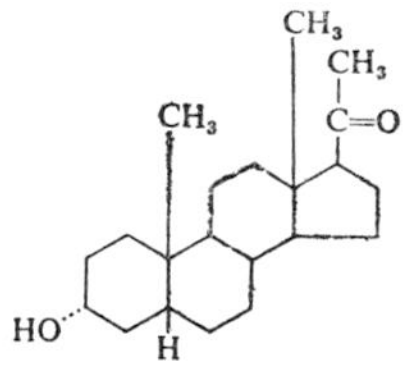	318·5	long needles from benz.
40	Pregnenolone	Δ5-Pregnene-3β-ol-20-one	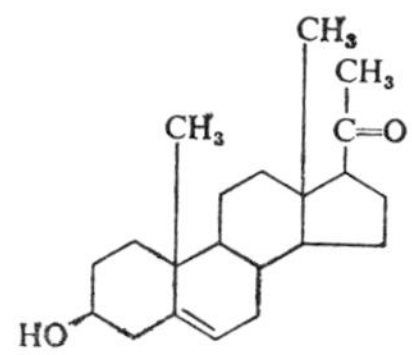	316·5	needles from aq. EtOH
41	Progesterone	Δ4-Pregnene-3,20-dione; lutocyclin; proluton; progestin	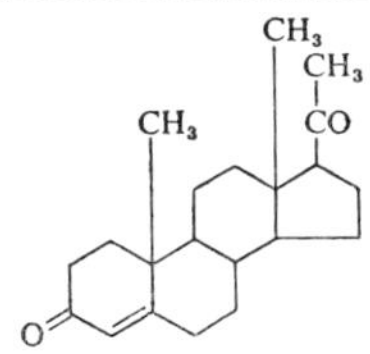	314·4	α, prisms from EtOH β, needles from pet. eth.
42	Strophanthidin		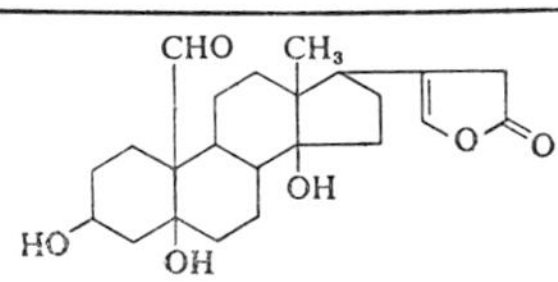	404·5; Hydrate, 413·5	orthorhombic crys $+\frac{1}{2}H_2O$
43	Tachysterol (and Dihydro-tachysterol)		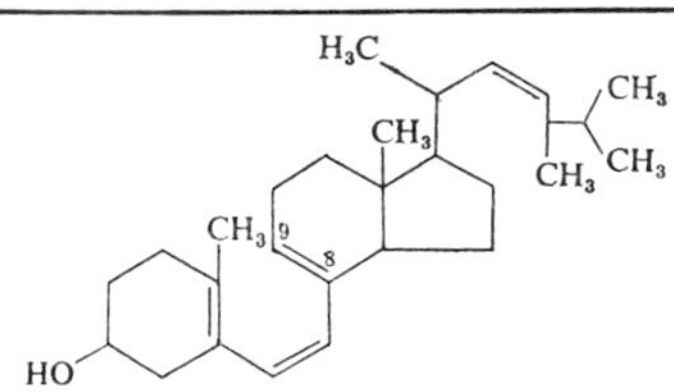 In Dihydrotachysterol the 8,9 bond is saturated	396·6 Dihydro, 398·6	oil Dihydro, needles
44	Testosterone	17β-Hydroxy-Δ4-androstene-3-one; Δ4-androstene-17β-ol-3-one	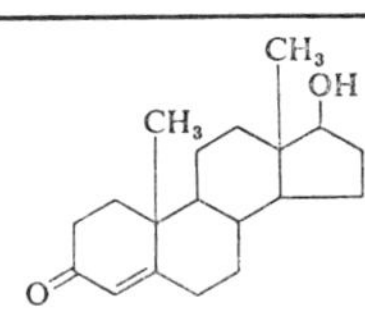	288·4	needles from acet
45	Tetrahydro-cortisol	Pregnane-3α,11β,17α,21-tetrol-20-one	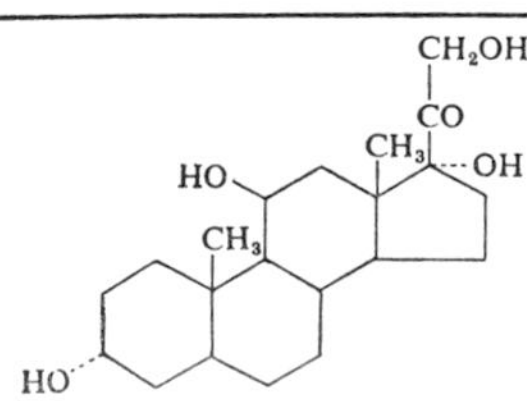	366·5	cryst.

M.p.	$[\alpha]^t_D$	Solubility	References	General remarks
'alues reported 44, 149, ınd 154. J.B.C. **172,** '63 (1948); 'ieser and 'ieser]	+107[26] (c = 0·6 in EtOH)	s. eth.-benz. (1:9), benz., EtOH, MeOH	ISOL. *J.B.C.* **172,** 263 (1948) PREP. *Helv. chim. Acta* **29,** 33 (1946)	Found in human and porcine pregnancy urine. Also in cases of human hyperfunction of adrenal cortex as urinary steroid and in bovine bile [*Fed. Proc.* 7, 178 (1948)].
90–3	+28[20] (in EtOH)	v. sp. s. H_2O; 17 $CHCl_3$; 2 EtOH	PREP. *Ber.* **67,** 1611 (1934) *J.A.C.S.* **71,** 1840 (1949) *J.B.C.* **174,** 925 (1948)	Isolated from pig testis [*Helv. chim. Acta* **26,** 975, 2222 (1943)].
127–31 121	+172 to +182 (c = 2 in dioxan)	i. H_2O; s. EtOH, acet., conc. H_2SO_4	ISOL. *J.B.C.* **107,** 321 (1934)	Absorption max. at 240 mμ. Natural hormone of corpus luteum. 1 mg = 1 I.U. The two crystal types are polymorphic forms of a single substance.
1–5; ıor.	+43·1[25] (c = 2·8 in MeOH)	i. H_2O, eth.; s. EtOH, MeOH, benz., $CHCl_3$, acet., gl. acetic	*J.B.C.* **54,** 253 (1922) Stoll, *The Cardiac Glycosides,* Pharm. Press, London (1937)	Formed by enzymatic or acid hydrolysis of glycosides in *Strophanthius apocynaceae.* Extremely toxic.
	−70[18] (in pet. eth.)	i. H_2O, MeOH; s. $CHCl_3$, EtOH, eth.	*Z.P.C.* **252,** 151 (1938) *Z.P.C.* **260,** 119 (1939)	Not precipitated by digitonin.
ıydro, -7	Dihydro, +97[22] (in $CHCl_3$)	Dihydro, as above		Dihydro, absorption max. 242 mμ $E^{1\%}_{1\,cm}$ 870, 251 mμ $E^{1\%}_{1\,cm}$ 1010, 261 mμ $E^{1\%}_{1\,cm}$ 650.
	+104–6 (in dioxan) +109[24] (c = 4 in EtOH)	i. H_2O; s. EtOH, eth., most organic solvents, veg. oils	ISOL. *Z.P.C.* **233,** 281 (1935) SYN. (partial) *Z.P.C.* **237,** 89 (1935) PREP. *Ber.* **71,** 2278 (1938)	Testicular origin. Converted in man to androsterone, aetiocholanolone and *epi*-androsterone. Available as testosterone propionate, M. wt. 344·5, M.p. 118–22, $[\alpha]^{25}_D$ +83 to 90 (c = 1 in dioxan), i. H_2O, s. EtOH, eth., $CHCl_3$, acet., pyr. Administration to man raises urinary 17-ketosteroids.
cetate, -11	+91[24] (diacetate in $CHCl_3$)	s. acet., benz., $CHCl_3$	ISOL. *J.B.C.* **205,** 87 (1953) SYN. (partial) *J.A.C.S.* **75,** 2356 (1953)	Found as conjugate in human urine. Major metabolite of hydrocortisone.

12. Steroids

No.	*Name*	*Synonyms*	*Structure*	*M. wt.*	*Physical form*
46	Tetrahydro-cortisone	Pregnane-3α,17α,21-triol-11,20-dione	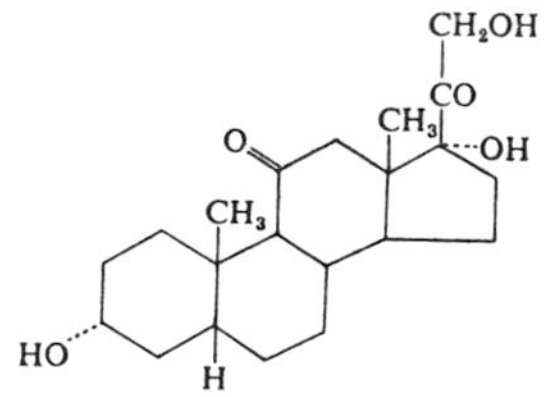	364·5	cryst.
47	Triamcinolone	9α-Fluoro-11β,16α,17α,21-tetrahydroxy-1,4-pregnadiene-3,20-dione	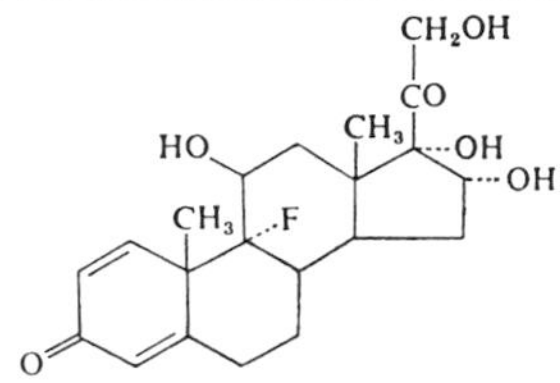	394·4	solvated cryst.

M.p.	$[\alpha]^t_D$	*Solubility*	*References*	*General remarks*
Diacetate, 232–4	$+93–95^{24}$ (c = 0·6 diacetate in acetone)	s. acet., benz., $CHCl_3$	PREP. *J.A.C.S.* **70**, 1454 (1948)	Found in human urine [*J.B.C.* **194**, 337 (1952)]. Major metabolite of hydrocortisone.
260–2	$+75^{25}$ (in acet.)	s. Et acetate, acet., EtOH, $CHCl_3$	*J.A.C.S.* **78**, 5693 (1956); **81**, 1689 (1959)	Absorption max. 238 mμ (ε 15 800). Diacetate (16,21), M.p. 187 solvated, 235 dry, $[\alpha]^{25}_D$ +22 (in $CHCl_3$), absorption max. 239 mμ (ε 15 200). Used pharmacologically as 16,17 acetonide.

13. Porphyrins and Related Compounds

General references

Works of general importance which have been quoted extensively in the tables are abbreviated as follows:

1. H. Fischer and H. Orth, *Die Chemie des Pyrrols*, vol. 2, Akademische Verlagsgesellschaft M.B.H., Leipzig (1937). Abbreviated as Fischer–Orth.
2. R. Lemberg and J. W. Legge, *Haematin Compounds and Bile Pigments*, 1st ed., Interscience, New York (1949). Abbreviated as Lemberg–Legge.
3. C. H. Gray, *The Bile Pigments*, Methuen, London (1953). Abbreviated as Gray.
4. J. E. Falk, *Porphyrins*, Elsevier, Amsterdam (1964). Abbreviated as Falk.
5. *Abderhalden's Handbuch der Biolog. Arbeitsmethoden*, Abt. **1**, Teil 11, p. 169 (1936). Abbreviated as Fischer–Abderhalden.
6. A. Vanotti, *Porphyrins*, Hilger and Watts, London (1954). Abbreviated as Vanotti.

Additional literature

Handbook of Biological Data, ed. W. S. Spector, pp. 35–36, Table 26 III, Division of Biology and Agriculture, The National Academy of Sciences (1956).

Handbook of Respiration, eds. D. S. Dittmer and R. M. Grebe, pp. 118–23, ibid. (1958).

A. BILE PIGMENTS AND RELATED COMPOUNDS

Revised by R. LEMBERG (*Royal North Shore Hospital, Sydney, Australia*)

The common, naturally occurring bile pigments are all formally derived from protoporphyrin-IX (cf. porphyrins) by oxidative fission of the α-methene linkage. They are therefore designated IXα and the arrangement of the side chains is thereby fixed. The side chains are either identical with those of protoporphyrin, or the vinyl groups are replaced by ethyl (giving *meso* compounds), or in the phycochromoproteins probably by an α-substituted ethyl rather firmly linked to protein.

The biological origin of the bile pigments in vertebrates is usually by oxidation of haem compounds, particularly of haemoglobin, leading at first to biliverdin. Bile pigments in invertebrates and algae may be formed in a different manner.

A ring written in the formulae in the lactim form 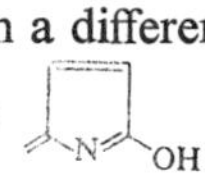 can be present in the prototropic lactam form 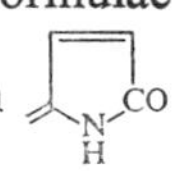 and a ring written in the formulae as α-hydroxypyrrole 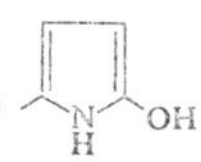 in the tautomeric 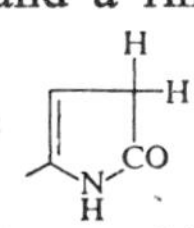 and 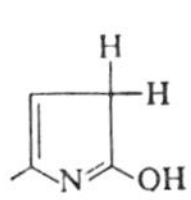 forms. This enables compounds such as stercobilin, mesobilene, or biliverdin to form metal complexes in which one metal atom of, e.g., Cu or Zn is bound to all four nitrogens of an approximately planar ring structure. This ring is probably stabilized by hydrogen bonds between the terminal α (>CO) and α′ (⩾COH) groups forming rings such as that shown below (Lemberg and Legge, p. 118).

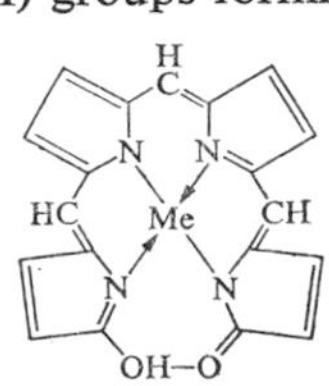

The bile pigments undergo a physiological hydrogenation from the most 'aromatic' biliverdin to the colourless stercobilinogen which affects the tetrapyrrolic system as well as the vinyl side chains.

13. Porphyrins and Related Compounds

No.	Name	Synonyms	Formula	M. wt.	Absorption spectrum Solvent	λmax mμ (ε mM)
1	Biliverdin	Dehydro-bilirubin, bilatriene-IXα	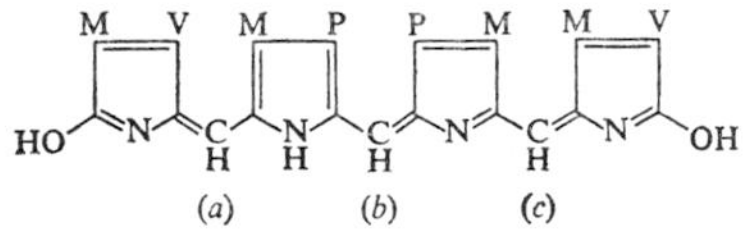 (M = CH_3, V = $CH{=}CH_2$, P = $CH_2{\cdot}CH_2{\cdot}CO_2H$)	582·7	MeOH	392 (25) 640 (10·4)
1*a*	— hydro-chloride		$C_{33}H_{34}O_6N_4{\cdot}HCl$	619·1	MeOH 5% HCl	377 (48) 680 (28) 372 (47) 665–70 (23·5)
1*b*	— dimethyl ester		$C_{35}H_{38}O_6N_4$	610·7		
1*c*	— dimethyl ester ferri-chloride	'Green haemin ester', of Warburg	$C_{35}H_{38}O_6N_4{\cdot}HFeCl_4$	809·4		
2	Bilirubin	Biladiene (*a,c*)-IXα	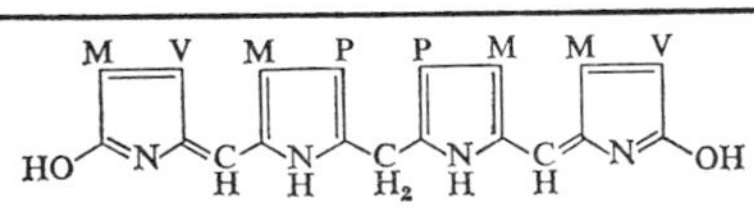 (M, V, P, see 1)	584·7	CHCl₃ serum	450 (56–61) 460 (42–57)
2*a*	— dimethyl ester		$C_{35}H_{40}O_6N_4$	612·7		
3	Meso-biliverdin	Dehydro-meso-bilirubin, glaucobilin, meso-bilatriene-IXα	As 1 with V replaced by C_2H_5	586·7	$CHCl_3$	640
3*a*	— ferri-chloride	'Ferrobilin'	$C_{33}H_{38}O_6N_4{\cdot}HFeCl_4$	785·4		
3*b*	— dimethyl ester		$C_{35}H_{42}O_6N_4$	614·7	dioxan benz. 5% HCl in MeOH	286 (17·8) 363 (47) 6 (6 (309 363 6 (

hysical rm	*M.p.*	*Solubility*	*Occurrence*	*Preparation*	*Determination*	*General remarks*
ue- een edles MeOH)	Blackens	v.s. alkalis, hot gl. acetic, hot MeOH; sl. s. $CHCl_3$, eth. (extr. from eth. in 2% HCl)	Bile of birds, amphibia; dog placenta ('uteroverdin'). Egg shells ('oocyan'). Fishes and invertebrates. Human meconium in path. conditions, tissues and fluids	SYN. *Z.P.C.* **258**, 9 (1939) *Z.P.C.* **274**, 231 (1942) ISOL. *Proc. R. Soc.* **B 110**, 362 (1932) PREP. *Ann.* **499**, 25 (1932) *B.J.* **28**, 978 (1934) *B.J.* **35**, 363 (1941) *J.C.S.* **1961**, 2264	*B.J.* **35**, 363 (1941)	Decomposes in conc. H_2SO_4 at 100°. Gmelin reaction positive. Van den Bergh and Ehrlich reactions negative. With zinc acetate+I_2 blue-green bilipurpurin complex, λ_{max} 637 mμ, intense red fluorescence.
e green edles l. HCl)		s. hot MeOH, gl. acetic; sl. s. dil. HCl		*See* 1		
e- en dle- sms	216–33	s. MeOH, $CHCl_3$, eth.; i. pet. eth., H_2O		*See* 1 *Bull. Soc. Chim. biol.* **27**, 621 (1945)		Two crystal forms (*B.J.* **28**, 978 (1934)).
o- oitic g es OH)	No definite M.p.	s. hot MeOH-HCl		*Ber.* **63**, 1816 (1930) *B.J.* **29**, 1325 (1935)		
nocl. es or allel- eds, asion- fine ets Cl_3) ur able w to brown	Blackens	s. alkalis, hot $CHCl_3$; sl. s. gl. acetic; v. sl. s. EtOH, eth.; i. H_2O, acids	Bile, gallstones (Ca salt); old haemorrhages ('haematoidin'); trace in normal serum; path. in tissues, serum, urine in jaundice, in faeces on medication with wide-spectrum antibiotics. In bile and serum partly as glucuronide esters ('direct bilirubin')	SYN. *Z.P.C.* **274**, 231 (1942) ISOL. Lemberg–Legge, p. 120 Gray, p. 121 *J.B.C.* **202**, 305 (1953)	Lemberg–Legge, pp. 153–5 Gray, pp. 109, 131 [*B.J.* **57**, 514 (1954)]	Dry solid stable; $CHCl_3$ soln. stable in dark; alkaline soln. rapidly oxidizes. Gmelin positive; Van den Bergh reaction positive, free bilirubin only in the presence of alcohol, etc. ('indirect reaction'), glucuronides without alcohol ('direct reaction'). Ehrlich reaction negative. Zn acetate+I_2 as 1.
ge- le- ns	198–200	v.s. $CHCl_3$, gl. acetic, benz.; s. hot MeOH; sl. s. eth.; i. pet. eth.		Fischer–Orth, p. 637		
t ns OH); es, tes	316–18 d., sinters 210–20	s. alkalis, hot MeOH; sl. s. eth., $CHCl_3$, dil. HCl; i. H_2O	Prosthetic group of green-blue chromoproteins of insect integuments and haemolymph; free in some invertebrates	SYN. Fischer–Orth, pp. 705–7 PREP. *B.J.* **45**, 199 (1949)		Stable to conc. H_2SO_4 at 100°. Colour reactions as 1. Zn-bilipurpurin complex, λ_{max} 627 mμ.
es cetic)	265	s. MeOH; sl. s. $CHCl_3$, gl. acetic		Fischer–Orth, p. 703		Dimethyl ester, violet rods, M.p. 244.
l_3- th.); s H); gular oic	218–25 SYN. 232	v.s. $CHCl_3$; s. hot MeOH; sl. s. eth., MeOH, benz.		*See* 3		

No.	Name	Synonyms	Formula	M. wt.	Absorption spectrum Solvent	λmax mμ (ε mM)
4	Meso-bilirubin	Meso-biladiene (*a*,*c*)-IXα	As 2 with V replaced by C_2H_5	588·7	$CHCl_3$	425 (62)
4*a*	— dimethyl ester		$C_{35}H_{44}O_6N_4$	616·8	dioxan	296 (2·6) 426 (71)
5	Meso-biliviolin	Meso-biladiene (2′*a*,5′*b*)	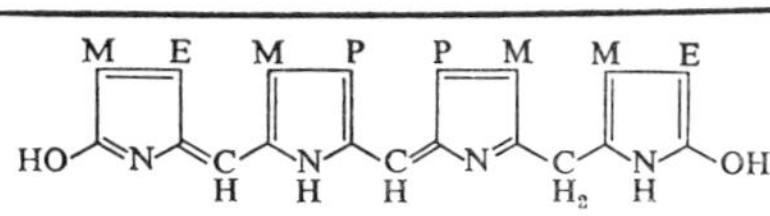 (E = C_2H_5, M, P, see 1)	588·7	$CHCl_3$	570
5*a*	— hydro-chloride		$C_{33}H_{40}O_6N_4 \cdot HCl$	625·2	$CHCl_3$-HCl aq. HCl	607 (2·1) 598
6	Meso-bilierythrin	Meso-bilirhodin	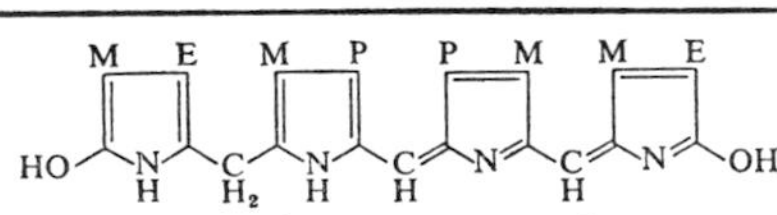 (M, P, E, see 5) (? structure uncertain)	588·7	$CHCl_3$	595?
6*a*	— hydro-chloride		$C_{33}H_{40}O_6N_4 \cdot HCl$	625·2	$CHCl_3$-HCl aq. HCl	312 576 557
7	Mesobilene-(*b*)-IXα	Urobilin, Urobilin-IXα	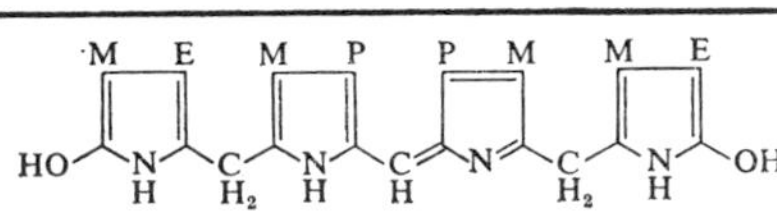 (M, P, E, see 5)	590·7	dioxan	330 (3·6) 452 (26)
7*a*	— hydro-chloride		$C_{33}H_{42}O_6N_4 \cdot HCl$	627·2	dioxan EtOH MeOH-HCl	380 (6·6) 494 (45 232 (17) 378 (7·2) 490 (50 (rev. sp 494
8	Meso-bilane-IXα	Uro-bilinogen, mesobili-rubinogen	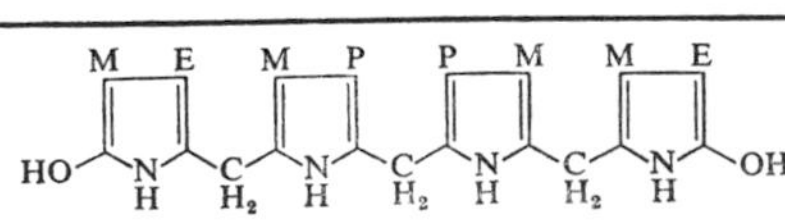 (M, P, E, see 5)	592·7		colourless

Physical form	M.p.	Solubility	Occurrence	Preparation	Determination	General remarks
el. oblong h. leaflets CHCl$_3$); ne eedles eth., gl. cetic); risms pyr.)	315–21	s. CHCl$_3$, pyr., ethyl acetate, alkalis; sl. s. gl. acetic; v. sl. s. eth. EtOH; i. H$_2$O, acids	In small intestine and bile; in faeces after medication with wide-spectrum antibiotics	SYN. *Z.P.C.* **245**, 257 (1937) PREP. *Z.P.C.* **268**, 225 (1941)	*See* 2	More s. in CHCl$_3$ than 2. Colour reactions as 2, but Zn acetate+I$_2$, λ_{max} 627 mμ.
el. pindle orm, short risms or ectangular aflets	240	v.s. CHCl$_3$; sl. s. MeOH; i. eth., H$_2$O		*Z.P.C.* **245**, 269 (1937) Fischer–Orth, p. 650		Monohydrochloride, red hexagonal leaflets; M.p. 190 (196–9) after darkening; v.s. CHCl$_3$.
morph.		v.s. alcohols, CHCl$_3$, gl. acetic, alkalis; s. eth. (extracted from eth. into 0·1 N-HCl), acids; i. H$_2$O, dil. acetic	Characteristic prosthetic group (modified by linkage to protein) of phycocyanins of red or blue algae and blue-violet *Aplysia* chromopeptides. 'Phycocyanobilin'	SYN. *Z.P.C.* **264**, 64 (1940) ISOL. *Z.P.C.* **221**, 145 (1933) Phycocyanobilin: *Ann.* **477**, 195 (1930) *Biochemistry* **2**, 375 (1963)	*B.J.* **57**, 514 (1954)	Unstable. Characteristic Zn complex in EtOH, strong red fluorescence, λ_{max} 625 (575) mμ. The bilipurpurins, biladiene-(*a,b*)-ones (*c*) and related compounds are different but spectroscopically similar compounds, oxidation products of bilirubins and biliverdins.
st.	165					
morph.		as 5	Characteristic prosthetic group (modified by linkage to protein) of phycoerythrins and of red *Aplysia* chromopeptides, but see *J.A.C.S.* **89**, 5976 (1967)	SYN. *Z.P.C.* **237**, 8 (1935) Phycoerythrobilin: *Ann.* **477**, 195 (1930) *B.J.* **80**, 2P (1961)		Highly unstable. Zn complex in EtOH, orange fluorescence, λ_{max} 583. The mesobilirhodin of Siedel and phycoerythrobilin of Lemberg were apparently partly isomerized to violinoid and urobilinoid pigments.
orph.						
nge-red dles or sms	190 SYN. 177 (darkens 158, sinters 171)	v.s. MeOH, EtOH, gl. acetic, alkali; s. CHCl$_3$, acet.; sl. s. eth. (extracted from eth. by dil. acetic)	Smaller part of 'stercobilin' and 'urobilin' of faeces and path. urine	SYN. *Z.P.C.* **242**, 101 (1936) PREP. Fischer–Orth, pp. 685–6 Gray, p. 126	Lemberg–Legge, pp. 156–8 Gray, pp. 133–7	Unstable, readily dehydrogenated to mesobiliviolin and mesobiliverdin, e.g. by FeCl$_3$. Crystals retain CHCl$_3$, ? compound. Combines readily with Zn, Cu. Zn complex with Zn acetate in EtOH, strong green fluorescence, λ_{max} 509 mμ. Pentdyopent reaction positive. Optically inactive.
ge- boat pindle ns t.)	191–200 (CHCl$_3$)	v.s. MeOH, EtOH, gl. acetic; s. CHCl$_3$; sl. s. acet., benz., H$_2$O				From CHCl$_3$ small rectangular orange-red cryst. prisms on further purification; M.p. not sharp, retains CHCl$_3$.
ns, ocl.	197–203	v.s. alkalis, NH$_4$OH; s. eth., benz., ethyl acetate; sl. s. H$_2$O, pet. eth.	Smaller part of 'stercobilinogen' and 'urobilinogen' of faeces and path. urine	Fischer–Orth, pp. 692–3 Gray, pp. 123–4	*See* 7	Unstable; crystals darken even in absence of O$_2$ and light. In soln. oxidizes in air to 7. Ehrlich aldehyde reaction positive, Van den Bergh and Gmelin reactions negative. FeCl$_3$ oxidizes via 7, 6, 5 to 3.

13. Porphyrins and Related Compounds

No.	Name	Synonyms	Formula	M. wt.	Absorption spectrum Solvent	λ_{max} mμ (ε mM)
9	Stercobilin	*l*-Urobilin, tetrahydro-mesobilene-(*b*)-IXα	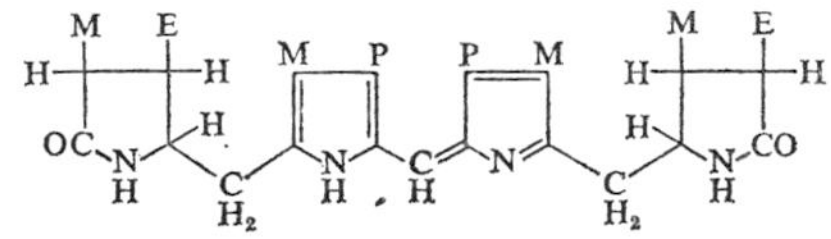 (M, P, E, see 5)	594·8	dioxan EtOH	332 456 (4·0) (34) varies with pH, cf. Gray, pp. 35–36; λ_{ma} 490 (74) at pH 4·48
9*a*	— hydro-chloride		$C_{33}H_{46}O_6N_4 \cdot HCl$	631·2	dioxan EtOH $CHCl_3$ MeOH-HCl	228 350 490 (16·2) (8·1) (69) 228 372 488 (16·2) (8·5) (55) 493 (71) (rev. spectr 492
9*b*	— ferri-chloride		$C_{33}H_{46}O_6N_4 \cdot HFeCl_4$	793·4		
10	Sterco-bilinogen	*l*-Uro-bilinogen, tetrahydro-mesobilane-IXα	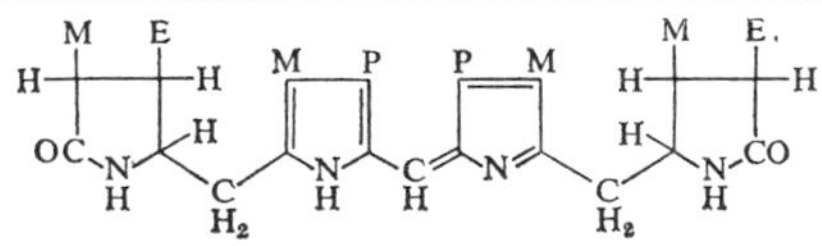 (M, P, E, see 5)	596·8		colourless

RELATED MONO-, DI-, AND TRI-PYRROLIC COMPOUNDS

No.	Name	Synonyms	Formula	M. wt.	Solvent	λ_{max} mμ (ε mM)
11	Porpho-bilinogen		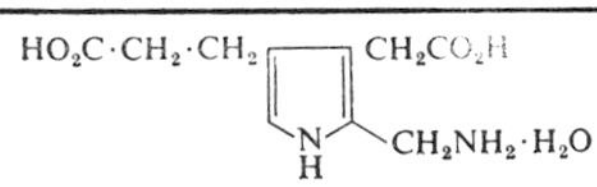	Hydrate, 244·2		210–12 (6·8–7·5)
12	Bilifuscins, meso-bilifuscins, propent-dyopent	'Körper II'	α-Oxydipyrromethenes of unknown constitution, or products derived therefrom by polymerization	?		
13	Prodigiosin		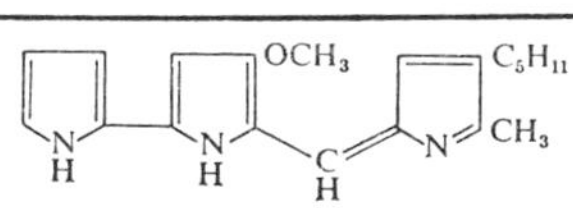	323·4	1% gl. acetic in $CHCl_3$ 85% EtOH 85% EtOH+ NH_4OH	540 (105–15) 535–40 470

Physical form	M.p.	Solubility	Occurrence	Preparation	Determination	General remarks
golden-yel. irregular cryst. (acet.); hygr.	236	v.s. EtOH, MeOH, gl. acetic, alkalis, NH_4OH, pyr.; s. $CHCl_3$, acet.; sl. s. H_2O, dil. acid, eth.; i. pet. eth.	Greater part of 'stercobilin' and 'urobilin' of faeces and path. urine	*J.B.C.* **105**, 469 (1934) *J.B.C.* **114**, 47 (1936) *Z.P.C.* **238**, 59 (1936) Gray, pp. 124–7 *Chemy Ind.* **1955**, 652	*See* 7 *B.J.* **44**, 105 (1949) *J. Lab. clin. Med.* **54**, 1 (1959) *J.B.C.* **218**, 633 (1956)	Stable. From $CHCl_3$ narrow prisms, M.p. 234–6, $[\alpha]^{20}_{6560}$ −824 (in gl. acetic). Zn complex in EtOH strong green fluorescence, λ_{max} 507mμ. Gmelin, Van den Bergh, pentdyopent and $FeCl_3$ reactions negative
ong yel. orisms $CHCl_3$)	120–65 not sharp, decomp.	v.s. EtOH; s. $CHCl_3$, acet.; sl. s. ethyl acetate, dil. HCl; i. eth., pet. eth.		*See* 9		From acetone M.p. 146–9. $[\alpha]^{20}_{5890}$ −1870 (in gl. acetic); −3500 to −3800 (in $CHCl_3$). $[\alpha]^{20}_{6900-7200}$ −1200 (in $CHCl_3$).
ed arallel-pipeds rom 5% HCl	187–90			*Z.P.C.* **233**, 39 (1935)		Stable dimethyl ester, orange-red prisms, dichroic, M.p. 160–2.
morph.		s. alcohols, alkalis, NH_4OH, $CHCl_3$; sl. s. eth.; i. H_2O	Greater part of 'stercobilinogen' and 'urobilinogen' of faeces and path. urine	*Z.P.C.* **208**, 101 (1932) *Z.P.C.* **238**, 59 (1936) Fischer–Orth, p. 696	*See* 9 8+10 det. as Ehrlich aldehyde pigment, Gray, p. 133	No optical activity found. Readily oxidizes to 9.
ol. rect-ngular rod rm yst.	Darkens 120–30; decomp. 170–80	s. dil. alkalis, NH_4OH, pyr.; almost i. H_2O, common organic solvents	Urine in acute porphyria	SYN. *J.A.C.S.* **78**, 505 (1956) PREP. *Nature, Lond.* **171**, 875 (1952) *B.J.* **57**, 476 (1954)	*Archs int. Med.* **93**, 643 (1954) *B.J.* **59**, 37 (1955) *J.B.C.* **219**, 435 (1956)	Aq. soln. unstable forms porphobilin in light, uroporphyrin on boiling. p*K'* = 3·70, 4·95, 10·1. Hydrochloride monohydrate, fine triclin. needles from 2N-HCl; M.p. 165–70 d. Red colour with Ehrlich aldehyde reagent. i. Hg salt. Lactam, M.p. 281–4.
scins, own orph. lymers om col. eso-ileucans'; opent-opents', l.		v.s. EtOH, acet., pyr., gl. acetic, ethyl acetate; sl. s. benz., $CHCl_3$; i. eth, pet. eth.	Claimed to occur as prosthetic group of polypeptide 'myobilin' in faeces in muscular dystrophy	ISOL. *Z.P.C.* **259**, 113 (1939) *Naturwissenschaften* **35**, 221 (1948); **36**, 219 (1949) *Z.P.C.* **316**, 78 (1959); **329**, 168, 182 (1962)	*J. clin. Invest.* **38**, 1166, 1175 (1959) *J. clin. Invest.* **41**, 1041 (1962)	According to Watson, fuscins are anabolic products, not derived by bilirubin breakdown. In contrast to propentdyopent they do not give the Stokvis pentdyopent reaction (conversion to red pigment by NaOH+ $Na_2S_2O_4$).
orph.; with een tallic tre	Sinters 70	s. EtOH, $CHCl_3$; i. H_2O, dil. acid, alkali	Cultures of *Serratia marcescens* (*B. prodigiosus*)	SYN. *J.A.C.S.* **84**, 635 (1962) ISOL. *Z.P.C.* **219**, 267 (1953) *B.J.* **46**, 220 (1950) *J.A.C.S.* **82**, 506 (1960)		Reversible pH effect on spectrum, p*K* ≏ 9 (? Na salt). Perchlorate, needles; M.p. 228; i. H_2O; s. $CHCl_3$ EtOH; sl. s. eth.

B. PORPHYRINS (EXCLUDING CHLOROPHYLL PORPHYRINS)

Revised by J. BARRETT (*Royal North Shore Hospital, Sydney, Australia*)

Porphyrins are derived formally from porphin

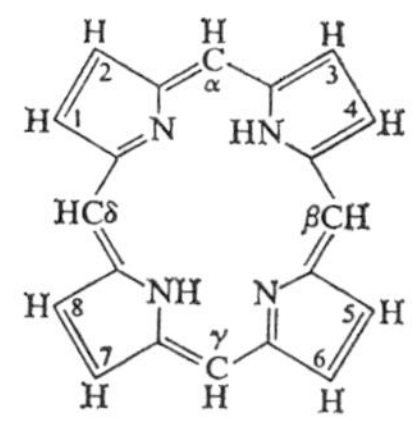

Porphin

by substitution of all or some of the 8 β-hydrogens by side-chains which may be alkyl, hydroxyalkyl, vinyl, carbonyl, or carboxylic in character. Positional isomers are possible depending on the distribution of these side-chains around the macrocyclic ring. In porphyrins of natural origin no pyrrole ring contains two identical side-chains, so that for porphyrins with only two kinds of side-chains (aetioporphyrin, coproporphyrin, uroporphyrin) only four isomers (I–IV, of which type III is the normal biological isomer) are possible. With three different substituents fifteen isomers are possible. Every porphyrin and metalloporphyrin known to have a metabolic function (prosthetic groups of haemoproteins, chlorophylls, vitamin B_{12}) is modelled on this pattern of side-chain substitution and conforms to isomer 9 (systematically related to aetioporphyrin III).

Porphyrins can be regarded as being essentially planar (diameter 8·5 Å, thickness 4·7 Å) but deviations from planarity occur in metal complexes, which with Fe-porphyrins may be of significance in the further coordination of nitrogenous ligands. Apart from solubility aspects, the side-chains determine the electron distribution on the nitrogens and thus affect the redox potential of the Fe-porphyrin complexes.

Modification of the conjugation of double bonds of the tetrapyrrole can occur giving green compounds, either by hydrogenation of a pyrrole (chlorophylls) or by oxidation (protoporphyrin photo-oxide). Spectra of such compounds are characterized by an intense absorption band in the red; λ_{max} and ε mM of the other visible bands are similar to the analogous porphyrin. Hydrogenation of the porphyrin nucleus at the two pyrrolenine nitrogens and all the methine bridge carbons yield porphyrinogens, intermediates in porphyrin biosynthesis; related partly hydrogenated porphyrins are also known. For extensive discussions of physical properties of porphyrins see Lemberg and Legge; Falk; Phillips, *Comprehensive Biochemistry*, vol. 9, pp. 34–72 (1963).

Identification and Estimation

Spectra are of primary importance. The position (λ_{max} mμ) and intensity (ε mM) of absorption maxima are influenced by the degree of electrophilicity of the β-substituents (—CHO > —$COCH_3$ > —CH=CH_2 > alkyl) and their position relative to other electrophilic substituents: e.g. 4-monoformyldeuteroporphyrin III > IV > II > I, rhodotype (R); 2:4-diformyldeuteroporphyrin IV > III > II > I, aetiotype (A); 2-hydroxyalkyl-4-vinyl-8-formyl-8-desmethyldeuteroporphyrin III > II > IV > I, oxorhodotype (OR). Substitution at a methine bridge as in phylloporphyrin (γ-methyl) gives phyllotype (P) spectra IV > II > III > I. Solvent effects are marked.

The ε mM of the Soret band of porphyrin di-cations is much greater than that of the corresponding neutral porphyrin, providing a sensitive means of analysis. Equations for the analysis of polycarboxylic porphyrins in aq. HCl are available (*B.J.* **75**, 620 (1960); Falk, p. 223).

Fluorometric assay though very sensitive requires strict control of experimental procedures because of other solutes and solvent effects.

Solubility

Natural free porphyrins are ampholytes (isoelectric point 3·5–4·5), hence s. in mineral acids and aq. alkalis, particularly NH_4OH. Solubility is markedly influenced by impurities and there is little precise information on the solubilities of the pure substances. In general, the free porphyrins are v.s. gl. acet., Et acetate, pyr., cyclohexanone; s. gl. acetic-eth. (except uroporphyrins), conc. H_2SO_4, and conc. NH_4OH; moderately s. $CHCl_3$, eth. (except uroporphyrins); sl. s. or i. alcohols; i. H_2O, pet. ether. The methyl esters have greater solubility in the organic solvents generally, s. benz., v.s. $CHCl_3$. Solubility in alkali is abolished and in aq. media is diminished. Metal complexes of porphyrins in general have a lowered solubility in organic solvents. Fe-porphyrins, v.s. pyr., acet.-HCl; i. or sl. s. mineral acids. Methyl esters of metal complexes are generally s. in organic solvents. Non-ionic detergents, e.g. Tween 80, increase solubility in aq. media. Though having a similar effect anionic or cationic detergents are less used in biochemical experiments. See Falk, p. 142 for extensive discussion of solubilities.

HCl no. of a porphyrin is defined as that concentration in per cent (w/v) which, from an equal volume of an eth. solution of the porphyrin, extracts two-thirds of the porphyrin. Et acetate-HCl no. which is used for Me esters of polycarboxylic porphyrins is similarly defined, Et acetate replacing eth.

Porphyrin Me esters generally crystallize well from MeOH-$CHCl_3$; polycarboxylic porphyrins from hot MeOH, porphyrins with carbonyl side-chains from $CHCl_3$-eth., metal complexes of porphyrins from benz. Double M.p. or polymorphism may occur. Cu complexes of porphyrin Me esters are less subject to polymorphism and M.p.'s are sharper. X-ray powder diagnosis may distinguish between certain isomers.

Me esters can be prepared from free porphyrins using diazomethane, or MeOH containing 15 per cent (w/v) anhydrous HCl or 5 per cent (w/v) conc. H_2SO_4 (preferably at 0°). Diazomethane, though rapid, may react with formyl side chains and has the disadvantage that it cannot be used for haemins (*B.B.A.* **71,** 150, 1963).

Paper chromatography is used extensively for identification of tetrapyrroles. (*See* Review, *J. Chromat.* **5,** 277, 1961.) Lutidine-H_2O solvent systems are used for determination of the number of free carboxyl groups. For this purpose paper electrophoresis is particularly useful for porphyrins with 4–8 carboxyls. Paper chromatography of the Me esters (*J.B.C.* **190,** 643, 1951) is preferable for porphyrins with electrophilic groups and for distinguishing between isomers.

Free haemins (*J.B.C.* **233,** 743, 1958) and their Me esters (*J.B.C.* **212,** 1, 1955) may be identified by this technique.

Infra-red spectra, though used mainly to identify functional groups (*Aust. J. scient. Res.* **4,** 519, 1951), may distinguish between isomeric forms, e.g. coproporphyrin I and III (*B.J.* **47,** 87 (1950); *J.B.C.* **234,** 251 (1959)).

General

All solvents must be peroxide-free and copper-free. Excessive exposure of tetrapyrroles to light should be avoided as photochemical alterations may occur.

No.	Name	Formula	M. wt.	Solvent	Absorption spectrum λmax mμ (ε mM)				
1	Chlorocruoroporphyrin (Spirographis porphyrin)	1:3:5:8-Tetramethyl-2-formyl-4-vinylporphin-6:7-dipropionic acid	564·6	eth.	642	583	555	514·5	
					592·5				
				dioxan	639	581	553	514	
					(2·3)	(7·9)	(12·4)	(10·3)	
				4% HCl	614	565			418
				20% HCl	616	565			421
2	— dimethyl ester		592·7	$CHCl_3$	644	585	560	520	421
					(2·3)	(9·3)	(14·8)	(10·6)	(161)
3	Coproporphyrin I	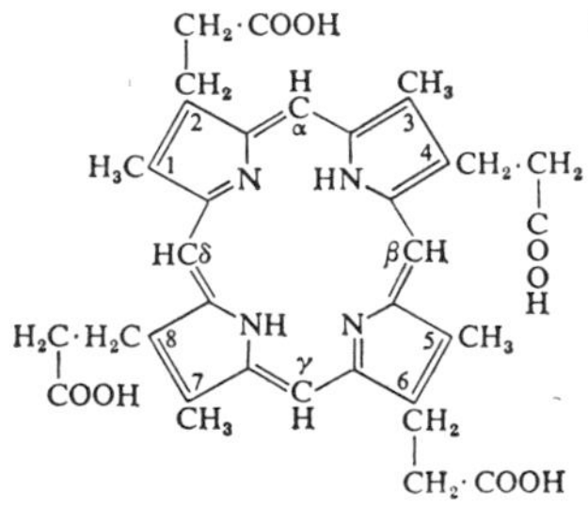 1:3:5:7-Tetramethylporphin-2:4:6:8-tetrapropionic acid	654·7	eth.	623·5	567·5	528	495	398
				25% HCl	593	550			406
					(5·5)	(16·2)			
				1 N-HCl	591	548			401
					(6·1)	(17·5)			(470)
				0·1 N-HCl					399·5
									(489)
4	— tetramethyl ester		710·8	$CHCl_3$	622	567	532	499·5	399·5
									(180)
				dioxan	621	567	529	497	
					(5·2)	(6·7)	(10·0)	(14·7)	
				3 N-HCl	591	548			
					(5·8)	(16·6)			
5	Coproporphyrin III	1:3:5:8-Tetramethylporphin-2:4:6:7-tetrapropionic acid	654·7	eth.	Spectroscopically identical with 3				
				0·1 N-HCl					
				1 N-HCl					
6	— tetramethyl ester		710·8	$CHCl_3$	Spectroscopically identical with 4				
				eth.					
				3 N-HCl	591	548			
					(5·4)	(16·1)			

Type	Physical form	M.p.	Occurrence	Preparation	Determination	General remarks
(R) (R)	fine needle-prisms (eth.)		As chlorocruorohaem, prosthetic group of chlorocruorin	SYN. *Z.P.C.* **272**, 1 (1941) PREP. *Z.P.C.* **242**, 139 (1936)		HCl no. = 4·6. Tween 80 solubilizes in aqueous buffers. 2+4-monoformyl-deuteroporphyrins intermediates in SYN.
(R)	short prisms ($CHCl_3$-MeOH)	278–82		PREP. *Aust. J. exp. Biol. med. Sci.* **30**, 162 (1952)		HCl oxidizes —CHO group. KOH should be used to obtain free porphyrin. Diformyldeuteroporphyrin and mono-+dicarboxylic-deuteroporphyrins by-products of PREP.
(A)	prisms, sometimes in clusters (from pyr.-gl. acetic)		Traces normal serum (esp. foetal), amniotic fluid, meconium. Normal human adult excretes 40–160 μg per 24 hr. Urine excretion increased in pathological conditions. Hedgehog spikes. Shell of mollusc *Pinctada vulgaris.* Micro-organisms yeasts, plants	SYN. Fischer–Orth, pp. 475, 484 *J.B.C.* **135**, 623 (1940) *Can. J. Chem.* **34**, 1768 (1956) PREP. Fischer–Orth, p. 480 ISOL. *J.B.C.* **227**, 505 (1957)	IDENT. *B.J.* **63**, 87 (1956) *J.B.C.* **227**, 505 (1957) *Scand. J. clin. Lab. Invest.* **10**, 319 (1958) EST. *Scand. J. clin. Lab. Invest.* **4**, 55 (1952) *B.J.* **75**, 622 (1960) *Meth. biochem. Anal.* **8**, 221 (1960)	HCl no. = 0·09. Et acetate-HCl no. = 0·35. Not extracted from dil. HCl by $CHCl_3$. Colloidal soln. in H_2O. Zn complex λ_{max} 575, 539, 408 mμ. Cu complex λ_{max} 561, 524, 400 mμ. Na, K salts s. H_2O and strong alkalis. Dihydrochloride, violet-red double pyramids, colloidal soln. in H_2O, ether, $CHCl_3$. Best source: meconium. Conveniently prepared by decarboxylation of uroporphyrin I.
(A)	fine, red-brown needles ($CHCl_3$-MeOH)	250–7		*See* 3	*See* 3 *B.J.* **39**, 239 (1945) *J.B.C.* **168**, 133 (1947)	HCl no. = 1·5. i. MeOH, eth. Quantitatively hydrolysed to free porphyrin by cold, conc. HCl in 10 hr. Cu complex, M.p. 284; sl. s. gl. acetic. Zn complex, M.p 299.
	cryst. with difficulty; globular aggregates		Traces in normal erythrocytes, urine (normal human adults excrete 20–80 μg/day) increased in pathological and toxic conditions. Owl feathers, many bacteria (*C. diphtheriae, Mycobacteria*) particularly in iron deficient media, yeasts. Frequently as Zn complex	SYN. Fischer–Orth, pp. 476, 490 *Can. J. Chem.* **34**, 1768 (1956) *J.C.S.* **1958**, 1430—as tetraethyl ester PREP. Chem., *J. org. Chem.* **25**, 1073 (1960) Biol., *Biochem. Preps.* **7**, 36 (1960) *See* 3	*See* 3	HCl no. = 0·09. Na, K salts, s. H_2O, strong alkalis. Dihydrochloride, red prisms, v.s. H_2O. Ethyl acetate-HCl no. = 3·5. Differentiated from 3 by thin-layer chromatography (*J. Chromat.* **10**, 236, 1963). Conveniently prepared by decarboxylation of uroporphyrin III.
	rosettes of fine needle-prisms ($CHCl_3$-MeOH)	140–60 (128–60) 170–80 (160–80)		*See* 5	*See* 3 and 4	HCl no. 1·5: Et acetate-HCl no. = 3·6. Double M.p.; s. MeOH; sl. s. ether. Cu complex, M.p. 206–10, v.s. gl. acetic. Relatively more soluble than 4 in non-polar solvents. May be differentiated from 4 by paper chromatography (*J.B.C.* **227**, 505 (1957)).

No.	Name	Formula	M. wt.	Absorption spectrum Solvent	λ_{max} mμ (ε mM)				
7	Deuteroporphyrin 9 (Schumm's coprato-porphyrin)	1:3:5:8-Tetramethylporphin-6:7-dipropionic acid	510·6	eth.	621·5	567	526	494	
				pyr.	621	566	530	497	
				25% HCl	591	548			404
				0·1 N-HCl	588	548			398
					(5·34)	(13·7)			(433)
8	— dimethyl ester		538·6	$CHCl_3$	620	565	530	496	399
									(175)
				dioxan	618	565	525	495	
					(4·3)	(6·8)	(8·6)	(16·0)	
9	Haematoporphyrin 9	1:3:5:8-Tetramethyl-2:4-di(α-hydroxyethyl)porphin-6:7-dipropionic acid	598·7	eth.	623	596	569·2	532	499·5
				pyr.	(4·35)	(1·26)	(6·57)	(9·04)	(14·7)
									402
									(175·5)
				25% HCl	595	552		407	
					(4·2)	(12·0)			
				5% HCl	591	549		402	
					(4·4)	(12·4)		(317)	
10	— dimethyl ester		626·7	$CHCl_3$	623	569	532	499	401
				pyr.	(4·3)	(6·7)	(9·0)	(14·8)	(175
11	Mesoporphyrin 9	1:3:5:8-Tetramethyl-2:4-diethylporphin-6:7-dipropionic acid	566·7	eth.	623	596	567	526	497
					(6·64)	(1·35)	(6·64)	(10·21)	(13·81
									395·5
									(158)
				$CHCl_3$	621	594	567	533	499
					(4·87)	(1·69)	(6·48)	(9·62)	(13·56
									400
									(166)
				25% HCl	593	550·5			
				0·1 N-HCl	590	547			399
					(5·55)	(15·1)			(455)
12	— dimethyl ester		594·7	$CHCl_3$	621	567	533·5	500·5	
				dioxan	620	567	528	496	
					(5·4)	(6·6)	(9·8)	(14·2)	
13	Protoporphyrin 9; Schumm's haemato-porphyroidin; Kammerer's porphyrin; Snapper's porphyrin; ooporphyrin	1:3:5:8-Tetramethyl-2:4-divinyl-porphin-6:7-dipropionic acid	562·7	eth.	633	576	538	503	
				dioxan	631	576	538	504	
					(5·2)	(6·5)	(10·8)	(14·8	
				25% HCl	602	557			411
					(5·9)	(16·4)			(278)
				2·7 N-HCl	598	554			408
					(5·75)	(13·5)			(262)

Type	Physical form	M.p.	Occurrence	Preparation	Determination	General remarks
(A) (A)	needles, prisms (pyr.-gl. acetic)		Faeces, putrefying blood, decaying meat	SYN. Fischer–Orth, pp. 407, 414 PREP. *J.A.C.S.* **74**, 6276 (1952) ISOL. *B.J.* **48**, 309 (1951) *J.B.C.* **202**, 781 (1953)	IDENT. *J.B.C.* **208**, 537 (1954) EST. *B.J.* **49**, 157 (1951)	HCl no. = 0·3. Ether/ 0·45% HCl, *K* = 0·36. Na salt, insol. in H_2O. Dihydrochloride, s. $CHCl_3$; extracted into $CHCl_3$ from 0·2% HCl. Cu complex from $CHCl_3$-acetic in needles, M.p. 335. Key compound in structure determination and preparation of model compounds of biochemical interest.
(A) (A)	clusters of bent needles, prisms ($CHCl_3$-MeOH)	222–4		PREP. Falk, p. 248	*See* 7	HCl no. = 2·0. Cu complex, M.p. 233–5.
(A)	Dihydrochloride; small thin needles forming spherical aggregates. K salt; needles		Of historical interest but occurrence in nature not established	PREP. *J.B.C.* **202**, 801 (1953) Fischer–Orth, p. 423	*See* 7	HCl no. = 0·1. Precipitates from strong NaOH; Na salt, s. H_2O; dehydrated in strong HCl. As optically inactive isomer prepared from protohaemin. Optically active isomer from cytochrome *c* (*Acta chem. scand.* **4**, 239 (1950)).
A)	thin plates ($CHCl_3$-MeOH)	212		PREP. Falk, p. 245 Vannotti, p. 40		For dimethyl ester-dimethyl ether, see *J.B.C.* **202**, 801 (1953). For dimethyl ester diacetate, see *Nature, Lond.* **183**, 1185 (1959).
A) A)	red, rhombic (eth.-gl. acetic) thin prisms		Faeces. By-product of removal of iron from protohaemin using hot ferrous-acetate or hydrazine method	SYN. Fischer–Orth, pp. 443, 448 PREP. *J.B.C.* **185**, 103 (1950) *B.J.* **45**, 163 (1949) *Meth. biochem. Anal.* **8**, 272 (1960) ISOL. *B.J.* **48**, 309 (1951)	*See* 7	HCl no. = 0·5. Na salt, sl. s. H_2O, precipitates from strong NaOH. More stable than protoporphyrin. A useful derivative of protohaem for biochemical purposes.
A) A)	bent red needles ($CHCl_3$-MeOH); long plates, with purple-green lustre	212–16		*See* 11		HCl no. = 2·5.
A) A)	platelets or needle-prisms (MeOH-KOH); platelets or rods monoclin. (pyr.); needle-prisms (eth.)		Harderian glands of rat. Egg shells. Immature erythrocytes. Ubiquitous in traces. *Tetrahymena* sp. As protohaem (q.v.) As monomethyl ester in algae and photosyn. bacteria	SYN. Fischer–Orth, p. 399 PREP. *Biochem. Preps.* **3**, 39 (1953) *B.J.* **63**, 87 (1956)	IDENT. *B.J.* **48**, 306 (1951) *B.J.* **55**, 101 (1953) *J.B.C.* **208**, 537 (1954) EST. *B.J.* **49**, 157 (1951) *B.J.* **75**, 622 (1960) *Aust. J. exp. Biol. med. Sci.* **33**, 483 (1955)	HCl no. = 2·5. Unstable in soln. esp. in light. Na salt, sl. s. H_2O, precipitates from strong alkalis. Tween 80 assists sol. in H_2O. K salt may be crystallized. Dihydrochloride, s. $CHCl_3$. Readily hydrated in dil. HCl to give 9 and 21 free porphyrins.

No.	Name	Formula	M. wt.	Absorption spectrum Solvent	λ_{max} mμ (ε mM)				
14	Protoporphyrin 9 dimethyl ester		590·7	$CHCl_3$	631	575	541	505	407
					(5·38)	(7·44)	(11·6)	(14·15)	(171)
				eth.	633	576	536	503	404
					(6·57)	(6·63)	(11·86)	(14·8)	(158)
				dioxan	630	575	537	503	
					(5·6)	(6·8)	(11·6)	(14·6)	
15	Uroporphyrin I (urinporphyrin)	Porphin-1:3:5:7-tetraacetic acid 2:4:6:8-tetrapropionic acid	830·7	25% HCl	597	554			410
				0·5 N-HCl	594	552			405
					(6·52)	(18·3)			(541)
16	— octamethyl ester		942·9	$CHCl_3$	627	572	536	502	406
					(4·18)	(6·85)	(9·35)	(15·8)	(215)
				dioxan	624	596	569	499	
					(3·93)	(1·39)	(9·26)	(15·25)	
17	Uroporphyrin III	Porphin-1:3:5:8-tetraacetic acid 2:4:6:7-tetrapropionic acid	830·7	0·5 N-HCl	Quantitatively identical with 15				
18	— octamethyl ester		942·9	$CHCl_3$ dioxan	Quantitatively identical with 16				
19	Heptacarboxylic porphyrin III (phriaporphyrin, pseudouroporphyrin)		786·7	10% HCl	593·7	551·5			407·

Type	Physical form	M.p.	Occurrence	Preparation	Determination	General remarks
(A) (A) (A)	long, thick prisms ($CHCl_3$-MeOH); needle prisms (benz.-gl. acetic)	224–30		*J.B.C.* **167**, 515 (1947) Falk, p. 241	*See* 13	HCl no. = 5·5. Converted to free porphyrin with alcoholic KOH.
	fine needles (pyr.-gl. acetic)		Traces in normal urine, increased excretion in pathological conditions (esp. congenital porphyria). Molluscan shells	SYN. *J.A.C.S.* **75**, 3040 (1953) ISOL. Fischer–Orth, p. 514 *B.J.* **50**, 202 (1952) PREP. Chem., *B.J.* **57**, 476 (1954) Enz., *J.B.C.* **233**, 501 (1958)	IDENT. *J.B.C.* **227**, 505 (1957) *B.J.* **55**, 105, 109, 867 (1953) *J.B.C.* **234**, 2751 (1959) *Clinica chim. Acta* **7**, 301 (1962) EST. *Scand. J. clin. Lab. Invest.* **8**, 73 (1956) *B.J.* **75**, 620 (1960) *B.J.* **60**, 703 (1955) *J. Chromat.* **10**, 141 (1963)	Readily yields coproporphyrin I by partial decarboxylation. Ethyl acetate HCl no. = 0·1; i. eth.
A) A)	curved filaments; concentrically grouped needles ($CHCl_3$-MeOH)	292–4			*See* 15 Vannotti, p. 40	HCl no. = 5·0, Wide variations in M.p. of impure samples in early literature (273–311). Crystallizes readily from MeOH (more rapidly than 18).
			Traces in normal urine, increased excretion in pathological conditions (esp. acute porphyria, as precursor porphobilinogen) and in experimental porphyria (e.g. Sedormid induced). As Cu complex, turacin, in *Turacos* feathers, *B.J.* **50**, 194 (1951)	ISOL. *B.J.* **55**, 109, 867 (1953) *J.B.C.* **227**, 505 (1957)	*See* 15	Ethyl acetate-HCl no. = 9·4. Readily yields coproporphyrin III by partial decarboxylation. Paper-electrophoresis a valuable method in the preparation of this and other polycarboxylic porphyrins, *Clinica chim. Acta* **7**, 301 (1962). Cu complex, turacin, thin needles; s. dil. alkalis; i. eth., $CHCl_3$, EtOH, gl. acetic. λ_{max} = 562·5, 526 mμ (alkali) and 583, 542 mμ (acid).
	curved filaments (benz.-pet. eth.)	264		*See* 15	*See* 15	Waldenström ester ('uroporphyrin III'), M.p. 255–61, is a mixture (*J.B.C.* **214**, 537 (1955)). Paper-chromatography distinguishes between isomers I and III, but the separation is not quantitative (*B.B.A.* **41**, 356 (1960); Falk, p. 277).
			Pathological conditions (esp. porphyria cutanea tarda); *in vitro* biosynthesis of uroporphyrin	ISOL. *J.B.C.* **227**, 505 (1957) *J.B.C.* **234**, 2741 (1959) *Clinica chim. Acta* **7**, 301 (1962) PREP. *J.B.C.* **234**, 2747 (1959)	*J.B.C.* **234**, 2747, 2751 (1959)	Ethyl acetate-HCl no. = 0·2.

No.	Name	Formula	M. wt.	Absorption spectrum Solvent	λ_{max} mμ (ε mM)					
20	Heptacarboxylic porphyrin III heptamethyl ester		884·9	$CHCl_3$	625	568·6	535·8	504·8	403·3	
				dioxan	625	569	534	500·5	403	
					(4·4)	(7·0)	(10·0)	(16·0)	(205·5)	
21	Monovinylmono-hydroxyethyldeutero-porphyrin 9	1:3:5:8-Tetramethyl-2(4)vinyl-4(2)α-hydroxyethyl porphin-6:7-dipropionic acid	580·6	eth.	626	572	533·5	502	404	
					(3·7)	(6·58)	(10·2)	(13·42)	(157·5)	
22	Cryptoporphyrin *a*, dimethyl ester	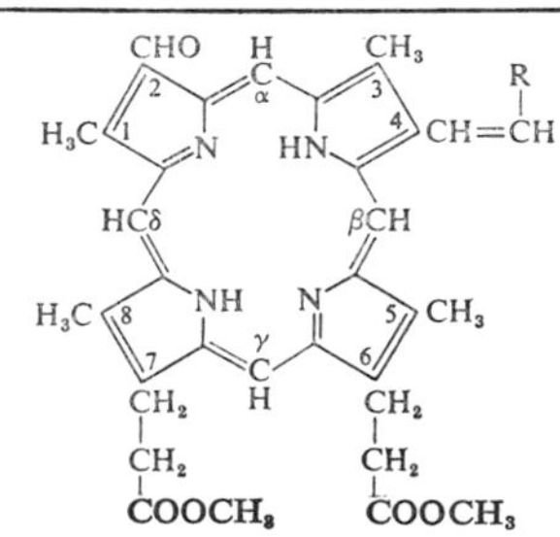 **(R = $C_{12}H_{25}$ to $C_{15}H_{31}$)**	761–793	$CHCl_3$	642·5	584	559	519	416	
					$E^{1\%}_{1\,cm.}$	31	127	194	148	
				10% HCl	613·5	563·5				
23	Cryptoporphyrin p_1, dimethyl ester	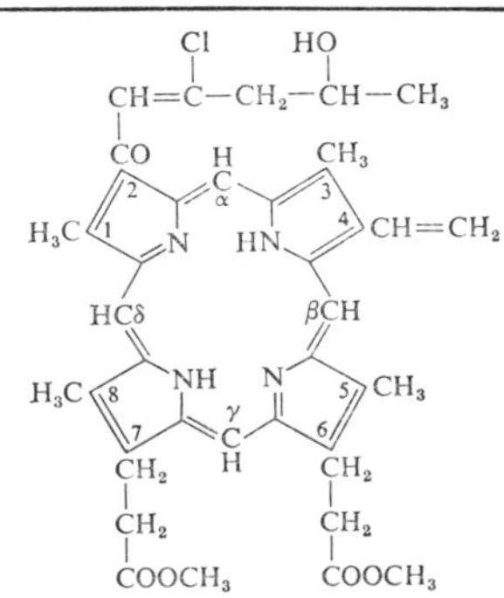	711·3	$CHCl_3$	641	584	557	517	418	
							(13·7)	(4·4)		
24	Cytodeuteroporphyrin, dimethyl ester	1:3:5-Trimethylporphin-6:7-dipropionic acid dimethyl ester	524·6	pyr.-eth.	618·5	593	571	565	521	48[illegible]
				$CHCl_3$	619			566	530	49[illegible]

Type	Physical form	M.p.	Occurrence	Preparation	Determination	General remarks
(A)	clusters of long needles	205		*See* 19	*See* 19	HCl no. = 4·0. Ethyl acetate-HCl no. = 8·1. Possibility of additional isomeric forms in III series. M.p. 213–15 from biosyn. prep. and urine isol. (*B.B.A.* **57**, 191 (1962)). Porphyrin of isomer I series (7-methylporphin-1:3:5-triacetic-2:4:6:8-tetrapropionic acid heptamethyl ester) has M.p. 253–5.
(A)			Recovered from *Chlorella* mutants. As impurity in preparations of haematoporphyrin, common by-product of the removal of iron from protohaemin	PREP. *B.J.* **78**, 799, 802 (1961) ISOL. *J.B.C.* **202**, 793 (1953) *B.J.* **87**, 186 (1963)	IDENT. *J.B.C.* **202**, 793 (1953) As dimethyl-ester, *Nature, Lond.* **183**, 1185 (1959)	HCl no. = 0·44; eth./0·1 N-HCl, $K = 0{\cdot}754$. Convenient intermediate in the preparation of monoformylmono-hydroxyethyl- and mono-acetylmonovinyl-deuteroporphyrin.
(R)	prisms; diamond-shaped leaflets; pentagonal plates	254–7 259–60 256–60	Ox heart-muscle, liver; pigeon breast muscle. Yeasts and bacteria (*S. lutea*), as haemin	*B.B.A.* **35**, 496 (1959)	EST. *B.B.A.* **35**, 496 (1959)	Found in crude porphyrin *a* preps. as free porphyrin. HCl no. = 4·0. As haemin from ox-heart muscle preps. (*J.B.C.* **233**, 743 (1958)). M. wt. calculated from specific extinction.
(R)	polymorphic leaves, platelets, or prisms	220–2	Artefact of preparation of protoporphyrin from whole blood by acetone-HCl method. Obtained from saline extracts of heart muscle as free haemin	*B.B.A.* **82**, 361 (1964)		Sl. s. in eth. Compounds in which the vinyl group is replaced by a second chlorinated ketonyl side-chain or in which the vinyl is hydrated are also obtained. (Cryptoporphyrins p_2 and p_3).
(A)	needles	198–202	Product of resorcinol degradation of haemin *a* and removal of Fe	SYN. *J.A.C.S.* **82**, 3183 (1960) PREP. *Z.P.C.* **292**, 174 (1953)	IDENT. *J.A.C.S.* **82**, 3183 (1960)	Free porphyrin, eth./0·4% HCl, $K = 0{\cdot}68$. Cu complex, M.p. 237–9. The three other possible isomers have been synthesized.

No.	Name	Formula	M. wt.	Absorption spectrum Solvent	λ_{max} mμ (ε mM)				
25	Porphyrin *a* (cytoporphyrin)	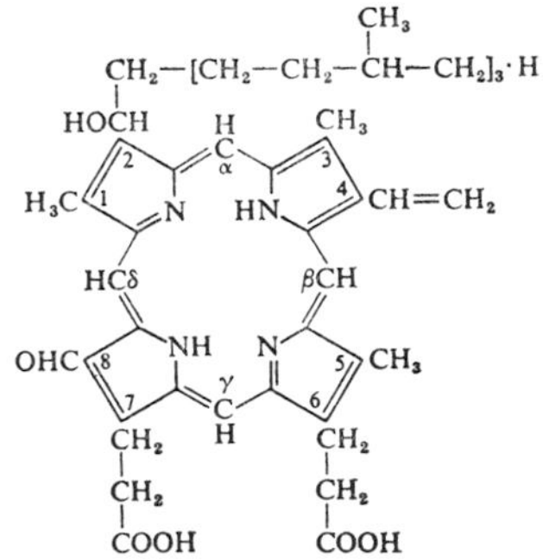 1:3:5-trimethyl-2-(α)hydroxy-alkyl-4-vinyl-8-formylporphin-6:7-dipropionic acid (See general remarks)	805·1	eth. CHCl$_3$ 5% HCl 25% HCl	647 (1·3) 646 614·8 619·0	582 (10·9) 584·5 559·1 564·2	558 (21) 563·5	518 (8·86) 520	414 (160) 418·5
26	Porphyrin *c*	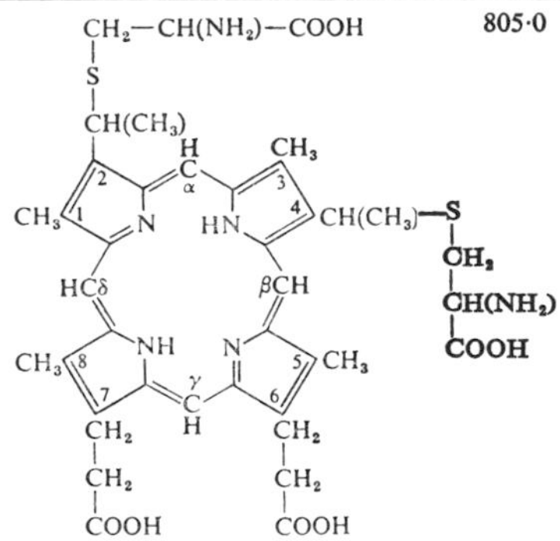	805·0	1 N-HCl	553 (16·5)				406 (312)
27	Aetioporphyrin III	1:3:5:8-Tetramethyl-2:4:6:7-tetraethylporphin	478·7	CHCl$_3$ dioxan	620 621 (5·18)	570·1 595 (1·36)	532·7 566 (5·95)	497·6 528 (9·5)	399·5 (160) 496 (13·6)
28	Diacetyldeutero-porphyrin 9, dimethyl ester	1:3:5:8-Tetramethyl-2:4-diacetylporphin-6:7-dipropionic acid dimethyl ester	622·7	CHCl$_3$ dioxan eth. 2·7 N-HCl	640 635 (3·58) 639 608 (6·68)	588 584 (6·56) 586 562 (13·6)	552 (6·56) 548 (7·79) 546·5	518 (12·14) 513 (14·11) 512·5	 420 (244)
29	Diformyldeutero-porphyrin 9, dimethyl ester	1:3:5:8-Tetramethyl-2:4-diformylporphin-6:7-dipropionic acid dimethyl ester	594·6	CHCl$_3$ eth.	651 (3·48) 648	595 (6·48) 593	562·5 (7·7) 557·5	526 (12·6) 521	435 (137·5)
30	Pyrroporphyrin 15, monomethyl ester	1:3:5:8-Tetramethyl-2:4-diethylporphin-7-propionic acid methyl ester	508·7	eth.-pyr.	620 (4·95)	594 (1·22)	566 (6·45)	527 (8·97)	496 (13·6)

Type	Physical form	M.p.	Occurrence	Preparation	Determination	General remarks
(OR) (OR)			As haem, prosthetic group of cytochrome oxidase (cytochrome $a+a_3$) and of cytochrome a_1 (bacteria, e.g. *E. coli*)	*B.J.* **78**, 793 (1961) As haemin: Ibid., *B.Z.* 337, 35 (1963)	EST. *Aust. J. exp. Biol. med. Sci.* 33, 483 (1955) By Cu titration, *B.J.* 49, 157 (1951)	Native porphyrin *a* (α form), HCl no. = 15. Transition to spectrally identical porphyrin *aβ*, HCl no. = 5, occurs on standing porphyrin *aα* in aq. HCl or acidified organic solvents. Alteration products may form during removal of iron from the haemin. Highly photosensitive. Cu complex, λ_{max} 598, 550 mμ. R group at position 2 unsaturated at undetermined position(s), see Chance *et al.*, *Haems and Haemoproteins*, Academic Press, 1966: in porphyrin *a* reduced by Pd-formic acid, 5:9:13-trimethyltetradecyl(*B.Z.*338,771(1963)).
			Derived from cytochrome *c* by hydrolysis	SYN. *B.B.A.* **38**, 351 (1960) *Acta chem. scand.* **17**, 47 (1963) PREP. *B.Z.* **298**, 242 (1938)		s. H_2O,; i. eth., Optically active. Amino-carboxylic acid groups, p*K* 5·7.
(A) (A)	Long prismatic needles from $CHCl_3$-pet. eth.	360–3	Coal, shale oils, coproliths	SYN. Fischer–Orth, p. 250 PREP. *Z.P.C.* **178**, 1 (1928) *B.J.* **74**, 417 (1960)		HCl no. = 3·0, i. alkali. Conveniently obtained by the decarboxylation of mesoporphyrin 9.
(A) (A) (A)	rhombic leaflets	234–6		SYN. *Ann.* **468**, 99, 108 (1929) PREP. *Nature, Lond.* **184**, 1988 (1959)		Sl. s. in eth., alcohols. Convenient prep. from haematoporphyrin. An intermediate in the prep. of porphyrins of biochemical interest. 2- and 4-monoacetyl-deuteroporphyrins by-product of SYN.
(A)	prisms ($CHCl_3$-eth.)	301–3		SYN. *Z.P.C.* **280**, 186 (1944) PREP. *J. org. Chem.* **25**, 1073 (1960) *Aust. J. exp. Biol. med. Sci.* **30**, 162 (1952)		Very sl. s. in eth. and alcohols. Free porphyrin by hydrolysis with KOH. Convenient intermediate for prep. of porphyrins of biochemical interest.
(A)	red-brown prisms; needles	241	By-product of chlorophyll *a* degradation	SYN. Fischer–Orth, p. 341 PREP. *Z.P.C.* **241**, 219 (1936)		HCl no. = 2·5. Free porphyrin, HCl no. = 1·3. 24 possible isomers, natural porphyrin isomer 15. Free porphyrin used as monocarboxylic marker in paper chromatography.

No.	Name	Formula	M. wt.	Absorption spectrum Solvent	λ_{max} mμ (ε mM)					
31	Chlorin a_2	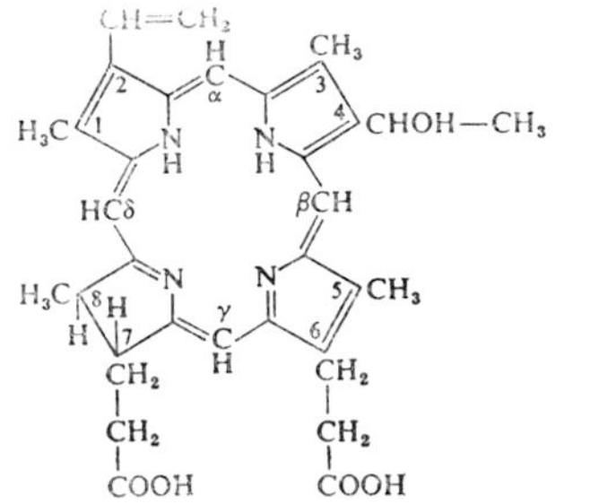	582·6(?)	eth.	653	598	573	534	503	405
					Ratio of intensities					
					3·3	0·3			1	12
				10% HCl	630		536			405
				20% HCl	647		530 (diffuse)			412
32	Uroporphyrinogen III (Hexahydrouro-porphyrin, urospectrin)	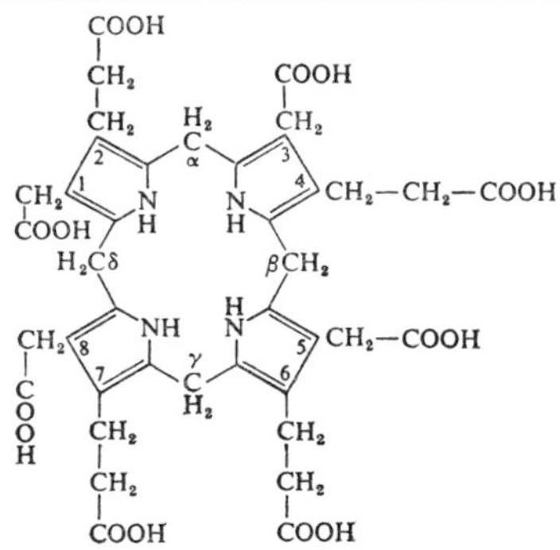	836·8	water					202 (50)	

Type	Physical form	M.p.	Occurrence	Preparation	Determination	General remarks
	obtained associated with lipid		As haemin prosthetic group of cytochrome a_2 in bacteria (*A. aerogenes*, *E. coli*)	PREP. *B.J.* 64, 626 (1956)	EST. *B.J.* **64**, 626 (1956)	Structure not definitive. HCl no. = 10. Conversion to a porphyrin may occur during removal of iron from the ferrochlorin. The ferrochlorin is best est. as the chloroferrichlorin (the haemin) λ_{max} 603–4 mμ; the pyridine haemochrome (λ_{max} 613–4 mμ) is extremely unstable.
			Present in urine esp. path. conditions. *J. Lab. clin. Med.* 37, 831 (1951); *Aust. J. exp. Biol. med. Sci.* **31**, 457 (1953). Intermediate in porphyrin biosynthesis	PREP. *J.B.C.* **232**, 1141 (1958) Falk, p. 219	EST. *J. Lab. clin. Med.* **37**, 831 (1951) *Nature, Lond.* **181**, 1592 (1958)	Readily oxidized by iodine to uroporphyrin, tetrahydro- (λ_{max} 500 mμ) and dihydro- (λ_{max} 737, 440 mμ) uroporphyrin as intermediates. Photocatalytically autooxidized. For other porphyrinogens see *J.B.C.* 236, 1173 (1961); Falk, p. 8.

C. IRON PORPHYRINS (HAEMS, HAEMATINS)

Revised by D. B. MORELL (*Royal North Shore Hospital, Sydney, Australia*)

Structure and nomenclature

The Fe atom of haems is coordinated to the four pyrrole nitrogens by bonds lying near the plane of the almost planar porphyrin ring. The fifth and sixth coordination positions of the Fe atom are directed perpendicularly to the porphyrin plane. The term 'haem' is preferred for generic use (e.g. haem-peptide, haemoprotein, ferrohaem, ferrihaem) irrespective of valency. A haematin is a ferric compound (e.g. alkaline haematin, neutral haematin (Lemberg & Legge, p. 170)). A haemin is a ferric compound in which an anion, usually a halogen, is coordinated to the iron atom in either the fifth or sixth coordination positions. Other nomenclature can be deduced from Table 1. Chlorins are derivatives of porphyrins in which the conjugation of the macro-ring is altered (*see* Porphyrin section). Their iron complexes are also termed haems, e.g. haem a_2 from cytochrome a_2 (*B.J.* **64,** 626 (1956)), Fe-chlorin (crystalline *Pseudomonas* oxidase, *B.B.A.* **67,** 407 (1963)). The general term 'haem' has sometimes been used also to describe the complexes of iron with non-porphyrin but closely related tetrapyrrolic compounds, e.g. verdohaem (*Proc. R. Soc.* **B138,** 386 (1951)) or biliverdin haem (*Rev. pure appl. Chem.* **6,** 1 (1956)).

Functional structure

The Fe atom of haems is conjugated with the conjugation of the macro-ring. Thus, alteration of the macro-ring conjugation as in haem a_2 or variation in conjugated β-pyrrole substituents affects the reactions of the Fe atom. This effect may be upon the redox potential as in haem *a* or haem a_2 (*Haematin Enzymes*, eds. J. E. Falk, R. Lemberg and R. K. Morton, p. 361, Pergamon Press (1961)) or upon reactivity, e.g. oxygen affinity in artificial haemoglobins (*Arch. B.B.* **85,** 37 (1959)). Other changes in the properties of the haem prosthetic group may be imposed by the nature and spatial arrangement of iron-protein bonds.

Assay of haems

Most commonly from extinction of the α-band of ferrohaemochrome. Also by differential ferro-ferrihaemochromes (*B.J.* **87,** 181 (1963)), provided ferrihaemochrome is fully oxidized. Haemochromes electrophilically substituted are difficult to maintain in the fully oxidized state.

Aqueous solution of haems

Haems are soluble in alkaline solutions (*see* Table 1) or at physiological pH in aqueous detergents (*B.J.* **87,** 181 (1963)).

Characterization of haem prosthetic groups—haemochromes

As a first approach to the identification of substituents at the β-pyrrole positions the spectrum of the dipyridine ferrohaemochrome (pyridine haemochromogen) is of value. The data in Table 1 apply to compounds having the same macro-ring conjugation as in protohaem. An electrophilic substituent moves the α-absorption maximum of the haemochrome towards the red; a second or third strong electrophilic group has much less effect in this respect than the first. Electrophilic substituents on opposite pyrroles (but not adjacent pyrroles) tend to abolish the β-band. Pyridine (20–30% v/v) is the standard base; for haemoproteins, alkali (0·1N–0·01N-NaOH) may be required to disrupt completely the Fe-protein bonds but can give erroneous or different band positions; for formylhaems (*Nature, Lond.* **193,** 373 (1962)), haems with side-chains labile to alkali (e.g. milk peroxidase, *B.B.A.* **71**, 157 (1963)), and haems substituted with unesterified carboxyls conjugated to the porphyrin conjugation (*Nature, Lond.* **192**, 750 (1961)), $Na_2S_2O_4$ is the usual reducer.

TABLE 1

Pyridine ferrohaemochrome	*α-band* (mμ)	*β-band* (mμ)	Δ *α-band* (mμ) (*ref. deutero-haemochrome*)
Deuterohaemochrome (2:4-dihydro-compound)	545	513	..
Mesohaemochrome (2:4-diethyldeutero-)	547	518	+2
From cytochrome *c* (2:4-di(-CH(SR)CH_3))	550	522	+5
Protohaemochrome (2:4-divinyldeutero-)	557	525	+12
2-Acetyldeuterohaemochrome	571	530	+26
From milk peroxidase (? structure)	565–71		+20–26
4-Formyldeuterohaemochrome	578	548	+33
From chlorocruorin (2-formyl-4-vinyldeutero-)	580	545	+35
Cryptohaemochrome *a* (formyl, vinyl, or vinylogue-)	581	(*B.B.A.* 35, 496 (1959))	+36
Oxorhodohaemochrome ester (2-acetyl-6-carboxylic ester-)	582	none	+37
2:4-Diformyldeuterohaemochrome	584	549	+39
From cytochrome oxidase-haemochrome *a* (2-hydroxyalkyl-4-vinyl-8-formyl-)	587	none	+42
From myeloperoxidase (? structure)	590	none	+45

TABLE 2

No.	*Name*	*Synonyms*	*Formula and M. wt.*	*5th and 6th co-ord. positions*	*Absorption spectrum* *Solvent*	λ_{max} mμ (ϵ mM Fe)
1	Ferroproto-haem IX	Ferroproto-porphyrin, protohaem, haem, reduced haematin	$C_{34}H_{32}O_4N_4Fe$ 616·5	H_2O, H_2O readily dis-placed by bases to form ferro-haemochromes e.g. 4	pH 7–12 borate or phosphate buffer	570–80 (5·5–6·5)
2	Ferriproto-haem IX	Hydroxyferriproto-porphyrin, alkaline haematin, haematin	$C_{34}H_{32}O_4N_4FeOH$ 633·5	H_2O, OH both ligands displaced by bases to form ferrihaemo-chromes, e.g. pyridine ferri-protohaemo-chrome, λ_{max} 558 mμ. Com-bines with CN^-	borate, pH 10·0 0·1 N-aq. NaOH 5×10^{-4} N-aq. NaOH 5×10^{-4} N-NaOH in 99% EtOH	600 (4·5) 610 (4·6), 385 (58·44) 385 (49) 403 (80)
3	Protohaemin IX	Chlorohaemin (abbreviation: haemin), chloro-ferriprotoporphyrin, haemin (Teichmann crystals), acetohaemin (acetate anion; acid haematin)	$C_{34}H_{32}O_4N_4FeCl$ 652·0	? H_2O, Cl, etc. as for 2	eth.-acetic (as ester) gl. acetic-75% EtOH	638, 540, 512, 407, 381 (*B.B.A.* **71,** 165 (1963)) 635, 510, 400 (90)
4	Pyridine ferro-protohaemo-chrome	Pyridine haemo-chromogen, dipyridine ferro-protoporphyrin IX	$C_{34}H_{32}O_4N_4Fe(NC_5H_5)_2$ 774·7	pyr., pyr.	0·2 N-NaOH-25% pyr.	557 (31–35), 525 (16–17·5)

Solubility	*Occurrence*	*Preparation*	*General remarks*
i. H_2O, dil. acids; sl. s. dil. alkalis; s. EtOH-eth.	Prosthetic group of de-oxygenated vertebrate haemoglobins, erythrocruorins, myoglobins, reduced cytochromes *b*, ? cytochrome *c* peroxidase, ? tryptophan pyrrolase	Reduction of 2, 3 Fischer–Orth, pp. 384, 201	Rapidly autoxidizes. Fe removed by HCl (e.g. *Aust. J. exp. Biol. med. Sci.* 34, 211 (1956)). Exists as dimer in solution.
i. H_2O, dil. acids, EtOH, eth., $CHCl_3$, acet.; sl. s. gl. acetic; s. dil. alkalis	Hydroxy-derivative of prosthetic group of methaemoglobins, meterythrocruorin, metmyoglobin, plant peroxidases, catalases, cytochromes *b*, methaemalbumin. In urine in pathological conditions in erythrocytes in malaria	3 in alkali Fischer–Orth, p. 388 Lemberg & Legge p. 170	Structure uncertain. Loose aggregates, dimer in aq. soln. Forms 1 on reduction with $Na_2S_2O_4$.
. H_2O, dil. acids; s. dil. alkalis, NH_4OH; s. org. bases; sl. s. gl. acetic, 70–80% EtOH; i. EtOH, eth., acet., $CHCl_3$; s. aq. HCl-EtOH, aq. HCl-acet.		*Org. Synth.* **Coll. 3**, 442 (1955) *J.B.C.* **112**, 89 (1935) *B.B.A.* **76**, 437 (1957) *J.B.C.* **228**, 123 (1957) Recrystallization tends to alter vinyl side chains.	Removal of Fe requires conc. H_2SO_4 (alteration contrast 1). Dimethyl ester, s. gl. acetic, $CHCl_3$; sl. s. MeOH; absorption bands in $CHCl_3$, 625, 565, 515 mμ. Estimation, *see* 4 and *J. gen. Microbiol.* **15**, 404 (1956). Stable form.
. aq. alkalis		*Z.P.C.* **70**, 217, 224 (1910) *Proc. R. Soc.* **B105**, 112 (1929) *J.B.C.* **146**, 605 (1942) *Acta chem. scand.* **7** 1284 (1953)	Autoxidizes to ferrihaemochrome (*see* 2, column 4) with some destruction. Estimation: *J.B.C.* **140**, 373, 387 (1941); *Acta chem. scand.* **7**, 1284 (1953).

D. CHLOROPHYLLS AND RELATED PIGMENTS

Revised by O. T. G. JONES (*Biochemistry Department, University of Bristol*)

Nomenclature

The chlorophyll pigments are magnesium complexes of various tetrapyrroles (e.g Formula 1). They can be considered as derivatives of protoporphyrin, a porphyrin which has two carboxylic acid groups; these may be free or esterified. Thus chlorophyll *a* has a carboxymethyl group at C_{10} and the phytol ester of propionic acid at C_7. Removal of magnesium, which is readily effected by mild acid treatment, yields a product known as a phaeophytin. Hydrolysis of the phytol ester bond of a chlorophyll yields a chlorophyllide: the metal-free chlorophyllide is known as a phaeophorbide.

All these compounds are highly coloured and fluoresce strongly except when dissolved in organic solvents under very strictly anhydrous conditions. Their characteristic absorption spectra are useful in the identification and determination of the pigments. The solubility of these compounds in HCl is often used, particularly as a guide to the presence or absence of esterifying alcohols. The HCl number is defined as that concentration of HCl (in % w/v) which, from an equal volume of an ether solution of

No.	*Name*	*Formula*	*M. wt.*	*Absorption spectrum*
1	Chlorophyll *a*	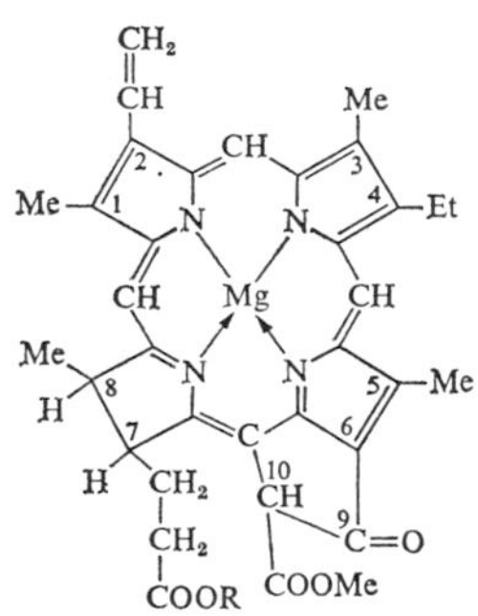 R = $C_{20}H_{39}$ (phytyl) $C_{55}H_{72}O_5N_4Mg$	893·5	Eth.: λ_{max}: 662 615 578 533·5 430 410; ϵ mM: 91·2 13·8 7·6 3·7 121 76·1. Acet.: λ_{max}: 663 615 580 535 430 410; ϵ mM: 75·05 14·03 7·75 3·47 94·71 68·9
2	Phaeophytin *a*	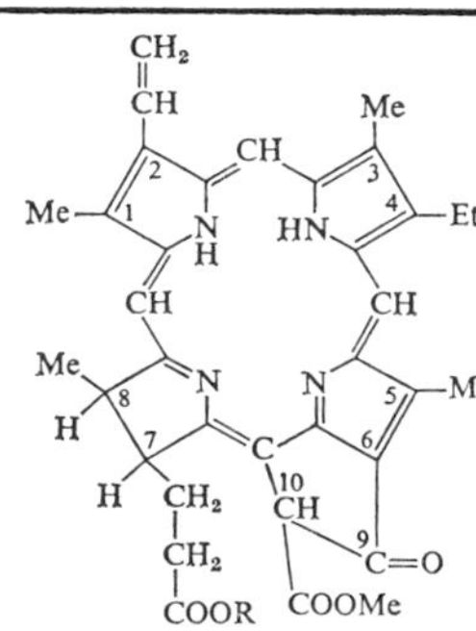 R = $C_{20}H_{39}$ (phytyl) $C_{55}H_{74}O_5N_4$	871·2	Eth.: λ_{max}: 667 609·5 560 534 505 471 408·5; ϵ mM: 55·5 8·5 3·1 11·0 12·7 4·4 115·8
3	Chlorophyllide *a*	As chlorophyll *a*, R = H $C_{35}H_{34}O_5N_4Mg$	614·9	As chlorophyll *a*

a pigment, extracts two-thirds of the pigment. The *phase test* is carried out by underlaying an ether solution of a chlorophyll with an equal volume of a 30% solution of KOH in MeOH. A coloured ring is formed at the interface of the two phases (Smith & Benitez, p. 192). The use of *thin layer chromatography* (e.g. *Planta*, **58,** 564 (1962)) permits rapid detection of chlorophylls in crude extracts.

The chlorophylls are unstable in light; they may undergo oxidation to allomerized chlorophylls if allowed to stand in air in methanolic or ethanolic solution.

The following references are recommended for further information.

1. H. Fischer and A. Stern, *Die Chemie des Pyrrols*, vol. 2, pt. ii, Akademische Verlagsgesellschaft M.B.H., Leipzig (1940). Cited in this section as Fischer & Stern.
2. J. H. C. Smith and A. Benitez, *Modern Methods of Plant Analysis*, eds. K. Paech and M. V. Tracey, vol. 4, p. 142, Springer-Verlag, Berlin (1955). Cited in this section as Smith & Benitez.
3. C. S. French, *Handb. PflPhysiol.* **5,** 252 (1960).
4. H. H. Strain, *Chloroplast Pigments and Chromatographic Analysis*, Pennsylvania State University (1958).
5. L. P. Vernon and G. R. Seely, *The Chlorophylls*, Academic Press, New York and London (1966). Cited in this section as Vernon & Seely.

olubility	*Occurrence*	*Preparation*	*Estimation*	*General remarks*
EtOH, acet., nz., eth.; s. pet. eth.; H_2O	All photosynthetic organisms evolving oxygen in photosynthesis, i.e. higher plants, green, red, and brown algae, diatoms, etc.	*Arch. B.B.* **53,** 228 (1954) Smith & Benitez, p. 143 *Nature, Lond.* **194,** 285 (1962) *B.B.A.* **58,** 486 (1962) *B.B.A.* **75,** 306 (1963)	Smith & Benitez, p. 154 For the determination of chlorophylls *a* and *b* in 80% acetone extracts of leaves, the equation of Arnon (*Pl. Physiol.* **24,** 1 (1949)) is used: $C_a = 12{\cdot}7 \times A_{663} - 2{\cdot}7 \times A_{645}$ $C_b = 22{\cdot}9 \times A_{645} - 4{\cdot}7 \times A_{663}$ C and C_b in mg/l.	Fluorescence max. (eth.) 668, 723. Phase test: yel. → green. Unstable, especially in light.
th., acet., nz., $CHCl_3$; s. EtOH, . eth.; i. H_2O	As for chlorophyll *a*, possibly due to decomposition of chlorophyll *a*	*Bot. Gaz.* **102,** 463 (1941) *B.B.A.* **58,** 486 (1962)	*Planta* **29,** 114 (1938–9)	Florescence max. (eth.) 672·5, 715. Phase test: positive. HCl no. ≈ 29. Unstable, especially in light.
h., acet.	Formed by the photoconversion of protochlorophyllide	Willstätter & Stoll, *Investigations on Chlorophyll* (transl. Schertz & Merz), Science Press, Lancaster, Pa. (1928)		Phase test: positive.

No.	*Name*	*Formula*	*M. wt.*	*Absorption spectrum*
4	Ethyl chlorophyllide *a*	As chlorophyll *a*, R = C_2H_5 $C_{37}H_{38}O_5N_4Mg$	643·0	As chlorophyll *a*
5	Methyl phaeophorbide *a*	As phaeophytin *a* R = CH_3 $C_{36}H_{38}O_5N_4$	606·7	As phaeophytin *a*
6	Chlorophyll *b*	As chlorophyll *a*, except 3, —CHO instead of —CH_3 $C_{55}H_{70}O_6N_4Mg$	907·5	Eth.: λ_{max}: 644 595 549 455 430 ε mM: 51·5 9·89 5·62 155 53·1 Acet.: 645 595 .. 455 .. ε mM: 47·0 10·3 .. 133·3 ..
7	Phaeophytin *b*	As phaeophytin *a*, except 3, —CHO instead of —CH_3 $C_{55}H_{72}O_6N_4$	885·2	Eth.: λ_{max}: 655 599 555 525·5 434 412·5 ε mM: 37·3 8·4 7·7 12·6 191 73·5
8	Ethyl chlorophyllide *b*	As chlorophyll *a*, except 3, —CHO instead of —CH_3 R = C_2H_5 $C_{37}H_{36}O_6N_4Mg$	657·0	As chlorophyll *b*
9	Methyl phaeophorbide *b*	As phaeophytin *a*, except 3, —CHO instead of —CH_3 R = CH_3 $C_{36}H_{36}O_6N_4$	620·7	As phaeophytin *b*
10	Protochlorophyll	As chlorophyll *a*, except bond between C atoms 7, 8 is unsaturated $C_{55}H_{70}O_5N_4Mg$	891·5	Eth.: λ_{max}: 623 571 535 432 ε mM: 35·6 13·3 6·4 289·7
11	Proto-phaeophytin	As protochlorophyll, but lacking Mg $C_{55}H_{72}O_5N_4$	869·2	Eth.: λ_{max}: 638 585 565 524 417 ε mM: 2·2 15·4 22·4 10·4 228·7
12	Proto-chlorophyllide (Mg vinyl-phaeoporphyrin a_5 monomethyl ester)	As protochlorophyll, R = H $C_{35}H_{32}O_5N_4Mg$	612·9	As protochlorophyll
13	Vinyl phaeoporphyrin a_5 monomethyl ester	As protophaeophytin, R = H $C_{35}H_{34}O_5N_4$	590·6	As protophaeophytin
14	Chlorophyll *c* (chlorofucine)	Probably a mixture of magnesium hexadehydrophaeoporphyrin a_5 monomethyl ester and magnesium tetradehydrophaeoporphyrin a_5 monoethyl ester (*J.A.C.S.* **88**, 5037 (1966))		Eth.: λ_{max}: 628 580 449 ϵ_{sp}: 15·8 15·7 169·7 Acet.: λ_{max}: 628 580 442 ϵ_{sp} 15·8 10·7 115·9

olubility	Occurrence	Preparation	Estimation	General remarks
. EtOH, acet.; . H_2O	Usually present in ethanolic extracts of leaf tissue, due to action of chlorophyllase	*Am. J. Bot.* **41**, 710 (1954)		Phase test: positive.
s. $CHCl_3$; . pyr.; l. s. EtOH, leOH, eth.; H_2O, pet. eth.	Does not occur naturally; may be used to characterize phaeophytin *a*	Fischer & Stern, p. 64 *Helv. chim. Acta* **16**, 183 (1933)	*Am. J. Bot.* **15**, 86 (1928) *Am. J. Bot.* **16**, 716 (1929)	Fluorescence max. (dioxan) 681·5, 717·5.
. EtOH, acet., enz., eth.; . s. MeOH; H_2O, pet. eth.	All higher plants and many green algae	Smith & Benitez, p. 143 *B.B.A.* **58**, 486 (1962)	Smith & Benitez, p. 154 For determination of chlorophyll *b* in 80% acetone extracts, *see* chlorophyll *a*	Fluorescence max. (eth.) 649, 708. Phase test: red → brown → green.
eth., acet., HCl_3, benz.; . s. MeOH, et. eth.; H_2O	As for chlorophyll *b* possibly due to decomposition of chlorophyll *b*	*See* phaeophytin *a*	*See* phaeophytin *a*	Fluorescence max. (eth.) 657, 707 Phase test: red → brown → green. HCl no. ≈ 35.
. s. eth., sl. s. EtOH	Usually present in alcoholic extracts of leaf tissue, due to chlorophyllase action	*Am. J. Bot.* **41**, 710 (1954)		
. s. eth., sl. s. EtOH	Does not occur naturally. May be used to characterize phaeophytin *b*	Fischer & Stern, p. 247 *Helv. chim. Acta* **16**, 183 (1933)	*See* methyl phaeophorbide *a*	Fluorescence max. (dioxan) 662, 713·5. HCl no. = 21.
EtOH, acet., nz., eth.; pet. eth., H_2O	Etiolated leaves of seedlings. A similar, but not identical pigment found in inner seed coats of Curcurbitaceae	Smith & Benitez, p. 172	Smith & Benitez, p. 176	Phase test: brown → yel. → red-brown. Fluorescence max. (acet.) 627, 685. Usually present in etiolated leaves in smaller amounts than protochlorophyllide.
eth., dioxan, r.; i. pet. eth.	Not certain if this occurs naturally	Smith & Benitez, p. 175		HCl no. = 25.
eth., . KOH	Etiolated leaves of seedlings. Mutants of *Chlorella*	*J.B.C.* **183**, 713 (1950)		Usually present in larger amounts than protochlorophyll in etiolated leaves.
lioxan, r., eth.; H_2O	Mutants of *Chlorella*	*J.B.C.* **183**, 713 (1950)		HCl no. ≈ 11.
MeOH, EtOH, acetate; H_2O	Brown algae, diatoms, dinoflagellates, symbiotic algae of sea anemones	Smith & Benitez, p. 162 *B.J.* **86**, 313 (1963) Vernon & Seely, p. 57		Fluorescence max. (eth.) 629, 690. Phase test: red → brown → green. HCl no. ≈ 12. The spectroscopic data given (from *B.J.* **86**, 313, (1963)) differ from those given in Smith & Benitez.

13. Porphyrins and Related Compounds

No.	Name	Formula	M. wt.	Absorption spectrum
15	Phaeophytin *c*	Chlorophyll *c*, lacking Mg		Variously reported, thus: *B.J.* **86**, 313 (1963) Eth.: λ_{max}: 625 594 573 530 430 or Smith & Benitez, p. 166 Eth.: λ_{max}: 641 589·5 564 521·5 421·5
16	Chlorophyll *d*	Not certain, possibly as chlorophyll *a*, except 2, —CHO instead of —CH=CH_2 (*Can. J. Chem.* 37, 507 (1959))		Eth.: λ_{max}: 688 643 595 548·5 512 447 392 ϵ_{sp}: 110·4 14·3 9·47 4·03 1·98 97·8 58·9
17	Phaeophytin *d*	Chlorophyll *d* without Mg (*see* chlorophyll *d*)		Eth.: λ_{max}: 692 631 576 547 516·5 476 421 382 ϵ_{sp}: 82·7 7·75 2·88 15·9 15·1 5·52 97·2 85·8
18	Bacterio-chlorophyll (*a*)	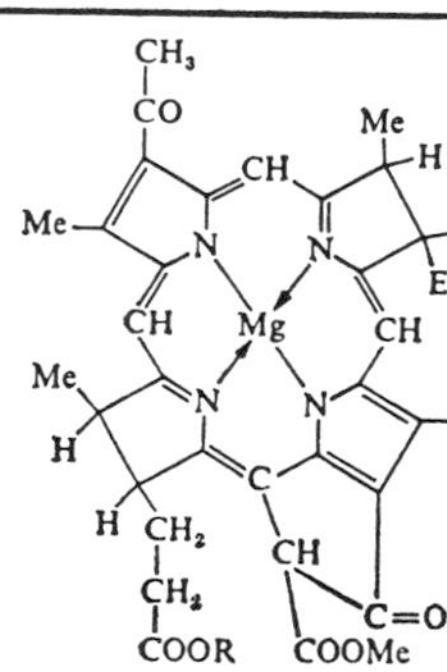 **R = $C_{20}H_{39}$ (phytyl)** $C_{55}H_{74}O_6N_4Mg$	911·5	Eth.: λ_{max}: 773 577 391·5 358·5 (697) (530) ϵ mM: 91·1 20·8 48·1 73·3 (9·1) (2·7) MeOH: λ_{max}: 772 608 .. 365 (685) ϵ mM: 42·0 15·4 .. 53·9 (8·6)
19	Bacterio-phaeophytin (*a*)	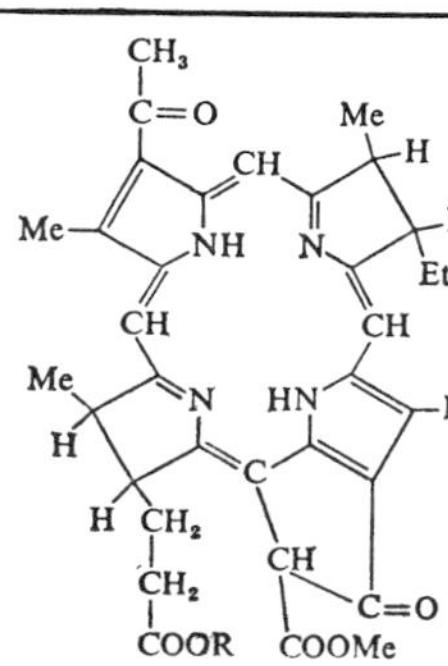 R = $C_{20}H_{39}$ (phytyl) $C_{55}H_{76}O_6N_4$	889·2	Eth.: λ_{max}: 749 680 625 525·5 384 357·5 ϵ mM: 67·5 10·7 3·6 28·3 62·7 113·7 $CHCl_3$: λ_{max}: 757·5 687 630 533 390 363 ϵ mM: 63·5 11·6 3·9 26·2 52·8 99·5
20	Methyl bacterio-chlorophyllide	As bacteriochlorophyll R = Me $C_{36}H_{38}O_6N_4Mg$	647·0	As bacteriochlorophyll
21	Methyl bacterio-phaeophorbide	As bacteriophaeophytin R = Me $C_{36}H_{40}O_6N_4$	624·7	As bacteriophaeophytin

olubility	Occurrence	Preparation	Estimation	General remarks
. MeOH, acet.	Not reported to occur naturally. Formed by acid treatment of chlorophyll *c*	Smith & Benitez, p. 166 *B.J.* **86**, 313 (1963)		Fluorescence max. (eth.) 649, 719. Phase test: yel. → green → brownish-yel. HCl no. ≈ 22.
. EtOH, eth., cet., benz.; . sl. s. pet. eth.	Some red algae	*J.B.C.* **151**, 1 (1943) Smith & Benitez, p. 167	*J.B.C.* **151**, 1 (1943) Smith & Benitez, p. 171	Fluorescence max. (eth.) 696, 752. Phase test: red → brown → green. HCl no. > 22. May exist in several isomeric forms.
. eth., acet., HCl$_3$, benz., et. eth.; . s. MeOH	Not reported to occur naturally; formed from chlorophyll *d* by acid treatment	*See* chlorophyll *d*		Acid treatment of chlorophyll *d* appears to yield a mixture of phaeophytins (*J.B.C.* **151**, 1 (1943)). Fluorescence max. (eth.) 701. Phase test: brown → green → brown. HCl no. > 35.
eth., acet., leOH, benz., yr.; i. pet. eth.	Purple and brown photosynthetic bacteria, some green sulphur bacteria	Smith & Benitez, p. 177 *Am. J. Bot.* **41**, 718 (1954) *Arch. B.B.* **53**, 228 (1954)	*Enzymologia* **5**, 244 (1938) *J. gen. Physiol.* **23**, 483 (1940) Smith & Benitez, p. 182	Phase test: yel. → brown → green. HCl no. ≈ 25. Fluorescence max. (EtOH) 805. More stable when pure than in crude extracts.
eth., acet., HCl$_3$, pyr.; . s. EtOH; pet. eth.	Not reported to occur naturally; formed from bacteriochlorophyll by acid treatment	*See* bacteriochlorophyll	*See* bacteriochlorophyll	Phase test: red-brown. HCl no. > 25.
eth., acet.	Does not occur naturally. Used to characterize bacteriochlorophyll	*Am. J. Bot.* **41**, 718 (1954)		
acet., eth., pyr.; sl. s. MeOH; H$_2$O, pet. eth.	Does not occur naturally. Used to characterize bacteriophaeophytin	*Ann.* **515**, 157 (1935)		HCl no. > 22.

No.	Name	Formula	M. wt.	Absorption spectrum
22	*Chlorobium* chlorophyll (650)	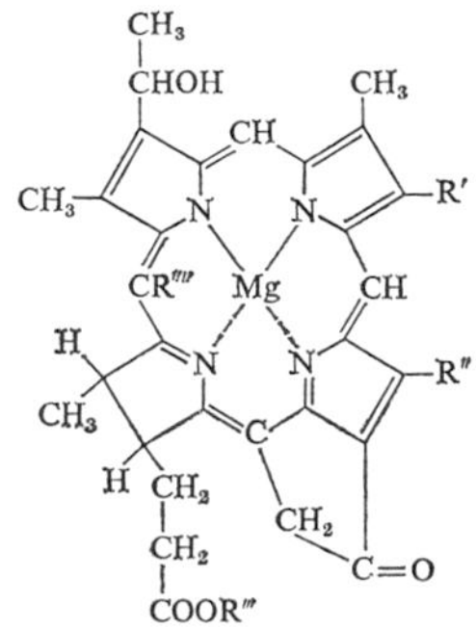 R groups, see General remarks		Eth.: λ_{max}: 650 612 575 530 425 406 ϵ_{sp} (for the unresolved mixture): 113·5 15·8 8·6 3·9 146 87·2 MeOH: λ_{max}: 659 612·5 .. .. 427 411 ϵ_{sp}: 82·3 18·0 .. .. 83·5 76·5 Acet.: λ_{max}: 654 612·5 577·5 530 427 406 ϵ_{sp}: 98·0 16·4 9·2 3·9 125·9 87·9
23	*Chlorobium* phaeophytin (650)	As *Chlorobium* chlorophyll (650), but lacking Mg		Eth.: λ_{max}: 660 605 555 532 503 470 405 Rel. abs. (for unresolved mixture): 49·4 6·6 2·5 9·8 8·9 3·1 100
24	*Chlorobium* phaeophorbides (650)	As *Chlorobium* chlorophyll (650), lacking Mg and with $R''' = H$ *See* Vernon & Seely, p. 112		λ_{max}, as for *Chlorobium* phaeophytin (650)
25	*Chlorobium* chlorophyll (660)	Similar to *Chlorobium* chlorophyll (650) $R'''' = CH_3$ or C_2H_5 Vernon & Seely, p. 112		Eth.: λ_{max}: 660 622 .. .. 432 412 ϵ_{sp}: 112·5 19·7 .. .. 175·5 89·7 MeOH: λ_{max}: 670 620 .. .. 435 419 ϵ_{sp}: 86·0 18·1 .. .. 97·8 86·1 Acet.: λ_{max}: 662·5 625 .. .. 433 413 ϵ_{sp}: 92·6 16·9 .. .. 142·8 88·8
26	Chlorobium phaeophytin (660)	As *Chlorobium* chlorophyll (660), lacking Mg		Eth.: λ_{max}: 665 607 .. 545 514 482 408 Rel. abs. 47·9 5·7 .. 13·3 8·9 3·3 100
27	Magnesium protoporphyrin	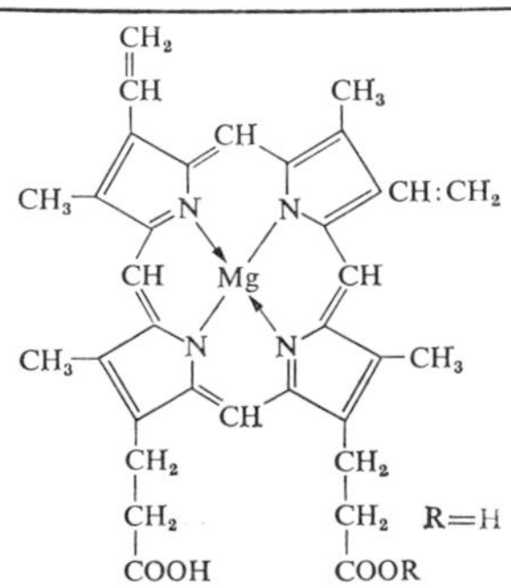 $C_{34}H_{32}O_4N_4Mg$	585·0	Eth.: λ_{max} 589 551 510 419 340 ϵ mM: 18·2 18·2 2·45 308 20·55
28	Magnesium protoporphyrin monomethyl ester	As magnesium protoporphyrin $R = —CH_3$ $C_{35}H_{34}O_4N_4Mg$	599·0	As magnesium protoporphyrin

Solubility	*Occurrence*	*Preparation*	*Estimation*	*General remarks*
s. eth., acet., MeOH; i. pet. eth.	Green sulphur bacteria	*B.B.A.* **41**, 478 (1960)		Negative phase test. Fluorescence max. (eth.) 653. The corresponding phaeophorbides, but not the chlorophylls themselves, have been separated into six components. R′ = C_2H_5, C_3H_7 or *iso*-C_4H_{10}; R″ = CH_3 or C_2H_5; R‴ = *trans-trans*-farnesyl ($C_{15}H_{25}$); R″″ = H. See Vernon & Seely, p. 112; (*Pl. Cell Physiol. Tokyo* **4**, 49 (1963)).
s. eth.	Not reported to occur naturally. Formed by acid treatment of *Chlorobium* chlorophyll (650)	*B.B.A.* **41**, 478 (1960)		Negative phase test.
s. eth.	Used in characterization of *Chlorobium* chlorophyll (650)	*Can. J. Chem.* **40**, 171 (1962)		Negative phase test. The mixture is extracted into 14% HCl. Six phaeophorbides have been separated with R′ = $CH_2{\cdot}CH(CH_3)_2$, C_3H_7 or C_2H_5 and R″ = C_2H_5 or CH_3
. eth., acet., MeOH; . pet. eth.	Green sulphur bacteria	*B.B.A.* **41**, 478 (1960)		Negative phase test. There is a series of 6 related pigments, as in the *Chlorobium* chlorophylls (650). Fluorescence max. (eth.) 663.
eth.	Formed by acid treatment of *Chlorobium* chlorophyll (660)	*B.B.A.* **41**, 478 (1960)		Negative phase test.
eth., dioxan, r.	Mutants of *Chlorella*	*J.B.C.* **175**, 333 (1948)		Possibly an intermediate in chlorophyll biosynthesis.
th., acet., xan, pyr.	Etiolated barley leaves, medium of *Rhodopseudomonas* spp.	*J.B.C.* **236**, 1168 (1961) *B.J.* **86**, 429 (1963)		The location of methyl ester on propionic acid at C_7 is not certain. Possibly an intermediate in chlorophyll biosynthesis.

14. Carotenoids

Revised by V. H. BOOTH (*Dunn Nutritional Laboratory, Cambridge*)

A selection of the most commonly occurring carotenoids is given here. More detailed information about these and the rarer members of the group can be obtained from the references in the table; and from the following books and reviews.

L. Zechmeister, '*Cis-trans* isomerization and stereochemistry of carotenoids and diphenylpolyenes', *Chem. Rev.* **34**, 267 (1944).

P. Karrer and E. Jucker, *Carotenoids* (trans. E. A. Braude), Elsevier, Amsterdam (1950).

T. W. Goodwin, *The Comparative Biochemistry of the Carotenoids*, Chapman and Hall, London (1952).

D. L. Fox, *Animal Biochromes and Structural Colours*, Cambridge University Press (1953).

T. W. Goodwin, *Moderne Methoden der Pflanzenanalyse*, eds. Paech & Tracey, vol. 3, p. 272, Springer-Verlag, Berlin (1955).

V. H. Booth, *Carotene, its Determination in Biological Materials*, Heffer, Cambridge (1957).

V. H. Booth, 'Mapping plant lipids by paper chromatography', *Chromatog. Rev.* **7**, 98 (1965).

A. Jensen, *Carotenoids of Norwegian Brown Seaweeds and of Seaweed Meals*, Norwegian Institute of Seaweed Research, Trondheim (1967).

The order of the carotenoids given in the table is approximately that of the sequence on chromatograms, the least strongly adsorbed members being at the beginning. Most carotenoids are soluble in acetone, benzene, and CS_2 but insoluble in water. Those at the top of the table are more soluble in hexane and other hydrocarbons, less soluble in alcohols, while those with hydroxyl groups and further down in the table are more soluble in alcohols.

The formula for β-carotene, No. 4, is

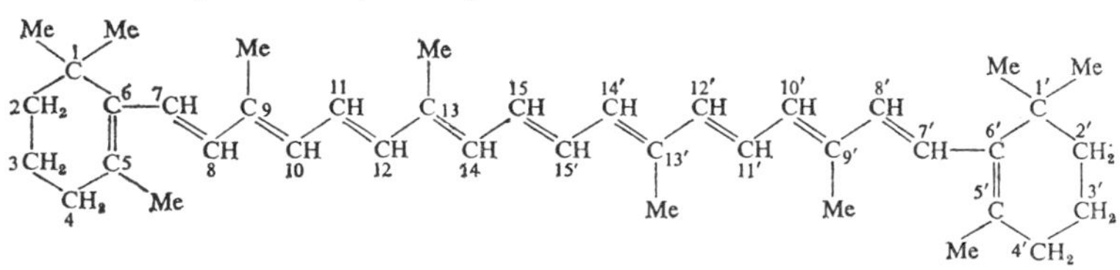

Since all carotenoids are related to β-carotene, only condensed formulae are shown in the table.

Nomenclature

Tentative rules for the nomenclature of carotenoids are given in *B.J.* **127**, 741 (1972); *Eur. J. Biochem.* **25**, 397 (1972).

14. Carotenoids

No.	Name	Formula	M. wt.	Spectral absorption maxima (mμ)				Physical form
1	Phytoene	7,8,11,12,12′,11′,8′,7′-Octahydrolycopene $C_{40}H_{64}$	545·0	Hexane	298	286	275	Colourless viscous oil
2	Phytofluene	7,8,12′,11′,8′,7′-Hexahydro-lycopene $C_{40}H_{62}$	542·9	Pet. eth. E, 1%, 1 cm	367–8	348 1350 (*cis*) 1540 (all-*trans*)	332	Colourless fluores-cent oil
3	α-Carotene	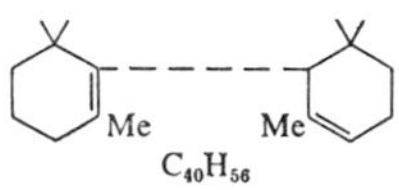 $C_{40}H_{56}$	536·9	Hexane E, 1%, 1 cm CS_2 E, 1%, 1 cm	475 509	445 2710 477 2180	420	Violet prisms and clusters from benz.-MeOH
4	β-Carotene (carotin)	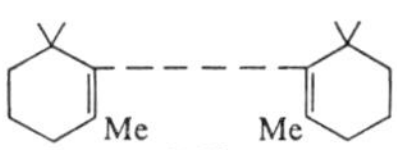 $C_{40}H_{56}$	536·9	Hexane E, 1%, 1 cm CS_2 E, 1%, 1 cm	482 520	451 2550 485 1940	425 450	Dark violet hexa-gonal prisms from benz.-MeOH
5	δ-Carotene	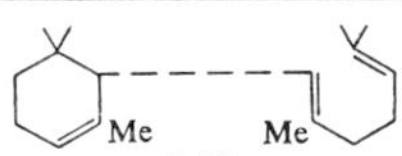 $C_{40}H_{56}$	536·9	Hexane	486	456	430	Long red needles from CS_2-hexane-EtOH
6	γ-Carotene	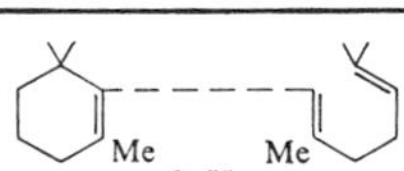 $C_{40}H_{56}$	536·9	Pet. eth. E, 1%, 1 cm CS_2	495 533·5	462 2720 496	431 463	Dark red prisms from benz.-MeOH
7	Helenien	Lutein dipalmitate $C_{72}H_{116}O_4$	1045·7	Hexane	475	455	420	Red needles from EtOH
8	Physalien	Zeaxanthin dipalmitate $C_{72}H_{116}O_4$	1045·7	Hexane	482	451	425	Red needles from benz.-MeOH
9	Lycopene	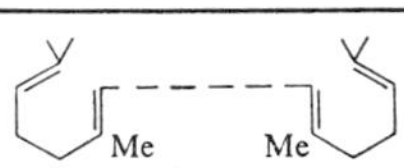 $C_{40}H_{56}$	536·9	Hexane E, 1%, 1 cm CS_2	506 547	474 3470 507	446 477	Long red needles from CS_2-EtOH
10	α-Carotene-5,6-epoxide	$C_{40}H_{56}O$	552·9	Hexane	471	442		Thin reddish-yello plates
11	Mutato-chrome (citroxan-thin)	β-Carotene-5,8-epoxide $C_{40}H_{56}O$	552·9	Pet. eth. CS_2	456 489·5	427 459		Yellow-orange lea lets from benz.-MeOH
12	Rhodoxan-thin	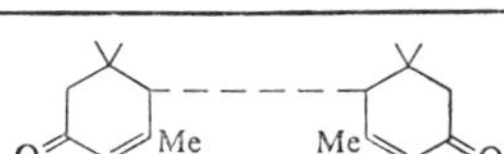 $C_{40}H_{50}O_2$	562·8	Hexane E, 1%, 1 cm CS_2	524 564	489 1900 525	458 491	Rosettes of dark violet needles from benz.-MeOH
13	α-Crypto-xanthin	3′-Hydroxy-α-carotene $C_{40}H_{56}O$	552·9	Hexane Benz.	475 488	446 457	421 433	
14	β-Crypto-xanthin (cryptoxan-thol)	3-Hydroxy-β-carotene $C_{40}H_{56}O$	552·9	Hexane E, 1%, 1 cm CS_2 E, 1%, 1 cm	483 518	451 2460 483 2040	425 453	Prisms from benz. MeOH
15	Spirilloxan-thin (rhodo-violascin)	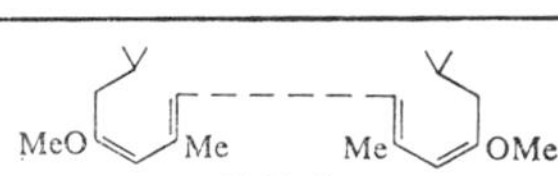 $C_{42}H_{60}O_2$	596·9	Benz. E, 1% ,1 cm CS_2 E, 1%, 1 cm	548 573·5	511 2470 534 1965	482 496·5	Deep red, spindle-shaped crystals fr benz.

M.p.	Occurrence	References	Remarks
	Small quantities in many leaves and fruits	*B.J.* **50**, 550 (1952) *Arch. B.B.* **44**, 159 (1953) *Arch. B.B.* **48**, 267 (1954)	Autoxidizes rapidly when pure. Optically inactive.
	Small amounts in many green plant tissues, fruits, and some flowers	*Arch. B.B.* **36**, 468 (1952) *Arch. B.B.* **46**, 100 (1953) *Arch. B.B.* **47**, 160 (1953) *Proc. chem. Soc.* **1961**, 261	*Cis*-form from tomatoes readily isomerizes to the more stable all-*trans*-form when illuminated. With $SbCl_3$ in $CHCl_3$ gives transient blue colour changing to purple.
187–8	Leaf and root of *Daucus carota*. Fruit of red palm. Often reported in other materials without distinction from geometric isomers of β-carotene	*Helv. chim. Acta* **16**, 641 (1933) *J.B.C.* **105**, 523 (1934) *J. Sci. Fd Agric.* **7**, 386 (1956)	$[\alpha]_{Cd}$ +385 (in benz.). With $SbCl_3$ in $CHCl_3$ gives blue colour absorbing maximally at 542 mμ. Half the vitamin activity of β-carotene.
183	Major carotenoid in green plant tissues and brown seaweeds. Widely distributed in plants and animals. Exceptionally concentrated in flower of *Narcissus*	*Z.P.C.* **64**, 47 (1910) *J.B.C.* **105**, 523 (1934) *J. Ass. off. agric. Chem.* **35**, 738 (1952) *Analyst* **77**, 171 (1952) *Meth. biochem. Anal.* **4**, 1 (1957)	Optically inactive. Vitamin A active. With $SbCl_3$ in $CHCl_3$ gives blue colour (λ_{max} 590 mμ).
140·5	Fruits of *Lycopersicum esculentum*	*Arch. B.B.* **88**, 59 (1960) *J.C.S.* **1965**, 2019	[α] +317 (in CS_2, using Corning filters nos. 242 and 244).
31–78	Leaf of *Cuscuta salina*, and of *Juniperis virginiana* infected with fungus. Some fruits and flowers. Many fungi. Major carotenoid in *Chlorobium* sp.	*Ber.* **66**, 407 (1933) *Proc. R. Soc.* **B128**, 275 (1940) *Science* **113**, 296 (1951)	Variations in M.p. from natural sources ascribed to different proportions of all-*trans*-γ-carotene and pro-γ-carotene.
2	Many flowers especially *Helenium autumnale*	*Z.P.C.* **197**, 147 (1931) *Ann.* **616**, 207 (1958)	
9·5	Fruit of *Physalis* sp., etc.	*Ber.* **63**, 1489 (1930) *Helv. chim. Acta* **12**, 499 (1949)	Almost insoluble in EtOH.
75	Major pigment in fruit of *Lycopersicum esculentum*, *Rosa canina*, and others	*Ber.* **65**, 1880 (1932) *Cereal Chem.* **15**, 310 (1938) *B.J.* **38**, 279 (1944) *Biochem. Preps.* **1**, 57 (1950)	Isomeric with β-carotene, but has no vitamin A activity.
75	Blossoms of *Ranunculus acer* and others	*Helv. chim. Acta* **28**, 471 (1945)	
53–4	Orange peel and numerous fruits	*Helv. chim. Acta* **27**, 1695 (1944) *Helv. chim. Acta* **28**, 427 (1945)	Unstable pale blue colour with conc. HCl.
9	Fruit of *Taxus baccata*. Leaves of many gymnosperms	*Ber.* **66**, 828 (1933)	Colours both layers in partition test. Red-violet colour with 25% HCl. Intense blue-violet colour with $SbCl_3$ in $CHCl_3$. Dioxime, M.p. 227–8.
	Capsicum annuum	*Ann.* **616**, 207 (1958)	$[\alpha]_C$ +360 (in benz.). Epiphasic with 90% MeOH, hypophasic with 95% MeOH.
9	Seed of *Zea mais*, fruit of *Physalis* sp., and small quantities in other fruits, some green tissues and a few flowers. Also eggs, butter, and blood	*Ber.* **66**, 1746 (1933)	When prefix omitted, β-form is understood. Half the vitamin A activity of β-carotene. Occurs esterified. Phase test as for α-cryptoxanthin. Dark blue colour (λ_{max} 590 mμ) with $SbCl_3$ in $CHCl_3$. Monoacetyl deriv., M.p. 117–18.
8	Major carotenoid of red and purple photosynthetic bacteria. Some fungi, e.g. *Neurospora crassa*	*Helv. chim. Acta* **18**, 1306 (1935) *Helv. chim. Acta* **19**, 3, 1019 (1936)	Blue colour (λ_{max} 642 mμ) with $SbCl_3$ in $CHCl_3$.

No.	Name	Formula	M. wt.	Spectral absorption maxima (mμ)				Physical form
16	Lutein (luteol, xanthophyll)	3,3′-Dihydroxy-α-carotene $C_{40}H_{56}O_2$	568·9	Hexane CS$_2$ E, 1%, 1 cm MeOH	477 508 474	447 475 2160 444	420 445 418	Violet prisms+ 1 MeOH from MeOH
17	Zeaxanthin (zeaxanthol)	3,3′-Dihydroxy-β-carotene $C_{40}H_{56}O_2$	568·9	Hexane E, 1%, 1 cm CS$_2$ E, 1%, 1 cm	483 517 	451 2480 482 2230	423 450 	Yellow plates from MeOH
18	Lutein epoxide (eloxanthin)	Lutein-5,6-epoxide $C_{40}H_{56}O_3$	584·9	Pet. eth. CS$_2$	471 501·5	442 472		Reddish-yellow crys tals from benz.-MeOH
19	Flavoxan-thin	5,8-Epoxylutein $C_{40}H_{56}O_3$	584·9	Hexane CS$_2$	450 479	421 449		Golden, clustered prisms from MeOH
20	Eschscholtz-xanthin	$C_{40}H_{54}O_2$	566·9	Pet. eth. CS$_2$	502 536	472 502	446 475	Purple-red crystals from ethyl acetate
21	Anthera-xanthin	5,6-Epoxyzeaxanthin $C_{40}H_{56}O_3$	584·9	CS$_2$ CHCl$_3$	510 490·5	478 460·5		Needles from benz.-MeOH; yellow leaf-lets from EtOH
22	Taraxanthin	$C_{40}H_{56}O_4$	600·9	Hexane EtOH CS$_2$	471 471 501	442 442 469	420 420 441	Ochre-yellow prism from MeOH
23	Violaxan-thin	5,6,5′,6′-Diepoxyzeaxanthin $C_{40}H_{56}O_4$	600·9	Hexane CS$_2$	472 501	443 470	417·5 440	Yellow-orange prisms from MeOH
24	Auroxan-thin	5,8,5′,8′-Diepoxyzeaxanthin $C_{40}H_{56}O_4$	600·9	EtOH E, 1%, 1 cm CS$_2$	428 454	403 1850 423	382 	Yellow needles from MeOH
25	Astacene (astacin)	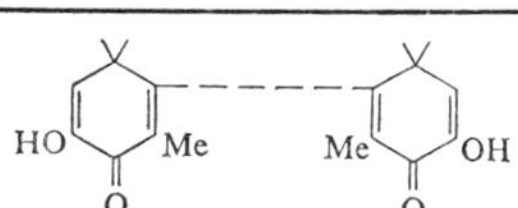 $C_{40}H_{48}O_4$	592·8	CS$_2$	500			Violet needles from pyr.-H$_2$O
26	Astaxanthin	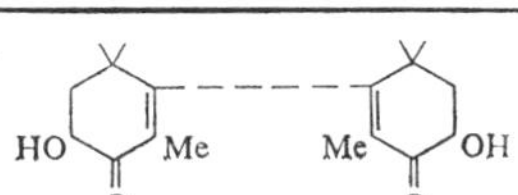 $C_{40}H_{52}O_4$	596·9	CS$_2$ Pyr.	502 513	 493	 476	Violet plates from pyr.
27	Bixin	$C_{25}H_{30}O_4$	394·5					
28	Crocetin (*trans*) (gardenin)	Polyene dicarboxylic acid $C_{20}H_{24}O_4$	328·4	Hexane CS$_2$	445 482	420 453	400 426	Brick-red rhombs from acetic anhy-dride
29	Capsanthin	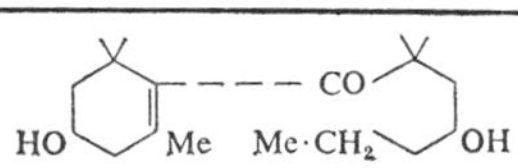 $C_{40}H_{58}O_3$	586·9	Pet. eth. E, 1%, 1 cm CS$_2$	504 542	474·5 1905 503	462 	Deep red prisms from MeOH; needl from pet. eth.

M.p.	Occurrence	References	Remarks
193	Major carotenol (xanthophyll) of green plant tissues. Extensively distributed in fruits, seeds, flowers. In eggs and many animal fats	*Z.P.C.* **197**, 141 (1931) *Helv. chim. Acta* **14**, 614 (1931) *J.A.C.S.* **65**, 1951 (1943)	$[\alpha]_{Cd}$+160 ($CHCl_3$). No vitamin A activity. Intense dark blue colour with $SbCl_3$ in $CHCl_3$. Green colour in conc. H_2SO_4 turning blue. Diacetyl deriv., M.p. 170. See helenien, No. 7.
215·5	Fruit seeds, and some flowers. Traces in green leaves, egg yolk	*Helv. chim. Acta* **13**, 268 (1930) *Helv. chim. Acta* **18**, 477 (1935) *Ber.* **72**, 1678 (1939)	$[\alpha]_D$ −40 to −45·2 ($CHCl_3$). Diacetyl deriv., M.p. 154–5. *See* physalien, No. 8.
192	Flowers and leaves	*Helv. chim. Acta* **28**, 300 (1945)	Very unstable towards acids, even in traces, being converted to flavoxanthin and chrysanthemaxanthin. Diacetyl deriv., M.p. 184–5.
184	Flower of *Ranunculus acer*, *Taraxacum officinale*, and a few others. Small quantities in green tissues and some fruits	*Z.P.C.* **213**, 192 (1932) *Helv. chim. Acta* **25**, 1144 (1942) *Helv. chim. Acta* **28**, 300 (1945)	Isomer of chrysanthemaxanthin. May be formed from lutein epoxide during extraction. $[\alpha]_C^{20}$ +190 (in benz.). Unstable blue colour with conc. HCl. Blue colour with $SbCl_3$ in $CHCl_3$. Diacetyl deriv., M.p. 157.
186	Flower of *Eschscholtzia californica*	*J. org. Chem.* **26**, 5061 (1961)	$[\alpha]_{6678}$ +225 ($CHCl_3$).
206	Anther of *Lilium* sp.	*Helv. chim. Acta* **18**, 1303 (1935) *Helv. chim. Acta* **28**, 300 (1945)	Similar to petaloxanthin. With $SbCl_3$ in $CHCl_3$ gives blue colour (λ_{max} 587 mμ). With conc. HCl slowly gives fairly stable blue colour. *cis*-Isomer, M.p. 110, isolated from *Lilium candidum* F.
184	Flower of *Taraxacum officinale* and others	*Arch. B.B.* **48**, 458 (1954) *Phytochem.* **3**, 229 (1964)	$[\alpha]_{6435}$ +200 (in ethyl acetate). Isomeric with violaxanthin. Found mainly as diester, taraxien, with some monoester.
200 (208)	Flower of *Viola tricolor* and many others. A few fruits. Important carotenol of green leaves	*Ber.* **64**, 326 (1931) *Helv. chim. Acta* **28**, 300 (1945) *Arch. B.B.* **48**, 458 (1954)	$[\alpha]_{Cd}$ +35 (in $CHCl_3$). Very unstable to acids. Soln. in conc. H_2SO_4 is indigo blue, in gl. acetic acid is green. Deep blue with $SbCl_3$ in $CHCl_3$. Dibenzoyl deriv., M.p. 217.
203	Flower of *Viola tricolor*	*Helv. chim. Acta* **25**, 1624 (1942) *Helv. chim. Acta* **28**, 300 (1945) *Arch. B.B.* **48**, 458 (1954)	Formed when violaxanthin is treated with dil. HCl. Very stable blue colour with 15% HCl.
240–3	Many animal tissues especially Crustacea shells, sometimes with astaxanthin	*Ber.* **66**, 488 (1933) *Ber.* **72**, 1688 (1939)	Found esterified (astacein) in shells of lobster. and crabs. Astacin is formed from ovoverdin, the astaxanthin-protein complex; thus some reported isolations of astacin may be in error. Optically inactive. Blue-green colour with $SbCl_3$ in $CHCl_3$. Diacetyl deriv., M.p. 235 d.; dipalmityl, M.p. 121.
215–16 d.	Characteristic carotenoid of many animal tissues, especially crustaceans. Some green algae, incl. *Haematococcus pluvialis*	*Ber.* **71**, 1879 (1938) *Ber.* **72**, 1688 (1939)	Occurs in chromoproteins, e.g. ovoverdin from lobsters, from which it is released by acids, organic solvents, and heat. In absence of air gives blue colour with alkalis. Optically inactive. Diacetyl deriv., M.p. 203–5; dipalmityl, M.p. 71·5–72·5.
cis, 196 *trans*, 220	Seed of *Bixa orellana*	*Helv. chim. Acta* **15**, 1218, 1399 (1932)	Formerly used for colouring foods. Naturally-occurring form is the labile *cis* isomer.
285	Flower of *Crocus sativus*, fruit of *Gardenia*, and various blossoms (as glycosides). *Cis*- and *trans*-isomers found as glycosides in saffron	*Helv. chim. Acta* **10**, 397 (1927) *Helv. chim. Acta* **13**, 392 (1930)	Occurs in stable *trans*-form (I- or α-crocetin) and a labile *cis*-form (II- or β-crocetin); *cis*-form converted to *trans*-form on heating or by catalysis with I_2 in pet. eth. No colour with conc. HCl. Stable dimethyl ester, M.p. 222·5.
175–6	Ripe fruit of *Capsicum* sp.; anthers of *Lilium tigrinum*	*Ann.* **454**, 54 (1927) *Ann.* **509**, 269 (1934)	$[\alpha]_{Cd}$ +36 ($CHCl_3$). With conc. HCl gives no colour, but deep blue colour with conc. H_2SO_4 and with $SbCl_3$ in $CHCl_3$. Also occurs esterified. Diacetyl deriv., M.p. 146·5; dibenzoyl, M.p. 121–2; dipalmityl, M.p. 95; distearyl, M.p. 84.

No.	*Name*	*Formula*	*M. wt.*	*Spectral absorption maxima* (mμ)				*Physical form*
30	Capsorubin	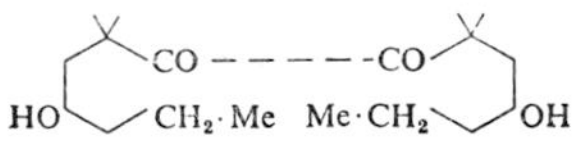 $C_{40}H_{60}O_4$	604·9	Pet. eth.	506	474	444	Violet-red needles from benz.-pet. eth.
				CS_2	541·5	503	468	
31	Fucoxanthin	5,5′-Dihydroxy-capsorubin(?) $C_{40}H_{56}O_6$(?)	632·9 (?)	Hexane	469	451	438	Brown-red prisms+3 MeOH from MeOH; needles from ether-pet. eth.
				E, 1%, 1 cm		760		
				CS_2	510	477	445	

M.p.	*Occurrence*	*References*	*Remarks*
201	Fruit of *Capsicum annuum*	*Ann.* **509**, 269 (1934) *Ann.* **516**, 30 (1935)	Violet colour, becoming deep blue, with conc. HCl. Diacetyl deriv., M.p. 179.
166–8	Characteristic carotenoid of Phaeophyceae, Chrysophyceae and diatoms	*Helv. chim. Acta* **14**, 614 (1931) *B.J.* **29**, 1369 (1935)	With conc. H_2SO_4 gives deep blue colour. Hydrochloride, $C_{40}H_{56}O_6 \cdot 4HCl$, M.p. 215. Pure compound optically inactive in benz. (also given as $[\alpha]_D^{18}$ $+72\pm9$ ($CHCl_3$)). Deep blue colour with 25% HCl.

15. Antimetabolites, Antibacterial Agents, and Enzyme Inhibitors

A. AMINO ACID ANALOGUES

By M. H. RICHMOND (*Department of Molecular Biology, University of Edinburgh*)

General references

1. D. W. Woolley, *A Study of Antimetabolites*, Wiley, New York (1952).
2. K. Dittmer, 'The structural bases of some amino acid antagonists and their microbiological properties', *Ann. N.Y. Acad. Sci.* **52,** 1274 (1950).
3. M. H. Richmond, 'The effect of amino acid analogues on growth and protein synthesis in microorganisms', *Bact. Rev.* **26,** 398 (1962).
4. W. Shive and C. G. Skinner, 'Amino acid analogues', *Metabolic Inhibitors,* eds. R. M. Hochster and J. H. Quastel, vol. 1, p. 1, Academic Press, New York (1963).

15. Antimetabolites, Antibacterial Agents, and Enzyme Inhibitors

No.	Name	Synonyms	Formula	M. wt.	Physical form
1	Allylglycine	2-Amino-4-pentenoic acid	$CH_2{=}CH \cdot CH_2 \cdot CH(NH_2) \cdot COOH$	115·1	col. cryst.
2	α-Amino-β-chloro-butyric acid		$CH_3 \cdot CH(Cl) \cdot CH(NH_2) \cdot COOH$	137·6	col. cryst.
3	3-(Aminomethyl)-cyclohexane glycine		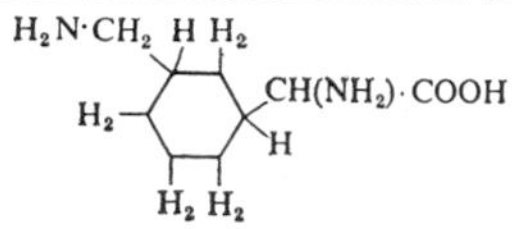	186·3	col. hygroscopic cryst.
4	*S*-(2-Aminoethyl)-cysteine		$NH_2 \cdot CH_2 \cdot CH_2 \cdot S \cdot CH_2 \cdot CH(NH_2) \cdot COOH$	164·2	col. cryst.
5	*p*-Aminophenyl-alanine		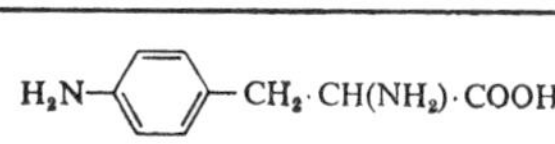	180·2	col. cryst. darkening in light
	Azaserine, *see* 15. D, Antibiotics				
6	7-Azatryptophan	α-Amino-β-(7-aza-3-indolyl)-propionic acid	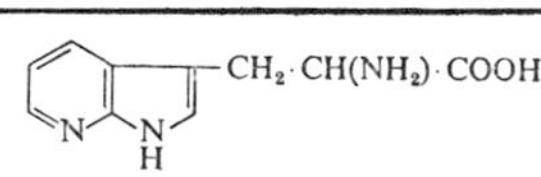	205·2; Hydrate, 223·2	fluffy needles
7	Azetidine-2-carboxylic acid		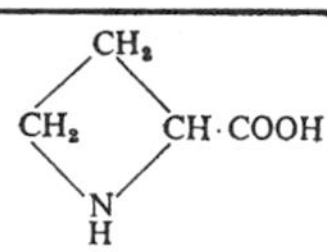	101·1	col. cryst.
8	β-(2-Benzothienyl)-α-aminopropionic acid	β-3-Thianaphthenylalanine	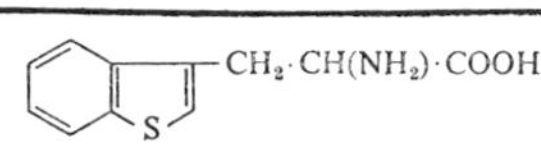	221·3	col. cryst.
9	Canavanine	α-Amino-γ-guanidioxy-*n*-butyric acid	$(HN)(H_2N){>}C \cdot NH \cdot O \cdot CH_2 \cdot CH_2 \cdot CH(NH_2) \cdot COOH$	176·2	col. cryst.
10	1-Cyclohexene-1-alanine		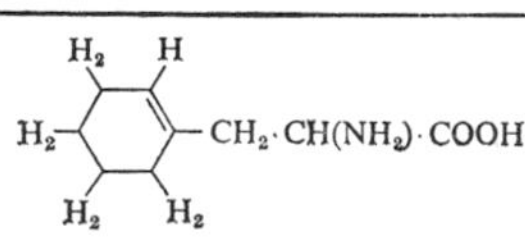	169·2	col. cryst.
11	3-Cyclohexene-1-alanine		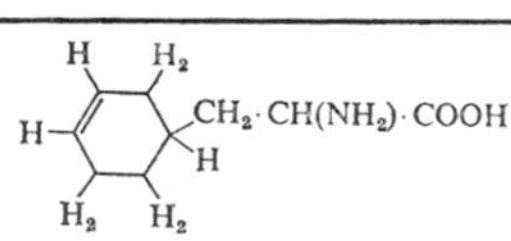	169·2	col. cryst.

M.p.	*Solubility*	*References*	*Use*	*General remarks*
255 d. (164 as HCl)	s. H_2O	SYN. *Ber.* **41**, 338 (1908) *J.A.C.S.* **70**, 3310 (1948) PROPERTIES *Ann. N.Y. Acad. Sci.* **52**, 1274 (1950)	Cysteine analogue	Inhibitory to growth of *E. coli*; reversal by cysteine not tested.
246 d.	sl. s. H_2O; s. acids	SYN. *J.B.C.* **234**, 2091 (1959) USE *J.B.C.* **236**, 1735 (1961)	Valine analogue	Inhibits valine incorporation into haemoglobin. Competitive inhibition of valine activating enzyme.
200–5 d. (as di-HCl salt)	s. H_2O	SYN. and USE *Arch. B. B.* **87**, 88 (1960)	Lysine analogue	Growth inhibitor of *L. dextranicum*; reversed by L-lysine.
192 d. (as HCl)	s. H_2O	SYN. *Experientia* **11**, 61 (1955) USE *P.S.E.B.M.* **100**, 222 (1959)	Lysine analogue	Potent competitive inhibitor of lysine incorporation into bone marrow cells.
245–50 d.	v. sl. s. H_2O; s. acids	SYN. *Ann.* **219**, 219 (1883) *J.A.C.S.* **74**, 4947 (1952) USE *B.J.* **54**, 1 (1953)	Tyrosine analogue	Inhibitory to growth of *E. coli*—reversed by tyrosine but not phenylalanine. May be incorporated at low levels into *E. coli* protein.
Hydrate, 257–9 d.	v. sl. s. H_2O; sl. s. acids	SYN. *J.A.C.S.* **77**, 457 (1955) USE *B.B.A.* **27**, 330 (1958)	Tryptophan analogue	Inhibits phage multiplication in *E. coli.* Incorporated into bacterial protein and into phage coat protein. Can be activated by pancreatic tryptophan activating enzyme.
Darkens above 200 d.	v.s. H_2O	SYN. *B.J.* **64**, 323 (1956) USE *B.B.A.* **71**, 459 (1963)	Proline analogue	Can replace proline in protein of *E. coli* and mung-bean (*Phaseolus aureus*).
248 d. (279–80)	v. sl. s. H_2O	SYN. *J.C.S.* **1949**, 1374 *J.A.C.S.* **70**, 3075 (1948)	Tryptophan antagonist	Growth inhibitor of *Str. haemolyticus*; reversed by tryptophan.
184 d.	v.s. H_2O	SYN. *J. Biochem., Tokyo* **23**, 181 (1936) ISOL. *B.J.* **59**, 221 (1955) USE *B.J.* **73**, 261 (1959)	Arginine analogue	Growth inhibitory to some strains of *S. aureus* and *E. coli.* May be incorporated into protein of Walker sarcocarcinoma and *S. aureus*. Acts as substrate to most enzymes normally acting on arginine. pK_a: 1. 7·40 (guanidinoxy-), 2. 9·25 (—COOH), 3. 11·50 (α—NH_2).
227 d.	sl. s. H_2O; s. acids	SYN. and USE *J.A.C.S.* **79**, 5209 (1957)	Phenylalanine antagonist	Growth inhibition of *L. dextranicum*; reversed by phenylalanine. No reversal by leucine.
258 d.	sl. s. H_2O; s. acids	SYN. and PROPERTIES *Arch. B. B.* **80**, 416 (1959)	Leucine antagonist	Growth inhibition of *L. dextranicum*; reversed by leucine but not by phenylalanine.

15. Antimetabolites, Antibacterial Agents, and Enzyme Inhibitors

No.	Name	Synonyms	Formula	M. wt.	Physical form
12	2-Cyclohexene-1-glycine		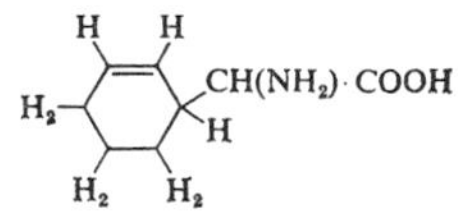	155·2	col. cryst.
13	3-Cyclohexene-1-glycine		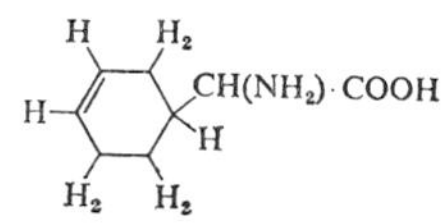	155·2	col. cryst.
14	β-(Cyclopentane)-alanine		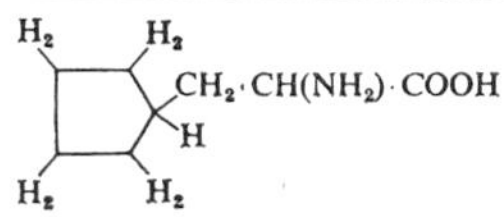	157·2	col. cryst.
15	β-(1-Cyclopentene)-1-alanine		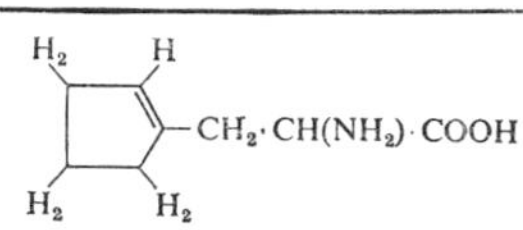	155·2	col. cryst.
	Diazooxonorleucine, *see* 15. D, Antibiotics				
16	Ethionine	*S*-Ethylhomocysteine	$CH_3\cdot CH_2\cdot S\cdot CH_2\cdot CH_2\cdot CH(NH_2)\cdot COOH$	163·2	col. plates
17	α-Fluoro-β-alanine		$NH_2\cdot CH_2\cdot CH(F)\cdot COOH$	107·1	col. cryst.
18	2-Fluorophenylalanine		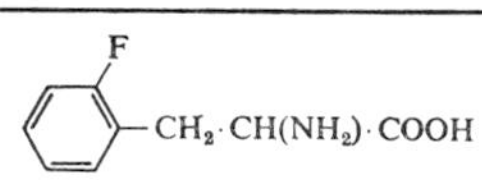	183·1	col. cryst.
19	3-Fluorophenylalanine		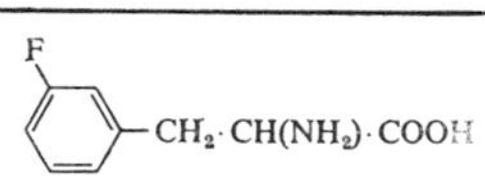	183·1	col. cryst.
20	4-Fluorophenylalanine		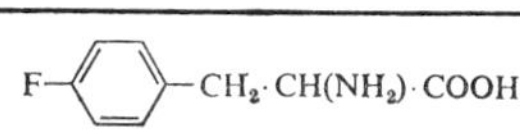	183·1	col. cryst.
21	5-Fluorotryptophan		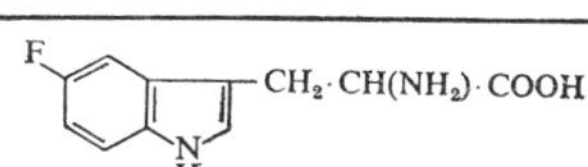	222·2	col. cryst.
22	6-Fluorotryptophan		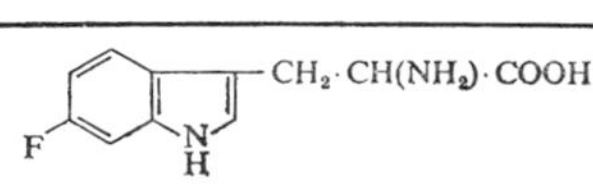	222·2	col. cryst.

M.p.	*Solubility*	*References*	*Use*	*General remarks*
290–3 d.	sl. s. H_2O; s. acids	SYN. and USE *J.A.C.S.* **79**, 5209 (1957)	Isoleucine antagonist	Growth inhibitory for *E. coli*; reversed by isoleucine.
312 d.	sl. s. H_2O	SYN. and USE *J.A.C.S.* **80**, 2698 (1958)	Isoleucine antagonist	Growth inhibitory for *E. coli*; reversed by isoleucine.
245 d.	sl. s. H_2O; s. acids	SYN. and USE *J.A.C.S.* **78**, 5116 (1956)	Leucine analogue	Growth inhibition of *S. lactis* and *L. dextranicum*; reversed by leucine but not phenylalanine.
245 d.	sl. s. H_2O; s. acids	SYN. and USE *J.A.C.S.* **78**, 5116 (1956)	Phenylalanine antagonist	Growth inhibition of *L. dextranicum* reversed by phenylalanine.
272 d.	s. H_2O	SYN. *J.B.C.* **124**, 519 (1938) USE *B.B.A.* **34**, 158 (1959)	Methionine analogue	Growth inhibitory to *E. coli*; effect reversed by methionine. May be incorporated into protein of mammals and bacteria in place of methionine. Activated by methionine activating enzymes.
190–5 d. (as HCl)	s. H_2O	SYN. and PROPERTIES *J.C.S.* **1961**, 4669	β-Alanine analogue	Structural analogue of β-alanine; potential inhibitor of CoA synthesis.
244–8 d.	sl. s. H_2O, dil. acids and alkalis	SYN. *J.A.C.S.* **72**, 1800 (1950) PROPERTIES *C.r. hebd. Séanc. Acad. Sci., Paris* **248**, 1870 (1959)	Phenylalanine analogue	May be incorporated into protein of *E. coli* in place of phenylalanine.
240–2 d.	sl. s. H_2O, dil. acids and alkalis	SYN. *J.A.C.S.* **72**, 1800 (1950) PROPERTIES *C.r. hebd. Séanc. Acad. Sci., Paris* **248**, 1870 (1959)	Phenylalanine analogue	Growth inhibitory to bacteria; reversed by phenylalanine.
259–61 d. (238–42)	*ca.* 10 mg./ml. H_2O; s. acids, alkalis	SYN. *J.A.C.S.* **72**, 1800 (1950); **74**, 4947 (1952) USE *B.B.A.* **31**, 347; **31**, 378 (1959) *J. molec. Biol.* **6**, 284 (1963)	Phenylalanine analogue	Growth inhibitor of *E. coli*. May be incorporated into cell protein in place of phenylalanine. Phenylalanine replaced randomly during biosynthesis of phosphatase by *E. coli*.
264–5 d.	v. sl. s. H_2O; s. acids, alkalis	SYN. *J.A.C.S.* **72**, 2296 (1950) PROPERTIES *Bull. Res. Coun. Israel* **2**, 308 (1952) *Jaarb. K. ned. Akad. Wet. Ser. C.* **57**, 8 (1954)	Tryptophan analogue	Probably inhibits same reaction as 6-fluorotryptophan (q.v.). Can be activated by pancreatic tryptophan activating enzyme.
	v. sl. s. H_2O; s. acids, alkalis	PROPERTIES *Bull. Res. Coun. Israel, Sect. A.* **10**, 1 (1961)	Tryptophan analogue	Inhibits synthesis of *N-o*-carboxyphenyl-D-ribosylamine-1-phosphate from anthranilic acid and phosphoribosepyrophosphate in tryptophan biosynthetic pathway. Can be activated by pancreatic tryptophan activating enzyme.

15. Antimetabolites, Antibacterial Agents, and Enzyme Inhibitors

No.	*Name*	*Synonyms*	*Formula*	*M. wt.*	*Physical form*
23	3-Fluorotyrosine		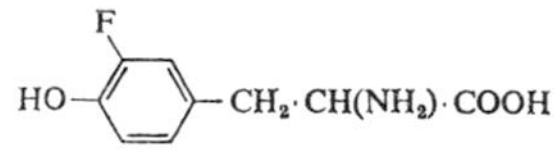	199·2	col. cryst.
24	Glutamic acid hydrazide	γ-Glutamylhydrazine	$H_2N\cdot NH\cdot CO\cdot CH_2\cdot CH_2\cdot CH(NH_2)\cdot COOH$	161·2	
25	Homoarginine	α-Amino-ε-guanidino-*n*-hexanoic acid	$\begin{matrix}HN\\H_2N\end{matrix}\!>C\cdot NH\cdot (CH_2)_4\cdot CH(NH_2)\cdot COOH$	188·2	col. needles
26	β-Methallylglycine	2-Amino-4-methyl-4-pentenoic acid	$\begin{matrix}H_3C\\H_2C\end{matrix}\!>C\cdot CH_2\cdot CH(NH_2)\cdot COOH$	129·2	col. cryst.
27	Methionine-sulphoximine	3-Amino-3-carboxypropylmethyl-sulphoximine	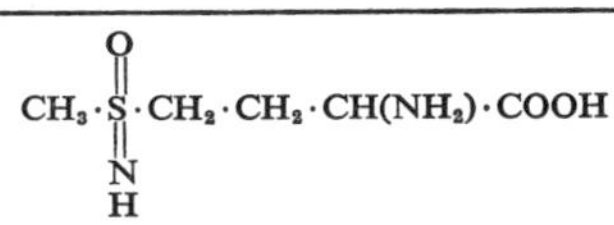	180·2	col. cryst. from hot H_2O
28	Methoxinine	*O*-Methylhomoserine	$CH_3\cdot O\cdot CH_2\cdot CH_2\cdot CH(NH_2)\cdot COOH$	133·2	col. flakes
29	ω-Methyllysine	α, ε-Diaminoheptanoic acid, ε-*C*-methyllysine	$CH_3\cdot CH(NH_2)\cdot (CH_2)_3\cdot CH(NH_2)\cdot COOH$	160·2	col. cryst.
30	*O*-Methylthreonine		$\begin{matrix}CH_3\cdot O\\H_3C\end{matrix}\!>CH\cdot CH(NH_2)\cdot COOH$	133·2	col. cryst.
31	4-Methyltryptophan		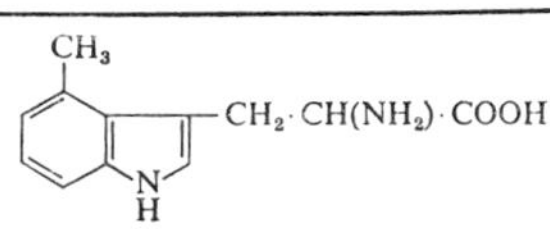	218·3	col. leaflets
32	5-Methyltryptophan		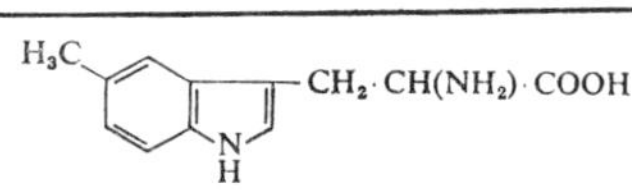	218·3	col. leaflets
33	6-Methyltryptophan		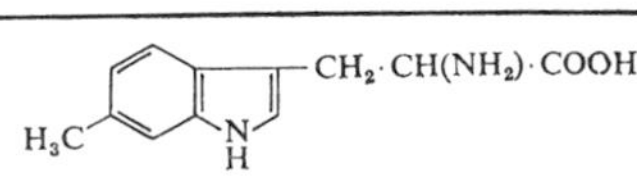	218·3	shining leaflets
34	Norleucine	α-Aminocaproic acid	$CH_3\cdot CH_2\cdot CH_2\cdot CH_2\cdot CH(NH_2)\cdot COOH$	131·2	col. leaflets

M.p.	*Solubility*	*References*	*Use*	*General remarks*
275–8 d.	v. sl. s. H_2O; s. acids, alkalis	SYN. and PROPERTIES *J.A.C.S.* **62**, 350 (1940)	Tyrosine analogue	May be incorporated into *E. coli* protein in place of tyrosine.
		USE *J.B.C.* **225**, 163 (1957)	Glutamine analogue	Inhibits at 10^{-3} M conversion of formylglycinamide ribotide to formylglycinamidine ribotide. Similar results with azaserine and diazo-oxo-norleucine.
Monosulphate, 183–8 (L-isomer)	s. H_2O	SYN. *J.B.C.* **180**, 1253 (1949); **183**, 139 (1950) USE *J.B.C.* **212**, 207, 617 (1955)	Arginine analogue	Growth inhibitor for some bacterial strains. Where effective, reversed by L-arginine.
252 d.	s. H_2O	SYN. *J.A.C.S.* **68**, 450 (1946) PROPERTIES *Ann. N.Y. Acad. Sci.* **52**, 1274 (1950)	Leucine analogue	Rather non-specific effects on growth of *E. coli*; reversal by leucine, isoleucine or valine.
220 d.	sl. s. H_2O	SYN. *Nature, Lond.* **165**, 735 (1950) *Chem. pharm. Bull. Tokyo* **8**, 177 (1960) USE *Nature, Lond.* **164**, 438; **164**, 439 (1949) *Nature, Lond.* **166**, 353 (1950)	Glutamine analogue	Inhibitory for *Leuconostoc mesenteroides* P60; reversed by glutamine. Formed as neurotoxin from methionine on 'agenizing' Zein in flour (*Nature, Lond.* **166**, 353 (1950)).
253 d.	s. H_2O	SYN. and USE *J.A.C.S.* **67**, 290 (1945)	Methionine analogue	Growth inhibitory to some strains of *E. coli*; reversed by L-methionine.
191 (as di-HCl)	s. H_2O	SYN. *J.A.C.S.* **73**, 4478 (1951) USE *J.B.C.* **204**, 417 (1953)	Lysine analogue	Growth inhibition of *S. faecalis* and *L. mesenteroides*; reversed by lysine. Incorporated in place of lysine in *S. aureus* cell wall.
	s. H_2O	SYN. *J.A.C.S.* **71**, 1096 (1949) USE *J.A.C.S.* **77**, 3109 (1955)	Isoleucine analogue	Competitive inhibition of leucine incorporation into Ehrlich ascites tumour cells. *Allo-O*-methylthreonine not active.
65–7 d.	sl. s. H_2O; s. acids	SYN. *J.C.S.* **1948**, 705 USE *B.J.* **62**, 488 (1956)	Tryptophan analogue	Growth inhibitor of *E. coli*. Inhibits tryptophan synthetase in *E. coli*. Not activated by pancreatic tryptophan activating enzyme.
64 d.	sl. s. H_2O; s. acids	SYN. *J.C.S.* **1948**, 705 USE *J.B.C.* **235**, 1098 (1960)	Tryptophan analogue	Not incorporated into protein. Competitive inhibition of tryptophan activating enzyme in liver and bacteria, but not itself activated. Inhibits synthesis of anthranilic acid from shikimic acid-5-phosphate and glutamate in *E. coli* by 'false' feedback inhibition. Completely inhibits phage synthesis.
58–60 d.	sl. s. H_2O; s. acids	SYN. *J.C.S.* **1948**, 705 USE *J. Bact.* **81**, 81 (1961)	Tryptophan analogue	Inhibition of tryptophan synthetase in *E. coli*. Competition of tryptophan activation by pancreatic enzyme but not itself activated.
1 d.	s. H_2O	SYN. *Org. Synth.* Coll. **1**, 1st edn. 40 (1932) USE *B.B.A.* **34**, 39 (1959)	Methionine analogue	May be incorporated into protein of *E. coli* in place of methionine. Competitive inhibition of methionine activation in *E. coli*. pK_a: 1. 2·39, 2. 9·76

No.	*Name*	*Synonyms*	*Formula*	*M. wt.*	*Physical form*
35	β-Phenylserine	β-Hydroxyphenyl-alanine	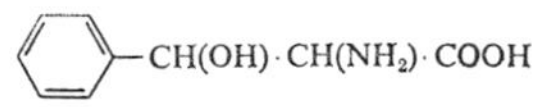 $-CH(OH)\cdot CH(NH_2)\cdot COOH$	181·2	col. cryst.
36	Selenomethionine		$CH_3\cdot Se\cdot CH_2\cdot CH_2\cdot CH(NH_2)\cdot COOH$	196·1	col. cryst.
37	2-Thiazolealanine		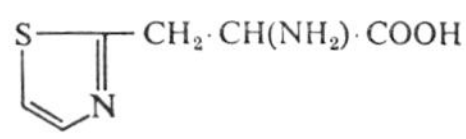 $CH_2\cdot CH(NH_2)\cdot COOH$	172·2	col. cryst.
38	β-2-Thienylalanine	2-Thiophene-alanine	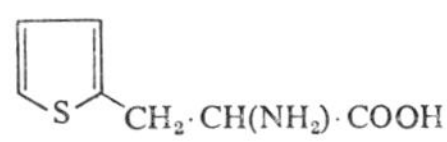 $CH_2\cdot CH(NH_2)\cdot COOH$	171·2	col. cryst.
39	β-3-Thienylalanine		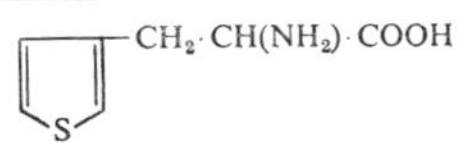 $CH_2\cdot CH(NH_2)\cdot COOH$	171·2	col. cryst.
40	5′,5′,5′-Trifluoro-leucine		$(F_3C)(H_3C)CH\cdot CH_2\cdot CH(NH_2)\cdot COOH$	185·2	col. cryst.
41	Tryptazan	α-Amino-β-(3-indazole)propionic acid	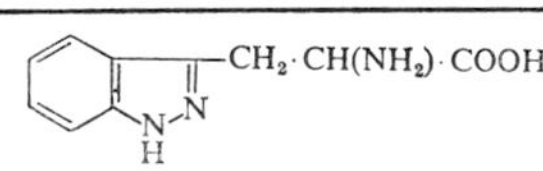 $CH_2\cdot CH(NH_2)\cdot COOH$	205·2	col. needles

M.p.	Solubility	References	Use	General remarks
190 d.	s. H_2O	SYN. *Ann.* 284, 36 (1894) USE *Folia microbiol.* 5, 207 (1960) *Science* 126, 445 (1957)	Phenylalanine analogue	Growth inhibitory to *E. coli*; reversed by phenylalanine and sometimes by tyrosine. Probably interferes with phenylalanine utilization and may be incorporated. Tyrosine reversal probably due to prior conversion to phenylalanine.
Not stated	s. H_2O	SYN. *Am. J. Bot.* 41, 345 (1954) USE *Fed. Proc.* 20, 695 (1961) *J.A.C.S.* 79, 5830 (1957)	Methionine analogue	Can replace methionine completely in protein of *E. coli*. Also found in protein of animals grazing in pastures rich in selenium compounds.
197–8 d.	s. H_2O	SYN. *J.A.C.S.* 72, 4526 (1950) USE *J.B.C.* 236, 2261 (1961)	Histidine analogue	Inhibition of histidine biosynthesis caused by 'false feedback' inhibition of synthesis of 'Compound III'.
273 d.	sl. s. H_2O; s. acids, alkalis	SYN. *J.B.C.* 166, 541 (1946) USE *B.B.A.* 31, 378 (1959)	Phenylalanine antagonist	Growth inhibition of bacteria; reversed by phenylalanine.
244–8 d.	sl. s. H_2O; s. acids	SYN. *J.A.C.S.* 71, 1205 (1949) PROPERTIES *Ann. N.Y. Acad. Sci.* 52, 1274 (1950)	Phenylalanine analogue	Incorporated into bacterial and mammalian protein in place of phenylalanine. Activated by phenylalanine activating enzymes.
Not stated	sl. s. H_2O	SYN. and PROPERTIES *Biochemistry* 2, 471 (1963)	Leucine analogue	Capable of replacing leucine completely for growth of a *leu*-auxotroph of *E. coli*. Protein synthesized in presence of analogue contains no leucine; all being replaced by analogue.
249–50 d.	sl. s. H_2O; s. acids	SYN. *J.A.C.S.* 74, 2009 (1952) USE *Arch. B.B.* 68, 112 (1957)	Tryptophan analogue	Incorporated in protein of *E. coli* in place of tryptophan. May be activated by pancreatic tryptophan activating enzyme.

B. PURINE AND PYRIMIDINE ANALOGUES

By C. I. DAVERN (*Division of Plant Industry, C.S.I.R.O., Canberra*)

General references

1. G. H. Hitchings and G. B. Elion, 'Purine analogues', *Metabolic Inhibitors*, eds. R. M. Hochster and J. H. Quastel, vol. 1, p. 215, Academic Press, New York (1963).
2. R. W. Brockman and E. P. Anderson, 'Pyrimidine analogues', *Metabolic Inhibitors*, eds. R. M. Hochster and J. H. Quastel, vol. 1, p. 239, Academic Press, New York (1963).
3. R. E. Handschumacher and A. D. Welch, 'Antimetabolites and nucleic acid metabolism', *The Nucleic Acids*, eds. E. Chargaff and J. N. Davidson, vol. 3, p. 453, Academic Press, New York (1960). Referred to in this section as *The Nucleic Acids*.
4. R. W. Brockman, 'Mechanisms of resistance to anticancer agents', *Adv. Cancer Res.* **7**, 129 (1963).

No.	*Name*	*Synonyms*	*Formula*	*M. wt.*	*Physical form*
1	8-Azaguanine	Guanazole, 5-amino-7-hydroxy-1-γ-triazolo-[*d*]-pyrimidine	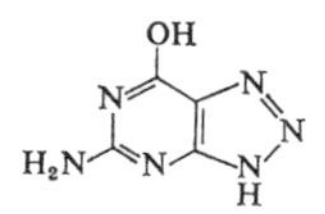	152·1	col. cryst.
2	6-Azauracil		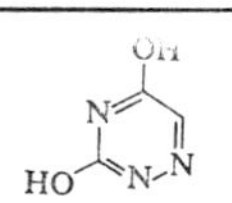	113·1	
3	5-Bromo-2′-deoxyuridine		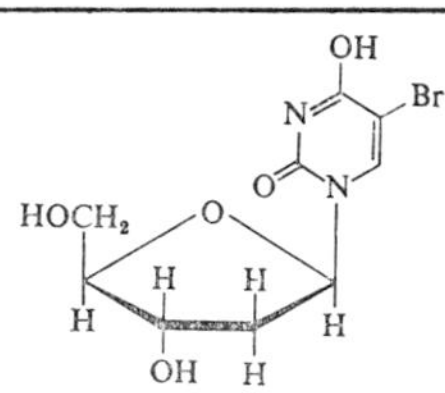	307·1	
4	5-Bromouracil		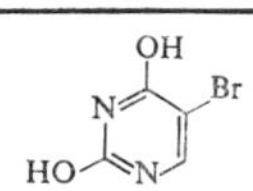	191·0	
5	2,6-Diaminopurine		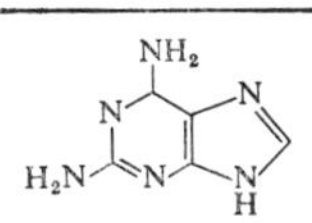	150·2	
	— sulphate		$(C_5H_6N_6)_2 \cdot H_2SO_4 \cdot H_2O$	416·4	wh. needles

M.p.	*Solubility*	*References*	*Use*	*General remarks*
Decomp. > 300	s. dil. acids	SYN. *J.A.C.S.* **67**, 290 (1945) USE *B.B.R.C.* **7**, 199 (1962)	Guanine analogue, causes translation errors from messenger RNA to protein	Incorporated into RNA.
	s. H_2O	SYN. *J.A.C.S.* **78**, 1938 (1956) REVIEWS *The Nucleic Acids*, p. 512 *Adv. Cancer Res.* **7**, 167 (1963) USE *Cancer Chemother. Rep.* No. **21**, 1 (1962) *J.B.C.* **235**, 764 (1960)	Inhibitor of RNA synthesis	Anabolized to azauridylic acid which inhibits formation of UMP from orotidylic acid; azauridine more effective than azauracil.
	s. H_2O	USE *J. molec. Biol.* **4**, 216 (1962) *J.B.C.* **235**, 1129 (1960)	Thymidine analogue, *see* 5-bromouracil	λ_{max} = 280 mμ, ϵ_{max} = 9250 at pH 2·0. pK_a: 8·1.
	s. H_2O	SYN. *Am. chem. J.* **29**, 478 (1903) USE *B.B.A.* **42**, 117 (1960) *J. molec. Biol.* **1**, 87 (1959)	Thymine analogue. Mutagen (induces GC → AT transition mutants). Density marker for DNA	Anabolized to bromodeoxyuridylic acid and to BUDR triphosphate. Incorporated into DNA where it may lead to blocking of further DNA synthesis in some organisms. Pox viruses particularly sensitive.
	$0{\cdot}24^{25}$, $0{\cdot}59^{100}$ H_2O	SYN. *J.A.C.S.* **70**, 3109 (1948) USE *J.A.C.S.* **74**, 2432 (1952) REVIEWS *Adv. Cancer Res.* **7**, 160 (1963) *The Nucleic Acids*, p. 493	Purine antagonist, especially of adenine containing cofactors of 1 carbon transfer reactions	pK_a: 1. < 1 2. 5·09 3. 10·77

15. Antimetabolites, Antibacterial Agents, and Enzyme Inhibitors

No.	*Name*	*Synonyms*	*Formula*	*M. wt.*	*Physical form*
6	5-Fluorodeoxy-uridine	5-Fluoro-2′-deoxy-uridine	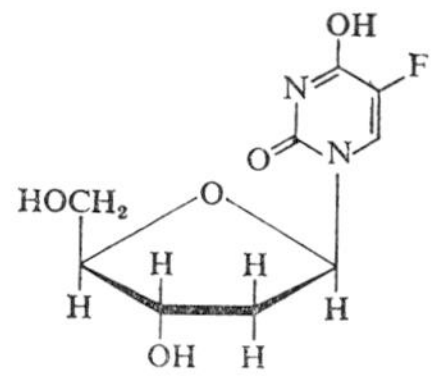	246·2	wh. cryst.
7	5-Fluorouracil	5-Fluoro-2:4-dihy-droxypyrimidine	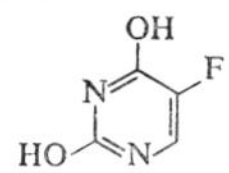	130·1	wh. powder
8	5-Iodo-2′-deoxy-uridine		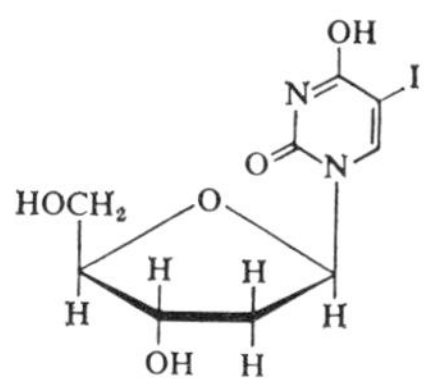	354·1	col. cryst.
9	6-Mercaptopurine	Purinethiol	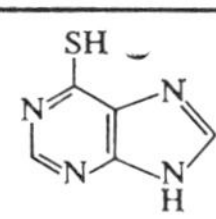	152·2; Hydrate, 170·2	yellow prisms $+1H_2O$, lost at 140°
10	6-Thioguanine	2-Amino-6-mercap-topurine	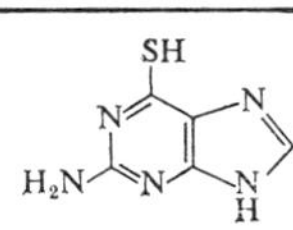	167·2	col. needles
11	Thiouracil	2-Mercapto-4-hydroxypyrimidine	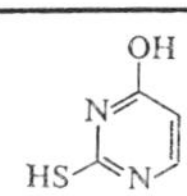	128·2	col. prisms
12	Uracil-6-sulphonic acid		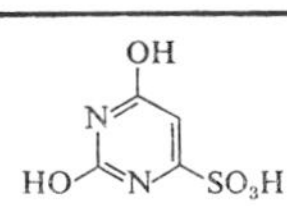	192·2	

M.p.	Solubility	References	Use	General remarks
	s. H_2O	SYN. and ACTION *Proc. natn. Acad. Sci., U.S.A.* **44**, 1004 (1958)	Inhibits DNA synthesis by blocking thymidylic acid synthetase when metabolized to fluorodeoxyuridylic acid	pK_a: 7·6.
282–3 d.	s. H_2O	SYN. *J.A.C.S.* **79**, 4559 (1957) ACTION *Proc. natn. Acad. Sci., U.S.A.* **44**, 1004 (1958) *C.r. hebd. Séanc. Acad. Sci., Paris* **250**, 4049 (1960)	Inhibits DNA synthesis; causes translation errors from messenger RNA to protein; causes transition mutations in RNA organisms. Cancer chemotherapy	Metabolized to fluorodeoxyuridylic acid which inhibits thymidylic acid synthetase and to fluorouridine triphosphate which is incorporated into RNA in the place of UTP. pK_a: 8·0.
	s. H_2O	SYN. *B.B.A.* **32**, 295 (1959) USE *Arch. Ophthal., N.Y.* **67**, 67 (1962) REVIEW *Cancer Chemother. Rep.* No. **6**, 29 (1960)	Thymidine analogue. Chemotherapy of herpes simplex keratitis	λ_{max} = 288 mμ, ϵ_{max} = 7770 at pH 2·0.
13–14 d.	s. H_2O	SYN. *J.A.C.S.* **74**, 411 (1952) USE *Nature, Lond.* **192**, 946 (1961) *J.B.C.* **192**, 505 (1951) *Clin. Pharmac. Ther.* **2**, 523 (1961) REVIEWS *Adv. Cancer Res.* **7**, 129, 235 (1963) *The Nucleic Acids*, p. 478	Cancer chemotherapy. Inhibitor NAD synthesis. Treatment of leukaemia	Interferes with purine interconversion; the nucleoside 5′-triphosphate interferes with NAD synthesis
		SYN. *J.A.C.S.* **77**, 1676 (1955) ACTION *Cancer Res.* **21**, 1590 (1961) REVIEW *Adv. Cancer Res.* **7**, 146 (1963)	Inhibits DNA synthesis after incorporation. Inhibits neoplasms and micro-organisms	Incorporated into DNA and to lesser extent into RNA.
40 d.	s. alkalis; 0·06 H_2O; v. sl. s. EtOH, eth., acids	USE *B.B.A.* **11**, 438 (1953) *B.B.A.* **33**, 269 (1959) *J. molec. Biol.* **3**, 166 (1961)	Uracil analogue. Causes translation errors from messenger RNA to protein	Incorporated into RNA, but not into DNA.
	s. H_2O	ACTION *J.B.C.* **223**, 677 (1956)	Inhibitor of pyrimidine anabolism	Competitive inhibitor of the formation of orotidylic acid from orotic acid.

C. VITAMIN ANALOGUES

By A. B. ROY (*Department of Physical Biochemistry, Australian National University, Canberra*)

General references

1. D. W. Woolley, 'Antimetabolites of the water-soluble vitamins', *Metabolic Inhibitors*, eds. R. M. Hochster and J. H. Quastel, vol. 1, p. 445, Academic Press, New York (1963).
2. T. H. Jukes and H. P. Broquist, 'Sulphonamides and folic acid antagonists', *Metabolic Inhibitors*, eds. R. M. Hochster and J. H. Quastel, vol. 1, p. 481, Academic Press, New York (1963).

No.	*Name*	*Synonyms*	*Formula*	*M. wt.*	*Physical form*
1	3-Acetylpyridine		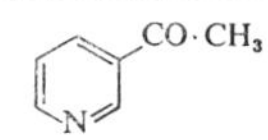	121·1	oil
2	Amethopterin	Methotrexate,4-amino-N^{10}-methylpteroyl-glutamic acid	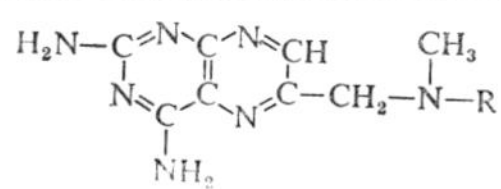 [R = benzoylglutamic acid]	454·5	yel. cryst.
3	2-Amino-2-methylpropanol		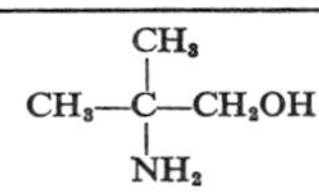	89·1	cryst. (or viscous oil)
4	Aminopterin	4-Aminopteroyl-glutamic acid	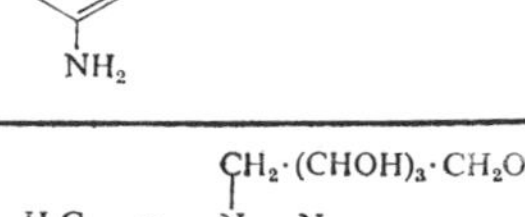 [R = benzoylglutamic acid]	Hydrate $+2H_2O$, 476·4; Anhyd., 440·4	yel. needles
5	*p*-Amino-salicylic acid	PAS	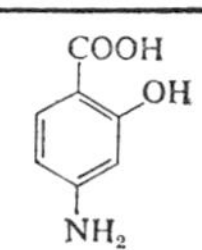	153·1	wh. powder
6	Chlororibo-flavin	6-Chloro-7-methyl-9-ribityl*iso*alloxazine	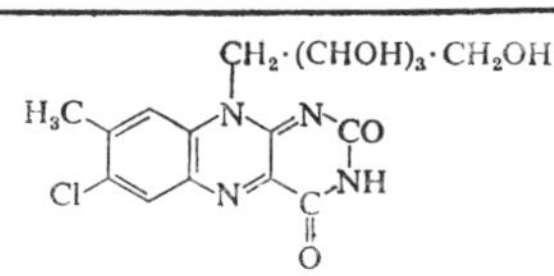	396·8	orange needles
7	Citral	3:7-Dimethylocta-2:6-dien-1-al	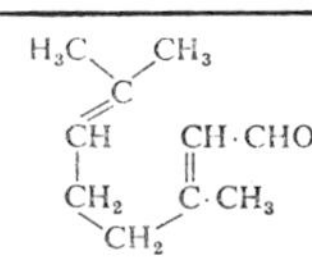	152·2	oil
8	4-Deoxypyri-doxine	2:4-Dimethyl-3-hydroxy-5-hydroxy-methylpyridine	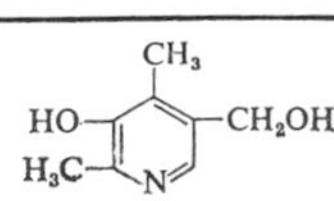	153·2	wh. cryst.

M.p.	*Solubility*	*References*	*Action*	*General remarks*
B.p. 90	s. H_2O, EtOH	*J.B.C.* **157**, 455 (1945)	Nicotinamide antagonist producing deficiency in several mammals and in chickens. Can be reversed by prior, but not subsequent administration of nicotinic acid	Not a good antimetabolite in bacteria. Probably forms an NAD analogue *in vivo*.
185–204	s. dil. HCl	*Chemistry and Biology of Pteridines*, pp. 290, 253 (1954) Ciba Symposium *The Nucleic Acids*, vol. 3, p. 456 (1960)	Folic acid antagonist. Reversed by FA itself, and by 5-formyltetrahydrofolic acid. Used to control leukaemia; dosage more readily controlled than in aminopterin. See *Adv. Cancer Res.* **7**, 192 (1963) for mechanisms of resistance	Inhibits dihydrofolate reductase. Various halogenated derivatives act similarly, *J. Pharmac. exp. Ther.* **128**, 419 (1960).
30	∞ H_2O; s. EtOH	*Fed. Proc.* **13**, 319 (1954)	Choline antagonist in rats, as judged by kidney changes	Inhibits choline oxidase *in vitro*.
	s. aq. NaOH; sl. s. H_2O	*See* Amethopterin	Folic acid antagonist, similar in action to amethopterin (q.v.). Used to control leukaemia	
50	s. EtOH; sl. s. H_2O	*J. Bact.* **57**, 573 (1949)	*p*-Aminobenzoic acid antagonist in tubercle bacillus. Can replace this factor in some strains of *E. coli*	May be incorporated into a folic acid-like molecule.
74	sl. s. H_2O	*Am. J. clin. Nutr.* **3**, 282 (1955) *Arch. B.B.* **78**, 10 (1958)	Potent anti-riboflavin action in bacteria and rats, although it can maintain some growth in the latter	Is converted to 5′-phosphate. *L. casei* can be trained to use antagonist as a flavin source.
p. 229	∞ EtOH, eth.; i. H_2O	*Proc. Nutr. Soc.* **15**, xv (1956)	In low doses (5 μg/kg body weight) causes damage to vascular endothelium in rabbits. Damage reversed by vitamin A	Only presumptive evidence that this is a vitamin A antagonist.
	s. H_2O; sl. s. EtOH	*P.S.E.B.M.* **61**, 125 (1946); **70**, 293 (1949)	An anti-pyridoxin in chickens. Inhibits the growth of most bacteria which require pyridoxin	In bacterial cells is phosphorylated to an inhibitor of amino-acid decarboxylases.

15. Antimetabolites, Antibacterial Agents, and Enzyme Inhibitors

No.	Name	Synonyms	Formula	M. wt.	Physical form
9	Desthiobiotin		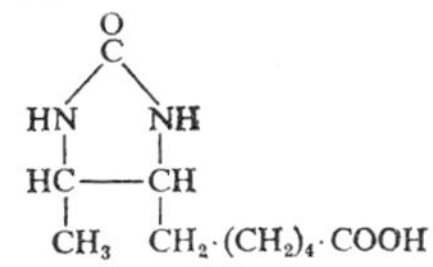	214·3	wh. needles
	Dicoumarol, *see* 15. H, Inhibitors of respiratory enzymes, photosynthesis and phosphorylation; uncoupling agents				
10	Diethylribo-flavin	6:7-Diethyl-9-ribityl*iso*-alloxazine	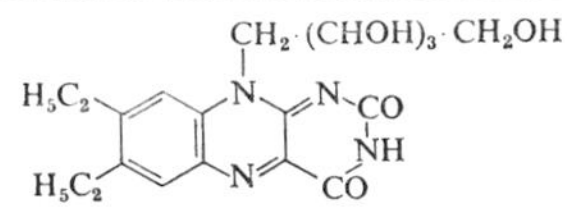	404·3	orange needles
11	α,α-Dimethyl-choline chloride		$(CH_3)_3\overset{+}{N}\cdot C(CH_3)_2\cdot CH_2OH \quad Cl^-$	167·7	cryst.
12	5-Fluoronico-tinic acid		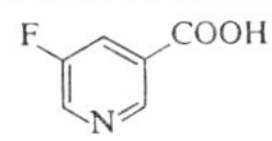	141·1	powder
13	Gammexane	Lindane, γ-hexachloro-cyclohexane	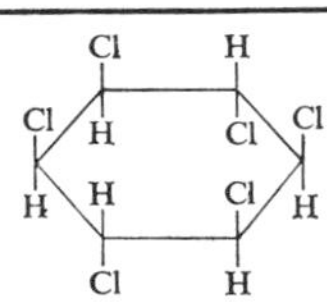	290·9	cryst.
14	Glucoascorbic acid	2:3-Enediol-D-gluco-heptono-1:4-lactone	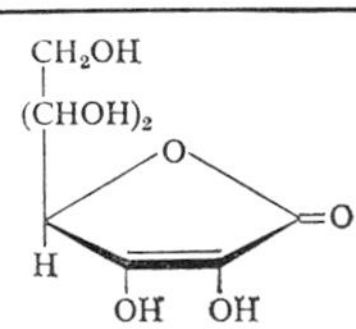	206·2	cryst.
15	Iproniazid	*iso*Nicotinic acid 2-*iso*-propylhydrazine, Mar-silid	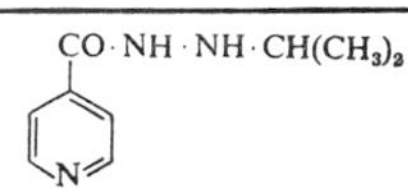	179·2	needles
16	Isoniazid	*iso*Nicotinic acid hydra-zide	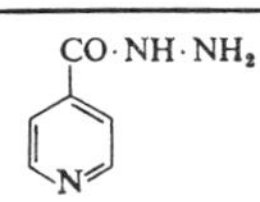	137·1	wh. cryst.
17	9-Methylfolic acid		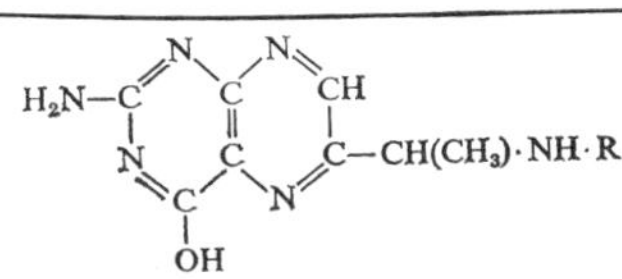 [R = benzoylglutamic acid]	455·4	
18	Oxythiamine chloride hydro-chloride		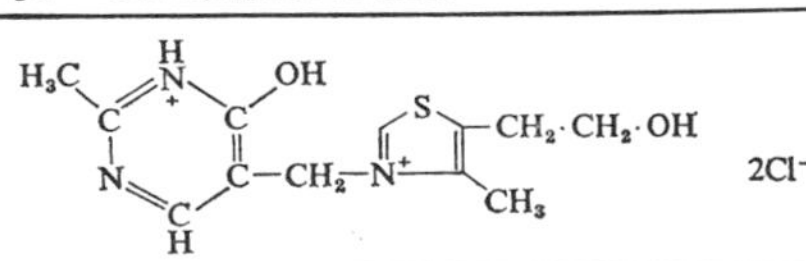	338·3	wh. needles
19	Pantoyltaurine		$HO\cdot CH_2\cdot C(CH_3)_2\cdot CH(OH)\cdot CO\cdot NH\cdot CH_2\cdot CH_2\cdot SO_3H$	255·3	wh. deliq. powder

M.p.	Solubility	References	Action	General remarks
DL-, 165	s. H_2O	*Science* 98, 497 (1943); 99, 203, 205 (1944)	Competes with biotin utilization of *L. casei* but stimulates growth of *Saccharomyces cerevisiae* in a biotin deficient medium	Only D-isomer active.
255	sl. s. H_2O	*J.B.C.* **188**, 459 (1951) *P.S.E.B.M.* **78**, 197 (1951) *J. Nutr.* **47**, 539 (1952)	Has an anti-riboflavin activity in the growing rat but can serve as sole source of flavin for *L. casei*	
	s. EtOH; i. eth.	*J.B.C.* **217**, 631 (1955)	Antimetabolite of choline in rats	
195–7	s. H_2O	*B.J.* **57**, 485 (1954)	Antimetabolite of nicotinic acid in micro-organisms; inhibition reversed competitively by nicotinic acid, nicotinamide or NAD	Converted to corresponding NAD derivative *in vivo*. Other isomers effective as follows 5F > 5Cl > 5Br > 2F and 6F.
113	v.s. acet.; sl. s. EtOH; i. H_2O	*Science* **108**, 556 (1948) *J.B.C.* **186**, 823 (1950)	Probably an antimetabolite of inositol in *Neurospora* and in plants. Powerful insecticide	Early commercial samples were mixtures of isomers—now 99% γ-isomer.
Hydrate, 01–5 Anhyd., 91	s. H_2O; sl. s. EtOH	*J. exp. Med.* **78**, 333 (1943) *Fed. Proc.* **3**, 97 (1944)	May be an antagonist of ascorbic acid; causes scurvy-like lesions when fed to rats, mice, and guinea pigs—only the latter respond to ascorbic acid	Effects cured in all species by feeding green plants.
13	s. H_2O, EtOH	*J. Am. pharm. Ass.* (Sci. Ed.) **42**, 457 (1953)	Antitubercular activity probably not related to anti-pyridoxine activity. Used as a 'psychic energiser' in depressed states	Inhibits amino acid decarboxylation *in vivo* and *in vitro*, and also amine oxidases.
70–3	v.s. H_2O; sl. s. EtOH, $CHCl_3$	*P.S.E.B.M.* **84**, 292 (1953); **85**, 389 (1954)	An antagonist of pyridoxin in some bacteria but not in mycobacteria as the effect in latter not reversed by pyridoxin. Causes peripheral neuritis in man, reversed by pyridoxin	Antibacterial action probably due to chelation of metals.
		J.B.C. **235**, 1780 (1960)	Folic acid antagonist	Probably causes a block at folic reductase level.
5 d.	s. MeOH; i. eth.	*P.S.E.B.M.* **72**, 165 (1949) *Fed. Proc.* **9**, 169 (1950)	Thiamine antagonist in chicken and mouse, effects reversed by thiamine	Unlike pyrithiamine is phosphorylated *in vivo* to an inhibitor of carboxylase.
	s. H_2O	*B.J.* **36**, 357, 364, 417 (1942)	Weak competitive antagonist of pantothenic acid in those bacteria which require this growth factor. No effect on bacteria which can synthesize pantothenic acid nor on rats, mice, or hamsters	

15. Antimetabolites, Antibacterial Agents, and Enzyme Inhibitors

No.	*Name*	*Synonyms*	*Formula*	*M. wt.*	*Physical form*
20	Pantoylthio-amido-4-chloro-benzene	4-[2-(Pantoylamino)-ethylsulphonamido]-chlorobenzene	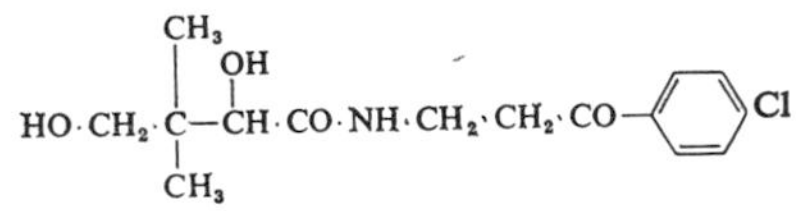	364·9	
21	Phenylpanto-thenone		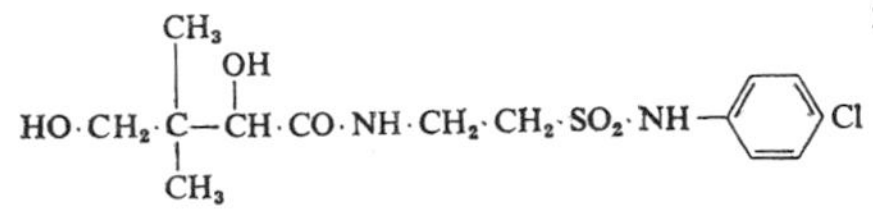	279·3	wh. cryst.
22	Pteroylaspartic acid, Mg salt		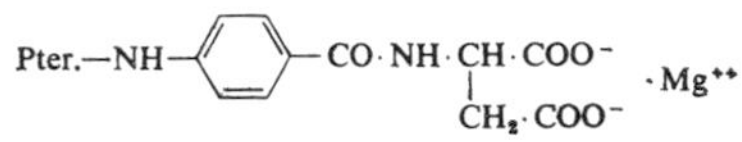	449·7	yel. needles
23	Pyridine-3-sul-phonic acid		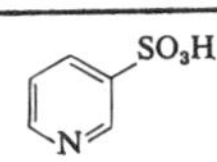	159·2	needles or plates
24	Pyrimethamine	2:4-Diamino-5-*p*-chlorophenyl-6-ethyl-pyrimidine	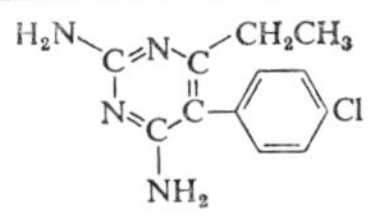	248·7	cryst.
25	Pyrithiamine bromide hydro-bromide	Neopyrithiamine	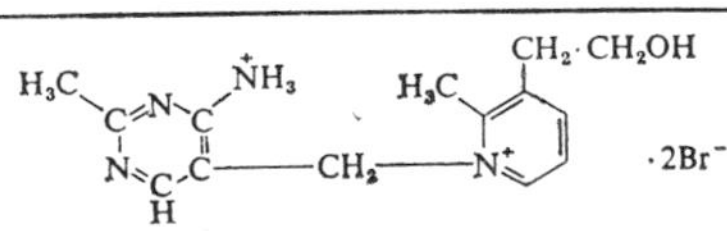	420·2	hygr. needles
26	Sulphadiazine	N^1-2-Pyrimidyl-sulphanilamide	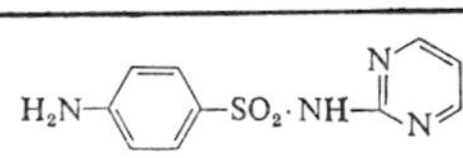	250·3	wh. cryst.
27	Sulphaguanidine	N^1-Guanylsulphanil-amide	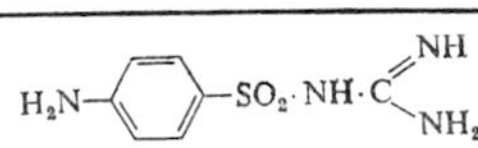	214·3	needles
28	Sulphamethazine	N^1-(4:6-Dimethyl-2-pyridimyl)sulphanil-amide	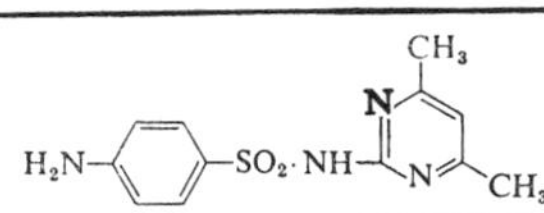	278·3	wh. cryst.
29	Sulphanilamide	*p*-Aminobenzene-sulphonamide	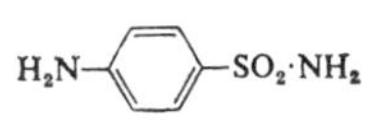	172·2	wh. cryst.
30	Sulphapyridine	N^1-2-Pyridylsulphanil-amide	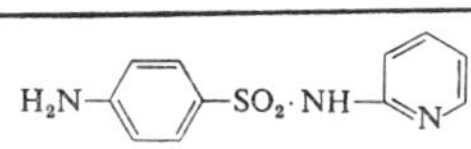	249·3	wh. cryst.
31	Sulphathiazole	N^1-2-Thiazolyl-sulphanilamide	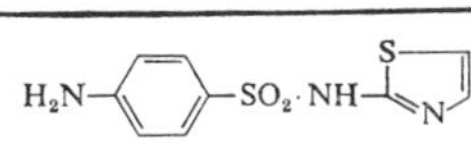	255·3	wh. cryst.
32	Toxopyrimidine	4-Amino-5-hydroxy-methyl-2-methylpyri-midine, 2-methyl-6-amino-5-hydroxy-methylpyrimidine	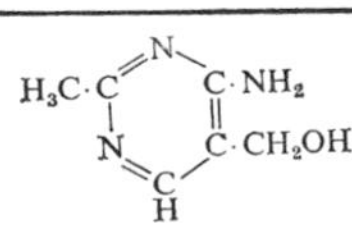	139·2	
33	Tromexan	Ethyl bis(4-hydroxy-coumaryl) acetate, BOEA, bis-3:3′-(4-oxycoumarinyl) ethyl acetate	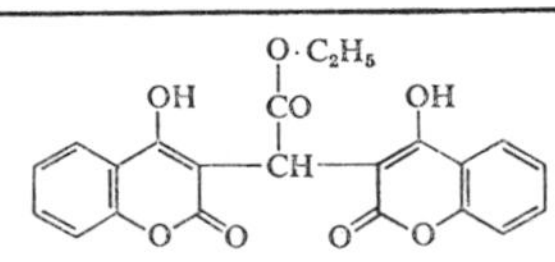	408·4	cryst.

M.p.	*Solubility*	*References*	*Action*	*General remarks*
110–12		*J.A.C.S.* **69**, 1393 (1947)	Pantothenic acid antagonist with anti-malarial and anti-streptococcal activity	Many other related compounds described in same reference.
126	v.s. EtOH; s. H_2O	*J.B.C.* **159**, 263 (1945)	Powerful antagonist of pantothenic acid in many micro-organisms, irrespective of dietary requirement for this factor. Effects reversed by pantothenic acid only in those species with dietary requirement	Formation of CoA inhibited by this analogue and by the even more effective tolylpantothenone.
	sl. s. H_2O	*J.B.C.* **170**, 323 (1947)	Folic acid antagonist	Mechanism of action unknown. Free acid unstable.
357 d.	v.s. H_2O; sl. s. EtOH	*J.B.C.* **157**, 455 (1945)	Nicotinamide antagonist in some micro-organisms and in nicotinic acid-deficient dogs	Forms an inhibitory analogue of NAD *in vivo*.
	sl. s. EtOH; i. H_2O	*Antibiot. Chemother.* **4**, 971 (1954); **7**, 630 (1957) *The Nucleic Acids*, vol. 3, p. 469 (1960)	Folic acid antagonist	Has antimalarial activity and used in control of toxoplasmosis.
20	s. H_2O, EtOH, $CHCl_3$	*Fed. Proc.* **9**, 169 (1950) *J.B.C.* **207**, 295 (1954)	Competitive antagonist of thiamine in micro-organisms and in higher animals. Effects produced differ from those caused by oxythiamine	Inhibits enzyme forming co-carboxylase but may have other effects.
52	s. dil. acid and alkali; sl. s. H_2O, EtOH	E. H. Northey, *The Sulphonamides and Allied Compounds*, Am. Chem. Soc. Monograph Series (1948)	All sulphonamides (*see* nos. 26–31) are antagonists of *p*-aminobenzoic acid, preventing the formation of folic acid	Forms Na salt, s. H_2O.
90–3	s. hot H_2O, dil. acid; sl. s. H_2O, EtOH			
76	s. dil. alkali; sl. s. H_2O			Forms Na salt, v.s. H_2O.
5–7	s. dil. acid and alkali; sl. s. H_2O, EtOH			Inhibits carbonic anhydrase at 10^{-6} M.
1–3	s. dil. acid and alkali; v. sl. s. H_2O			Forms Na salt, s. H_2O.
0–3	s. dil. acid			Forms Na salt, s. H_2O.
		Nature, Lond. **173**, 34; **174**, 275 (1954)	Causes convulsions and death in rats and mice. Effects reversed by pyridoxal	This compound is the pyrimidine moiety of thiamine.
mor- ous: 154–7 177–82	s. acet.; sl. s. EtOH; i. H_2O	*J. Lab. clin. Med.* **36**, 19 (1950)	Antagonist of vitamin K in mammals causing deficiency of prothrombin. See also *Metabolic Inhibitors*, vol. 1, p. 428 (1963) for other vitamin K antagonists	Used clinically as an anti-coagulant.

D. ANTIBIOTICS

By G. COLEMAN (*Department of Biochemistry, Australian National University, Canberra*)

General references

1. B. D. Davis and D. S. Feingold, 'Antimicrobial agents: mechanism of action and use in metabolic studies', *The Bacteria*, vol. 4, p. 343 (1962).
2. E. F. Gale, 'Mechanisms of antibiotic action', *Pharmac. Rev.* **15**, 481 (1963).
3. E. J. Modest, G. E. Foley, and S. Farber, 'Polypeptides and proteins as inhibitors', *Metabolic Inhibitors*, eds. R. M. Hochster and J. H. Quastel, vol. 1, p. 76, Academic Press, New York (1963). Cited in this section as *Metabolic Inhibitors.*
4. R. W. Brockman, 'Mechanisms of resistance to anticancer agents', *Adv. Cancer Res.* **7,** 83, 209 (1963). Cited in this section as *Anticancer Agents.*
5. P. J. Weiss, M. L. Andrew, and W. W. Wright, 'Solubility of antibiotics in twenty-four solvents; use in analysis', *Antibiotics Chemother.* **7,** 374 (1957).
6. J. H. Humphrey, D. A. Long, and W. L. M. Perry, 'Biological standards in biochemical analysis', *Meth. biochem. Anal.* **5,** 73 (1957).
7. D. C. Grove and W. A. Randall, *Assay Methods of Antibiotics: A Laboratory Manual,* Medical Encyclopedia, Inc., New York (1955).

No.	*Name*	*Synonyms*	*Formula*	*M. wt.*	*Physical form*
1	Actidione	Cycloheximide	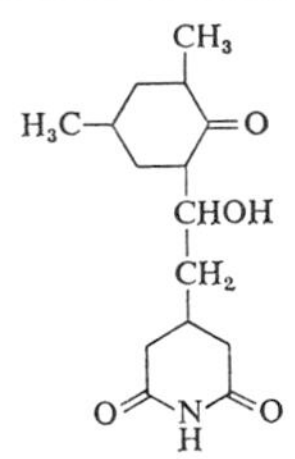	281·4	cryst. from H_2O containing a littl MeOH
2	Actinomycin		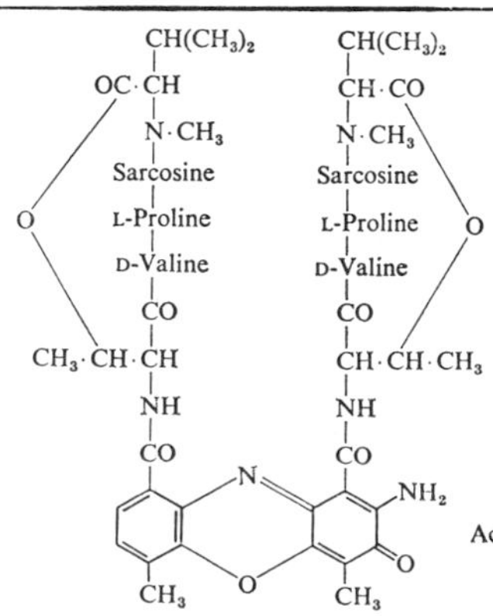 Actinomycin D	D, 1255·5	red cryst.
3	Amphomycin		An acidic polypeptide of unknown structure		Na^+ and Ca^{++} salts cryst.

M.p.	Solubility	Use	General remarks	References
15–17	v.s. H_2O and all common organic solvents except saturated hydrocarbons	Inhibits DNA and protein synthesis. Little or no activity against bacteria but effective against many yeasts and fungi, also reported to have effect on animal tumours	At the minimum growth inhibitory conc. DNA and protein synthesis in yeast completely blocked; RNA synthesis continues at slower rate. Inhibition not reversed by any of a number of metabolites tested. Actidione is weakly acidic. pK_a: 11·2. Rapidly inactivated by dil. alkali at R.T.	ISOL. and PROPERTIES *J.A.C.S.* **69**, 474 (1947). *J.A.C.S.* **70**, 1223 (1948). *J. Bact.* **56**, 283 (1948). ACTION *J. gen. Microbiol.* **19**, 497 (1958). *Antimicrobial Agents and Chemotherapy* **1961**, 237.
	v.s. acet., benz., $CHCl_3$, gl. acetic; s. ethyl acetate, MeOH, EtOH; sl. s. eth., H_2O; i. pet. eth.; s. dil. mineral acids; i. alkalis	Inhibits RNA synthesis. Broad spectrum; gram +ve more sensitive than gram −ve organisms. Active in mammalian systems—potent antitumour agent	Obtained as mixtures of closely related compounds, formed in different proportions by different strains of *Streptomyces*. The various actinomycins have the same chromophore but different peptide side chains. Actinomycin D is the most widely used of the group. Actinomycin inhibits DNA-primed RNA polymerase by complexing with DNA, via deoxyguanosine residues. At higher concentrations DNA polymerase inhibited. 0·25–0·75 μg/ml inhibits growth of *S. aureus* whereas 100 μg/ml is required to inhibit *E. coli*	ACTION *B.B.A.* **42**, 167 (1960). *B.B.A.* **47**, 610 (1961). *Proc. natn. Acad. Sci., U.S.A.* **48**, 1222 (1962). *Proc. natn. Acad. Sci., U.S.A.* **48**, 2094 (1962). *Science* **136**, 315 (1962). REVIEWS *Ann. N.Y. Acad. Sci.* **89**, 285 (1960). *Amino acids and Peptides with Antimetabolic Activity*, p. 123 (1958) Ciba Symp. *Metabolic Inhibitors*, p. 77. *Anticancer Agents*, p. 209.
	s. H_2O and lower alcohols; i. nonpolar solvents	Surface active compound. Primarily active against gram +ve bacteria	Acts on cell membrane—surface active compound. Similar chemical and biological properties to those of aspartocin (*see below*). Aqueous solution, at neutral pH, stable at R.T. for at least a month	*Antibiotics Chemother.* **3**, 1239 (1953). *Antibiotics Annual* **1959–60**, p. 195.

No.	*Name*	*Synonyms*	*Formula*	*M. wt.*	*Physical form*
4	Antimycin A		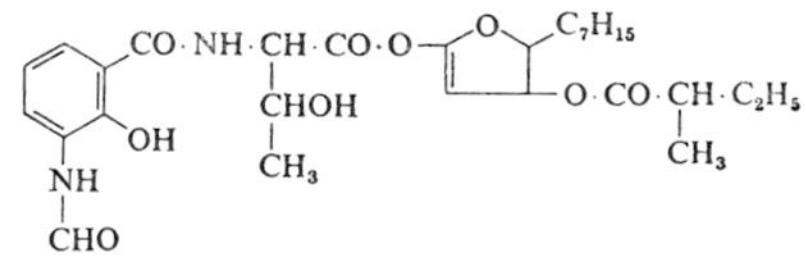 (probable structure)	548·6	col. cryst. from MeOH, aq. MeOH
5	Aspartocin		An acidic polypeptide which on hydrolysis gives L-Asp, L-Pro, L-Val, Gly, a fatty acid moiety and 3 unidentified ninhydrin-positive components		Microcryst. Na^+ and K^+ salts formed by addition of ethanolic soln. of NaOH or KOH to ethanolic soln. of drug
6	Azaserine	*O*-Diazo-acetyl-L-serine	$\overset{-}{N}=\overset{+}{N}=CH\cdot\overset{O}{\overset{\parallel}{C}}\cdot O\cdot CH_2\cdot\overset{NH_2}{\overset{\mid}{C}H}\cdot COOH$	173·1	orthorhombic pa[l] yel. to green crys[t.] from 90% EtOH
7	Bacitracin		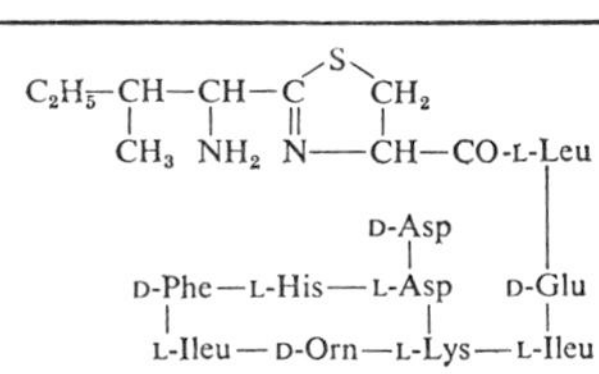 Bacitracin A	1411	grey-wh. powde[r]

M.p.	Solubility	Use	General remarks	References
39–40	v.s. eth., acet., $CHCl_3$, EtOH; sl. s. pet. eth., benz., CCl_4; i. H_2O and 5% HCl, Na_2CO_3, $NaHCO_3$	*In vitro* interrupts electron transport in all biological systems. Inhibits growth of fungi, no action on most bacteria	Interrupts the electron transport chain specifically between cytochromes *b* and c_1. Extremely potent fungicide, e.g. inhibits *Nigrospora sphaerica* growth at dilutions of 1 in 800 000 000. On synthetic medium growth of *Saccharomyces cerevisiae* completely inhibited by 8 μg/ml, on complex medium containing yeast extract and peptone no effect up to 40 μg/ml. Alcoholic solutions appear to be stable indefinitely under ordinary conditions	ISOL. and PROPERTIES *J.A.C.S.* **71**, 2436 (1949). ACTION *Arch. B.* **28**, 281 (1950). *A. Rev. Biochem.* **30**, 18 (1961). *J.B.C.* **237**, 2384 (1962). *B.B.R.C.* **8**, 421 (1962).
	s. MeOH, EtOH, gl. acetic; sl. s. H_2O, *n*-BuOH; i. acet., ethyl acetate. It is more readily s. in H_2O at $pH < 3{\cdot}0$ or $> 3{\cdot}6$. Rel. stable in aqueous soln.	Surface active compound. Primarily active against gram +ve bacteria; shows some activity towards Mycobacteria	Acts on cell membrane—surface active compound. Staphylococci and Streptococci do not easily develop resistance to it. Active against penicillin and tetracycline resistant strains. *In vitro* assay using gram +ve organisms showed 4–8 times activity of closely related amphomycin. Growth inhibitory concns (μg/ml): *S. aureus*, 8–15·5; *Strep. pyogenes*, 2–8; *B. subtilis*, 1–4; *E. coli*, > 250; Mycobacteria, 62	REVIEW *Antibiotics Annual* 1959–60, p. 194.
Decomp. 146–62	v.s. H_2O; s. aq. EtOH; sl. s. MeOH, EtOH, acet.	Inhibits purine synthesis. Active against several Clostridia sp., *Mycobacterium tuberculosis* and *Rickettsiae*. Also possesses antitumour activity. A few fungi including several yeasts are inhibited by this compound	A glutamine analogue, like DON, prevents transfer of amide group from glutamine to formylglycinamide ribotide in purine synthesis. Competition with glutamine is probably not its only role since it is also mutagenic. Bacteria in minimal medium show greater sensitivity than in complex medium (*E. coli* inhibited by 0·02 and 5·0 μg/ml and *B. subtilis* 1·0 and 6·6 μg/ml in minimal and complex medium, respectively). Aqueous solns. most stable at pH 8, stability rapidly falls off above and below this pH, can be heated at 100° in neutral aqueous soln. for 5 min. pK_a: 8·55. $E_{1\,cm}^{1\%}$ at 250·5 mμ = 1140	ISOL. and SYN. *Nature, Lond.* **173**, 72 (1954). *J.A.C.S.* **76**, 2878, 2887 (1954). ACTION *Arch. B.B.* **64**, 437 (1956). *Proc. natn. Acad. Sci., U.S.A.* **44**, 446 (1958). REVIEWS *Amino acids and Peptides with Antimetabolic Activity*, pp. 62, 75 (1958) Ciba Symp. *Anticancer Agents*, p. 183.
	v.s. H_2O, MeOH; s. EtOH; sl. s. acet., benz., eth.; i. $CHCl_3$	Inhibits cell wall synthesis. Effective against gram +ve bacteria, *Meningococcus* and *Gonococcus*	The bacitracins are a family of cyclic polypeptides of which bacitracin A is the main component. Resembles penicillin in action causing protoplast formation and accumulation of cell wall precursors. Rel. stable in acid soln.; unstable above pH 9	REVIEWS *Amino acids and Peptides with Antimetabolic Activity*, p. 205 (1958) Ciba Symp. *Biochemistry of some Peptide and Steroid Antibiotics*, by E. P. Abraham (1957) Ciba Lectures in Microbial Biochemistry.

No.	Name	Synonyms	Formula	M. wt.	Physical form
8	Carbomycin	Magnamycin	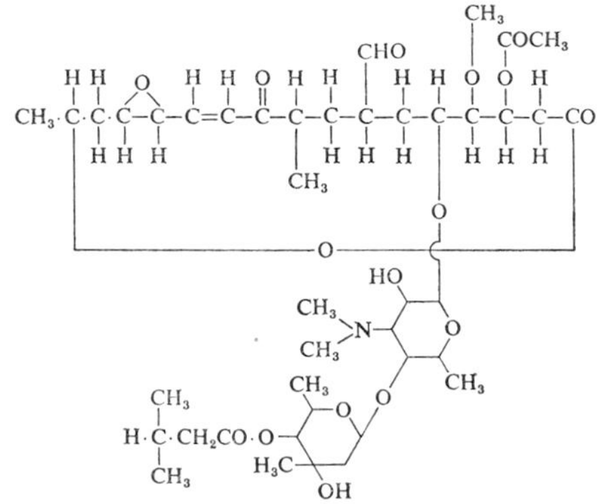	842·0	blunt needles from EtOH
9	Cephalosporin C		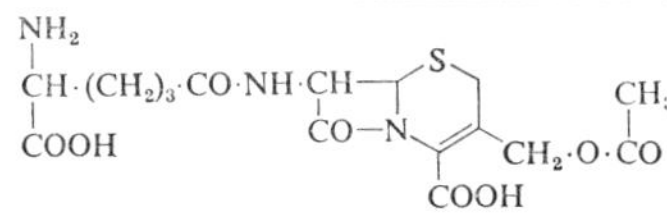	415·4	cryst. as sodium salt
10	Chloramphenicol	Chloromycetin, D(−)-threo-1-(*p*-nitrophenyl)-2-dichloroacetamido-1:3-propanediol	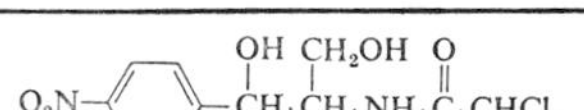	323·1	pale yel. needles from H_2O
11	Chlortetracycline	Aureomycin	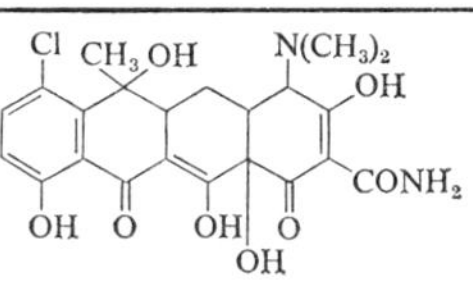	478·9	yel. cryst.
12	Circulin		Polypeptide related to polymyxin contains L-α,γ-Diaminobutyric acid, 6; L-Thr, 2; L-Ileu, 1; D-Leu, 1; and Fatty acid, 1 mole	~ 1400 for sulphate	exists as sulph and hydrochlori which are amor solids

p.	*Solubility*	*Use*	*General remarks*	*References*
4	v.s. MeOH, EtOH, acet., benz., $CHCl_3$, ethyl acetate; sl. s. H_2O	Probably inhibits protein synthesis, most active against gram +ve organisms	Member of macrolide group of antibiotics (*see* erythromycin). Aqueous soln. pptd. in 0·1M-HCl; diluted, stable for 1 week at +5°; after 2 weeks 7% loss of activity; more rapid loss of activity if frozen	*Antibiotics Chemother.* **2,** 441 (1952). *B.B.R.C.* **8,** 299 (1962). *Antibiotics Chemother.* **3,** 865 (1953).
	Sodium salt, readily soluble in water	Inhibits cell wall synthesis. Active against a wide range of bacteria	Action similar to penicillins causing lysis of growing bacterial cells by inhibiting polymerization of UDP-muramic acid peptides; approx. 0·1% activity of benzyl penicillin against *S. aureus* but more active against certain strains of *Salmonella typhi*. Induces penicillinase in *S. aureus* and *B. cereus* but resistant to penicillinase action. Attacked by cephalosporinase and by acetyl esterase, both found in many bacteria	ISOL. and PROPERTIES *B.J.* **62,** 651 (1956). *Nature, Lond.* **199,** 909 (1963). REVIEWS *Endeavour* **20,** 92 (1961). *Pharmac. Rev.* **14,** 473 (1962). *See also* Bacitracin reviews
7– 7	s. MeOH, EtOH, acet., ethyl acetate; sl. s. H_2O, eth.; i. benz., pet. eth.	Inhibits bacterial protein synthesis. Bacteriostatic to a wide variety of bacteria	RNA and DNA synthesis continue in the presence of the drug which inhibits protein synthesis by preventing peptide bond formation. Always considered specific inhibitor of bacterial protein synthesis; recently an effect on a cell-free mammalian system described. It inhibits bacterial growth at 10 μg/ml. Aqueous soln. stable at 0° between pH 2–9, decomp. on boiling	ACTION *J. molec. Biol.* **12,** 9 (1965). *Proc. natn. Acad. Sci., U.S.A.* **50,** 86 (1963). *Nature, Lond.* **201,** 397 (1964). REVIEW *Bact. Rev.* **25,** 32 (1961).
9 ro- ride, mp. 10	v.s. dioxan; sl. s. H_2O, EtOH, benz., acet.; i. eth. Hydrochloride, s. H_2O, MeOH	Broad spectrum antibiotic, bacteriostatic	Literature on mechanism of action meagre; said to prevent protein synthesis without affecting nucleic acid formation. Ability to chelate heavy metals suggested as being important action since under certain conditions added Fe^{++} or Mg^{++} reverses bacteriostasis. However possible that chelate represents inactive complex although there is evidence to the contrary. See data in Chelating Agents, p. 432. More recently the drug has been shown to inhibit transfer of amino acids from amino acyl s-RNA to ribosomes in a cell-free *E. coli* system. pK_a: 3·3, 7·44, 9·27	ACTION *B.J.* **53,** 493 (1953). *Nature, Lond.* **172,** 395 (1953). *Nature, Lond.* **177** 433 (1956). *J.B.C.* **235,** 616 (1960). *B.B.R.C.* **14,** 137 (1964).
iate, np. 3 o- ide, np. 5	Sulphate and hydrochloride, s. H_2O; sl. s. lower alcohols; i. acet. and H_2O-immisc. solvents	Surface active compound. Bactericidal to both gram +ve and −ve organisms	Rapidly causes disorganization of the cell membrane leading to loss of intracellular constituents. Exists in 2 forms, A and B, differing in nature of fatty acid residue; A contains (+)-6-methyloctanoic acid and B contains *iso*octanoic acid. Obtained as free base at pH 11; unstable in this form	*J. Bact.* **57,** 305 (1949). *J.B.C.* **181,** 95 (1949). *Science* **116,** 147 (1952). *Adv. Protein Chem.* **8,** 49 (1953). STRUCTURE *J. Biochem., Tokyo* **54,** 32 (1963).

No.	*Name*	*Synonyms*	*Formula*	*M. wt.*	*Physical form*
13	Colistin	Colimycin	Basic, cyclic polypeptide related to polymyxin, colistin A contains: L-Dab, 6 moles L-Thr, 2 ,, L-Leu, 1 ,, D-Leu, 1 ,, Moa, 1 ,, L-Dab = L-α,γ-diaminobutyric acid Moa = (+)-6-methyloctan-1-oic acid	Sulphate, A, 1414 B, 1400	normally obtaine as sulphate—a wh powder
14	Cycloserine	Oxamycin, D-4-amino-3-isoxazolidone	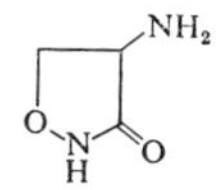	102·1	cryst.
15	DON	6-Diazo-5-oxo-L-norleucine	$\overset{-}{N}=\overset{+}{N}=CH\cdot\overset{O}{\overset{\Vert}{C}}\cdot CH_2\cdot CH_2\cdot\overset{NH_2}{\overset{\vert}{C}H}\cdot COOH$ $\updownarrow$ $N\equiv N\rightarrow CH\cdot$ etc. (resonance hybrid)	171·2	pale yel. cryst. from dil. EtOH
16	Erythromycin		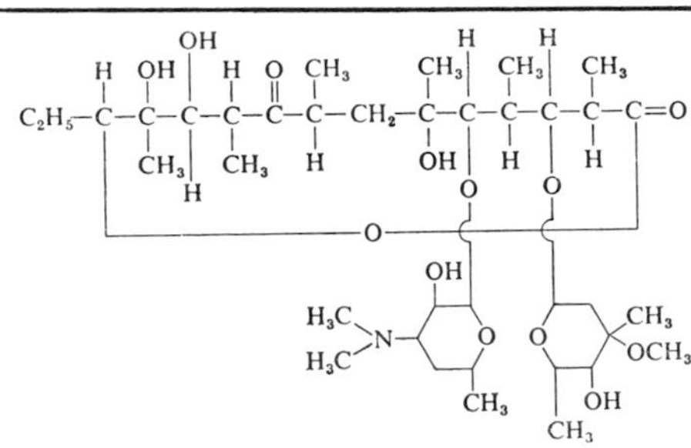	733·9	hydrated cryst. from H_2O
17	Gramicidin S		L-Val—L-Orn—L-Leu—D-Phe—L-Pro | L-Pro—D-Phe—L-Leu—L-Orn—L-Val	1141·4	cryst. from alco hol or aq. acet.

M.p.	*Solubility*	*Use*	*General remarks*	*References*
ulphate, A, de- omp. 05–10; B, ecomp. 06–12	Salts, s. H_2O; less s. lower alcohols; i. acet., H_2O-immisc. solvents	Surface active compound. Marked bactericidal activity against a wide variety of gram −ve bacteria and to a lesser degree against gram +ve bacteria and fungi	Crude material is a mixture of 3 components, colistin A and B being the major ones; B differs from A in that *iso*octanoic acid replaces the 6-methyl-octanoic acid. Action similar to polymyxin which it resembles; causes disorganization of the cell membrane. Solutions of colistin salts are relatively stable pH 2–6, stability decreases over pH 6. Growth inhibitory concentrations of sulphate (μg/ml) *E. coli*, 0·01–0·02; *B. cereus*, 11; *B. subtilis*, 33; *S. aureus*, *S. faecalis*, fungi, $>$ 100	PROPERTIES *Antibiotics Annual* **1959–60**, 41. *C.A.* **50**, 13374 (1956). STRUCTURE *J. Biochem., Tokyo* **54**, 25 (1963).
ecomp. 55–6	s. H_2O; sl. s. MeOH, propylene glycol	Inhibits cell wall synthesis in both gram +ve and gram −ve organisms	Prevents bacterial growth and causes lysis by blocking conversion of L-alanine to D-alanine and the formation of D-alanyl-D-alanine. Inhibition reversed competitively by D-alanine. Forms salts with acids and bases. Neutral or acid solutions are unstable. Aq. soln. buffered to pH 10 with Na_2CO_3 can be stored for a week at +4°	ACTION *J.A.C.S.* **81**, 3803 (1959). *J.A.C.S.* **82**, 998 (1960). REVIEW *Antimicrobial Agents Annual* **1960**, p. 328.
ecomp. 5–55	v.s. H_2O; s. aq. solns. of MeOH, EtOH, acet.; sl. s. abs. alcohols	Inhibits purine synthesis in bacterial and mammalian systems	Glutamine analogue interferes with the transfer of amide group from glutamine to formylglycinamide ribotide. At high concn. other glutamine-requiring reactions inhibited. Prevents the growth of exptl. tumours but toxic to animals. Of 57 strains of bacteria tested only 6 were sensitive to 12·5 μg/ml or less and of 104 fungi and yeasts examined only 5 yeasts inhibited by 50 μg/ml or less. Aqueous solutions should be kept at pH 4·5–6·5. Compd. rapidly destroyed in neutral aq. soln. at 100°. $E^{1\%}_{1\,cm}$ at 274 mμ = 683	SYN. *J.A.C.S.* **80**, 3941 (1958). ISOL. and PROPERTIES *J.A.C.S.* **78**, 3075 (1956). REVIEW *Amino acids and Peptides with Antimetabolic Activity*, pp. 62, 75 (1958) Ciba Symposium. *Anticancer Agents*, p. 183.
5–40 ter cuum ying)	v.s. MeOH, EtOH, benz., eth., acet., $CHCl_3$, ethyl acetate; slowly s. H_2O (2·1 mg/ml R.T.)	Inhibits protein synthesis. Most active against gram +ve organisms	Most widely used of macrolide group of antibiotics characterized by a large lactone ring with novel sugars, usually amino sugars, linked glycosidically. Mechanism of action not clear; inhibits protein synthesis but not nucleic acid formation. Solution 1–2 mg/ml sealed and frozen stable for several weeks	PROPERTIES *J.A.C.S.* **76**, 3121 (1954). *J.A.C.S.* **79**, 6062 (1957). ACTION *B.B.A.* **33**, 274 (1959).
–8	s. EtOH, eth., acet.; i. H_2O, acids, alkalis	Surface active agent and inhibitor of oxidative phosphorylation. Effective against gram +ve and some gram −ve organisms	Basic cyclic polypeptide produced by strain of *Bacillus brevis*. Acts as an uncoupler of oxidative phosphorylation in intact cells and cell-free preparations; in the latter phosphorylation is uncoupled without affecting oxidation at 8×10^{-6} M. As cationic detergent disorganizes protoplast membrane allowing leakage of intracellular constituents, as does tyrocidin (*J. gen. Microbiol.* **1**, 77 (1947)). Other gramicidins (A, B, and C) which occur in the tyrothricin complex produced by other strains of *B. brevis* are neutral peptides characterized by the presence of 2-aminoethanol; they are known to uncouple oxidative phosphorylation, but are not strongly surface active (*Adv. Enzymol.* **4**, 153 (1944))	STRUCTURE *B.J.* **41**, 496 (1947). ACTION *Adv. Enzymol.* **4**, 153 (1944). *J.B.C.* **219**, 853 (1956). *B.B.A.* **62**, 556 (1962). REVIEWS *Adv. Protein Chem.* **8**, 61 (1953). *Pharmac. Rev.* **15**, 497 (1963). *Metabolic Inhibitors*, p. 87.

15. Antimetabolites, Antibacterial Agents, and Enzyme Inhibitors

No.	Name	Synonyms	Formula	M. wt.	Physical form
18	Hadacidin	*N*-Formyl-hydroxyamino-acetic acid	$OHC{-}N(OH){-}CH_2{-}COOH$	119·1	Both free acid an monosodium sa cryst.
19	Kanamycin		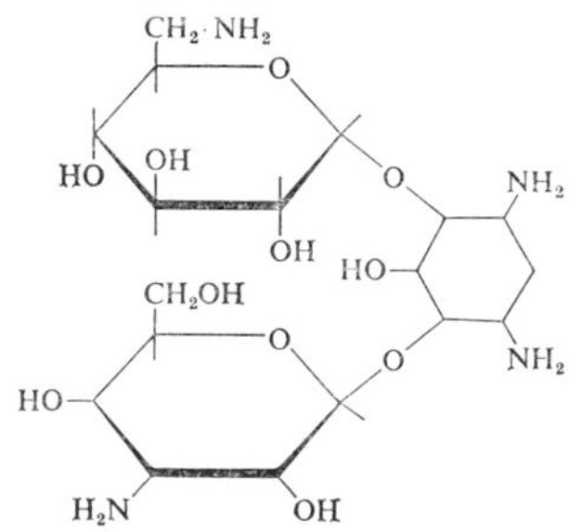	484·5	Hydrated sulphate, flat, pale yel. prisms from dil. MeOH
20	Mitomycin		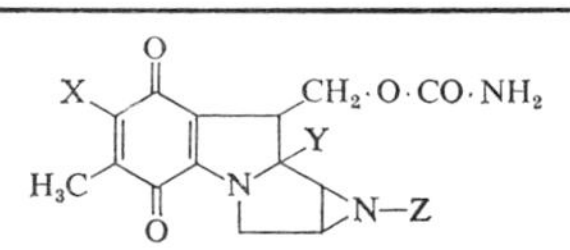 *X* *Y* *Z* mitomycin A H_3CO OCH_3 H ,, B H_3CO OH CH_3 ,, C H_2N OCH_3 H	C, 334·3	A, reddish cryst B, purplish cryst C, purple or de violet cryst.
21	Neomycin		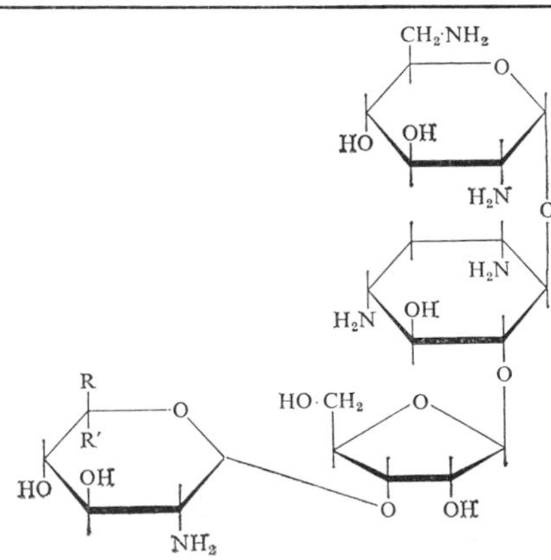 *R* *R'* neomycin B —H $—CH_2·NH_2$,, C $—CH_2·NH_2$ —H	B and C, 614·7	amorph. base forming amorp hydrochlorides

M.p.	*Solubility*	*Use*	*General remarks*	*References*
Free acid 119–20 Mono-sodium salt, decomp. 205–10	Cryst. acid, s. H_2O, MeOH, EtOH, acet., eth.; Monosodium salt, s. H_2O, MeOH; i. EtOH	Inhibits purine biosynthesis in bacterial and mammalian systems. Exhibits some antitumour activity	Formed by *Penicillium frequentans.* Inhibits growth of human adenocarcinoma-1 in embryonated egg. Stops biosynthesis of AMP and dAMP; acts as analogue of L-aspartate which can reverse the inhibition. Acts by inhibiting adenylosuccinate synthetase, involved in conversion of IMP to adenylosuccinic acid. The free acid is unstable and in soln. hydrolyses to give formic acid and hydroxyaminoacetic acid. pK_a: 3·5, 9·1	ISOL. and PROPERTIES *Biochemistry* **1**, 340 (1962). ACTION *J.B.C.* **237**, 1932, 1937 (1962).
Sulphate, decomp. over wide temp. range > 250	s. H_2O and dil. water-misc. solvents; nearly i. MeOH, EtOH, acet., eth., pet. eth., $CHCl_3$	Affects cell membrane and possibly also inhibits protein synthesis. Broad spectrum antibiotic though rel. inactive against Streptococci, Diplococci, and Clostridia	Not studied extensively but evidence points to same site of action as streptomycin (*see below*). Aqueous solutions retain more than 90% of their activity after autoclaving for 1 hr at 120°. Standard bactericidal concentration, against *E. coli*, 40 μg/ml (*B.B.A.* **55**, 787 (1962))	STRUCTURE *J.A.C.S.* **80**, 4115 (1958). ACTION *B.B.A.* **55**, 787 (1962). REVIEW *Ann. N.Y. Acad. Sci.* **76**, art. 2, 17 (1958).
[illegible], 159–1 d. [illegible], 182– d. [illegible], > 360 d.	s. H_2O	Inhibits DNA synthesis. Broad spectrum antitumour activity and strong bactericidal action against gram +ve and gram −ve organisms and acid-fast bacilli	Group of cpds. of which C is most widely used since the least toxic and with most potent antitumour activity. At low concns. DNA of cells actively synthesizing RNA and protein converted to acid sol. products. Evidence suggests primary action leads to scission of DNA strands. Complete inhibition of net DNA synthesis in *E. coli* by 10 μg/ml. Drug stable in aq. soln. pH 6–9, can be stored at +5° for 1 week with little loss of activity. Readily decomposed by light	STRUCTURE *J.A.C.S.* **84**, 3185 3187, 3188 (1962). ACTION *B.B.A.* **45**, 608 (1960). *B.B.A.* **55**, 277, 558 (1962). REVIEW *Anticancer Agents* p. 212.
[illegible], 225–[illegible] d.	s. H_2O; sl. s. MeOH	Affects cellular permeability barrier and possibly inhibits protein synthesis also. Active against many gram +ve and gram −ve bacteria	Polybasic antibiotic which has action resembling that of streptomycin (*see below*). Occurs as complex of three components A, B, and C. Component B, which is obtained as the sulphate and hydrochloride, appears to be the one most widely used. Aqueous soln. stable pH 2–9. Standard bactericidal concn., against *E. coli*, 3 μg/ml (*B.B.A.* **55**, 787 (1962))	STRUCTURE *J.A.C.S.* **75**, 1018 (1953). *J.A.C.S.* **84**, 3218 (1962). ACTION *B.B.A.* **55**, 787 (1962).

No.	*Name*	*Synonyms*	*Formula*	*M. wt.*	*Physical form*
22	Novobiocin		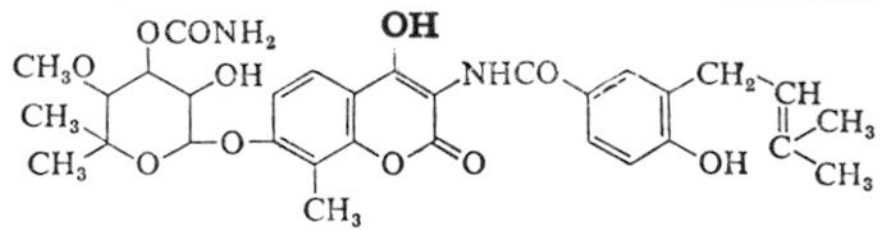	612·7	pale yel. orthorhombic cryst. from EtOH. Monosodium salt minute wh. cryst
23	Nystatin		Polyene antibiotic, structure unknown		light yel. powder
24	Oleandomycin		Not completely elucidated, it is a polyhydroxyepoxypolymethylketolactone of macrolide type containing glycosidically bound desosamine and L-oleandrose $C_{35}H_{61}NO_{12}$	688	Free base, col. cryst. from aq. MeOH or aq. acet. Hydrochlo ide, long needles from ethyl aceta
	Oligomycin, *see* 15. H, Inhibitors of respiratory enzymes, photosynthesis, and phosphorylation; uncoupling reagents				
25	Oxytetracycline	Terramycin	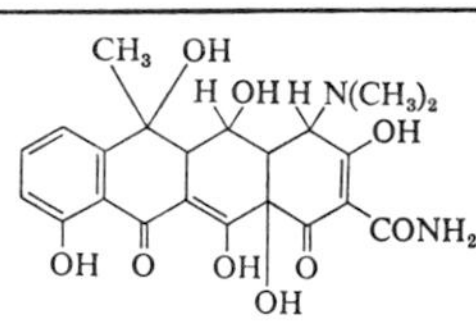	460·4 (anhyd.)	Dihydrate, need from water. Hydrochloride, needles from MeOH, platel from water at 5 Disodium salt hydrate, yel. cr tals
26	Paromomycin	Humatin	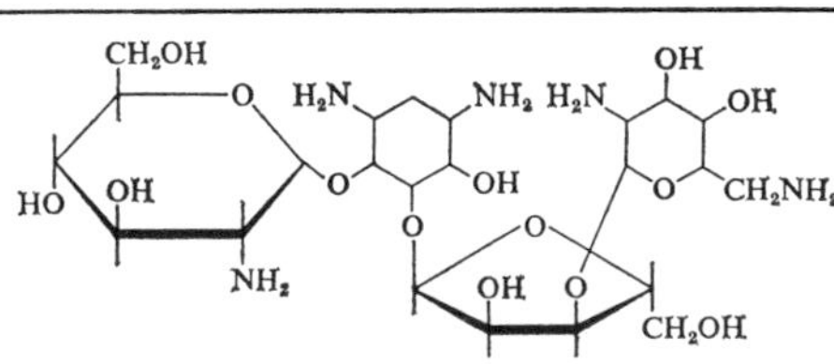	615·7	amorph. wh. powder
27	Penicillin		All penicillins have the β-lactam-thiazolidine structure shown below: 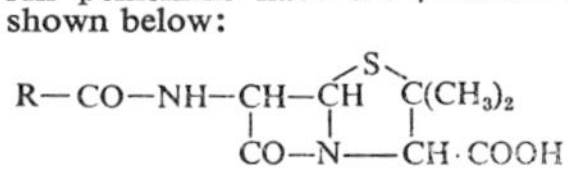 Penicillin G, benzylpenicillin R=PhCH$_2$—	334·4 (free acid) 356·4 (Na salt)	Free acid, amo wh. powder. Sodium salt, cr from MeOH-e acetate

M.p.	*Solubility*	*Use*	*General remarks*	*References*
152–6 decomp. Na salt, d. > 220	s. aq. soln. pH > 7·5, acet., lower alcohols, ethyl acetate; Monosodium salt, freely s. H_2O	Causes damage to membrane of growing gram +ve bacterial cells	Destroys permeability barrier of growing cells although no large-scale cell lysis. Causes *S. aureus* to accumulate cell wall precursors but this is probably a secondary effect. The drug is sensitive to light. pK_a: 4·3, 9·1	STRUCTURE *J.A.C.S.* **78**, 2019 (1956). *J.A.C.S.* **80**, 5168 (1958). ACTION *Arch. B.B.* **85**, 176 (1959). *B.B.A.* **33**, 280 (1959). *Science* **136**, 316 (1962).
	s. MeOH, EtOH, propylene glycol; pract. i. H_2O	Acts on cell membrane. No action on bacteria, active against yeasts and fungi	Acts on cell membrane which it affects in the absence of growth causing leakage of intracellular constituents. Solutions and aqueous suspensions are unstable, heat, light, and oxygen accelerate decomposition. Aqueous suspension, pH 7, is stable to heating at 100° for 10 min	STRUCTURE *Science* **121**, 147 (1955) ACTION *Ann. N.Y. Acad. Sci.* **89**, 122, 134 (1960). *J. Bact.* **82**, 889 (1961). REVIEW *Trans. N.Y. Acad. Sci.* ser. 2, **19**, 447 (1957).
Free base, 110 d. Hydrochloride, 134–5	s. MeOH, EtOH, acet., dil. acid; sl. s. H_2O; pract. i. hexane, CCl_4	Probably inhibits protein synthesis. Inhibits growth of gram +ve bacteria and Mycobacteria, also effective against some gram −ve organisms and viruses	Member of macrolide group of antibiotics. Action little studied, possibly inhibits protein synthesis by analogy with erythromycin (*see above*). pK_a: 8·5	STRUCTURE *J.A.C.S.* **80**, 3777 (1958). *Antibiotics Annual* **1957–8**, p. 476.
Dihydrate, 181–2 d. Hydrochloride, 179–82 d.	Dihydrate, s. MeOH, EtOH, acet.; sl. s. H_2O, pH 7. Hydrochloride, v.s. H_2O; s. MeOH, EtOH, acet.	Bacteriostatic; said to inhibit protein synthesis. Active against gram +ve, gram −ve, and acid-fast bacteria	*See* Chlortetracycline. Very unstable in soln., stable in dry state. See also data in Chelating Agents, p. 433. pK_a: 3·1, 7·26, 9·11	STRUCTURE *J.A.C.S.* **74**, 3708 (1952). *See* Chlorotetracycline.
	s. H_2O; mod. s. MeOH; sl. s. EtOH	Possibly inhibits protein synthesis and affects permeability barrier of bacterial cells. Effective against a variety of gram −ve bacilli and strains of Staphylococci	Polybasic antibiotic not investigated in detail. Thought to have action similar to that of streptomycin (*see below*). Available as sulphate and hydrochloride. Structure of paromomycin II very similar to that of neomycin B and C. *J.A.C.S.* **84**, 3219 (1962)	STRUCTURE *J.A.C.S.* **81**, 3480, 3482 (1959). *Antibiotics Annual* **1959–60**, p. 293.
Na salt, 215 d.	Free acid, s. MeOH, EtOH, eth., acet., ethyl acetate; sp. s. H_2O; i. pet. eth. Sodium salt, v.s. H_2O; sl. s. EtOH; pract. i. acet., eth. $CHCl_3$, ethyl acetate	Inhibits cell wall formation. Active mainly against gram +ve organisms less effective with gram −ve and acid-fast bacteria	Blocks cell wall formation in growing cells resulting in accumulation of uracil nucleotides of muramic acid peptides and in the formation of protoplasts preceding lysis. Interferes with the transfer of the muramic acid peptide from its UDP carrier to polymerized position in the cell wall; mechanism of interference is not known. Resistant strains of susceptible organisms occur which produce inducible penicillinase. The free acid retains its activity when dry but is rapidly inactivated by small amounts of water	REVIEWS *Antimicrobial Agents Annual* **1960**, p. 328. *The Bacteria* **4**, 360 (1962). Newer synthetic penicillins: *Metabolic Inhibitors*, p. 92.

No.	Name	Synonyms	Formula	M. wt.	Physical form
28	Pikromycin	Picromycin	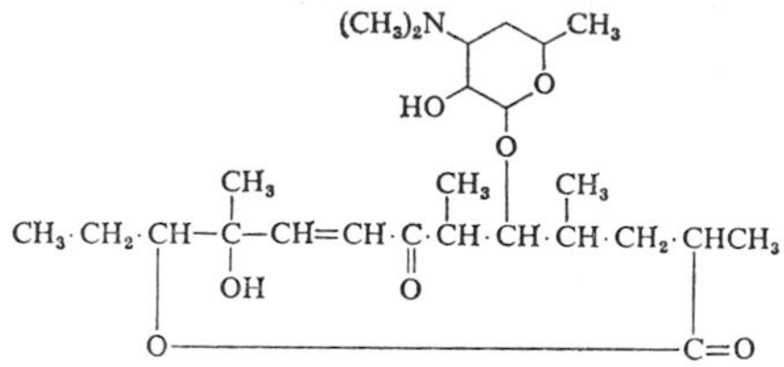	469·6	rect. platelets from MeOH
29	Polymyxin	Aerosporin formerly used as synonym for polymyxin A, now a trade name for polymyxin B sulphate	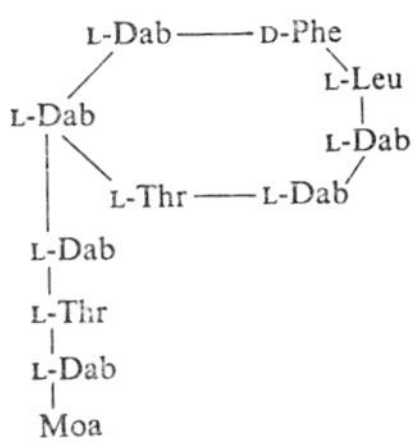 **Polymyxin B_1** (*J. Biochem., Tokyo* **54**, 555 (1963). See also *Nature* **202**, 1211 (1964) where structure is limited to either 7α or 8γ ring) L-Dab = L-α,γ-diaminobutyric acid Moa = (+)-6-methyloctan-1-oic acid	approx. 1250 for A, B, D, and E	D hydrochloride, wh. powder. B sulphate, wh. powder

Note: Most structural studies carried out on polymyxin B which was separated into two components differing only in the nature of their fatty acid component (B_1 contains (+)6-methyloctanoic acid and B_2, *iso*octanoic acid). There is some confusion in the literature as to the configuration of Phe and Leu in the ring—in 1953 (*Adv. Protein Chem.*) incorrectly designated L-Phe and D-Leu. However, this error was perpetuated through the biochemical literature. Correct configuration of these amino acids, D-Phe and L-Leu, through chemical literature where most of structural work reported, e.g. *J.A.C.S.* **76**, 4892 (1954) onwards.

No.	Name	Synonyms	Formula	M. wt.	Physical form
30	Polypeptin		Consists of 2 closely related components each related to the polymyxins, having a cyclic structure and a side chain containing (+)6-methyloctan-1-oic acid The major component accounts for 80% of the material	Major component: Free base, 1145 Sulphate, 1292	Normally obtained as sulphate, form of which depends on cryst. solvent—gives triangular prisms from conc. soln. in warm 65% EtOH cooled to 20°
31	Psicofuranine	6-Amino-9-D-psicofuranosylpurine	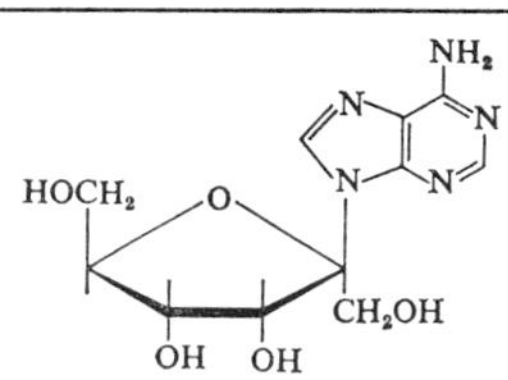	296·3	needle-shaped cryst.
32	Puromycin	Stylomycin	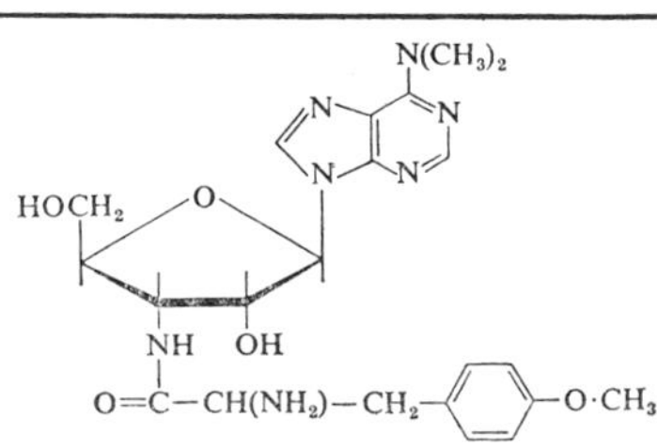	471·5	wh. cryst.

M.p.	Solubility	Use	General remarks	References
169·5–70	Freely s. acet., benz., $CHCl_3$, ethyl acetate; mod. s. MeOH, EtOH, eth.; v. sp. s. H_2O, pet. eth.	Possibly inhibits protein synthesis	Little studied member of macrolide group of antibiotics (*see* erythromycin)	ISOL. *Naturwissenschaften* **37**, 138 (1950). *Ber.* **84**, 284 (1951). STRUCTURE *Ber.* **90**, 605 (1957). *Helv. chim. Acta* **40**, 119 (1957).
D hydrochloride, 228–30 d.	Free bases, sl. s. H_2O and almost i. alcohol. D hydrochloride, v.s. H_2O, MeOH; s. decrease as M. wt. alcohol increases; i. eth., acet., esters, hydrocarbons. B sulphate, v.s. H_2O; sl. s. MeOH, EtOH, acet.; i. pet. eth.	Surface active compounds, bactericidal to gram +ve and gram −ve organisms. Polymyxin group differs from other cationic surface active agents in being more active against gram −ve than gram +ve bacteria	5 known polymyxins A, B, C, D, and E synthesized by *B. polymyxa*; a given strain of the organism in general synthesizes only one polymyxin. All 5 compounds have similar chemical and biological properties. The bactericidal action is due to combination with and disorganization of the cell membrane (*J. gen. Microbiol.* **9**, 54 (1953)). Action antagonized by cations (*J. gen. Microbiol.* **10**, 491 (1954)). Used in preparation of cell-free nitroreductase (*Nature, Lond.* **184**, 1565 (1959)). Mortality > 99·5%, in 20 min, when *E. coli* and *Ps. denitrificans* (1 mg dry wt./ml) treated with 20 and 25 μg polymyxin/ml	REVIEWS *Adv. Protein Chem.* **8**, 49 (1953). *Bact. Rev.* **20**, 14 (1956). *Strategy of Chemotherapy*, Soc. Gen. Microbiol. Symp. **8**, 62 (1958). *Metabolic Inhibitors*, p. 88. STRUCTURE *J. Biochem., Tokyo* **54**, 555 (1963). *Nature, Lond.* **202**, 1211 (1964).
Sulphate (mixture) 235 d.	Dry cryst. sulphate, s. ethylene glycol, gl. acetic, pyr.; sl. s. H_2O, solubilized by Na or NH_4 acetate; rapidly s. MeOH and EtOH, ppts. on standing; i. acet., eth., benz.	Surface active agent. Inhibits growth of bacteria and fungi	Basic peptide which, like polymyxin, causes disorganization of cell membranes	REVIEW *Adv. Protein Chem.* **8**, 49 (1953).
212–14 d.		Inhibits purine synthesis, possesses antitumour in addition to antibacterial properties	Structural analogue of adenosine; acts by inhibiting the conversion of xanthosine-5-phosphate (XMP) to GMP by XMP aminase. Inhibition of growth of *S. aureus* by drug reversed by guanine, guanosine, and GMP	STRUCTURE *J.A.C.S.* **81**, 1767 (1959). ACTION *J. Bact.* **80**, 30 (1960). *B.B.R.C.* **3**, 596 (1960). *Cold Spring Harb. Symp. quant. Biol.* **26**, 323 (1961). REVIEW *Anticancer Agents*, p. 163.
175·5–77	Free base, sp. s. H_2O as well as organic solvents. Dihydrochloride and monosulphate, readily s. H_2O	Inhibits protein synthesis. Prevents growth of bacteria, algae, protozoa, and mammalian cells	Causes premature release of partially formed protein chains from ribosomes; possible that it displaces the terminal transfer RNA binding polypeptide chain to ribosome resulting in the release of the chain with a molecule of puromycin attached. Evidence of reversal of inhibition by washing inhibited ribosomes has been obtained. Puromycin is a diacidic base. pK_a: 6·8, 7·2	STRUCTURE *J.A.C.S.* **80**, 2736 (1958). ACTION *B.B.A.* **55**, 865 (1962). *J.B.C.* **237**, 477 (1962). *B.B.R.C.* **7**, 326 (1962).

No.	Name	Synonyms	Formula	M. wt.	Physical form
33	Ristocetin		Consists of two components ristocetins A and B both complex amino acid-containing oligosaccharides of unknown structure	approx. 4000	Sulphate, cryst.
34	Spiramycin		Unknown, empirical formula $C_{22-24}H_{34-44}NO_{7-8}$		Free base, amorph. powder. Sulphate, cryst.
35	Streptolin		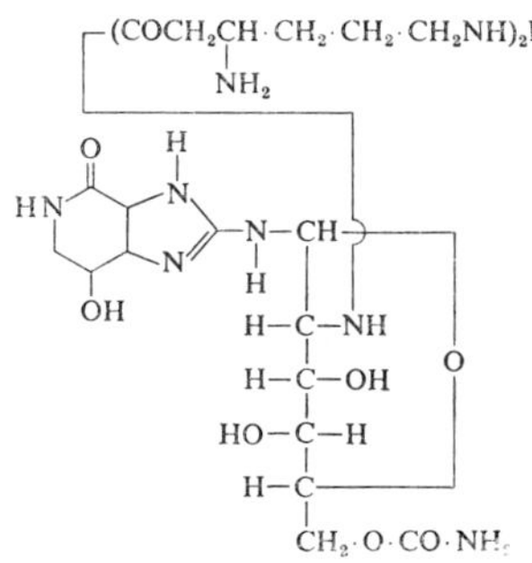	630·7	non-cryst., isol. as hydrochloride in the form of a gummy mass
36	Streptogramin group of antibiotics. This group includes: Streptogramin Ostreogrycin PA 114 Staphylomycin M_1 Mikamycin. All these complex antibiotics consist of at least two components belonging to two major groups, A and B	Group A: Streptogramin A Ostreogrycin A PA 114 A Staphylomycin M_1	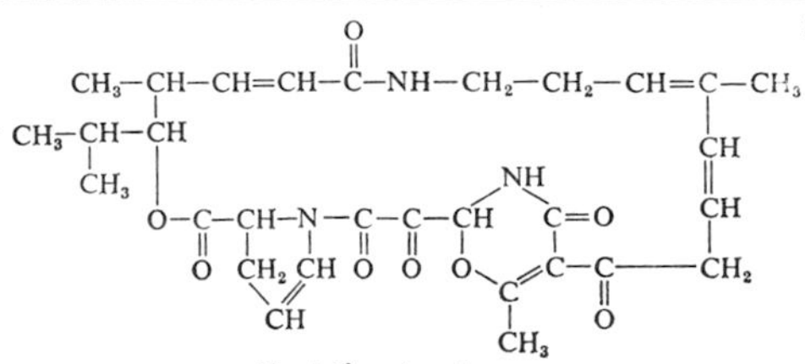 Tentative structure Streptogramin A, Ostreogrycin A, PA 114 A, Staphylomycin M_1 } Identical	567·6	col. cryst.
		Mikamycin A	Mikamycin A is different and its structure is not yet known		
		Group B: Streptogramin B Ostreogrycin B PA 114 B Mikamycin B	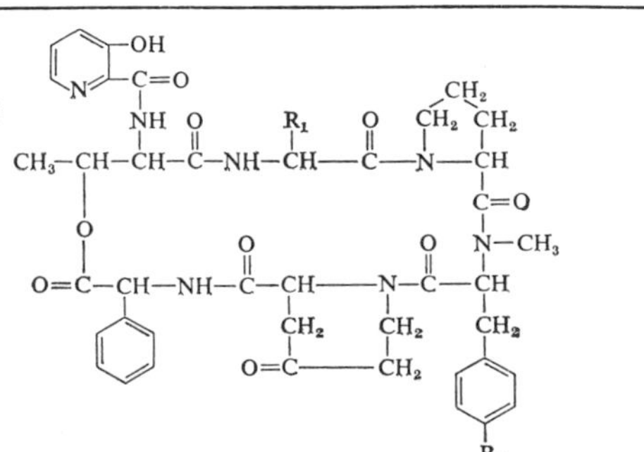 Streptogramin B, Ostreogrycin B, PA 114 B, Mikamycin B } R_1 = —CH_2—CH_3; R_2 = —$N(CH_3)_2$	867·0	col. prisms from MeOH, col. needles from toluene
		Staphylomycin S	Staphylomycin S R_1 = —CH_2—CH_3; R_2 = —H	823·9	col. cryst.

M.p.	*Solubility*	*Use*	*General remarks*	*References*
	s. acidic soln.; much less s. aq. soln. in neutral pH range; i. organic solvents	Inhibits cell wall synthesis. Effective against gram +ve bacteria and Mycobacteria	Ristocetin A and B and their partial hydrolysis products like several other antibiotics, e.g. penicillin, induce accumulation of cell wall precursors in *S. aureus*. Inhibition of cell wall synthesis is a selective effect and protein synthesis is not affected. Both components show good stability in aq. acid soln. but are readily inactivated pH > 7. Min. growth inhibitory concn. both A and B with *S. aureus*, 15 μg/ml	GENERAL *Antibiotics Annual* **1959–60, p. 497.** *Antimicrobial Agents Annual* **1960, p. 10.** ACTION *J.B.C.* **238,** 2264 (1963).
	Free base, sl. s. H_2O; s. most organic solvents. Sulphate, s. H_2O, MeOH, EtOH, BuOH	Possibly inhibits protein synthesis. Active against gram +ve and a few gram −ve bacteria and some Rickettsiae	Antibiotic which has been little studied, classified in the macrolide group (*see* erythromycin)	GENERAL *Antibiotics Annual* **1958–9, p. 204.** *Antimicrobial Agents Annual* **1960, p. 459.**
	s. H_2O	Active against a wide range of gram +ve and gram −ve bacteria	Mechanism of action not studied, possibly similar to that of streptomycin. Molecule possesses 4 basic centres. pK_a: 7·5, 8·4, 9·3, 10·6. Forms crystalline helianthate	STRUCTURE and PROPERTIES *J.A.C.S.* **75,** 2036 (1953). *J.A.C.S.* **83,** 4295 (1961).
162–5 d.	s. $CHCl_3$, acet., EtOH, MeOH; v. sl. s. H_2O	Inhibit protein synthesis. Bacteriostatic, active mainly against gram +ve cocci	Mixtures of groups A and B are synergistic and bactericidal. Effective 0·02–1·8 μg/ml against gram +ve cells, 10–100 μg/ml against gram −ve. Only staphylomycin and mikamycin are used clinically as topical agents. They do not distribute well through the tissues from the site of application. Only a very small amount is recovered in urine	STRUCTURE *B.J.* **68,** 24P (1958). *J.C.S.* **1960,** 2286. *J.A.C.S.* **82,** 4414 (1960). *C.A.* **57,** 16738*g* (1962). A.R. Todd–IUPAC, Brussels (1962). ACTION *B.B.A.* **61,** 849 (1962). *J. gen. Microbiol.* **42,** 93 (1966). *Symp. Soc. gen. Microbiol.* **16,** 181 (1966).
266–8	s. $CHCl_3$, dil. acid, aq. NaOH; sl. s. MeOH, benz., toluene; i. H_2O, eth.	Inhibitors of protein, nucleic acid, and cell wall synthesis by an unknown mechanism. Bacteriostatic, active mainly against gram +ve bacilli		
240–2	v. s. $CHCl_3$; s. acet., ethyl acetate, dioxan; sl. s. eth., MeOH, EtOH, benz.; i. H_2O, pet. eth.			

No.	*Name*	*Synonyms*	*Formula*	*M. wt.*	*Physical form*
37	Streptomycin	*N*-Methyl-L-glucosaminido-streptosido-streptidine	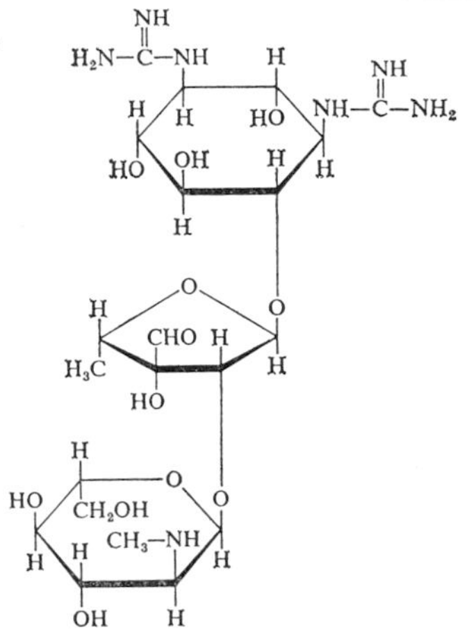	581·6	Base, sulphate and hydrochloride all hygroscopic wh. powders
38	Subtilin		Basic, cyclic polypeptide the structure of which has not been fully elucidated	min. value 3420	amorph. wh. powder
39	Tyrocidin		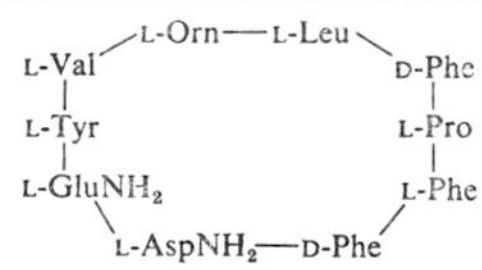 ***Tyrocidin A*** Tyrocidin B has L-Tryp in place of L-Phe above	Tyrocidin A, 1287	Hydrochloride of tyrocidin complex obtained as fine needles from MeOH or EtOH+HCl
	Valinomycin, *see* 15. H, Inhibitors of respiratory enzymes, photosynthesis, and phosphorylation; uncoupling reagents				
40	Vancomycin		Large molecule containing D-glucose and aspartic acid, detailed structure obscure	3200–3500	Isolated as hydrochloride, a wh. solid
41	Viomycin		Unknown, appears to be a peptide containing guanidine $C_{18}H_{31-33}N_9O_8$		Free base and sulphate exist as purple cryst.

M.p.	*Solubility*	*Use*	*General remarks*	*References*
Sulphate, 192	s. H_2O; salts, v.s. H_2O; almost i. EtOH, acet., eth., $CHCl_3$	Affects permeability barrier of bacterial cells and probably also inhibits protein synthesis. Active against gram +ve and gram −ve bacteria but not against Rickettsiae, viruses or fungi	Action not clear; streptomycin resistance and dependence can occur. May be two different sites of affinity in the bacterial cell. One involves the ribosomes and leads to bacteriostasis by inhibiting protein synthesis. The second involves the wall-membrane complex; this is the bactericidal lesion. It requires growth for its expression and results in breakdown of the cellular permeability barrier. Drug is relatively stable pH 1–10 but decomposes fairly readily outside this range. Standard bactericidal concn., against *E. coli*, 50 μg/ml (*B.B.A.* 55, 787 (1962)). More recently streptomycin has been shown to cause misreading of the genetic code (*Proc. natn. Acad. Sci., U.S.A.* **51**, 883 (1964))	REVIEW *The Bacteria* **4**, 381 (1962).
	s. dil. acids, 80% EtOH; sp. s. H_2O, pH 6–9; i. EtOH, acet., eth., pet. eth.	Surface active agent. Effective primarily against gram +ve bacteria	Surface active, basic polypeptide which rapidly disorganizes the cell membrane	*Adv. Protein Chem.* **8**, 57 (1953). *J.A.C.S.* **81**, 696, 701 (1959).
Complex hydrochloride, 240 d.	Complex hydrochloride, s. 95% EtOH, gl. acetic, pyr; sl. s. H_2O, acet., EtOH; i. eth., hydrocarbons, $CHCl_3$	Surface active agent. Effective against gram +ve and gram −ve bacteria	'Tyrocidin' is a family of basic homeomeric peptides, certain of which are cyclic, related to each other and characterized by the possession of ornithine. Three major components have been separated, A, B, and C; A has been studied in the most detail. Disorganizes cell membrane permeability	STRUCTURE *J.A.C.S.* **76**, 688 (1954). *J.A.C.S.* **77**, 6627 (1955). REVIEWS *Adv. Enzymol.* **4**, 153 (1944). *Adv. Protein Chem.* **8**, 60 (1953).
	Hydrochloride, s. H_2O; mod. s. dil. MeOH; i. acet., eth., higher alcohols	Inhibits cell wall synthesis. Active against gram +ve organisms esp. Staphylococci resistant to other antibiotics	Like penicillin inhibits incorporation of amino acids into the cell wall of *S. aureus*. Also causes accumulation of hexosamine-containing uridine nucleotides; however, not reported to produce lysis of protoplasts. Min. growth inhibitory concn. 2·5 μg/ml against *S. aureus*	PROPERTIES *Antibiotics Annual* **1955–6**, p. 606. ACTION *B.B.R.C.* **6**, 167 (1961). *B.B.A.* **52**, 403 (1961).
Sulphate, 280 d.	Sulphate, s. H_2O; rel. i. MeOH, EtOH, eth., acet., benz., ethyl acetate	Possibly affects cell membrane and protein synthesis. Used in TB therapy	Action thought to be similar to that of streptomycin. Used in form of sulphate; solutions adjusted to pH 5–6 are quite stable	

E. TRYPANOCIDAL COMPOUNDS

By B. A. NEWTON (*Sub-Department of Chemical Microbiology, Department of Biochemistry, University of Cambridge*)

General reference

B. A. Newton, 'Trypanocidal agents', *Metabolic Inhibitors*, eds. R. M. Hochster and J. H. Quastel, vol. 2, pp. 285–310, Academic Press, New York (1963).

No.	*Name*	*Synonyms*	*Formula*	*M. wt.*	*Physical form*
1	Atoxyl	Sodium *p*-aminophenyl arsonate, Protoxyl, Arsamin	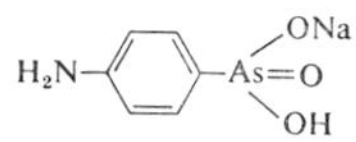	239·0; Tetra-hydrate, 311·1	wh. powder or needles
2	Homidium bromide	2:7-Diamino-10-ethyl-9-phenylphenanthridinium bromide, Ethidium bromide	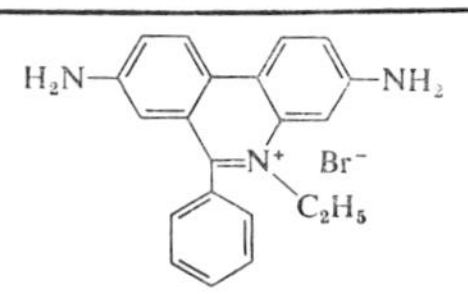	394·3	dark red cryst. or powder
3	Quinapyramine	4-Amino-6-(2-amino-6-methylpyrimidin-4-yl-amino)-quinaldine-1:1′-dimethyl sulphate, Antrycide	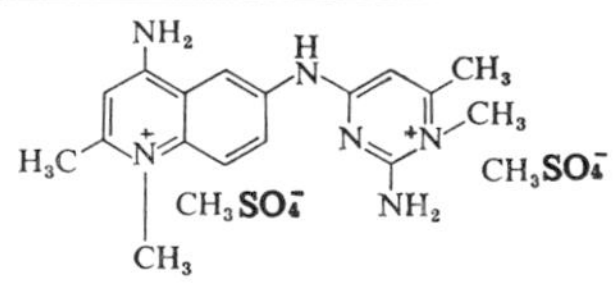	532·6	wh. powder
4	Suramin	Hexasodium *sym.* bis-(*m*-aminobenzoyl-*m*-amino-*p*-methylbenzoyl-1-naphthyl-amino-4:6:8-trisulphonate) carbamide Antrypol, Bayer 205, Germanin, Fourneau 309	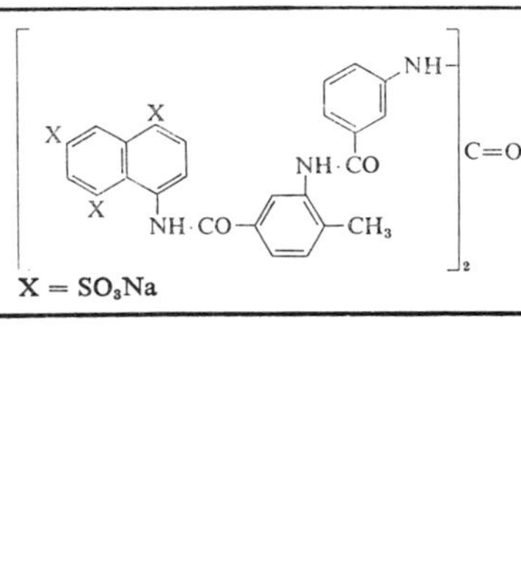 X = SO_3Na	1429·2	wh. or creamy wh. powder

M.p.	pK_a	*Solubility*	*References*	*General remarks*
232		sl. s. H_2O, EtOH	REVIEW *Pharmac. Rev.* 3, 107 (1951)	General inhibitor of SH-enzymes. *See also* Marpharsan in 15. I, THIOL REAGENTS.
247–9		s. H_2O, EtOH, MeOH	REVIEW *Expl Parasit.* 12, 274 (1962)	Potent inhibitor of DNA synthesis *in vivo* (*J. gen. Microbiol.* **17**, 718 (1957)); inhibits DNA synthesis by cell-free DNA-polymerase (*B.J.* **86**, 562 (1963)) and RNA synthesis by cell-free DNA-dependent RNA-polymerase (*J. gen. Microbiol.* **33**, x (1963)). Also inhibitor of enzyme synthesis in bacteria (*B.B.A.* **34**, 325 (1959)) and bacteriophage development (*J. gen. Microbiol.* **6**, 1 (1952)). Probably acts by forming a complex with DNA. (*Symp. Soc. gen. Microbiol.* **16**, 235 (1966).)
		s. H_2O	REVIEW *Expl Parasit.* **12**, 274 (1962)	Inhibitor of RNA and protein synthesis in flagellates (Biological Council Symposium on *Drugs, Parasites, and Hosts*, p. 142, Churchill (1962)). Causes intracellular aggregation of ribosomes in sensitive organisms (*B.J.* **84**, 109P (1962)). *See also Symp. Soc. gen. Microbiol.* **16**, 213 (1966).
		freely s. H_2O; sp. s. 95% EtOH; i. benz., eth., $CHCl_3$		Inhibits trypsin, fumarase, hyaluronidase, urease, hexokinase, succinic dehydrogenase, choline dehydrogenase, ribonuclease, β-galactosidase, and lysozyme. Active against these enzymes at concentrations within the range 10^{-4}–10^{-5} M (*B.J.* **47**, 158 (1950)). Unstable in solution. Has been used in a rapid method for determination of the isoelectric point of certain sensitive enzymes, the method being particularly useful in early stages of enzyme purification (*B.J.* **50**, 421 (1952)).

F. SURFACE ACTIVE COMPOUNDS

By B. A. NEWTON (*Sub-Department of Chemical Microbiology, Department of Biochemistry, University of Cambridge*)

General references

1. F. W. Putnam, 'The interactions of proteins and synthetic detergents', *Adv. Protein Chem.* **4,** 79 (1948).
2. H. N. Glassman, 'Surface active agents and their application in bacteriology', *Bact. Rev.* **12,** 105 (1948).
3. B. A. Newton, 'Surface-active bactericides', *The Strategy of Chemotherapy, Symp. Soc. gen. Microbiol.* **8,** 62 (1958).
4. R. D. Hotchkiss, 'The nature of the bactericidal action of surface active agents', *Ann. N.Y. Acad. Sci.* **46,** 479 (1946).

No.	*Name*	*Synonyms*	*Formula*	*M. wt.*
1	Cetylpyridinium chloride	1-Hexadecylpyridinium chloride, Ceepryn chloride, Cepacol chloride, Cetamium	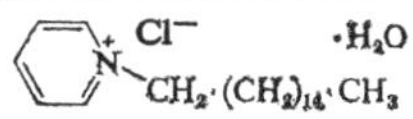	358·0
2	Cetyltrimethyl-ammonium bromide	Cetavlon, Cetrimide, CTAB, Cetylamine, Quamonium	$(CH_3)_3\cdot \overset{+}{N}(C_{16}H_{33})\cdot Br^-$	364·5
3	Dioctyl sodium sulphosuccinate	Aerosol OT, bis(2-ethylhexyl) sodium sulphosuccinate	$H_2C\cdot CO\cdot O\cdot CH_2\cdot CH(C_2H_5)\cdot (CH_2)_3\cdot CH_3$ $NaO_3S\cdot CH\cdot CO\cdot O\cdot CH_2\cdot CH(C_2H_5)\cdot (CH_2)_3\cdot CH_3$	444·6
4	Emasol 4130	Polyoxyethylene sorbitan monoleate		
	Gramicidin S, *see* 15. D, Antibiotics			
5	Lubrol W			
6	Nonidet P40			
	Polymyxin, *see* 15. D, Antibiotics			
7	Sodium lauryl sulphate	Sodium dodecyl sulphate, Irium	$\left[CH_3\cdot(CH_2)_{10}\cdot CH_2{-}O{-}\overset{O\uparrow}{\underset{\downarrow O}{S}}{-}O\right]Na$	288·4

Physical form	Solubility	General remarks
wh. powder	v.s. H_2O, EtOH, $CHCl_3$; v. sl. s. benz., eth.	Cationic detergent. Bactericidal, active at alkaline pH against both gram +ve and −ve organisms. Denatures proteins (*Adv. Protein Chem.* **4**, 79 (1948)) and disorganizes bacterial cell membranes in a manner similar to CTAB. Has been used to modify cell permeability. Reverses the surface charge on bacteria (*J. Bact.* **51**, 149 (1946)). M.p. 77–83.
creamy wh. powder	v.s. EtOH, MeOH; s. H_2O (c. 100 g/l.)	Cationic detergent. Commercial product a mixture of alkyl ammonium bromides (c. 80% CTAB). Bactericidal, activity annulled by soaps and anionic detergents active at alkaline pH against both gram +ve and gram −ve organisms. Disorganizes cell membranes, releasing amino acids, purines, pyrimidines, and other small molecules (*J. gen. Microbiol.* **5**, 391 (1951)). Used to render cells permeable to substrates in enzyme assays, to accelerate enzyme action (*B.J.* **45**, 325 (1949)), and in the isolation of nucleic acids (*B.B.A.* **10**, 607 (1953)). Denatures protein (*Adv. Protein Chem.* **4**, 79 (1948)). ASSAY. *Research* **2**, 247 (1947).
waxy solid	s. H_2O (18 g/l. at 30°) CCl_4, acet., benz., MeOH	Anionic detergent. Slightly hygroscopic, stable in acid and neutral solution, hydrolyses in alkaline solutions. Bactericidal activity increases as pH falls, active only against gram +ve bacteria at neutral pH but active against gram +ve and −ve at pH 4 (*Bull. int. Ass. Milk Deal.* **33**, 491 (1941)).
amber coloured viscous liquid	v.s. H_2O; s. EtOH	Non-ionic synthetic detergent resembling Tween 80. Hydrophilic and lyophilic balance = 16·5. Used extensively as a 1% solution in 0·1 M-tris or phosphate buffer at pH 7·4 for extraction and solubilization of cytochrome *a* from mammalian tissues (*J. Biochem., Tokyo* **46**, 917 (1959); *J.B.C.* **235**, 845 (1960)).
waxy wh. solid	s. H_2O, EtOH	Non-ionic synthetic detergent, a condensate of cetyl alcohol and polyoxyethylene ether. Used in conjunction with deoxycholate as 0·5% soln. in 0·25 M-sucrose to fractionate proteins from mammalian microsomes and to prepare ribonucleoprotein particles (*B.J.* **70**, 254 (1958); *Expl Cell Res.* **23**, 517 (1961)). A 0·05% solution in buffers facilitates the separation of serum proteins by paper electrophoresis (*Clin. Chem.* **6**, 413 (1960)).
pale yel. viscous liq.	∞ H_2O; s. EtOH. *iso*PrOH, diethyl eth., acet., benz.	Non-ionic detergent and wetting agent. An alkyl phenol/ethylene oxide condensate. Used as a 1·5% (v/v) solution in 0·2 M-phosphate buffer at pH 7·2, containing 0·006 M-$MgCl_2$ to solubilize lipid material and allow the isolation of endosperm proteoplasts (*Aust. J. biol. Sci.* **16**, 375 (1963); **17**, 102 (1964)).
wh. or creamy wh. powder or cryst.	s. H_2O, EtOH	Anionic detergent, commercial product is a mixture of alkyl sulphates. Bactericidal activity is greatest at low pH and at pH 4 it is active against gram +ve and −ve organisms. Causes disaggregation of cell walls of gram −ve bacteria (*J. gen. Microbiol.* **23**, 137 (1960)). Used to separate nucleic acid from protein: RNA (*J.A.C.S.* **75**, 4041 (1953)); DNA (*J.B.C.* **190**, 165 (1951)). Releases certain animal viruses from host cells (*J. gen. Microbiol.* **20**, 61 (1959)). Denatures protein (*Adv. Protein Chem.* **4**, 79 (1948)).

No.	*Name*	*Synonyms*	*Formula*	*M. wt.*
8	Triton W.R. 1339	*p-iso*Octylpolyoxy-ethylene phenol polymer, Triton A 20, Alevaire, Superinone	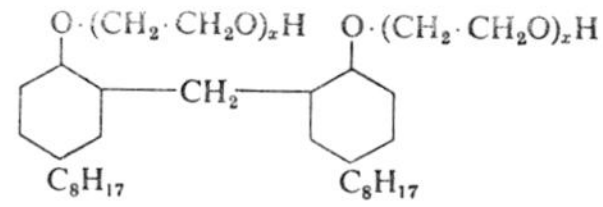	
9	Tween 80		A complex of polyoxyethylene ethers of mixed partial oleic esters of sorbitol anhydrides.	

Physical form	*Solubility*	*General remarks*
col. liq.	v.s. H_2O	Non-ionic detergent. Anti-tuberculous activity *in vivo* (*Nature, Lond.* **168,** 150 (1951)). Causes swelling and disruption of mitochondria and a stimulation of rhodanese activity in isolated mitochondria (*B.B.A.* **33,** 267 (1959)). REVIEW: Influence of certain surface-active agents on the host-parasite relationship in experimental tuberculosis in *CIBA Foundation Symposium on Experimental Tuberculosis*, p. 299 (1955).
amber, viscous liq.	v.s. H_2O; s. EtOH, MeOH, Et acetate, toluene	Non-ionic detergent. Little or no antibacterial activity. Used to promote submerged growth of tubercle bacilli (opt. concn. 0·1%) (*J. exp. Med.* **83,** 409 (1946)). May be metabolized to release oleic acid which is growth inhibitory to some bacteria (*Annls Inst. Pasteur, Paris* **85,** 277 (1953)). Induces a change from smooth to rough forms in some bacteria (*C.r. Séanc. Soc. Biol., Paris* **146,** 820 (1952)). Used in fractionation of tissue culture cells (*Proc. R. Soc.* **B156,** 521 (1962)). Hydrophilic and lyophilic balance = 15·0.

G. CHOLINESTERASE INHIBITORS

By D. R. CURTIS (*Department of Physiology, Australian National University, Canberra*)

General references

1. *Handbuch der Experimentellen Pharmakologie*. XV. *Cholinesterases and Anticholinesterase Agents*, Springer-Verlag, Berlin (1963).
2. R. D. O'Brien, 'Organophosphates and carbamates', *Metabolic Inhibitors*, eds. R. M. Hochster and J. H. Quastel, vol. 2, p. 205, Academic Press, New York (1963).

No.	*Name*	*Synonyms*	*Formula*	*M. wt.*	*Physical form*
1	1:5-Bis-(4-allyl-dimethyl-ammoniumphenyl)-pentane-3-one dibromide	284C51 (297C50 = diiodide)	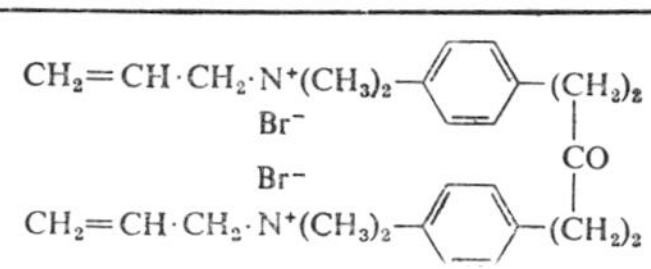	566·4	wh. cryst. powder
2	*N-p*-Chlorophenyl-*N*-methylcarbamate of *m*-hydroxyphenyl-trimethylammonium bromide	NU1250 (R02–1250)	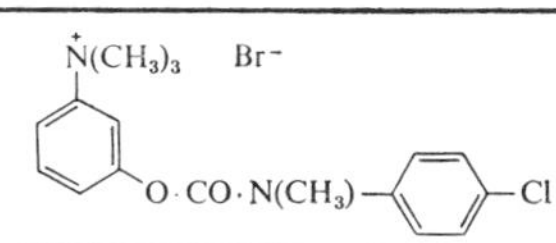	399·7	wh. cryst. powder
3	Di*iso*propylphosphofluoridate	DFP, di*iso*propyl-fluorophosphonate	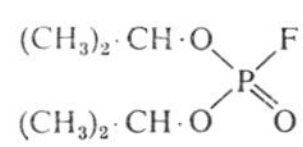	184·2	col. liq.
4	Dimethylcarbamate of 2-hydroxy-5-phenyl-benzyltrimethylammonium bromide	NU683 (R02–0683)	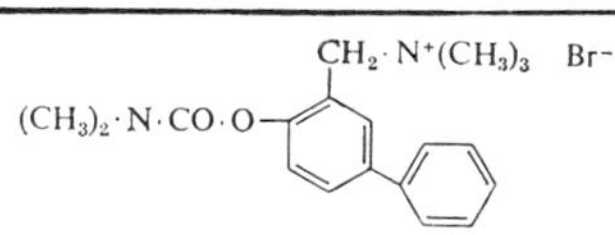	393·3	wh. cryst. powder
5	Neostigmine bromide	Prostigmine	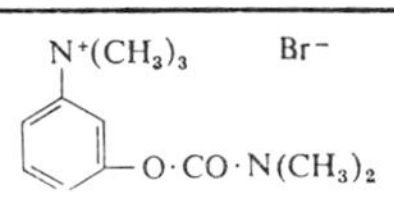	303·2	wh. cryst. powder
6	Physostigmine	Eserine	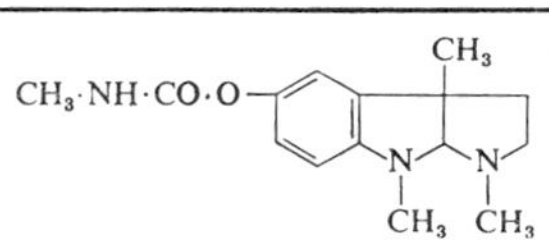	275·3	col. cryst. prisms (unstable form)
7	Tetraethylpyrophosphate	TEPP	$O{:}P(OC_2H_5)_2{\cdot}O{\cdot}P(OC_2H_5)_2{:}O$	290·2	col. hygr. oil
8	1:5-Bis-(4-trimethyl-ammoniumphenyl)-pentane-3-one diiodide	62C47	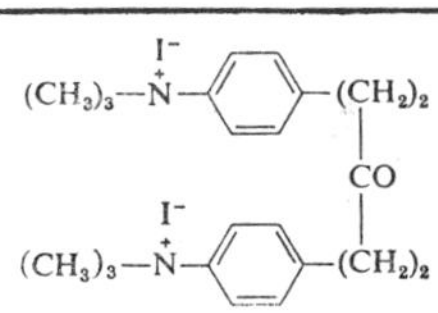	608·4	wh. cryst. powder

M.p.	*Solubility*	*References*	*Use*	*General remarks*
179–80	s. H_2O	*B.J.* **54**, 695 (1953) *Meth. biochem. Anal.* **5**, 1 (1957) *B.J.* **62**, 62 (1956)	Acetylcholinesterase inhibitor at 10^{-5}–10^{-6} M	10^{-3} M solutions stable 36 hr.
152–3	s. H_2O	*B.J.* **44**, 260 (1949) *Meth. biochem. Anal.* **5**, 1 (1957)	Acetylcholinesterase inhibitor at 10^{-6}–10^{-7} M	For 'specific' anticholinesterases see *Meth. biochem. Anal.* **5**, 1 (1957).
B.p. 183	s. organic solvents, veg. oils; $1{\cdot}54^{25}$ H_2O	*B.J.* **53**, 62 (1953) *Br. J. Pharmac. Chemother.* **2**, 173 (1947); **8**, 208 (1953)	Pseudocholinesterase inhibitor at 10^{-7}–10^{-9} M. Trypsin, chymotrypsin (esterase and proteinase) at 10^{-3}–10^{-5} M	Unstable aq. soln., HF formed. Soln. in oil stable 117°. Store in dry *iso*propanol. Absorbed through skin.
	s. H_2O	*B.J.* **40**, 192 (1946) *Meth. biochem. Anal.* **5**, 1 (1957)	Pseudocholinesterase inhibitor at 10^{-8} M	
167 d.	v.s. cold H_2O; s. EtOH	*J.B.C.* **146**, 85 (1942)	Brain, red blood cell and plasma cholinesterase inhibitor at 10^{-7}–10^{-8} M	Protect solutions from light.
105 (86)	s. EtOH, $CHCl_3$, eth.; sl. s. H_2O	*B.J.* **36**, 746 (1942) *J.B.C.* **146**, 85 (1942)	Serum and muscle cholinesterase inhibitor at 10^{-5}–10^{-8} M	pK_a: 6·12, 12·24. Must be kept in dark. Sulphate, M. wt. 648·8; M.p. 145; v.s. H_2O; s. EtOH, $CHCl_3$. Salicylate, M. wt. 413·5; M.p. 185–7; s. H_2O.
	s. EtOH, H_2O. Soln. hydrolyses to EtOH and H_3PO_4	*J.B.C.* **179**, 543 (1949)	Brain and plasma cholinesterase inhibitor at 10^{-8}–10^{-9} M. Plant acetylesterase inhibitor at 10^{-6} M	No effect on trypsin; reacts v. slowly with chymotrypsin; compare DFP.
244	s. H_2O	*B.J.* **62**, 62 (1956) *Br. J. Pharmac. Chemother.* **9**, 138 (1954) *Meth. biochem. Anal.* **5**, 1 (1957)	Acetylcholinesterase inhibitor at 10^{-5}–10^{-6} M	

H. INHIBITORS OF RESPIRATORY ENZYMES, PHOTOSYNTHESIS AND PHOSPHORYLATION; UNCOUPLING REAGENTS

By C. A. APPLEBY (*Division of Plant Industry, C.S.I.R.O., Canberra*)

General references

1. J. L. Webb, *Enzyme and Metabolic Inhibitors*, 4 volumes, Academic Press, New York (1963).
2. R. M. Hochster and J. H. Quastel, eds., *Metabolic Inhibitors*, 2 volumes, Academic Press, New York (1963).
3. F. Bendall, 'Inhibition and activation of enzymes', *Modern Methods of Plant Analysis*, eds. H. F. Linskens and M. V. Tracey, vol. 6, p. 424, Springer-Verlag, Berlin (1963).

Substances shown as inhibiting electron transport will consequently inhibit oxidative phosphorylation, photosynthesis, and photophosphorylation. Certain substances (e.g. dinitrophenol) which uncouple or inhibit phosphorylation, or inhibit the oxygen evolving step of photosynthesis, may have no effect on, or even stimulate electron transport.

No.	*Name*	*Synonyms*	*Formula*	*M. wt.*	*Physical form*
1	3-Amino-1*H*-1:2:4-triazole	Amizol	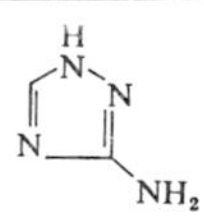	84·1	col. cryst. from EtOH
2	Amytal, Na salt	Na 5-ethyl-5-*iso*amyl-barbiturate, amobarbital, Somnal	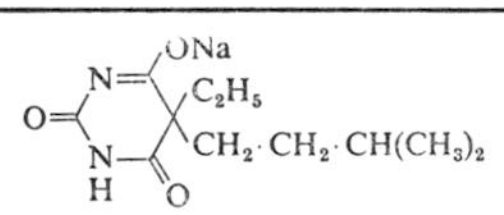	248·3	wh. hygr. powder
	Antimycin A, *see* 15. D, Antibiotics				
3	Arsenic acid, Na salt	Sodium arsenate	$Na_2HAsO_4 \cdot 7H_2O$	Hydrate, 312·0	col. monocl. cryst.
4	Arsenious acid	Arsenic trioxide, arsenolite	As_2O_3 ($As_2O_3 + 3H_2O \rightleftharpoons 2As(OH_3)$)	197·8	wh. powder
5	—, Na salt	Sodium *meta*-arsenite	$NaAsO_2$	129·9	wh. hygr. powder
6	Atebrin hydrochloride	Atabrine, mepacrine, quinacrine, SN390	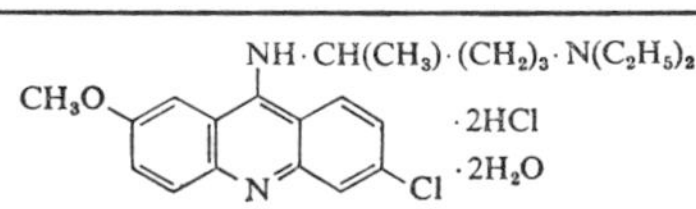	Hydrate, 508·9	yel. needles
7	Carbon monoxide		CO	28·0	col. gas

M.p.	*Solubility*	*References*	*Use or action*	*General remarks*
159	s. H_2O, EtOH, MeOH, $CHCl_3$; i. eth., acet.	SYN. *Org. Synth.* 26, 11 (1946) ACTION *B.J.* **68**, 468 (1958)	Irreversible inhibitor of catalase in presence of H_2O_2 at 2×10^{-2} M; no action on peroxidase	Commercial grade, used as herbicide, generally contains catalase anti-inhibitory impurity. Inhibits riboflavin biogenesis, *Science* **132**, 622 (1960).
	v.s. H_2O; v. sl. s. eth.	ACTION *Acta chem. scand.* 9, 198 (1955) *B.B.R.C.* **8**, 92 (1962) *J.B.C.* **238**, 418, 1124 (1963)	Inhibits $NADH_2$ oxidizing enzymes and some other flavoproteins at 10^{-3} M; and succinic dehydrogenase at 10^{-2} M	May also inhibit energy transferase reactions at NAD-flavoprotein phosphorylation site.
120–30	s. H_2O; sl. s. EtOH	ACTION *J.B.C.* **236**, 1510 (1961)	Uncouples substrate level and oxidative phosphorylation at 10^{-2} M; uncoupling increases with time and is not complete	Phosphorylysis replaced by arsenolysis. pK_a: 2·25, 6·77, 11·53.
Anhyd., ublimes 93	s. acids, alkalis; sl. s. H_2O (2^{25}, $11{\cdot}5^{100}$); sl. s. EtOH, eth.		Inhibits dehydrogenases containing dithiols, e.g. α-ketoglutaric dehydrogenase, at 10^{-4} M. Also uncouples oxidative phosphorylation	Dissolve in alkali to prepare arsenite solution. pK_a: 9·22. Weedicide, pesticide.
	s. H_2O; sl. s. EtOH		As above	Commercial salt not satisfactory; *see above*.
48 d.	s. H_2O, MeOH, EtOH; i. eth., acet.	ACTION *Acta chem. scand.* 15, 1629 (1960)	Inhibits some flavoprotein enzymes at 10^{-4} M. Uncouples oxidative and photophosphorylation at 10^{-3} M. Inhibits ATPase	Antimalarial. pK_a: 7·5, 10·1.
B.p. −190	s. benz., Cu_2Cl_2 soln.; sl. s. H_2O (α = 0·02 at 20°)	USE *Arch. B.B.* 53, 239 (1954)	Inhibits wide range of metalloenzymes, including hydrogenase and haemoglobins, at low concs., and cytochrome oxidase at 50–95% (in gas phase)	Light reversible CO inhibition is characteristic of cytochrome oxidase and other haemproteins. Cu^+ and other metal carbonyls not light-sensitive. CAUTION: CO is respired by many tissues and micro-organisms.

No.	*Name*	*Synonyms*	*Formula*	*M. wt.*	*Physical form*
8	2-Chloro-4:6-bis-(ethylamino)-*s*-triazine	Simazin	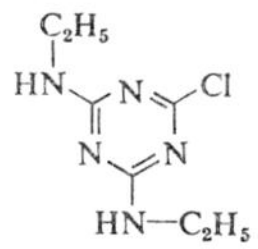	201·7	cryst. from EtOH, MeOH
9	3-(*p*-Chlorophenyl)-1:1-dimethylurea	CMU, Monuron	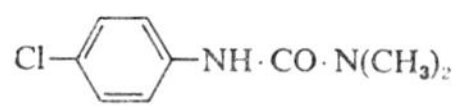	198·7	wh. prisms from MeOH
10	Chlorpromazine	Largactil	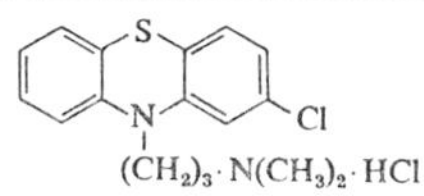	355·3	wh. cryst.
11	2:6-Dibromophenol		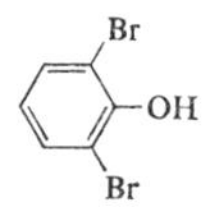	251·9	col. needles
12	2:4-Dichlorophenol		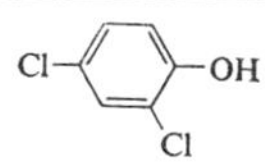	163·0	col. needles
13	3-(3:4-Dichlorophenyl)-1:1-dimethylurea	DCMU, Diuron	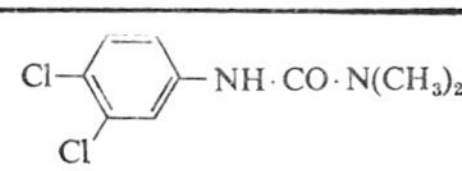	233·1	wh. cryst.
14	Dicoumarol	Bishydroxycoumarin, Dicoumarin	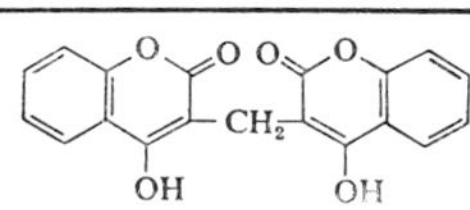	336·3	wh. cryst.
15	Diethyldithiocarbamic acid, Na salt	DIECA	$(C_2H_5)_2N \cdot CS \cdot SNa$	171·3	
16	2:4-Dinitrophenol		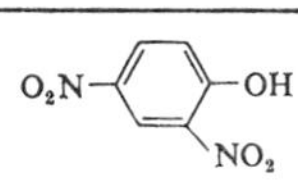	184·1	yel. plates
17	α:α′-Dipyridyl		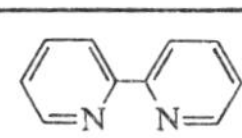	156·2	
	Gramicidin S, *see* 15. D, Antibiotics				
18	2-*n*-Heptyl-4-hydroxyquinoline-*N*-oxide	HOQNO	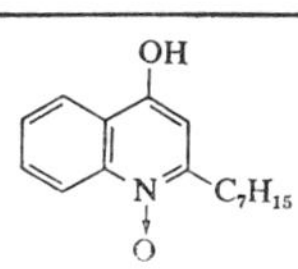	259·4	wh. cryst. from EtOH
19	Hydrazoic acid	Hydrogen azide	HN_3	43·0	col. liq.
	—, Na salt	Sodium azide	NaN_3	65·0	col. cryst.

M.p.	*Solubility*	*References*	*Use or action*	*General remarks*
26–7	sl. s. dioxane, ethyl cellosolve, EtOH, MeOH; pract. i. H_2O	ACTION *Pl. Physiol.* **34**, 432 (1959)	Inhibits oxygen evolution in photosynthesis	Herbicide.
71	s. EtOH, MeOH, acet.; v. sl. s. H_2O	ACTION *Arch. B.B.* **90**, 184 (1960) *B.B.A.* **19**, 548 (1956)	Inhibits O_2 evolution step of photosynthesis at 10^{-6}–10^{-7} M	Herbicide.
79–80 d.	v.s. H_2O; s. MeOH, EtOH; i. eth.	ACTION *B.J.* **72**, 204; **73**, 16 (1959)	Uncouples and inhibits oxidative phosphorylation at 10^{-3}–10^{-4} M	Sedative, *see* Drugs.
5–57	v.s. EtOH, eth.; sl. s. H_2O	ACTION *J.B.C.* **238**, 439 (1963)	Uncouples phosphorylation at 10^{-4}–10^{-5} M. *See* dinitrophenol	Higher concs. inhibit many mitochondrial enzymes.
5 p. 210	0·45[19] H_2O; s. EtOH, $CHCl_3$, eth., benz.		Inhibits catalase at 10^{-5} M; no effect on other haem enzymes below 10^{-4} M	Uncouples phosphorylation in some tissues.
8–9	v. sl. s. H_2O (42 ppm); v. sl. s. hydrocarbon solvents	*See* CMU	*See* CMU	Herbicide.
7–93	s. alkalis; sl. s. $CHCl_3$; i. H_2O, EtOH, eth.	ACTION *J.B.C.* **238**, 439 (1963) *B.Z.* **333**, 111 (1960)	Uncouples oxidative phosphorylation at 2×10^{-5} M; inhibits vit. K reductase	Med. use as anticoagulant. *See* Drugs.
	s. H_2O; sl. s. EtOH	USE *J. exp. Bot.* **3**, 310 (1952) STABILITY. *B.B.A.* **36**, 538 (1959)	Irreversible inhibition of Cu enzymes at 10^{-3} M. Inhibits diamine oxidase, *B.J.* **59**, 609 (1955)	May also react with Zn, Fe, and other metallo-enzymes. Unstable in acid solutions. *See also* data in Chelating Agents.
[illegible]	s. benz.; sl. s. EtOH, eth.; 0·56[18] H_2O	ACTION *B.B.A.* **48**, 221 (1961)	Uncouples oxidative phosphorylation at 10^{-5}–10^{-4} M by causing hydrolysis of first high-energy intermediate at each phosphorylation site; stimulates mitochondrial ATPase	Does not uncouple substrate-level phosphorylation. pK_a: 4·1.
	v.s. EtOH, eth., $CHCl_3$; sl. s. H_2O.		May inhibit Fe^{++} enzymes at 10^{-8} M	*See also* data in Chelating Agents.
–60	s. EtOH; v. sl. s. H_2O. Make stock soln. in 0·01 N-NaOH, 50 μg/ml.	ISOL. and SYN. *B.J.* **63**, 124 (1956) ACTION *B.J.* **63**, 130 (1956)	Inhibits cytochrome systems at or near cytochrome *b*, at 10^{-5}–10^{-8} M	Active against some bacterial systems not inhibited by antimycin.
[illegible] 37 d.	Free acid, ∞ H_2O; s. EtOH Salt, s. H_2O; i. eth.	*Arch. B.* **23**, 141 (1949)	Inhibits catalase, Fe enzymes at 10^{-3} M; uncouples phosphorylation at 10^{-4} M; inhibits O_2 evolution in photosynthesis	Not effective at alkaline pH, since active form is undissoc. acid. (Use HCN or H_2S at alkaline pH.) pK_a: 4·72.

15. Antimetabolites, Antibacterial Agents, and Enzyme Inhibitors

No.	*Name*	*Synonyms*	*Formula*	*M. wt.*	*Physical form*
20	Hydrogen cyanide	Hydrocyanic acid	HCN	27·0	col. liq. or gas
	—, K salt	Potassium cyanide	KCN	65·1	col. deliq. cryst.
21	Hydrogen sulphide		H_2S	34·1	col. gas
	—, Na salt		$Na_2S\cdot 9H_2O$	Hydrate, 240·2	col. deliq. cryst.
22	Hydroxylamine hydrochloride		$NH_2OH\cdot HCl$	69·5	col. cryst.
23	2-*n*-Nonyl-4-hydroxyquinoline-*N*-oxide		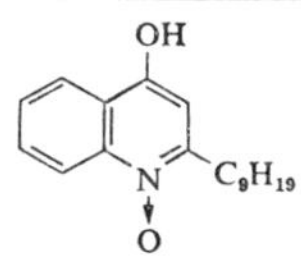	287·4	wh. cryst. from EtOH
24	Oleic acid		$CH_3\cdot(CH_2)_7\cdot CH{=}CH\cdot(CH_2)_7\cdot COOH$	282·5	col. needles
25	Oligomycin		A mixture of three compounds: A $C_{24}H_{40}O_6$ B $C_{22}H_{36}O_6$ C $C_{28}H_{46}O_6$ All are neutral unsaturated optically-active alcohols. Exact formulae not known	A424·6 B396·5 C478·7	col. cryst. ,, ,,
26	Pentenyl guanidine sulphate	Galegine sulphate, 4-methyl-3-butenyl-guanidine sulphate	$(NH_2)_2\cdot C{:}N\cdot CH_2\cdot CH{=}C(CH_3)_2\cdot H_2SO_4$	225·3	col. cryst.
27	1:10-Phenanthroline	*o*-Phenanthroline hydrate	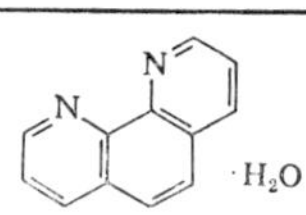	Hydrate, 198·2	wh. cryst. powder
28	Phenylurethane	Phenylethyl carbamate, ethylcarbanilate	$C_6H_5\cdot NH\cdot COO\cdot C_2H_5$	165·2	wh. cryst.
29	Quinine		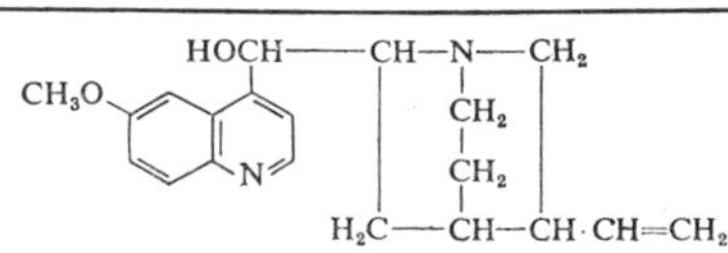	324·4	triboluminescent wh. needle from EtOH
30	Rotenone		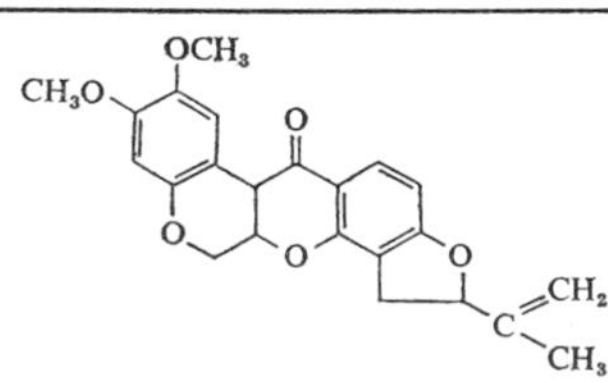	394·4	col. orthorh. plates

M.p.	*Solubility*	*References*	*Use or action*	*General remarks*
−14; B.p. 26	Free acid, ∞ H_2O, EtOH; sl. s. eth.	MANOMETRY *Meth. med. Res.* **1**, 307 (1948)	Inhibits by complexing with metals in metallo-enzymes, e.g. cytochrome oxidase, at 10^{-3}–10^{-5} M; or by forming cyanhydrins with carbonyl groups	Check metal inhibition activity with azide, CO or hydrogen sulphide. High concs. cyanide may be respired. Active form is undissoc. acid. pK_a: 9·14.
634	Salt, v.s. H_2O; s. EtOH			
B.p. −62	Gas, s. CS_2; sl. s. H_2O		Inhibits metallo-enzymes at 10^{-3} M. Not a carbonyl reagent	Sulphide is respired by some tissues and micro-organisms. pK_a: 7·04, 14·9.
920 d.	Salt, s. H_2O; i. eth.			
151	v.s. H_2O, EtOH; i. eth.	*Arch. B.* **23**, 141 (1949)	Inhibits catalase; also inhibits O_2 evolution in photosynthesis at 10^{-4} M	Also inhibits alcohol dehydrogenases and vitamin B_6 enzymes; carbonyl reagent forming oximes. pK_a: 6·2.
148–9	s. EtOH; v. sl. s. H_2O. Make stock soln. in 0·001 N-NaOH 5 μg/ml.	*See* HOQNO	As HOQNO, although 3–10 times more active	Commercially available; less soluble than HOQNO.
4	∞ EtOH, eth.; s. benz.; i. H_2O	ACTION *B.B.A.* **62**, 509 (1962)	Uncouples oxidative phosphorylation. Inhibits 2:4-dinitrophenol-stimulated ATPase. Active at 120 μmoles/g protein	Action reversed by adding serum albumin. *See also* data in Lipids.
A140–1 B160–1 C195–200	s. EtOH, benz.; i. acet., H_2O	ACTION *J. Biochem., Tokyo* **49**, 493 (1961) *Arch. B.B.* **78**, 587 (1958) *B.B.R.C.* **7**, 70 (1962)	Inhibits oxidative phosphorylation at all phosphorylation sites and hence inhibits coupled respiration. Active at 1 μg/mg protein	This inhibitor does not inhibit the formation of all high energy intermediates, but only phosphorylated intermediates. Respiratory inhibition relieved by 2:4-dinitrophenol.
	s. EtOH; sl. s. H_2O	ACTION *J.B.C.* **238**, 401, 410 (1963)	Inhibits oxidative phosphorylation at the site between NAD and cytochrome *b*	Inhibitory action of related alkyl guanidines increases with chain length of the alkyl group.
3–94; nhyd. 17	s. EtOH, eth.; sl. s. H_2O, benz.	USE *Arch. B.* **23**, 141 (1949) *B.B.A.* **62**, 327 (1962)	Inhibits O_2 evolution in photosynthesis, possibly by Zn or Mn chelation; inhibits some Fe enzymes at 10^{-8} M; inhibits glutamic dehydrogenase	*See also* data in Chelating Agents. pK_a: 4·96.
2–53	s. EtOH, eth.; sl. s. H_2O	ACTION *Arch. B.* **23**, 141 (1949)	Inhibitor of O_2 evolution in photosynthesis, at 10^{-3}–10^{-4} M	
7 d.	v.s. EtOH; sl. s. eth.; v. sl. s. H_2O. Hydrochloride, v.s. H_2O	ACTION *J.B.C.* **159**, 239 (1945); **163**, 553 (1946)	Inhibits some flavoprotein enzymes at 10^{-3} M	Also inhibits choline esterases. Mode of action as an antimalarial is unknown. pK_a: 4·13, 8·3.
3	s. EtOH, acet., eth.; i. H_2O	ACTION *J.B.C.* **238**, 418, 1124 (1963)	Inhibits electron transfer between $NADH_2$ and flavin at 10^{-7} M. Reaction site is titrated	Insecticide and fish poison. Isolated from derris root. Vitamin K_3 releases rotenone inhibition.

No.	*Name*	*Synonyms*	*Formula*	*M. wt.*	*Physical form*
31	Thyroxine		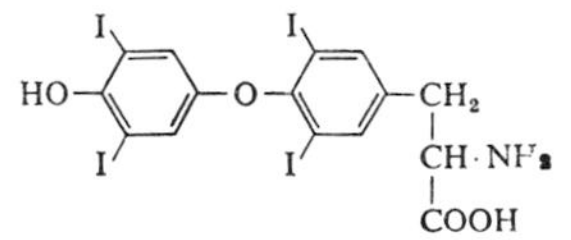	776·9	wh. needles
32	Valinomycin		Cyclic molecule, containing 2 L-val, 2 D-val, 2 L-lactic acid, and 2 D-α-hydroxy-*iso*valeric acid residues, linked by alternating ester and amide bonds to form a 24-membered ring.	740·9	col. cryst.

M.p.	*Solubility*	*References*	*Use or action*	*General remarks*
DL- 231–3 d. L- 235–6 d.	s. dil. alkali; i. H_2O, EtOH and org. solvents.	ACTION *B.J.* **60**, 122 (1955)	Uncouples mitochondrial oxidative phosphorylation at 5×10^{-5} M	Requires preincubation with particles, may affect their structure. *See also* data in Amino Acids.
190	s. acet. eth.; i. H_2O	ACTION *Arch. B.B.* **84**, 546 (1959)	Uncouples oxidative and photophosphorylation at 10^{-7}–10^{-8} M. Activates ATPase	In photophosphorylation only one of two phosphorylation sites may be affected. Antibiotic, isolated from *Strep. fulvissimus*.

I. THIOL REAGENTS

By P. A. TRUDINGER (*Division of Plant Industry, C.S.I.R.O., Canberra*)

Uses

1. Detection of essential —SH groups in enzymes as indicated by inhibition of enzymic activity. (*Note*: (*a*) Combination of —SH groups with thiol reagents may in some cases alter the configuration of the enzyme protein or may mask reactive sites through steric effects with a consequent loss of activity; (*b*) protection of enzymic activity by substrate against inhibition by thiol reagents is a more definitive test for the essential requirement for —SH.)
2. Quantitative estimation of —SH in proteins.
3. Histological localization of —SH groups.

General comments

(*a*) Differences in reactivity of the —SH groups in proteins may lead to different results depending upon the thiol reagent used and the time of its exposure to the protein.

No.	*Name*	*Synonyms*	*Formula*	*M. wt.*	*Physical form*

ALKYLATING REAGENTS—MALEIMIDE DERIVATIVES

Class characteristics. Reaction 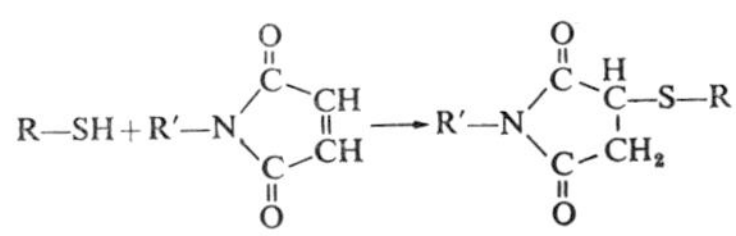 essentially irreversible, fairly specific for —SH at low concentration, rapid reaction.

No.	*Name*	*Synonyms*	*Formula*	*M. wt.*	*Physical form*
1	*N*-(4-Dimethylamino-3:5-dinitrophenyl)-maleimide		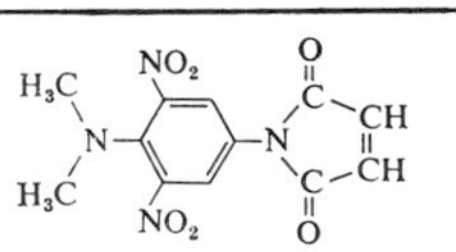	306·2	orange cryst.
2	*N*-Ethylmaleimide	NEM	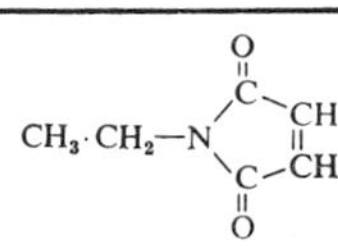	125·1	col. cryst.
3	*N*-(4-Hydroxy-1-naphthyl)-isomaleimide	HNI	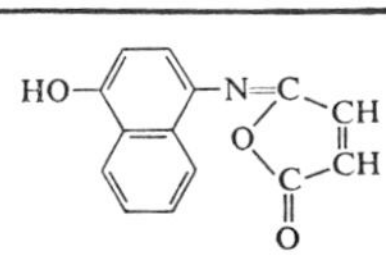	239·2	
4	*N*-(4-Hydroxy-1-naphthyl)-maleimide		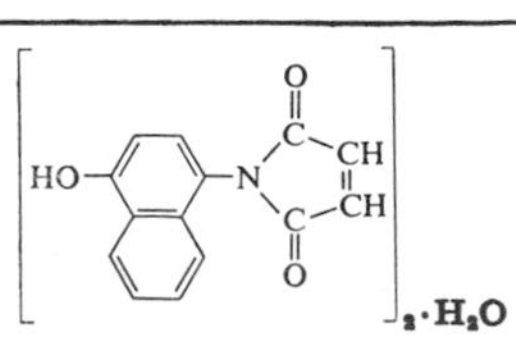	496·4	tan, amorph.

(*b*) Due to possible reactions between thiol reagents and protein groups other than —SH, tests for —SH should be carried out, wherever possible, with more than one type of reagent and at low concentrations. The concentrations of thiol reagents for thiol enzyme inhibition listed are *representative only*. Much variation may be experienced depending upon the enzyme preparation and conditions employed. Compounds insoluble in water are generally added to the medium as a concentrated solution in a suitable solvent (controls with an equivalent amount of solvent should be included). In these cases the concentrations listed refer to the *total* amounts of thiol reagents added but may not, in fact, be the concentrations of reagents in solution.

General references

1. Properties and reactions of thiol groups. *Adv. Enzymol.* **11,** 201–66 (1951). *The Enzymes*, Ed. by Boyer, P.D., Lardy, H. and Myrbäck, K., Academic Press, New York, 2nd ed., vol. 1, pp. 511–88 (1959). *Biochem. Soc. Symp.* No. 17 (1959). *Chem. Rev.* **41,** 151 (1947).
2. Quantitative analysis. *Meth. biochem. Anal.* **1,** 1–26 (1954). *Meth. biochem. Anal.* **10,** 43–70 (1962).

M.p.	*Solubility*	*Uses*	*General remarks*
79–81	sp. s. H_2O; s. acet., EtOH, acetic acid; aqueous solutions by dilution of EtOH soln. with H_2O	Coloured complex with —SH used in detection of —SH-containing peptides on paper chromatograms and electrophoretograms, *B.B.A.* **45,** 429 (1960)	Unstable in alkali.
ublimes 4	v.s. H_2O	Enzyme inhibitor at 10^{-3} M. Mitotic inhibitor. ^{14}C-NEM for quantitative determ. of mercaptans, *J.A.C.S.* **77,** 3922 (1955); *Analyt. Chem.* **30,** 1291 (1958)	Absorption max. in H_2O at 218, 302 mμ. Stable at pH 5 (22 hr). Slow hydrolysis to *N*-ethylmaleamate at pH 7—rate increased at higher pH values (use fresh solutions). Reaction between NEM and glutathione complete within 1 min at R.T. and pH 7. Reaction rate decreases at lower pH values, *J.A.C.S.* **77,** 3922 (1955). Reaction product of NEM+RSH gives intense, unstable red colour in alkali: used for detection on chromatograms, *Science* **123,** 981 (1956). Slow reaction of NEM with peptide-NH_2, imidazoles, *J.A.C.S.* **82,** 4600 (1960). Purification of ^{14}C-NEM, *Analyt. Biochem.* **5,** 60 (1963).
3–4	s. EtOH	As *N*-(4-hydroxy-1-naphthyl)-maleimide (chromatography of thiols, *B.J.* **65,** 512 (1957))	U.v. max. at 209, 237, 280, 310 mμ. Rate of reaction with glutathione, complete in secs. at pH 8, very slow at pH 2. Detection of —SH on chromatograms (after diazotization of HNI–RSH complex), 0·3 μm-mole (0·1 μm-mole under u.v.).
2 d.		Histochemical localization of —SH after formation of azo dye by coupling with tetra-azotized diorthoanisidine	PREP. and USE: *J.A.C.S.* **77,** 4613 (1955) [also *N*-(1-naphthyl)-, *N*-(4-acetoxy-1-naphthyl)-, *N*-(5-hydroxy-1-naphthyl)- derivatives and *N*-(4-hydroxy-1-naphthyl)-isomaleimide].

No.	Name	Synonyms	Formula	M. wt.	Physical form

ALKYLATING REAGENTS—HALOGENATED COMPOUNDS

Class characteristics. Reaction R—SH+R′X → R—S—R′+HX, essentially irreversible; *not highly specific.*

No.	Name	Synonyms	Formula	M. wt.	Physical form
5	α-Bromobenzyl cyanide	α-Bromophenylaceto-nitrile, α-bromo-α-tolunitrile	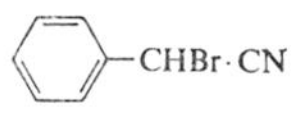	196·1	cryst. mass
6	ω-Chloroaceto-phenone	α-Chloroaceto-phenone, phenacyl chloride	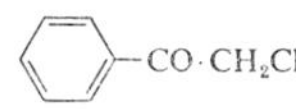	154·6	cryst.
7	Iodoacetamide		$ICH_2 \cdot CO \cdot NH_2$	185·0	
8	Iodoacetic acid —, Na salt		$ICH_2 \cdot COOH$ $ICH_2 \cdot COONa$	186·0 208·0	col. cryst.
9	Mustard gas	Bis-(2-chloroethyl)-sulphide	$(ClCH_2 \cdot CH_2)_2S$	159·1	col. oily liq.

TRIVALENT ARSENICALS

Class Characteristics. Reaction $2RSH + R'—As{=}O \rightarrow (RS)_2{=}As—R' + H_2O$

The arsenicals are generally very specific for —SH. Arsenite and monosubstituted derivatives hav a particularly strong affinity for dithiols with closely related —SH groups; lipoic acid containir enzymes therefore sensitive. The reactions are generally reversed by thiols and, more particularl dithiols (e.g. BAL (2:3-dimercaptopropanol)). The following compounds are representative, mar others have been tested.

General references. Mode of action: *Biochem. Soc. Symp.* No. 2, pp. 28–37 (1948); Review: *Met bolic Inhibitors*, Vol. 2, pp. 99–118 (1963).

Caution: The majority of organic arsenicals are highly toxic—handle with care.

No.	Name	Synonyms	Formula	M. wt.	Physical form
10	2-Amino-4-arsenoso-phenol hydrochloride	Mapharsen, Mapharside, 3-amino-4-hydroxy-phenylarsenoxide HCl, 3-amino-4-hydroxy-arsenosobenzene HCl, Oxophenarsine HCl	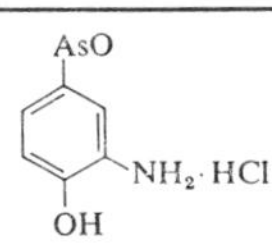	235·5	wh. deliq. powder
11	3-Amino-4-hydroxy-phenyldichloroarsine hydrochloride	Dichloromapharside, Halarsol, Dichlorophenarsine	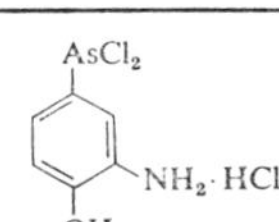	290·4	wh. deliq. powder
	Arsenious oxide, Na arsenite	*see* 15. H, Inhibitors of respiratory enzymes, photosynthesis, and phosphorylation; uncoupling reag			

M.p.	Solubility	Uses	General remarks
29	sl. s. H_2O; s. EtOH, eth., acet., ethylene glycol monomethyl ether	Enzyme inhibitor at 10^{-3}–10^{-4} M	Strong lachrymator. PREP. *Org. Synth.* Coll. **3**, 347 (1955).
95 B.p. 247	s. EtOH, benz., eth., ethylene glycol monomethyl ether; i. H_2O	Enzyme inhibitor at 10^{-3}–10^{-4} M	Lachrymatory. PREP. *Ber.* **44**, 1542 (1911).
95	s. H_2O	Enzyme inhibitor at 10^{-3} M. Determination of —SH and —S—S— groups, *B.B.A.* **23**, 643 (1957)	As for iodoacetate.
82–83	Free acid, s. H_2O, EtOH; sl. s. eth. Salt, s. H_2O	Enzyme inhibitor at 10^{-3} M. Titration of —SH groups (*a*) estimation of liberated I^-, *J.B.C.* **132**, 657 (1940) (*b*) manometric, *J.B.C.* **114**, 601 (1936) (*c*) isolation of *S*-carboxymethyl-cysteine, *J.B.C.* **233**, 1359 (1958)	Slow decomp. in solution; store away from light. Reacts also with —NH_2 and phenolic —OH (more slowly than with —SH). Increased rate of reaction at high pH values (pH 9) indicates that reaction is probably with RS^-. pK_a 3·13. Triosephosphate dehydrogenase is the 'classic' sensitive enzyme.
3	s. EtOH, eth., $CHCl_3$, benz.	General reagent for protein carboxyl, sulphydryl, and perhaps imidazole groups, *Adv. Protein Chem.* **3**, 187 (1947). Inhibits yeast hexokinase, phosphokinases, and some peptidases (e.g. pepsin) at 10^{-3} M, *B.J.* **42**, 60 (1948); *Nature, Lond.* **158**, 432 (1946)	*General references* relating to the cytotoxic action of alkylating agents such as sulphur and nitrogen mustards: 1. W. C. J. Ross, *Biological Alkylating Agents*, Butterworths, London (1962). 2. G. P. Wheeler, 'Mechanism of action of cytotoxic alkylating agents', *Cancer Res.* **22**, 651 (1962). 3. R. W. Brockman, 'Mechanisms of resistance to anti-cancer agents', *Adv. Cancer Res.* 7, 129 (1963). 4. S. M. Johnson and F. Bergel, 'Biological alkylating agents' in *Metabolic Inhibitors*, vol. 2, pp. 161–92 (1963).
	v.s. H_2O, alk., acid; sl. s. EtOH, $CHCl_3$	Enzyme inhibitor at 10^{-3}–10^{-4} M. Trypanosomiasis chemotherapy, *Pharmac. Rev.* **3**, 107 (1951)	BAL protects at 10^{-3}–10^{-4} M.
200	s. H_2O	Enzyme inhibitor at 10^{-4}–10^{-5} M.	Some decomp. to Mapharsen in H_2O—accelerated by alkali.

No.	*Name*	*Synonyms*	*Formula*	*M. wt.*	*Physical form*
12	*p*-Arsenosobenzamide	Benzamide-*p*-arsenious oxide	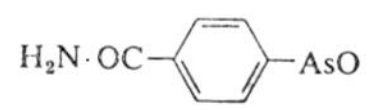	211·0	
13	γ-(*p*-Arsenosophenyl)-*n*-butyric acid, Na salt	Butarsen	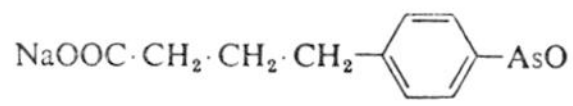	276·1	amorph. powder
14	Arsphenamine	3:3′-Diamino-4:4′-dihydroxyarseno-benzene dihydrochloride, Salvarsan, Ehrlich 606	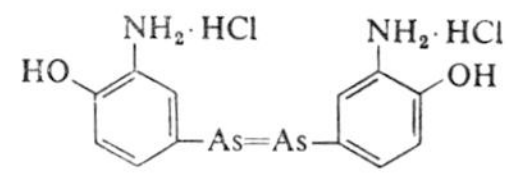	439·0; Di-hydrate, 475·0	light yel. deliq. powder
15	Dichloro-(2-chloro-vinyl)-arsine	Lewisite	$ClCH{=}CHAsCl_2$	207·3	col. liquid
16	Diphenylchloroarsine	Diphenylarsenious chloride	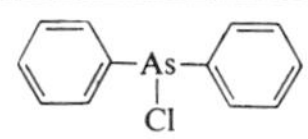	264·6	wh. powder
17	Methyldichloroarsine		$CH_3 \cdot AsCl_2$	160·9	col. liquid
18	Phenylarsenoxide	Arzene	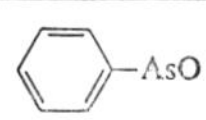	168·0	col. cryst.

ORGANIC MERCURIALS

Class characteristics. Reaction RSH+R′HgX → R—S—HgR′+HX. Generally fairly high specificit at low concentration, reversed by thiols (e.g. mercaptoethanol); may react with other protein group at high concentration.

Have high affinity for —SH and react rapidly—useful for quantitative determination of —SH.

Note: Inorganic Hg^{++} salts (and those of other heavy metals) have also been used as —SH enzym inhibitors and for —SH analysis. Anion constitution of medium may affect reactivity and specificity the reactive species may be derivatives formed with buffer anions.

General references. Preparation: *Metal-organic Compounds*, pp. 82–86, *Adv. in Chem. Series*, No. 23 Am. Chem. Soc. (1959); Review: *Metabolic Inhibitors*, vol. 2, pp. 119–44 (1963).

19	*p*-Chloromercuri-benzene sulphonic acid		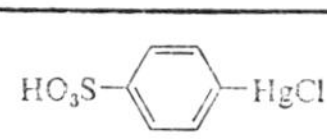	393·2	
20	*p*-Chloromercuri-benzoic acid, Na salt		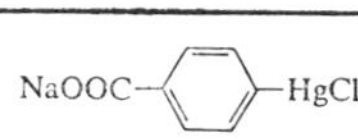	379·2	amorph. wh. powder or cryst.
21	1-(4-Chloromercuri-phenylazo)-naphthol-2		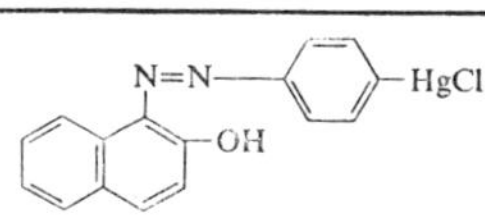	483·3	red needles
22	Ethylmercuric chloride		$CH_3 \cdot CH_2 \cdot HgCl$	265·1	silvery iridescent leaflets
23	Mersalyl	Mercusal, Salygran, Neptal, Na salt of Mersalyl acid	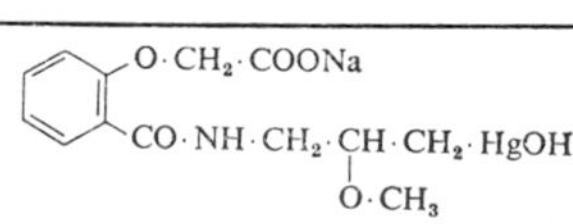	505·9	bitter cryst., deliq.

M.p.	*Solubility*	*Uses*	*General remarks*
	i. H_2O	Enzyme inhibitor at 10^{-3} M	PREP. *J.C.S.* 1930, 669—prep. of a number of other arsenicals described.
126	s. H_2O (> 2%)	Enzyme inhibitor at 10^{-4}–10^{-5} M	PREP. *J.A.C.S.* **62**, 3012 (1940).
	s. H_2O, EtOH, glycerol; v. sl. s. $CHCl_3$, eth.	Antisyphilitic drug. Enzyme inhibitor at 10^{-4}–10^{-5} M	Aqueous solution *ca.* pH 3; oxidizes on exposure to air.
·1 B.p. 190^{760} d., 6–$77^{12\cdot5}$	s. organic solvents; i. H_2O, mineral acids	Enzyme inhibitor at 10^{-4}–10^{-5} M	Hydrolysed by alkalis. BAL partially protects. Powerful vesicant.
4 B.p. 180^{10}	s. EtOH, eth., benz.; $0{\cdot}006^{20}$ H_2O	Enzyme inhibitor at 10^{-3}–10^{-4} M	Reacts only with one —SH group. PREP. *J. Soc. Chem. Ind., Lond.* **68**, 289 (1949).
–59 .p. 133–6	v.s. EtOH, eth.; sl. s. H_2O	Enzyme inhibitor at 10^{-3} M	Hydrolyses in water to methyl arsenoxide ($CH_3As{=}O$). PREP. *Ann.* **107**, 269 (1858).
19	s. EtOH, benz.; i. H_2O	Enzyme inhibitor at 10^{-3}–10^{-4} M	Gives dichlorophenylarsine if warmed with HCl.
	v.s. H_2O	Enzyme inhibitor at 10^{-6} M. Titration of —SH groups in proteins, *J.B.C.* **203**, 563 (1953)	PREP. *J.A.C.S.* **58**, 2308 (1936).
	s. H_2O, alkali; i. acid. Dissolve in 0·2 N-NaOH and carefully neutralize to pH 8.	Enzyme inhibitor at 10^{-5} M. Titration of —SH groups in proteins	In some cases inhibition reversed by ethylenediamine-tetra-acetate. Pptd. by phosphate at pH 7. Solubility increased in presence of pyrophosphate, glycylglycine, tris. Increase in u.v. absorption on formation of mercaptide used in —SH analysis, *J.A.C.S.* **76**, 4331 (1954).
·5–293 d.	i. H_2O; sl. s. EtOH, $CHCl_3$	Histological location of —SH, *Anat. Rec.* **110**, 231 (1951)	PREP. *J.A.C.S.* **70**, 3522 (1948).
·5; limes	$1{\cdot}4^{18}$ H_2O; sl. s. EtOH, $CHCl_3$	Enzyme inhibitor at 10^{-4}–10^{-6} M. Fungicide	Steam distils. Tends to evolve diethyl mercury—accelerated by H_2O and organic materials.
	100 H_2O; 33 EtOH; i. eth., $CHCl_3$	As mersalyl acid	Gradually decomposed by light.

No.	*Name*	*Synonyms*	*Formula*	*M. wt.*	*Physical form*
24	Mersalyl acid	*o*-[(3-Hydroxymercuri-2-methoxypropyl)-carbamyl]-phenoxyacetic acid	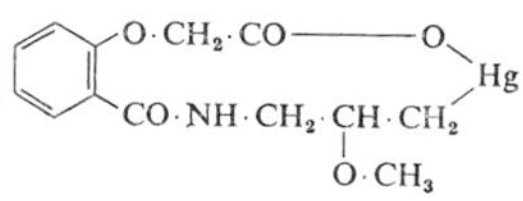	465·9	
25	Methylmercuric nitrate		CH_3HgNO_3	277·7	wh. deliq. cyst.
26	Phenylmercuric acetate	Mercuriphenyl acetate	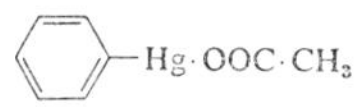	336·8	wh. lustrous prisms
27	Phenylmercuric chloride	Mercuriphenyl chloride	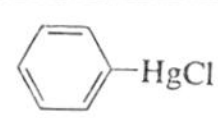	313·2	wh. satiny leaflets
28	Phenylmercuric nitrate (basic)	Merphene, Merphenyl nitrate, Phemernite, Phenmerzyl nitrate, Mercuriphenyl nitrate	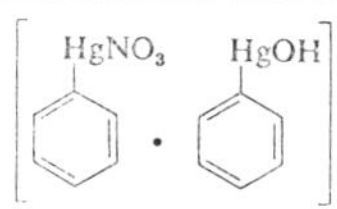	634·4	grey or wh. powder

OXIDIZING COMPOUNDS

General reaction $2RSH \rightarrow R{-}S{-}S{-}R + 2H^+ + 2e$ reversible. Iodine and oxidized glutathione have also been used.

No.	*Name*	*Synonyms*	*Formula*	*M. wt.*	*Physical form*
29	*o*-Iodosobenzoic acid		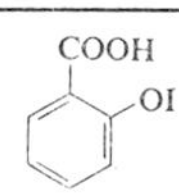	264·0	leaflets
30	Porphyrindine		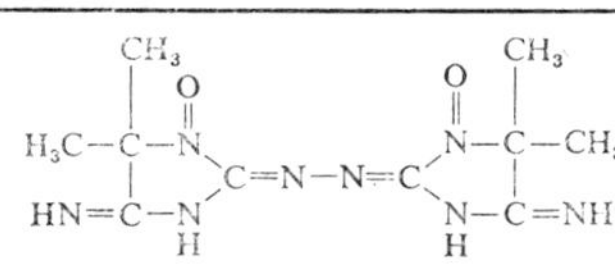	280·3 (anhyd.)	dark blue prisms (with $2H_2O$)

MISCELLANEOUS COMPOUNDS

No.	*Name*	*Synonyms*	*Formula*	*M. wt.*	*Physical form*
31	Acrylonitrile	Propene nitrile, vinyl cyanide, fumigrain	$CH_2{=}CH{-}CN$	53·1	flammable liq.
32	Allicin		$CH_2{=}CH\cdot CH_2{-}SO$ $\vert$ $CH_2{=}CH\cdot CH_2{-}S$	162·3	col. oil

M.p.	*Solubility*	*Uses*	*General remarks*
	v.s. chloride or alkaline solutions (up to 1 g/ml); solution accompanied by ring opening with formation of HgCl or HgOH derivatives	Diuretic. Enzyme inhibitor at 10^{-3} M	The C—Hg bond unstable below pH 5 with liberation of free Hg, accelerated by—SH.
59	s. H_2O	Enzyme inhibitor, fungicide. Estimation of reactive —SH in enzymes, *J.B.C.* **214**, 589 (1955)	Prep. by reacting methylmercuric iodide (CH_3HgI) with $AgNO_3$, *J.A.C.S.* 52, 2820 (1930); also for ethylmercuric nitrate, butylmercuric nitrate, benzylmercuric nitrate.
approx. 149	0·17 H_2O; s. EtOH	Enzyme inhibitor at 10^{-4}–10^{-5} M. Herbicide	
250–2	0·005 H_2O	Enzyme inhibitor at 10^{-3}–10^{-4} M. Herbicide	
178–84 d.	0·08 H_2O; sl. s. EtOH	Enzyme inhibitor at 10^{-3}–10^{-4} M. Germicide Fungicide Antiseptic	
> 200 d.	s. hot H_2O, hot EtOH, alkalis; sp. s. H_2O, EtOH	Enzyme inhibitor at 10^{-3}–10^{-4} M. Estimation of —SH (iodometric)	Reacts incompletely with —SH. Rel. specific for —SH at pH 7. Reacts also with thioether of methionine and —S—S— at pH values below 7.
183 d.	s. H_2O	Enzyme inhibitor at 10^{-4}–10^{-5} M. Estimation of —SH (back titration of porphyrindine with ascorbate), *Meth. biochem. Anal.* **1**, 1 (1954)	Not specific; reacts also with hydroxyphenyl groups of tyrosine. Unstable; store in desiccator over $CaCl_2$ at 0°. PREP. *J. Pharm. Soc. Japan* 74, 1059 (1954); see also *J.A.C.S.* 66, 1652 (1944). E_0', pH 7, +0·57 v. Oxidized form blue, in solution; reduced, colourless.
−82 B.p. $78{\cdot}5^{760}$ Flash pt. 0	s. H_2O; misc. usual org. solvs.	Detection cysteine residues in proteins (*S*-carboxyethyl cysteine in acid hydrolysates), *Arch. B.B.* 95, 470 (1961)	Reaction R—SH + CH_2=CH—CN → R—S—CH_2CH_2CN. V. poisonous—handle in hood. Explosive mixtures with air.
B.p. $78\text{–}80^{16}$	2·5 H_2O	Enzyme inhibitor at 10^{-4}–10^{-5} M. Antibacterial agent	Active principle of garlic. Major product of reaction with RSH is C_3H_5—S—S—R. ISOL. *J.A.C.S.* **66**, 1950 (1944). ENZYME ACTION, *B.J.* 63, 514 (1956).

J. MISCELLANEOUS ENZYME INHIBITORS

By A. B. ROY (*Department of Physical Biochemistry, Australian National University, Canberra*)

No.	*Name*	*Synonyms*	*Formula*	*M. wt.*	*Physical form*
1	Acetazolamide	5-Acetamido-1:3:4-thiadiazole-2-sulphonamide, Diamox	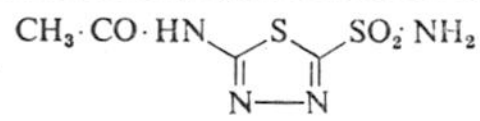	222·3	wh. cryst. from H_2O
2	*N*-Acetylglucosaminonolactone	2-Acetamido-2-deoxygluconolactone	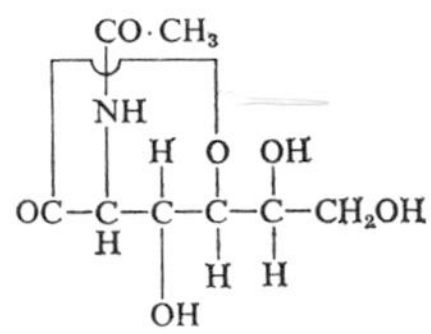	219·2	wh. powder; v. deliq.
3	Adenosine-5′-monosulphate, Ba salt		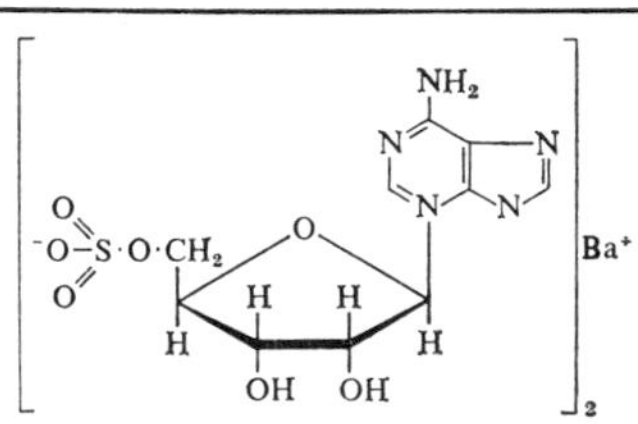	830·0	col. cryst.
4	α-Amino-methoxyphenyl-methane sulphonic acid	1-Amino-1-(*p*-methoxyphenyl)-methane sulphonic acid, AMPS	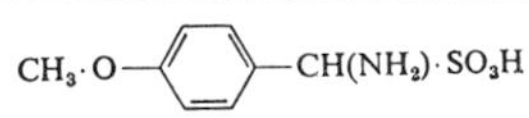	217·2	
5	Amphenone B	3:3-Bis-(*p*-aminophenyl)-butan-2-one	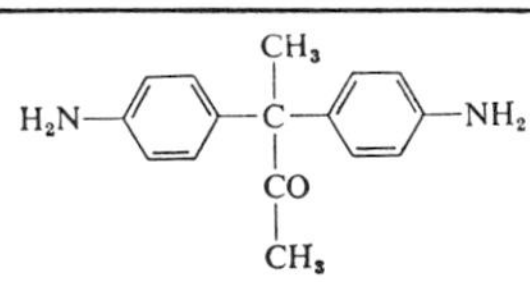	254·3	cryst.
6	Antabuse	Tetraethylthiuram-disulphide	$(H_5C_2)_2\cdot N\cdot \overset{S}{\overset{\Vert}{C}}\cdot S\cdot S\cdot \overset{S}{\overset{\Vert}{C}}\cdot N\cdot (C_2H_5)_2$	296·5	col. cryst.
7	2-Benzyl-imidazole		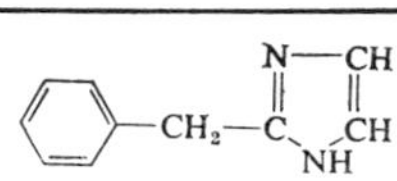	158·2	col. needles
8	5-Chlorofuroic acid		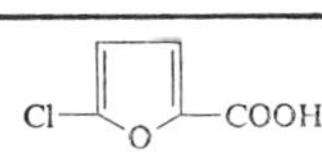	146·5	wh. leaflets
9	*m*-Dimethyl-aminophenyl methyl-carbamate·HCl		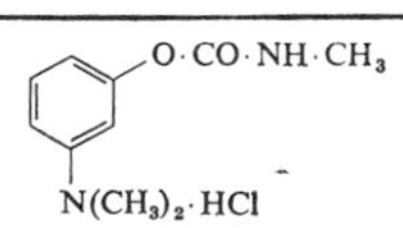	230·7	wh. prisms
10	Flavianic acid	2:4-Dinitro-1-naphthol-7-sulphonic acid	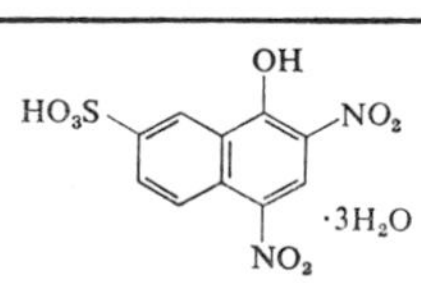	Hydrate, 368·3	yel. needles
11	Fluoroacetic acid —, Na salt		$FCH_2\cdot COOH$ $FCH_2\cdot COONa$	78·0 100·0	wh. cryst. col. cryst.

M.p.	*Solubility*	*References*	*Examples of action*	*General remarks*
258 d.	sl. s. H_2O	*Z.P.C.* **316,** 172 (1959) *J.B.C.* **238,** 945 (1963)	Non-comp. inhibits carbonic anhydrase at 10^{-8} M	pK_a = 7·2. Used as a diuretic. Abs. max. 270 mμ (ε = 7900).
	s. H_2O	*B.J.* **69,** 467 (1958)	Comp. inhibits β-*N*-acetylglucosaminidase at 10^{-5} M	In general aldonolactones comp. inhibit corresponding glycosidases, *B.J.* 65, 389 (1957); **82,** 225 (1962).
	s. H_2O	*J. Biochem., Tokyo* **43,** 153 (1956) *Nature, Lond.* **184,** 1227 (1959)	Inhibits amino acid oxidase at 10^{-3} M by competing with adenylic acid moiety of FAD	
		J. exp. Med. **99,** 105; **100,** 329 (1954)	Inhibits uptake of influenza virus by chorioallantoic cells	
138	Di-HCl, s. H_2O, EtOH	*Science* **133,** 613 (1961) *J.B.C.* **222,** 565 (1956)	Inhibits hydroxylation reactions and so corticoid production by adrenal cortex *in vivo* and in perfused gland	Many side reactions in intact animal, especially on thyroid gland.
70	s. EtOH, $CHCl_3$	*B.Z.* **329,** 17 (1957)	Inhibits oxidation of acetaldehyde *in vivo* probably by inhibiting glyceraldehyde dehydrogenase. Inhibits yeast alcohol dehydrogenase	Used in treatment of alcoholism
125	s. H_2O, EtOH	*Arch. B.* **27,** 94 (1950)	Inhibits penicillinase at 10^{-3} M	
79	s. EtOH; sl. s. H_2O	*J.B.C.* **224,** 591 (1957)	Inhibits L-glutamic dehydrogenase: mechanism mixed comp.–non-comp.	
70	s. EtOH, acet.	*B.J.* **25,** 1147 (1931)	Inhibits liver esterase at 10^{-6} M	
00	s. H_2O, EtOH	*J.B.C.* **233,** 1128 (1958)	Inhibits phosphate-activated glutaminase at 10^{-3} M: non-comp. with glutamine.	
	s. H_2O, EtOH	*J.B.C.* **217,** 213 (1955); **218,** 823 (1956)	Forms fluorocitrate (q.v.) *in vivo* through action of acetyl CoA synthetase and citrate synthase	pK_a = 2·66.

15. Antimetabolites, Antibacterial Agents, and Enzyme Inhibitors

No.	*Name*	*Synonyms*	*Formula*	*M. wt.*	*Physical form*
12	Fluorocitric acid		FCH·COOH HO·C·COOH CH_2·COOH	210·1	anhyd., col. needles hydrated, col. cryst.; both v. deliq.
	—, Ba salt		$[Ba_3(C_6H_4O_7F)_2]_2\cdot H_2O$	1652·8	
13	β-Fluorooxalo-acetic acid	1-Fluoro-2-oxo-succinic acid	HOOC·CO·CHF·COOH	150·1	cryst.
14	δ-Guanidino-valeric acid		NH, NH_2 >CH·NH·CH_2·CH_2·CH_2·CH_2·COOH	160·2	cryst.
15	Hydroxylamine		NH_2OH	33·0	wh. needles or col. liq.
16	MER 25	1-[*p*-(2-Diethylamino-ethoxy)-phenyl]-1-phenyl-2-(*p*-methoxy-phenyl)-ethanol	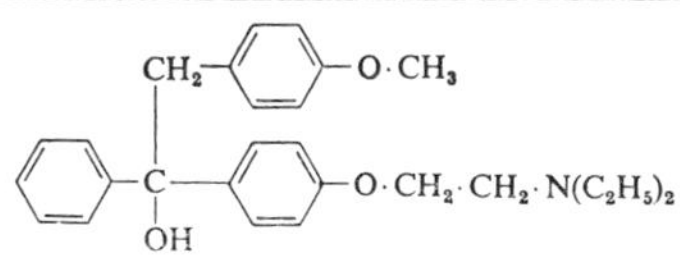	419·6	
17	Ouabain	G-Strophanthin	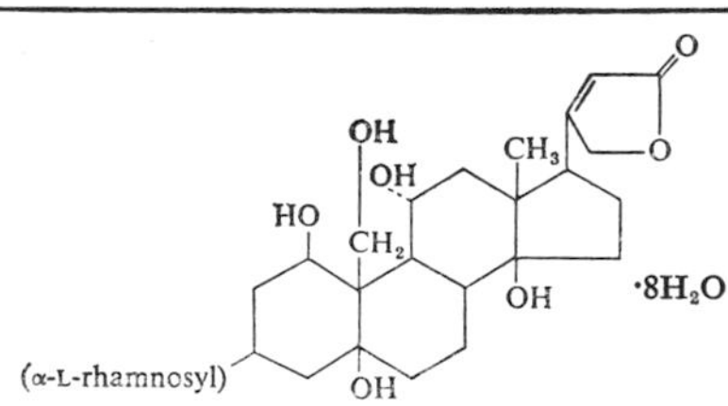	Hydrate, 728·8	shiny plates of octahydrate
18	Oxamic acid		COOH $CONH_2$	89·1	col. cryst.
19	Parapyruvate	γ-Methyl-γ-hydroxy-α-ketoglutaric acid	CH_3 HOOC·C·CH_2·CO·COOH OH	176·1	
20	Phenethyl alcohol	2-Phenylethanol	$C_6H_5\cdot CH_2\cdot CH_2OH$	122·2	col. liq.
21	2-Phenylcyclo-propylamine hydrochloride	SKF *trans*-385	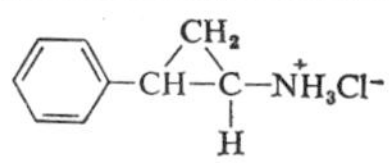	169·7	col. needles
22	Phenyl-β-D-thiogalactoside		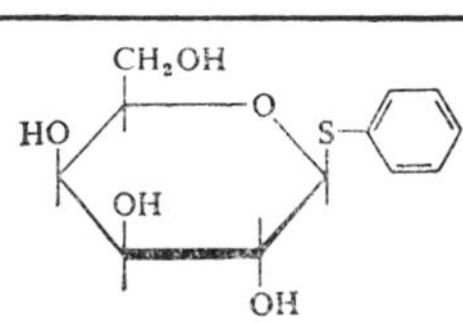	272·3	
23	Phloretin		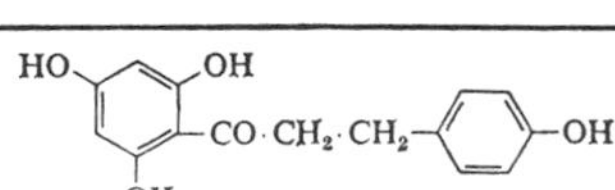	274·3	col. needles

M.p.	*Solubility*	*References*	*Examples of action*	*General remarks*
	s. H_2O, EtOH, eth.	*B.J.* **58**, 473 (1954) Peters, *Biochemical Lesions and Lethal Synthesis*, Pergamon Press (1963) *J.B.C.* **239**, 425 (1964) *J.B.C.* **244**, 2966 (1969)	Inhibits aconitase at 10^{-5} M	Difference between natural and synthetic compounds probably due to presence of different stereoisomers.
86	s. H_2O	*Biochem. Pharm.* **1**, 207 (1958)	Comp. inhibits malate dehydrogenase at 10^{-3} M	Crystalline acid decomposes on standing.
265	s. H_2O, EtOH	*J.B.C.* **231**, 379 (1958)	Comp. inhibits carboxypeptidase B at 10^{-3} M	Similar action by δ-aminovaleric acid and ε-aminocaproic acid which also inhibits plasmin.
33	s. H_2O, EtOH	*J.B.C.* **233**, 1135 (1958)	Inhibits amino acid decarboxylases at 10^{-5} M. Also γ-aminobutyrate–α-oxoglutarate transaminase and serine and threonine dehydrases. Inhibits glucose oxidase by unknown mechanism	Similar inhibition by most carbonyl reagents which combine with pyridoxal phosphate.
		Endocrinology **63**, 295 (1958)	Powerfully inhibits *in vivo* the action of steroid and non-steroid oestrogens	
Anhyd., 190 Hydrate, 130	s. H_2O, EtOH	*B.J.* **84**, 110; **85**, 495 (1962)	Inhibits cation transport and some K^+-dependent ATP-ases (at 10^{-6} M) under certain conditions	
210	s. H_2O; v. sl. s. EtOH	*J.B.C.* **234**, 1143 (1959)	Inhibits heart lactic dehydrogenase at 10^{-5} M by competing with pyruvate	Has been used to inhibit glycolysis in neoplastic cells.
	s. H_2O	*J.B.C.* **221**, 359, 369 (1956)	Specifically inhibits at 10^{-3} M the oxidation of α-oxoglutarate in tissue preps.	Parapyruvate exists in equilibrium with the corresponding lactone, the latter amounting to 25% at equilibrium.
B.p. 19–21	s. EtOH, eth.; $1{\cdot}6^{20}$ H_2O	*J. Bact.* **83**, 738 (1962) *J. Am. pharm. Ass.* **42**, 6 (1953)	Inhibits DNA synthesis without affecting protein and RNA synthesis at 0·25%. At higher conc. protein and RNA synthesis inhibited and cells no longer elongate	Bacteriostatic to a wide variety of bacterial species (exception: *Streptococci*). Gram −ve susceptible at 0·27%, gram +ve a 0·5%.
	s. EtOH; i. eth.	*Helv. chim. Acta* **43**, 439 (1960)	Inhibits amine oxidase, essentially irreversibly, at 10^{-7} M	Both *cis*- and *trans*- isomers active. Neither has significant effect on diamine oxidase.
12	s. H_2O	*B.B.A.* **7**, 585 (1951)	Comp. inhibits β-galactosidase at 10^{-3} M	Is not an inducer of β-galactosidase in *E. coli.*
64–71 d.	s. EtOH, acet., acetic acid; i. H_2O, eth.	*J.B.C.* **135**, 733 (1940); **234**, 3022 (1959)	Inhibits muscle phosphorylase and also uptake of glucose by erythrocytes	Mechanism of action on erythrocytes not clear.

15. Antimetabolites, Antibacterial Agents, and Enzyme Inhibitors

No.	*Name*	*Synonyms*	*Formula*	*M. wt.*	*Physical form*
24	Phloridzin	Phlorhizin, asebotin	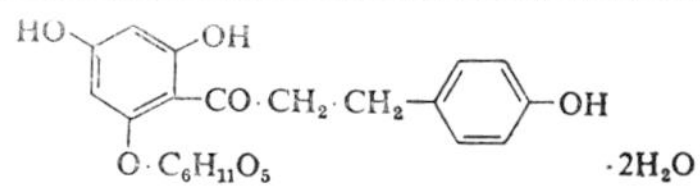	Hydrate, 472·4	silky wh. needles
25	Polyphloretin phosphate		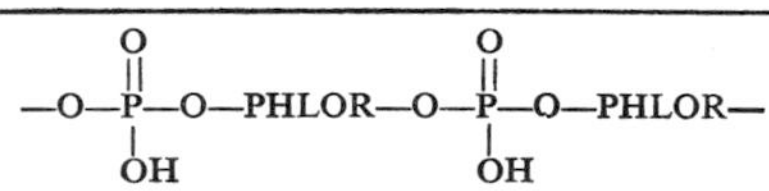	15 000	light green or brown powder
26	Potassium selenate		K_2SeO_4	221·2	col. rh. cryst.
27	Proflavin dihydrochloride	3:6-Diamino acridinium chloride hydrochloride	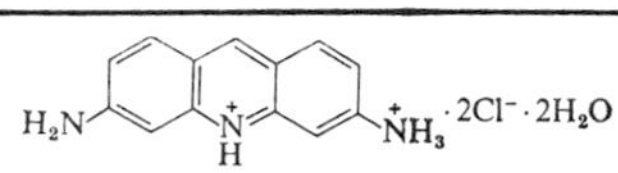	318·2	orange-red cryst.
28	Propylgallate	Tenox PG	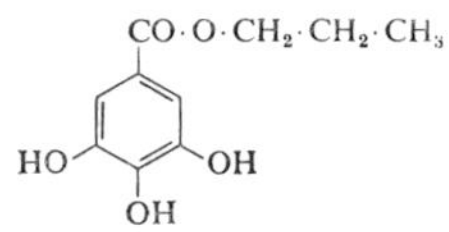	212·2	cryst.
29	*iso*Propylhydrazine		$(CH_3)_2CH\cdot NH-NH_2$	74·1	col. liq.
30	6-Pteridylaldehyde	2-Amino-4-hydroxy-6-formylpteridine	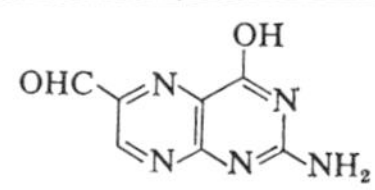	191·2	yel. powder
31	Pyrogallol	Pyrogallic acid	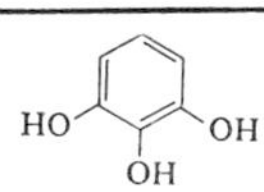	126·1	wh. cryst.; darken in air and light
32	Riboflavin-5-sulphate		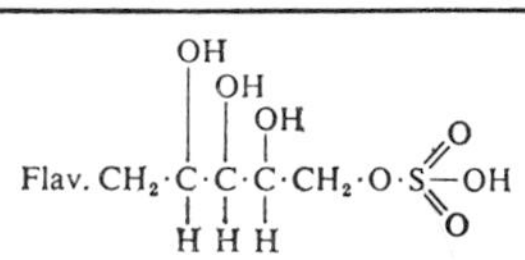	456·4	yel. cryst.
33	Saccharolactone	D-Glucaro-1:4-lactone	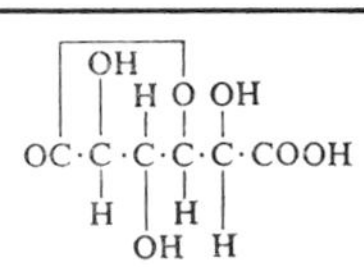	192·1	col. cryst.
34	Sodium fluoride		NaF	42·0	wh. cubic cryst.
35	Sodium sulphite		$Na_2SO_3\cdot 7H_2O$	252·2	col. monocl. cryst. effl.
36	SKF 525–A	2-Diethylaminoethyl 2-diphenylpropylacetate	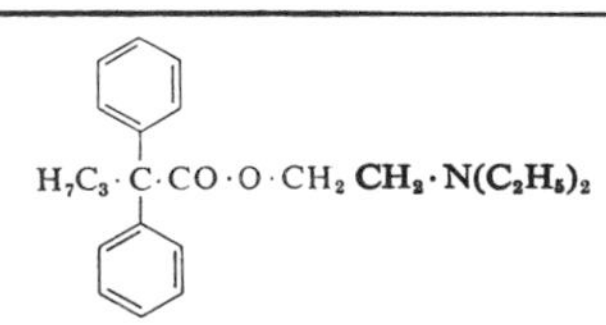	353·5	
37	SU 4885	Metopirone, 2:3-bis(3-pyridyl)-2-methylpropan-3-one	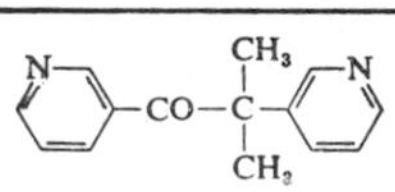	226·3	

M.p.	*Solubility*	*References*	*Examples of action*	*General remarks*
108; solidifies 138; remelts 170	v.s. hot H_2O; s. EtOH; v. sl. s. eth.	*J.B.C.* **135**, 733 (1940) *Arch. B.B.* **81**, 508 (1959)	Non-comp. inhibition of muscle, but not potato, phosphorylase. Inhibits phosphatases and UDPG-glycogen transglucosylase	Causes glucosuria by prevention of glucose reabsorption in renal tubules.
	s. H_2O	*Acta chem. scand.* **7**, 913 (1953)	Inhibits alkaline phosphatase at 0·025 μg/ml and hyaluronidase at 0·1 μg/ml	Other polyphosphates act similarly.
	s. H_2O	*Proc. natn. Acad. Sci., U.S.A.* **41**, 880 (1955)	Inhibits ATP-sulphurylase and many reactions involving sulphate	
	s. H_2O; v. sl. s. eth.	*J. molec. Biol.* **3**, 18 (1961) *Symp. Soc. gen. Microbiol.* **16**, 241 (1966)	Powerful mutagen, probably through its combination with DNA by intercalation	Inhibits DNA polymerase *in vitro* but not RNA polymerase.
150	s. EtOH, eth.; v. sl. s. H_2O	*Arch. B.B.* **42**, 293 (1953)	Inhibits lipoxidase at 10^{-4} M	Used as an anti-oxidant in foods.
	s. H_2O, EtOH	*Helv. physiol. pharmac. Acta* **18**, C27 (1960)	Inhibits diamine oxidase at 10^{-9} M	No inhibition of monoamine oxidase.
		J.B.C. **180**, 399 (1949)	Inhibits milk xanthine oxidase at 10^{-9} M	
131	s. H_2O, EtOH, eth.	*Science* **130**, 800 (1959)	Comp. inhibits catechol–*O*-methyl transferase at 10^{-5} M	Potentiates action of adrenalin and noradrenalin *in vivo*.
	s. H_2O	*J. Biochem., Tokyo* **43**, 153 (1956) *Nature, Lond.* **184**, 1227 (1959)	Inhibits amino acid oxidase at 10^{-5} M by competing for riboflavin moiety of FAD	Does not prevent FMN combining with 'old yellow enzyme', *Nature, Lond.* **180**, 922 (1957).
Hydrate, 90	s. H_2O, acet.	*B.J.* **52**, 464 (1952)	Comp. inhibits β-glucuronidase at 10^{-5} M	The lactone is formed to about 30% on boiling a solution of potassium hydrogen saccharate for 30 min. It is unstable at a pH greater than 6.
	s. H_2O	*B.Z.* **310**, 384 (1941)	Inhibits many Mg^{2+}-requiring enzymes such as enolase and acid phosphatase	pK_a 3·2 (free acid).
	s. H_2O; sl. s. EtOH	*B.J.* **59**, 8 (1955) *Adv. Enzymol.* **22**, 205 (1960)	Inhibits sulphatases at 10^{-4} M or less	General reagent for cleaving protein disulphide bonds, *Chem. Rev.* **59**, 583 (1959).
		Science **121**, 603 (1955) *J. Pharm. exp. Ther.* **112**, 49, 55 (1954)	Inhibits many 'detoxifying' enzymes of the liver microsomes, especially those requiring $NADPH_2$ and O_2	Potentiates the action of many drugs (e.g. barbiturates) *in vivo*.
		J. mednl pharm. Chem. **1**, 407 (1959) *Science* **128**, 478 (1958); **133**, 613 (1961)	*In vivo* inhibits 11β-hydroxylation by the adrenal cortex and so alters corticoid production	Many side effects on other endocrine glands.

15. Antimetabolites, Antibacterial Agents, and Enzyme Inhibitors

No.	Name	Synonyms	Formula	M. wt.	Physical form
38	L(+)-Tartaric acid	*d*-Tartaric acid, D(+)-tartaric acid (See *J.B.C.* **207**, 275 (1954))	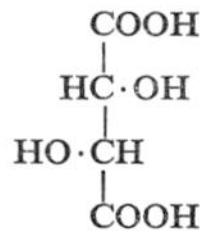	150·1	col. monocl.
39	*meso*-Tartaric acid	*i*-Tartaric acid	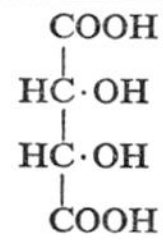	150·1	col. plates
40	D-Threose-2:4-diphosphate		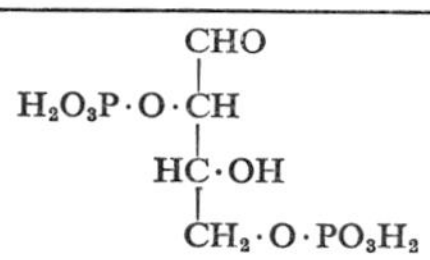	280·1	
41	2:6:8-Trichloropurine		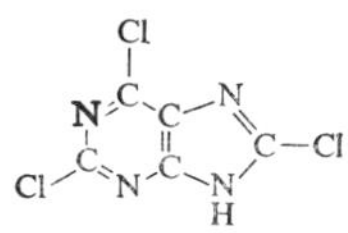	223·5	platelets of pentahydrate
42	Triparanol	MER 29, 1-[*p*-(2-diethylamino-ethoxy)-phenyl]-1-(*p*-tolyl)-2-(*p*-chlorophenyl)-ethanol	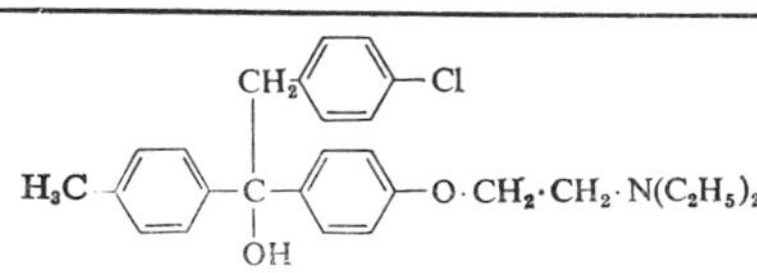	438·0	

M.p.	*Solubility*	*References*	*Examples of action*	*General remarks*
170	s. H_2O, EtOH; i. benz.	*B.J.* **45**, 51 (1949) *J.B.C.* **227**, 879 (1957)	Inhibits acid phosphatase (liver, kidney, and prostate) at 10^{-3} M	D(−)-isomer inactive. Erythrocyte or plasma enzyme not inhibited—basis of clinical differentiation.
140	s. H_2O, EtOH	*J.A.C.S.* **82**, 5482 (1960)	Inhibits fumarase at 10^{-5} M	
	s. H_2O	*J.B.C.* **234**, 2510, 2517 (1959)	Non-comp. inhibition of glyceraldehyde-3-phosphate dehydrogenase	Inhibitor not isolated but prepared by oxidation of corresponding arabitol phosphate.
Hydrate, 187	sl. s. H_2O; v. sl. s. EtOH, acet.	*The Enzymes*, vol. 8, p. 291 (1963)	Inhibits uricase at 10^{-6} M	Other tri-substituted purines act similarly.
		B.B.R.C. **2**, 63 (1960)	*In vivo* causes a block in cholesterol synthesis from mevalonate with an accumulation of desmosterol	

16. Drugs and Other Pharmacologically Active Compounds

Revised by D. F. SHARMAN (*A.R.C. Institute of Animal Physiology, Babraham, Cambridge*)

Fluorescence data

A = wavelength of maximum activation (mμ); F = wavelength of maximum fluorescence (mμ).

16. Drugs and Other Pharmacologically Active Compounds

No.	*Name*	*Synonyms*	*Formula*	*M. wt.*	*Physical form*	*M.p.*
1	Alloxan	Mesoxalylurea	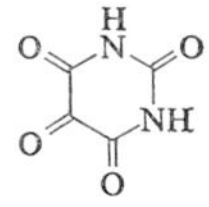	Anhyd., 142·1; Hydrate, 160·1	Monohydrate, col. rh. prisms, efflor.; anhyd., yel. powder	Monohydrate, decomp. 256
2	Amphetamine	Benzedrine, 1-phenyl-2-aminopropane, (±α-)-methylphenethylamine; (+)-isomer: dexamphetamine	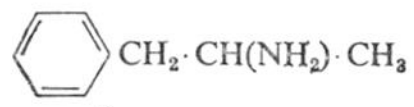 Sulphate, $(C_9H_{13}N)_2 \cdot H_2SO_4$	135·2 Sulphate, 368·5	liq. with acrid taste; slightly volatile	B.p. 200 d. SO_4 melts > 300 d.
3	Antipyrine	Phenazone, 1-phenyl-2,3-dimethyl-5-pyrazolone	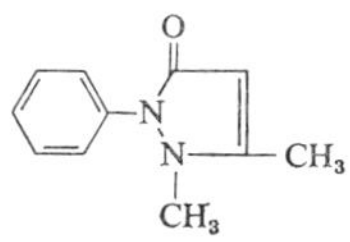	188·2	small cryst. or wh. powder	111–13
4	Apomorphine hydrochloride		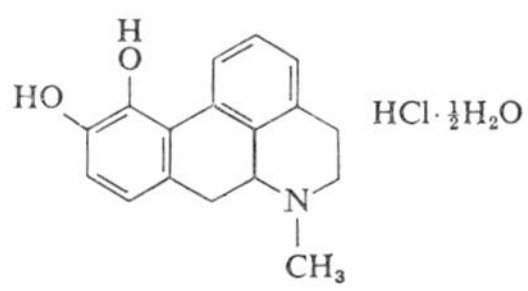	312·8	cryst; decomposes, turns green in light and air	170 d.
5	Atropine	DL-Hyoscyamine	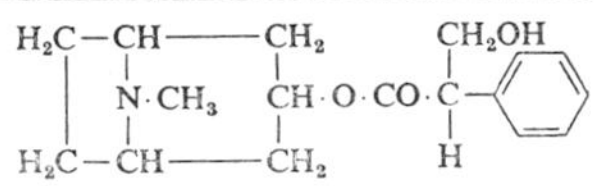 Sulphate, $(C_{17}H_{23}O_3N)_2 \cdot H_2SO_4 \cdot H_2O$	289·4 Sulphate, 694·8	col. microcryst. Sulphate, col. cryst.	114–16 Sulphate, 191–6
6	Banthine bromide	Methantheline bromide, 2-diethylaminoethylxanthene-9-carboxylate methobromide	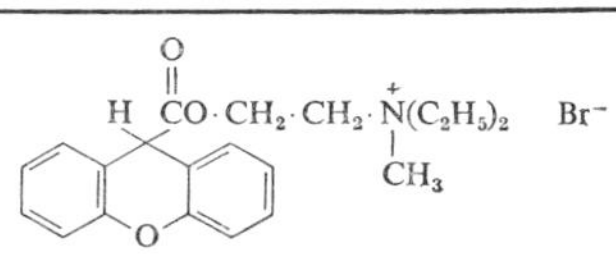	420·3	wh. cryst. sl. hygr.; bitter taste	171–7
7	Barbiturate anaesthetics and hypnotics					
	(*a*) Amylobarbitone	Amytal, 5-ethyl-5-isoamylbarbituric acid	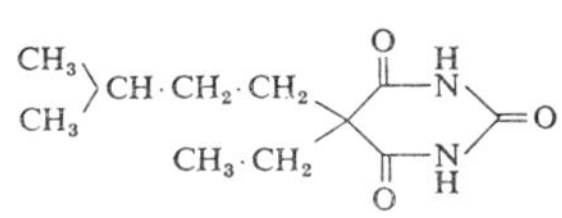	226·3; Na salt, 248·3	col. cryst.	156–8
	(*b*) Barbitone	Barbital, veronal, 5,5-diethylbarbituric acid, 5,5-diethylmalonylurea. Na salt, barbitone soluble	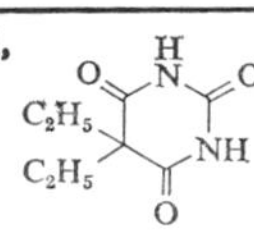	184·2 Na salt, 206·2	wh. cryst.	189–92

Solubility	*Action*	*Route*	*Absorption and fate*	*General remarks*	*References*
s. H_2O, EtOH; sl. s. $CHCl_3$; i. eth.	Cytotoxic, diabetogenic. At 10^{-3} M inhibits skeletal muscle hexokinase; inhibition reversed by cysteine. Succinic dehydrogenase also inhibited	i.v., oral	Absorbed orally, parenterally. Rapidly destroyed. Part reduced to alloxantin	Cellular mechanism unknown. Action very rapid. Prevented by SH compounds, nicotinic acid. Diabetogenic dosage: Dogs, 50–70 mg/kg i.v. Rabbits, 200 mg/kg i.v. Rats, 50 mg/kg i.v. Reversibly nephrotoxic above diabetogenic dosage. Fluorescent product with *o*-phenylene diamine	*Physiol. Rev.* **28,** 304 (1948). *Lancet* **2,** 384 (1943). PREP. *Org. Synth.* **32,** 6 (1952).
s. EtOH, eth., acids, $CHCl_3$; sl. s. H_2O. Sulphate, s. H_2O; sl. s. EtOH; i. eth.	Central stimulant, peripheral sympathomimetic	oral, i.v.	Absorbed G.I.T. Part deaminated, part excreted unchanged	Dextrorotatory form has twice the potency of racemate. Stronger inhibitor of amine oxidase than ephedrine. Used in barbiturate intoxication	*J. Pharmac. exp. Ther.* **68,** 419 (1940). EST. *J. Lab. clin. Med.* **32,** 913 (1947).
50 H_2O; v.s. $CHCl_3$, EtOH; s. eth.	Analgesic, antipyretic	oral	Rapidly absorbed G.I.T. Plasma peak 1–2 hr. Rapidly metabolized in dogs, slower in man. 40% oxidized to 4-hydroxyantipyrine and conjugated with glucuronic acid	Has been used as a measure of body water (second ref.)	*J. Pharmac. exp. Ther.* **98,** 97 (1950). *J.B.C.* **179,** 31 (1949). EST. *J. Pharm. Pharmac.* **2,** 393 (1950). *J. Am. pharm. Ass.* **22,** 947 (1933).
sl. s. H_2O, HCl, EtOH; v. sl. s. $CHCl_3$, eth.	Centrally acting emetic. C.N.S. depressant	s.c., oral, i.v., i.m.	Absorbed all routes	Emetic dose in the dog 2–10 mg	*Pharmac. Rev.* **5,** 193 (1953).
0·2 H_2O, 2^{100} H_2O; 33 EtOH; 3 benz.; 1·8 eth.; 50 $CHCl_3$; s. oils, oleic acid, glycerol. Sulphate, 200 H_2O; 25 EtOH; i. benz., $CHCl_3$, eth.	Antagonist of muscarinic actions of acetylcholine. Central excitant and depressant	i.m., oral, topical	Rapidly absorbed by G.I.T., from mucosal surfaces and to some extent from intact skin. Disappears quickly from the blood. The tissues, especially liver, hydrolyse it to tropine and tropic acid. In man about 10% excreted in urine. Species differences in occurrence of atropinase. Blackbird and most strains of rabbit are resistant	Reduces salivary and gastric secretions. Pupil of the eye dilated and accommodation paralysed. Sweat glands inhibited. Tolerance soon develops in man. Unstable to autoclaving.	EST. *J. Pharm. Pharmac.* **4,** 1001 (1952). *J. Pharm. Pharmac.* **5,** 169, 608 (1953). *J. Am. pharm. Ass. Sci. Edn.* **41,** 602 (1952).
s. H_2O (> 10%)	Anticholinergic	oral, i.v., i.m.	Absorbed G.I.T.	Qualitatively resembles atropine (less potent). In lab. animals delays gastric emptying and intestinal transit time. Aq. soln. unstable on keeping	*Gastroenterology* **14,** 301 (1950). *J. Pharmac. exp. Ther.* **99,** 245 (1950).
			After absorption barbiturates distributed throughout the tissues	Readily cross placental barrier	*Pharmac. Rev.* **1,** 217 (1949).
sl. s. H_2O; s. EtOH, eth., $CHCl_3$. Na salt, s. H_2O, EtOH; i. eth.	Hypnotic of intermediate duration	oral	Degraded by the liver	Fluor., A 265 mμ F 410 mμ (pH 14)	
0·84 H_2O; s. EtOH, eth., $CHCl_3$, acet. Na salt, s. H_2O	Hypnotic, sedative (long lasting)	oral	Readily absorbed. Not bound to plasma proteins, excreted mainly by the kidney	Onset of effect is slow. Often used as sodium salt. Phenobarbitone is also long lasting	*J. Pharmac. exp. Ther.* **101,** 296 (1951). *Fed. Proc.* **11,** 640, 653 (1952).

No.	Name	Synonyms	Formula	M. wt.	Physical form	M.p.
7	(c) Pentobarbitone sodium	Nembutal, sodium 5-ethyl-5-(1-methylbutyl)-barbiturate	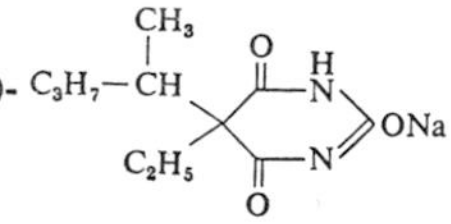	248·3	wh. cryst. powder or granules	128·5–130 (free acid)
	(d) Thiopentone sodium	Pentothal sodium	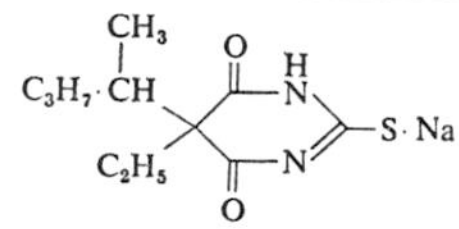	264·3	yel.-wh. hygr. powder. Alliaceous odour	
8	Bemegride	β-Ethyl-β-methylglutarimide	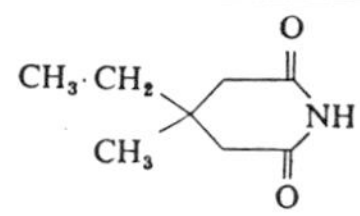	155·2	col. odourless cryst. powder	127
9	3,4-Benzpyrene		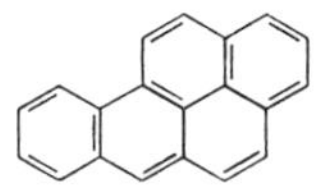	252·3	yel. plates and needles	179
10	Caffeine	1,3,7-Trimethylxanthine, theine, methyltheobromine	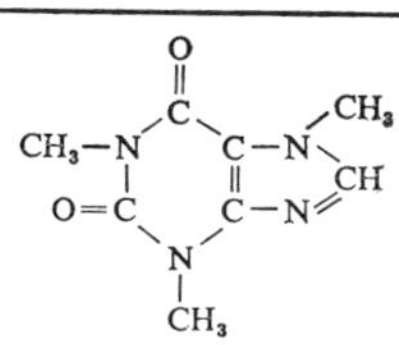 Hydrochloride, $C_8H_{10}N_4O_2 \cdot HCl \cdot 2H_2O$ Sulphate, $C_8H_{10}N_4O_2 \cdot H_2SO_4$	194·2; Hydrate, 212·2 HCl, 266·7 Sulphate, 292·2	wh. needles from EtOH; prisms by sublimation	Anhyd. 237; sublimes above 178
11	Camphor	*d*-2-Camphanone	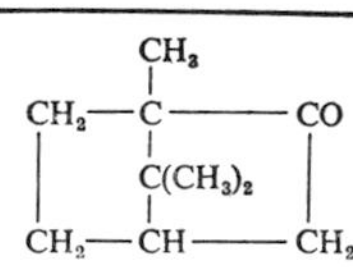	152·2	transparent cryst. with aromatic odour	176–7; sublimes at room temp. B.p. 204
12	Chloral hydrate	Trichloroethylidene glycol	$CCl_3 \cdot CH(OH)_2$	165·4	large wh. cryst.	57–58
13	Chloralose	α-D-Glucochloralose, Glucochloral, Somio, Chloralosane	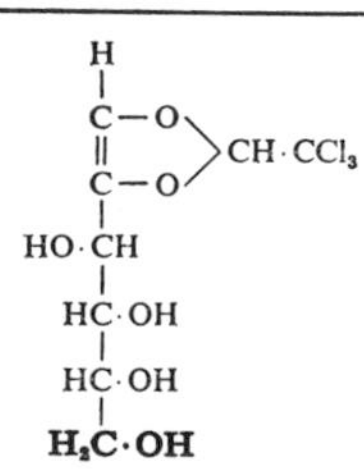	309·5	col. cryst. powder	187
14	Chlorpromazine	10-(γ-Dimethylaminopropyl)-2-chlorophenothiazine HCl, thorazine, largactil	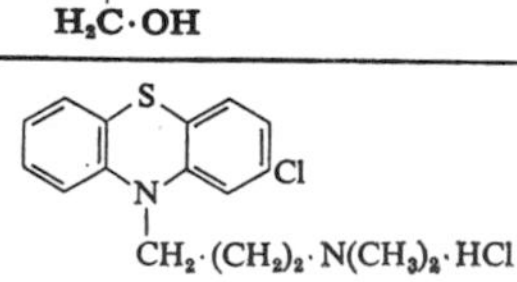	355·3	whitish-grey powder; changes colour when exposed to light	179–80

Solubility	*Action*	*Route*	*Absorption and fate*	*General remarks*	*References*
s. H_2O, EtOH; i. eth.	Hypnotic of short duration used as surgical anaesthetic in animals (dose 35–40 mg/kg i.p.)	oral, i.v., i.p.	50% bound to plasma proteins. Degraded by the liver	Fluor., A 265 mμ F 440 mμ (pH 13–14)	EST. *J. Pharmac. exp. Ther.* **109**, 26 (1953).
s. H_2O, EtOH; i. eth., benz.	Very short acting general anaesthetic	i.v.	75–80% bound to plasma proteins. Rapidly taken up by body fat, degraded by the liver	Solns. are unstable. Immediate onset of anaesthesia. Fluor., A 315 mμ F 513 mμ (pH 13–14)	
s. H_2O, acet.	Analeptic. Used to antagonize barbiturates	i.v.		Often used in conjunction with amiphenazole (2,4-diamino-5-phenylthiazole)	PREP. *J.C.S.* **1927**, 600. *Nature, Lond.* **173**, 402 (1954).
s. benz., toluene, xylene.; sp. s. EtOH, MeOH; i. H_2O	Carcinogenic agent	all	Hydroxylated in positions 5, 8 and 10. Some metabolites excreted in the bile	Fluor. in conc. H_2SO_4, A 521 mμ (470 mμ) F 548 mμ (493 mμ)	*J.C.S.* **1933**, 396. *J.C.S.* **1950**, 1112.
s. hot H_2O, EtOH, acet., $CHCl_3$, benz.; sl. s. cold H_2O; sp. s. eth.	Stimulates C.N.S.: cortex > medulla > cord. Vasoconstrictor	oral	Readily absorbed by G.I.T., and blood levels persist 6–12 hr. Partially demethylated and oxidized and excreted as 1-methyluric acid		*J.B.C.* **162**, 309 (1946).
v.s. $CHCl_3$, MeOH, EtOH, acet., eth., benz.; sp. s. H_2O	Stimulates C.N.S.; convulsant	oral, i.m.	Rapidly absorbed all sites. Oxidized to camphorol and excreted in urine combined with glucuronic acid	Oxime deriv., M.p. 118	
s. H_2O, EtOH, eth., $CHCl_3$	Central depressant	oral	Readily absorbed G.I.T. Most reduced to trichloroethanol (hypnotic), part of which is conjugated with glucuronic acid	Soln. may be sterilized by boiling. Used for large animal narcosis	*J. Pharmac. exp. Ther.* **92**, 49 (1948). *J. Pharmac. exp. Ther.* **95**, 360 (1949). *Bull. Johns Hopkins Hosp.* **95**, 1 (1954). EST. *Analyst* **71**, 97 (1946).
s. warm H_2O, eth., gl. acetic; i. pet. eth.	Hypnotic, used as anaesthetic in large animals	i.v.		Must be free from β-chloralose which has central stimulant properties and can be removed by warming 1% soln. to 90°, cooling to 50°, and filtering at 50°	*Handb. exp. Pharmak.* Erg. **2**, 127. M. Denavit, Thesis, University of Paris, 1963.
s. H_2O, $CHCl_3$, EtOH, MeOH	Central depressant, adrenolytic, antifibrillatory, antiedemic, hypothermic, antipyretic, antiemetic, local anaesthetic	oral, i.m.	Readily absorbed G.I.T. Highest blood level 3 hr. Distribution or metabolism unknown. Little urinary excretion (7–8% rabbits). Metabolized to the sulphoxide	Enhances analgesic and hypnotic drugs and disrupts conditioned reflexes. A 5% aq. soln. stable at least 1 day and has pH 4·9. Fluor., A 350 mμ F 480 mμ (pH 11)	*Arch. int. Pharmacodyn. Thér.* **92**, 305 (1953).

16. Drugs and Other Pharmacologically Active Compounds

No.	Name	Synonyms	Formula	M. wt.	Physical form	M.p.
15	Cocaine	Benzoylmethyl-ecgonine	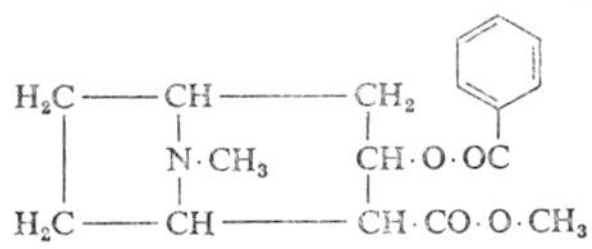	303·3; HCl, 339·8	wh. cryst. powder	96–98; HCl, 197
16	Colchicine		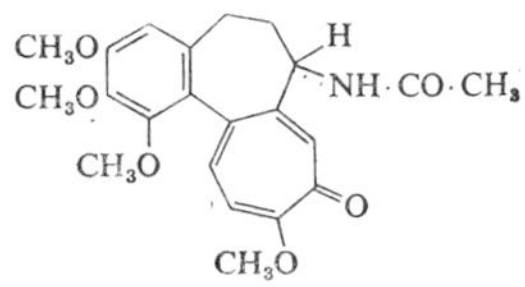	399·4	pale yel. powder; darkens in light	142–50
17	Dichloro-iso-prenaline hy-drochloride	D.C.I.	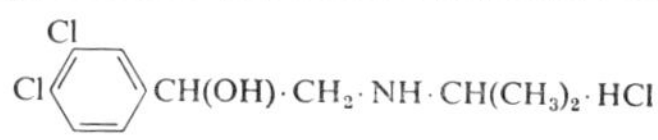	284·7	wh. cryst. powder	
18	Dicoumarol	Bishydroxy-coumarin, 3,3′-methylene-bis(4-hydroxy-coumarin)	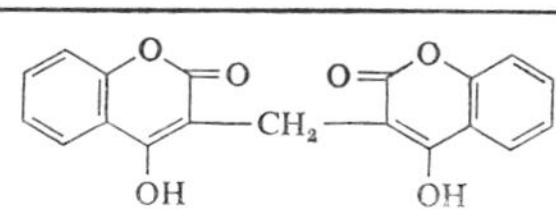	336·3	wh. hexag. prisms	287–93
19	3,5-Diethoxy-carbonyl-1,4-dihydro-2,4,6-trimethyl-pyridine	Collidine derivative	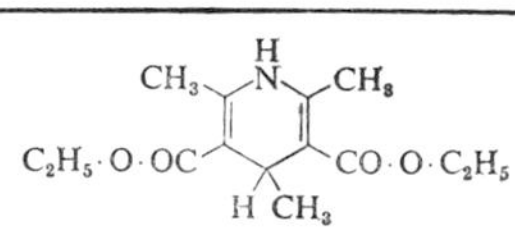	267·4	almost wh. cryst.	128
20	Dihydro-β-erythroidine		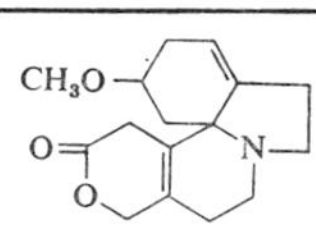	275·3	col. cryst. powder	85–86 d.; HBr salt, 242 d.
21	Diphenhydra-mine	Benadryl HCl, 2-(benzhydryl-oxy)-*N*,*N*-di-methylethyl-amine hydro-chloride	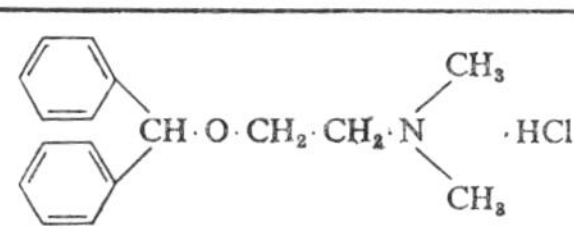	291·8	cryst. powder	161–2
22	Ephedrine	*l*-Ephedrine, α-(1-methyl-aminoethyl)-benzyl alcohol, *l*-1-phenyl-2-methylamino-propanol	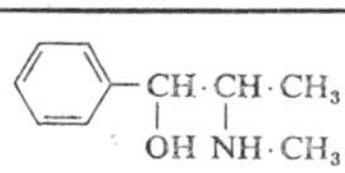	165·2; HCl, 201·7	waxy cryst.; decomp. in light; HCl, wh. needles	38; HCl, 216–20
23	Gallamine triethiodide	Flaxedil	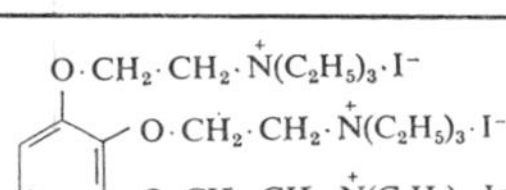	891·6	cryst. powder	145–50

Solubility	Action	Route	Absorption and fate	General remarks	References
0·16[25], 0·38[80] H_2O; 20[25] EtOH; 26·3 eth.; s. $CHCl_3$, benz. Hydrochloride, v.s. H_2O; s. EtOH, $CHCl_3$, glycerol; i. eth.	Local anaesthetic, central excitant and depressant. Enhances effects of catecholamines	i.m., s.c., mucous membrane	Absorbed readily from all sites including mucous membrane. Orally given, is largely hydrolysed in G.I.T. Detoxified by the liver, some excreted unchanged	$[\alpha]_D^{20}$ −29 (c = 2 in EtOH), −48 (c = 2 in benz.); Hydrochloride, −70 to −72 (c = 2 in H_2O). Addiction and tolerance develop on prolonged use; local anaesthetic but more toxic than procaine	EST. *J. Ass. off. agric. Chem.* **31**, 781 (1948). *J. Pharm. Pharmac.* **4**, 636 (1952). *J. Pharm. Pharmac.* **5**, 608 (1953). DETECTION *Analyst* **72**, 253 (1947). *Analyst* **75**, 169 (1950).
4 H_2O; v.s. EtOH, $CHCl_3$; s. eth.	Mitotic arrest (plants and animals); uricosuric	oral, injection	Excreted in bile, and by small intestine. Renal elimination slight (cumulative)	Effect is on metaphase. Less toxic than cinchophen. Aurichloride only salt. Forms cryst. compounds with $CHCl_3$ decomposed at 60°	*Nature, Lond.* **155**, 141 (1945). *J. Pharmac. exp. Ther.* **106**, 261 (1952). *J.A.C.S.* **81**, 6341 (1959).
s. H_2O	Selectively blocks some inhibitory effects of adrenaline and isoprenaline	i.v.		Useful in isolated organ preparation	*J. Pharmac. exp. Ther.* **122**, 480 (1958).
sl. s. $CHCl_3$; sp. s. H_2O, EtOH; s. aq alkalis, organic bases	Blood anticoagulant. Uncouples phosphorylation associated with oxidation of butyrate by liver mitochondria. At 10^{-5} M inhibits $NADH_2$ oxidase activity of heart muscle preps.	oral	Absorbed (variably) from G.I.T. Transformed slowly into intermediates. Bound to plasma proteins (especially albumin) up to 99% at dosage levels. Little urinary excretion	Acts by competitive interference with hepatic utilization of vitamin K in prothrombin synthesis. Other hepatic functions unaffected. Vitamin K does not affect disappearance rate from plasma. Latent period 24–96 hr (man)	*J. Pharmac. exp. Ther.* **99**, 409 (1950). PREP. *Harvey Lect.* **39**, 162 (1943–4).
	Causes hepatic porphyria	oral		Intense blue fluorescent substance	*P.S.E.B.M.* **100**, 583 (1959). PREP. *B.J.* **83**, 1 (1962).
Base, s. $CHCl_3$, EtOH HBr. s. H_2O, EtOH	Neuromuscular and ganglionic blocking agent. Inhibits cholinergic synaptic transmission to Renshaw cells	oral		Longer acting than β-erythroidine and six times as active	*J.A.C.S.* **75**, 2550 (1953). *J. Physiol.* **131**, 154 (1956). *J. cell. comp. Physiol.* **34**, 327 (1949).
s. H_2O, EtOH, $CHCl_3$; sp. s. eth., benz.	Antihistaminic	oral	Readily absorbed. Peak tissue concentration in 60 min. Concentration: lungs > spleen > kidney > liver > brain > muscle > skin. Excreted kidney, some unchanged, rest as unidentified degradation products, in 20–24 hr	Protective against death from anaphylactic shock, in dogs and guinea-pigs	*Ann. N.Y. Acad. Sci.* **50**, 1142 (1950). *J.B.C.* **179**, 403 (1949).
s. H_2O, EtOH, $CHCl_3$, eth., oils. HCl and sulphate, s. H_2O, EtOH; i. eth.	Sympathomimetic. Competitive inhibitor of choline dehydrogenase	oral, s.c.	Readily absorbed G.I.T. Over 50% eliminated by kidney in 12 hr. Unchanged in man. Dog excretes it mostly as norephedrine	Predominant alkaloid of *Ephedra* spp. Aq. soln. stable to light, air, and heat	*J. Physiol.* **94**, 87 (1938). *J. Pharmac. exp. Ther.* **109**, 62 (1953).
s. H_2O, EtOH; sp. s. acet., eth., benz., $CHCl_3$	Neuromuscular blocking agent	i.v.	Large fraction of dose excreted in urine within 2 hr	Little action on ganglia	*Lancet* **1**, 726 (1949).

16. Drugs and Other Pharmacologically Active Compounds

No.	Name	Synonyms	Formula	M. wt.	Physical form	M.p.
24	Guanethidine	Ismelin, [2-(octahydro-1-azocinyl)-ethyl]guanidine sulphate	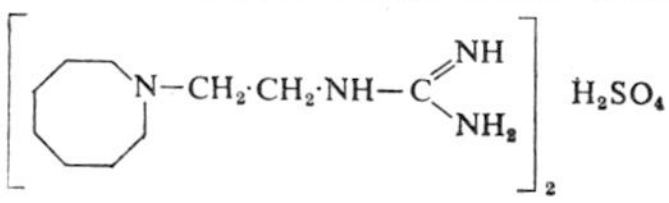	494·8	wh. cryst. powder	276–81 d.
25	Hemicholinium bromide	HC3	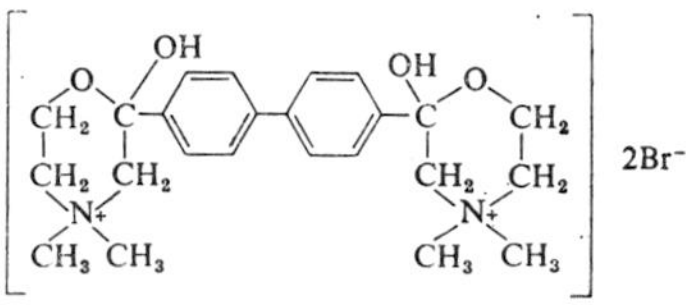	574·4	wh. cryst. powder	
26	Heparin (Na salt)		Heteropolysaccharide with repeating 4-*O*-(α-D-glucuronido)-D-glucosamine-*N*-sulphate units linked by α-(1 → 4) hexosaminidic bonds and bearing between one and two *O*-sulphate groups per disaccharide	approx. 16 000–17 000	wh. amorph. powder; isolated as Na salt	
27	Hyoscine	Scopolamine	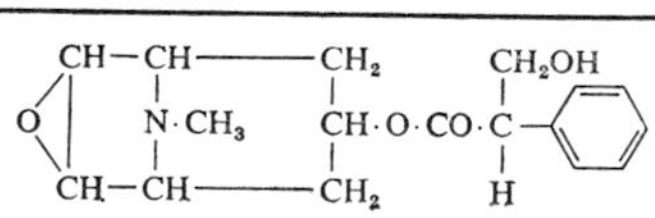	303·3	col. syrup	Monohydrate, 55
			Hydrobromide, $C_{17}H_{21}O_4N \cdot HBr \cdot 3H_2O$	HBr, 438·3	HBr, cryst.	Anhyd. HBr, 194
28	Insulin		A protein containing 51 amino-acid residues. For complete structure *see B.J.* **60**, 541 (1955)	5734	cryst.	
29	Lysergic acid derivatives					
	(*a*) Lysergic acid diethylamide	L.S.D. 25 Delysid is the tartrate	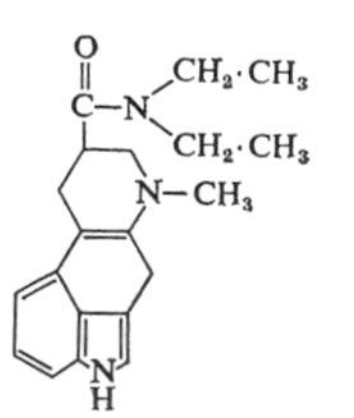	323·4; anhyd. tartrate, 796·9	Cryst. powder (base and salt)	83 (base); 198–200 (tartrate)

Solubility	Action	Route	Absorption and fate	General remarks	References
5 H_2O at pH 6	Anti-hypertensive. Blocks post-ganglionic adrenergic transmission; depletes catecholamines in peripheral tissues	oral, s.c.		Does not penetrate blood brain barrier easily	PREP. *Experientia* **15**, 267 (1959). *J. Pharmac. exp. Ther.* **128**, 22 (1960). *P.S.E.B.M.* **103**, 871 (1960).
s. H_2O	Respiratory paralysant. Blocks cholinergic transmission by interfering with ACh synthesis				*J. Pharmac. exp. Ther.* **115**, 127 (1955). *Br. med. Bull.* **13**, 157 (1957).
s. H_2O; v. sp. s. EtOH, eth., $CHCl_3$	Anticoagulant	i.v., i.m., s.c.	Destroyed in G.I.T. After i.v. injection, disappears rapidly from plasma	May be sterilized by autoclaving, 110°, 30 min. α- and β-forms known. Has chylocytic properties (*see* ref. 2). $[\alpha]_D$ +65 (in H_2O)	*Can. J. med. Sci.* **30**, 353 (1952). *Science* **98**, 19 (1943). *Brit. med. Bull.* **11**, 62 (1955). *Meth. biochem. Anal.* **7**, 253 (1959). *Adv. Carbohyd. Chem.* **10**, 335 (1955).
. H_2O, EtOH, th., $CHCl_3$. Hydrobromide, . H_2O, EtOH; p. s. $CHCl_3$; . eth.	Antagonist of muscarinic actions of acetylcholine. Central excitant and depressant	oral	Rapidly absorbed from G.I.T. mucous membranes. Only 1% excreted in urine	$[\alpha]_D$ −33·1 (in H_2O)	EST. *Q. Jl Pharm. Pharmac.* **15**, 238 (1942).
. H_2O	Produces hypoglycaemia	i.m., i.v., s.c.	Rapidly absorbed from injection site, disappears from circulation, and is bound by tissues. Believed to be destroyed by insulinase present in muscle, lixer, kidney; none excreted	Zn insulin cryst. = 22 units/mg. Rapidly destroyed by proteolytic enzymes of G.I.T. Impure samples usually contaminated with glucagon, which mobilizes hepatic glycogen and increases blood sugar level	EST. *British* or *U.S. Pharmacopœia*. *J. Endocr.* **14**, 82 (1956). *Biochem. Preps.* **8**, 103 (1961). ISOL. *Biochem. Preps.* **6**, 28 (1958). A and B chains: *Biochem. Preps.* **8**, 70 (1961).
. benz.; H_2O. 'artrate, s. H_2O	Psychotomimetic, antagonist of 5-HT	oral	Poorly absorbed G.I.T. Excretion mainly through liver. Converted to water-soluble metabolites. *In vitro* guinea pig liver forms 2-oxy-L.S.D.	Effective in minute doses, 0·5–1·0 μg/kg to produce psychotomimetic effect. Fluor., A 325 mμ F 465 mμ (pH 7)	*Helv. chim. Acta* **38**, 421 (1955). *Psychotropic Drugs*, p. 37, Elsevier (1957).

No.	Name	Synonyms	Formula	M. wt.	Physical form	M.p.
29	(*b*) 2-Bromo-lysergic acid diethylamide	BOL 148	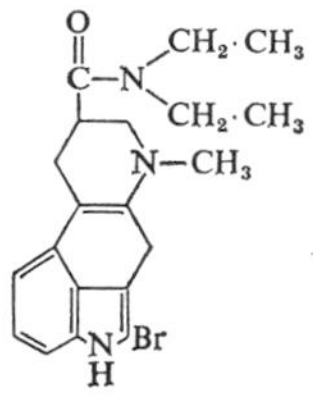	402·3	needles; acid tartrate, white needles	120–7; acid tartrate, 130–40
	(*c*) Ergotamine tartrate	Gynergen, Femergan	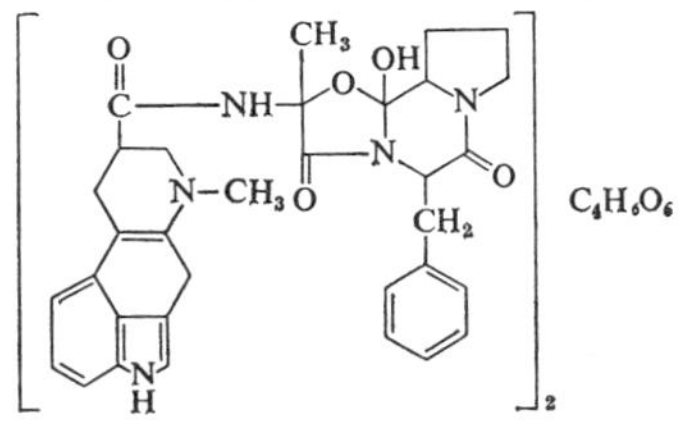	1313·5	cryst. powder	203 d.
30	Mechlorethamine hydrochloride	Mustargen, methyl-bis-(β-chloroethyl)-amine hydrochloride	$CH_3\cdot N(CH_2\cdot CH_2Cl)_2\cdot HCl$	192·5	hygr. cryst.	109–10
31	Mephenesin	Myanesin, 3-*O*-toloxy-1,2-propanediol	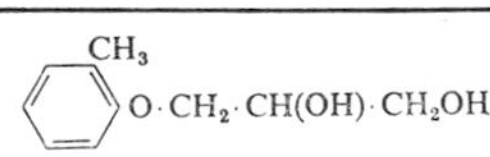	182·2	wh. cryst.; bitter taste	69–70
32	Mepyramine	Neoantergan, Anthisan, Pyrilamine	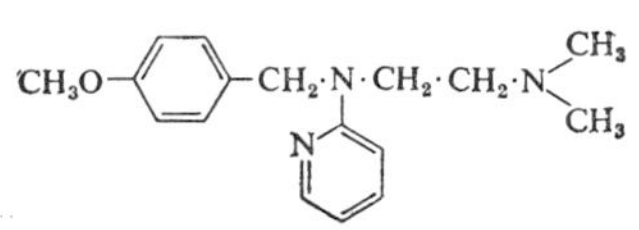	Base, 285·4 Maleate, 401·4	oily liquid cryst. powder	 100–1
33	Methonium compounds (*a*) Hexamethonium	Hexamethylene-bis(trimethyl-ammonium), hexameton chloride. Bromide: Vegalysen	$(CH_3)_3\overset{+}{N}{-}[CH_2]_6{-}\overset{+}{N}(CH_3)_3$ Cl^- Cl^-	Chloride, 273·3	Chloride, wh. cryst. hygr. powder	289–92 d.
	(*b*) Decamethonium	Decamethylene-bis(trimethyl-ammonium). Bromide: Syncurine	$(CH_3)_3\overset{+}{N}{-}[CH_2]_{10}{-}\overset{+}{N}(CH_3)_3$ Br^- Br^-	Bromide, 418·4	col. cryst.	255–67 d.
	(*c*) Suxamethonium bromide	Succinyl choline, bis(2-dimethyl-aminoethyl) succinate bis-(methobromide), Brevidil M.	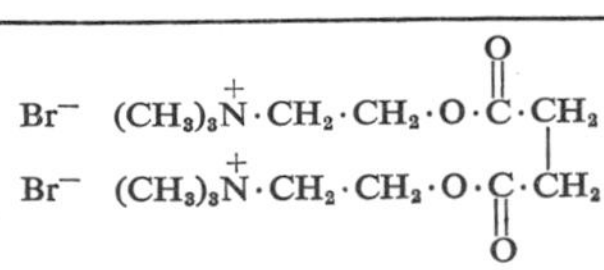	Bromide, 450·2; Chloride, (dihydrate) 397·3	hygr. cryst. hygr. cryst.	225 156–63 (dihydrate)

Solubility	Action	Route	Absorption and fate	General remarks	References
s. $CHCl_3$. Tartrate, s. H_2O	5-HT antagonist. No psychotomimetic action			Fluor., A 315 mμ F 460 mμ (pH 1)	PREP. *Helv. chim. Acta* **40,** 2160 (1957). *Arch. exp. Path. Pharmak.* **228, 146** (1956).
H_2O, EtOH	Vasoconstrictor. Oxytocic. Blocks α-adrenergic effects	oral, i.v.	Irregular absorption G.I.T.	Protect from light and heat. Hydrogenated derivatives have less ability to stimulate smooth muscle	*Helv. chim. Acta* **28,** 1283 (1945).
v.s. H_2O; s. EtOH	Cytotoxic, mitotic arrest, mutagenic	i.v.	Absorbed from G.I.T. and parenteral sites (local reaction). Active form is extremely short-lived. None excreted	Local vesicant. Mean lethal dose may produce delayed death in laboratory animals. In neutral or alkaline soln. rapid cyclization to highly reactive quaternary ammonium compound occurs	*Pharmac. Rev.* **2,** 281 (1950). *P.S.E.B.M.* **80,** 503 (1952).
s. common organic solvents; sl. s. H_2O	Skeletal muscle relaxant (centrally acting)	oral, i.m., i.v.	Rapidly absorbed and metabolized. 50% appears conjugated, and 2% free, in urine	Relaxant action due to selective subcortical and spinal synaptic depression. Fluor., A 280 mμ F 315 mμ (pH 1)	*P.S.E.B.M.* **68,** 339 (1948). *J. Pharmac. exp. Ther.* **111,** 293 (1954).
Maleate, v.s. H_2O; s. EtOH	Antihistaminic	oral, topical, i.v., i.m.	Readily absorbed G.I.T.	pH of 10% soln. 5·1; free base precipitates at pH 7·5–8·0	*Ann. N.Y. Acad. Sci.* **50,** 1089 (1950).
H_2O, EtOH; eth., $CHCl_3$	Ganglionic blocking agent	oral, s.c., i.m., i.v.	Poorly absorbed G.I.T.; distributed extracellular fluids; excreted unchanged in urine	pH of 10% aq. soln. 5·5–6·5. Can be autoclaved	*Br. J. Pharmac. Chemother.* **4,** 381 (1949).
H_2O, EtOH; s. $CHCl_3$; eth.	Neuromuscular blocking agent	i.v.	Similar to hexamethonium	Aqueous soln. stable. Produces block by depolarization; does not pass placental barrier	*Br. J. Pharmac. Chemother.* **3,** 298 (1948).
H_2O; sl. s. OH; i. eth.	Short-acting neuromuscular blocking agent	i.v.	Rapid enzymic hydrolysis by non-specific plasma choline esterase; 5–15% excreted in urine	Solutions slightly acidic, not stable	*J. Pharmac. exp. Ther.* **99,** 458 (1950).

16. Drugs and Other Pharmacologically Active Compounds

No.	Name	Synonyms	Formula	M. wt.	Physical form	M.p.
34	Methyl cholanthrene		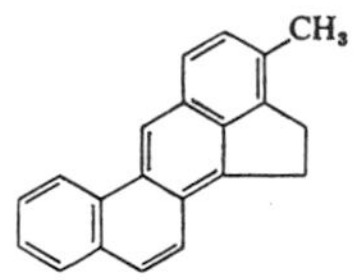	268·3	pale yel. cryst.	179–80
35	Metrazol	Pentylenetetrazol, leptazol, cardiazol	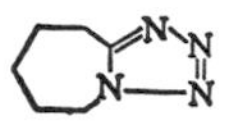	138·2	wh. odourless cryst.	57–60
36	Morphine		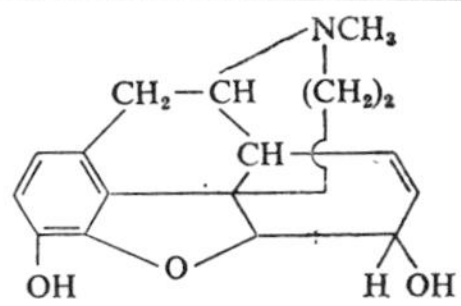 H_2O	Hydrate, 303·3; Anhyd., 285·3	cryst. (needles, rh. prisms) $+H_2O$	Anhyd., 254 d.
			Hydrochloride, $C_{17}H_{19}NO_3 \cdot HCl \cdot 3H_2O$	HCl (trihydrate), 375·8;	HCl, needles; bitter taste	HCl, 250 d.
			Sulphate, $(C_{17}H_{19}NO_3)_2 \cdot H_2SO_4 \cdot 5H_2O$	Sulphate (pentahydrate), 758·8	SO_4, needles or cubes; bitter taste	SO_4, decomp. 250
37	Muscarine	Quaternary trimethyl ammonium salt of 2-methyl-3-hydroxy-5-(aminomethyl)-tetrahydrofuran	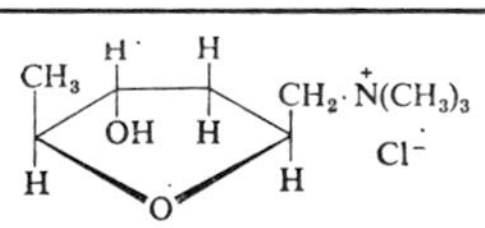	209·8	chloride, hygr. cryst.	180–1
38	Nethalide	Alderlin, Pronethalol	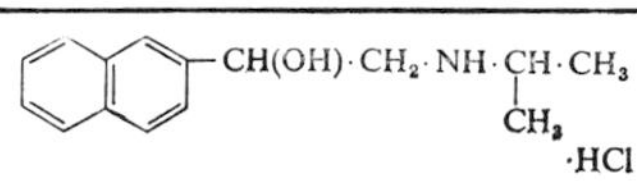	265·8	wh. cryst.	209–10
39	Nicotine		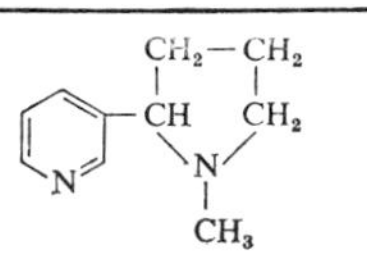	162·2	col. oil; burning taste	B.p. 247
			Hydrochloride, $C_{10}H_{14}N_2 \cdot 2HCl$	Di-HCl, 235·2	Dihydrochloride hygr. cryst.	
40	Nikethamide	Coramine, anacardone, *N,N*-diethylnicotinamide	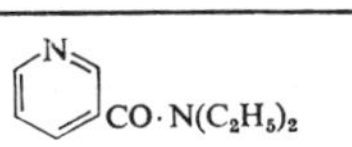	178·2	viscous oil; faint bitter taste	22–24
41	Phenoxybenzamine	Dibenzyline, dibenyline, *N*-(2-chloroethyl)-*N*-(1-methyl-2 phenoxyethyl)-benzylamine	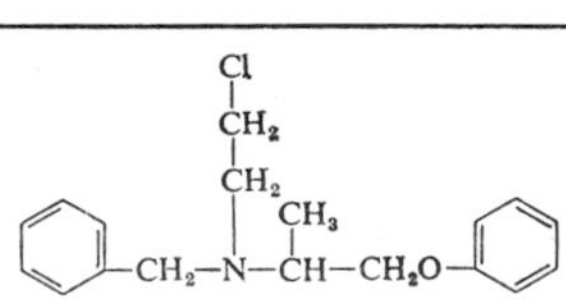	303·8	cryst.	38–40; Hydrochloride, 137·5–40

Solubility	*Action*	*Route*	*Absorption and fate*	*General remarks*	*References*
s. benz., toluene, xylene; sl. s. amyl alcohol; i. H_2O	Carcinogenic	applied locally		Protect skin when working with this substance. Water-soluble derivative is methyl cholanthrene choleic acid	
v.s. H_2O, EtOH; s. $CHCl_3$, CCl_4, eth.	Central nervous system stimulant	i.v., oral	Rapidly absorbed, 75% excreted unchanged in urine. Metabolite temporarily stored in the liver	Will protect against toxic doses of central depressants. No direct effect on the heart	*Klin. Wschr.* **4**, 1678 (1925). *J. Neuropath. exp. Neurol.* **2**, 132 (1943).
s. alkalis; sl. s. EtOH, MeOH; sp. s. H_2O, eth., $CHCl_3$ HCl and ulphate. . H_2O; sl. s. EtOH; i. eth., $CHCl_3$	On C.N.S., narcotic and analgesic, respiratory depressant	oral, i.v.	Readily absorbed G.I.T. The majority is excreted, mainly as an unknown conjugated form in the urine	Loses H_2O of cryst. at 110°. $[\alpha]^{20}_{D}$ −133 to −135 (c = 1 in EtOH). HCl, $[\alpha]^{20}_{D}$ −97 to −99 (c = 2 in H_2O). SO_4, $[\alpha]^{25}_{D}$ −107 to −109 (c = 2 in H_2O). Addiction and tolerance develop. Central excitation sometimes observed. Diacetylmorphine = heroin; morphine methyl ether = codeine. Morphine can be converted to a fluorescent derivative by treatment with conc. H_2SO_4 and then make alkaline with NH_4OH. Fluorescence in isobutanol, A 365 mμ F 420 mμ	IDENTIFICATION *Am. J. Pharm.* **109**, 219 (1937). EST. *Q. Jl Pharm. Pharmac.* **19**, 350 (1946). *Analyst* **62**, 440, 851 (1937). *J. Pharm. Pharmac.* **4**, 547 (1952). *J. Pharm. Pharmac.* **5**, 795 (1953).
.s. H_2O, EtOH; sl. s. $CHCl_3$, eth., cet.	Parasympathomimetic	oral, i.v.	Excreted unchanged in the urine	Aqueous solution very stable	*Helv. chim. Acta* **41**, 229 (1958).
H_2O	Blocks inhibitory effects of adrenaline			Converts the blood pressure response of the pithed rat to adrenaline to a purely pressor response. Propanolol is more active.	*J. Physiol.* **168**, 939 (1963). *Lancet* **2**, 311 (1962).
ase and ydrochloride, H_2O, EtOH, MeOH, $CHCl_3$	Cholinomimetic at ganglia and neuromuscular junction, central stimulant		Absorbed rapidly from G.I.T., mucous membranes, and skin. Mainly metabolized in liver, kidney, and lungs but 10–20% excreted unchanged in man	Tolerance develops. Nornicotine is demethylated nicotine	*Chem. Rev.* **29**, 123 (1941). EST. *Analyt. Chem.* **22**, 430 (1950). *Analyt. Chem.* **24**, 1831 (1952). *Ind. Engng Chem. analyt. Edn* **18**, 508 (1946).
H_2O, eth., OH, $CHCl_3$	Analeptic; respiratory, cardiovascular stimulant	i.v., i.m.	Absorbed all sites	Convulsant in toxic doses. Peripheral vasconstrictor. More effective against volatile anaesthetics than barbiturates	*J. Pharmac. exp. Ther.* **91**, 362 (1947).
benz. Cl, s. EtOH, pylene col; s. H_2O	Adrenergic blocking agent	i.v., oral	20–30% absorbed G.I.T.; derivatives excreted in urine and bile	Does not block inhibitory adrenergic responses. I.v. must be given slowly	*J. Pharmac. exp. Ther.* **101**, 379 (1951).

16. Drugs and Other Pharmacologically Active Compounds

No.	Name	Synonyms	Formula	M. wt.	Physical form	M.p.
42	Picrotoxin	Cocculin	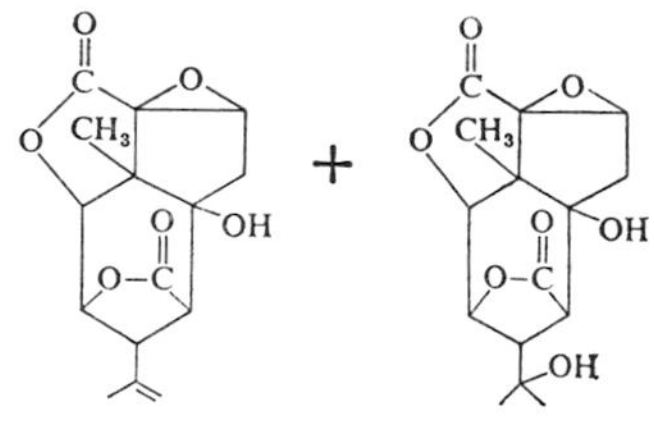 Picrotoxinin + Picrotin	Picrotoxinin, 292·3; Picrotin, 310·3	shiny rh. leaflets	203
43	Pilocarpine		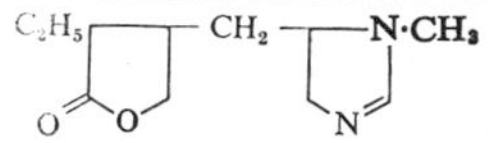	208·2	oil or cryst; HCl, hygr. cryst.	34
44	Probenecid	Benemid, *p*-(dipropyl-sulphamyl)-benzoic acid	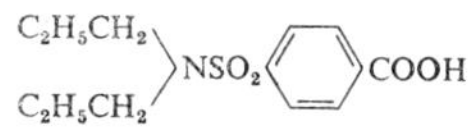	285·4	cryst.	198–200
45	Procaine	Ethocaine, diethylamino-ethyl-*p*-amino-benzoate	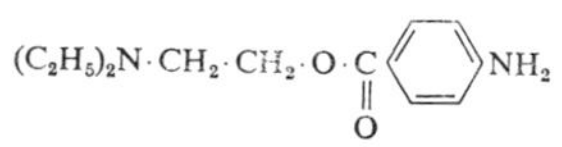	236·3; HCl, 272·8	HCl, needles; numbing bitter taste	Anhyd., 61; HCl, 154–6
46	Promethazine	Phenergan	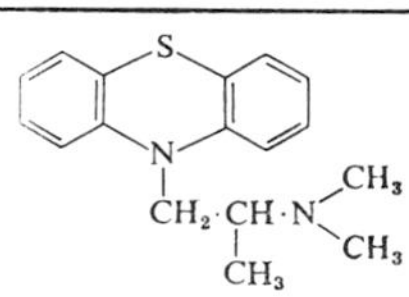	284·4	cryst.	60; HCl, 230–2 d.
47	Propylthio-uracil	6-Propyl-2-thio-uracil	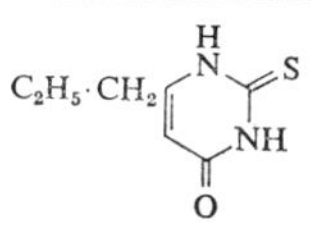	170·2	wh. cryst.; bitter taste	219
48	Pyridine-2-aldoxime methiodide	2-PAM	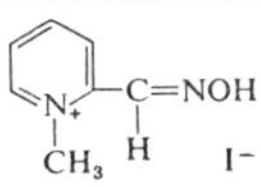	264·1	yel. cryst.	224–5
49	Reserpine	3,4,5,Tri-methoxyben-zoyl methyl reserpate, Serpasil	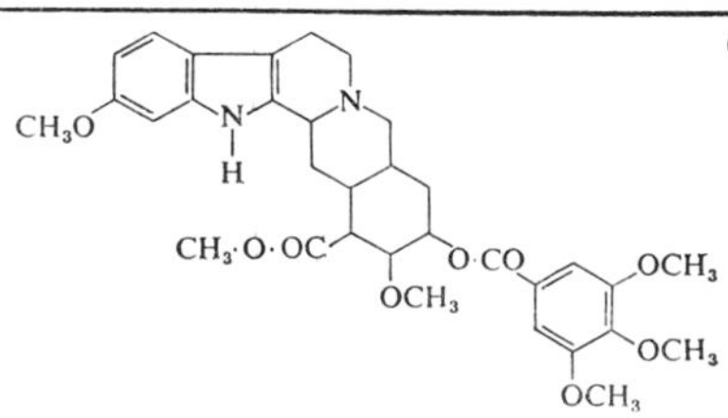	608·7	long prisms	264–5 d.

Solubility	Action	Route	Absorption and fate	General remarks	References
)·3 H_2O; 8·3 EtOH; v.s. alkalis; sl. s. $CHCl_3$, eth.	C.N.S. stimulant and convulsant	i.v.	Absorbed all channels; leaves blood rapidly. Distribution unknown. Only present in urine if large amounts ingested	Bitter principle of *Anamirta cocculus*. Equimolecular compound of picrotin and picrotoxinin. Antidote to barbiturates. Protect from light	*J.B.C.* **151**, 651 (1943).
. H_2O, EtOH, $CHCl_3$; sp. s. eth., benz.; pet. eth.	Parasympathomimetic (selective action on tissue innervated by post-ganglionic cholinergic nerves)	oral, s.c.	After absorption most excreted in conjugated form	Nitrate generally used. Resembles muscarine and arecoline. Atropine antagonist. Stimulant to gastric secretion, miotic, diaphoretic	*Gastroenterology* **2**, 201 (1944). *J. invest. Derm.* **4**, 453 (1950).
H_2O; s. $CHCl_3$, alkalis	Inhibitor of renal tubular transport	oral	Absorbed rapidly by G.I.T. Portion bound plasma proteins. Urinary excretion (free form) low. Slow conjugation with glucuronic acid	Decreases elimination of organic acids (e.g. *p*-aminosalicylic acid, *p*-aminobenzoic acid). Inhibits glycine conjugation by preventing benzoyl-CoA formation	*Am. J. Physiol.* **166**, 625 (1951). *P.S.E.B.M.* **74**, 772 (1950).
H_2O, EtOH; . s. $CHCl_3$, :h. Cl, s. H_2O; 2·5 95% tOH; sl. s. HCl_3; i. eth.	Local anaesthetic	infiltration	Readily absorbed after parenteral administration. Hydrolysed to PABA and diethylaminoethanol by choline esterase	Used as hydrochloride. Procaine-sulphonamide antagonism exists (interferes with sulphonamide estimation). 0·2–2·0% for nerve block. Soln. unstable and slowly oxidized especially in the presence of heavy metals and alkali. Fluor., A 275 mμ F 345 mμ (pH 11)	*J. Pharmac. exp. Ther.* **104**, 122 (1952). *J. Pharmac. exp. Ther.* **94**, 359 (1948).
Cl, v.s. H_2O; EtOH, HCl_3	Antihistaminic, anticholinergic	oral, i.m., topical	Readily absorbed G.I.T.	pH of 10% aq. soln. 5·3	*J. Pharm. Pharmac.* **5**, 279 (1953).
s. H_2O, OH, $CHCl_3$, h.; i. benz.	Goitrogenic	oral	Readily absorbed G.I.T. 60% destroyed, 40% excreted in 24 hr	Interferes with synthesis of thyroxine, triiodothyronine. Thyroid hyperplasia occurs in response to thyrotrophic hormone secretion. Less toxic than thiouracil	*Physiol. Rev.* **30**, 194 (1950). EST. *J. Pharm. Pharmac.* **5**, 101 (1953).
H_2O	Reactivator of ACh esterase inhibited by organo-phosphorus compounds	i.p., s.c., oral		pK_a 8·0	*B.B.A.* **18**, 168 (1955). *Handb. exp. Pharmak.* Erg. XV, 921 (1963).
$CHCl_3$, nz., gl. acetic; s. H_2O. Cl, s. H_2O. SO_4, s. H_2O	Hypotensive tranquillizer. Sedative	oral, s.c.	Absorbed G.I.T. Trimethoxybenzoic acid excreted in urine of mice. Up to 15% unchanged in faeces	pK_a 6·6. Releases catechol amines and 5-HT from stores in tissues. Fluor., A 300 mμ F 375 mμ (pH 1)	*Helv. chim. Acta* **37**, 59 (1954). *J. Neurochem.* **1**, 8 (1956). *J. Pharmac. exp. Ther.* **116**, 84 (1956).

16. Drugs and Other Pharmacologically Active Compounds

No.	Name	Synonyms	Formula	M. wt.	Physical form	M.p.
50	Stilboestrol	Diethylstilboestrol, DES, *trans*-4,4′-dihydroxy-αβ-diethylstilbene	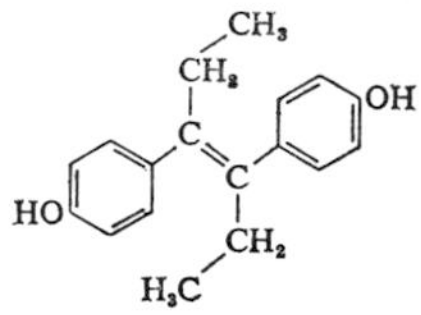	268·3	wh. cryst. powder	169–72 (104 dipropionate)
51	Strychnine		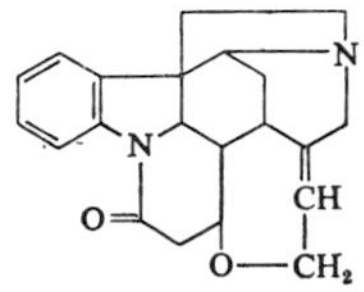 $C_{21}H_{22}N_2O_2$	334·4	col. rh. cryst.; v. bitter taste	268 d.
			Hydrochloride, $C_{21}H_{22}N_2O_2\cdot HCl\cdot 2H_2O$	HCl, 406·9	efflor. cryst.	
			Sulphate, $(C_{21}H_{22}N_2O_2)_2\cdot H_2SO_4\cdot 5H_2O$	Sulphate, 857·0	efflor. cryst.	Anhyd. SO_4 200 d.
52	Tetraethylammonium chloride	TEA chloride, etamon chloride	$(C_2H_5)_4N^+\ Cl^-$	165·7 (anhyd.)	deliq. cryst.; prisms$+4H_2O$	Hydrate, 37·5
53	Trimethadione	Tridione, 3,5,5-trimethyl-2,4-oxazolidinedione	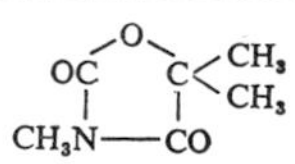	143·1	wh. cryst.; bitter taste; camphorous odour	46
54	Tubocurarine chloride	*d*-Tubocurarine chloride	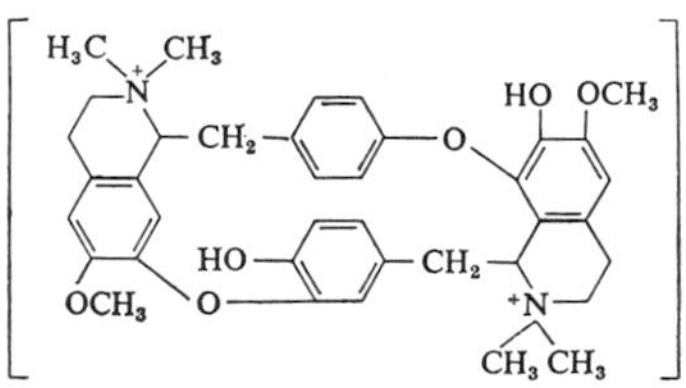 $2Cl^-\ \ 5H_2O$	Anhyd., 695·7; Hydrate, 785·8	hex. and pent. platelets (from water)	Anhyd., decomp. 274–5; Hydrate, 268–9
55	Urethane	Ethyl carbamate	$NH_2\cdot CO\cdot OC_2H_5$	89·1	wh. prisms or needles; taste salty	50

Solubility	Action	Route	Absorption and fate	General remarks	References
s. dil. aq. alkalis, acet., eth., $CHCl_3$, vegetable oils; i. H_2O	Oestrogenic	oral	Readily absorbed G.I.T. About 20% excreted in urine (conjugated)	Synthetic oestrogen. Used in replacement therapy. Not stored in fat	*J. Endocr.* **8**, 291 (1952).
s. $CHCl_3$; sl. s. benz., EtOH; sp. s. H_2O, eth.	Blocks postsynaptic inhibition. Convulsant	oral, i.m.	Readily absorbed by G.I.T. and from injection sites. Rapidly enters tissues especially C.N.S. Mainly destroyed by liver but some excreted unchanged		EST. *J. Am. pharm. Ass., Sci. Edn.* **40**, 291 (1951).
Hydrochloride and sulphate, s. H_2O; sl. s. $CHCl_3$, EtOH; . eth.					
.s. H_2O, EtOH, $CHCl_3$, acet.	Ganglionic blocking agent	i.m.	Poor absorption G.I.T. Rapid, quantitative excretion by kidney (glomerular and tubular)	Sympathetic and parasympathetic ganglionic transmission blocked. Raises excitation threshold for acetylcholine	*Pharmac. Rev.* **2**, 61 (1950). *J. Pharmac. exp. Ther.* **91**, 210 (1947).
H_2O (solubility increased by urethane); .s. EtOH, $CHCl_3$, eth.	Anticonvulsant		Readily absorbed G.I.T. In man and dogs demethylation to inactive 5,5-dimethyloxazolidine-2,4-dione occurs	Highly specific antagonist to pentylenetetrazol-induced convulsions. Some variable analgesic effect	*Physiol. Rev.* **28**, 409 (1948). *J. Pharmac. exp. Ther.* **108**, 11 (1953).
, alkalis; sp. s. H_2O, EtOH, MeOH; i. $CHCl_3$, acet. pyr.	Autonomic blocking agent	i.v. (i.m.)	Distributed throughout body tissues; not bound plasma proteins. About 30% excreted in urine (man)	Quaternary base isolated from *Chondrodendron tomentosum*. In presence of moisture anhyd. form is rapidly converted to pentahydrate. Action brief	*J. Pharmac. exp. Ther.* **105**, 299 (1952).
.s. H_2O, EtOH, $CHCl_3$, eth.; s. vegetable oils, glycerol	Cytotoxic, mitotic inhibitor; weak hypnotic	oral, i.p.	Absorbed rapidly G.I.T., greater part rapidly metabolized	Mechanism of cytotoxic effects undetermined. Less potent than nitrogen mustards. Used as an anaesthetic for small animals (1·2–1·5 g/kg i.p.) and fish (1:40 000)	*B.J.* **44**, 528 (1949). *J.B.C.* **177**, 941 (1949).

17. Stability Constants of Metal Complexes

By W. J. O'SULLIVAN (*Department of Medicine, University of Sydney*)

The general order of complexing ability of metal ions may be expressed as: alkali metals (Na^+, K^+, etc.) < alkaline earths (Mg^{2+}, Ca^{2+}, etc.) < transition metals.

Alkali and alkaline earths combine most strongly with oxyanions, the transition metals with N and to a lesser extent with S; metals such as Zn and Hg combine most strongly with S. For the divalent ions of the transition metals the complexing ability usually follows the Irving-Williams series, viz. Mn < Fe < Co < Ni < Cu > Zn.

Stability constants

For the reaction between metal (M) and ligand (L), $M+L \rightleftharpoons ML$, the stability constant is defined by $K_1 = \dfrac{[ML]}{[M][L]}$.

The metal may combine with more than one molecule of ligand, e.g.

$$\text{for } ML+L \rightleftharpoons ML_2, \quad K_2 = \frac{[ML_2]}{[ML][L]}, \text{ etc.}$$

Experimentally, where more than one complex is formed, the *cumulative stability constants* are determined. These are defined by

$$\beta_2 = K_1 K_2,$$

$$\beta_3 = K_1 K_2 K_3, \text{ etc.}\dagger$$

Constants are taken mainly from the Chemical Society publications (ref. 1) and also from other compilations (refs. 2–4). For methods of determination of stability constants, see Rossotti and Rossotti (ref. 5) and for information on many chelating agents, see Sandell (ref. 6) and (for biological systems) Seven (ref. 7). As far as possible, all results are quoted as at 25–30°, at ionic strengths ranging from 0·01 to 0·5 and the pK_a values obtained under the same conditions. The effect of these variables should not however be overlooked (ref. 5). (N.B. Many gaps in the table may be due to lack of information rather than to the fact that complexes are not formed.)

Use of the tables

(*a*) *Conversion of absolute to 'apparent' constants*

Unless indicated otherwise, the stability constants are expressed as absolute values, i.e. independent of pH. In practice, it is more usual to require the 'apparent' value at a particular pH. An apparent stability constant considers all forms of complexing species, whereas an absolute considers only the most anionic,

i.e.
$$K_{app} = \frac{[ML]}{[M]([L]_T - [ML])} = \frac{[ML]}{[M][L]_{T'}}$$

where $[L]_{T'}$ is the sum of all the individual uncomplexed forms of the ligand present in solution.

To a first approximation, where the pK_a of the ligand is more than one unit above the pH under consideration, the log of the absolute stability constant is reduced by log α,

† Other stability constants which may occur are $K^M_{MHL} = \dfrac{[MHL]}{[M][HL]}$ for the reaction $M+HL \rightleftharpoons MHL$, and $K^M_{M_2L} = \dfrac{[M_2L]}{[M][ML]}$ for the reaction $M+ML \rightleftharpoons M_2L$.

the difference between the pK_a and the pH, to give the log of the apparent stability constant, e.g. for α-alanine; $pK_{a_2} = 9{\cdot}9$.

At pH 7·0, $\log\alpha = pK_a - \text{pH} = 9{\cdot}9 - 7{\cdot}0 = 2{\cdot}9$.

$$\therefore \quad \log K_1\,(\text{app})\,(Cu^{2+}) = 8{\cdot}5 - 2{\cdot}9 = 5{\cdot}6.$$

To convert cumulative constants to apparent values:

$$\log\beta_2\,(\text{app}) = \log\beta_2 - 2\log\alpha,$$
$$\log\beta_3\,(\text{app}) = \log\beta_3 - 3\log\alpha, \quad \text{etc.}$$

In Table A, the apparent stability constants at pH 7·0 and pH 8·0 have been tabulated for EDTA. Note that for a nitrogen base, designated as L in the tables (e.g. *o*-phenanthroline), the apparent stability constants will be indistinguishable from the absolute stability constants at pH values two or more units above the pK_a value.

More exactly,
$$\alpha = \frac{[H^+]^n}{K_{a_1}K_{a_2}\ldots K_{a_n}} + \frac{[H^+]^{n-1}}{K_{a_2}K_{a_3}\ldots K_{a_n}} + \ldots + \frac{[H^+]}{K_{a_n}} + 1.$$

Thus, for EDTA,
$$\alpha = \frac{[H^+]^4}{K_{a_1}K_{a_2}K_{a_3}K_{a_4}} + \frac{[H^+]^3}{K_{a_2}K_{a_3}K_{a_4}} + \frac{[H^+]^2}{K_{a_3}K_{a_4}} + \frac{[H^+]}{K_{a_4}} + 1.$$

At pH 7·0, for EDTA, $\alpha = 2{\cdot}084 \times 10^3$; $\log\alpha = 3{\cdot}3$.

For Mg–EDTA at pH 7·0;
$$\log K_1\,(\text{app}) = 8{\cdot}7 - 3{\cdot}3 = 5{\cdot}4.$$

(*b*) *Calculation of free metal ion concentration*

(i) Simple stability constants

From the equations
$$K_1 = \frac{[ML]}{[M][L]} \quad \text{and} \quad [M]_T = [M] + [ML]$$

the free metal concentration is
$$[M] = \frac{[M]_T}{1 + K_1[L]} = \frac{[M]_T}{1 + (K_1[L]_{T'}/\alpha)}.$$

A. TABLE OF CHELATING AGENTS

No.	*Name*	*Synonyms*	*Formula*	*M. wt.*	pK_a
1	Ammonium *N*-nitrosophenylhydroxylamine	Cupferron	$C_6H_5 \cdot N(NO) \cdot ONH_4$	155·1	4·2
2	Ammonium purpurate	Murexide	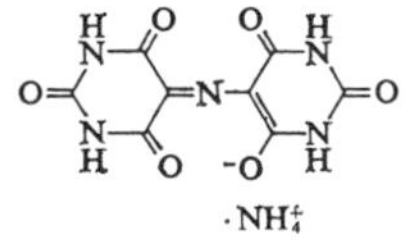	284·2 Hydrate, 302·2	9·2 10·5
3	α-Benzoin oxime	Cupron	$C_6H_5 \cdot CHOH \cdot C(:NOH) \cdot C_6H_5$	227·3	
4	2:3-Butanedione dioxime	Dimethylglyoxime, diacetyl dioxime	$CH_3 \cdot C(:NOH) \cdot C(:NOH) \cdot CH_3$	116·1	< 2 12·8

N.B. For strong chelating agents (viz. $\log K_1 > 5$)

$$[L]_{T'} = [L]_T - [M]_T.$$

The above equation may also be expressed in the form

$$[L]_T = \frac{[M]_T}{K_1[M]} - \frac{1}{K_1} + [M]_T - [M]$$

so that using $[L] = [L]_T - [ML]$, the concentrations of the species, [M], [L], and [ML] may be calculated under a given set of conditions.

(ii) Cumulative stability constants

In this case,

$$[M] = \frac{[M]_T}{1+K_1[L]+\beta_2[L]^2} = \frac{[M]_T}{1+(K_1[L]_{T'}/\alpha)+\beta_2\{([L]_{T'})^2/\alpha^2\}}$$

where L exists as more than one ionic species and $\beta_2 = K_1K_2$. A similar procedure is used for β_3, β_4, etc., where appropriate. (See ref. 3 for further details.)

References

1. *Stability Constants of Metal-Ion Complexes* (1964). Compiled by L. G. Sillén and A. E. Martell. Special Publication No. 17, The Chemical Society, London.
2. A. E. Martell and M. Calvin, *Chemistry of the Metal Chelate Compounds*, Prentice-Hall, Englewood Cliffs, N.J. (1952).
3. S. Chaberek and A. E. Martell, *Organic Sequestering Agents*, Wiley, New York (1959).
4. K. B. Yatsimirskii and V. P. Vasil'ev, *Instability Constants of Complex Compounds*, Pergamon Press, London (1960).
5. F. J. C. Rossotti and H. Rossotti, *The Determination of Stability Constants*, McGraw-Hill, New York (1961).
6. E. B. Sandell, *Colorimetric Determinations of Traces of Metals*, Interscience, New York (1959).
7. M. J. Seven (ed.), *Metal Binding in Medicine*, Lippincott, Philadelphia (1960).

Main form of Ligand at pH 7·0	*Type of stability constant*	*Log stability constant†* Mg	Ca	Mn	Fe	Co	Ni	Cu	Zn	*Remarks*
L^-										Soluble in H_2O and C_2H_5OH. Metal complexes insoluble in H_2O, soluble in CCl_4; used in solvent extraction separations. Reagent and complexes generally unstable.
H_4L^-	K_1		5							Soluble in H_2O. Forms soluble coloured complexes with divalent metals. Used particularly for analysis of Ca^{2+} concentration; also for Cu^{2+}, Ni^{2+}, Co^{2+}. Other complexes too unstable for analytical purposes (ref. 3).
H_2L										Slightly soluble in H_2O. Complexes (insoluble in H_2O) with heavy metals. Green ppt. with Cu^{2+}; yellow ppt. with vanadates. Used for estimation of Mo(VI).
HL										Insoluble in H_2O; soluble in C_2H_5OH. Forms soluble complexes with Co^{2+}, Cu^{2+}, Fe^{2+}; insoluble complex with Ni^{2+}. Used for quantitative estimation of Ni^{2+}.

† N.B. These are not thermodynamic constants.

17. Stability Constants of Metal Complexes

No.	Name	Synonyms	Formula	M. wt.	pK_a
5	*trans*-1:2-Diaminocyclohexan-tetra-acetic acid	CDTA	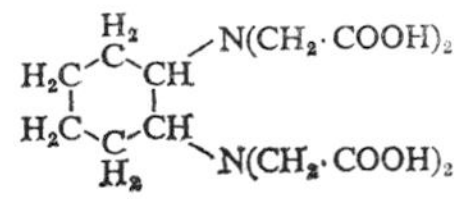	346·3	2·43 3·52 6·12 12·35
6	4:5-Dihydroxybenzene-1:3-disulphonic acid	Catechol-3:5-disulphonic acid, 'Tiron'	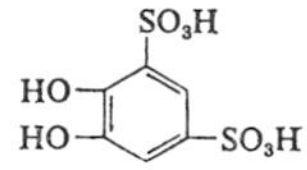	270·2; Disodium salt, 314·2	7·7 12·6
7	2:3-Dimercapto-1-propanol	BAL, dimercaprol	$CH_2.OH$ | $HC.SH$ | $CH_2.SH$	124·2	
8	Diphenylthiocarbazone	Dithizone	$C_6H_5\cdot N{:}N\cdot CS\cdot NH\cdot NH\cdot C_6H_5$	256·3	4·5
9	2:2′-Dipyridyl	α:α′-Dipyridyl	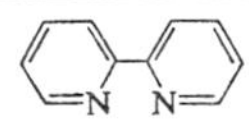	156·2	4·4
10	3:6-Disulpho-1:8-dihydroxy-naphthalene	Chromotropic acid	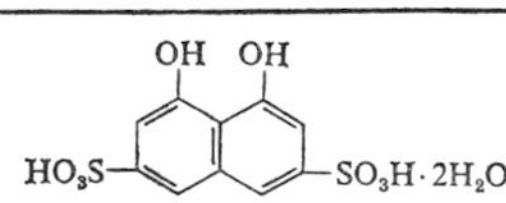	Hydrate, 356·3	5·4 (15·6)
11	Dithio-oxamide	Rubeanic acid	$HN{=}C{-}C{=}NH$ (each C bearing SH) SH SH	120·2	10·6
12	Eriochromeschwarz T	1-(1-Hydroxy-2-naphthylazo)-2-hydroxy-5-nitro-4-naphthalene sulphonic acid	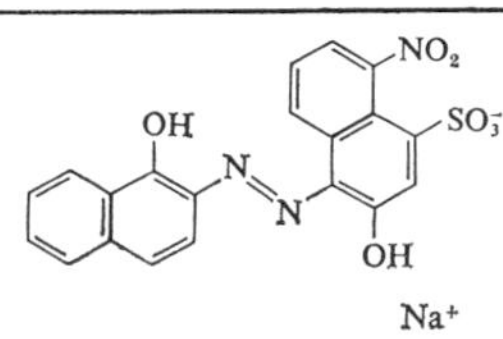	439·4; Na salt, 461·4	6·3 11·6
13	Ethylene diamine	1:2-Diaminoethane	$NH_2\cdot CH_2\cdot CH_2\cdot NH_2$	60·1	7·2 10·2
14	Ethylene diaminetetra-acetic acid	EDTA, versene, sequestrol	$(HOOC\cdot CH_2)_2N\cdot CH_2\cdot CH_2\cdot N(H_2C\cdot COOH)_2$	292·2	2·0 2·67 6·16 10·26
	—, Na_2 salt		$C_{10}H_{14}O_8N_2Na_2\cdot 2H_2O$	372·3	

Main form of Ligand at pH 7·0	*Type of stability constant*	*Log stability constant* Mg	Ca	Mn	Fe	Co	Ni	Cu	Zn	*Remarks*
HL^{3-}	K_1	11·0	13·2	17·4		19·6		22·0	19·3	Used in preventing precipitation of Mn in 3N alkali, during the estimation of organic compounds in alkaline solution.
H_2L^{2-}	K^M_{MHL}	2·0	2·2			3·1	3·0	5·5	3·3	N.B. K_{app} (Ca^{2+}) = 1·8 at pH 7·2. Used in colorimetric estimation of Fe^{3+} (ref. 6).
	K_1	6·9	5·8	8.6		9·5	10·0	14·5	10·4	
H_2L	K_1			5·2					13·5	Insoluble in H_2O. General chelator of heavy metals. Used in therapeutic treatment of Pb, As, Hg poisoning.
	β_2			10·4			23·0		23·0	
L										Dithizone and its complexes insoluble in H_2O; soluble in organic solvents. Used in extraction of heavy metal contaminants from aqueous solutions. Complexes highly coloured and used for analytical determination of many metals, e.g. Zn (ref. 6); *Arch. B.B.* **46**, 345 (1953); *J.B.C.* **237**, 1129 (1962). PREP. *Org. Synth.* **25**, 38 (1945).
L	K_1	0·5		2·5	4·3				5·4	
	β_2								9·8	
	β_3			6·3	17·3			17·9	13·5	
H_3L^-	K_1							2·8		Soluble in H_2O. Complexes (soluble in H_2O and usually coloured) heavy metals (ref. 6); also Al^{3+}, Be^{2+}.
H_2L										Soluble in aqueous ethanol. Forms coloured complexes with transition and heavy metals (ref. 6). Used particularly in localization of Cu (green precipitate) on chromatograms and in histochemical preparations (ref. 7). Other complexes soluble in H_2O, except Co and Ni complexes soluble in acid solutions.
HL^{2-}	K_1	7	5·5						13	Soluble in H_2O. Forms coloured complexes with a large number of divalent metal ions (ref. 3). Used particularly for analytical determination of Mg^{2+}. (See ref. 3 for other metal indicators.)
HL	K_1	0·4		2·7	4·3	5·9	7·6	10·7	6·0	
	β_2			4·8	7·5	10·7	14·0	20	11·0	
	β_3			5·7	9·5	13·8	18·5		13·0	
HL^{3-}	K_1	8·7	10·6	14·0	14·2	16·0	18·6	18·8	16·4	(log K_1(Na^+) = 1·7) Used as a metal buffer (ref. 3) and in metal titrations. Used to eliminate inhibition of enzyme catalysed reactions due to traces of heavy metals. See *B.J.* **79**, 584 (1961); *B.B.A.* **64**, 83 (1962); **77**, 142 (1963). Poor complexing ability with Ag: *J.B.C.* **236**, 1225 (1961). See refs. 1 and 3 for analogues of EDTA.
	K_1 (app) at pH 7·0	5·4	7·3	10·7	10·9	12·7	15·3	15·5	13·1	
	K_1 (app) at pH 8·0	6·4	8·3	11·7	11·9	13·7	16·3	16·5	14·1	

No.	*Name*	*Synonyms*	*Formula*	*M. wt.*	pK_a
15	*o*-Hydroxybenzaldehyde oxime	Salicylaldoxime	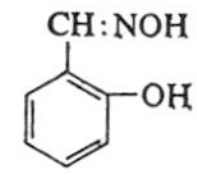	137·1	~ 12
16	*o*-Hydroxybenzoic acid	Salicylic acid	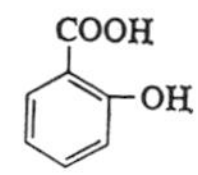	138·1	3·0 13
17	8-Hydroxyquinoline	Oxine, 8-quinolinol	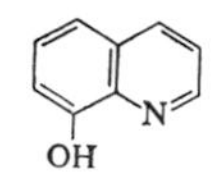	145·2	5·1 9·9
18	8-Hydroxyquinoline- 5-sulphonic acid		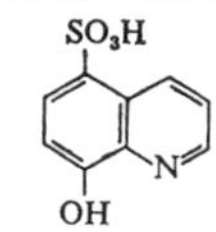	225·2	1·3 4·1 8·7
19	4-Methyl-1:2-dimercapto- benzene	Dithiol	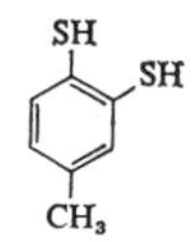	156·3	
20	5-Nitro-1:10-phenanthroline		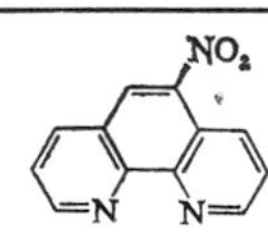	225·2	3·5
21	*o*-Phenanthroline	1:10-phenanthroline, OP	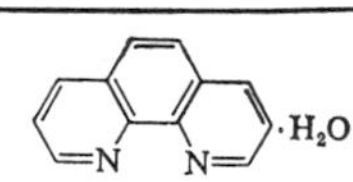	Hydrate, 198·2	5·0
22	Potassium ethyl xanthate	Potassium xanthogenate	$C_2H_5O \cdot CS \cdot SK$	160·3	
23	Sodium diethyl dithiocarbamate		$(C_2H_5)_2N \cdot CS \cdot SNa \cdot 3H_2O$	225·3	
24	2-Thenoyl-2-furoylmethane		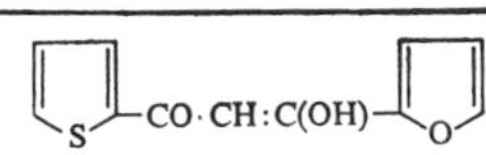	220·3	12·3
25	Thenoyl trifluoroacetone	4:4:4-trifluoro-1-(2-thienyl)- 1:3-butanedione, TTA	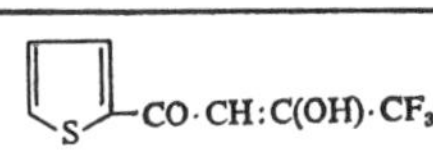	222·2	~ 9 (?)
26	Thiourea	Thiocarbamate	$NH_2 \cdot CS \cdot NH_2$	76·1	

Main form of Ligand at pH 7·0	Type of stability constant	Log stability constant Mg	Ca	Mn	Fe	Co	Ni	Cu	Zn	Remarks
HL^-	K^{M}_{MHL}	0·6	0·9			8·1	3·8	4·2		Slightly soluble in H_2O. Complexes with heavy metals; yellow-green ppt. with Cu^{2+}.
HL^-	K_1		0·5	5·9	6·6	6·7	7·0	10·6		Slightly soluble in H_2O. Forms strong complexes with Cu^{2+}, Al^{3+}, Fe^{3+}. Used to remove Be (log K_1 = 4·3; cf. log K_1 (Ca^{2+}) = 0·5) in Be poisoning.
HL	K_1 β_2	4·7	3·3	6·8 12·6	8·0 15·0	9·1 17·2	9·9 18·7	12·2 23·4	8·5 17·6	Only slightly soluble in H_2O. Mg and Ca complexes sparingly soluble. Others insoluble.
HL^-	K_1 β_2	4·8 8·4	3·5	6·9	8·4 15·1	8·8 15·9	9·8 18·5	12·5 23·1	8·7 16·2	Higher solubility of both ligand and complexes than for oxine.
H_2L										Slightly soluble in aqueous alkali; soluble in organic solvents. Forms slightly soluble coloured complexes with heavy metals.
L	K_1 β_3				5·1 18	6·3 16·6	7·0 20·4	8·0 17·7	5·5	Other substituted 1:10-phenanthrolines (e.g. 5-bromo-, 5-methyl) have similar chelating ability. 2-Substituted compounds have weaker chelating properties.
L	K_1 β_2 β_3	1·5	0·5	3·9 7·0 10·0	5·9 21	7·3 14·0 20·0	8·6 16·7 24·0	6·3 12·5 18	6·4 12·1 17·0	Used in removal of Zn from Zn-metalloenzymes: *J.B.C.* 235, 64 (1960). Also for spectrophotometric determination of iron (ref. 6).
L										Soluble in H_2O but solutions unstable. Forms coloured complexes (insoluble in H_2O) with heavy metals. Used for analysis of Mo.
L										Soluble in H_2O but solutions unstable. Metal complexes insoluble in H_2O. Used in immiscible solvents to extract heavy metals; also for colorimetric determination of Cu, Ni, Co.
HL										Insoluble in H_2O, soluble in organic solvents. Complexes (insoluble in H_2O) with heavy metals.
HL										Slightly soluble in H_2O; soluble in C_6H_6. Complexes (usually insoluble in H_2O, soluble in C_6H_6) with heavy metals. Used in solvent extraction procedures.
										Soluble in H_2O. Forms soluble complexes with heavy metals. Used particularly as a masking agent for Cu^{2+}. Fairly strong reducing agent.

B. METAL BINDING PROPERTIES OF COMPOUNDS USED IN BIOCHEMISTRY

No.	Name	pK_a	*Principal form of Ligand at* pH 7·0	*Type of constant*	*Log stability constant* Mg	Ca	Mn	Fe	Co	Ni	Cu	Zn
	ANIONS†‡											
1	Cyanide CN^-		L^-	β_4						12	25	16·9
				β_6				35	19			
2	Phosphate, PO_4^{3-}	2·1 7·2 12·0	HL^{2-}	K^M_{MHL}	2·5	2·2	2·6					
3	Pyrophosphate, $P_2O_7^{4-}$	1·0 2·5 6·1 8·45	HL^{3-}	K_1	5·7	5·0			7·4	5·8	6·7	
				β_2						7·3	9·0	6·5
4	Thiocyanate, SCN^-		L^-	K_1				1·0	1·2			1·6
				β_2						1·8	5·2	
5	Thiosulphate, $S_2O_3^{2-}$		L^{2-}	K_1	1·8	2·0	2·0	2·2	2·1	2·1		2·4
				β_2							12·3	
6	Triphosphate, $P_3O_{10}^{5-}$	< 2 5·43 7·87	HL^{4-}	K_1	5·8	5·0			8·1	7·9	9·8	
				K^M_{MHL}	3·7	3·1						
7	Sulphate, SO_4^{2-}		L^{2-}	K_1	2·4	2·3	2·3	2·3	2·5	2·4	2·2	2·3

AMINO ACIDS AND RELATED COMPOUNDS

No.	Name	pK_a	Principal form of Ligand at pH 7·0	Type of constant	Mg	Ca	Mn	Fe	Co	Ni	Cu	Zn
1	α-Alanine	2·34 9·87	$HL^\pm$	K_1	2·0	1·2	3·1		4·8	6·0	8·5	5·1
				β_2			6·1	7·3	8·6	10·7	15·4	9·4
2	β-Alanine	3·52 10·26	$HL^\pm$	K_1						4·6	7	4
				β_2				4	7	8	12·6	
3	α-Aminobutyric acid	2·55 9·76	$HL^\pm$	K_1				3·4	4·3			4·6
				β_2					7·6			8·3
4	Arginine	2·17 9·10 12·48	$H_2L^{2+,-}$	K_1	1·3		2·0	3·2	3·9			
				β_2					7·1	9·2	13·7	7·8
				β_3					9·2			
5	Asparagine	2·14 8·85	$HL^\pm$	K_1					4·6			
				β_2	4·0		4·5	6·5	8·3	10·6	14·9	8·7
				β_3					10·0			
6	Aspartic acid	1·94 3·70 9·62	$HL^{2-,+}$	K_1	2·4	1·6	3·7		5·9	7·1	8·6	5·8
				β_2				8·5	10·2	12·4	15·4	10·2
7	Cysteine	1·96 8·48 10·55	$H_2L^\pm$	K_1	< 4		4·1	6·2	9·3			9·9
				β_2				11·8	16·9	19·3		18·7
8	Glutamic acid	2·30 4·28 9·67	$HL^{2-,+}$	K_1	1·9	1·4	3·3	4·6		5·9	7·9	5·5
				β_2					8·1	10·3	14·6	9·5

† *Other anions.* AsO_4^{3-}, CO_3^{2-} generally form insoluble salts with divalent metals; Cl^-, possible very weak complexes with Mn, Fe, Cu; F^-, weak complexes with Mg, Ni, Cu, Zn but usually gives insoluble salts, strong complexes with tri- and tetravalent cations; NO_3^-, possible weak complexes with Co, Cu. NH_3 forms very weak complexes with Mg, Ca, Mn, stepwise complexes with Fe, Co, Ni, Cu, Zn.

‡ *Hydrolysis of metal ions.* Divalent metal ions combine with OH^- according to the equation $M^{2+}+OH^- \rightleftharpoons M(OH)^+$. The further reaction $M(OH)^+ + OH^- \rightleftharpoons M(OH)_2$ results in the formation of the insoluble hydroxide. pK_a values for the formation of $M(OH)^+$, and the approximate pH at the onset of precipitation of $M(OH)_2$, are respectively: Mg, 11·4, 10; Ca, 12·7, 12; Mn, 9·5, 9; Fe, 9·5, 9; Co, 10·2, 8; Ni, 10·6, 8; Cu, 8·0, 6; Zn, 9·6, 6.

No.	Name	pK_a	Principal form of Ligand at pH 7·0	Type of constant	Log stability constant Mg	Ca	Mn	Fe	Co	Ni	Cu	Zn
9	Glycine	2·24	HL±	K_1	3·4	1·4	2·9	4·3	3·8	5·7	8·1	5·2
		9·85		β_2			5·5	7·8	8·5	10·5	15·0	9·5
				β_3					10·8			
10	Glycylglycine	2·91	HL±	K_1	1·1	1·2	2·2		2·9	4·5	6·0	3·8
		8·22		β_2					5·2	7·9	11·6	6·6
11	Histamine	6·10	HL^+	K_1					5·2	6·8	9·6	5·7
		9·8		β_2					8·7	11·7	16·2	8·7
				β_3					10	14·9		
2	Histidine	1·82	HL±	K_1			4					6·7
		6·05		β_2			7·7	9·3	13·9	15·9	18·3	11·8
		9·17										
3	Imidazole	7·1	HL^+, L	K_1		0·1(?)	1·6	3·3	2·4	2·9	4·2	2·0
				β_2			2·9	6·4	4·4	5·4	7·7	4·2
				β_3					6·0	7·3	10·1	6·6
				β_4					7·2	8·7	12·5	9·5
4	Leucine	2·36	HL±	K_1			2·8	3·4	4·6	5·6	7·9	4·9
		9·60		β_2			5·5		8·3	10·2	14·3	8·9
5	Lysine	2·18	$H_2L^{2+,-}$	K_1			2	4·5				
		9·18		β_2					6·8	8·8	13·7	7·6
		10·72										
6	Methionine	2·20	HL±	K_1								4·4
		9·10		β_2				6·7	7·9		14·8	8·5
7	Norleucine	2·25	HL±	β_2	< 4		5	8·6	9·4	11·1	15·4	10·4
		9·96										
8	Ornithine	1·96	$H_2L^{2+,-}$	K_1			< 2	5·0	4·0	4·9	6·9	4·1
		8·65		β_2					6·9	8·5	12·5	7·3
		10·7										
	Phenylalanine	1·85	HL±	β_2				6·3	7·9		14·7	
		9·13										
	Proline	1·93	HL±	β_2	< 4		5·5	8·3	9·3	11·3	16·8	10·2
		10·68										
	Serine	2·20	HL±	K_1		1·4						
		9·64		β_2				7·0	8·0		14·5	
	Tryptophan	2·38	HL±	β_2	< 4		5	7·6	8·5	10·2	15·9	9·3
		9·39										
	Tyrosine	2·20	H_2L±	K_1	2	1·5	2·4					
		9·19		β_2				7·1	8·1	10·1	15·0	9·1
		10·43										
	Valine	2·3	HL±	K_1			2·8		4·6		8·1	5·0
		9·7		β_2			5·6	6·8	8·4		14·9	8·1

CARBOXYLIC ACIDS

Name	pK_a	Principal form of Ligand at pH 7·0	Type of constant	Mg	Ca	Mn	Fe	Co	Ni	Cu	Zn
Acetic acid	4·64	L^-	K_1	0·5	0·5	1·2	1·4	1·5	0·7	1·6	1·0
			β_2					1·9	1·3	2·7	
Citric acid	3·0	HL^{3-}	K_1							18	6·2
	4·7		$K^{M}_{MH_3L}$		1·2						
	6·4		$K^{M}_{MH_2L}$	1·6	3·1	2·1	2·1		3·4		3·0
	(16)		K^{M}_{MHL}	3·3	4·9	3·5	3·1		5·1	14	4·9
Formic acid	3·77	L^-	K_1		0·8					2·0	
Fumaric acid	3·02	L^{2-}	K_1		2·0	1·0				2·5	
	4·39										
Gluconic acid	3·56	L^-	K_1	0·7	1·2					18	1·7

17. Stability Constants of Metal Complexes

No.	Name	pK	Principal form of Ligand at pH 7·0	Type of constant	Log stability constant Mg	Ca	Mn	Fe	Co	Ni	Cu	Zn
6	Lactic acid	3·7	L^-	K_1	0·9	1·1				2·2		1·9
				β_2					1·7		2·7	
7	Maleic acid	1·92 6·22	L^{2-}	K_1		2·4	1·7			2·0	3·9	2·0
8	Malic acid	3·26 4·68	L^{2-}	K_1	1·6	1·9	2·2				3·4	2·8
9	Malonic acid	2·7 5·3	L^{2-}	K_1	1·9	1·5	3·3		3·7	4·0	5·6	2·8
				β_2				2·2			8·2	
10	Oxalic acid	1·14 3·85	L^{2-}	K_1	2·6	3	3·9	4·7	4·7	5·3		4·9
				β_2	4·4		5·3	9·2	6·7	12·9	8·5	7·4
				β_3				14·4		14		8·2
11	Propionic acid	4·7	L^-	K_1	0·5	0·5					2·2	1·0
12	Pyruvic acid	2·5	L^-	K_1		0·8					2·2	
13	Succinic acid	4·07 5·28	L^{2-}	K_1	1·2	1·2			0·1		3·3	1·8
14	Tartaric acid	2·88 3·94	L^{2-}	K_1	1·4	1·8					3·1	2·7
				β_2				5			5·1	

MISCELLANEOUS COMPOUNDS OF BIOLOGICAL INTEREST

No.	Name	pK	Principal form of Ligand at pH 7·0	Type of constant	Mg	Ca	Mn	Fe	Co	Ni	Cu	Zn
1	Adenine	4·18 9·7	HL	K_1					4·2	4·8	7·1	
				β_2							13·5	
2	Aureomycin	3·3 7·44 9·27	$H_2L > HL^-$	K_1			4·3	5·7	4·8		7·6	4·5
				β_2				10·4			12·6	
3	Flavine adenine dinucleotide (FAD)			K_{app} pH 8·2	2·0	2·0	2·4		2·4			
4	Flavine mononucleotide (FMN)			K_{app} pH 8·2	2·1	2·1	2·2		2·4			
5	Guanosine	2·2 9·3	HL	K_1				4·3	3·2	3·8	6	4·6
6	Glucose-1-phosphate	1·11 6·13	HL^{2-}	K_1		2·5	2·3					
	Glucose-6-phosphate	0·94 6·11	HL^{2-}	K_1			2·3					
8	Hypoxanthine	1·98 8·94 12·1	HL	K_1			2·4	3·9	3·8	4·7	6·2	
9	Inosine	1·2 8·8	HL	K_1				3	2·6	3·3	5	
10	Phosphoarginine	< 2, 2·0, 4·5, 9·6 11·2	$HL^{3-,+}$	K^{M}_{MHL}	2·0							
11	Phosphocreatine	2, 2·7, 4·5	$HL^{3-,+}$	K^{M}_{MHL}	1·6	1·3	2·0					
12	Phosphoenolpyruvic acid			K_1	2·3		2·7		3·5	2·3		3·0
13	2-Phosphoglyceric acid			K_1	2·4		3·1		3·0	2·9		3·4
14	Pteroylglutamic acid (Folic acid)	8·26 (4-Hydroxy)	HL^{2-}	β_2			6	7·9	8·1	9·0	7·8	7·5
15	Pyridine	5·45	L	K_1				0·7	1·1		2·5	1·4
				β_2					1·5	1·2	4·4	1·1
16	Pyridoxamine	3·37 8·0 10·1	$H_2L^{2+,-}$	K_1			3·6		5·1	6·0	10·2	5·7
				β_2					9·6	10·9	16·0	

No.	Name	pK_a	Principal form of Ligand at pH 7·0	Type of constant	Log stability constant Mg	Ca	Mn	Fe	Co	Ni	Cu	Zn
17	Riboflavin	9·9	HL	K_1			3·4	7·1	3·9	4·1		5·6
				β_2							13	
18	Terramycin	3·10 7·26 9·1	$H_2L > HL^-$	K_1	3·8		4·3	5·6	5·1	5·8	7·2	4·6
				β_2			8·0	10·4		10·6	12·2	
19	Xanthosine	2·5 5·67	L^-	K_1				2	2·8	3·0	3·4	2·4

C. METAL NUCLEOTIDE COMPLEXES

Detailed information is presented for the alkali metals and for Mg^{2+}, Ca^{2+}, and Mn^{2+} complexes with ADP and ATP. There is considerable variation in the values available from the literature (see *The Enzymes*, vol. 2, p. 3, Academic Press, New York (1960)) and this table is based largely on the results of Burton (*B.J.* **71,** 388 (1959)) and O'Sullivan and Perrin (*B.B.A.* **52,** 612 (1961); *Biochemistry* **3,** 18 (1964)). (Cf. *The Enzymes*, vol. 6, p. 515, Academic Press, New York (1962).) Where the values are 'apparent' stability constants, the pH is reported.

Other metal nucleotide complexes

In general the substitution of a deoxyribose sugar for ribose or changing the identity of the purine or pyrimidine base would only slightly alter the magnitude of the stability constants (*The Enzymes*, vol. 2, p. 3, Academic Press, New York (1960); *Biochemistry* **3,** 18 (1964); *Acta chem. scand.* **12,** 528 (1958)). Thus these figures are a fairly reliable guide for complexes formed by other nucleotides with Mg^{2+} and Ca^{2+} and possibly Mn^{2+}.

Values for complexes with other metals have been reported: $CoATP^{2-}$, 4·62; $CoADP^-$, 3·68 (*Acta chem. scand.* **12,** 528 (1958)); $SrATP^{2-}$, 3·03; $SrADP^-$, 2·50 (*J.A.C.S.* **78,** 2376 (1956)); $CoATP^{2-}$, 4·71; $NiATP^{2-}$, 4·54; $ZnATP^{2-}$, 4·80; $CuATP^{2-}$, 5·77 (*Helv. chim. Acta* **44,** 935 (1961)). All values expressed as log *K*.

Estimates for metal complexes with DNA and RNA have also been reported: MgDNA, 2·10; CaDNA, 2·10; MnDNA, 2·44; MgRNA, 2·32; CaRNA, 2·32 (*Arch. B.B.* **72,** 66 (1957)). All values expressed as log *K*. Measurements at $\mu = 0{\cdot}15$, pH 7·2 (0·011M-Na barbital).

Complex	Conditions	log *K*	References
$MgATP^{2-}$	0·11M-tributylethylammonium ion, 25°, pH 8·4	4·58	*B.J.* **71,** 388 (1959)
	0·1M-tris, 30°, pH 8·0	4·30	*B.B.A.* **52,** 612 (1961)
	0·1M-triethanolamine buffer, 30°, pH 8·0	4·89	*Biochemistry* **3,** 18 (1964)
	0·1M-*N*-ethylmorpholine, 30°, pH 8·0	4·86	*J. Biochem., Tokyo* **54,** 17 (1963)
	0·165M-Na^+, pH 7·4, 37°	4·18	*Biochemistry* **3,** 18 (1964) corrected according to *B.J.* **71,** 388 (1959)
$CaATP^{2-}$	0·1M-tributylethylammonium ion, 25°, pH 8·0	4·45	*B.J.* **71,** 388 (1959)
	0·1M-*N*-ethylmorpholine, pH 8·0, 30°	4·49	*Biochemistry* **3,** 18 (1964)
	0·165M-Na^+, pH 7·4, 37°	3·82	*Biochemistry* **3,** 18 (1964) corrected according to *B.J.* **71,** 388 (1959)
$NaATP^{3-}$	0·1M-*N*-ethylmorpholine, pH 8·0, 30°	1·18	*Biochemistry* **3,** 18 (1964)
	0·2M-tetramethylammonium ion, 25°	1·0	*The Enzymes*, vol. 6, p. 515, Academic Press, New York (1962) *J.B.C.* **208,** 615 (1954)

17. Stability Constants of Metal Complexes

Complex	*Conditions*	log *K*	*References*
$KATP^{3-}$	0·1M-*N*-ethylmorpholine, pH 8·0, 30°	1·15	*Biochemistry* **3**, 18 (1964)
	0·2M-tetramethylammonium ion, 25°	1·0	*The Enzymes*, vol. 6, p. 515, Academic Press, New York (1962) *J.B.C.* **208**, 615 (1954)
$MnATP^{2-}$	0·1M-tetraethylammonium chloride + 0·05 M-tris, pH 7·5	4·88	*Nature, Lond.* **193**, 1037 (1962)
	0·05M-*N*-ethylmorpholine, pH 7·5, 25°	5·0	*J.B.C.* **241**, 3104 (1966) *B.B.A.* **127**, 35 (1966)
	0·05M-KNO_3+0·05M-tris, pH 7·05, 38°	4·85	*Arch. B.B.* **92**, 94 (1961)
$MgADP^{-}$	0·085M-tributylethylammonium bromide + 0·025M-triethanolamine, pH 7·9, 25°	3·34	*B.J.* **71**, 388 (1959)
	0·1M-*N*-ethylmorpholine, pH 8·0, 30°	3·60	*Biochemistry* **3**, 18 (1964)
$CaADP^{-}$	0·085M-tributylethylammonium bromide + 0·025M-triethanolamine pH 8·8, 25°	2·89	*B.J.* **71**, 388 (1959)
	0·1M-*N*-ethylmorpholine, pH 8·0, 30°	3·34	*Biochemistry* **3**, 18 (1964)
$NaADP^{2-}$	0·2M-tetraethylammonium bromide, 25°	0·65	*The Enzymes*, vol. 6, p. 515, Academic Press, New York (1962) *J.B.C.* **208**, 615 (1954)
$KADP^{2-}$	,,	0·68	,,
$MnADP^{-}$	0·1M-tetramethylammonium chloride + 0·05M-tris, pH 7·5	4·00	*Nature, Lond.* **193**, 1037 (1962)
	0·1M-*N*-ethylmorpholine, pH 8·0, 30°	4·40	*Biochemistry* **3**, 18 (1964)
	0·05M-KNO_3+0·05M-tris, pH 7·05, 38°	3·89	*Arch. B.B.* **92**, 94 (1961)

18. Artificial Substrates and Biochemical Reagents

By K. M. JONES (*Department of Biochemistry, University of Leicester*)

A. ELECTRON DONORS, CARRIERS, AND ACCEPTORS

No.	*Name*	*Synonyms*	*Formula*	*M. wt.*
1	Benzyl viologen	1,1′-Dibenzyl-4,4′-bipyridylium dichloride	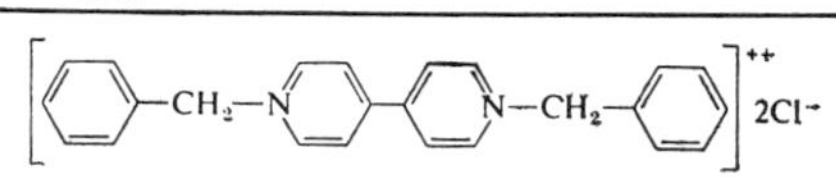	409·4
2	Blue tetrazolium	3,3′-(3,3′-Dimethoxy-4,4′-biphenylylene)-bis[2,5-diphenyl-2*H*-tetrazolium chloride]; Blue T; BT	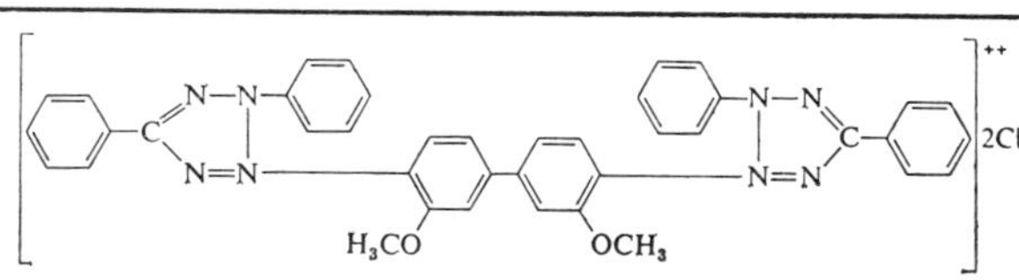	727·7
3	Brilliant cresyl blue	7-(Diethylamino)-3-imino-8-methyl-3*H*-phenoxazine hydrochloride	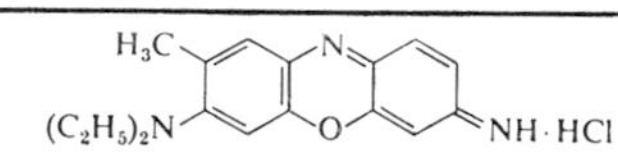	317·8; Hydrate, 335·8
4	2,6-Dichlorophenol-indophenol, Na salt	2,6-Dichloroindophenol; *N*-(*p*-Hydroxyphenyl)-2,6-dichloro-*p*-benzoquinoneimine	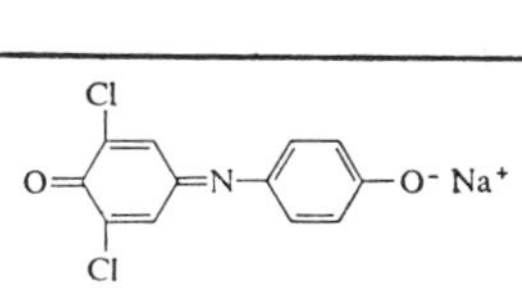	290·1; Hydrate, 326·1; Free acid, 268·1

Physical properties	Solubility	Preparation	Use	General remarks
col. cryst.; E_0' −0·359 v (30°, independent of pH)	s. H_2O, MeOH; i. acet.	*J. gen. Physiol.* **16,** 859 (1933)	Low potential electron acceptor and carrier. Oxidized form colourless to pale yellow, reduced form blue to violet. Reduced compd. v. readily oxidized by O_2; benzyl viologen used either anaerobically or as carrier to O_2 or non-autoxidizable acceptors. Reduced compd. used as an electron donor	Reduced by dithionite, borohydride. Stable reduced compd. at neutral pH formed by addition of one electron. *Reduced compd.*: λ_{max} 555 mμ at room temp. At higher temp. 555 mμ peak diminishes and peak at 598 mμ appears. At 80° only 598 mμ peak is visible.
col. needles; M.p. 245–7 *Reduced compd.*: blue-black needles; M.p. 244	sl. s. H_2O; v.s. MeOH, EtOH, $CHCl_3$; i. acet., eth., Et acetate *Reduced compd.*: i. H_2O; s. most organic solvents	*Chem. Rev.* **55,** 355 (1955) *Cancer Res.* **10,** 113 (1950) *Analyst* **83,** 532 (1958)	Electron acceptor. Oxidized form colourless; reduced form (bis-formazan) blue to black. Reduced by flavoprotein enzymes, rate increased by intermediate electron carriers such as phenazine methosulphate. Hydrogen acceptor in Hill reaction, *Acta chem. scand.* **15,** 1629 (1961). In estimation and detection on chromatograms of reducing steroids, especially adrenocortical steroids with α-ketol group, Dorfman, *Meth. Horm. Res.* **1,** 199 (1962); *Analyt. Biochem.* **2,** 1 (1961)	Not appreciably photolabile. *Reduced compd.*: λ_{max} about 520 mμ (in EtOH), varies widely in other solvents. Not oxidized by O_2.
green needles+ H_2O from dil. EtOH; E_0' +0·047 v pH 7, 30°)	s. H_2O, EtOH, acet., gl. acetic; i. eth., benz.		Electron acceptor. Oxidized form blue, reduced form colourless. Reduced by flavoprotein enzymes, but not by soluble succinic dehydrogenase	Unstable in aq. soln., esp. alkaline solns., or as solid in presence of H_2O. Spectrum depends upon conc.; at 40 mg/l λ_{max} 625 mμ, at 1 g/l λ_{max} 575 mμ. Reduced by dithionite. Recryst. from pet. eth. Commercial product is now usually diethylamino compd., but may also be, esp. in older literature, dimethylamino compd. which has similar properties. *Reduced compd.*: reoxidized by air at pH 7 and above, but *not* below pH 6·4. Reoxidized by ferricyanide at all pHs.
ark green powder ·$2H_2O$; hydration omewhat variable; E_0' +0·217 v H 7, 30°)	sl. s. H_2O; v.s. EtOH	*Public Health Reports, U.S.* Suppl. No. 69 (1928)	Electron acceptor. Oxidized form blue at neutral pH, pink in acid, reduced form colourless. Reduced by flavoprotein enzymes; used in their assay, often with phenazine methosulphate as intermediate electron carrier. Addition of phenazine methosulphate allows coupling to nicotinamide nucleotide-linked dehydrogenases. Reduced compd. only v. slowly oxidized by O_2, so exclusion of air *not* necessary. Volumetric reagent, e.g. for ascorbic acid	Solid stable for years in air if kept dark, decomp. by heat and light. Aq. solns. decomp. slowly at neutral pH, rapidly below pH 3 or if strongly alkaline, and must be standardized daily for volumetric use. Reduced by ascorbic acid, dithionite, borohydride, reduced phenazine methosulphate, reduced ubiquinones, reduced vitamin K. Commercial preparations often impure. λ_{max} approx. 600 mμ ϵ_{600} 16 100 (pH 7).

No.	*Name*	*Synonyms*	*Formula*	*M. wt.*
5	Diethylsafranin	3-(Diethylamino)-7-amino-5-phenyl-phenazinium chloride	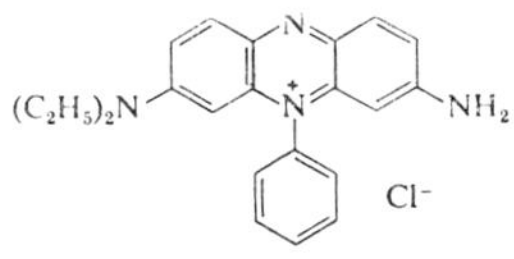	378·9
6	Guaiacol	*o*-Hydroxyanisole; *o*-Methoxyphenol	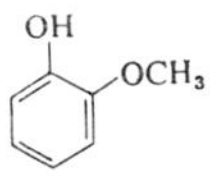	124·1
7	Hydroquinone	Quinol; 1,4-Benzenediol	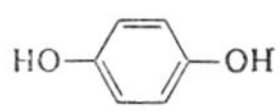	110·1
8	Iodonitrotetra-zolium	2-*p*-Iodophenyl-3-*p*-nitrophenyl-5-phenyl-2*H*-tetrazolium chloride; INT	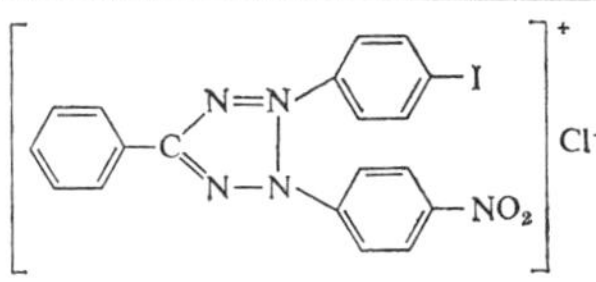	505·7
9	Menadione	Vitamin K_3; Menaphthone; 2-Methyl-1,4-naphthoquinone	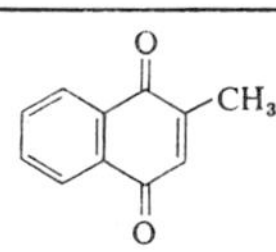	172·2
10	Methylene blue	Methylthionine chloride; 3,7-Bis-(dimethylamino)-phenazathionium chloride	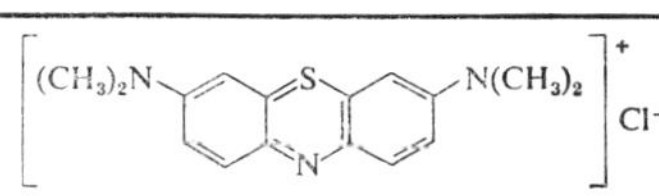	319·9

Physical properties	*Solubility*	*Preparation*	*Use*	*General remarks*
E_0' −0·251 v (pH 7)	s. H_2O	*Expl Cell Res.* **5**, 69 (1953)	Reduced compd. used as hydrogen donor in fumarate reductase—*Meth. biochem. Anal.* **4**, 307 (1957)—and similar reactions. Oxidized form red, reduced form colourless. Reduced form v. readily oxidized by O_2, generally prepared *in situ* by action of dithionite on oxidized form	Unstable esp. to acid and to air; prepare fresh daily. Generally impure because starting material, Janus Green B, is impure. λ_{max} 555 mμ, ε approx. 49 000.
wh. or sl. yel. cryst. mass or col. to yel. liq.; M.p. 28; B.p. 204–6	1·5 H_2O; ∞ EtOH, $CHCl_3$, eth., gl. acetic		Hydrogen donor in assay of peroxidase, *Meth. biochem. Anal.* **1**, 357 (1954). On oxidation forms tetraguaiacol which has λ_{max} at 470 mμ. Colour fades rapidly	Protect from light.
col. hexagonal prisms; dimorphous; stable form from H_2O; M.p. 170–1; B.p. 286–7; pK_a 9·85, 11·4	7 H_2O; s. EtOH, eth., acet.; sl. s. benz.		Electron donor. Reduces cytochrome c. Antioxidant	Keep well closed and protected from light. Soln. oxidizes in air, v. rapidly in presence of alkali.
buff or cream powder; M.p. 229 *Reduced compd.*: red-purple needles; M.p. 185–6	$0·5^{25}$ H_2O *Reduced compd.*: i. H_2O; s. most organic solvents	*J.A.C.S.* **72**, 3629 (1950)	Electron acceptor. Oxidized form colourless, reduced form reddish purple. Readily reduced by flavoprotein enzymes; rate may be increased by intermediate electron carriers such as phenazine methosulphate. Used in assay of dehydrogenases by non-enzymic coupling to $NADH_2$ or $NADPH_2$ with phenazine methosulphate, *J.B.C.* **235**, 499 (1960); *Analyt. Biochem.* **1**, 317 (1960)	Much less photolabile than triphenyltetrazolium. Soln. stable at 5° for months. Reduced by reducing sugars, ascorbic acid, NH_2OH in alkaline soln., by reduced phenazine methosulphate, reduced ubiquinones, reduced vitamin K at neutral pH. *Reduced compd.* (formazan): λ_{max} about 500 mμ (varies slightly with solvent). Not oxidized by O_2.
bright yel. needles; M.p. 105–7; E_0' +0·408 v (pH 0, 25°)	1·7 EtOH; 10 benz.; s. eth., $CHCl_3$, CCl_4; i. H_2O	*J.B.C.* **133**, 391 (1940)	Electron carrier. Reduced by flavoprotein enzymes. Oxidation-reduction may be followed at 262 mμ. Frequently used as an electron carrier to O_2 or non-autoxidizable acceptors such as indophenols or tetrazolium salts. Cofactor of cyclic photophosphorylation	Stable in air but decomp. by sunlight. Solns. stable at 120°, but destroyed by reducing agents or alkalis. In hexane, λ_{max} 244, ε 19 800 λ_{max} 253 264 328 mμ ε 19 700 16 800 3100 In aq. buffer pH 6·24, λ_{max} 250 263–4 340 mμ *Reduced compd.* (menadiol): greyish-wh. powder, M.p. 160–7, PREP. *J.B.C.* **133**, 391 (1940), λ_{max} 241 330 mμ (in aq. buffer pH 6·24). Readily oxidized by air at neutral or alkaline pH, very slowly oxidized at pH 6·3 and below.
dark green cryst.+ –5 H_2O; E_0' +0·011 v (pH 7, 30°)	4·3 H_2O; 1·5 EtOH; sl. s. $CHCl_3$; i. eth. *Reduced compd.*: v. sl. s. H_2O	*Reduced compd.*: *Angew. Chem.* **68**, 352 (1962)	Electron acceptor. Oxidized form blue; reduced form colourless. Reduced by flavoprotein enzymes, but not by soluble succinic dehydrogenase; rate often increased by intermediate electron carriers such as phenazine methosulphate. Reduced compd. readily reoxidized in air, so methylene blue is either used anaerobically or as carrier to O_2	Oxidizes on standing as solid and esp. in soln. to give demethylated forms. Loses H_2O of cryst. only with partial decomp. Spectrum depends upon concentration; at 10^{-5} M λ_{max} 665 mμ. Above 10^{-4} M main peak between 610 and 570 mμ tending to lower wavelengths at higher concs. Peak at 665 mμ falls and virtually disappears at 10^{-3} M. See *J.A.C.S.* **77**, 4197 (1955). Reduced by dithionite, reduced flavins, reduced phenazine methosulphate, reduced quinones. Possesses vitamin E activity. *Reduced compd.*: Tends to stick to glass surfaces. Reoxidized by O_2 or anaerobically by light; oxidation rate increases with pH. Stable under N_2 in dark.

No.	Name	Synonyms	Formula	M. wt.
11	Methyl viologen	1,1′-Dimethyl-4,4′-bipyridylium dichloride	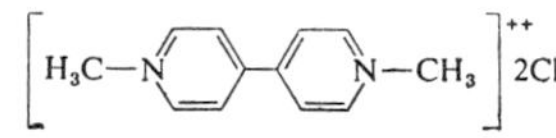	257·2
12	Neotetrazolium	3,3′-(4,4′-Biphenylylene)-bis[2,5-diphenyl-2*H*-tetrazolium chloride]; NeoT; NT	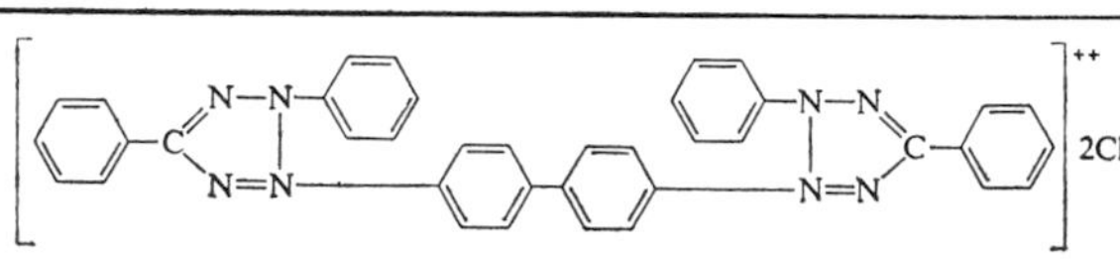	667·6
13	Nitroblue tetrazolium	3,3′-(3,3′-Dimethoxy-4,4′-biphenylylene)-bis[2-(*p*-nitrophenyl)-5-phenyl-2*H*-tetrazolium chloride]; NitroBT	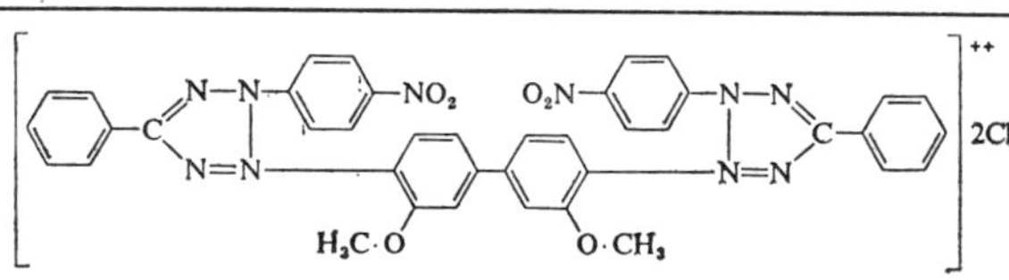	817·7
14	Phenazine methosulphate	*N*-Methyl-phenazinium methylsulphate; PMS	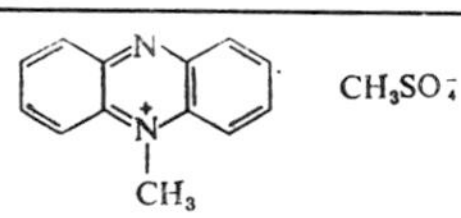	306·3

Physical properties	Solubility	Preparation	Use	General remarks
col. needles+H_2O, lose H_2O at 50°; E_0' −0·446 v (30°, independent of pH)	s. H_2O, MeOH; i. acet.	*J. gen. Physiol.* **16**, 859 (1933)	V. low potential electron acceptor. Oxidized form colourless, reduced form blue to violet. Reduced compd. v. readily oxidized by O_2, so methyl viologen is used anaerobically or as carrier to O_2 or non-autoxidizable acceptor. Reduced compd. used as electron donor, e.g. in hydrogenase reaction	Reduced by dithionite, borohydride. Stable reduced form at neutral pH formed by addition of one electron. The 1,1′-dimethyl-4,4′-bipyridylium ion, usually as the dimethosulphate, is a herbicide, 'Paraquat'. Estimation, *Nature, Lond.* **199**, 1011 (1963). *Reduced compd.*: λ_{max} 601 mμ, shoulder at 570 mμ.
col. needles; M.p. 260–78 *Reduced compd.*: dark violet needles; M.p. 219–20 d.	s. H_2O *Reduced compd.*: i. H_2O; s. most organic solvents	*Chem. Rev.* **55**, 355 (1955)	Electron acceptor. Oxidized form pale yellow, reduced form (bis-formazan) magenta. Reduced by flavoprotein enzymes, rate increased by intermediate electron carriers such as phenazine methosulphate. Use in assay of succinoxidase, *B.J.* **73**, 314 (1959)	Not sensitive to sunlight, no decomp. of soln. in 4 hr in direct sunlight. Reduced by reducing sugars, ascorbic acid, NH_2OH at alkaline pH, by reduced phenazine methosulphate, reduced ubiquinones, reduced vitamin K_3 at neutral pH. *Reduced compd.*: λ_{max} about 520 mμ (varies widely with solvent). Not oxidized by O_2.
cryst. containing solvent; trihydrate, M.p. 156 d.; anhydrous chloride hydroxide, M.p. 134 *Reduced compd.*: black cryst.; M.p. 270–2 d.	s. H_2O *Reduced compd.*: i. H_2O; s. most organic solvents	*J.A.C.S.* **78**, 6139 (1956) *J.A.C.S.* **81**, 3771 (1959)	Electron acceptor. Oxidized form colourless; reduced form (bis-formazan) blue to black. Rapidly reduced by flavoprotein enzymes, rate increased by electron carriers such as phenazine methosulphate. Most commonly used tetrazolium salt for histochemical detection of dehydrogenases, see Burstone, *Enzyme Histochemistry*, Academic Press (1962). Used, with phenazine methosulphate, in detection of dehydrogenases on electrophoretograms, *Meth. Enzymol.* **6**, 958 (1963)	Not appreciably photolabile. *Reduced compd.* (bis-formazan): has v. marked substantivity for protein, e.g. *not* extracted into Et acetate from aq. suspension containing gelatin. λ_{max} approx. 550 mμ (varies widely with solvent).
yel. to brown parallelepipeds from EtOH; M.p. 167; E_0' +0·080 v (pH 7, 30°) *Reduced compd.*: M.p. 164	v.s. H_2O *Reduced compd.*: v. sl. s. H_2O	*Meth. biochem. Anal.* **4**, 307 (1957) *Reduced compd.*: *J.B.C.* **239**, 3964 (1964)	Electron acceptor and electron carrier. Oxidized form yellow, reduced form colourless, green semiquinone sometimes observed. Rapidly reduced by flavoprotein enzymes, incl. succinic dehydrogenase—*Meth. biochem. Anal.* **4**, 307 (1957). Reduced compd. v. readily oxidized by O_2, so PMS normally used in assays as electron carrier between enzymes and O_2, cytochrome c, or less readily autoxidizable electron acceptors e.g. indophenols or tetrazolium salts. H_2O_2 formed on autoxidation of $PMSH_2$ and since PMS completely inhibits catalase, other provision to remove H_2O_2, e.g. CN^- or 8-hydroxyquinoline, may be necessary. PMS reduced non-enzymically by $NADH_2$ and $NADPH_2$; used to couple dehydrogenases to other electron acceptors, e.g. indophenols, tetrazolium salts. Electron carrier in cyclic photophosphorylation and stimulates Hill reaction. Reduced compd. used as an electron donor, e.g. to reduce cytochrome c or in photosynthetic expts. For use in enzymic reactions best to use enzymically reduced material (tissue prep.+$NADH_2$)	Solid stable years in dark. Prepare solns. in H_2O *not* neutral buffers; such solns. keep frozen and in dark for several months. Unstable to light, forming pyocyanine and other products; in sunlight decomp. in 5–10 min, but takes hours in diffuse light. Stabilized by polyvalent cations. Reduced by dithionite, borohydride, $NADH_2$, $NADPH_2$, ascorbic acid, reduced ubiquinones, reduced vitamin K. Reacts with —SH compds., incl. —SH enzymes. λ_{max} 387 mμ ε 26 300 (pH 2–8); Δε (ox-red) 25 000. *Reduced compd.*: Solid stored 2–3 weeks in air at −20°, but in soln. and at working temp. v. rapidly oxidized by O_2. Rapidly reduces cytochrome c, indophenol dyes, tetrazolium salts, and many other electron acceptors.

No.	Name	Synonyms	Formula	M. wt.
15	*p*-Phenylene diamine	1,4-Diaminobenzene	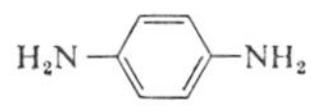	108·1
16	Potassium ferricyanide		$K_3[Fe(CN)_6]$	329·3
17	Pyocyanine		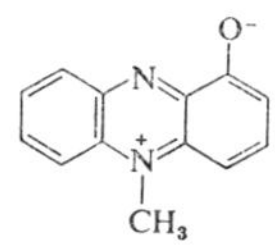	210·2; Hydrate, 228·3
18	Pyrogallol	1,2,3-Trihydroxy-benzene	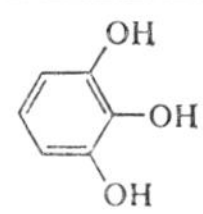	126·1
19	Sodium boro-hydride		$NaBH_4$	37·8
20	Sodium dithionite	Sodium hydrosulphite; Sodium sulphoxylate	$Na_2S_2O_4 \cdot 2H_2O$	210·2; Anhydrous, 174·1
21	Tetramethyl-phenylene diamine		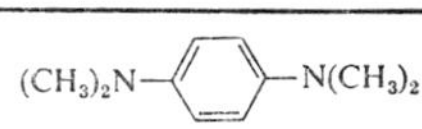	164·3; Dihydro-chloride, 237·2
22	2,3′,6-Trichloro-phenolindo-phenol, Na salt	2,3′,6-Trichloro-indophenol; *o*-Chlorophenolindo-2,6-dichlorophenol	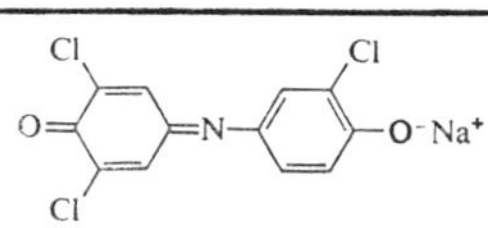	324·5; Free acid, 302·5
23	Triphenyl-tetrazolium	2,3,5-Triphenyl-tetrazolium chloride; Tetrazolium salt; TTZ; TTC	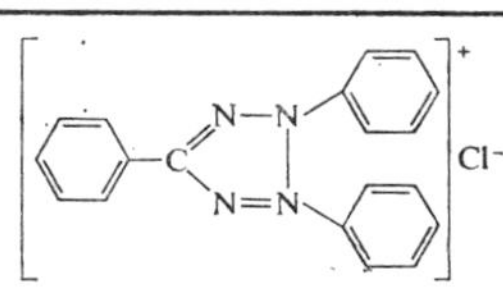	334·8

Physical properties	*Solubility*	*Preparation*	*Use*	*General remarks*
wh. cryst., darken on exposure to air; M.p. 145–7; B.p. 267; pK_a 2·67, 6·16	1 H_2O; s. hot H_2O, EtOH, $CHCl_3$, eth.		Electron donor. Reduces cytochrome c	Store in dark and well closed.
monocl. red cryst.; decomp. on heating; E'_0 +0·360 v (pH 7)	48·8^{25} H_2O; sl. s. MeOH, EtOH, acet.		Electron acceptor and mild oxidizing agent. Reduction may be followed by decrease in OD at 400 mμ. Reduced at several sites in electron transport chain. Oxidizes reduced cytochrome c	Aq. soln. decomp. slowly on standing, protect from light. Oxidizes —SH groups to —S—S—.
dark blue needles+1 H_2O from H_2O; loses H_2O *in vacuo* over P_2O_5 at 50°; M.p. 133; E'_0 −0·034 v (pH 7, 30°)	v.s. $CHCl_3$; s. hot H_2O, hot EtOH, acet., gl. acetic, pyr., phenol, Et acetate; sl. s. cold H_2O, benz.; i. eth., pet. eth., CCl_4	*Org. Synth.* Coll. 3, 753 (1955) *J.C.S.* 1937, 1704	Electron acceptor and carrier. Oxidized form blue, reduced form colourless. Very effective cofactor of cyclic photophosphorylation, *Pl. Physiol.* 34, 240 (1959). Reduced pyocyanine used as an electron donor in fumarate reductase; best prepared enzymically with tissue prep.+$NADH_2$, *J.B.C.* **229**, 759 (1957)	Solid stable weeks in dry and dark, decomp. on long storage. Reduced by dithionite, borohydride, and in alkaline soln. by glucose. Formed by cultures of *Pseudomonas aeruginosa.* λ_{max} 239 312 379 690 mμ (pH 7–8) ϵ_{700} 3400 (pH 7). *Reduced compd.*: V. rapidly oxidized by O_2.
wh. cryst.; M.p. 133; B.p. 309; pK_{a1} 9·0	62·5^{25} H_2O; 78^{25} EtOH; 64^{25} eth.; sl. s. benz., $CHCl_3$, CS_2		Hydrogen donor in peroxidase assay, *Meth. biochem. Anal.* **1**, 357 (1954). On oxidation forms purpurogallin, which has λ_{max} at 430 mμ ϵ 2470. Oxygen absorber in strongly alkaline solution, see p. 617	Poisonous. Keep well closed and protected from light. Aq. soln. oxidizes in air, rapidly when alkaline. Strong reducing agent.
cubic cryst.; decomp. > 300	10 isopropylamine; 3 pyr.; 1 morpholine; 0·8 dimethyl cellosolve; s. H_2O; sl. s. tetrahydrofuran		Powerful reducing agent, reduces many physiological and artificial electron carriers. Reduces pyridoxal phosphate Schiff's bases to stable —CH_2—NH— links	Solid stable if dry, decomp. in moist air. Reacts slowly with water at room temp.
monocl. cryst. or yel. powder; decomp. 52	25·4^{20} H_2O; s. alkalis, dil. acids; i. EtOH		Powerful reducing agent, used to reduce many physiological and artificial electron carriers including NAD, NADP, flavins and cytochromes	Oxidizes in air, readily when damp or in soln., but dry solid only v. slowly.
eaflets from aq. EtOH or ligroin; M.p. 51; B.p. 260; E'_0 +0·26 v (pH 7)	v.s. EtOH, eth., $CHCl_3$, benz.; s. ligroin; sp. s. H_2O		Electron donor. Reduces cytochrome c; generally used in catalytic amounts with ascorbate as bulk electron donor	Keep solid protected from light. Soln. unstable. Dihydrochloride, cryst.
green cryst.+up to 17% H_2O; E'_0 +0·219 v (pH 7, 30°)	s. H_2O; v.s. EtOH	*Public Health Reports, U.S.* Suppl. No. 69 (1928) *Reduced compd.*: *J.B.C.* **179**, 865 (1949) *J.B.C.* **211**, 183 (1954)	Electron acceptor. In neutral soln., oxidized form blue, reduced form colourless. Reduced by flavoprotein enzymes. Used as acceptor in Hill reaction. Reduced compd. used as electron donor, e.g. in nitrate reductase. Oxidation by O_2 occurs v. slowly	Solid stable in air if kept dark, decomp. slowly in light. Aq. solns. decomp. on standing, esp. at acid pH. Reduced by ascorbic acid, dithionite, reduced phenazine methosulphate. λ_{max} approx. 645 mμ ϵ 27 000 (pH 7·3). *Reduced compd.*: Stable several days under H_2 at R.T.
solvated needles, lose solvent on heating; M.p. 243 d.; E'_0 −0·080 v (pH 7) *Reduced compd.*: red leaflets; M.p. 173·5	25 H_2O; s. MeOH, EtOH; sl. s. acet., $CHCl_3$; i. eth. *Reduced compd.*: i. H_2O; s. most organic solvents	*Chem. Rev.* **55**, 355 (1955) *Science* **111**, 385 (1950)	Electron acceptor. Oxidized form colourless to pale yellow, reduced form red. Slowly reduced by flavoprotein enzymes, rate increased by intermediate electron carriers such as phenazine methosulphate or pyocyanine. For testing seed viability, *Science* **113**, 751 (1951). Indicator of bacterial growth in bioautography, *Appl. Microbiol.* **2**, 29 (1954). Least toxic to bacteria of tetrazolium salts. Review of uses, *Tetrazolium Salts*, B.D.H. Ltd., Poole, England	Turns yellow on exposure to light. Decomp. by visible or u.v. light. Nonenzymic reduction by reducing sugars, ascorbic acid, NH_2OH requires alkaline pH. *Reduced compd.* (formazan): λ_{max} about 490 mμ (varies slightly with solvent). Not oxidized by O_2.

B. SUBSTRATES FOR PEPTIDASES

Natural peptides used as peptidase substrates are included in Table 1, Amino Acids, Amines, Amides, Peptides, and their Derivatives.

Preparation

References quoted usually describe the preparation of the particular substance concerned. Many of these methods could be improved by using modern techniques of peptide synthesis. See, for example, Greenstein & Winitz, *Chemistry of the Amino Acids*, vol. 2, p. 763, Wiley (1961); *Adv. Protein Chem.* **12,** 465 (1957); *Adv. org. Chem.* **3,** 159 (1963); Neurath (ed.), *The Proteins*, 2nd ed., vol. 1, p. 53, Academic Press (1963).

Assay of peptidases

Methods of assay of peptidases, using natural and artificial substrates are described in *Meth. biochem. Anal.* **2,** 215 (1955), **4,** 171 (1957); *Meth. Enzymol.* **2,** 3–114 (1955); Bergmeyer, *Methods of Enzymatic Analysis*, pp. 800–36, Academic Press (1963).

No.	*Name*	*Synonyms*	*Formula*	*M. wt.*	*Physical properties*
1	*N*-Acetyl-L-tyrosine ethyl ester	ATEE	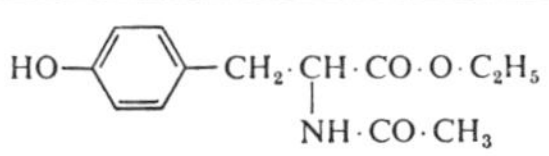	251·3; Hydrate, 269·3	pale cream powder $+1H_2O$; M.p. 87–88; $[\alpha]^{20}_D$ +24 (c = 1 in EtOH)
2	α-*N*-Benzoyl-L-arginin-amide hydrochloride	BAA	$H_2N—C(=NH)—NH·(CH_2)_3·CH(NH·CO·C_6H_5)·CO·NH_2$ ·HCl	313·8; Hydrate, 331·8; Free base, 277·3	cryst. $+1H_2O$; sinters 120–3, loses H_2O 135–40, decomp. > 260; $[\alpha]^{25}_D$ −17·2 (in H_2O)
3	α-*N*-Benzoyl-L-arginine ethyl ester hydrochloride	BAEE	$H_2N·C(=NH)·NH·(CH_2)_3·CH(NH·CO·C_6H_5)·CO·O·C_2H_5$ ·HCl	342·8; Free base, 306·4	hygr. cryst.; M.p. 129·5–131; $[\alpha]^{22}_D$ −17·5 (c = 2 in H_2O)
4	*N*-Benzoyl-L-tyrosine ethyl ester		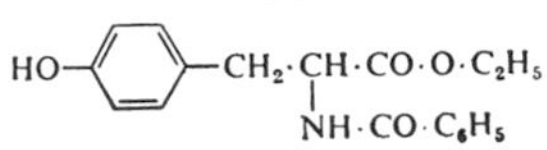	313·4	cryst.; M.p. 122–3; $[\alpha]^{20}_D$ −23·7 (c = 3·7 in EtOH)
5	Carbobenzoxy-L-glutamyl-L-tyrosine	Benzyloxycarbonyl-L-glutamyl-L-tyrosine	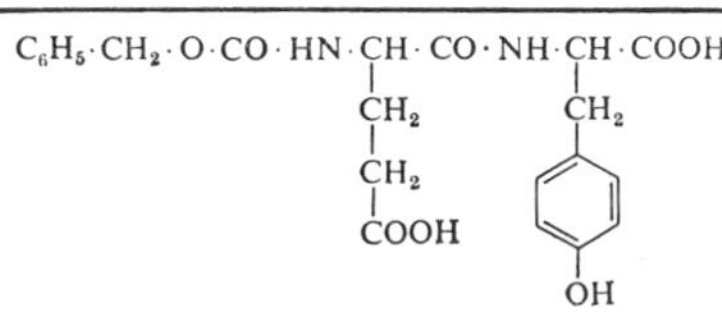	444·4	
6	Carbobenzoxy-glycyl-L-phenylalanine	Benzyloxy-carbonylglycyl-L-phenylalanine	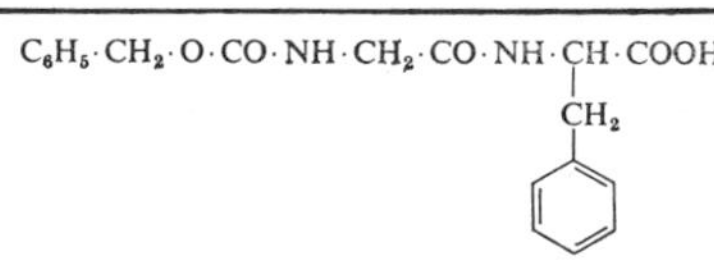	356·4	cryst.; M.p. 127; $[\alpha]^{18}_D$ +41·5 (c = 2 in EtOH)
7	Glycyl-L-phenylalanin-amide acetate		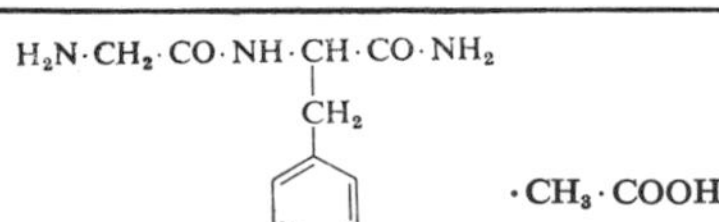	281·3; Free base, 221·3	cryst.; $[\alpha]^{26}_D$ +28·8 (c = 5 in H_2O)

Solubility	Preparation	Use	General remarks
v. sl. s. H_2O; s. hot H_2O	*J.C.S.* **1953**, 1448 *J.B.C.* **203**, 755 (1953) See also *J.B.C.* **98**, 295 (1932)	Substrate for assay of chymotrypsin. Hydrolysis followed by decrease in O.D. at 237 mμ (pH 7), *B.B.A.* **16**, 570 (1955), or by appearance of carboxyl gps., *Meth. biochem. Anal.* **2**, 215 (1955), **4**, 171 (1957)	Supersaturated solns. (0·01M–0·02M), stable for 6–12 hours, prepared by dissolving at 85° and rapid cooling to room temp. (25°). Stronger solns. must be maintained at elevated temp.
s. H_2O	*Biochem. Preps.* **6**, 61 (1958) *J.B.C.* **127**, 643 (1939)	Substrate for assay of trypsin, papain, cathepsin B, ficin, bromelin. Hydrolysis followed by release of carboxyl gps. or of ammonia, *Meth. biochem. Anal.* **2**, 215 (1955); *Biochem. Preps.* **6**, 61 (1958)	Soln. keeps for months at 5° with thymol as preservative.
s. H_2O	*Biochem. Preps.* **6**, 61 (1958) *J.B.C.* **127**, 643 (1939) *J.B.C.* **233**, 1387 (1958)	Substrate for assay of trypsin, papain, ficin. Hydrolysis followed by increase in O.D. at 253 mμ (pH 8), *B.B.A.* **16**, 570 (1955), or by release of carboxyl groups, *Meth. biochem. Anal.* **2**, 215 (1955), **4**, 171 (1957)	Hydrolyses slowly in soln., 4% in 24 hr at 4° and pH 8. Methyl ester, PREP. *J.B.C.* **172**, 221 (1948), v. hygr. wh. glass, store *in vacuo*.
v. sl. s. H_2O; s. aq. MeOH		Substrate for assay of chymotrypsin, completely resistant to trypsin. Hydrolysis followed by increase in O.D. at 256 mμ, *Can. J. Biochem. Physiol.* **37**, 1393 (1959), or by release of carboxyl gps., *Meth. biochem. Anal.* **2**, 215 (1955), **4**, 171 (1957)	
s. hot H_2O	*Z.P.C.* **224**, 17 (1934) *B.J.* **59**, 69 (1955)	Substrate for assay of pepsin and cathepsin A. Hydrolysis followed by release of amino N, *Meth. biochem. Anal.* **2**, 215 (1955)	
s. H_2O, EtOH	*J.C.S.* **1952**, 2069 *J.B.C.* **170**, 221 (1947) *J.B.C.* **134**, 225 (1940)	Substrate for assay of carboxypeptidase A. Hydrolysis followed by release of amino N, *Meth. biochem. Anal.* **2**, 215 (1955	
s. H_2O	*J.B.C.* **204**, 891 (1953) *J.B.C.* **145**, 253 (1942)	Substrate for assay of cathepsin C, also hydrolysed by chymotrypsin. Hydrolysis followed by release of NH_3 or of carboxyl groups, *Meth. biochem. Anal.* **2**, 215 (1955), or by transfer to hydroxylamine, *Meth. Enzymol.* **2**, 64 (1957)	

No.	Name	Synonyms	Formula	M. wt.	Physical properties
8	Glycyl-L-tyrosinamide acetate		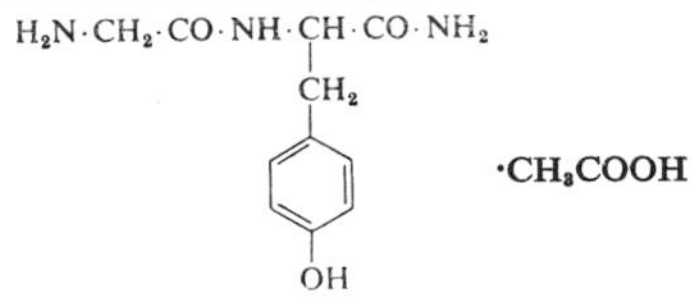	297·3; Free base, 237·3	cryst.; $[\alpha]_D^{22}$ +28·0 (c = 10 in H_2O)
9	Hippuryl-L-arginine	Benzoylglycyl-L-arginine	$C_6H_5\cdot CO\cdot NH\cdot CH_2\cdot CO\cdot NH\cdot CH(COOH)\cdot(CH_2)_3\cdot NH\cdot C(=NH)\cdot NH_2$	335·4	M.p. 182–6; $[\alpha]_D^{20}$ −2·8 (c = 2 in MeOH)
10	Hippuryl-L-phenylalanine	Benzoylglycyl-L-phenylalanine	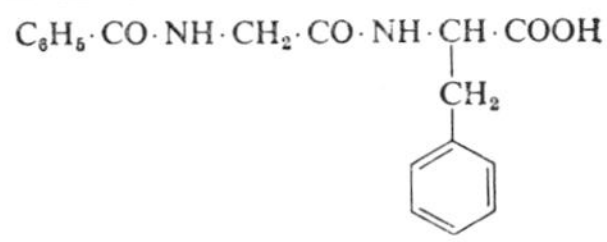	326·4	$[\alpha]_D^{25}$ +39 (c = 5 in 95% EtOH)
11	L-Leucinamide hydrochloride		$(CH_3)_2CH\cdot CH_2\cdot CH(NH_2)\cdot CO\cdot NH_2\cdot HCl$	166·7; Free base, 130·2	long needles from MeOH-eth.; M.p. 244–5 d.; $[\alpha]_D^{25}$ +10·0 (c = 1 in H_2O)
12	α-*N*-Toluene-*p*-sulphonyl-L-arginine methyl ester hydrochloride	*p*-Tosyl-L-arginine methyl ester hydrochloride; TAME	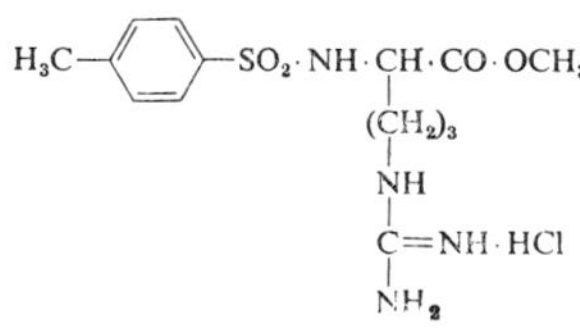	378·9; Free base, 342·4	M.p. 147·5–148; $[\alpha]_D^{18}$ −14·4 (c = 4 in H_2O)
13	L-Tyrosine ethyl ester hydrochloride		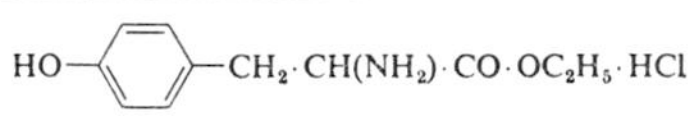	245·7; Free base, 209·2	M.p. 166–8

Solubility	*Preparation*	*Use*	*General remarks*
s. H_2O	*J.B.C.* **204**, 891 (1953) *J.B.C.* **145**, 253 (1942)	Substrate for assay of cathepsin C, also hydrolysed by chymotrypsin. Hydrolysis followed by release of NH_3 or of carboxyl groups, *Meth. biochem. Anal.* **2**, 215 (1955), or by transfer to hydroxylamine, *Meth. Enzymol.* **2**, 64 (1957)	Slow spontaneous hydrolysis occurs at pHs above 7·8, even at 4°. Negligible over 2–3 hour period but significant after a few days storage.
s. H_2O, MeOH	*J.B.C.* **231**, 379 (1958)	Substrate for assay of carboxypeptidase B. Hydrolysis followed by increase in O.D. at 254 mμ, *J.B.C.* **235**, 2272 (1960), or by release of amino N, *Meth. biochem. Anal.* **2**, 215 (1955)	
		Substrate for assay of carboxypeptidase A. Hydrolysis followed by increase in O.D. at 254 mμ, *J.B.C.* **238**, 3884 (1963), or by release of amino N, *Meth. biochem. Anal.* **2**, 215 (1955)	
s. H_2O, MeOH	*Biochem. Preps.* **6**, 35 (1958)	Substrate for assay of leucine aminopeptidase. Hydrolysis followed by release of NH_3 or of carboxyl groups, *Biochem. Preps.* **6**, 35 (1958); *Meth. biochem. Anal.* **2**, 215 (1955)	Soln. keeps several weeks at pH 8·5 and 5° with thymol added as preservative.
s. H_2O	*J.B.C.* **208**, 85 (1954)	Substrate for assay of trypsin, not attacked by chymotrypsin. Also hydrolysed by papain, plasmin, and thrombin. Hydrolysis followed by release of carboxyl groups, *Meth. biochem. Anal.* **2**, 215 (1955), **4**, 171 (1957)	Hydrolyses slowly above pH 9.
v. sl. s. H_2O; s. aq. MeOH	*Biochemistry* **1**, 12 (1962) *B.B.A.* **16**, 570 (1955)	Substrate for assay of trypsin, not hydrolysed by chymotrypsin. Hydrolysis followed by decrease in O.D. at 233·5 mμ (pH 6·5), *B.B.A.* **16**, 570 (1955), or by release of carboxyl groups, *Meth. biochem. Anal.* **2**, 215 (1955), **4**, 171 (1957)	Hydrolyses slowly in soln., 4% in 24 hr at 4° and pH 7. Free ester, prisms, M.p. 108–9, $[\alpha]_D^{20}$ + 20·4 (c = 4·85 in EtOH).

C. SUBSTRATES AND INDUCERS FOR GLYCOSIDASES

Preparation

References quoted generally describe the preparation of the particular compound concerned. In some cases, more recent methods may be more suitable. For discussions of general methods of glycoside synthesis, see *Adv. Carbohyd. Chem.* **12,** 157 (1957); Whistler & Wolfrom (eds.), *Methods in Carbohydrate Chemistry*, vol. 2, pp. 326–89, Academic Press (1963); thioglycosides, see also *Adv. Carbohyd. Chem.* **18,** 123 (1963).

No.	*Name*	*Synonyms*	*Formula*	*M. wt.*	*Physical properties*
1	Ethyl thio-α-D-glucoside	Ethyl 1-thio-α-D-glucopyranoside; Thioethyl-α-D-glucoside; α-TEG	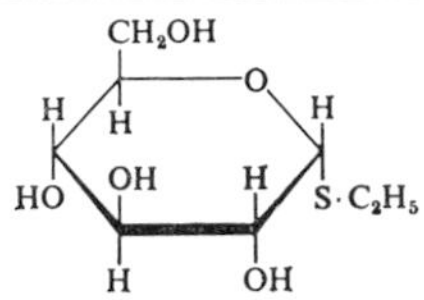	224·3	needles; M.p. 117; $[\alpha]_D^{20}$ +261·5 (c = 2 in H_2O)
2	Ethyl thio-β-D-glucoside	Ethyl 1-thio-β-D-glucopyranoside; Thioethyl-β-D-glucoside; β-TEG	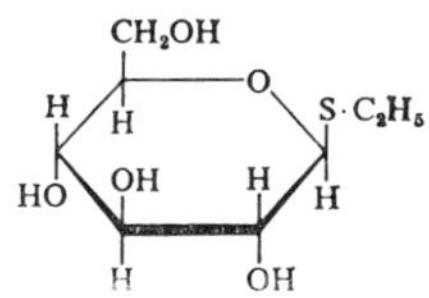	224·3; Hydrate, 242·3	cryst.+1H_2O, M.p. 42–44; Anhyd., M.p. 99·5; $[\alpha]_D$ −55 (c = 4 anhyd. in H_2O)
3	Isopropyl thio-β-D-galactoside	Isopropyl 1-thio-β-D-galactopyranoside; IPTG	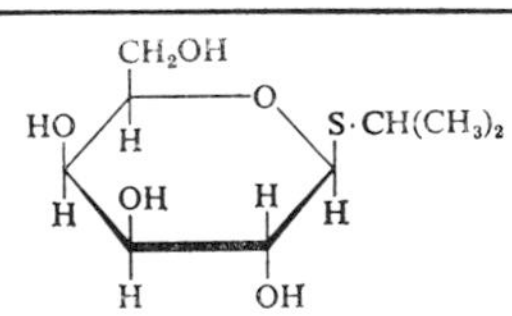	238·3	col. needles; M.p. 109·5–110·5; $[\alpha]_D^{22}$ −31·4 (in H_2O)
4	Methyl thio-β-D-galactoside	Methyl 1-thio-β-D-galactopyranoside; Thiomethyl galactoside; TMG	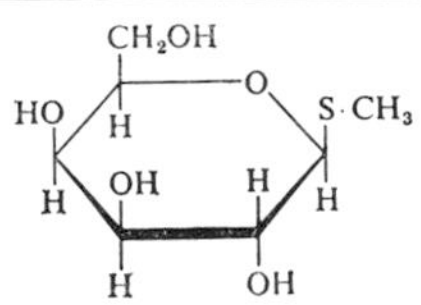	210·3	col. needles; M.p. 174–5; $[\alpha]_D^{20}$ +10·7 (in H_2O)
5	*o*-Nitrophenyl β-D-galactoside	*o*-Nitrophenyl β-D-galactopyranoside; Niphegal; ONPG	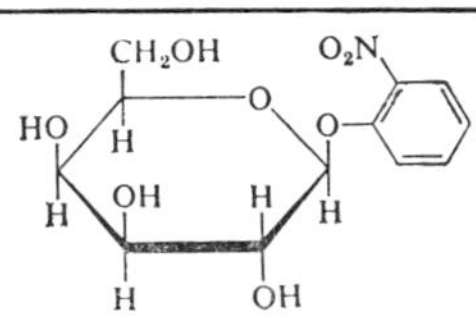	301·3	needles; M.p. 193–4; $[\alpha]_D^{18}$ −52 (c = 1 in H_2O)
6	*o*-Nitrophenyl β-D-glucoside	*o*-Nitrophenyl β-D-glucopyranoside	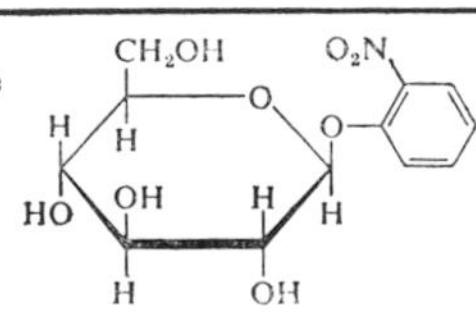	301·3	needles+H_2O from H_2O; Hydrate, M.p. 130–1, Anhyd., M.p. 168–70; $[\alpha]_D^{18\cdot5}$ −140·4 (c = 2·14 anhyd. in H_2O)
7	*p*-Nitrophenyl *N*-acetyl-β-D-glucosaminide	*p*-Nitrophenyl 2-acetamido-2-deoxy-β-D-glucopyranoside	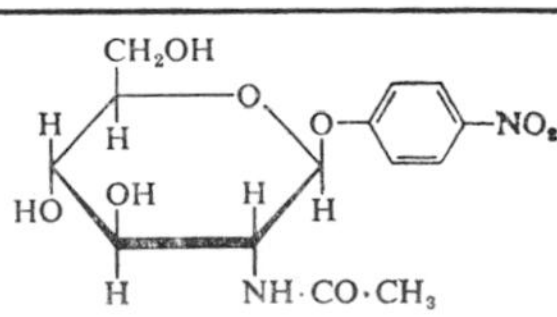	342·3	M.p. 210–12; $[\alpha]_D^{20}$ −15 (c = 0·5 in H_2O)

Solubility	*Preparation*	*Use*	*General remarks*
s. H_2O	*J.A.C.S.* **61**, 1450 (1939) *Adv. Carbohyd. Chem.* **18**, 123 (1963) *Methods in Carbohydrate Chemistry*, eds. Whistler & Wolfrom. vol. 2, pp. 354, 368, Academic Press (1963) *B.B.A.* **82**, 538 (1964)	Inducer of α-glucosidase; *not* hydrolysed by this enzyme	Tetra-acetyl deriv., M.p. 95, $[\alpha]_D^{20}$ +19 (c = 1·6 in $CHCl_3$).
s. H_2O, EtOH; sl. s. acet.; v. sl. s. eth.	*Can. J. Chem.* **29**, 1079 (1951) *Adv. Carbohyd. Chem.* **18**, 123 (1963) PURIF. *J. Bact.* **84**, 24 (1962)	Inducer of β-glucosidase (cellobiase), *not* hydrolysed by this enzyme, *B.B.A.* 36, 47 (1959)	Loses H_2O of cryst. *in vacuo* at 65°. Tetra-acetyl deriv., M.p. 82·5–83, $[\alpha]_D$ −28 (c = 0·9 in $CHCl_3$).
v. s. H_2O, MeOH, EtOH; sl. s. acet., $CHCl_3$; i. eth.	*Adv. Carbohyd. Chem.* **18**, 123 (1963) *Ber.* **89**, 2215 (1956)	Inducer of β-galactosidase and β-galactoside permease; *not* hydrolysed by β-galactosidase, *B.B.A.* **31**, 525 (1959). Substrate for thiogalactoside transacetylase, *J.B.C.* **237**, 253 (1962)	Tetra-acetyl deriv., syrup.
s. H_2O, MeOH; . eth., $CHCl_3$	*Methods in Carbohydrate Chemistry*, eds. Whistler & Wolfrom, vol. 2, p. 368, Academic Press (1963) *Adv. Carbohyd. Chem.* **18**, 123 (1963) *Ber.* **86**, 873 (1953) *Mh. Chem.* **94**, 290 (1963)	Inducer of β-galactosidase and β-galactoside permease; *not* hydrolysed by β-galactosidase, *B.B.A.* **31**, 525 (1959)	Tetra-acetyl deriv., M.p. 110–11, $[\alpha]_D^{17}$ +4 (c = 2 in $CHCl_3$).
. H_2O, MeOH	*Methods in Carbohydrate Chemistry*, eds. Whistler & Wolfrom, vol. 2, p. 335, Academic Press (1963) *J.A.C.S.* **72**, 4325 (1950)	Substrate for the assay of β-galactosidase (lactase). Hydrolysis followed by release of *o*-nitrophenol which is yellow in alkaline soln. (λ_{max} 420 mμ ε 21 300 at pH 10·2), *Adv. Carbohyd. Chem.* **16**, 239 (1961); *Meth. Enzymol.* **1**, 241 (1957)	Tetra-acetyl deriv., M.p. 172–172·5, $[\alpha]_D^{18}$ +70 (c = 1·9 in $CHCl_3$).
. H_2O	*B.J.* **57**, 1 (1954)	Substrate for β-glucosidase, hydrolysed by emulsin enzyme, *B.J.* **57**, 1 (1954), but not by that from *Stachybotrys atra*, *Aust. J. biol. Sci.* **8**, 541 (1955). Hydrolysis followed by release of *o*-nitrophenol which is yellow in alkaline soln. (λ_{max} 420 mμ ε 21 300 at pH 10·2)	Loses H_2O of cryst. *in vacuo* over P_2O_5 at 110°. Tetra-acetyl deriv., M.p. 150–2 $[\alpha]_D^{20}$ +45 (in $CHCl_3$).
·78^{20} H_2O	*Biochem. Preps.* **10**, 118 (1963) *B.J.* **69**, 467 (1958)	Substrate for assay of *N*-acetyl-β-D-glucosaminidase. Hydrolysis followed by release of *p*-nitrophenol which is yellow in alkaline soln. (λ_{max} 400 mμ ε 18 300 at pH 10·2), *B.J.* **78**, 106 (1961)	Sensitive to daylight or u.v. but not tungsten light in strongly alkaline soln. but stable at pH 9·2 or below. λ_{max} 300 mμ ε 10 800 (in 0·1N-NaOH). *p*-Nitrophenyl 2,3,4,6-tetra-acetyl-β-D-glucosaminide, M.p. 240–1, $[\alpha]_D^{20}$ −47 (c = 0·5 in pyr.).

No.	Name	Synonyms	Formula	M. wt.	Physical properties
8	*p*-Nitrophenyl β-D-galactoside	*p*-Nitrophenyl β-D-galactopyranoside	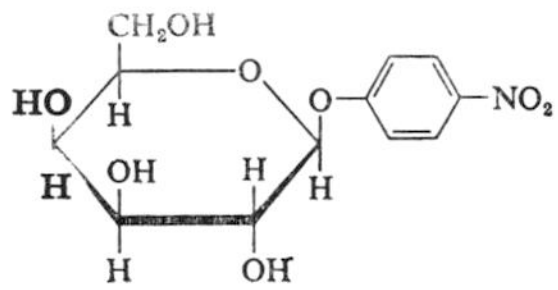	301·3	cryst.; M.p. 181–2; $[\alpha]_D^{21}$ −84 (c = 0·3 in H_2O)
9	*p*-Nitrophenyl α-D-glucoside	*p*-Nitrophenyl α-D-glucopyranoside	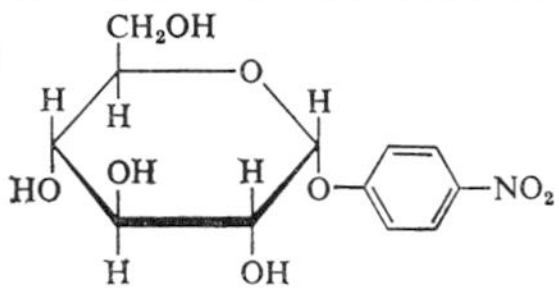	301·3	prisms; M.p. 216–17; $[\alpha]_D^{17}$ +215 (c = 1 in H_2O)
10	*p*-Nitrophenyl β-D-glucoside	*p*-Nitrophenyl β-D-glucopyranoside	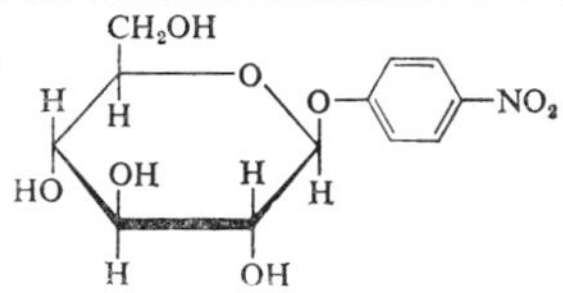	301·3	col. needles from H_2C dry *in vacuo* at 90°; Anhyd., M.p. 164–5; $[\alpha]_D$ −103 (c = 1 anhyd. in H_2O)
11	Phenolphthalein β-D-glucuronide	Phenolphthalein β-D-glucopyranosiduronic acid	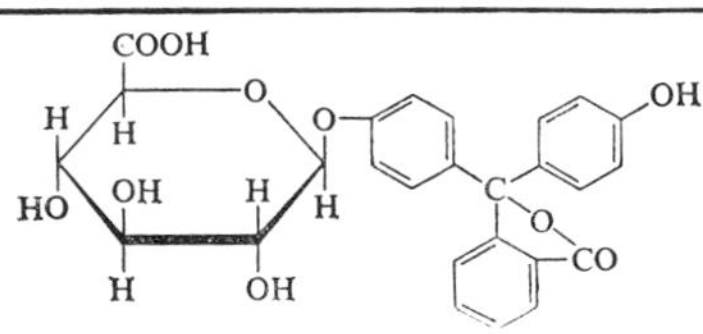	494·5	
12	—, cinchonidine salt		$C_{26}H_{22}O_{10} \cdot C_{19}H_{22}N_2O$	788·9; Methanolate, 820·9	wh. needles + 1MeOH M.p. 210–11
13	Phenyl *N*-acetyl-β-D-glucosaminide	Phenyl 2-acetamido-2-deoxy-β-D-glucopyranoside	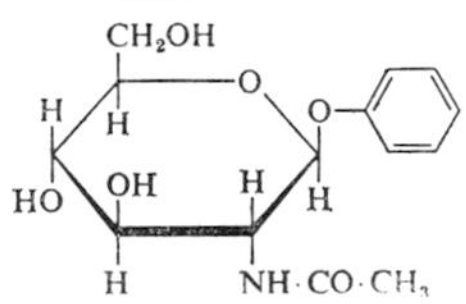	297·3	needles; M.p. 249–5 $[\alpha]_D^{25}$ −10·3 (c = 1·3 H_2O)
14	Phenyl α-D-galactoside	Phenyl α-D-galactopyranoside	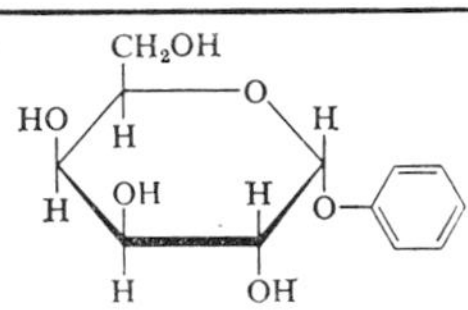	256·3; Hydrate, 274·3	cryst. + $1H_2O$; Anhyd. M.p. 146; $[\alpha]_D$ +217 (H_2O)
15	Phenyl α-D-glucoside	Phenyl α-D-glucopyranoside	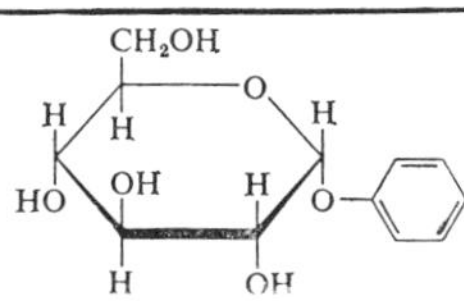	256·3; Hydrate, 274·3	needles + $1H_2O$; Anhyd., M.p. 174–5; $[\alpha]_D^{20}$ +180 (in H_2O)
16	Phenyl β-D-glucoside	Phenyl β-D-glucopyranoside	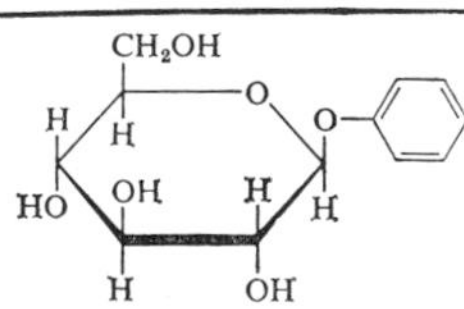	256·3; Hydrate, 292·3	cryst. + $2H_2O$, M.p. 144–5; Anhyd., M.p 175–6; $[\alpha]_D$ −72 (anhyd. in H_2O)
17	Phenyl β-D-glucuronide	Phenyl β-D-glucopyranosiduronic acid	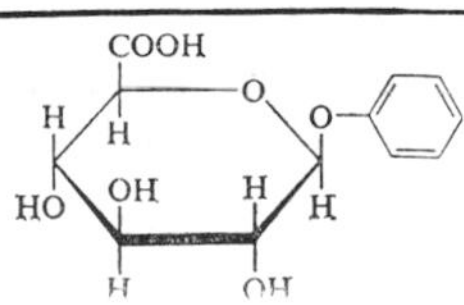	270·2; Dihydrate, 306·3	cryst. + $2H_2O$, M.p. 160–1; Anhyd., M.p 161–2; $[\alpha]_D$ −91 (in H_2O); pK_a 3·42

Solubility	*Preparation*	*Use*	*General remarks*
s. H_2O, MeOH	*B.J.* **83,** 331 (1962)	Substrate for assay of β-galactosidase (lactase). Hydrolysis followed by release of *p*-nitrophenol which is yellow in alkaline soln. (λ_{max} 400 mμ ε 18 300 at pH 10·2), *B.J.* **83,** 331 (1962)	Tetra-acetyl deriv., M.p. 138, $[\alpha]_D^{23}$ −12 (c = 0·5 in $CHCl_3$).
s. H_2O	*J.A.C.S.* **64,** 690 (1942)	Substrate for the assay of α-glucosidases (maltase and isomaltase). Hydrolysis followed by release of *p*-nitrophenol which is yellow in alkaline soln. (λ_{max} 400 mμ ε 18 300 at pH 10·2), *B.B.A.* **30,** 28 (1958)	Tetra-acetyl deriv., M.p. 113, $[\alpha]_D^{20}$ +200 (c = 2 in $CHCl_3$).
s. H_2O	*J.A.C.S.* **64,** 690 (1942) *B.J.* **57,** 1 (1954)	Substrate for assay of β-glucosidase (cellobiase). Hydrolysis followed by release of *p*-nitrophenol which is yellow in alkaline soln. (λ_{max} 400 mμ ε 18 300 at pH 10·2), *B.Z.* **337,** 146 (1963); *J.B.C.* **233,** 1113 (1958)	Tetra-acetyl deriv., M.p. 174–5, $[\alpha]_D^{20}$ −41 (c = 2 in $CHCl_3$).
s. H_2O	*Adv. Carbohyd. Chem.* **14,** 381 (1959) *Meth. Enzymol.* **3,** 55 (1957) *B.B.A.* **97,** 597 (1965) *Meth. biochem. Anal.* **15,** 77 (1967)	Substrate for the assay of β-glucuronidase. Hydrolysis followed by formation of phenolphthalein which is red in alkaline soln., max. colour development at pH 10·3–11·2 (λ_{max} approx. 550 mμ ε 26 600), *Adv. Carbohyd. Chem.* **14,** 381 (1959); *Meth. Enzymol.* **1,** 262 (1957); *Meth. biochem. Anal.* **15,** 77 (1967)	Soln. stable at 0° for months. λ_{max} 420 mμ ε 130 (pH 10).
s. H_2O			
$1{\cdot}6^{20}$ H_2O	*J.B.C.* **191,** 607 (1951) *J.C.S.* **1957,** 4754 *J.C.S.* **1961,** 879	Substrate for the assay of *N*-acetyl-β-D-glucosaminidase. Hydrolysis followed by release of phenol or of *N*-acetylglucosamine, *B.J.* **65,** 464 (1957)	Phenyl 2,3,4,6-tetra-acetyl-β-D-glucosaminide, M.p. 204–5, $[\alpha]_D^{25}$ −21 (c = 2 in $CHCl_3$).
s. H_2O	*Adv. Carbohyd. Chem.* **12,** 157 (1957) *J.C.S.* **1960,** 3421	Substrate for assay of α-galactosidase (melibiase). Hydrolysis followed by release of phenol which causes increase in OD at 285 mμ in alkaline soln., *Adv. Carbohyd. Chem.* **16,** 239 (1961)	Tetra-acetyl deriv., M.p. 131–2, $[\alpha]_D$ +176 (in $CHCl_3$).
s. H_2O	*Adv. Carbohyd. Chem.* **12,** 157 (1957) *J.A.C.S.* **64,** 690 (1942)	Substrate for the assay of α-glucosidases. Hydrolysis followed by release of phenol, *J. Bact.* **73,** 186 (1957)	Tetra-acetyl deriv., M.p. 115, $[\alpha]_D^{20}$ +169 (c = 2 in $CHCl_3$).
s. H_2O	*Adv. Carbohyd. Chem.* **12,** 157 (1957) *B.J.* **57,** 1 (1954)	Substrate for assay of β-glucosidase (cellobiase). Hydrolysis followed by release of phenol, *Aust. J. biol. Sci.* **8,** 541 (1955); *B.Z.* **337,** 146 (1963)	Loses H_2O of cryst. at 130–40° *in vacuo*. Tetra-acetyl deriv., M.p. 125–6, $[\alpha]_D^{20}$ −22·5 (c = 2 in $CHCl_3$).
s. H_2O	*B.J.* **45,** 65 (1949) *B.J.* **68,** 617 (1958) *Adv. Carbohyd. Chem.* **12,** 157 (1957) *J.A.C.S.* **77,** 3310 (1955)	Substrate for assay of β-glucuronidase. Hydrolysis followed by release of phenol, *Adv. Carbohyd. Chem.* **14,** 381 (1959)	Store soln. at 0°.

D. SUBSTRATES FOR PHOSPHATASES

For naturally occurring phosphate esters see Table 3, Phosphate Esters.

No.	*Name*	*Synonyms*	*Formula*	*M. wt.*	*Physical properties*
1	Bis(*p*-nitrophenyl) phosphate, Ca salt		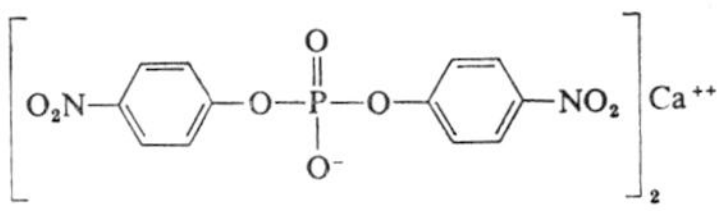	718·4; Na salt, 362·2; Free acid, 340·2	
2	*o*-Carboxyphenyl phosphate	Salicylyl phosphate	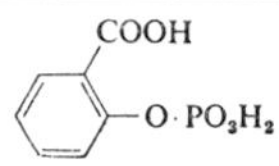	218·1	non-hygr. needles; M.p. 154–5; pK_a 0·95, 3·5, 6·11
3	α-Naphthyl phosphate, acid Na salt		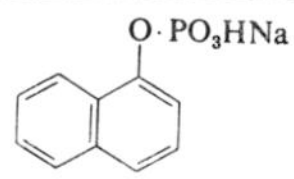	246·1; Free acid, 224·2	wh. cryst.
4	*p*-Nitrophenyl phosphate, Na_2 salt		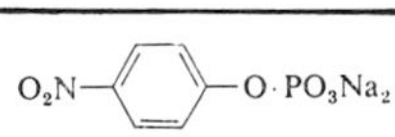	263·1; Free acid, 219·1	light yel. cryst.; hydration variable
5	*p*-Nitrophenyl thymidine 3′-phosphate, NH_4 salt		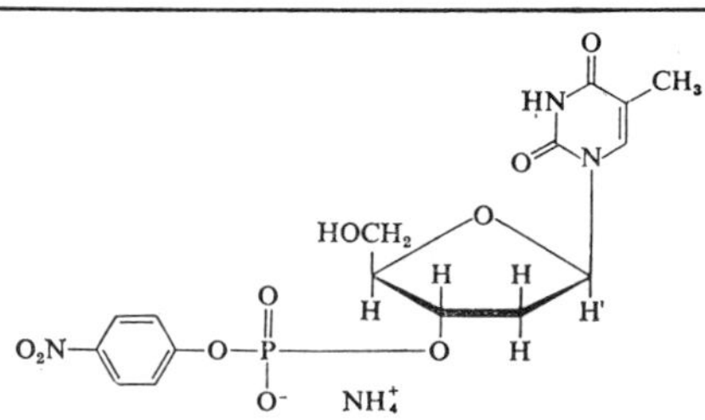	Free acid, 443·3; NH_4 salt, 460·3	anhyd. cryst.
6	*p*-Nitrophenyl thymidine 5′-phosphate Na salt		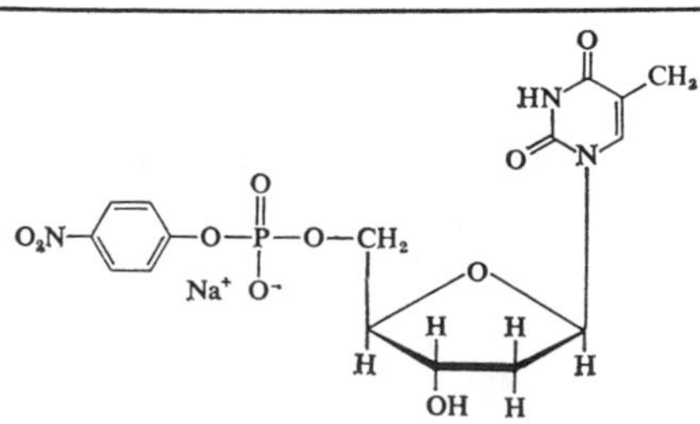	465·3; Hydrate, 519·3; Free acid, 443·3	cryst. + $3H_2O$; loses H_2O at 100° under reduced pressure

Solubility	*Preparation*	*Use*	*General remarks*
s. H_2O	*J. Biochem., Tokyo* **34**, 23 (1941) *B.B.A.* **18**, 370 (1955)	Substrate for phosphodiesterases, *J.B.C.* **198**, 293 (1952). Hydrolysis releases *p*-nitrophenol which is yellow in alkaline soln. (λ_{max} 400 mμ ε 18 300 at pH 9–10). Early methods used 440 mμ, but 400 mμ preferable	Store in cold, dry and dark. Soln. keeps weeks in cold if sl. acid but deteriorates rapidly if alkaline. Virtually no absorbance at 400 mμ in alkali. Na salt, wh. cryst. powder, M.p. 174–6.
v.s. H_2O, EtOH, dioxan; i. pet. eth., toluene	*Arch. B.B.* **51**, 139 (1954) *B.J.* **47**, 93 (1950)—Ba salts	Phosphomonoesterase substrate, *Arch. B.B.* **51**, 139 (1954). Hydrolysis followed by increase in absorbance at 310 mμ due to release of salicylic acid. λ_{max} for salicylic acid is at 295–300 mμ; use of 310 mμ avoids slight absorbance due to the phosphate and to protein. Advantage that salicylic acid absorbs over whole pH range, ϵ_{310} 1900 above pH 5, at lower pH ϵ_{310} rises to 3200 at pH 1	Non-enzymic hydrolysis occurs at max. rate at pH 5·2, slowly at room temp., complete in 1 hr at 80–90°. Stable in soln. above pH 8, almost completely stable below pH 2.
s. H_2O	*J.A.C.S.* **72**, 624 (1950)	Substrate for phosphomonoesterases, especially prostatic enzyme, *Am. J. clin. Path.* **32**, 88 (1959). Hydrolysis releases α-naphthol which is estimated colorimetrically after coupling with a diazonium salt, e.g. tetrazotized *o*-dianisidine, or by fluorimetry, *B.J.* **76**, 32P (1960). Useful for detection of phosphatases on electrophoretograms	Stable in soln. above pH 8, but slow hydrolysis occurs below pH 6. Free acid, wh. cryst., M.p. 155–6, pK_a 0·97, 5·85.
s. H_2O	*J.B.C.* **196**, 175 (1952)	Substrate for phosphomonoesterases, *J.B.C.* **164**, 321 (1946); Bergmeyer, *Methods of Enzymatic Analysis*, p. 783, Academic Press (1963), gives higher rates than glycerol phosphate, phenyl phosphate, or phenolphthalein phosphate. Hydrolysis releases *p*-nitrophenol which is yellow in alkaline soln. (λ_{max} 400 mμ ε 18 300 at pH 9–10). *p*-Nitrophenyl phosphate has slight absorbance at 400 mμ, so 405–20 mμ sometimes used	Store solid in cold and dark. Soln. decomposes slowly; store in cold and dark and renew every few weeks. Completely hydrolysed by N-HCl in 3 hr at 100°. λ_{max} 290 mμ (pH 2·3) 310 mμ (pH 9·2) ε 9500 (all pHs). Free acid, pK_{a_2} 5·70.
s. H_2O	*J.A.C.S.* **81**, 4651 (1959) *Meth. Enzymol.* **6**, 646 (1963)	Substrate for spleen phosphodiesterase and enzymes of similar specificity, *Meth. Enzymol.* **6**, 245 (1963). Not hydrolysed by venom enzyme. Hydrolysis releases *p*-nitrophenol which is yellow in alkaline soln. (λ_{max} 400 mμ ε 18 300 at pH 9–10)	λ_{max} 270·5 mμ ε 15 400.
[s]. H_2O, MeOH; [i]. eth.	*Biochem. Preps.* **8**, 100 (1961)	Substrate for venom phosphodiesterase and enzymes of similar specificity, *Meth. Enzymol.* **6**, 237 (1963). Gives rates many times higher than bis(*p*-nitrophenyl) phosphate. Not hydrolysed by spleen enzyme. Hydrolysis releases *p*-nitrophenol which is yellow in alkaline soln. (λ_{max} 400 mμ ε 18 300 at pH 9–10)	λ_{max} 270 mμ ε 16 250 (pH 2).

No.	Name	Synonyms	Formula	M. wt.	Physical properties
7	Phenolphthalein phosphate, Na_5 salt	Phenolphthalein diphosphate	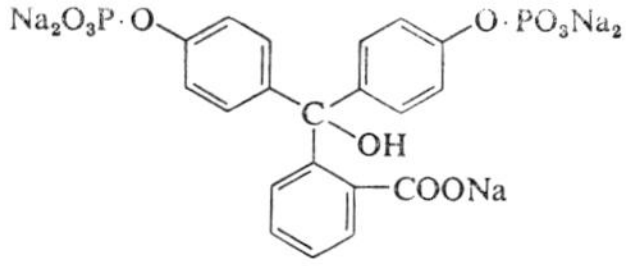	606·2; Free acid, 496·3	amorphous
8	Phenyl phosphate, Na_2 salt		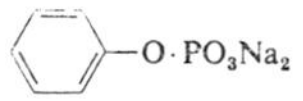	218·1; Free acid, 174·1	wh. cryst.

Solubility	*Preparation*	*Use*	*General remarks*
s. H_2O	*J.B.C.* **159**, 399 (1945) *J.B.C.* **173**, 449 (1949)	Substrate for phosphomonoesterases, *J.B.C.* **159**, 399 (1945); Bergmeyer, *Methods of Enzymatic Analysis*, p. 779, Academic Press (1963). Hydrolysis releases phenolphthalein which is red (λ_{max} approx. 550 mμ) in alkaline soln., max. colour at pH 10·3–11·4	Stable if stored cold, dry and dark. No absorbance at 550 mμ in alkaline soln.
s. H_2O, MeOH; s. eth.	*B.J.* 33, 1182 (1939) *J.A.C.S.* **77**, 3524 (1955) *J.C.S.* **1958**, 1963	Substrate for phosphomonoesterases, *Meth. biochem. Anal.* **4**, 257 (1957); Bergmeyer, *Methods of Enzymatic Analysis*, p. 785, Academic Press (1963). Hydrolysis releases phenol which may be estimated colorimetrically or by increase in absorbance at 287 mμ in alkaline soln., *B.B.A.* **52**, 36 (1961)	Keep cold, dry and dark. Solns. deteriorate slowly; store in cold and prepare fresh every 1–2 weeks. Free acid, M.p. 94, pK_{a2} 5·73.

E. SUBSTRATES FOR SULPHATASES

By A. B. ROY (*Department of Physical Biochemistry, Australian National University, Canberra*)

For sulphate esters of naturally occurring substances see Table 4, Sulphate Esters, and for macromolecular sulphate esters, see Table 19, Macromolecules.

Assay of sulphatases. See *Meth. biochem. Anal.* **4,** 211 (1957).

No.	*Name*	*Synonyms*	*Formula*	*M. wt.*	*Physical properties*
1	*p*-Acetylphenyl sulphate, K salt		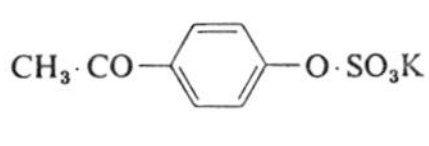	254·3	cryst. needles
2	2-Naphthyl sulphamate, K salt	2-Naphthylamine *N*-sulphate, K salt	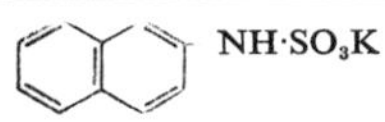	261·3	
3	Nitrocatechol sulphate	2-Hydroxy-5-nitro-phenyl sulphate	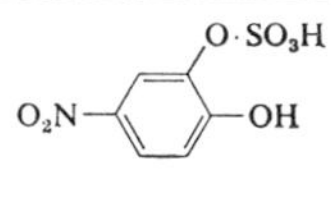	Mono-K salt, 273·3; K_2 salt, 311·4	Mono-K salt, anhyd. leaflets, decomp. 245–80; K_2 salt, needles+$1H_2O$, prisms+$2H_2O$.
4	*p*-Nitrophenyl sulphate, K salt		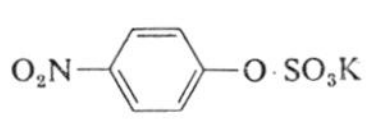	257·3	cryst.
5	Phenyl sulphate K salt		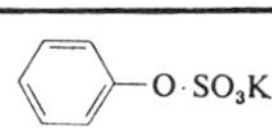	212·3	rh. plates

Solubility	*Preparation*	*Use*	*General remarks*
s. H_2O	*B.J.* 53, 444 (1953)	Substrate for the assay of arylsulphatase, *B.J.* 53, 444, 452 (1953); *Meth. biochem. Anal.* **4**, 211 (1957). Hydrolysis releases *p*-hydroxyacetophenone which has λ_{max} 323 mμ in 0·1N-NaOH and λ_{max} 327·5 mμ ε 21 700 in EtOH–0·5N-NaOH (2:1)	Spectrum, λ_{max} 252·5 mμ ε 11 450, ϵ_{323} 70 in 0·1N-NaOH, $\epsilon_{327\cdot5}$ 75 in EtOH–0·5N-NaOH (2:1).
s. H_2O	*B.J.* 65, 417 (1957)	Substrate for *N*-sulphatase (sulphamatase)	Found in urine after ingestion of 2-naphthylamine. EST. *B.J.* **74**, 49 (1960).
s. H_2O	*B.J.* **68**, 519 (1958) *Meth. biochem. Anal.* **4**, 211 (1957) *J.C.S.* **1951**, 2861	Substrate for assay of arylsulphatase, *Meth. biochem. Anal.* **4**, 211 (1957); *B.J.* 53, 12 (1953). Hydrolysis releases nitrocatechol which has λ_{max} 515 mμ ε 11 200 in alkaline soln. Colour fades rapidly but stabilized by quinol+ Na_2SO_3, *B.J.* 53, 12 (1953)	Store in cold, decomp. slowly at R.T. pK_a (phenol) *ca.* 6·5. K_2 salt has variable H_2O of cryst., anhyd. by drying over P_2O_5 *in vacuo*, and explodes on strong heating. Spectrum, λ_{max} 405–10 mμ ε 18 150 in 0·1N-NaOH.
6^{17} H_2O; v. sl. s. EtOH	*J.C.S.* **1929**, 141 *J.B.C.* 170, 391 (1947) ^{35}S. *B.J.* 74, 154 (1960)	Substrate for the assay of arylsulphatase, *Meth. biochem. Anal.* **4**, 211 (1957). Hydrolysis releases *p*-nitrophenol which has λ_{max} 400 mμ ε 18 300 in alkaline soln.	Solid decomp. on standing to nitrophenol and $KHSO_4$. May decomp. autocatalytically on attempted recrystallization from H_2O unless soln. kept alkaline. Neutral soln. stable; fairly rapid hydrolysis in acid. Decomp. in alkali catalysed by protein, *B.J.* **65**, 668 (1957). Spectrum, λ_{max} 280 mμ ε 17 000 in 0·1N-NaOH.
14^{17} H_2O; $0{\cdot}7^{17}$ EtOH; v.s. hot H_2O, hot EtOH	*J.C.S.* **1926**, 684 *Meth. biochem. Anal.* **4**, 211 (1957)	Substrate for the assay of arylsulphatase, *Meth. biochem. Anal.* **4**, 211 (1957); *Meth. Enzymol.* **2**, 328 (1955). Phenol released on hydrolysis	

F. SUBSTRATES FOR ESTERASES AND LIPASES

Any ester is a potential esterase substrate. Hydrolysis may be followed by measurement of acid released, by titration, e.g. in a pH stat (*Meth. biochem. Anal.* **4**, 171, 1957), or by release of CO_2 from a bicarbonate buffer in a Warburg manometer, or by measurement of unhydrolysed ester by the hydroxamic acid method, *J.B.C.* **180**, 249 (1949).

No.	*Name*	*Synonyms*	*Formula*	*M. wt.*	*Physical properties*
1	Acylsalicylic acids	2-Acyloxybenzoic acids	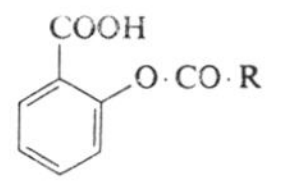	120·1+ M. wt. of *acid* OR 165·1+R; Acetyl, 180·2	Acetyl, needles, M.p. 135; Higher homologues, cryst. solids
2	β-Naphthyl esters	2-Naphthyl esters	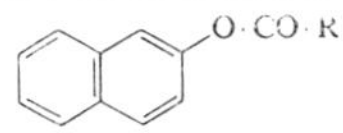	126·2+ M. wt. of *acid* OR 171·2+R; Acetate, 186·2; Laurate, 326·5	wh. solids; Acetate, M.p. 70; Laurate, M.p. 58–60; Stearate, M.p. 73–75
3	*p*-Nitrophenyl esters			121·1+M. wt. of *acid* OR 166·1+R; Acetate, 181·2	Acetate, pyramidal cryst., M.p. 81; Propionate, wh. needles, M.p. 62–63; *n*-Butyrate, liq.
4	Phenyl esters		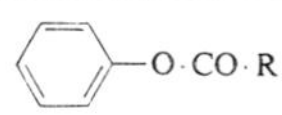	76·1+M. wt. of *acid* OR 121·1+R; Acetate, 136·2	Acetate, liq., d_{15}^{15} 1·081, B.p. 195·7; Propionate, prisms, M.p. 20, B.p. 211; Higher homologues, liq. or low melting cryst. solids
5	Triacetin	Glyceryl triacetate; Acetin	$CH_2·O·CO·CH_3$ | $CH·O·CO·CH_3$ | $CH_2·O·CO·CH_3$	218·2	cryst., M.p. 3·2; col. liq., d_4^{25} 1·156; B.p. 258–60
6	Tributyrin	Glyceryl tributyrate; Butyrin	$CH_2·O·CO·CH_2·CH_2·CH_3$ | $CH·O·CO·CH_2·CH_2·CH_3$ | $CH_2·O·CO·CH_2·CH_2·CH_3$	302·4	col. liq., bitter taste, d^{21} 1·027; B.p. 305–10

Solubility	Preparation	Use	General remarks
sl. s. H_2O, decreasing with increasing chain length of acid; s. alkali; s. organic solvents	*J.B.C.* **199**, 357, 365 (1952)	Substrates for assay of esterases. Hydrolysis releases salicylic acid which has λ_{max} 290–300 mμ, not found in its esters, *J.B.C.* **199**, 357 (1952)	Keep solns. in cold and prepare fresh daily.
sl. s. H_2O, decreasing with increasing chain length of acid; s. EtOH, acet., eth., $CHCl_3$	*J. natn. Cancer Inst.* **9**, 415 (1949) *J.B.C.* **181**, 343 (1949) *Arch. B.B.* **42**, 337 (1953)	β-Naphthyl acetate used as substrate for assay of esterases, *J. clin. Invest.* **29**, 31 (1950); β-naphthyl laurate for assay of lipase, *J.B.C.* **181**, 343 (1949), Bergmeyer, *Methods of Enzymatic Analysis*, p. 776, Academic Press (1963). Hydrolysis releases β-naphthol which may be estimated colorimetrically by coupling with a diazotized amine	Stock solns. in acet. keep at 4° for at least 14 days. Dilute with water or buffer, to form soln. or emulsion depending on chain length of acid, immediately before use.
Acetate, $0{\cdot}06^{25}$ H_2O; $0{\cdot}03^{25}$ 0·025 M-$NaHCO_3$–CO_2 buffer pH 7·5; s. organic solvents	*J.B.C.* **170**, 467 (1947)	Substrates for assay of esterases. Hydrolysis followed by release of acid (see above) or of *p*-nitrophenol which is yellow in alk. soln., λ_{max} 400 mμ ϵ 18 300, *J.B.C.* **170**, 467 (1947). Also hydrolysed, particularly acetate, by chymotrypsin and trypsin, *B.J.* **50**, 672 (1952), **56**, 288 (1954)	Slow spontaneous hydrolysis occurs at neutral pH, for which correction must be made. Store solid in dark. To prepare soln. or emulsion, dissolve in MeOH and dilute with water or buffer.
Acetate, sl. s. H_2O, higher homologues, i. H_2O; s. EtOH, eth., acet., $CHCl_3$		Substrates for assay of esterases. Hydrolysis releases phenol which may be estimated colorimetrically, *B.J.* **57**, 692 (1954)	Commercial samples often contain some free phenol, purification, *B.J.* **57**, 692 (1954).
0·685 H_2O; s. EtOH, eth., benz., $CHCl_3$		Substrate for assay of esterases. Hydrolysis followed by release of acid, see above	
i. H_2O; s. EtOH, eth., acet.	*J.A.C.S.* **47**, 2249 (1925)	Substrate for assay of esterases and lipase, *J. Lab. clin. Med.* **33**, 1047 (1948). Hydrolysis followed by release of acid, see above	

G. THIOL (SULPHYDRYL) COMPOUNDS

These compounds are used primarily to protect enzymes against inactivation, caused by oxidation of —SH groups or by traces of heavy metals. Cysteine, cysteamine and glutathione (see Table 1, Amino Acids, Amines, Amides, Peptides, and their Derivatives) are also frequently used for this purpose.

No.	*Name*	*Synonyms*	*Formula*	*M. wt.*	*Physical properties*
1	2,3-Dimercaptopropan-1-ol	British anti-Lewisite; BAL; Dimercaprol; 1,2-Dithioglycerol	CH_2SH | CHSH | CH_2OH	124·2	viscous col. to yel. liq.; pungent odour; d^{20} 1·2463; B.p. $86–90^{1}$
2	Dithiothreitol	*threo*-2,3-Dihydroxy-1,4-dithiolbutane	CH_2SH | CHOH | CHOH | CH_2SH	154·3	fine needles from eth.; sl. hygr.; M.p. 42–43; E_0' −0·33 v (pH 7)
3	2-Mercaptoethanol	Monothioethylene glycol	$HS\cdot CH_2\cdot CH_2\cdot OH$	78·1	liq.; characteristic odour; B.p. 157d.^{748}, 68^{20}, $53{\cdot}5^{10}$; d^{25} 1·1196
4	Thioglycollic acid	Mercaptoacetic acid	$HS\cdot CH_2\cdot COOH$	92·1	liq.; strong unpleasant odour; d^{20} 1·325; M.p −16·5; B.p. 108^{15}; pK_a 1. 3·68 2. 10·7
5	—, Na salt		$HS\cdot CH_2\cdot COONa$	114·1	hygr. cryst.

Solubility	*Preparation*	*Use*	*General remarks*
6·8[20] H_2O (slow decomp.); s. EtOH, eth., vegetable oils	*J.C.S.* **1947,** 592 *J.C.S.* **1948,** 1393 *J. org. Chem.* **23,** 551 (1958) *C.A.* **58,** 11203*f* (1963)	Protects many enzymes from inactivation (used at about 10^{-3} M), since an excess of dimercaptopropanol maintains protein —SH groups in reduced state and it is a strong chelating agent for heavy metals. Combines with trivalent As compds. Reverses inhibition, esp. of pyruvic and α-ketoglutaric oxidases, by trivalent arsenicals and will cause reversal in many cases of inhibition by heavy metal reagents. Conversely, inactivates many enzymes and other proteins containing disulphide links or heavy metal prosthetic groups, e.g catalase, peroxidase, carbonic anhydrase. Used medicinally, sometimes as less toxic glucoside, as antidote in arsenical and heavy metal poisoning. REVIEW. *Physiol. Rev.* **29,** 168 (1949)	Pure liq. stable if kept O_2-free in sealed containers, oxidizes slowly in air. Aq. soln. oxidizes to disulphide in air, rate negligible at pH 5 but rapid in alkaline soln. ESTIMATION. *B.J.* **41,** 360 (1947); *B.J.* **42,** 52 (1948); *Analyt. Chem.* **27,** 951 (1955); *Meth. biochem. Anal.* **1,** 1 (1954).
s. H_2O, MeOH, EtOH, acet., $CHCl_3$, warm eth.	*J.C.S.* **1949,** 248 *Biochemistry* **3,** 480 (1964)	Protects thiol compds. and —SH groups in proteins against oxidation and reduces disulphides. Low redox potential relative to most thiol compds. ensures that compds. acted upon are completely reduced to —SH form, *Biochemistry* **3,** 480 (1964)	Relatively slowly oxidized by air. Tetra-acetyl deriv., M.p. 73. Cyclic disulphide (*trans*-4,5-dihydroxy-*o*-dithiane), M.p. 132, λ_{max} 283 mμ.
∞ H_2O, EtOH, eth., benz.	*J.C.S.* **1948,** 1892	Protects many enzymes from inactivation (generally used at about 0·01M), since an excess of mercaptoethanol maintains protein —SH groups in reduced state. Also forms mercaptides with heavy metals. In some cases inhibition rather than activation is observed. Used to maintain readily oxidized substances particularly thiols, such as CoASH, and tetrahydrofolic acid in reduced state (concs. 0·01M–1·0M)	Pure liq. decomp. only slowly in air, 8% in 6 months. Aq. solns. readily oxidized in air to disulphide, esp. at alkaline pH. Decomp. by mineral acids esp. HCl.
∞ H_2O, EtOH, eth., $CHCl_3$, benz., most organic solvents		Protects many enzymes against inactivation (usually at 10^{-3} M to 10^{-2} M); an excess of thioglycollate maintains protein —SH groups in reduced state and it forms mercaptides with heavy metals. Frequently used in bacteriological media to maintain reducing conditions	Readily oxidized by air, esp. at alkaline pHs.
v.s. H_2O; sl. s. EtOH			

H. REAGENTS FOR PROTEIN MODIFICATION

End group and sequence analysis of proteins

For details of methods, see:

J. P. Greenstein & M. Winitz, *Chemistry of the Amino Acids*, vol. 2, p. 1512, Wiley (1961).
Meth. biochem. Anal. **2,** 359 (1955).
P. Alexander and R. J. Block (eds.), *A Laboratory Manual of Analytical Methods of Protein Chemistry*, vol. 2, p. 421, Pergamon (1960).
J. Leggett Bailey, *Techniques in Protein Chemistry*, 2nd ed., Elsevier (1967).
H. Neurath (ed.), *The Proteins*, 2nd ed., vol. 1, p. 311, Academic Press (1963).

No.	*Name*	*Synonyms*	*Formula*	*M. wt.*	*Physical properties*
1	Benzyloxycarbonyl chloride	Carbobenzoxy chloride; Carbobenzyloxy chloride; Benzyl chloroformate	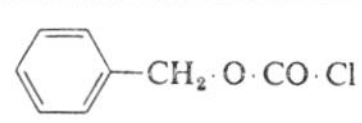	170·6	oily liq., acrid odour; B.p. 103^{20}, 85–87^{7}
2	1-Dimethylamino-naphthalene-5-sulphonyl chloride	Dansyl chloride	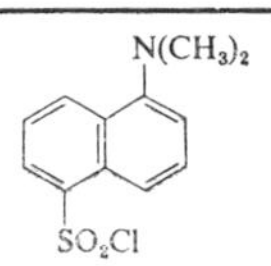	269·8	yel. or orange cryst.; M.p. 74–76
3	Fluorescein isothiocyanate	FITC	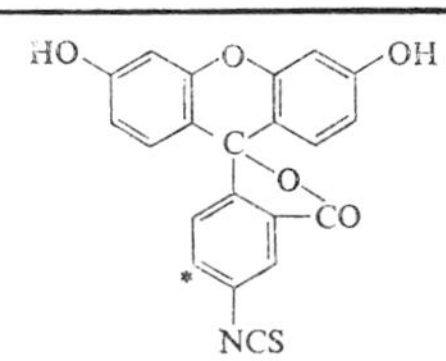	389·4	bright yel. powder
4	1-Fluoro-2,4-dinitro-benzene	2,4-Dinitrofluoro-benzene; DNFB	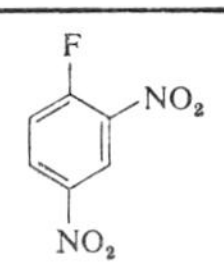	186·1	oily liq. or cryst. from eth. or EtOH; M.p. 26 B.p. 130^{1}
5	*p*-Iodophenyl-sulphonyl chloride	Pipsyl chloride	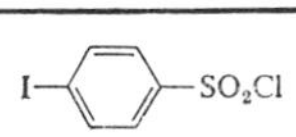	302·5	col. cryst.; M.p. 86; sublimes 150^{8}
6	Lissamine Rhodamine B	RB 200; Sulpho-rhodamine B	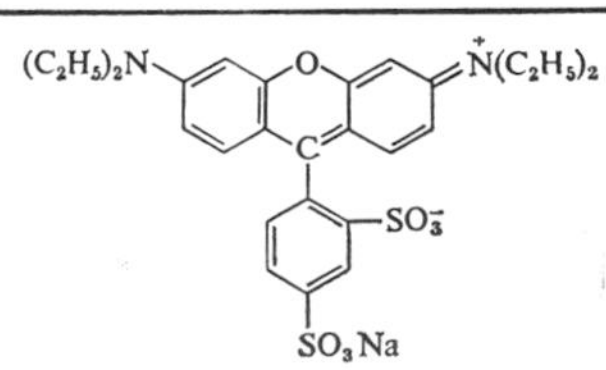	580·7	red powder

Solubility	*Preparation*	*Use*	*General remarks*
Decomp. H_2O, hot EtOH; s. eth.	*Org. Synth.* **Coll. 3**, 167 (1955) *J.C.S.* **1950**, 3213	Reacts with —NH_2 and —SH groups at pH 7–9, 20° forming benzyloxycarbonyl (carbobenzoxy, CBZ) derivs. Benzyloxycarbonyl group removed by reduction. Used in protein modification. Chief use as protecting group in peptide synthesis	Lachrymator. Decomp. to CO_2 and benzyl chloride on heating to 100–50°.
i. H_2O; s. acet., pyr., benz., dioxan	*B.J.* **51**, 155 (1952)	Reacts with —NH_2 groups to attach a fluorescent dimethylaminonaphthalenesulphonyl (DANS) group. Used for molecular weight studies by fluorescence polarization, *Adv. Protein Chem.* **8**, 415 (1953), for fluorescent protein tracing using immunological and other techniques, R. C. Nairn (ed.), *Fluorescent Protein Tracing*, 2nd ed., Livingstone (1964), and for amino end group analysis on an ultramicro scale, *B.J.* **89**, 379, 59P (1963)	Only v. slowly decomp. by H_2O. Solid stable over $CaCl_2$ for months. Frequently used adsorbed on Celite. Absorption max. of conjugates 340 mμ, fluorescence max. of conjugates 525 mμ.
s. H_2O	*Analyt. Biochem.* **7**, 74 (1964)	Used, frequently adsorbed on Celite, to add a fluorescent group to proteins, e.g. for fluorescent antibody tracing, R. C. Nairn (ed.), *Fluorescent Protein Tracing*, 2nd ed., Livingstone (1964); *Nature, Lond.* **193**, 167 (1962)	Decomp. in H_2O, solid stable at least a year in stoppered container at R.T. Two isomers known; that shown is probably fluorescein isothiocyanate II. The other isomer (FITC I) has isothiocyanate group in position marked with asterisk, *J. org. Chem.* **26**, 1292 (1961). Absorption max. of conjugates 495 mμ, fluorescence max. of conjugates *ca.* 520 mμ.
s. benz., eth., organic solvents; i. H_2O	*Biochem. Preps.* **3**, 120 (1953) *B.J.* **41**, 558 (1947) *J.C.S.* **1954**, 3091	Combines with —NH_2, —SH, phenolic —OH and imidazole >NH groups under mildly alkaline conditions forming dinitrophenyl (DNP) derivs. Used in identification of amino terminal amino acids of peptides and proteins, see *B.J.* **39**, 507 (1945); *B.J.* **53**, 353 (1953); *Meth. Enzymol.* **4**, 221 (1957); and general references above	Vesicant, avoid skin contact. Tends to darken on standing especially in light. DNP derivs. of amino acids decomp. in light.
s. organic solvents	*Meth. Enzymol.* **4**, 238 (1957) *J.A.C.S.* **71**, 249 (1949)	Reacts with —NH_2 and phenolic —OH groups in proteins to form stable *p*-iodophenylsulphonyl (pipsyl) derivs. Use in sequence determinations, *Meth. Enzymol.* **4**, 238 (1957)	Radioactive substance, especially ^{131}I, tends to become coloured over long periods, but is satisfactory for use. Non-radioactive material is stable.
s. H_2O; sl. s. EtOH	Acid chloride, *J. gen. Chem. U.S.S.R.* **32**, 1476 (1962)	Used as acid chloride, frequently adsorbed on Celite, to add a fluorescent group to proteins, e.g. for fluorescent antibody tracing, R. C. Nairn (ed.), *Fluorescent Protein Tracing*, 2nd ed., Livingstone (1964); *Nature, Lond.* **193**, 167 (1962)	Absorption max. of conjugates 575 mμ, fluorescence max. of conjugates 595 mμ. Acid chloride is slowly decomp. by H_2O.

No.	*Name*	*Synonyms*	*Formula*	*M. wt.*	*Physical properties*
7	Phenyl isothiocyanate		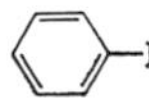—NCS	135·2	col. liq., d_4^{25} 1·1288; M.p. −21; B.p. 218, 95^{12}

Solubility	*Preparation*	*Use*	*General remarks*
i. H_2O; s. EtOH, eth.	*Org. Synth.* Coll. **1**, 447 (1941)	Combines with $—NH_2$ groups to form phenylthiocarbamyl derivs. These may be removed from a peptide forming the phenylthiohydantoin (PTH) derived from the amino-terminal amino acid (Edman degradation). Use in peptide sequence studies, see *Meth. biochem. Anal.* **2**, 359 (1955); *A. Rev. Biochem.* 33, 597 (1964); *Biochemistry* **2**, 992 (1963); *J.B.C.* **237**, 2547 (1962); and general references above	

19. Macromolecules

With contributions by R. W. BAILEY (*Plant Chemistry Laboratory, Department of Scientific and Industrial Research, Palmerston North, New Zealand*); P. COHN (*Chester Beatty Research Institute, Chalfont St. Giles*); *and* F. S. WUSTENNAN (*Department of Biochemistry, University College, Cardiff*)

No.	*Name*	*Structure*	*Approx. M. wt.*	*Physical form*
1	Albumin (egg); ovalbumin	A cryst. protein obtained from egg white	45 000–46 000	needles or elongated prisms, often forming rosettes
2	Amylopectin	Branched polymer of amylose chains joined through α 1 → 6 links	200 000–400 000	amorph. (X-ray)
3	Amylose	Linear chains of glucose units joined through α 1 → 4 (maltose) links	50 000–150 000	cryst. (X-ray)
4	Avidin	A basic protein prepared from egg white. Probably contains a carbohydrate moiety	66 000–70 000	isoelectric point 10·5
5	Casein (caseinogen in Great Britain)	A phosphoprotein consisting of a mixture of α, β, and γ forms	Unfractionated casein, 75 000–100 000	wh. amorph. powder
6	Cellulose (and DEAE, CM, and phosphorylated derivatives)	Linear chains of glucose units joined through β 1 → 4 (cellobiose) links DEAE– [cellulose]—O—C_2H_4—$N(C_2H_5)_2$ CM– [cellulose]—O—CH_2—COOH Phosphorylated [cellulose]—O—PO_3H_2	600 000 'native'	wh. powder cryst. (X-ray)
7	Chitin	Linear chains of β 1 → 4 linked *N*-acetylglucosamine units		cryst. (X-ray)
8	Chondroitin	Linear heteropolysaccharide with repeating 3-*O*-(β-D-glucuronido)-*N*-acetyl-D-galactosamine units linked by β (1 → 4) hexosaminidic bonds	25 000–30 000	Na salt; wh. amorph. powder
9	Chondroitin 4-sulphate and chondroitin 6-sulphate (chondroitin sulphates A and C)	Linear heteropolysaccharides with repeating 3-*O*-(β-D-glucuronido)-*N*-acetyl-D-galactosamine 4-sulphate or 3-*O*-(β-D-glucuronido)-*N*-acetyl-D-galactosamine 6-sulphate units linked by β (1 → 4) hexosaminidic bonds	30 000–50 000	Na salt; wh. amorph. powder

$[\alpha]^t_D$	*Solubility*	*References*	*General remarks*
	s. H_2O	*B.J.* **30**, 227 (1936) *The Proteins*, eds. Neurath and Bailey, vol. 2A, p. 443, Academic Press, New York (1954)	Isoelectric point, pH 4·58. As normally prepared is electrophoretically heterogeneous. Contains about 0·12% P.
$+201^{20}$ (in aq. NaCl) −61 (tricarbanilate)	s. H_2O, formamide	REVIEW. *Handb. PflPhysiol.* **6**, 154 (1958) PREP. *Modern Methods of Plant Analysis*, vol. 2, p. 166, Springer, Berlin (1955).	Stains red with I_2. Minor component of plant starch.
$+201^{20}$ (in aq. NaCl) −82·5 (tricarbanilate)	s. dil. alk., formamide	REVIEW. *Handb. PflPhysiol.* **6**, 154 (1958) PREP. *Modern Methods of Plant Analysis*, vol. 2, p. 166, Springer, Berlin (1955)	Stains intense blue with I_2. Major component of plant starch.
	s. H_2O	*Arch. B.B.* **39**, 80 (1952) *B.J.* **89**, 591 (1963) *B.J.* **92**, 16c (1964)	Unstable to heat. Forms stable complex with biotin and consequently inhibits biotin-dependent enzymes. One mole avidin binds 4 of biotin.
	sp. s. H_2O; s. dil. alk. and mineral acids; i. EtOH, eth. α-Casein is less soluble in 50% aq. EtOH than β	Unfractionated, *Org. Synth.* **Coll. 2**, 120 (1943) *J.A.C.S.* **66**, 1725 (1944) *The Proteins*, eds. Neurath and Bailey, vol. 2A, p. 397, Academic Press, New York (1954) *Analyt. Biochem.* **9**, 423 (1964) *J.A.C.S.* **84**, 4929 (1962)	Isoelectric points: α, 4·0–4·1; β, 4·5; γ, 5·8–6·0. Ca caseinate is water insoluble. α-Casein contains about 1% P and is attacked by prostatic phosphatase while β contains 0·6% P and is not attacked.
	i. H_2O, EtOH, eth., $CHCl_3$; 's' in conc. H_2SO_4, on adding H_2O gives ppt. hydrocellulose s. (1) Cu hydroxide dissolved in NH_4OH (2) $ZnCl_2$ in HCl (3) diethyldibenzylammonium hydroxide	REVIEW. *Methods in Carbohydrate Chemistry*, vol. 3 (1963) PREP. *Modern Methods of Plant Analysis*, vol. 2, p. 197, Springer, Berlin (1955) DEAE, CM, phosphorylated: *Biochem. Preps.* **8**, 39, 45, 47 (1961)	p*K'* DEAE, 9·5; CM, 3·5; P-cellulose < 2, 6·7.
+14 to $+56^{20}$ (in conc. HCl)	s. conc. acids; i. H_2O	REVIEW. *Adv. Carbohyd. Chem.* **15**, 371 (1960)	
approx. −20 (−24·7 and −29·6) (c = 2·5 g Ca salt in H_2O)	s. H_2O	PREP. *J.B.C.* **211**, 605 (1954) EST. *See* hyaluronic acid	
4-sulphate, −28 to −32 6-sulphate, −16 to −22	s. H_2O	PREP. These two polymers are usually isolated together with other acidic polysaccharides from connective tissue and then separated by chromatography or by fractional precipitation of calcium salts from ethanol-water mixtures *B.B.A.* **21**, 506 (1956) 4-sulphate, *Meth. Enzymol.* **3**, 20 (1957) 6-sulphate, *J.B.C.* **215**, 685 (1955) EST. *See* hyaluronic acid	The two chondroitin sulphates are also distinguished by their infrared spectra in the region 1000–700 cm^{-1}. Chondroitin 6-sulphate can be estimated in the presence of the 4-sulphate by a colorimetric procedure (*B.B.A.* **53**, 509 (1961)). Sulphated chondroitin 6-sulphate is found in the connective tissue of cartilaginous fish, *B.B.A.* **58**, 92 (1962).

No.	Name	Structure	Approx. M. wt.	Physical form
10	Deoxyribonucleic acid (DNA; thymonucleic acid; chromonucleic acid)	A usually twin-stranded polynucleotide containing D-2-deoxyribose and adenine, guanine, cytosine, and thymine. 5-Hydroxymethylcytosine, usually glucosylated, present in T_2 bacteriophage; small amounts of 5-methylcytosine in DNA of some species. Usually found combined with protein (e.g. histone) in animal tissues	6–120 million according to source and method of preparation	Na salt; wh. fibrous solid, v. hygr.
11	Dermatan sulphate (β-heparin, chondroitin sulphate B, dermatoidin sulphate)	Linear heteropolysaccharide with repeating 3-*O*-(α-L-iduronido)-*N*-acetyl-D-galactosamine 4-sulphate units linked by β (1 → 4) hexosaminidic bonds	20 000–30 000	Na salt; wh. amorph. powder
12	Dextran	Linear chains of α 1 → 6 (isomaltose) linked glucose. Often α 1 → 3 or α 1 → 2 branches	v. high	amorph.
13	Glycogen (animal starch)	Branched polymer of amylose chains joined through α 1 → 6 links. Yields D-glucose on acid hydrolysis	1–10 million	wh. amorph. powder
14	Gum arabic (acacia)	Ca-Mg salt of complex polymer of L-arabinose, L-rhamnose, galactose, and glucuronic acid	250 000–300 000	amorph.
15	Haemoglobin (Hb; reduced haemoglobin; deoxygenated haemoglobin; ferrohaemoglobin)	A conjugated Fe-containing blood protein in which a water molecule and globin are attached to the Fe of protohaem. See *Comp. Biochem. Physiol.* **4**, 429 (1962)	67 000	purple cryst., flat plates, prisms, monoclin.
16	Heparan sulphate (heparitin sulphate, heparin monosulphate)	Heteropolysaccharide with alternating D-glucosamine (some *N*-acetyl, some *N*-sulphate) and D-glucuronic acid residues. *O*-sulphate groups also present. Detailed structure not yet established	Lower than that of heparin (17 000–20 000)	Na salt; wh. amorph. powder
17	Histones	A series of basic proteins prepared from the nucleoproteins of animal tissues (e.g. thymus, liver, erythrocytes). Tryptophan is absent	8400–57 000	wh. powder

$[\alpha]_D^t$	Solubility	References	General remarks
	sl. s. H_2O s. 1–3M salt, forms viscous solution; s. alkalis; i. org. solvents	PREP. *J. molec. Biol.* **3**, 208 (1961) *Nature, Lond.* **191**, 1375 (1961) *Prog. nucl. Acid Res.* **3**, 1 (1964) EST. *The Nucleic Acids*, vol. 2, p. 2, Academic Press, New York (1955) *B.J.* **62**, 315 (1956) *J.B.C.* **213**, 107 (1955) *Meth. biochem. Anal.* **1**, 287 (1954); **6**, 1 (1958); **14**, 113 (1966)	Much more stable in alkaline soln. than ribonucleic acid. With acids (2% HCl, 10 min., 100°) purine bases quantitatively removed forming apurinic acid.
approx. −50 to −80	s. H_2O	PREP. *J.B.C.* **233**, 541 (1958) or from similar sources as the chondroitin sulphates: *B.B.A.* **21**, 506 (1956) EST. *See* hyaluronic acid	
+200 to +220[25] (in formamide)	s. H_2O, formamide	REVIEW. *Adv. Carbohyd. Chem.* **15**, 341 (1960)	'Clinical' dextrans are acid-degraded dextrans.
+191 to +199[20] (in H_2O)	v.s. H_2O, giving opalescent soln.; s. hot EtOH; i. cold EtOH	REVIEW. *Adv. Carbohyd. Chem.* **12**, 262 (1957) PREP. *J.A.C.S.* **64**, 2349 (1942) *J.B.C.* **199**, 97 (1952) *Makromol. Chem.* **12**, 79 (1954) EST. *Aust. J. biol. Sci.* **9**, 139 (1956) *J.B.C.* **220**, 583 (1956)	Weakly reducing towards alkaline Cu soln. Very stable to hot alkali. Reddish-brown colour with I_2 soln.
−28 to −30 (free acid in H_2O)	s. dil. acid, hot H_2O	REVIEW. F. Smith & R. Montgomery, *Chemistry of Plant Gums and Mucilages*, Reinhold, New York (1959)	
	s. H_2O. See *Haemoglobin*, p. 269, Butterworth, London (1949)	PREP. *J.B.C.* **127**, 123 (1939) *Arch. B.* **21**, 224 (1949) *J.B.C.* **185**, 231 (1950) *J. Lab. clin. Med.* **46**, 255 (1955) EST. Lemberg & Legge, *Hematin Compounds and Bile Pigments*, p. 295, Interscience, New York (1949) *Lancet* **2**, 971 (1948) *Nature, Lond.* **175**, 903 (1955)	Must be stored in an inert atmosphere as readily converted to oxyhaemoglobin by O_2 and carboxyhaemoglobin with CO. λ_{max} 275 430 555 760 900 ϵ 31 135 13·5 0·4 0·2 Isoelectric point, 6·8.
pprox. +40 to -80	s. H_2O	PREP. *J.B.C.* **235**, 3283 (1960) *B.B.A.* **29**, 443 (1958) EST. *See* hyaluronic acid	Heparan sulphate is the name for a family of related polysaccharides related to heparin but containing some *N*-acetyl groups.
	s. H_2O, dil. acids; i. NH_4OH	REVIEW. Phillips, *Prog. Biophys. biophys. Chem.* **12**, 211 (1961)	Heat coagulated protein soluble in dil. acid. Isoelectric point pH 10–11.

No.	Name	Structure	Approx. M. wt.	Physical form
18	Hyaluronic acid	Linear heteropolysaccharide with repeating 3-*O*-(β-D-glucuronido)-*N*-acetyl-D-glucosamine units linked by β (1 → 4) hexosaminidic bonds	0·1–10 million	Na salt; wh. fibrous solid hygr.
19	Inulin	A polysaccharide consisting of chains of about 30 fructofuranose units. On hydrolysis yields D-fructose	3000–5000	col. hygr. cryst.
20	Keratan sulphate (keratosulphate)	Linear heteropolysaccharide with repeating 4-*O*-(β-D-galactosido)-*N*-acetyl-D-glucosamine 6-sulphate units linked by β (1 → 3) hexosaminidic bonds	10 000–20 000	Na salt; wh. amorph. powder
21	β-Lactoglobulin	A cryst. protein obtained from milk	35 000–42 000	cubic cryst.
22	Laminarin	Linear chains of β 1 → 3 (laminaribiose) linked glucose units		amorph.
23	Levan (bacterial)	Chains of β 2 → 6 linked fructofuranose units branched through β 2 → 1 links	high	amorph.
24	Myoglobin (horse muscle)	A globin containing about 0·3% Fe. See *Angew. Chem.* **75**, 595 (1963); *Comp. Biochem. Physiol.* **4**, 429 (1962)	18 500–18 800 (horse muscle)	
25	Pectic acid	Linear chains of α 1 → 4 linked galacturonic acid units	60 000–80 000	
26	Protamines salmine—salmon clupein—herring	A series of simple basic proteins prepared from the nucleoproteins of fish spermatozoa. They give predominantly basic amino acids (arginine) on acid hydrolysis and no tryptophan or S-amino acids. Salmine—90% protein N is arginine	Salmine, 8000	wh. powder

$[\alpha]^t_D$	*Solubility*	*References*	*General remarks*
approx. −70 to −80	s. H_2O	PREP. *B.B.A.* 69, 574 (1963)—Bovine synovial fluid *J.B.C.* 239, 726 (1964)—Streptococci broth cultures *B.J.* 92, 34P (1964)—Human umbilical cord EST. This normally requires preliminary separation of the desired fraction from a complex mixture of similar polysaccharides (*Meth. biochem. Anal.* 8, 145 (1960); *Biochem. Soc. Symp.* 20, 39 (1961)) followed by colorimetric analysis of the component monosaccharide units (*Meth. biochem. Anal.* 2, 313 (1955); *Meth. Enzymol.* 3, 73 (1957))	
$-40{\cdot}2^{15}$ (in H_2O); acetate, −34 (in $CHCl_3$)	sp. s. H_2O, EtOH	PREP. *Modern Methods of Plant Analysis*, vol. 2, p. 189, Springer Berlin (1955) *J.B.C.* 51, 275 (1922) EST. *P.S.E.B.M.* 74, 117 (1950) *Clinica chim. Acta* 1, 470 (1956) *Klin. Wschr.* 41, 615 (1963)	M.p. 178 d. Enzymically hydrolysed by *Aspergillus niger* emulsin and by yeast invertase.
approx. +5	s. H_2O	PREP. *J.B.C.* 205, 611 (1953)—Bovine cornea *Acta chem. scand.* 11, 668 (1957)—Nucleus pulposus EST. *See* hyaluronic acid and general remarks	Keratan sulphate can be estimated in the presence of other acidic aminopolysaccharides by a colorimetric procedure (*Analyt. Biochem.* 4, 10, 1962). Sulphated keratan sulphate is found in the connective tissues of cartilaginous fish.
$-30{\cdot}4^{25}$ (in acetate buffer pH 4·8, $\mu = 0{\cdot}1$)	s. H_2O	PREP. *B.J.* 58, 332 (1954) *Biochem. Preps.* 4, 23 (1955) EST. *Acta chem. scand.* 16, 2067 (1962)	Bovine: isoelectric point, pH 5·1–5·2.
$-12{\cdot}8^{15}$ (c = 3·5 in H_2O)	s. H_2O	PREP. *Modern Methods of Plant Analysis*, vol. 2, p. 178, Springer, Berlin (1955)	
−45 (Strep. levan in H_2O)	s. H_2O	PREP. *J.B.C.* 140, 105 (1941)	
	s. H_2O	PREP. *Arch. B.B.* 91, 319 (1960) *J.B.C.* 236, 2238 (1961) EST. *Arch. B.B.* 91, 310 (1960) *Nature, Lond.* 198, 1201 (1963) REVIEW. *Mendel Bull.* 1963, 62	Three forms of myoglobin can be separated by electrophoresis.
$+250$ to $+280^{20}$	s. dil. acids	REVIEW. Z. I. Kertesz, *The Pectic Substances*, Interscience (1951) *B.J.* 47, 437 (1950)	Plant pectins are metal salts of partial Me esters of pectic acid.
	s. H_2O, dil. acids, NH_4OH	PREP. *J. gen. Physiol.* 30, 101 (1946) PURIFICATION. *B.B.A.* 91, 416 (1964) REVIEW. *The Proteins*, eds. H. Neurath and K. Bailey, vol. 2, p. 39, Academic Press (1954) *Adv. Protein Chem.* 15, 1 (1960)	Not coagulated by heat. Slowly dialyses. Non-antigenic.

No.	Name	Structure	Approx. M. wt.	Physical form
27	Ribonucleic acid (RNA; PNA; pentose nucleic acid; yeast nucleic acid)	A polynucleotide containing D(−)-ribose and adenine, guanine, cytosine, and uracil; pseudouridine and alkyl-substituted adenine and guanine present in small amounts particularly in transfer-RNA (s-RNA); found combined with protein in nucleus and cytoplasm (ribosomes and cell sap)	10 000–2 million	wh. powder
28	Tobacco mosaic virus		40×10^6	minute rods 18×300 mμ
29	Xylan	Linear chains of β 1 → 4 linked xylose units	10 000–20 000	amorph.

$[\alpha]_D^t$	*Solubility*	*References*	*General remarks*
	sl. s. H_2O, solns. of salts of alk. metals; i. org. solvents (amine salts s. in org. solvents). Transfer RNA s. 1–3M-NaCl	PREP. *B.J.* **96**, 266 (1965) *B.J.* **93**, 5C (1964) *B.B.R.C.* **13**, 61 (1963) *Progr. nucl. Acid Res.* **3**, 1 (1964) EST. *J.B.C.* **198**, 297 (1952); **221**, 635 (1956) *The Nucleic Acids*, vol. 2, p. 2, Academic Press, New York (1955) *Meth. biochem. Anal.* **1**, 287 (1954); **6**, 1 (1958); **14**, 113 (1966)	Readily hydrolysed by alkalis (e.g. N-KOH, 18 hr, 37°) to oligo- and mononucleotides; dil. acid (e.g. N-HCl at 100°) releases purine bases and pyrimidine nucleotides.
	s. H_2O, saline	PREP. *Biochem. Preps.* **9**, 132 (1962)	Sedimentation coefficient 194 S (∞ dilution). Isoelectric point pH 3·5.
-78 to -109^{20} (in 2–4% alk.)	s. dil. alk.; i. H_2O	REVIEW. *Modern Methods of Plant Analysis*, vol. 2, p. 221, Springer, Berlin (1955) *Handb. PflPhysiol.* **6**, 254 (1958)	Part of plant hemicellulose fraction.

20. pH and Buffers

Revised by H. A. McKENZIE (*Department of Physical Biochemistry, Australian National University, Canberra*)

Physiological Media

Revised by R. M. C. DAWSON

THE STANDARDIZATION AND MEASUREMENT OF pH

GENERAL REFERENCES

R. G. Bates, *Determination of* pH: *Theory and Practice*, 2nd ed., Wiley, New York (1964); R. G. Bates and E. A. Guggenheim, *Pure Appl. Chem.* **1**, 163 (1960).
V. Gold, pH *Measurements—Their Theory and Practice*, Methuen, London (1956).
G. Mattock, pH *Measurement and Titration*, Heywood, London (1961).
British Standard 1647: 1950 'pH Scale'. British Standards Institution, 24 Victoria St., London, S.W. 1.
Japanese Industrial Standard Z 8802–1958

NOTES ON pH MEASUREMENT

These notes apply to pH determination using the usual commercial pH assemblies with glass electrodes. For more specialized work the general references at the beginning of this section should be consulted.

Calibration. At least two standard buffer solutions (p. 479) *should be used to calibrate the* pH *assembly.*

Temperature. The standard solutions used to calibrate the pH assembly and the unknowns must all be at the same temperature. This requirement is not dispensed with by use of the 'temperature' compensator control on the pH meter which usually only compensates for the 'slope factor' (pH–e.m.f. relationship) and sometimes also for the zero shift.

NOTES ON THE PROPERTIES OF BUFFER SOLUTIONS

Buffer capacity (*buffer value*). In the tables of buffers the van Slyke buffer value, $\beta = db/d\text{pH}$, is given where possible; db is an increment of a strong base, in equivalents, added to 1 litre of buffer solution. An increment of strong acid, equivalent in effect to a negative increment, $-db$, of strong base produces a decrease in pH. Therefore $db/d\text{pH}$ is always positive.

Where the buffer value is not available in the tables it can be determined experimentally but can also be calculated from theoretical considerations. For a weak acid system,

$$\beta = \frac{db}{d\text{pH}} \approx 2{\cdot}303\left(\frac{cKc_\text{H}}{(K+c_\text{H})^2}+c_\text{H}+c_\text{OH}\right),$$

where c is the *total* molar concentration of weak acid HA and its salt MA; K is the dissociation constant of HA, c_H and c_OH are the concentrations of H_3O^+ and OH^- respectively.

Between pH 3 and 11 the buffer value is determined almost wholly by the first term within the brackets. The maximum buffer effect for a given value of c is found when $c_\text{H} = K$ (pH $\approx$ pK), i.e. when there are present equivalent amounts of HA and MA. The actual buffer value, β_max, is then given by:

$$\beta_\text{max} = \frac{2{\cdot}303}{4}\,c$$

(interionic effects impose a practical upper limit for β of approx. 0·2).

If the ratio of HA to MA is increased or decreased tenfold, i.e. 10:1 or 1:10, the pH $\approx$ pK+1 and pK−1 respectively. The buffer capacity is then only about one-third of the maximum value. If the pH lies within the range of pK−1 and pK+1 the buffer capacity is appreciable, but outside this range it falls off to such an extent as to be of little value. **Therefore a given system only has useful buffer action in a range of one pH unit on either side of the p*K* of the weak acid.**

The same equation applies to systems consisting of a weak base (B) and its conjugate acid (BH^+) using K_{bh}, the dissociation constant of BH^+ (where $pK_{bh} = pK_w - pK_b$).

While aqueous solutions of strong acids and bases are not normally classified as buffer solutions they do display 'buffer capacity' at pH values below about 2·4 and above pH 11·6 ($db/d\text{pH} \approx 2{\cdot}303(c_\text{H}+c_\text{OH})$).

Dilution value. The dilution values ($\Delta\text{pH}_{1/2}$) given in the tables refer to the change of pH suffered by a solution of initial concentration c_i, upon dilution with an equal volume of pure water.

$$\Delta\text{pH}_{1/2} = (\text{pH})_{c_i/2} - (\text{pH})_{c_i}.$$

It is positive when the pH increases with dilution and negative when it decreases.

Dilution values ($\Delta\text{pH}_{1/2}$) *for equimolal amine buffer solutions between* pH 4·5 *and* 9·5 *in* pH *units*

(Bates, *Ann. N.Y. Acad. Sci.* **92**, 341 (1961))

m (*molality*)	$\Delta\text{pH}_{1/2}$	m	$\Delta\text{pH}_{1/2}$
0·0025	−0·007	0·025	−0·019
0·005	−0·010	0·05	−0·023
0·01	−0·013	0·1	−0·028
0·02	−0·017		

Salt effects. The effect on the pH of adding neutral salt to a buffer solution is readily predicted in a qualitative manner from a consideration of the buffer equilibria (see Bates (1964)).

Some indication of the magnitude of the effects to be expected is given in the following tables.

Salt effect caused by addition of neutral salt (0·1M) *to typical buffers*

(From Bates (1964))

Solution	ΔpH
0·005M-HCl	+0·10
0·005M-NaOH	+0·10
0·005M-CH_3COOH	0
0·005M-NH_3	0
0·005M-CH_3COOH–0·005M-CH_3COONa	−0·10
0·005M-NH_3–0·005M-NH_4Cl	+0·10

Salt effects on three standard buffers

(From Bates (1964))

Buffer solution	ΔpH 0·02M *added salt*	ΔpH 0·05M *added salt*
0·05M-KH phthalate (added KCl)	−0·019	−0·044
0·025M-KH_2PO_4–0·025M-Na_2HPO_4 (added NaCl)	−0·022	−0·051
0·01M-$Na_2B_4O_7$ (added NaCl)	−0·014	−0·035

Approximate salt effects (*in* pH *units*) *for amine buffer solutions at* 25°

(Bates, *Ann. N.Y. Acad. Sci.* **92**, 341 (1961))

m	*Salt effect for* Δ*I equal to*†			
(*molality*)	0·01	0·02	0·05	0·1
0·01	+0·016	+0·027	+0·049	+0·070
0·02	+0·011	+0·020	+0·039	+0·058
0·05	+0·006	+0·012	+0·024	+0·039
0·1	+0·003	+0·007	+0·015	+0·025

Temperature effects. The effect of temperature on the pH of the buffer solutions is given in the tables where possible. There is a considerable variation in the magnitude of *d*pH/*dt* for the different buffers.

Metal ion effects. Bjerrum first noted a correlation between the affinity for hydrogen ions of a *closely related* series of ligands and their affinity for a given metal ion. *Thus all buffers are potential ligands for forming metal complexes.*

Caution must be exercised in the use of buffers in the investigation of metal complexes (see, e.g. *Aust. J. Chem.* **14**, 562 (1961)). Some workers consider the interaction of certain nitrogen base buffers with alkali and alkaline earth metal ions is negligible and may be small with transition metal ions, e.g. *N*-ethylmorpholine, triethanolamine, and collidine. However, such buffers should not be used in a particular instance without prior investigation.

† Molality of added salt, m_s, is given by $m_s = \Delta I$ (uni-univalent salts such as NaCl, KNO_3), $m_s = \frac{1}{3}\Delta I$ (ternary salts such as Na_2SO_4 or $Ba(NO_3)_2$).

REVISED N.B.S. STANDARD BUFFER SOLUTIONS FOR pH MEASUREMENTS FROM 0° TO 95°

(Bates, *J. Res. natn. Bur. Stand.* **66A**, 179 (1962))

PRIMARY STANDARDS

Composition and properties of the five primary standard buffers at 25° (see notes on preparation, below).

	Buffer solution				
	Tartrate	*Phthalate*	*Phosphate D*	*Phosphate E*	*Borate*
Buffer substance	$KHC_4H_4O_6$	$KHC_8H_4O_4$	KH_2PO_4 Na_2HPO_4	KH_2PO_4 Na_2HPO_4	$Na_2B_4O_7\cdot 10H_2O$
g/l soln. at 25°	Saturated at 25°	10·12	[b]3·39 [c]3·53	[b]1·179 [c]4·30	3·80
Molality (m)	0·0341	0·05	[a]0·025	[b]0·008695 [c]0·03043	0·01
Molarity (M)	0·034	0·04958	[a]0·02490	[b]0·008665 [c]0·03032	0·009971
Density (g/ml)	1·0036	1·0017	1·0028	1·0020	0·9996
pH at 25°	3·557	4·008	6·865	7·413	9·180
Dilution value, $\Delta pH_{\frac{1}{2}}$	+0·049	+0·052	+0·080	[d]+0·07	+0·01
Buffer value, β equiv./pH	0·027	0·016	0·029	0·016	0·020
Temp. coeff. $dpH(S)/dt$ units/°C	−0·0014	+0·0012	−0·0028	−0·0028	−0·0082

[a] Concentration of each phosphate salt. [b] KH_2PO_4. [c] Na_2HPO_4.
[d] Calculated value.

Recommended standard values of pH(S) for primary standard buffers (estimated limits of accuracy ±0·005 over the temperature range 0–60° and ±0·008 from 60–90°).

Temp. (° C)	*Buffer* pH				
	Tartrate	*Phthalate*	*Phosphate D*	*Phosphate E*	*Borate*
0		4·003	6·984	7·534	9·464
5		3·999	6·951	7·500	9·395
10		3·998	6·923	7·472	9·332
15		3·999	6·900	7·448	9·276
20		4·002	6·881	7·429	9·225
25	3·557	4·008	6·865	7·413	9·180
30	3·552	4·015	6·853	7·400	9·139
35	3·549	4·024	6·844	7·389	9·102
38	3·548	4·030	6·840	7·384	9·081
40	3·547	4·035	6·838	7·380	9·068
45	3·547	4·047	6·834	7·373	9·038
50	3·549	4·060	6·833	7·367	9·011
55	3·554	4·075	6·834		8·985
60	3·560	4·091	6·836		8·962
70	3·580	4·126	6·845		8·921
80	3·609	4·164	6·859		8·885
90	3·650	4·205	6·877		8·850
95	3·674	4·227	6·886		8·833

Notes on the preparation of the above standard buffer solutions

The compositions of the above solutions to which pH(S) values have been assigned by the N.B.S., using the Bates–Guggenheim convention, are **on the molal scale.** Errors in pH(S) resulting from the use of an x molar solution in place of an x molal solution are small for the dilute solutions presented, but if third decimal accuracy is required the compositions of the solutions must be adjusted more carefully. Consequently the density of the standard solutions is listed above, together with the corresponding molarity to enable the solutions to be prepared precisely by volume methods.

The buffer solutions should be stored in bottles of borosilicate glass (e.g. Pyrex) or of polyethylene (pure). The tartrate solution is subject to mould growth accompanied by an increase in the pH value; it must therefore be freshly made every few days or a few crystals of thymol added as a preservative. Mould may appear slowly in the phthalate buffer and sediment may appear in the phosphate buffers. It is recommended that these buffers be remade every month.

Of the buffer salts only Na_2HPO_4 is appreciably hygroscopic. The tartrate, phthalate, and phosphates may be dried at 110° for 1–2 hr before use. Potassium tetroxalate dihydrate should not be dried at temperatures above 60°, nor should borax be heated above normal room temperature. Good quality distilled water should be used to prepare the buffer solutions (specific conductance should be less than 2×10^{-6} ohm^{-1} cm^{-1} at 25°).

SECONDARY STANDARDS

Composition and properties of the two secondary standard buffers at 25°.

	Buffer solution	
	Tetroxalate	*Calcium hydroxide*
Buffer substance	$KH_3(C_2O_4)_2 \cdot 2H_2O$	$Ca(OH)_2$
g/l of soln. at 25°	12·61	Saturated at 25°
Molality (*m*)	0·05	0·0203
Molarity (M)	0·04962	0·02025
Density (g/ml)	1·0032	0·9991
pH at 25°	1·679	12·454
Dilution value, $\Delta pH_{\frac{1}{2}}$	+0·186	−0·28
Buffer value, β equiv./pH	0·070	0·09
Temp. coeff. dpH(S)/dt units/°C	+0·001	−0·033

Recommended standard values of pH(S) for the secondary buffer standards.

Temp.	*Buffer* pH	
(° C)	*Tetroxalate*	*Calcium hydroxide*
0	1·666	13·423
5	1·668	13·207
10	1·670	13·003
15	1·672	12·810
20	1·675	12·627
25	1·679	12·454
30	1·683	12·289
35	1·688	12·133
38	1·691	12·043
40	1·694	11·984
45	1·700	11·841
50	1·707	11·705
55	1·715	11·574
60	1·723	11·449
70	1·743	
80	1·766	
90	1·792	
95	1·806	

Note. See above for remarks on drying potassium tetroxalate dihydrate.

APPROXIMATE pK_a VALUES OF SUBSTANCES USEFUL FOR BUFFER SYSTEMS

pK_a *at* 25°	*Compound*	ΔpH/Δt (pH *units per* °C)
1·27	k_1 Oxalic acid	
1·97	k_1 Maleic acid	
2·15	k_1 Phosphoric acid	
2·35	k_1 Glycine†	
2·95	k_1 Phthalic acid†	
3·02	k_1 Fumaric acid	
3·04	k_1 Tartaric acid	
3·13	k_1 Citric acid†	
3·14	k_1 Glycylglycine	
3·17	Furoic acid	
3·71	k_1 ββ′-Dimethylglutaric acid†	
3·75	Formic acid	
4·04	Barbituric acid	
4·20	Benzoic acid	
4·21	k_1 Succinic acid†	
4·27	k_2 Oxalic acid	
4·37	k_2 Tartaric acid	
4·38	k_2 Fumaric acid	
4·76	Acetic acid†	0·000
4·76	k_2 Citric acid†	
5·05	k_2 Malic acid	
5·41	k_2 Phthalic acid†	
5·64	k_2 Succinic acid†	
6·04	k_2 Histidine	
6·12	k_3 Pyrophosphoric acid	
6·24	k_2 Maleic acid†	
6·27	Cacodylic acid†	
6·34	k_2 ββ′-Dimethylglutaric acid†	
6·35	k_1 Carbonic acid†	
6·39	5(4)-Hydroxymethylimidazole	
6·40	k_3 Citric acid	
6·65	k_2 Glycerol 2-phosphoric acid	
6·85	k_1 Ethylenediamine	−0·027
6·95	Imidazole†	
6·98	k_2 Arsenic acid	
7·20	k_2 Phosphoric acid†	−0·003
7·43	2:4:6-Collidine†	
7·52	5(4)-Methylimidazole	
7·67	*N*-Ethylmorpholine†	
7·76	Triethanolamine†	−0·020
7·98	Diethylbarbituric acid†	−0·014
8·08	Tris(hydroxymethyl)aminomethane†	−0·028
8·25	Glycylglycine	−0·026
8·36	2:5(4)-Dimethylimidazole	
8·79	2-Amino-2-methyl-1:3-propanediol†	−0·029
8·80	2-Amino-2-ethyl-1:3-propanediol	
8·88	Diethanolamine†	−0·025
8·95	k_4 Pyrophosphoric acid	
9·11	4-Aminopyridine	−0·028
9·21	Serine	−0·025
9·24	Boric acid†	
9·25	Ammonia	−0·031
9·50	Ethanolamine	−0·030
9·54	Ephedrine	

† A table of buffer composition is given for these compounds in the next section.

pK_a *at* 25°		*Compound*	ΔpH/Δ*t* (pH *units per* °C)
9·66		Hydroxyproline	
9·69		2-Amino-2-methyl-1-propanol	−0·032
9·74		Leucine	
9·78		Glycine†	−0·026
9·80		Trimethylamine	
9·87		α-Alanine	−0·027
9·93	k_2	Ethylenediamine	−0·029
10·00		Aspartic acid	
10·24		β-Alanine	−0·028
10·33	k_2	Carbonic acid†	−0·009
10·56		γ-Aminobutyric acid	−0·030
10·57		*n*-Propylamine	
10·62		Methylamine	
10·63		Ethylamine	
10·64		*n*-Butylamine	
10·72		Triethylamine	
10·77		Dimethylamine	
10·93	k_2	Hexamethylenediamine	−0·034
10·93		Diethylamine	
11·12		Piperidine	−0·031
12·38	k_3	Phosphoric acid†	

† A table of buffer composition is given for these compounds in the next section.

p*K* values for many other compounds are given in the main tables of biochemical compounds.

Preparation of buffers. Buffers may be prepared from these or other suitable compounds by the addition of acid or alkali as appropriate. The amount of acid or alkali required can be calculated from the Henderson–Hasselbalch equation

$$\text{pH} = \text{p}K + \log_{10}\frac{[\text{salt}]}{[\text{acid}]}.\ddagger$$

The table below gives [salt]/[acid] ratios corresponding to pH values between p*K*−1 and p*K*+1, which represents the useful buffering range of a buffer system.

pH	[salt]/[acid]‡
p*K*−1·0	0·10
−0·9	0·13
−0·8	0·16
−0·7	0·20
−0·6	0·25
−0·5	0·32
−0·4	0·40
−0·3	0·50
−0·2	0·63
−0·1	0·79
p*K*	1·0
p*K*+0·1	1·26
+0·2	1·58
+0·3	2·00
+0·4	2·51
+0·5	3·16
+0·6	3·98
+0·7	5·01
+0·8	6·31
+0·9	7·94
+1·0	10·0

‡ [base]/[salt] ratio for cation buffers.

BUFFER SOLUTIONS FOR pH 1–13

Data are given in this section for miscellaneous buffer solutions which have wide application in biochemistry. Their concentration and ionic strength can be altered readily to make them more suitable for specific purposes. In general the pH values of these solutions have not been determined with high precision, and are only given to the first decimal place. In other cases, marked with an asterisk, the pH values have been accurately determined and are given to two decimal places.

Clark and Lubs solutions, pH 1·0–2·2*

(Bower and Bates, *J. Res. natn. Bur. Stand.* **55**, 197 (1955))

25 ml 0·2M-KCl (14·919 g/l), *x* ml 0·2M-HCl; diluted to 100 ml with H_2O.

pH, 25°	*x*	*Buffer value* (β)
1·00	67·0	0·31
1·10	52·8	0·24
1·20	42·5	0·19
1·30	33·6	0·16
1·40	26·6	0·13
1·50	20·7	0·10
1·60	16·2	0·077
1·70	13·0	0·060
1·80	10·2	0·049
1·90	8·1	0·037
2·00	6·5	0·030
2·10	5·1	0·026
2·20	3·9	0·022

For HCl–KCl buffers of constant ionic strength, see p. 499–500.

p-Toluene sulphonic acid–sodium p-toluene sulphonate buffer solutions, pH 1·2–2·0 *at* 25°

(German and Vogel, *Analyst* **62**, 271 (1937))

p-Toluene sulphonic acid monohydrate, $C_7H_8O_3S \cdot H_2O$, M. wt. 190·12
Sodium *p*-toluene sulphonate, $NaC_7H_7O_3S \cdot H_2O$, M. wt. 212·02

Maximum value of $db/d\text{pH} \approx 0{\cdot}21$

x ml 0·2M-*p*-toluene sulphonic acid monohydrate (38·024 g/l), *y* ml 0·2M-sodium *p*-toluene sulphonate (42·40 g/l); diluted to 100 ml with H_2O.

pH, 25°	*x* ml 0·2M-*acid*	*y* ml 0·2M-Na *salt*
1·2	42·0	8·0
1·3	31·6	18·4
1·4	24·8	25·2
1·5	18·9	31·1
1·6	15·35	34·65
1·7	12·6	37·4
1·8	10·6	39·4
1·9	8·7	41·3
2·0	6·9	43·1

Glycine–HCl *buffer solutions*, pH 2·2–3·6 *at* 25°

(Sørensen, *B.Z.* **21,** 131 (1909); Gomori, *Meth. Enzymol.* **1,** 141 (1955))

Glycine, $C_2H_5NO_2$, M. wt. 75·07
25 ml 0·2M-glycine (15·01 g/l), *x* ml 0·2N-HCl; diluted to 100 ml with H_2O.

pH, 25°	*x* ml 0·2N-HCl
2·2	22·0
2·4	16·2
2·6	12·1
2·8	8·4
3·0	5·7
3·2	4·1
3·4	3·2
3·6	2·5

Clark and Lubs solutions, pH 2·2–4·0*

(Bower and Bates, *J. Res. natn. Bur. Stand.* **55,** 197 (1955))

50 ml 0·1M-KH phthalate (20·42 g/l), *x* ml 0·1M-HCl; diluted to 100 ml with H_2O.

pH, 25°	*x*	*Buffer value* (β)
2·20	49·5	
2·30	45·8	0·036
2·40	42·2	0·035
2·50	38·8	0·034
2·60	35·4	0·033
2·70	32·1	0·032
2·80	28·9	0·032
2·90	25·7	0·033
3·00	22·3	0·034
3·10	18·8	0·033
3·20	15·7	0·030
3·30	12·9	0·026
3·40	10·4	0·023
3·50	8·2	0·020
3·60	6·3	0·018
3·70	4·5	0·017
3·80	2·9	0·015
3·90	1·4	0·014
4·00	0·1	0·014

Citric acid–Na_2HPO_4 (*McIlvaine*) *buffer solutions*, pH *approx.* 2·6–7·6

(McIlvaine, *J.B.C.* **49,** 183 (1921))

Citric acid monohydrate, $C_6H_8O_7 \cdot H_2O$, M. wt. 210·14; 0·1M-solution contains 21·01 g/l.
Na_2HPO_4, M. wt. 141·98; 0·2M-solution contains 28·40 g/l, or $Na_2HPO_4 \cdot 2H_2O$, M. wt. 178·05; 0·2M-solution contains 35·61 g/l.
x ml 0·1M-citric acid and *y* ml 0·2M-Na_2HPO_4 mixed.

pH	*x* ml 0·1M-*citric acid*	*y* ml 0·2M-Na_2HPO_4
2·6	89·10	10·90
2·8	84·15	15·85
3·0	79·45	20·55
3·2	75·30	24·70
3·4	71·50	28·50
3·6	67·80	32·20
3·8	64·50	35·50
4·0	61·45	38·55
4·2	58·60	41·40
4·4	55·90	44·10
4·6	53·25	46·75
4·8	50·70	49·30
5·0	48·50	51·50
5·2	46·40	53·60
5·4	44·25	55·75
5·6	42·00	58·00
5·8	39·55	60·45
6·0	36·85	63·15
6·2	33·90	66·10
6·4	30·75	69·25
6·6	27·25	72·75
6·8	22·75	77·25
7·0	17·65	82·35
7·2	13·05	86·95
7·4	9·15	90·85
7·6	6·35	93·65

Universal buffer solutions (*Britton and Robinson type*), pH 2·6–12·0

(Johnson and Lindsey, *Analyst* **64,** 490 (1939))

For the range 2–12 see also:

Prideaux and Ward, *J.C.S.* **125,** 426 (1924); H. T. S. Britton, *Hydrogen Ions*, vol. 1, p. 364, Chapman and Hall, London (1955); Coch Frugoni, *Gazz. chim. ital.* **87,** 403 (1957).

1 litre of mixture for titration contains citric acid (6·008 g), KH_2PO_4 (3·893 g), H_3BO_3 (1·769 g), diethylbarbituric acid (5·266 g).
100 ml of this mixture is titrated with *x* ml 0·2N-NaOH to give the required pH (18°).

pH	*x*	pH	*x*	pH	*x*
2·6	2·0	5·8	36·5	9·0	72·7
2·8	4·3	6·0	38·9	9·2	74·0
3·0	6·4	6·2	41·2	9·4	75·9
3·2	8·3	6·4	43·5	9·6	77·6
3·4	10·1	6·6	46·0	9·8	79·3
3·6	11·8	6·8	48·3	10·0	80·8
3·8	13·7	7·0	50·6	10·2	82·0
4·0	15·5	7·2	52·9	10·4	82·9
4·2	17·6	7·4	55·8	10·6	83·9
4·4	19·9	7·6	58·6	10·8	84·9
4·6	22·4	7·8	61·7	11·0	86·0
4·8	24·8	8·0	63·7	11·2	87·7
5·0	27·1	8·2	65·6	11·4	89·7
5·2	29·5	8·4	67·5	11·6	92·0
5·4	31·8	8·6	69·3	11·8	95·0
5·6	34·2	8·8	71·0	12·0	99·6

Citric acid–sodium citrate buffer solutions, pH 3·0–6·2

(N. Hemington and R. M. C. Dawson, unpublished data)

Citric acid monohydrate, $C_6H_8O_7 \cdot H_2O$, M. wt. 210·14; 0·1M-solution contains 21·01 g/l.
Trisodium citrate dihydrate, $C_6H_5O_7Na_3 \cdot 2H_2O$, M. wt. 294·12; 0·1M-solution contains 29·41 g/l.
x ml 0·1M-citric acid and *y* ml 0·1M-trisodium citrate mixed.

pH	*x* ml 0·1M-*citric acid*	*y* ml 0·1M-*trisodium citrate*
3·0	82·0	18·0
3·2	77·5	22·5
3·4	73·0	27·0
3·6	68·5	31·5
3·8	63·5	36·5
4·0	59·0	41·0
4·2	54·0	46·0
4·4	49·5	50·5
4·6	44·5	55·5
4·8	40·0	60·0
5·0	35·0	65·0
5·2	30·5	69·5
5·4	25·5	74·5
5·6	21·0	79·0
5·8	16·0	84·0
6·0	11·5	88·5
6·2	8·0	92·0

β:β′-Dimethylglutaric acid–NaOH *buffer solutions*, pH 3·2–7·6 *at* 21°

This buffer was outlined by Stafford, Watson, and Rand, *B.B.A.* **18,** 318 (1955), for use in enzyme studies where low u.v. absorption of the buffer was required. No details of mixtures were given. The following approximate pH data were kindly supplied by R. Hems.

β:β′-Dimethylglutaric acid, $C_7H_{12}O_4$, M. wt. 160·2.
50 ml 0·1M-β:β′-dimethylglutaric acid (16·02 g/l), *x* ml 0·2N-NaOH; diluted to 100 ml with H_2O.

pH, 21°	*x* ml 0·2N-NaOH
3·2	4·15
3·4	7·35
3·6	11·0
3·8	13·7
4·0	16·65
4·2	18·4
4·4	19·9
4·6	20·85
4·8	21·95
5·0	23·1
5·2	24·5
5·4	26·0
5·6	27·9
5·8	29·85
6·0	32·5
6·2	35·25
6·4	37·75
6·6	42·35
6·8	44·0
7·0	45·2
7·2	46·05
7·4	46·6
7·6	47·0

Sodium acetate–acetic acid buffer solutions, pH *approx.* 3·7–5·6

Sodium acetate trihydrate, $CH_3COONa \cdot 3H_2O$, M. wt. 136·09; 0·2M-solution contains 27·22 g/l.
x ml 0·2M-NaOAc and *y* ml 0·2M-HOAc mixed.

pH, 18°	*x* ml 0·2M-NaOAc	*y* ml 0·2M-HOAc
3·7	10·0	90·0
3·8	12·0	88·0
4·0	18·0	82·0
4·2	26·5	73·5
4·4	37·0	63·0
4·6	49·0	51·0
4·8	59·0	41·0
5·0	70·0	30·0
5·2	79·0	21·0
5·4	86·0	14·0
5·6	91·0	9·0

Succinic acid–NaOH *buffer solutions*, pH 3·8–6·0 *at* 25°

(Gomori, *Meth. Enzymol.* **1**, 141 (1955))

Succinic acid, $C_4H_6O_4$, M. wt. 118·09.
25 ml 0·2M-succinic acid (23·62 g/l), *x* ml 0·2N-NaOH; diluted to 100 ml with H_2O.

pH, 25°	*x* ml 0·2N-NaOH
3·8	7·5
4·0	10·0
4·2	13·3
4·4	16·7
4·6	20·0
4·8	23·5
5·0	26·7
5·2	30·3
5·4	34·2
5·6	37·5
5·8	40·7
6·0	43·5

Clark and Lubs solutions, pH 4·1–5·9*

(Bower and Bates, *J. Res. natn. Bur. Stand.* **55,** 197 (1955))

50 ml 0·1M-KH phthalate (20·42 g/l), *x* ml 0·1M-NaOH; diluted to 100 ml with H_2O.

pH, 25°	*x*	*Buffer value* (β)
4·10	1·3	0·016
4·20	3·0	0·017
4·30	4·7	0·018
4·40	6·6	0·020
4·50	8·7	0·022
4·60	11·1	0·025
4·70	13·6	0·027
4·80	16·5	0·029
4·90	19·4	0·030
5·00	22·6	0·031
5·10	25·5	0·031
5·20	28·8	0·030
5·30	31·6	0·026
5·40	34·1	0·025
5·50	36·6	0·023
5·60	38·8	0·020
5·70	40·6	0·017
5·80	42·3	0·015
5·90	43·7	0·013

Sodium cacodylate–HCl *buffer solutions*, pH 5·0–7·4 *at* 15°

(Plumel, *Bull. Soc. Chim. biol.* **30,** 129 (1948))

Sodium cacodylate trihydrate, $Na(CH_3)_2AsO_2 \cdot 3H_2O$, M. wt. 214·02.
50 ml 0·1M-$Na(CH_3)_2AsO_2 \cdot 3H_2O$ (21·40 g/l), *x* ml 0·1N-HCl; diluted to 100 ml with H_2O.

pH, 15°	*x* ml 0·1N-HCl
5·0	46·75
5·2	45·05
5·4	42·6
5·6	39·2
5·8	34·8
6·0	29·55
6·2	23·85
6·4	18·75
6·6	13·3
6·8	9·3
7·0	6·3
7·2	4·15
7·4	2·7

Sodium hydrogen maleate–NaOH *buffer solutions*, pH 5·2–6·8 *at* 25°

(Temple, *J.A.C.S.* **51**, 1754 (1929))

Sodium hydrogen maleate, $NaHC_4H_2O_4 \cdot 3H_2O$, M. wt. 192·11.
0·2M-solution is prepared by dissolving in H_2O, 23·2 g maleic acid and mixing with 200 ml 1N-NaOH and diluting to 1 litre with H_2O.
25 ml 0·2M-NaH maleate, *x* ml 0·1M-NaOH; diluted to 100 ml with H_2O.

Approximate pH, 25°	*x* ml 0·1M-NaOH
5·2	7·2
5·4	10·5
5·6	15·3
5·8	20·8
6·0	26·9
6·2	33·0
6·4	38·0
6·6	41·6
6·8	44·4

Na_2HPO_4–NaH_2PO_4 *buffer solutions*, pH 5·8–8·0 *at* 25°

(Gomori, after Sørensen, *Meth. Enzymol.* **1**, 143 (1955))

$Na_2HPO_4 \cdot 2H_2O$, M. wt. 178·05; 0·2M-solution contains 35·61 g/l.
$Na_2HPO_4 \cdot 12H_2O$, M. wt. 358·22; 0·2M-solution contains 71·64 g/l.
$NaH_2PO_4 \cdot H_2O$, M. wt. 138·01; 0·2M-solution contains 27·6 g/l.
$NaH_2PO_4 \cdot 2H_2O$, M. wt. 156·03; 0·2M-solution contains 31·21 g/l.
x ml 0·2M-Na_2HPO_4, *y* ml 0·2M-NaH_2PO_4; diluted to 100 ml with H_2O.

pH, 25°	*x* ml 0·2M-Na_2HPO_4	*y* ml 0·2M-NaH_2PO_4
5·8	4·0	46·0
6·0	6·15	43·85
6·2	9·25	40·75
6·4	13·25	36·75
6·6	18·75	31·25
6·8	24·5	25·5
7·0	30·5	19·5
7·2	36·0	14·0
7·4	40·5	9·5
7·6	43·5	6·5
7·8	45·75	4·25
8·0	47·35	2·65

Clark and Lubs solutions, pH 5·8–8·0*

(Bower and Bates, *J. Res. natn. Bur. Stand.* **55,** 197 (1955))

50 ml 0·1M-KH_2PO_4 (13·60 g/l), *x* ml 0·1M-NaOH; diluted to 100 ml with H_2O.

pH, 25°	*x*	*Buffer value* (*β*)
5·80	3·6	
5·90	4·6	0·010
6·00	5·6	0·011
6·10	6·8	0·012
6·20	8·1	0·015
6·30	9·7	0·017
6·40	11·6	0·021
6·50	13·9	0·024
6·60	16·4	0·027
6·70	19·3	0·030
6·80	22·4	0·033
6·90	25·9	0·033
7·00	29·1	0·031
7·10	32·1	0·028
7·20	34·7	0·025
7·30	37·0	0·022
7·40	39·1	0·020
7·50	40·9	0·016
7·60	42·4	0·013
7·70	43·5	0·011
7·80	44·5	0·009
7·90	45·3	0·008
8·00	46·1	

Sodium bicarbonate–5% CO_2 *buffer solutions*, pH 6·0–8·0 *at* 37°

Calculated from the Henderson–Hasselbalch equation,

$$\mathrm{pH} = \mathrm{p}K' + \log\frac{[\mathrm{HCO_3^-}]}{[\mathrm{CO_2}]}.$$

Concentrations of bicarbonate are approximately correct when atmospheric pressure varies between 725 and 760 mm Hg. Temperature: for temperatures below 37° (down to 20°) the bicarbonate concentration given in the tables should be decreased by approximately 1·88% per degree to give the required pH.

pH, 37°	*Conc. of* $NaHCO_3$ (*M. wt.* 84·02) *in equilibrium with gas phase containing* 5% CO_2
6·0	$5{\cdot}86\times10^{-4}$ M
6·2	$9{\cdot}29\times10^{-4}$ M
6·4	$1{\cdot}47\times10^{-3}$ M
6·6	$2{\cdot}33\times10^{-3}$ M
6·8	$3{\cdot}70\times10^{-3}$ M
7·0	$5{\cdot}86\times10^{-3}$ M
7·2	$9{\cdot}29\times10^{-3}$ M
7·4	$1{\cdot}47\times10^{-2}$ M
7·6	$2{\cdot}33\times10^{-2}$ M
7·8	$3{\cdot}70\times10^{-2}$ M
8·0	$5{\cdot}86\times10^{-2}$ M

Imidazole (*glyoxaline*)–HCl *buffer solutions*, pH 6·2–7·8 *at* 25°

(Mertz and Owen, *P.S.E.B.M.* **43**, 204 (1940))

Imidazole, $C_3H_4N_2$, M. wt. 68·08.
25 ml 0·2M-imidazole (13·62 g/l), *x* ml 0·2N-HCl; diluted to 100 ml with H_2O.

pH, 25°	*x* ml 0·2N-HCl
6·2	21·45
6·4	19·9
6·6	17·75
6·8	15·2
7·0	12·15
7·2	9·3
7·4	6·8
7·6	4·65
7·8	3·0

2:4:6-*Trimethylpyridine* (2:4:6-*collidine*)–HCl *buffer solutions*, pH 6·4–8·3

(Gomori, *P.S.E.B.M.* **62**, 33 (1946))

2:4:6-Trimethylpyridine, $C_8H_{11}N$, M. wt. 121·18.
25 ml 0·2M-2:4:6-trimethylpyridine (24·24 g/l), *x* ml 0·2N-HCl; diluted to 100 ml with H_2O.

pH		
23°	37°	*x* ml 0·2N-HCl
6·4	6·4	22·5
6·6	6·5	21·25
6·8	6·7	20·0
6·9	6·8	18·75
7·0	6·9	17·5
7·1	7·0	16·25
7·2	7·1	15·0
7·3	7·2	13·75
7·4	7·3	12·5
7·5	7·4	11·25
7·6	7·5	10·0
7·7	7·6	8·75
7·8	7·7	7·5
7·9	7·8	6·25
8·0	7·9	5·0
8·2	8·1	3·75
8·3	8·3	2·5

Triethanolamine hydrochloride–NaOH *buffer solutions*, pH 6·8–8·6 *at* 20°

(R. Hems, unpublished)

Triethanolamine hydrochloride, $C_6H_{15}NO_3 \cdot HCl$, M. wt. 185·7.
The hydrochloride is prepared by dissolving pure triethanolamine in 1 vol. of ethanol, neutralizing with conc. HCl, and cooling to 0°. M.p. 178·9°.
50 ml 0·1M-triethanolamine hydrochloride (18·57 g/l), *x* ml 0·1N-NaOH; diluted to 100 ml with H_2O.

$$\frac{dpH}{dt} = -0{\cdot}020 \text{ pH units/degree.}$$

pH, 20°	*x* ml 0·1N-NaOH
6·8	6·00
7·0	9·00
7·2	12·15
7·4	15·80
7·6	20·05
7·8	26·00
8·0	31·50
8·2	36·00
8·4	40·00
8·6	46·00

Sodium 5:5-*diethylbarbiturate* (*veronal sodium*; *barbitone sodium*)–HCl *buffer solutions*, pH 6·8–9·6 *at* 18°

(Britton and Robinson, *J.C.S.* **1931,** 1456)

Sodium 5:5-diethylbarbiturate, $C_8H_{11}N_2O_3Na$, M. wt. 206·18; 0·04M-solution contains 8·25 g/l.
x ml 0·04M-sodium diethylbarbiturate and *y* ml 0·2N-HCl mixed.

pH, 18°	*x* ml 0·04M-*sodium diethylbarbiturate*	*y* ml 0·2N-HCl
6·8	100	18·4
7·0	100	17·8
7·2	100	16·7
7·4	100	15·3
7·6	100	13·4
7·8	100	11·47
8·0	100	9·39
8·2	100	7·21
8·4	100	5·21
8·6	100	3·82
8·8	100	2·52
9·0	100	1·65
9·2	100	1·13
9·4	100	0·70
9·6	100	0·35

Dimethylleucylglycine buffer solutions, pH 7·0–8·8

(Leonis, *C.r. Trav. Lab. Carlsberg, Ser. Chemie* **26**, 357 (1948))

N-Dimethylleucylglycine, $C_{10}H_{20}O_3N_2 \cdot \frac{3}{2}H_2O$, M. wt. 243·3.
Stock solution contains 4·866 g $C_{10}H_{20}O_3N_2 \cdot \frac{3}{2}H_2O$ and 2·338 g NaCl dissolved in 100 ml H_2O.
Solution A contains 50 ml stock solution+50 ml H_2O and is 0·1N in the dipeptide and 0·2M in NaCl.
Solution B contains 50 ml stock solution+50 ml 0·2M-NaOH and is 0·1N in dipeptide–NaOH and 0·2M in NaCl.

pH	ml A	ml B
7·0	90·0	10·0
7·2	80·0	20·0
7·4	70·0	30·0
7·5	65·0	35·0
7·6	60·0	40·0
7·7	55·0	45·0
7·8	50·0	50·0
7·9	45·0	55·0
8·0	40·0	60·0
8·1	35·0	65·0
8·2	30·0	70·0
8·4	20·0	80·0
8·8	10·0	90·0

N-Ethylmorpholine–HCl *buffer solutions*, pH 7·0–8·2 *at* 20°

(Prof. A. Albert, private communication)

N-Ethylmorpholine, $C_6H_{13}NO$, M. wt. 115·17.
N-Ethylmorpholine should be dried and freshly distilled (B.p. 138–9°, 763 mm).
50 ml 0·2M-*N*-ethylmorpholine (23·03 g/l), *x* ml 1N-HCl; diluted to 100 ml with H_2O.

pH, 20°	*x* ml 1N-HCl
7·0	8·0
7·2	7·1
7·4	6·1
7·6	5·0
7·8	4·0
8·0	2·9
8·2	2·0

Tris(hydroxymethyl)aminomethane buffer solutions, pH 7·1–8·9 *at* 25°*
(Bates and Bower, *Analyt. Chem.* **28,** 1322 (1956))
$C_4H_{11}NO_3$, M. wt. 121·14.
50 ml 0·1M-tris† (12·114 g/l), *x* ml 0·1M-HCl; diluted to 100 ml with H_2O.

$$I = 0{\cdot}001x.$$
$$d\text{pH}/dt \approx -0{\cdot}028 \text{ pH units/deg.}$$

pH, 25°	*x*	*Buffer value* (β)	$\Delta pH_{\frac{1}{2}}$‡
7·10	45·7	0·010	
7·20	44·7	0·012	
7·30	43·4	0·013	
7·40	42·0	0·015	
7·50	40·3	0·017	−0·02
7·60	38·5	0·018	
7·70	36·6	0·020	
7·80	34·5	0·023	
7·90	32·0	0·027	
8·00	29·2	0·029	−0·02
8·10	26·2	0·031	
8·20	22·9	0·031	
8·30	19·9	0·029	−0·01
8·40	17·2	0·026	
8·50	14·7	0·024	
8·60	12·4	0·022	
8·70	10·3	0·020	−0·01
8·80	8·5	0·016	
8·90	7·0	0·014	

† Tris solutions absorb CO_2 from the air (see Bates and Hetzer, *Analyt. Chem.* **33,** 1285 (1960)).
‡ Calculated.

*2-Amino-2-methyl-*1:3-*propanediol*–HCl *buffer solutions*, pH 7·8–9·7
(Gomori, *P.S.E.B.M.* **62,** 33 (1946))
2-Amino-2-methyl-1:3-propanediol, $C_4H_{11}NO_2$, M. wt. 105·14.
25 ml 0·2M-2-amino-2-methyl-1:3-propanediol (21·03 g/l), *x* ml 0·2M-HCl; diluted to 100 ml with H_2O.

pH		
23°	37°	*x* ml 0·2N-HCl
9·7	9·6	2·5
9·6	9·4	3·75
9·4	9·3	5·0
9·3	9·1	6·25
9·1	9·0	7·5
9·0	8·9	8·75
9·0	8·8	10·0
8·9	8·8	11·25
8·8	8·7	12·5
8·7	8·6	13·75
8·6	8·5	15·0
8·5	8·4	16·25
8·4	8·3	17·5
8·3	8·2	18·75
8·2	8·1	20·0
8·0	7·9	21·25
7·8	7·7	22·5

Diethanolamine–HCl *buffer solutions*, pH 8·0–10·0 *at* 25°

(J. Lowenstein, unpublished)

Diethanolamine, $C_4H_{11}NO_2$, M. wt. 105·14; B.p. 268·8° at 760 mm.
25 ml 0·2M-diethanolamine (21·02 g/l), *x* ml 0·2N-HCl; diluted to 100 ml with H_2O.

pH, 25°	*x* ml 0·2N-HCl
8·0	22·95
8·3	21·0
8·5	18·85
8·7	16·35
8·9	13·55
9·1	10·2
9·3	7·8
9·5	5·55
9·7	3·45
10·0	1·8

Clark and Lubs solutions, pH 8·0–10·2*

(Bower and Bates, *J. Res. natn. Bur. Stand.* **55**, 197 (1955))

50 ml of a mixture 0·1M with respect to both KCl and H_3BO_3 (7·455 g KCl and 6·184 g H_3BO_3/l), *x* ml 0·1M-NaOH; diluted to 100 ml with H_2O.

pH, 25°	*x*	*Buffer value* (β)
8·00	3·9	
8·10	4·9	0·010
8·20	6·0	0·011
8·30	7·2	0·013
8·40	8·6	0·015
8·50	10·1	0·016
8·60	11·8	0·018
8·70	13·7	0·020
8·80	15·8	0·022
8·90	18·1	0·025
9·00	20·8	0·027
9·10	23·6	0·028
9·20	26·4	0·029
9·30	29·3	0·028
9·40	32·1	0·027
9·50	34·6	0·024
9·60	36·9	0·022
9·70	38·9	0·019
9·80	40·6	0·016
9·90	42·2	0·015
10·00	43·7	0·014
10·10	45·0	0·013
10·20	46·2	

Borate buffer solutions, pH 8·1–9·0 *at* 25°*

(Bates and Bower, *Analyt. Chem.* **28**, 1322 (1956))

50 ml 0·025M-$Na_2B_4O_7 \cdot 10H_2O$ (9·525 g/l), x ml 0·1M-HCl; diluted to 100 ml with H_2O.

$I \approx 0{\cdot}025$.

$dpH/dt \approx 0{\cdot}008$ unit/deg.

pH, 25°	x	*Buffer value* (β)	$\Delta pH_{\frac{1}{2}}$
8·10	19·7	0·009	+0·07
8·20	18·8	0·010	
8·30	17·7	0·011	
8·40	16·6	0·012	
8·50	15·2	0·015	+0·05
8·60	13·5	0·018	
8·70	11·6	0·020	
8·80	9·4	0·023	+0·04
8·90	7·1	0·024	
9·00	4·6	0·026	+0·02

Glycine–NaOH *buffer solutions*, pH 8·6–10·6 *at* 25°

(Gomori, after Sørensen, *Meth. Enzymol.* **1**, 145 (1955))

Glycine (aminoacetic acid), $C_2H_5NO_2$, M. wt. 75·07.
25 ml 0·2M-glycine (15·01 g/l), x ml 0·2N-NaOH; diluted to 100 ml with H_2O.

$$\frac{dpH}{dt} = -0{\cdot}026 \text{ pH units/degree.}$$

pH, 25°	x ml 0·2N-NaOH
8·6	2·0
8·8	3·0
9·0	4·4
9·2	6·0
9·4	8·4
9·6	11·2
9·8	13·6
10·0	16·0
10·4	19·3
10·6	22·75

Sodium carbonate–sodium bicarbonate buffer solutions, pH 9·2–10·8

(Delory and King, *B.J.* **39**, 245 (1945))

$Na_2CO_3 \cdot 10H_2O$, M. wt. 286·2; 0·1M-solution contains 28·62 g/l.
$NaHCO_3$, M. wt. 84·0; 0·1M-solution contains 8·40 g/l.
x ml 0·1M-Na_2CO_3 and y ml 0·1M-$NaHCO_3$ mixed.

pH			
20°	37°	x ml 0·1M-Na_2CO_3	y ml 0·1M-$NaHCO_3$
9·2	8·8	10	90
9·4	9·1	20	80
9·5	9·4	30	70
9·8	9·5	40	60
9·9	9·7	50	50
10·1	9·9	60	40
10·3	10·1	70	30
10·5	10·3	80	20
10·8	10·6	90	10

Borate buffer solutions, pH 9·3–10·7 *at* 25°*

(Bates and Bower, *Analyt. Chem.* **28,** 1322 (1956))

50ml 0·025M-$Na_2B_4O_7 \cdot 10H_2O$ (9·525 g/l), x ml 0·1M-NaOH; diluted to 100 ml with H_2O.

$$I = 0{\cdot}001(25+x).$$

$$d\text{pH}/dt \approx -0{\cdot}008 \text{ unit/deg.}$$

pH, 25°	x	*Buffer value* (β)	$\Delta\text{pH}_{\frac{1}{2}}$
9·30	3·6	0·027	+0·01[a]
9·40	6·2	0·026	+0·01[b]
9·50	8·8	0·025	
9·60	11·1	0·022	+0·01[a], +0·01[b]
9·70	13·1	0·020	
9·80	15·0	0·018	+0·01[b]
9·90	16·7	0·016	
10·00	18·3	0·014	
10·10	19·5	0·011	−0·01[a]
10·20	20·5	0·009	0·00[b]
10·30	21·3	0·008	
10·40	22·1	0·007	
10·50	22·7	0·006	
10·60	23·3	0·005	
10·70	23·8	0·004	

[a] Measured. [b] Calculated.

Carbonate buffer solutions, pH 9·7–10·9 *at* 25°*

(Bates and Bower, *Analyt. Chem.* **28,** 1322 (1956))

50 ml 0·05M-$NaHCO_3$ (4·20 g/l), x ml 0·1M-NaOH; diluted to 100 ml with H_2O.

$$I = 0{\cdot}001(25+2x).$$

$$d\text{pH}/dt \approx -0{\cdot}009 \text{ unit/deg.}$$

pH, 25°	x	*Buffer value* (β)	$\Delta\text{pH}_{\frac{1}{2}}$
9·70	6·2	0·013	+0·02[a], +0·03[b]
9·80	7·6	0·014	
9·90	9·1	0·015	+0·03[b]
10·00	10·7	0·016	+0·04[a]
10·10	12·2	0·016	+0·04[a]
10·20	13·8	0·015	
10·30	15·2	0·014	+0·02[b]
10·40	16·5	0·013	
10·50	17·8	0·013	
10·60	19·1	0·012	+0·03[a]
10·70	20·2	0·010	0·00[b]
10·80	21·2	0·009	
10·90	22·0	0·008	

[a] Measured. [b] Calculated.

Phosphate buffer solutions, pH 11·0–11·9 *at* 25°*

(Bates and Bower, *Analyt. Chem.* **28**, 1322 (1956))

50 ml 0·5M-Na_2HPO_4 (7·10 g/l), x ml 0·1M-NaOH; diluted to 100 ml with H_2O.

$$I = 0{\cdot}001(77+2x).$$

$$dpH/dt \approx -0{\cdot}025 \text{ unit/deg.}$$

pH, 25°	x	*Buffer value* (β)	$\Delta pH_{\frac{1}{2}}$
11·00	4·1	0·009	
11·10	5·1	0·011	−0·06[a], −0·07[b]
11·20	6·3	0·012	
11·30	7·6	0·014	
11·40	9·1	0·017	−0·09[a], −0·10[b]
11·50	11·1	0·022	
11·60	13·5	0·026	
11·70	16·2	0·030	−0·15[b]
11·80	19·4	0·034	−0·13[a], −0·17[b]
11·90	23·0	0·037	

[a] Measured. [b] Calculated.

Hydroxide–chloride buffer solutions, pH 12·0–13·0 *at* 25°*

(Bates and Bower, *Analyt. Chem.* **28**, 1322 (1956))

25 ml 0·2M-KCl (14·91 g/l), x ml 0·2M-NaOH; diluted to 100 ml with H_2O.

$$I = 0{\cdot}001(50+2x).$$

$$dpH/dt \approx -0{\cdot}033 \text{ unit/deg.}$$

pH, 25°	x	*Buffer value* (β)	$\Delta pH_{\frac{1}{2}}$[b]
12·00	6·0	0·028	−0·28
12·10	8·0	0·042	
12·20	10·2	0·048	−0·28
12·30	12·8	0·060	
12·40	16·2	0·076	
12·50	20·4	0·094	−0·28
12·60	25·6	0·12	
12·70	32·2	0·16	
12·80	41·2	0·21	−0·28
12·90	53·0	0·25	
13·00	66·0	0·30	−0·27

[b] Calculated.

BUFFERS OF CONSTANT IONIC STRENGTH

Buffer solutions of varying pH but fixed ionic strength can be prepared most readily in monobasic acid and monoacid base systems providing the acid or base is sufficiently weak that the contribution of its ionization to the total ionic strength is negligible.

The molar ionic strength (I) of a buffer solution can be calculated from:

$$I = \tfrac{1}{2} \sum m_i z_i^2,$$

where m_i is the molarity of a particular ion and z_i is its charge.

In the weak acid systems the final concentration of MA (the salt of HA) need only be sufficiently great to yield adequate buffer capacity. The ionic strength can be raised to the required level with strong electrolyte (KCl or NaCl). Weak base buffer mixtures of constant I are similarly prepared (B·HX, the HX form of the weak base B, is kept at low concentration.)

HCl–KCl *mixtures of constant ionic strength* (I), pH 1·0–2·2 *at* 25°*

(Bower and Bates, *J. Res. natn. Bur. Stand.* **55**, 197 (1955))

$$I = 0{\cdot}1.$$

(The first table gives data in terms of molarity of HCl and KCl; the second in terms of volumes of 0·2M-HCl and 0·2M-KCl solutions mixed together.)

Molarity of HCl	*Molarity of* KCl	pH	*Buffer value* (β)
0·10	0	1·11	0·23
0·09	0·01	1·15	0·21
0·08	0·02	1·20	0·18
0·07	0·03	1·26	0·16
0·06	0·04	1·33	0·14
0·05	0·05	1·41	0·12
0·04	0·06	1·50	0·092
0·03	0·07	1·63	0·069
0·02	0·08	1·80	0·046
0·01	0·09	2·11	0·023
0·005	0·095	2·41	0·012
0·002	0·098	2·80	0·004
0·001	0·099	3·11	0·002

x ml 0·2M-HCl, y ml 0·2M-KCl (14·919 g/l); diluted to 100 ml with H_2O gives $I = 0·1$ (0·002xM-HCl, 0·002yM-KCl).

pH, 25°	x	y	*Buffer value* (β)
[a](1·00)	67·0	0	0·31
[b](1·10)	51·2	0	0·24
1·20	40·7	9·3	0·19
1·30	32·3	17·7	0·15
1·40	25·7	24·3	0·12
1·50	20·1	29·9	0·093
1·60	16·0	34·0	0·074
1·70	12·8	37·2	0·059
1·80	10·2	39·8	0·047
1·90	8·1	41·9	0·037
2·00	6·5	43·5	0·030
2·10	5·2	44·8	0·024
2·20	4·2	45·8	0·019

[a] $I = 0·134$. [b] $I = 0·102$.

Constant ionic strength buffer solutions of Miller and Golder for electrophoresis

(Miller and Golder, *Arch. Biochem.* **29,** 420 (1950))

Composition of 0·1 and 0·2 I buffer solutions pH 2·0 to 12·0 at 2°.
Solution to be made up to 2 l to give indicated pH.

pH	*For* 0·1 I, x ml 5·0M-NaCl	*For* 0·2 I, y ml 5·0M-NaCl	1·0M-*glycine*–1·0M-NaCl	2·0N-HCl	2·0N-NaOH	2·0M-*sodium acetate*	8·5M-*acetic acid*	0·5M-Na_2H-PO_4	4·0M-NaH_2-PO_4	0·5M-*sodium veronal*
2·0	32	72	10·6	14·7						
2·5	32	72	22·8	8·6						
3·0	32	72	31·6	4·2						
3·5	32	72	36·6	1·7						
4·0	32	72				20·0	33·7			
4·5	32	72				20·0	11·5			
5·0	32	72				20·0	3·7			
5·5	32	72				20·0	1·2			
6·0	32	72						9·2	6·6	
6·5	32	72						16·6	3·7	
7·0	32	72						22·7	1·6	
7·5	32	72						24·3	0·5	
8·0	32	72		10·4						80·0
8·5	32	72		5·3						80·0
9·0	32	72		2·0						80·0
9·5	32	72	34·5		2·7					
10·0	32	72	28·8		5·6					
10·5	32	72	23·2		8·4					
11·0	32	72	19·6		10·2					
11·5	32	72	17·6		11·2					
12·0	32	72	15·2		12·4					

McIlvaine type buffer systems of constant ionic strength

(Especially suitable for polarography)

(Elving, Markowitz, and Rosenthal, *Analyt. Chem.* **28**, 1179 (1956))

pH *desired at 25°*	*Composition* g/l *solution* $Na_2HPO_4 \cdot 12H_2O$	citric acid·H_2O	*Buffer system ionic strength* M	g KCl *added per litre of solution to produce ionic strength of:* 1·0M	0·5M
2·2	1·43	20·6	0·0108	74·5	37·2
2·4	4·44	19·7	0·0245	72·7	35·4
2·6	7·80	18·7	0·0410	71·5	34·2
2·8	11·35	17·7	0·0592	70·2	32·9
3·0	14·7	16·7	0·0771	68·7	31·4
3·2	17·7	15·8	0·093	67·6	30·3
3·4	20·4	15·0	0·112	66·2	28·9
3·6	21·5	14·2	0·128	64·9	27·6
3·8	25·4	13·6	0·142	64·0	26·7
4·0	27·6	12·9	0·157	62·8	25·5
4·2	29·7	12·3	0·173	61·7	24·4
4·4	31·6	11·7	0·190	60·4	23·1
4·6	33·4	11·2	0·210	58·9	21·6
4·8	35·3	10·7	0·232	57·2	19·9
5·0	36·9	10·2	0·256	55·5	18·2
5·2	38·4	9·75	0·278	53·8	16·5
5·4	40·0	9·29	0·302	52·1	14·8
5·6	41·5	8·72	0·321	50·6	13·3
5·8	43·3	8·32	0·336	49·5	12·2
6·0	45·2	7·74	0·344	48·9	11·6
6·2	47·5	7·12	0·358	47·9	10·6
6·4	49·6	6·47	0·371	46·9	9·62
6·6	52·1	5·72	0·385	45·8	8·50
6·8	55·4	4·79	0·392	44·5	7·23
7·0	58·9	3·70	0·427	42·7	5·44
7·2	62·3	2·74	0·457	40·4	3·10
7·4	65·0	1·91	0·488	38·2	0·488
7·6	67·2	1·35	0·516	36·0	
7·8	68·6	0·893	0·540	34·3	
8·0	69·6	0·589	0·559	32·9	

Preparation of amine buffers of constant ionic strength

(Bates, *Ann. N.Y. Acad. Sci.* **92,** 341 (1961))

A stock solution of an amine salt (e.g. B·HCl) is prepared with added neutral salt. The concentration of the amine salt need only be sufficient for adequate buffering and neutral salt is added to yield the desired ionic strength. The NaOH solution added to increase the pH will dilute the solution and lower the ionic strength unless sufficient neutral salt is added to this reagent exactly to compensate for the dilution.

When this is done, the pH of the buffer solution may be shifted throughout the entire range of the buffer system without altering the ionic strength appreciably. The only restriction is that the amount of NaOH added should not exceed the amount of amine salt present. Representative compositions of amine hydrochloride stock solutions and of the alkaline reagents needed for the preparation of buffer solutions of five different ionic strengths are given in the table following.

Amine buffer solutions of constant ionic strength: composition of stock solutions

Ionic strength	*Solution of amine salt* B·HCl (M)	NaCl (M)	*Solution of alkali* NaOH (M)	NaCl (M)
0·05	0·02	0·03	0·1	0·05
0·1	0·02	0·08	0·1	0·1
0·15	0·02	0·13	0·1	0·15
0·2	0·02	0·18	0·1	0·2
0·25	0·02	0·23	0·1	0·25
0·05	0·05	—	0·2	0·05
0·1	0·05	0·05	0·2	0·1
0·15	0·05	0·1	0·2	0·15
0·2	0·05	0·15	0·2	0·2
0·25	0·05	0·2	0·2	0·25

Buffers of constant and low ionic strength for spectrophotometric p*K determinations* ($I = 0{\cdot}01$)

(Perrin, *Aust. J. Chem.* **16,** 572 (1963))

All quantities in a final volume of 100 ml.

Chloroacetic acid			*Formic acid*			*Acetic acid*		
pH	0·1M-*acid* (ml)	0·1M-KOH (ml)	pH	0·1M-*acid* (ml)	0·1M-KOH (ml)	pH	0·1M-*acid* (ml)	0·1M-KOH (ml)
2·20	50·99	2·76	3·20	41·34	9·30	4·10	51·26	9·91
2·30	42·18	4·31	3·30	34·99	9·45	4·20	43·03	9·93
2·40	35·38	5·51	3·40	30·28	9·55	4·30	36·17	9·94
2·50	29·98	6·46	3·50	25·88	9·65	4·40	30·87	9·95
2·60	25·82	7·19	3·60	22·62	9·72	4·50	26·67	9·96
2·70	22·46	7·79	3·70	20·21	9·78	4·60	23·14	9·97
2·80	19·94	8·23	3·80	18·05	9·82	4·70	20·58	9·98
2·90	17·85	8·60	3·90	16·36	9·86	4·80	18·38	9·98
3·00	16·21	8·89	4·00	15·03	9·89	4·90	16·69	9·99
3·10	14·95	9·12	4·10	14·00	9·91	5·00	15·34	9·99
3·20	13·89	9·30	4·20	13·21	9·93	5·10	14·28	9·99
3·30	13·11	9·45	4·30	12·54	9·94	5·20	13·42	9·99
3·40	12·46	9·55	4·40	12·05	9·95	5·30	12·78	9·99
Max. interpolation 0·011 pH unit			Max. interpolation 0·007 pH unit			Max. interpolation 0·034 pH unit		

All quantities in a final volume of 100 ml.

Phosphoric acid

pH	0·02M-KH_2PO_4 (ml)	0·01M-Na_2HPO_4 (ml)
6·40	30·21	13·19
6·50	27·45	15·05
6·60	24·60	16·94
6·70	21·66	18·90
6·80	18·97	20·68
6·90	16·40	22·41
7·00	13·96	24·04
7·10	11·72	25·52
7·20	9·73	26·85
7·30	7·99	28·00
7·40	6·54	28·97
7·50	5·32	29·78
7·60	4·27	30·49
7·70	3·41	31·05

Max. interpolation 0·028 pH unit

Succinic acid

pH	0·1M-*acid* (ml)	0·05M-KOH (ml)
3·60	45·95	19·21
3·70	36·93	19·27
3·80	31·84	19·27
3·90	27·12	19·24
4·00	23·29	19·21
4·10	19·72	19·11
4·20	17·50	19·00
4·30	15·37	18·84
4·40	13·73	18·67
4·50	12·24	18·42
4·60	11·06	18·15
4·70	10·12	17·90

Succinic acid (cont'd)

pH	0·02M-*acid* (ml)	0·05M-KOH (ml)
4·80	46·04	17·57
4·90	41·62	17·15
5·00	38·12	16·80
5·10	35·01	16·42
5·20	32·15	16·02
5·30	29·88	15·68
5·40	27·70	15·34
5·50	25·89	15·05
5·60	24·33	14·78
5·70	22·94	14·53
5·80	21·95	14·35
5·90	20·82	14·13
6·00	20·07	14·00
6·10	19·41	13·88
6·20	18·87	13·77

Max. interpolation 0·032 pH unit

All quantities in a final volume of 100 ml.

Boric acid

pH	0·025M-$Na_2B_4O_7$ (ml)	0·1M-H_3BO_3 (ml)
8·50	20·00	38·62
8·60	20·00	29·89
8·70	20·00	22·97
8·80	20·00	16·62
8·90	20·00	11·21
9·00	20·00	6·89
9·10	20·00	3·07
9·20	20·00	0·60

pH	0·025M-$Na_2B_4O_7$ (ml)	0·01M-KOH (ml)
9·30	18·30	8·56
9·40	16·47	17·62
9·50	15·01	24·97
9·60	13·74	31·25
9·70	12·94	35·29

Max. interpolation 0·048 pH unit

Carbonic acid

pH	0·02M-$NaHCO_3$ (ml)	0·01M-Na_2CO_3 (ml)
9·60	29·64	13·64
9·70	26·26	15·92
9·80	23·05	18·08
9·90	20·32	19·80
10·00	17·41	21·89
10·10	14·47	23·92
10·20	11·76	25·79
10·30	9·32	27·51
10·40	7·35	28·95
10·50	5·32	30·43
10·60	3·61	31·77

Max. interpolation 0·037 pH unit

Tris(hydroxymethyl)-aminomethane

pH	0·1M-TRIS (ml)	0·1M-HCl (ml)
7·70	12·97	10·00
7·80	13·68	10·00
7·90	14·67	10·00
8·00	15·84	10·00
8·10	17·28	10·00
8·20	19·14	10·00
8·30	21·52	10·00
8·40	24·44	10·00
8·50	28·18	10·00
8·60	32·90	10·00
8·70	38·87	10·00
8·80	46·41	10·00
8·90	55·22	10·00

Max. interpolation 0·032 pH unit

All quantities in a final volume of 100 ml.

Citric acid			*Butylamine*		
pH	$0{\cdot}002$M-*acid* (ml)	$0{\cdot}01$M-Na_3 *citrate* (ml)	pH	$0{\cdot}2$M-*free base* (ml)	$0{\cdot}1$M-HCl (ml)
5·80	33·12	19·78	10·30	6·45	9·85
5·90	28·88	19·41	10·40	6·83	9·81
6·00	25·10	19·07	10·50	7·30	9·76
6·10	21·45	18·75	10·60	7·90	9·69
6·20	18·26	18·46	10·70	8·65	9·61
6·30	15·27	18·17	10·80	9·59	9·51
6·40	12·73	17·92	10·90	10·78	9·39
6·50	10·47	17·70	11·00	12·28	9·23
6·60	8·58	17·51	11·10	14·16	9·03
6·70	6·99	17·37	11·20	16·53	8·78
Max. interpolation			11·30	19·52	8·46
0·004 pH unit			11·40	23·28	8·07
			11·50	28·02	7·57
			11·60	33·97	6·94
			Max. interpolation 0·053 pH unit		

BUFFERS FOR ELECTROPHORESIS

(See p. 500 for electrotrophoresis buffers of constant ionic strength)
The buffer systems described in other sections can form the basis of electrophoretic buffers; it is preferable to use univalent buffers of known and constant ionic strength.

Numerous buffer solutions for zone electrophoresis (paper, gel, column) have been described in the literature; since many of these have been developed for a single specific purpose only a limited number are given in the tables of this section. For further data see Bloemendahl, *Zone Electrophoresis*, Elsevier, Amsterdam (1963).

Univalent buffer systems for electrophoresis

(B. S. Magdoff, *Laboratory Manual of Analytical Methods of Protein Chemistry*, eds. P. Alexander and R. J. Block, vol. 2, p. 170, Pergamon, London (1960); and J. C. Nichol, *J.A.C.S.* **72,** 2367 (1950))

In moving boundary electrophoresis it is important that the buffer ion of low mobility has the same sign as the protein ion (e.g. see *B.B.A.* **65,** 148 (1962)). Some data on the mobilities of common buffer ions are given here.

Weak acid or base	$pK_{25°}$	*Ion mobility* $\times 10^5$ *at* $0{\cdot}1$N (cm^2/V sec)
Glycine	2·3	+15·6
Lactic acid	3·8	−13·1
Acetic acid	4·7	−16·6
Cacodylic acid	6·2	−10·1
Diethylbarbituric acid	7·9	−10·2
Triethanolamine	7·9	+9·1
Tris(hydroxymethyl)-aminomethane	8·1	
Diethanolamine	9·0	+11·4
Glycine	9·7	
{ Sodium		+22·2
{ Chloride		−37·0

Buffer solutions suitable for paper electrophoresis of proteins

pH	*I*	*Components/l solution*
4·4	0·2	Na_2HPO_4, 9·44 g Citric acid, 10·3 g
4·5	0·1	NaCl, 3·51 g NaOAc, 3·28 g Adjust to pH 4·5 with N-HCl
6·5	0·1	KH_2PO_4, 3·11 g Na_2HPO_4, 1·49 g
7·8	0·12	$NaH_2PO_4 \cdot H_2O$, 0·294 g Na_2HPO_4, 3·25 g
8·6	0·05	Diethylbarbituric acid, 1·84 g Sodium diethylbarbiturate, 10·30 g
8·6	0·075	Diethylbarbituric acid, 2·76 g Sodium diethylbarbiturate, 15·45 g
8·6	0·1	Diethylbarbituric acid, 3·68 g Sodium diethylbarbiturate, 20·6 g
8·9	—	Tris(hydroxymethyl)aminomethane (Tris), 60·5 g Ethylenediaminetetraacetic acid (EDTA), 6·0 g Boric acid, 4·6 g (0·5M in Tris; 0·021M in EDTA; 0·075M in H_3BO_3)

Buffer solutions for starch gel electrophoresis

Typical buffers which have been used are given below, but see also Smithies, *Adv. Protein Chem.* **14,** 65 (1959).

pH *of gel* 8·5 (Smithies, *Adv. Protein Chem.* **14,** 68 (1959)).

Gel buffer: 0·021M-H_3BO_3, 0·0084M-NaOH.
Electrode buffer: 0·3M-H_3BO_3, 0·06M-NaOH.

pH *of gel* 7·8 (Ashton, *Nature, Lond.* **180,** 917 (1957)).

Gel buffer: 20 ml electrode buffer diluted to 1 litre with H_2O.
Electrode buffer: 42 g/l Na_2HPO_4 titrated to pH 7·8 with saturated KH_2PO_4.

Discontinuous buffer (Poulik, *Nature, Lond.* **180,** 1477 (1957)).

Gel buffer: 0·076M-Tris–0·005M-citric acid.
Electrode buffer: 0·30M-H_3BO_3–0·06M-NaOH.

HCOOH–NaOH–*mercaptoethanol–urea buffer solutions*

(See Smithies, *Arch. B.B. Suppl.* **1,** 125 (1962).)

Volatile buffer solutions for high voltage electrophoresis

The useful range of the various systems is given below, followed by a few specific reported mixtures.

pH *range*	*System*
approx. 2	Acetic acid–formic acid
2·3–3·5	Pyridine–formic acid
3·5–6·0	Pyridine–acetic acid
3·0–6·0	Trimethylamine†–formic acid (or acetic)
5·5–7·0	Collidine–acetic acid
7·0–12·0	Trimethylamine†–carbon dioxide
6·0–10·0	Ammonia–formic acid (or acetic)
6·5–11·0	Mono- (or tri-)ethanolamine–hydrochloric acid
8·0–9·5	Ammonium carbonate–ammonia

† For use of triethylamine buffers, *see* Porath, *Nature, Lond.* **175,** 478 (1955).

Typical volatile buffer mixtures

pH	*Constituents*
1·9	CH_3COOH (87 ml glacial), HCOOH (25 ml 88%) to 1 l with H_2O
2·1	HCOOH (25 ml 88%) to 1 l with H_2O
3·1	Pyridine (5 ml), CH_3COOH (100 ml glacial) to 1 l with H_2O
3·5	Pyridine (5 ml), CH_3COOH (50 ml glacial) to 1 l with H_2O
4·7	Pyridine (25 ml), CH_3COOH (25 ml glacial) to 1 l with H_2O
6·5	Pyridine (100 ml), CH_3COOH (4 ml glacial) to 1 l with H_2O
7·9	0·03M-NH_4HCO_3
8·9	$(NH_4)_2CO_3$ (20 g/l solution)

APPROXIMATE pH OF SOME COMMON REAGENTS AT ROOM TEMPERATURE

Data from R. G. Bates, *Determination of* pH: *Theory and Practice*, 2nd ed., Wiley, New York (1964))

Substance	*Molarity*	pH
Acid benzoic	Saturated	2·8
Acid boric	0·1	5·3
Acid citric	0·1	2·1
Acid hydrochloric	0·1	1·1
Acid oxalic	0·1	1·3
Acid salicylic	Saturated	2·4
Acid succinic	0·1	2·7
Acid tartaric	0·1	2·0
Acid trichloroacetic	0·1	1·2
Alum, ammonium	0·05	4·6
Alum, potassium	0·1	4·2
Ammonia water	0·1	11·3
Ammonium chloride	0·1	4·6
Ammonium oxalate	0·1	6·4
Ammonium phosphate, primary	0·1	4·0
Ammonium phosphate, secondary	0·1	7·9
Ammonium sulphate	0·1	5·5
Barbital sodium	0·1	9·4
Borax	0·1	9·2
Calcium hydroxide	Saturated	12·4
Potassium acetate	0·1	9·7
Potassium bicarbonate	0·1	8·2
Potassium bioxalate	0·1	2·7
Potassium carbonate	0·1	11·5
Potassium phosphate, primary	0·1	4·5
Sodium acetate	0·1	8·9
Sodium benzoate	0·1	8·0
Sodium bicarbonate	0·1	8·3
Sodium bisulphate	0·1	1·4
Sodium carbonate	0·1	11·5
Sodium hydroxide	0·1	12·9
Sodium phosphate, primary	0·1	4·5
Sodium phosphate, secondary	0·1	9·2

PHYSIOLOGICAL MEDIA

Krebs mammalian Ringer solutions

Parts by volume

Solutions required (all approximately isotonic with serum)	*Krebs–Henseleit original Ringer bicarbonate*† *A*	*Krebs original Ringer phosphate* *B*	*Krebs improved Ringer I*† *C*	*Krebs improved Ringer II* *D*	*Krebs improved Ringer III* *E*	*Krebs substrate fortified serum*†
0·90% NaCl (0·154M)	100	100	80	83	95	100 vol. serum prepared from rapidly cooled blood
1·15% KCl (0·154M)	4	4	4	4	4	
1·22% $CaCl_2$ (0·11M)	3‡	3‡	3‡		3‡	
2·11% KH_2PO_4 (0·154M)	1	1	1	1	1	
3·8% $MgSO_4\cdot 7H_2O$ (0·154M)	1§	1§	1§	1§	1§	
1·3% $NaHCO_3$	21‖		21‖	3	3	
0·1M-Phosphate buffer pH 7·4 (17·8 g $Na_2HPO_4\cdot 2H_2O$ + 20 ml N-HCl diluted to 1 l)		21				
0·16M-Na pyruvate (or L-lactate)			4	4	4	3
0·1M-Na fumarate			7	7	7	6
0·16M-Na-L-glutamate			4	4	4	3
0·3M-(5·4%) glucose			5	5	5	5
0·1M-Na phosphate buffer [100 vol. 0·1M-Na_2HPO_4 (1·78% $Na_2HPO_4\cdot 2H_2O$)+25 vol. 0·1M-NaH_2PO_4 (1·38% $NaH_2PO_4\cdot H_2O$)]				18	3	

† Gassed with 5% CO_2 in gas phase.
‡ Twice the conc. of ionized Ca in serum (*Nature, Lond.* **184**, 1315 (1959)).
§ For human serum-substitute replace 50% with 0·154M-$MgCl_2$.
‖ Gassed with 100% CO_2 for 1 hr before mixing with other solutions.

Notes. A and *B. Krebs and Henseleit bicarbonate and phosphate Ringer* (*Z.P.C.* **210,** 33 (1932); **217,** 193 (1933)). Cl^- ions about 20 per cent higher than in mammalian serum.

C. Krebs improved Ringer I (*B.B.A.* **4,** 249 (1950)). Conc. of electrolytes and organic acids similar to mammalian serum, and contains intrinsic substrate.

D. Krebs improved Ringer II. Low bicarbonate, Ca^{++} *free* (*B.B.A.* **4,** 249 (1950)). Suitable for measurement of CO_2 production by direct CO_2 absorption. Valuable for minced tissues and homogenates as higher and steadier rates of respiration obtained in Ca-free media. Concentration of phosphate is 20 times higher and bicarbonate 10 times lower than physiological.

E. Krebs improved Ringer III. Low phosphate, bicarbonate, and CO_2. Suitable for measurement of CO_2 production by direct CO_2 absorption. Concentration of Ca about twice that of the ionized Ca of serum. Limited buffering capacity.

Storage. A composite solution containing the NaCl, KCl, $CaCl_2$, KH_2PO_4, and $MgSO_4 \pm 3$ vols. $NaHCO_3$ solution will not precipitate Ca or Mg. The danger of microfloral contamination is avoided if the *individual* solutions are made up at five times the required concentrations and diluted before use. Solutions of organic acid salts and glucose should be sterilized, frozen, or freshly prepared.

Other Ringer solutions

The following salts and glucose are dissolved in water to produce 100 ml solution. Solutions containing $NaHCO_3$ should not be sterilized by heating since the loss of CO_2 causes a more alkaline reaction. They may be sterilized by filtration through a Seitz, Berkefeld or similar filter.

	Ringer (frog heart) (g)	*Locke† (mammalian heart)* (g)	*Tyrode‡ (rabbit intestine)* (g)	*Amphibian Ringer* (g)	*Marine mollusc saline* (g)	*Marine crustacea saline* (g)	*Elasmobranch saline* (g)
NaCl	0·65	0·9§	0·8	0·65	2·34	2·92	1·64
KCl	0·014	0·042	0·02	0·025		0·075	0·089
$CaCl_2$ (anhyd.)	0·012	0·024	0·02	0·03	0·56	0·44	0·11
$MgCl_2$ (anhyd.)			0·01‖		0·76		
$NaHCO_3$	0·02	0·01–0·03	0·1	0·02 (pH 7·0–7·4)			0·038
NaH_2PO_4 (anhyd.)	0·001		0·005				0·006
Glucose	0·2	0·1–0·25	0·1				0·1
Urea							2·16

† Locke, *Zentbl. Physiol.* **14,** 670 (1900).
‡ Tyrode, *Arch. int. Pharmacodyn. Thér.* **20,** 205 (1910).
§ For cold-blooded animals reduce NaCl to 0·65 g.
‖ Pernow, *Acta physiol. scand.* **29,** Suppl. 105 (1953), uses $MgCl_2 \cdot 6H_2O$.

Artificial sea water

(i) Prepared from solutions isotonic with sea water. Atlantic sea water is 3·50–3·55% saline while North Sea sea water is 3·4–3·5%.

		ml
0·54M	NaCl	739·6
0·54M	KCl	18·05
0·36M	$MgCl_2$	145·7
0·36M	$CaCl_2$	28·0
0·44M	Na_2SO_4	63·0
0·54M	$NaHCO_3$	4·6
0·54M	NaBr	1·05 (for most purposes NaCl can be substituted)

(ii) Prepared from the following salts dissolved in water and diluted to 1 litre.
24·7 g NaCl; 0·7 g KCl; 6·3 g $MgSO_4 \cdot 7H_2O$; 4·6 g $MgCl_2 \cdot 6H_2O$; 1·0 g anhyd. $CaCl_2$; 0·2 g $NaHCO_3$.

21. Methods for the Detection of Biochemical Compounds on Paper and Thin Layer Chromatograms, with some notes on separation

Reference works on chromatography

1. E. Lederer and M. Lederer, *Chromatography*, 2nd ed., van Nostrand, Princeton, N.J. (1957).
2. R. J. Block, E. L. Durrum, and G. Zweig. *A Manual of Paper Chromatography and Paper Electrophoresis*, 2nd ed., Academic Press, New York (1958).
3. I. M. Hais and K. Macek, *Handbuch der Papierchromatographie*, Gustav Fischer Verlag, Jena (1958).
4. Ivor Smith (ed.), *Chromatographic and Electrophoretic Techniques*, 3rd ed., 2 vols., W. Heinemann, London (1969).
5. E. Stahl (ed.), *Dünnschicht-Chromatographie*, Springer-Verlag, Berlin (1962). (English translation by Cambridge Consultants Ltd., Springer-Verlag, Berlin, and Academic Press, New York (1965)).
6. Kurt Randerath, *Thin-layer Chromatography*, Academic Press, New York (1963) (Translated from the German by D. D. Libman, *Dünnschicht-Chromatographie*, Verlag Chemie GMBH, Weinheim/Bergstr (1962)).
7. E. V. Truter, *Thin Film Chromatography*, Cleaver-Hume Press, London (1963).
8. I. M. Hais and K. Macek (ed.), *Paper Chromatography: A Comprehensive Treatise*, 3 vols., Academic Press, New York and London, and Czechoslovak Academy of Sciences, Prague (1964).

1. ACIDS

Revised by J. B. DAVENPORT (*Division of Food Preservation, C.S.I.R.O., Ryde, New South Wales*)

VOLATILE FATTY ACIDS

The separation of volatile aliphatic acids is reviewed in *J. Chromat.* **1,** 70 (1958). It is recommended there that the acids be run as their morpholine salts in the solvent system butanol–cyclohexane–propylene glycol–0·880 ammonia–morpholine–water (30:30:10:0·7:0·07:3·5) for the separation of the straight chain acids, and in the system benzyl alcohol saturated with 1·5N-ammonia for the *iso* series. An evaluation of methods of separation using other derivatives has been discussed in a review in *Fette Seifen Anstrichmittel* **64,** 679 (1962).

Free volatile fatty acids can only be detected on paper by pH indicator methods. The formation of heavy-metal soaps, which can be used for the higher fatty acids, is not applicable as the soaps of the volatile fatty acids are too soluble in water. If unsaturation is present, methods listed under higher fatty acids and lipids may be applicable.

1. *Indicators*

Spray with 0·04% bromocresol green in EtOH or H_2O, adjusted to a blue colour (pH 7·5) with NaOH. Anions give yellow spots and cations deep blue spots on a pale blue background, or if bromothymol blue is used, a green background. Sensitivity is 5 μg. If the chromatogram has been run in a solvent containing NH_3 or ethylamine these colours are given only if, before spraying, the paper is dried at 95° for 5 min to decompose salts (*B.J.* **47,** 598 (1950)). If the paper is dried at R.T. for a short time and then sprayed with 2% bromocresol green in EtOH, ammonium or ethylamine salts give blue spots on a greenish-yellow background (*Nature, Lond.* **166,** 522 (1950)).

Modified procedures

(i) Spray with 0·05% bromophenol blue in 0·2% aq. citric acid. Acids give blue spots on an orange-yellow ground. This is claimed to be better than bromocresol green made alkaline with NaOH (*Analyt. Chem.* **23,** 1033 (1951)).

(ii) Spray with 0·04% bromocresol purple in B.P. formalin–EtOH (1:5) adjusted to pH 5 with NaOH. Expose sprayed paper to NH_3. Acids give yellow spots on a purple background (*B.J.* **50,** 60 (1952)).

(iii) Spray with 0·1% aq. thymol blue, adjusted to a deep blue colour (pH 10) with NaOH. Ammonium salts give yellow spots on a blue ground (*B.J.* **55,** 824 (1953)).

(iv) Spray with a solution containing 0·04% each of methyl red and bromothymol blue in formalin–EtOH (1:4) adjusted to pH 5·2 with 0·1N-NaOH. Dip in NH_3 vapour several times, returning the paper to air between each dip. Acids give orange or red spots on a dark green ground (*Analyst* **78,** 641 (1953)).

HIGHER FATTY ACIDS

The separation and detection of higher fatty acids on impregnated papers is reviewed in *Chromat. Rev.* **4,** 160 (1962). See also *Meth. biochem. Anal.* **4,** 131 (1957). Thin layer chromatography of fatty acids is described in *Fette Seifen Anstrichmittel* **62,** 1014 (1960) and **64,** 81 (1962).

Higher fatty acids may be detected by (*a*) the use of indicators, (*b*) the use of lipophilic dyes, (*c*) the formation of heavy metal soaps, or (*d*) reaction with the olefinic bonds if the fatty acids are unsaturated. Kaufmann (*Fette Seifen Anstrichmittel* **58,** 492 (1956) has reviewed methods especially of the types (*c*) and (*d*) above and considered their use in quantitative estimations particularly using the soaps of radioactive heavy metals.

Indicators, liposoluble dyes, and metal salts are not now commonly used for the detection of higher fatty acids in *complex* mixtures. Acidic phospholipids would react with indicators and many phospholipids form complexes with metal salts. Any of the general sprays for lipids are routinely used for higher fatty acids.

2. *Indicators*

Spray with 0·4% bromothymol blue in methyl cellosolve. Acids give yellow spots on a blue ground (*B.J.* **54,** xxxix (1953)).

3. *Lipophilic dyes*

Spray with 0·1% Rhodamine B in H_2O or 0·5N-HCl. In u.v. light fatty acids show a clear red fluorescence. Sensitivity 10–100 μg (*Angew. Chem.* **66,** 330 (1954)).

Nile blue is also used (*Fette Seifen* **53,** 390 (1951)) as well as fluorescent indicators, quinine, acridine orange, chlorophyll, anthracene, etc. (*Fette Seifen* **54,** 7 (1952)).

4. *Metallic soaps*

(i) Dip in 1% aq. Pb acetate and wash in water. After drying, expose to H_2S. Acids give brown spots on a white or pale tan ground. 0·5 μg of stearic acid may be detected. Instead of exposing to H_2S the paper may be dipped in sat. aq. solution of the K salt of rhodizonic acid followed by washing in water until the water is colourless. Purple spots of Pb rhodizonate on a pale pink background result. This is slightly less sensitive than the H_2S treatment (*Arch. B.B.* **56,** 1 (1955)).

(ii) Dip in 1% ammoniacal $AgNO_3$. Wash in water, the last wash containing a drop of HCl. A dip in ammonium sulphide gives brown-black spots (*Bull. Soc. Chim. biol.* **36,** 415 (1954)).

(iii) Immerse the air-dried chromatogram for 15 min in a 0·1% mercuric acetate solution containing 0·5 ml acetic acid/litre. Remove excess mercuric acetate by washing in running tap-water for 45 min. Dry in air and spray with a 0·2% solution of *s*-diphenylcarbazide in 95% ethyl alcohol. Mercuric salts of acids give purple spots which are stable for several days (*Analyt. Chem.* **31,** 1616 (1959)).

5. *Reaction with unsaturated centres*

Spray with 0·5% osmic acid. Leave overnight. Unsaturated acids give black spots (*J. exp. Bot.* **4,** 173 (1953)).

See also Lipids, 5.

HIGHER FATTY ACID ESTERS

6. *Sudan IV*

Spray with 1% Sudan IV in acetone–H_2O (1:1). This spray has been used for esters of long chain fatty acids (C_{10}–C_{22}) (*Experientia* **4,** 270 (1948)).

7. *Hydroxylamine-ferric chloride*

Spray plates or papers with alkaline hydroxylamine reagent, dry briefly, spray with ethereal acid ferric chloride reagent prepared as below. Purple spots appear quickly on a yellow background (*J. Lipid Res.* **3,** 471 (1962)).

Alkaline hydroxylamine. Dissolve 10 g $NH_2OH \cdot HCl$ in 25 ml water, dilute to 100 ml with ethanol, mix with 26 ml of saturated aq. NaOH diluted to 200 ml with ethanol. Filter off NaCl ppt.

Acid ferric chloride. Grind 10 g $FeCl_3 \cdot 6H_2O$ and 20 ml HCl (37% w/v) in pestle and mortar, shake resulting solution with 300 ml ether.

FATTY ACID DERIVATIVES

Hydroxamic acids

8. *Ferric chloride*

Spray with 5% $FeCl_3 \cdot 6H_2O$ in 0·1N-HCl in 95% EtOH. Acids up to C_{10} give purple spots on a yellow ground; C_{12}–C_{22} acids give brown spots. 0·01–0·02 μmole detected (*J.B.C.* **184,** 769 (1950)).

Hydrazides

9. *Silver nitrate*

Spray with *n*-BuOH saturated with 10% ammoniacal $AgNO_3$. Hydrazides give brown spots. 10 μg acetic acid hydrazide is detected (*J. Jap. Chem.* **4,** 557 (1950)).

NON-VOLATILE ACIDS (*other than higher fatty acids*)

A review by Howe (*J. Chromat.* **3,** 389 (1960)) deals with the behaviour of many organic acids in various solvents, and Ferraz and Relvas (*J. Chromat.* **6,** 505 (1961)) give the colours of many with various sprays.

GENERAL METHODS

10. *Indicators*

After strongly acid chromatographic solvents, unless they contain cineole to assist in the removal of the acid, papers are dried for 1 hr at 60°, then at R.T. for 2–3 hr. Spray with 0·04% bromophenol blue in 95% EtOH, adjusted to a purple tint (pH 5) with NaOH, or with bromocresol green indicator adjusted to a blue tint. A few drops of NH_4OH added just before spraying assists in giving a vivid contrast (*B.B.A.* **10,** 471 (1953)). Bromothymol blue can also be used and is a more sensitive indicator but the colour given with bromophenol blue is more stable (*Nature, Lond.* **168,** 511 (1951)). The combination of *alkaline* $KMnO_4$ with acid-base indicators is said to yield different colours with different organic acids, so making their identification easier (*J. Chromat.* **4,** 241 (1960)).

After alkaline solvents, when acids are separated as ammonium salts, *see* 1, or use one of the following sprays.

(i) Heat the paper at 95° for 5 min and then spray with 0·04% aq. chlorophenol red, pH 4·7. Anions give bright yellow spots on a mauve ground (*Nature, Lond.* **167,** 441 (1951)).

(ii) Spray with B.D.H. Universal indicator, adjusted to pH 9–10 with NaOH (*J.C.S.* **1951,** 2197).

(iii) Spray with a solution containing 50 mg phenol red in 20 ml 96% EtOH+2 ml M-NaOH, diluted to 100 ml with H_2O. Acids give bright yellow spots on a red ground (*B.J.* **48,** 467 (1951)).

11. *Dimethylglyoxime–nickel biuret*

The paper is first allowed to dry in air and then well steamed to remove all traces of volatile acidic solvent. Dip in (*a*) 1% dimethylglyoxime in 95% ethanol. Partially dry and then spray with (*b*) freshly prepared alkaline nickel biuret solution: 1 g nickel sulphate heptahydrate is dissolved in 50 ml H_2O, and 1 g biuret then dissolved, with warming. Add 10 ml 1N-NaOH and allow to stand 30 min before being filtered to remove precipitated nickel hydroxide. The acids appear as stable pink to red spots on a colourless background. After 2 min wash twice in 400–500 ml ethanol–0·88 NH_3 (1:1) for 2 min. Sensitivity 10 μg (*J. Chromat.* **14,** 549 (1964)).

12. *Glucose–silver nitrate*

Spray with 3% glucose. Dry. Then dip in a mixture of 3 ml 50% w/v $AgNO_3$+200 ml acetone. Heat at 100° for 3 min. White spots on a dark ground are given due to inhibition of $AgNO_3$ reduction by acid (cf. *Chemy Ind.* **1951,** 479). Follow by 1% Na thiosulphate to fix the spots (*Nature, Lond.* **172,** 1188 (1953)).

13. *Mercurochrome*

Spray with 0·1% mercurochrome in EtOH. Acids give white spots on a pink ground; in u.v. light, violet spots on a greenish-yellow fluorescent ground (*Analyt. Chem.* **25,** 659 (1953)).

14. *Nessler reagent*

Expose the dry paper to NH_3 vapour. Dip in Nessler reagent (*see* Biochemical Reagents section, p. 619). Intense orange spots are produced on a light background. The reaction is given by any acid which forms an ammonium salt (*J.A.C.S.* **73,** 1387 1951)).

Diazotized p-nitroaniline has also been recommended for the detection of ammonium salts of aliphatic acids (*J. Chromat.* **4,** 350 (1960)).

15. *Multiple spray for amino acids+acids+sugars*

Spray with (*a*) 0·2% ninhydrin in BuOH saturated with water and dry at 70°. Mark amino acids (1–5 μg) and then spray with (*b*) 0·1% methyl red in EtOH adjusted with NaOH to the pH where the soln. just turns orange on paper. Dry in air. Organic acids (25 μg) give red spots. Then spray with (*c*) 3:5-dinitrosalicylate (*see* Carbohydrates, 19). Dry in air, then heat at 105° until dark spots of reducing sugars (15 μg) appear. Store in the dark at R.T. for 2 weeks. Non-reducing sugars give grey-green spots (60 μg) (*Analyt. Chem.* **26,** 248 (1954)).

KETO ACIDS

See also reviews in *Meth. biochem. Anal.* **5,** 127, 139, 161 (1957); **6,** 145 (1958), for the determination of α-keto acids.

16. *Semicarbazide hydrochloride*

Spray with 0·1% semicarbazide hydrochloride in 0·15% aq. Na acetate. Heat at 110°. Free keto acids appear as dark spots on a faintly fluorescent background in u.v. (*J.A.C.S.* **74,** 4253 (1952)). *See also* Aldehydes and Ketones, 1.

17. *o-Phenylenediamine*

Spray with 0·05% *o*-phenylenediamine in 10% aq. trichloroacetic acid. Heat at 100° for 2 min. In u.v. α-keto compounds show a yellow-green fluorescence (*Naturwissenschaften* **36,** 219 (1949)).

KETO ACID DERIVATIVES

2:4-Dinitrophenylhydrazones

18. *Colour*

Yellow colour of hydrazones turns to various shades of red with 10% Na_2CO_3 or dilute NaOH (*Nature, Lond.* **163,** 568 (1949)).

Quinoxalinols

19. *Ultraviolet light*

Yellow fluorescence in u.v. is shown by quinoxalinol derivatives (*B.J.* **52,** 38 (1952)).

20. *2-Chloro-4-nitrophenyldiazoniumnaphthyl-2-sulphonate*

Spray with a 0·1% aq. solution. Pyruvic acid quinoxalinol gives a pink spot; dimethylpyruvic, benzoylformic, and ketoglutaric acid derivatives are negative (*B.J.* **52,** 38 (1952)).

Nitroquinoxalinols

21. *Colour*

A yellow colour in visible light is shown by nitroquinoxalinol derivatives (50 μg). This is accentuated by a spray of 2% KOH in EtOH. In u.v. the spots are dull brown on a purplish background (*B.J.* **52,** 38 (1952)).

PHENOLIC ACIDS

22. *2:6-Dibromoquinone-4-chloroimide**

Spray with a 0·33% solution of 2:6-dibromoquinone-4-chloroimide in dry dioxan-acetone (4:1). Then spray with dilute ammonia. Phenolic compounds give blue, green, and grey colours (*J. Chromat.* **1,** 338 (1958)). Cf. Phenols, 3.

* Warning: This compound can be an explosive risk at temperatures of 50 °C and above.

23. *Ferric chloride*

Spray with 2% $FeCl_3 \cdot 6H_2O$ in water or with a saturated solution of anhydrous ferric chloride in anhydrous dioxan or chloroform. Most phenolic compounds give red-violet spots. Pyrocatechol derivatives give green spots (*J. Chromat.* **1,** 338 (1958)). Cf. Phenols, 10.

TRICARBOXYLIC ACIDS

24. *Furth–Hermann reagent*

Spray with acetic acid–pyridine (1:9). Heat at 100° for 5 min. Tricarboxylic acids give yellow to red spots showing fluorescence in u.v. Glucuronic and ascorbic acids give yellow spots; aconitic, brown; itaconic, orange (*Analyt. Chem.* **24,** 489 (1952); *J. Chromat.* **6,** 505 (1961)).

AROMATIC ACIDS

25. *Fluorescent hydroxy derivatives*

Spray with 0·3% hydrogen peroxide. Irradiate the wet chromatogram with u.v. light. Within a few minutes aromatic acids give blue fluorescent spots (*J. Chromat.* **10,** 511 (1963)).

HYDROXY ACIDS

26. *Cupric acetate—rubeanic acid*

Hydroxy acids forming complexes with copper can be determined by retention analysis. Develop the chromatogram in the second direction with 1% cupric acetate in tetrahydrofuran–water (95:5). Dry and spray with 1% rubeanic acid. Colourless areas in a grey-green ground give an estimate of the amount of hydroxy acid present (*Angew. Chem.* **63,** 258 (1951)). This method has also been used for amino acids (*Angew. Chem.* **63,** 171 (1951)).

27. *Lead tetra-acetate oxidation*

α-Hydroxy and pyruvic acids are detected by this method. *See* Carbohydrates, 43.

TRITERPENOID AND STEROID ACIDS

28. *Phosphomolybdic acid*

Spray heavily with 10% phosphomolybdic acid in 95% ethanol. Heat the wet paper at 100° for 5 min. Gives blue spots on a greenish-yellow background (*J. Chromat.* **8,** 32 (1962)). Cf. Steroids, 34.

UNSATURATED ACIDS

29. *Osmic acid*

See Higher fatty acids, 5.

URONIC ACIDS

See Carbohydrates.

---

2. ALDEHYDES AND KETONES

1. 2:4-*Dinitrophenylhydrazine*

Spray with 0·4% 2:4-dinitrophenylhydrazine in 2N-HCl. Carbonyl compounds give yellow spots which turn red-brown when treated with 10% NaOH and α-dicarbonyl compounds give a purple colour (*Nature, Lond.* **172,** 455 (1953); **164,** 1093 (1949)). *See also* a review on the chromatographic separation of carbonyl compounds in *J. Chromat.* **8,** 433 (1962).

2. *Orcinol*

Spray with 0·5 g orcinol+15 g trichloroacetic acid in 100 ml H_2O-saturated *n*-BuOH. Different coloured spots are given for aldehydes depending on the time and temp. of heating (e.g. heat at 25° for 5–10 min; 50°, 1 or 10 min; 100°, 1 or 5 min). Characteristic colours, mostly pinks, are given with vanillin and other aromatic aldehydes (*Chemist Analyst* **41,** 5 (1952)).

3. *Ammoniacal silver nitrate*

This reagent (cf. Carbohydrates, 1) has been used for methylglyoxal which gives a brownish spot. Presumably all aldehydes react (*Arch. B.B.* **57,** 20 (1955)).

2:4-*Dinitrophenylhydrazine derivatives of volatile aldehydes and ketones*

4. *Sodium hydroxide*

Spray with 10% NaOH. The yellow coloured spots of 2:4-dinitrophenylhydrazones turn red-brown (*Nature, Lond.* **170,** 579 (1952)).

3. AMINES

Revised by H. WEIL-MALHERBE (*National Institute of Mental Health, Washington, D.C.*)

The paper chromatography of amines is such a vast field that it cannot be dealt with adequately in a few introductory remarks. For a more thorough treatment the reader is referred to the general treatises on paper chromatography previously mentioned (p. 512). References to Thin-layer Chromatography (TLC) unless accompanied by other quotation pertain to E. Stahl (ed.), *Dünnschicht-Chromatographie*, Springer-Verlag, Berlin (1962).

Only some recent contributions of interest to the worker in the area of animal biochemistry and pharmacology will be mentioned here.

The phenolic amines of human urine were studied two-dimensionally with *n*-butanol–acetic acid–water (4:1:1) as the first solvent and *iso*-propanol–conc. ammonia–water (8:1:1) as the second solvent (*J.B.C.* **237,** 208 (1962)). For improved resolution the following solvent systems have been recommended: *tert*-amyl alcohol–17% aq. methylamine (4:1) in the first direction (to be used at a temperature of about 32° C) and either *sec*-butanol–pyridine–acetic acid–water (604:10:41:100) or nitroethane–70% aq. acetic acid (9:4) in the second direction (both at about 21° C) (*Nature, Lond.* **195,** 174 (1962)).

For the *detection of basic drugs in urine and tissue extracts* the organic phase of the system *n*-butanol–formic acid–water (12:1:7) has been used (*Z.P.C.* **292,** 94 (1953); *Z.P.C.* **305,** 53 (1956)). In another widely used method the paper is buffered by dipping in 5% sodium dihydrogen citrate and dried, before development in *n*-butanol–2% aq. citric acid (1:1, upper layer) (*Nature, Lond.* **173,** 1143 (1954)). Factors affecting the reproducibility of the method, such as equilibration of the paper with solvent vapours, the water content of the solvent, the temperature, the size of the tank and the number of sheets in the tank, have been studied (*J. Pharm. Pharmac.* **15,** 390 (1963)). A similar system—paper buffered by dipping in 0·25M-citrate buffer, pH 5·7; solvent: azeotropic dioxan–citric acid–0·880NH_3 (400 ml: 1·6 g: 0·6 ml) has been used for the separation of phenothiazine metabolites in urine (*J. Pharmac. exp. Ther.* **141,** 377 (1963)).

For the *separation of glycerylphosphoryl bases* formed during the hydrolysis of phospholipids, the following method has been described (*B.J.* **75,** 45 (1960); *B.J.* **84,** 497 (1962)): the chromatogram is developed in the first direction with phenol saturated with water–acetic acid–ethanol (100:10:12) as solvent. This is followed in the second direction either by chromatography in methanol–formic acid–water (80:13:7) (after removing phenol with ether) or, preferably, by ionophoresis in a pyridine–acetic acid buffer pH 3·6.

GENERAL METHODS

1. *Inspection in short-wave* (253 *mμ*) *and long-wave* (366 *mμ*) *ultraviolet light*

Fluorescent amines include kynurenine (pale blue), *o*-aminoacetophenone (pale blue), 3-hydroxykynurenine (green), anthranilic acid (purple), aminosalicylic acid (blue), xanthopterine (yellow-green), many drugs and alkaloids (*B.J.* **52,** 3 (1952)).

Other compounds, possessing single or condensed aromatic rings, may be visible as dark spots on a faintly fluorescent background.

2. *Indicators, for the detection of bases*

Thoroughly remove basic or acidic solvents in current of hot air. Spray with one of the following reagents:

(i) 0·05% bromocresol green in 95% ethanol, adjusted to green colour (pH 6–7) with dilute NaOH (*Univ. of Texas Publication*, no. **5109,** 30 (1951)).

(ii) mixture (1:1) of saturated ethanolic solutions of methyl orange and congo red (*Arch. B.B.* **59,** 484 (1955)).

If spots do not show up, expose paper alternately to vapours of NH_3 and HCl.

(iii) Spray with 1% solution of tetraphenylborosodium in butanone saturated with water. Dry, then spray with 0·015% solution of a flavon-3-ol in methanol (e.g. fisetin, quercetin, hyperin, or rutin) (*J. Chromat.* **11,** 364 (1963)). Spots are orange to red.

PRIMARY AMINES

3. *Ninhydrin*

One of the following ninhydrin sprays may be used:

(i) 0·1% in *n*-butanol, saturated with water. Heat at 105° for 5 min (*Arch. B.* **24,** 179 (1949)).

(ii) 0·2% in *iso*propanol–pyridine (80:20). Heat at 105° for 2–3 min (*J. Lab. clin. Med.* **41,** 802 (1953)). Aliphatic amines blue-red, tyramine purple, tryptamine purple-brown, histamine red-brown, noradrenaline and 5-hydroxytryptamine brown.

(iii) 0·2% in mixture of abs. ethanol, acetic acid and 2:4:6-collidine (50:10:2). Immediately before use, mix 25 parts with 1·5 parts of a 1% solution of $Cu(NO_3)_2 \cdot 3H_2O$ in abs. ethanol. Spray and dry for 1·5–2 min at 105° (*Analyt. Chem.* **31,** 926 (1959)). Also applicable for TLC. Polychromatic spots are obtained with a mixture of amino acids.

Ninhydrin is specific for the aliphatic or alicyclic primary amino group. Secondary, tertiary, and quaternary amines, amides, and amino-substituted aromatic compounds do not react. Exception: proline gives yellow spot, probably due to opening of ring.

4. *o-Acetoacetylphenol or 2-acetoacetyl-4-methylphenol*

Spray with 0·1% solution of *o*-acetoacetylphenol (*J.C.S.* **1952,** 3215) or 2-acetoacetyl-4-methylphenol (*J.C.S.* **1954,** 1157) in *n*-butanol. Primary aliphatic or alicyclic amines show brilliant greenish-yellow fluorescence in u.v. Does not react with secondary amines, primary aromatic amines, or amino acids.

SECONDARY AMINES

5. *Sodium nitroprusside–acetaldehyde*

Immediately before spraying mix equal volumes of 5% sodium nitroprusside in 10% aqueous acetaldehyde and 2% sodium carbonate (*Pharmazie* **11,** 533 (1956)). Alternatively, spray first with nitroprusside-acetaldehyde solution, then, when the paper is almost dry, with 2% sodium carbonate (*J. Pharmac. exp. Ther.* **125,** 283 (1959)). May also be used in TLC. Secondary amines appear as blue spots.

TERTIARY AMINES, QUATERNARY AMMONIUM COMPOUNDS, AND ALKALOIDS

6. *Iodoplatinate*

Mix 5 ml of 5% platinum chloride in 1N-HCl with 45 ml 10% potassium iodide and 100 ml water. Protect the reagent against light. After spraying wash out excess from paper with water (*Analyt. Chem.* **28,** 1289 (1956)). For TLC a mixture (1:1) of 0·3% $PtCl_4$ and 6% KI may be used (*J. Chromat.* **6,** 61 (1961)).

7. *Dragendorff's reagent*

Stock solutions:

Soln. I: Dissolve 17 g basic bismuth nitrate and 200 g tartaric acid in 800 ml water.

Soln. II: Dissolve 160 g potassium iodide in 400 ml water.

Mix solutions I and II. Protect from light. For spraying mix 50 ml stock, 100 g tartaric acid and 500 ml water.

Alkaloids appear as orange spots (sensitivity about 5 μg) (*Bull. Soc. Chim. biol.* **35,** 1225 (1953)).

Modification for TLC: Stock solution: boil 2·6 g bismuth carbonate, 7 g sodium iodide and 25 ml acetic acid for a few minutes. After 12 hr filter from precipitate of sodium acetate. Mix 20 ml of filtrate with 8 ml ethyl acetate and store in brown bottle.

Spray solution: mix 10 ml stock, 25 ml acetic acid, and 60 ml ethyl acetate.

Sensitivity can be enhanced by a second spray with 0·05–0·1N-H_2SO_4. The most favourable concentration and amount of acid should be ascertained in a trial experiment.

8. *Iodine*

2% solution in ethanol (*Nature, Lond.* **163,** 651 (1949)). Cf. Lipids, 5; Steroids, 36.

For TLC: 0·5% solution in chloroform, or treat with iodine vapour.

Iodine is a relatively unspecific reagent which forms brown spots with many organic compounds.

SPECIAL METHODS

Many reagents used for the detection of particular amines or groups of amines interact with functions other than the amino group and will, therefore, be found in other sections. To avoid undue duplication only a few selected reagents which are less commonly used for the detection of other classes of compounds will be described here.

ETHANOLAMINE

9. *Benzoquinone*

Spray with 0·5 g benzoquinone in 10 ml pyridine+40 ml *n*-butanol (*Bull. Soc. Chim. biol.* **33,** 862 (1951)). Ethanolamine gives a brown-red spot at room temperature. Serine reacts feebly at 100°, choline not at all.

CHOLINE

10. *Phosphomolybdic acid*

Spray with (*a*) 2% aq. phosphomolybdic acid. Wash the paper in a large vol. *n*-butanol for 5 min, then in running water. Dip in (*b*) freshly prepared 0·4% stannous chloride in 3N-HCl (*J.B.C.* **175,** 67 (1948)). Spots of choline phosphomolybdate are reduced to molybdenum blue. Sensitivity 5–10 μg. This method is also positive for sphingosine.

Modification for TLC: spray with (*a*) 1% phosphomolybdic acid in 1:1 mixture of ethanol–chloroform. Dry for 3 min. Then spray with (*b*) 1% stannous chloride in 3N-HCl. Dry for 10 min.

11. *Potassium ferrocyanide–cobalt chloride*

Spray with (*a*) 1% aq. $K_4Fe(CN)_6$. Then spray with (*b*) 0·5% aq. cobalt chloride (*J. Am. pharm. Ass.* **42,** 680 (1953)). Choline gives a green spot. Sensitivity 10 μg. Also suitable for TLC.

CHOLINE ESTERS

12. *Hydroxylamine–ferric chloride*

Hydroxylamine solution: (*a*) dissolve 20 g $NH_2OH \cdot HCl$ in 50 ml water and dilute to 200 ml with 95% ethanol; (*b*) dissolve 50 g KOH in minimum amount of water and dilute to 500 ml with 95% ethanol. Mix 1 vol. of (*a*) with 2 vol. of (*b*) and filter from precipitated KCl. The mixture is stable for 2 weeks in the cold. It is best kept at −10°.

Ferric chloride solution: dissolve 10 g of finely powdered $FeCl_3 \cdot 6H_2O$ in 20 ml conc. HCl. Shake with 200 ml ether until a homogeneous solution is formed.

Spray first with NH_2OH solution, dry at room temp., then spray with $FeCl_3$-solution (*B.J.* **51,** 348 (1952)). Any organic ester gives a purple spot on a yellow ground. Sensitivity for carboxylic esters, 0·5–2 μg. Also suitable for TLC. Cf. Carbohydrates, 49; Acids, 7.

CYANAMIDES, GUANIDINES

See Amino acids, 22, 23.

GLUTARIMIDES, CARBAMATES, UREIDES

13. *Sodium hypochlorite*

Dilute a solution of NaOCl containing 10–13% available chlorine with 4 vol. water. Spray and dry paper in current of air for 1 hr to remove excess chlorine. Then spray with 2% starch solution containing 1% KI (I. Smith, *Chromatographic and Electrophoretic Techniques*, 2nd ed., Heinemann, London (1960)). Spots appear blue-black on colourless or pale blue background.

o-AMINOPHENOLS

14. *Urorosein test*

Expose damp paper to nitrous fumes generated in beaker from $NaNO_2$ and HCl (*B.J.* **52**, 3 (1952)). *o*-Aminophenols give yellow spots, turning brown. The reaction is also positive for indoles.

o-, *m*-, AND *p*-AMINOPHENOLS

15. *Ammoniacal silver nitrate*

Spray with 1:1 mixture of 0·1N-$AgNO_3$ and 5N-NH_3, prepared immediately before use (*B.J.* **50**, 228 (1951)).

16. *Salicylaldehyde*

Spray with 1% soln. of salicylaldehyde in ethanol containing 5% (v/v) acetic acid. Dry at room temp. (*B.J.* **50**, 228 (1951)). Yellow fluorescent spots appear.

AROMATIC AMINES, SULPHONAMIDES

17. *Coupling with diazonium salts*

(i) *Diazotized sulphanilic acid*: *see* Amino acids, 14; Phenols, 2 (ii). This reagent has been used for the detection of histamine, tyramine, tryptamine, and 5-hydroxytryptamine (*B.J.* **49**, 651 (1951); *Archs int. Pharmacodyn. Thér.* **88**, 296 (1951)). Some phenols develop a colour after spraying with diazotized sulphanilic acid, whereas the majority do so only after a second spray with alkali.

(ii) *Diazotized p-nitroaniline*. To a stock solution of 0·2% *p*-nitroaniline in 1N-HCl (5 ml) add 50 ml 0·1N-HCl, then 1 ml 5% $NaNO_2$. When the solution has become colourless, leave in ice for a few minutes. Keep cold until ready to spray. Immediately afterwards spray with ice-cold 20% K_2CO_3 (*Can. J. Biochem. Physiol.* **36**, 295 (1958)). Metanephrine, normetanephrine, *N*-methylmetanephrine, tyramine, hordenine, give purple spots; *p*-sympatol and octopamine, red; 3-*O*-methyldopamine, olive; phenylethylamine and phenylethanolamine, crimson; 5-hydroxytryptamine, dark red (*J.B.C.* **237**, 208 (1962); *Clinica chim. Acta* **6**, 851 (1961)). This spray has also been used for sulphonamides (*B.J.* **48**, 400 (1951)). For quantitative colorimetric estimation the spots are eluted with alkaline methanol (methanol–2% Na_2CO_3, 2:1) (*Nature, Lond.* **191**, 599 (1961); *Clinica chim. Acta* **5**, 447 (1960)) or alkaline *tert*-butanol (*tert*-butanol–H_2O–10% Na_2CO_3, 5:5:1) (*J.B.C.* **237**, 208 (1962); *Clinica chim. Acta* **6**, 851 (1961)). *See* Phenols, 2 (i).

(iii) *Diazotized p-anisidine*. Mix equal volumes of 1% soln. of *p*-anisidine in ethanol containing 0·11N-HCl and 10% (v/v) soln. of amyl nitrite in ethanol. Allow to stand for some minutes before spraying. Dry the paper in current of air. While still slightly damp expose it to NH_3 vapours or spray with ethanolic KOH (*B.J.* **49**, 463 (1951)).

Modification: replace half of the *p*-anisidine with sulphanilamide (*B.J.* **80**, 193 (1961)). Several other diazonium compounds have been used.

18. *Diazotization of amines on paper, followed by coupling reaction*

Spray with 0·2% $NaNO_2$ in 0·1N-HCl *or* 0·1% $NaNO_2$ in acetic acid containing 1 drop conc. HCl per 100 ml. (0·2% $NaNO_2$ in 10% trichloroacetic acid has been used before reagent vii). Wait 1–3 min, then spray with one of the following coupling reagents:

(i) *N-Ethyl-α-naphthylamine* (*Ekman's reagent*). 0·2% soln. of *N*-ethyl-α-naphthylamine hydrochloride in ethanol (*Acta chem. scand.* **2,** 383 (1948)). Aromatic amines give red-violet spots.

(ii) *N*-(1-*Naphthyl*)*ethylenediamine* (*Bratton–Marshall reagent*). Spray with 5% ammonium sulphamate soln. to decompose excess nitrite. Then spray with 1% aq. soln. of *N*-(1-naphthyl)ethylenediamine hydrochloride (*Can. J. Biochem. Physiol.* **37,** 1493 (1959)). Spots: kynurenine purple, tryptophan yellow, 4-aminoimidazole-5-carboxamide magenta, creatinine orange, urocanic acid pale brown, 2-aminohippuric acid purple. Sulphonamides give intensely coloured compounds (*Analyt. Chem.* **21,** 1402 (1949)).

(iii) *Dimethyl-α-naphthylamine*. Spray with 1% aq. solution (*Nature, Lond.* **168,** 877 (1951)). This has been used for sulphonamides which give red or pink spots. Sensitivity 1 μg.

(iv) *Alkaline β-naphthol*. Spray with 1% soln. in N-NaOH. Aminophenols give red to red-violet spots (*B.J.* **54,** 225 (1953)). This spray has also been used for sulphonamides (*Naturwissenschaften* **39,** 133 (1952)).

Modification for TLC: Spray with (*a*) 1% $NaNO_2$ in 1N-HCl. Then spray with (*b*) 0·2% β-naphthol in 1N-KOH. Dry at 60°.

(v) *Phenol*. Spray with 1% phenol in N-NaOH (*Aust. J. Sci.* **11,** 208 (1949)). *o*-Aminobenzoic acid gives an orange colour; *m*- and *p*-aminobenzoic acids and sulphonamides give yellow spots.

(vi) *Hexylresorcinol*. Spray with 0·5% soln. in 2N-NaOH (*B.J.* **60,** 62 (1955)). Various colours are given by aromatic amines.

(vii) 1-*Amino*-8-*naphthol*-5:6-*disulphonic acid*. Spray with 0·2% soln. (*Naturwissenschaften* **39,** 135 (1952)). Sulphonamides give red colours.

INDOLEAMINES

19. *p-Dimethylaminobenzaldehyde* (*Ehrlich's reagent*)

Spray with one of the following solutions:

'Normal Ehrlich's': 2% *p*-dimethylaminobenzaldehyde in 1·3N-HCl.

'Strong Ehrlich's': 2% *p*-dimethylaminobenzaldehyde in 6N-HCl (*J. clin. Path.* **8,** 73 (1955)).

At pH of 'normal' reagent aromatic amines appear immediately, while indoles appear slowly. In the strongly acid solution indole colours appear rapidly, but the aromatic amines appear more gradually, as the excess HCl evaporates from the paper.
Modifications:

(i) 2 g *p*-dimethylaminobenzaldehyde dissolved in 80 ml 95% ethanol+20 ml conc. HCl (*Can. J. Biochem. Physiol.* **37,** 1493 (1959)).

(ii) 2 g *p*-dimethylaminocinnamaldehyde in 100 ml 6N-HCl+100 ml ethanol (*B.J.* **69,** 60P (1958)).

(iii) 0·1% *p*-dimethylaminocinnamaldehyde in 1N-HCl (*Chromat. Rev.* **3,** 92 (1961)). *p*-Dimethylaminocinnamaldehyde is more sensitive but less specific than *p*-dimethylaminobenzaldehyde. A purple, red, or blue spot appearing after spraying with Ehrlich's reagent is presumptive evidence for the presence of a substance with an indole or pyrrole ring. Urea, aromatic amines, sulphonamides, allantoin, xanthurenic, and urocanic acids give yellow to orange colours.

20. *Ninhydrin–acetic acid*

Dip paper in 0·25% solution of ninhydrin in acetone containing 10% (v/v) acetic acid. Heat for 2–3 min at 90–100° (*Nature, Lond.* **172,** 772 (1953)).

Tryptamine and 5-hydroxytryptamine give blue-green fluorescent spots. Very sensitive test, capable of revealing 0·02 μg 5-HT.

21. *α-Nitroso-β-naphthol*

Spray with (*a*) 0·1% α-nitroso-β-naphthol in 95% ethanol. Dry and apply (*b*) 2·5% $NaNO_2$: 2N-HCl = 4:100, mixed immediately before spraying (*J.B.C.* **215,** 337

(1955)). The reagent is specific for 5-hydroxyindoles, but it is not very sensitive and is not able to detect less than 10–20 μg.

22. *Tetrazotized di-o-anisidine*

Dissolve 100 mg tetrazotized di-*o*-anisidine in 30 ml water. Immediately before spraying, add 20 ml borate buffer, pH 9·0 (*Archs Neurol. Psychiat., Chicago* **79**, 336 (1958)). Hydroxyindoles and xanthurenic acid give blue colour; indoles, indoxyl, adrenochrome, and many aromatic amines do not react.

23. *Formaldehyde*–HCl, *for TLC*

Spray with freshly prepared mixture of 10 ml 35% formaldehyde soln., 10 ml 25% HCl and 20 ml ethanol. Dry at 100° for 5 min. Indoles form yellow or green fluorescent spots. The sensitivity of the reaction (0·005–0·01 μg) is intensified by exposure to vapours of *aqua regia* (conc. HCl–conc. HNO_3, 3:1).

PHENOTHIAZINES

24. *Sulphuric acid*

Spray with mixture of conc. H_2SO_4–water–95% ethanol (1:1:8) (*J. Pharmac. exp. Ther.* **141,** 377 (1963)). Phenothiazine, promazine, and chlorpromazine yield yellow, orange, and pink colours respectively. Phenolic derivatives give purple or blue spots. Colour production with sulphoxides is catalysed by u.v. light. The same spray may be used for TLC (*J. Pharmac. exp. Ther.* **139,** 160 (1963)).

25. *Sulphuric acid–ferric nitrate*

Spray with (*a*) conc. H_2SO_4–95% ethanol (1:1). Then spray with (*b*) 2% ferric nitrate soln. Dry in stream of warm air (*Arzneimittel-Forsch.* **9,** 121 (1959)). The colours are similar to those produced by sulphuric acid alone.

CATECHOLAMINES

The tendency of catecholamines to undergo oxidation, particularly at a pH above 6, is the overriding consideration in their chromatography. Basic solvent systems have to be avoided for this reason. Phenol and *n*-butanol, with the addition of aqueous solutions of various acids, are the solvents most frequently used (*Acta chem. scand.* **4,** 1185 (1950); *Nature, Lond.* **161,** 851 (1948); *J. Pharm. Pharmac.* **3,** 22 (1951); *Br. J. Pharmac. Chemother.* **6,** 8 (1951)). Especially with phenol as solvent, the chromatograms are run in an atmosphere of SO_2, CO_2, or nitrogen and, as a further protection against oxidation, the paper may be treated with a dilute solution of ascorbic acid (50 mg per 100 ml) before use.

Two-dimensional chromatography of catecholamines seems to be uncommon, but improved resolution of a mixture of adrenaline, noradrenaline, dopamine, dopa, and 3:4-dihydroxyphenylacetic acid has been obtained by carrying out a first run in 88% aq. phenol followed by a second run in the *opposite* direction in *n*-butanol, saturated with 1N-HCl (*Nature, Lond.* **195,** 178 (1962)).

Catecholamines may form complexes or compounds with trichloroacetic acid (*Nature, Lond.* **169,** 797 (1952)) or with lactic acid (*B.J.* **48,** 203 (1951)) during the processing of tissue extracts and these may appear on the chromatogram as separate spots.

Acetylation of catecholamines prior to their separation on paper or by TLC has been recommended (*Experientia* **15,** 80 (1959); *Analyt. Biochem.* **2,** 387 (1961); *Arch. Pharm., Berl.* **32,** 125 (1962)).

Methods for the detection of catecholamines on paper chromatograms fall into three groups: (1) those based on oxidation to coloured 'chromes' (e.g. adrenochrome) or their decomposition products, (2) those based on the formation of fluorescent condensation products with formaldehyde or ethylenediamine, and (3) those based on reactions with the phenolic or amino-function of the molecule or simply on its reducing power. The reactions of the third group are not only less specific but as a rule also less sensitive than those of the first and second groups. Since the reagents of the third group (ammoniacal silver nitrate, ferric chloride, diazonium salts, etc.) are described in other sections, they will not be considered here.

For quantitative estimation the approximate position of catecholamine spots is usually located with the aid of a guide strip. After their elution from the paper they are estimated by bioassay (*Br. J. Pharmac. Chemother.* **6,** 8 (1951)) or by fluorimetry (*B.J.* **67,** 65 (1957)).

26. *Potassium ferricyanide*

Spray with 0·44% $K_3Fe(CN)_6$ in 0·2M-phosphate buffer, pH 7·8 (*Nature, Lond.* **161,** 851 (1948)) or, when the chromatogram has been run in an acidic solvent, in 0·2M-Na_2HPO_4 soln. to give pH 8·3 (*J. Pharm. Pharmac.* **3,** 22 (1951)). Colours may be intensified by exposure to ammonia vapour. Adrenaline forms a pink spot turning yellow, noradrenaline a lavender spot turning brown, and dopamine a lavender spot. Limit of sensitivity about 2 μg (*Science* **109,** 534 (1949)). Smaller quantities may be detected by green fluorescence in u.v. (*J. Physiol.* **113,** 123 (1951)).

N-Methyladrenaline gives no colour when oxidized since no indole ring closure is possible, but the ferricyanide is bleached by reduction (*Nature, Lond.* **161,** 851 (1948)). The reduced ferrocyanide may be demonstrated by a drop of very dilute copper sulphate solution resulting in a red colour. The surrounding, unreduced ferricyanide turns brown.

Ferrocyanide formation may also be demonstrated by the Prussian blue reaction: spray with soln. containing 5 g ferric sulphate, anhyd., and 75 ml 85% H_3PO_4 per litre (*Science* **109,** 534 (1949)). This reaction, indicating merely the presence of a reducing compound, is less specific than the colour formation observed after the single ferricyanide spray.

27. *Exposure to ammonia vapour*

Adrenaline shows apple-green fluorescence in u.v. light (*Nature, Lond.* **165,** 729 (1950)). Sensitivity 10 μg.

28. *Exposure to vapours of iodine and ammonia*

Adrenaline and noradrenaline form brilliant red spots turning brown (*Boll. Soc. ital. Biol. sper.* **26,** 1230 (1950)). Sensitivity, about 25 μg/3 cm^2.

29. *Iodine, for TLC*

Spray with solution of 0·5 g iodine in 100 ml chloroform and observe fluorescence in u.v. light. Sensitivity 0·005 μg.

30. *Potassium iodate*

Spray with 1% aq. KIO_3. Heat at 100–110° for not more than 2 min. Like the two preceding ones this test is based on the formation of iodo-chromes. Adrenaline (1 μg) gives a pink spot, turning brown, noradrenaline (2 μg) a violet spot, turning brown, dopamine an orange-brown spot (*Br. J. Pharmac. Chemother.* **6,** 665 (1951)). Isopropyl noradrenaline red, epinine orange (*Lancet* **1957** (1), 715).

31. *Ferricyanide–formaldehyde*

Spray with a freshly prepared mixture of 0·66% $K_3Fe(CN)_6$ and 40% formaldehyde (9:1), and heat at 100° for 5 min (*Nature, Lond.* **171,** 1160 (1953)). In a modification (*Lancet* **1957** (1), 715) the $K_3Fe(CN)_6$ solution is made up in a 0·6M-phosphate buffer, pH 5·9.

Adrenaline, noradrenaline, dopamine, isopropyl noradrenaline, and epinine give red to purple spots (sensitivity 1–2 μg) which show yellow-green fluorescence in u.v. light (sensitivity 0·2 μg).

32. *Ferricyanide or iodine, followed by Ehrlich's reagent*

Following oxidation of catecholamines to indoles, blue pigments are formed by reaction with Ehrlich's reagent.

First spray: 0·2% $K_3Fe(CN)_6$ in water or 0·001N-iodine in 0·2M-acetate buffer, pH 6 (*Scand. J. clin. Lab. Invest.* **6**, 78 (1954)) or 0·01N-iodine in 0·6M-phosphate buffer, pH 5·9 (*Lancet* **1957** (1), 715). Dry in current of cold air for 3–5 min.

Second spray: 4 g *p*-dimethylaminobenzaldehyde in 380 ml ethanol+80 ml conc. HCl. Detects 0·2 μg adrenaline or noradrenaline.

33. *Ethylenediamine–ammonia*

Spray with 2:8 mixture of redist. ethylenediamine and 2N-ammonia (*J.B.C.* **208**, 741 (1954)) or 10% (w/v) ammonia (*J. clin. Path.* **10**, 138 (1957)). Catecholamines, as well as other catechol derivatives, give yellow to brown spots showing brilliant yellow fluorescence in u.v. light. Sensitivity 0·1 μg adrenaline.

34. *Ferricyanide or iodine–ethylenediamine*

This combination is intended to accelerate the oxidative step preceding the condensation with ethylenediamine and thereby minimize side reactions (*Nature, Lond.* **181**, 768 (1958)).

Spray with solution of 0·1% $K_3Fe(CN)_6$ or 0·01N-I_2, both in 5% (v/v) aq. ethylenediamine. Dry for 5 min at 50°.

Dip reagents: Dip in 1% solution of iodine in carbon tetrachloride, blot and before the paper is completely dry, dip in 1% solution of ethylenediamine in *iso*propanol. Blot and dry at R.T. for 24 hr. Detects 0·05 μg of catecholamines.

CATECHOLAMINE TRIACETATES

35. *Ferric chloride–potassium ferricyanide*

Spray with (*a*) 10% KOH in methanol–water (1:1). Then spray with (*b*) freshly prepared mixture of 1% $FeCl_3$ and 2% $K_3Fe(CN)_6$ (*Experientia* **15**, 80 (1959)).

36. *Blue tetrazolium reagent*

Spray with (*a*) 10% KOH in methanol–water (1:1). Then spray with (*b*) 0·2% aq. sol. of triphenyltetrazolium chloride (*Analyt. Biochem.* **2**, 387 (1961)).

37. *TLC of catecholamine triacetates*

Spray with 40% H_3PO_4. Heat for 7 min at 110°. Then spray with 5% phosphomolybdic acid in ethanol and heat for 2 min at 110°.

Alternative method: dissolve 3 g vanillin in 100 ml abs. ethanol and add dropwise 3 ml conc. H_2SO_4. Spray and heat at 110° for 7 min (*Arch. Pharm., Berl.* **295/67**, *Mitt. dt. pharm. Ges. pharm. Ges. DDR* **32**, 125 (1962)).

4. AMINO ACIDS, PEPTIDES, AND PROTEINS

Revised by R. E. OFFORD (*M.R.C. Laboratory of Molecular Biology, Cambridge*)

Choice of separating system

The best systems for most compounds of this class are the ion-exchange columns to be found in the commercial amino acid analysers (*Analyt. Chem.* **30**, 1190 (1958)). Paper and thin layer methods, however, are often more rapid and more convenient. They have a greater flexibility, and quite elegant separations can be achieved with very small amounts of material.

A useful system for amino acids is electrophoresis on paper at pH 1·9 in an aqueous medium 8% with respect to acetic acid, 2% with respect to formic. Ambiguities can be resolved by chromatographic development at right angles with *sec.*-butanol–3% aq. ammonia (5:2) (*Analyt. Biochem.* **3**, 173 (1962)). This system provides a complete separation for the amino acids normally occurring in protein hydrolysates and is useful for many of the related compounds.

See also:

P. Alexander and R. J. Block (eds.), *A Laboratory Manual of Analytical Methods of Protein Chemistry*, vol. 2, Pergamon Press (1960). General.

R. J. Block, E. L. Durrum, and G. Zweig, *Paper Chromatography and Paper Electrophoresis*, 2nd ed., chap. 5, Academic Press (1958). General. Includes a list of over a hundred solvent systems for special purposes.

J. Leggett Bailey, *Techniques in Protein Chemistry*, 2nd edn., Elsevier (1967). Apparatus and technique.

M. Brenner and A. Niederwieser, 'Dünnschicht-Chromatographie von Aminosäuren', *Experientia* **16**, 378 (1960). The use of thin layer methods.

Detection

Some of the general reagents for amino acids are non-destructive and allow the subsequent estimation or re-running of the spots concerned (*see* 1 (v), 3, 4, 6, 7 (ii) below).

In the methods below, dipping is to be preferred to spraying as it gives a more even result. It cannot be applied where the substances on the paper are soluble in the reagents—for example, when the latter are aqueous solutions. On the whole the method given is that recommended by the original authors, but either dipping or spraying may be selected with the above considerations in mind.

GENERAL REAGENTS

By far the best all round reagent for a preliminary investigation is ninhydrin as it is the most sensitive and uncomplicated.

1. *Ninhydrin*

(i) For general use as a locating agent use 0·25% w/v ninhydrin in acetone (*Analyt. Chem.* **23**, 823 (1951)). The spots may be developed by heating at 100° for 5 min, or for a lighter background, by leaving at room temperature for a few hours. The amino acids give purple spots except for histidine and glycine (red-grey); phenylalanine, tyrosine, and aspartic acid (blue); tryptophan (brown); asparagine (dirty yellow); proline (yellow). The sensitivity ranges from 0·2 μg for glycine to about 2 μg for histidine.

(ii) For identification by colour use 50 ml of 0·1% ninhydrin in ethanol plus 2 ml collidine. Some workers add 10 ml CH_3COOH. The less pure the collidine the better the colours. Heat over a sand bath, observing the colours as they come up. The colours given by each amino acid are best learnt by experience, but note particularly that tyrosine changes colour a few seconds after it comes up and that many of the colours fade within a few minutes to purple and blue.

(iii) Some workers prefer a modification of 1 (ii) incorporating copper ion. It is claimed that the colour differences (a full list is given in *Analyt. Chem.* **31**, 926 (1959)) are such as to enable identification of all amino acids, no matter how close their R_F's, after a 35-cm run in *n*-butanol–acetic–water (4:1:5).

The reagent consists of (*a*) 0·2% ninhydrin in 50 ml ethanol+10 ml of glacial acetic acid+2 ml of collidine. (*b*) 1% $Cu(NO_3)_2 \cdot 3H_2O$. A fresh mixture of 25 ml of (*a*) and 1·5 ml of (*b*) is sprayed onto the paper which is dried and heated in the oven for 1·5 to 2 min at 105°. This reagent has been used on thin layer plates. The plates are dried, the reagent is sprayed on and the plates are reheated so that the colours may be seen as they come up.

(iv) The addition of cadmium ion stabilizes the colour complex. Most amino acids give red colours except for glycine (orange) and proline (yellow). Use 1% ninhydrin in acetone (100 vol.) and a solution of 1 g cadmium acetate in 100 ml acetic acid+50 ml water (15 vol.). The colours may be eluted with 96% ethanol and read quantitatively in the spectrophotometer (*Z.P.C.* **309,** 219 (1957)).

(v) 0·05% ninhydrin in acetone on heating at 70° for 15 min gives only a faint colour, but destroys very little of the substances present (*Arch. B.B.* **35,** 443 (1952)). After ringing the spot excess ninhydrin can be washed away in acetone.

(vi) For the detection of *N*-methyl amino acids (which normally give a very weak colour with ninhydrin) in the presence of free amino acids (*J. Chromat.* **4,** 251 (1960)) use the following reagent. Mix equal vols. of 0·33% ninhydrin in *tert*-butanol and glacial acetic–water–pyridine (1:5:5). Spray, and heat for 10–15 min at 100–110°. Primary and *N*-methyl amino acids give purple spots of comparable intensity. *N*-methyl amino acids are distinguished by their feeble colour on spraying with ninhydrin in water saturated *n*-butanol, 2% with respect to acetic acid.

(vii) A buffered ninhydrin solution containing a reducing agent for maximum colour development has been described (*Arch. B.B.* **35,** 443 (1952)).

(viii) A large number of modifications of the use of ninhydrin are listed (*see* Block *et al.*, as quoted above, p. 124). Most have little advantage over those already mentioned.

(ix) If the solvents used are likely to leave an alkaline deposit, reagents 1 (i), 1 (ii), and 1 (iv) may be made 10% with respect to acetic acid. If there is likely to be an acidic deposit pyridine may be used similarly.

(x) Ninhydrin stained papers fade on exposure to the air. For temporary storage they may be kept in nitrogen in the dark. A permament record may be made (*Nature, Lond.* **168,** 77 (1951)) by spraying with a $Cu(NO_3)_2$ reagent. To 1 ml of saturated solution of $Cu(NO_3)_2$ add 0·2 ml of 10% HNO_3 and make up to 100 ml in 95% ethanol. If ninhydrin reagent 1 (vii) has been used the papers will not be well preserved by this method. It is best to varnish the papers by dipping in a saturated solution of perspex in chloroform. For the very best results the papers should be washed (*Nature, Lond.* **166,** 1000 (1956)) before running the chromatogram.

2. *Isatin*

See also proline and hydroxyproline, Amino acids, 25.

One disadvantage of ninhydrin is the ease with which proline can be masked by other spots. Two reagents have been described which overcome this difficulty, and also provide a range of colours for the amino acids (*Z.P.C.* **304,** 21 (1956)—colour plate included).

(i) Dissolve 1 g isatin+1·3 g zinc acetate in 70–80 ml warm *iso*propanol. After cooling add 1 ml pyridine.

(ii) Dissolve 1 g isatin+1·5 g zinc acetate in 93 ml warm *iso*propanol+3 ml of water. Add 1 ml of glacial acetic acid on cooling.

The two reagents give slightly different ranges of colour. In both cases spray, dry, and heat at 80–85° for 10 min. The background may be washed out by a quick rinse in water without displacing the amino acid colours.

3. *Ultraviolet light*

(i) The amino group can react with free aldehyde groups in the paper. The resulting Schiff's bases fluoresce blue in u.v. light. Heat the paper at 100° for 30 min. *N*-substituted amino acids give dark spots (*P.S.E.B.M.* **71,** 88 (1949)). The sensitivity is somewhat lower than ninhydrin, and in some cases a significant quantity of material may undergo irreversible combination.

(ii) Spray with 0·2% salicylaldehyde in acetone. The Schiff's bases may be decomposed by spraying with water and exposure to air (*Annali Chim.* **43,** 338 (1953)).

(iii) Soak the paper in 0·01% 1:2-naphthoquinone-4-sulphonate (Folin's reagent) in methanol. Heat at 110°–120° for 10 min. It is claimed (*J. Chromat.* **3,** 415 (1960)) that this method is more sensitive than ninhydrin for detecting amino acids with the exception of asparagine, lysine, and tryptophan.

In (ii) and (iii) the spots are also visible in normal light.

4. *Iodine*

A non-destructive method giving positive results for many nitrogenous compounds (including amino acids), carbohydrates, and steroids. The paper, or thin layer plate is exposed to I_2 vapour produced by a few crystals in a glass tank. After 10–30 sec it is removed and the rapidly fading brown spots marked with pencil (*Nature, Lond.* **194,** 1171 (1962)). Alternatively, the paper may be sprayed with I_2 in CCl_4 (*Analyt. Chem.* **27,** 1519 (1955)) or with petroleum ether (60–80° fraction) saturated with I_2 (*B.J.* **50,** 370 (1952)).

5. *Chlorine*

Useful for amino acids, N blocked amino acids (q.v.) and peptides (q.v.). The test is said to be specific for the N—C bond and so solvents such as pyridine and collidine must be removed (*Ber.* **87,** 1103 (1954)). The paper or thin layer plate is washed with ether and then acetone–ethanol, 1:1, in which amino acids and most peptides are insoluble. Expose for 5 min to Cl_2 from a tray containing equal volumes of satd. $KMnO_4$ and 10% HCl. Remove, allow excess Cl_2 to disappear and dip in a solution of equal volumes saturated *o*-tolidine* in 2% acetic acid and 0·05N-KI. Blue-black spots are given on a lighter background. It is claimed that background colour is reduced if the chlorinated paper is exposed to ammonia vapour for 10 sec before dipping (*J. Chromat.* **3,** 499 (1960)). Formation of the *N*-chloro derivative using *tert*-butyl hypochlorite (1% in cyclohexane) has been recommended (*J.B.C.* **237,** 1619 (1962)), followed by spraying with 1% starch in 1% KI. The sensitivity to amino acids varies. Methionine, cysteine, cystine, and tyrosine are scarcely detected at all.

* Warning: *o*-tolidine has been listed as carcinogenic. The 1% starch–1% KI mixture may be used in its place with only slightly inferior results.

6. *Indicators*

A rather insensitive method, which rests on the buffering power of acids, bases, and ampholytes (useful for *N*-substituted amino acids). The dyes often do not interfere with subsequent work. The technique is to spray with a *ca.* 0·1% solution of indicator. For example:

(i) *Tropaeolin OO*, subsequently exposing to HCl vapour (*Recl Trav. chim. Pays-Bas Belg.* **68,** 717 (1949)).

(ii) *Bromothymol blue* (Na salt), dip in 0·2% acetic acid (*Nature, Lond.* **167,** 724 (1951)).

(iii) *Bromothymol blue–formalin–KOH*, for use after neutral solvents (*Nature, Lond.* **170,** 664 (1952)).

7. *Other methods*

Occasionally substances left on the paper give high backgrounds with ninhydrin, etc. If these cannot be removed, a number of other reagents can be employed depending on the circumstances.

(i) *Folin's reagent.* (*See* Amino acids, 3 (iii).) If it is intended to view the spots in visible light spray with (*a*) 0·3 g Na 1:2-napthoquinone-4-sulphonate in 10 ml H_2O diluted to 300 ml with acetone. Heat at 80° for 3–5 min. Amino acids give light spots. Dip for 30–60 sec in a fresh solution of 2 ml 5N-NaOH diluted to 100 ml with EtOH, plus 30 ml of (*a*). Dry at room temperature. Most colours are in the blue-green except proline and hydroxyproline (orange); tyrosine (grey); tryptophan (brown). Ultraviolet may still be used (*Naturwissenschaften* **39,** 548 (1952)).

(ii) *Orcinol.* Spray with 0·1% orcinol in ethanol 0·004N with respect to sulphuric acid. Dry. Heat at 110–120° for 30 min. The amino acids protect the cellulose against hydrolysis and appear as white spots on a red violet background. The edges are better seen in the u.v. The method is non-destructive and sensitive (*Nature, Lond.* **168,** 202 (1952)).

(iii) Other reagents described are alloxan (*Analyt. Chem.* **28,** 501 (1956)) and acid permanganate (*Chem. Listy* **44,** 43 (1950)).

α-AMINO ACIDS

8. *Copper complexes to distinguish between α- and other amino acids*

Ninhydrin gives purple colours with β-, γ-, δ-, and ε-amino acids as well as with α-amino acids. The copper complexes of the latter do not. Before running in a two-dimensional system (water-saturated phenol followed by collidine–lutidine) dust along the path of movement in the first step with powdered basic $CuCO_3$. A duplicate should be run without $CuCO_3$. On staining the completed chromatograms with ninhydrin α-amino acids and *N*-methyl amino acids will show up only on the untreated paper. β-Amino acids give blue colours on the treated paper only if present in large amounts; γ-, δ-, and ε-amino acids react normally (*Nature, Lond.* **164,** 441 (1949)).

A more recent procedure for copper complexing involves running and drying the chromatogram in the usual way, and then dipping in a mixture of sat. cupric nitrate–acetone (0·4:100), and drying. α-Amino acids no longer react with ninhydrin, while other amino compounds do (*B.B.A.* **29,** 446 (1958)).

D-AMINO ACIDS

9. D-*Amino acid oxidase* (*to distinguish between* D- *and* L-*amino acids*)

Run two duplicate papers. Spray one with a solution of D-amino acid oxidase in 0·06 M-pyrophosphate buffer, pH 8·3. Incubate for 2½ hours at 37° in moist oxygen. Dry and spray both papers with ninhydrin. Only L-amino acids and glycine will remain on the treated paper (*B.J.* **42,** lix (1948)). Alternatively the α-keto acids (q.v.) formed from the D-amino acids may be detected by the use of a 2:4-dinitrophenylhydrazine spray (*Revue can. Biol.* **9,** 3 (1950)).

SPECIFIC REAGENTS

Where, for some reason, it has not been possible to identify a spot by position and colour with one of the general tests, reagents exist which are specific for single amino acids or groups of amino acids.

AMINO ACIDS WITH AROMATIC AND HETEROCYCLIC RINGS

The separation and identification of compounds in this class and many related ones have been extensively reviewed (*J. Chromat.* **1,** 338 (1958) and **4,** 458 (1960)).

TYROSINE

10. *α-Nitroso-β-naphthol*

Dip in (*a*) 0·1% α-nitroso-β-napthol in acetone. Dry at room temperature. Dip in (*b*) acetone 10% with respect to nitric acid (add conc. HNO_3 to acetone). Allow to dry and heat progressively from one edge in a position where the paper can be seen. The yellow colour of the paper lightens when any area has been heated sufficiently. Tyrosine is indicated by a red colour, with a sensitivity of the order of 1 μg. Tryptophan gives a grey or brown colour with less sensitivity. Phenol and collidine should be removed (see also *B.B.A.* **9,** 704 (1952)). This reagent is not listed as a carcinogen. Its structural similarity to some of those that are has, however, been remarked upon.

Tyrosine is also detected in the Pauly test (*see* Histidine, 14).

TRYPTOPHAN AND RELATED COMPOUNDS

11. *Ehrlich's reagent*

(i) Dip in 1% w/v *p*-dimethylaminobenzaldehyde in acetone–conc. HCl (9:1). Stand at room temperature for a few minutes. Tryptophan gives a purple spot (*Nature, Lond.* **171,** 43 (1953)), pyrroles and related compounds give red spots.

(ii) Alternatively, spray with 2% *p*-dimethylaminobenzaldehyde in 5% HCl. Dry at room temperature. Tryptophan gives a purple colour, aromatic amines and citrulline yellow; oxykynurenine, kynurenine, and 2-amino-3-hydroxyacetophenone give orange spots (*B.J.* **52,** 3 (1952)). Cf. Amines, 19.

12. *Ultraviolet light*

(i) Dry the paper at room temperature. Tryptophan gives little or no colour (what little there is is due to decomposition products and is usually slightly ahead of the true spot). Some related compounds are readily seen, for example, kynurenine (blue); kynurenic acid (blue-green); hydroxykynurenic acid (greenish-yellow); aminoacetophenone (sky-blue); 2-amino-3-hydroxyacetophenone (yellow); xanthurenic acid (blue); anthranilic acid (blue-violet); hydroxyanthranilic acid (sky-blue) (*B.J.* **52,** 3 (1952)). Aromatic solvents sometimes interfere.

(ii) Spray with perchloric acid (70–72%)–water (6:1). Tryptophan gives a stable and intense green-blue fluorescence within 10 min. Subsequent spraying with 1% $FeCl_3$ gives a reddish-yellow colour. Indoleacetic acid responds to this test with a faint pinkish fluorescence (*J.A.C.S.* **70,** 2615 (1948)).

13. *Acid terephthalaldehyde*

Spray with 0·2% terephthalaldehyde in acetone, 10% with respect to acetic acid. Heat at 105° for 3 min. Tryptophan gives a blue spot, tryptamine yellow-green. This reagent is extremely sensitive (*see also* Histidine, 15).

HISTIDINE

14. *Pauly reagent*

Solution I (1% sulphanilic acid in N-HCl) and solution II (5% $NaNO_2$ aq.) are kept in the refrigerator. Equal volumes are mixed, still being kept cold, 5 min. before use. Spray, taking care not to displace the spots by flooding the paper. Then spray with 15% Na_2CO_3. Histidine and other imidazoles give red colours at once. Coloured spots are also given with reduced sensitivity by histamine (rose-brown); tyrosine (rose); xanthine, diiodotyrosine (orange); thiamin, tryptophan, hordenine, hydroxykynurenine (orange-red); adenine (pink); guanine (orange-purple); catechol (purple); ergothionine (red); thiolhistidine (light orange). A modification (*B.J.* **49,** 463 (1951)) reduces interference by tyrosine. Spray with 0·1% *p*-anisidine in ethanolic 0·11N-HCl–10% ethanolic amyl nitrite (1:1). Dry in air at R.T. Spray with 1% KOH in ethanol. Recryst. *p*-anisidine may not work.

Residual solvents such as phenol and collidine must be washed out with acetone and ether. Many other diazotized compounds give similar ranges of colours.

15. *Terephthalaldehyde*

Spray with 0·2% terephthalaldehyde in acetone. Heat at 105° for 10 min. Histidine gives a yellow-green spot. Tryptophan gives a brown spot in the u.v. The reagent is very sensitive, especially for histidine (*Nature, Lond.* **173,** 314 (1954)).

PHENYLALANINE

16. *Ninhydrin*–$NaHCO_3$

Stain the chromatogram with ninhydrin (1 (i)). On spraying the heated paper with dilute (0·15 to 10%) $NaHCO_3$, only the phenylalanine spot is stable (*B.B.A.* **19,** 366 (1956)).

SULPHUR-CONTAINING AMINO ACIDS

The chromatographic separation of members of this class has been reviewed (*Arch. B.B.* **54,** 114 (1955)). The best reagent for detection is platinic iodide or its modification employing palladium.

17. *Platinic iodide*

(i) Dip in 0·002M-chloroplatinic acid–M-KI–2N-HCl–acetone (4:0·25:0·4:76). Intensify with HCl vapour after drying at room temperature. Bleached areas on a pink ground are given by cystine, cysteine, methionine, cystathionine, lanthionine, djenkolic acid, methionine sulphoxide, etc. After using a phenol or collidine solvent papers must first be washed in acetone–ether (1:1) (*Analyt. Chem.* **23,** 823 (1951)).

(ii) For greater contrast (the background is dark brown) replace the H_2PtCl_6 solution in (i) with 0·002M-$PdCl_2$ in 0·1N-HCl (*Analyt. Chem.* **23,** 823 (1951)).

18. *Azide–iodine*

Spray with 0·05N-I_2 in 50% ethanol containing 1·5% NaN_3. White spots on a light brown ground are given by cysteine immediately, then cystine (15 min), then methionine (60 min). The spots are best seen in u.v. This spray also detects thiamin (*Science* **113,** 582 (1951)).

19. *Nitroprusside*

Reagent (*a*): mix together 1·5 g Na nitroprusside in 5 ml 2N-H_2SO_4+95 ml MeOH+10 ml 28% NH_3. Filter. Dip in this soln. Red colours are given with —SH compounds. While the paper is still damp dip in (*b*) 2% NaCN in 95% MeOH. The cleavage of —S—S— bonds by this reagent causes red colours to appear in a few seconds to 10 min. Sensitivity for cystine, 1 μg. If the detection of —SH compounds is not required use an equal vol. of (*a*) and (*b*) made up in double concentrations. Arginine gives an orange spot on a pale yellow ground, turning grey-blue on an intense green ground (*Analyt. Chem.* **23,** 823 (1951)).

GLYCINE

20. *o-Phthalaldehyde*

Spray with 0·2% *o*-phthalaldehyde in acetone (for preparations of this reagent see Block & Bolling, *The Amino Acid Composition of Foods*, pp. 346–8, Thomas, Springfield, Ill. (1951)). Heat at 50° for 10 min. A green spot is given with glycine, chocolate brown in u.v. (at 365 mμ); NH_4^+ ion gives a dark grey spot; histidine and tryptophan show intense yellow fluorescence at 365 mμ. This spray cannot be used after aromatic solvents (*Science* **109,** 339 (1949)).

SERINE

21. *Nessler's reagent*

Nessler's reagent is added to solid periodic acid until the precipitate first formed just redissolves. Spray. Aliphatic hydroxyamino acids give dark brown spots (*B.J.* **40,** 33 (1946)).

ARGININE

22. *Sakaguchi*

Dip in 0·1% 8-hydroxyquinoline in acetone. Dry in air. Spray carefully with a soln. of 0·2 ml Br_2 in 100 ml 0·5N-NaOH. Orange-red spots are given by arginine and other guanidines. Taurocyamine and glycocyamine give only transient colours (*Nature, Lond.* **172,** 1100 (1953)).

GUANIDINES

23. *α-Naphthol–diacetyl*

Spray with 0·1 ml diacetyl+15 ml 1% α-naphthol in 6% NaOH, freshly mixed. Let stand for 2–10 min. Blue-violet spots on a beige ground are given by guanidine, its disubstituted derivatives (e.g. creatine), and monosubstituted derivatives (e.g. arginine, glycocyamine) with less sensitivity. Creatinine gives a negative result (*B.B.A.* **14,** 71 (1954)).

ORNITHINE

24. *Vanillin*

Spray with 0·2% vanillin in acetone followed by 0·1% KOH in ethanol. Heat at 110° for 10 min. Ornithine gives a red spot, as do proline and hydroxyproline (*Nature, Lond.* **173,** 314 (1954)).

IMINO ACIDS (*proline and hydroxyproline*)

25. *Isatin*

(i) Spray with 0·2% isatin in *n*-butanol, 4% with respect to acetic acid. Heat at 105° for 15 min. Stable spots are given by proline and hydroxyproline (blue) and pipecolinic acid (blue-green). Many amino acids give colours in this range which fade after a few hours at room temperature (*B.B.A.* **5,** 81 (1950)). *See also* 2.

To obtain only the blue spots of proline and hydroxyproline, wash the paper, after developing, in N-HCl and then in water.

(ii) To distinguish between proline and hydroxyproline, dip as above and then in Ehrlich's reagent (*see* 11). All the colours given by isatin are removed except that of hydroxyproline which turns from blue to cerise.

MULTIPLE SPRAYING

Ninhydrin (1 (i)) may be followed by α-nitroso-β-napthol (10) or Ehrlich's reagent (11). It may also be followed, with diminished sensitivity, by the Pauly test (14) or the Sakaguchi (22). Isatin may be preceded by ninhydrin or followed by Ehrlich's reagent or α-nitroso-β-napthol, the latter with diminished sensitivity. Ehrlich's reagent may be followed by the Sakaguchi even if it was preceded by ninhydrin or isatin. The non-destructive methods (3) and (4) do not interfere with any subsequent test. *See also* a more recent and very full account in *B.B.A.* **107,** 386 (1965).

Iodinated amino acids—see Thyroxine in Hormones.

AMINO ACID DERIVATIVES

The separation of various classes of these compounds has been described: DNP-amino acids and phenylthiohydantoins (*Meth. biochem. Anal.* **2,** 360, 383 (1955); *J. Chromat.* **2,** 225 (1959)); hydrazides (*Bull. chem. Soc. Japan* **25,** 214 (1952)); 'dansyl' amino acids (*B.J.* **89,** 59P (1963)). If the derivative still has a free amino group it can be detected by ninhydrin.

DNP-AMINO ACIDS

1. *Visual inspection*

Quite small quantities of these compounds can be seen by their yellow colour. They may be distinguished from the common artefact dinitrophenol by inspection in the u.v. (dinitrophenol appears much more black than any other spot) (*Nature, Lond.* **162,** 152 (1948)).

PHENYLTHIOHYDANTOINS AND HYDANTOINS

2. *Iodine–azide*

Before running the chromatogram, dip the paper in 0·5% starch solution and dry. After running, dry at room temp. and spray with a mixture of equal volumes of 0·01M-I_2 in 0·5M-KI and 0·5M-sodium azide (*see* reference for phenylthiohydantoins above). Phenylthiohydantoins and hydantoins give bleached areas on a dark ground.

HYDRAZIDES

3. *Ammoniacal silver nitrate*

Spray with 10% $AgNO_3$ solution–ethanol (1:4) having added enough strong ammonia to dissolve the precipitate first formed. Hydrazides give brown spots on leaving the paper at room temperature for a few minutes. Hydrazine gives a rapidly appearing black spot.

Hydrazides give a range of colours with ninhydrin–collidine (Amino acids, 1 (ii)).

'DANSYL' AMINO ACIDS

4. *Ultraviolet light*

'Dansyl' amino acids in extremely small amounts can be seen as yellow spots in u.v. light. Dansyl-OH gives a green-blue spot.

N-METHYL AMINO ACIDS

5. *p-Nitrobenzoyl chloride*

Dip in 0·2% *p*-nitrobenzoyl chloride in benzene. Dry. Dip in pyridine–petroleum ether (1:10). Orange colours lasting only a few minutes are given by *N*-methyl amino acids and ring compounds such as pipecolinic acid. Amino acids give no colour.

See also Amino acids, 1 (vi) and 6.

ACETYL AMINO ACIDS

6. *See* Amino acids, 5

As these compounds are somewhat soluble in acetone–ethanol the paper cannot be washed with this reagent. The paper is washed with ether and then sprayed with enough acetone–ethanol to keep the paper moist during the chlorination. Acetyl derivatives of those amino acids which are not detected in this test will give feeble colours.

PEPTIDES

Separation

Electrophoresis is to be preferred to chromatography where possible as it gives sharper spots and is less dependent on changes in conditions. Several pH's are used, including pH 1·9 (basic groups fully ionized, nearly all carboxyls completely suppressed, the sulphonic acid group partly charged); pH 3·5 (the terminal carboxyl group and the carboxyls of aspartic and glutamic acids are discharged to an extent depending on neighbouring groups); pH 6·5 (all carboxyls fully charged save in exceptional cases, most α-NH_2 groups fully charged, basic side chains fully charged except that of histidine, which is charged to an extent depending upon neighbouring groups) (*Nature, Lond.* **176,** 72 (1955) and *B.B.A.* **28,** 539 (1958)). The most generally used chromatographic systems are butanol–acetic acid–water (3:1:1 for most applications (*B.J.* **89,** 349 (1963)); 4:1:5 gives better separation for basic peptides but is more troublesome).

It is often valuable to combine electrophoretic with chromatographic separations. R_F values for 88 synthetic peptides and 29 amino acids in 15 solvent systems are given in *J. Chromat.* **1**, 513 (1958). For preparative work electrophoresis should be used last in order to sharpen up the bands, and to avoid the risk of the partial destruction of some amino acids during acid hydrolysis after elution from the paper (*B.J.* **89,** 341 (1963)).

Detection

1. *Ninhydrin*

Methods 1 (i), 1 (iv), and 1 (v) (*see* Amino acids) are recommended. Heating is to be avoided if possible. Some peptides, particularly large, cyclic, or acetylated ones, give poor colour yields. Most glycine and some asparagine *N*-terminal peptides give yellow colours with 1 (i), 1 (iv), 1 (v). Some serine and threonine *N*-terminal peptides give yellow colours with 1 (iv). Valine and isoleucine *N*-terminal peptides are slow to come up and sometimes give a low colour yield. Proline *N*-terminal peptides give a very faint yellow colour which is usually missed.

2. *Ultraviolet light*

See Amino acids, 3.

Ultraviolet methods can be used for peptides with free amino groups. Heating is to be avoided, as some peptides cannot then be eluted in good yield.

3. *Iodine*

See Amino acids, 4.

4. *Chlorine*

See Amino acids, 5.

This method is of especial value for those peptides which do not give good ninhydrin colours. The intensity of colour given is roughly proportional to the number of peptide bonds. In particular cases, however, the sensitivity may vary widely from that expected. Peptides largely consisting of those amino acids not detected will themselves often not be detected.

5. *Phenylisothiocyanate*

Spray with pyridine–water–triethylamine–phenylisothiocyanate (150:50:6:2) and leave in an atmosphere of the same mixture for 3 hr to allow conversion of peptides to phenylthiocarbamyl derivatives. Wash three times with benzene, twice with ethylene chloride. Dry 30 min at R.T. Locate spots with u.v. light by the use of a fluorescent screen. Prewashing of papers is necessary before running chromatograms (*B.B.A.* **71,** 210 (1963)).

6. *Elution*

In the last resort elute the paper in strips and heat samples at 100–110° with 6N-HCl overnight. Those samples in which free amino acids appear on hydrolysis came from strips on which there was peptide.

7. *More specific reagents for peptides*

Some of the specific reagents for amino acids will show the presence of the amino acid concerned in a peptide. The remarks above about multiple staining apply equally to the use of these reagents for peptides. The numbers given below are those of the reagent in the section on Amino acids.

Tyrosine peptides will be detected by α-nitroso-β-naphthol (10); tryptophan peptides are detected by the Ehrlich's reagent (11); histidine by the Pauly (14) (*N*-terminal histidine in a peptide gives a more brown colour than the usual pink); sulphur-containing peptides by platinic iodide (17); arginine by the Sakaguchi (22); proline and hydroxyproline, if *N*-terminal, by isatin (25); serine if *N*-terminal by Nessler's reagent (21).

PROTEINS

A list of some proteins separated by paper chromatography is given in Block, Durrum, & Zweig, p. 166 (reference at beginning of Amino acids section). No general methods are in use and paper electrophoresis (Block, Durrum, & Zweig, p. 508) or cellulose acetate strip electrophoresis is more common. Thin-layer methods have been applied to proteins both on 'conventional' supports and on such materials as Sephadex (*B.J.* **91,** 222 (1964)).

Detection

Iodine and *Chlorine* (Amino acids, 4 and 5) may be employed with paper and thin-layer separations of proteins. Proteins may show as dark areas in u.v. light (*Nature, Lond.* **168,** 685 (1951)).

1. *Haemin–protein complexes*

When proteins have been chromatographed as haemin complexes they are detected by spraying with the mixture: 1 vol. saturated soln. of benzidine in EtOH+1 vol 3% H_2O_2, made acid with CH_3COOH. A blue colour is given by haemin complexes (*Science* **110,** 447 (1949)). Warning: Benzidine is carcinogenic.

2. *Dye binding methods*

(i) *Amido black* 10 *B* (naphthaline black 12 B200, buffalo black). Soak the paper in a saturated solution of the dye in methanol–acetic acid (9:1) for 10 min. Agitate occasionally. The excess dye can be rinsed out with several changes of methanol–acetic acid (9:1) until the bands show up as dark areas on a light blue background. The colour can be eluted with 50% methanol and read in the spectrophotometer.

(ii) *Azocarmine G.* Use a saturated solution in methanol–acetic acid–water (5:1:1). Soak the paper in the dye for 10 min and then wash out the background with 10% acetic acid (*Naturwissenschaften* **37,** 93 (1950)). The colour can be eluted with 0·1M-NaOH.

(iii) *Procion brilliant blue RS* and *coomassie brilliant blue R250*. Recently an extensive study has been made of the usefulness of these two dyes and the following staining procedures are recommended for cellulose acetate strips after electrophoresis, although they are equally well suited to work on filter paper, agar, and starch gel (*B.B.A.* **71,** 377 (1963)).

Procion blue: immerse strips in dye-bath (5 g/l procion blue and 20 ml/l conc. HCl in MeOH) for 5 min at R.T. Wash strips twice in MeOH for 5 min. Dry strips, either stretched on wooden frame or, preferably, in a photographic glazer, at 60° for about 5 min. Sensitivity 2 μg/cm^2.

Coomassie blue: fix protein by immersing electrophoretic strips in 200 g/l sulphosalicylic acid in water, for 1 min. Transfer strips to dye-bath (2·5 g/l coomassie blue in glass-distilled water) for 5 min. Remove background by four rinses of 5 min each in distilled water. Dry strips at 90° for 15 min. Sensitivity 0·5 μg/cm^2.

Procion blue is about three times less sensitive than coomassie blue, while azocarmine, amido black, and bromphenol blue are 5–10 times less so. Coomassie blue, although preferred for sensitivity, is not quantitative at higher protein concentrations. For quantitative assay, procion blue is preferable since it is more reliable in reproducibility and accuracy.

3. *Proteins with enzymatic activity*

Make a plate of 2% agar containing a suitable substrate (*B.J.* **51,** 123 (1952)). Place the moist chromatogram on the plate and incubate for some hours. The reaction products are then revealed by suitable tests (*see* the other parts of this table). An example is the use of 1% soluble starch in buffered (pH 7·0) agar to detect salivary amylase by means of the starch–iodine reaction.

It is also possible to spray the substrate directly on to the paper. For example, catalase is detected by spraying with 0·5% H_2O_2 and after 20 min spraying with a reagent containing $FeCl_3$–1% K ferricyanide (*Aust. J. biol. Sci.* **6,** 77 (1953)—contains many other examples).

Proteolytic enzymes may be detected by laying the paper (buffered at pH 6·8 with 0·067M-phosphate) on the gelatin side of a piece of photographic film. Incubate at 30° for 20–60 min, still keeping the paper moist. A clear zone on the film indicates the position of proteolytic activity (*Angew. Chem.* **63,** 44 (1951)).

A further list of such methods will be found in Block, Durrum, & Zweig (see above), p. 166.

5. ANTIBIOTICS

Revised by E. P. ABRAHAM (*Sir William Dunn School of Pathology, Oxford*)

GENERAL

The antibiotics comprise compounds of widely different chemical structures and as a group they have little in common other than antimicrobial activity. Thus bioautography is the only general method for their detection on paper after chromatography or electrophoresis. In a typical procedure paper strips or sheets are placed on the surface of nutrient agar plates bulk-seeded with a suitable test organism. After 15–30 min the paper is peeled off and the plates incubated overnight (*J. gen. Microbiol.* **6,** 47 (1952); *Nature, Lond.* **172,** 545 (1953)). Clear zones of inhibition are seen on the plates.

Chemical methods for the detection of antibiotics on paper vary widely in their nature and specificity. But certain methods are applicable to classes of antibiotics whose members have chemical features in common. For example, the ninhydrin reaction can be used with a number of peptide antibiotics, including the polymyxins (*Science* **116,** 147 (1952)). The procedure of Rydon and Smith, consisting of *N*-chlorination followed by reaction with starch–iodide (*Nature, Lond.* **169,** 922 (1952)), can be used with antibiotics containing peptide or amide groupings. Convenient modifications of this procedure have been described (*B.J.* **84,** 157 (1962)). A variety of antibiotics, including some of the cephalosporins, puromycin, and novobiocin (*Antibiotics Annual* (1956–7), p. 1035), have absorption spectra which result in their appearance as dark spots when the paper is viewed in u.v. light after chromatography in a suitable solvent system. Some, including the tetracyclines (*Antibiotics Chemother.* **7,** 292 (1957)), can be revealed by fluorescence in u.v. light.

Solvent systems used for paper chromatography vary widely according to the physical properties and stabilities of the antibiotics concerned. Examples are provided by solvents used for different penicillins (*J. Bact.* **57,** 101 (1949); *Nature, Lond.* **172,** 545 (1953); *Proc. R. Soc.* **B 154,** 490 (1961)), cephalosporins (*Antibiotics Chemother.* **12,** 689 (1962); *B.J.* **62,** 651 (1956)), streptomycin (*J.A.C.S.* **72,** 3598 (1950)), kanamycin (*J. Antibiot., Tokyo* Ser. A, **10,** 228 (1957)), neomycins (*J.A.C.S.* **82,** 3938 (1960); **83,** 643 (1961)), the tetracyclines (*Antibiotics Chemother.* **5,** 640 (1955)), macrolide antibiotics (erythromycins (*J.A.C.S.* **79,** 6074 (1957)) and oleandomycin (*J. Chromat.* **5,** 126 (1961)), the actinomycins (*Antibiotics Chemother.* **10,** 221 (1960)), and polymyxins (*Antibiotics Chemother.* **6,** 196 (1956)).

Thin-layer chromatography on silica gel G (Merck) or alumina G (Merck) is suitable for a number of antibiotics and appears to be particularly useful with the macrolides (*J. Antibiot., Tokyo* Ser. A, **16,** 56 (1963); *J. Chromat.* **14,** 127 (1964)) and actinomycins (*J. Chromat.* **13,** 238 (1964)).

PENICILLINS AND CEPHALOSPORINS

1. *Bioautographs*

The agar plates used may be seeded with *Bacillus subtilis* (*Nature, Lond.* **158,** 675 (1946)), *Micrococcus pyogenes* var *aureus* (*J. Bact.* **57,** 101 (1949)), or (for penicillin N or cephalosporin C (*B.J.* **62,** 651 (1956)) an avirulent strain of *Salmonella typhi.* The cephalosporins retain their activity when the paper is sprayed with penicillinase from *Bacillus cereus* in 1% gelatin (*B.J.* **79,** 408 (1961)). *Alcaligenes faecalis* ATCC 8750 is much more sensitive to cephalosporin C than to penicillin N (*Antimicrobial Agents and Chemotherapy*, p. 682 (1962)).

2. *Starch–iodine after hydrolysis of β-lactam ring*

(i) The starch–iodine solution is composed of 0·01M-iodine in 3mM-KI (10 ml), M-phosphate buffer, pH 7·0 (1 ml), and 2% (w/v) sodium starch glycollate in water (9 ml). When the paper is sprayed with this solution compounds with potential sulphydryl groups (but not the penicillins with a closed β-lactam ring) appear as pale spots on a deep blue background. The paper is then sprayed with a mixture of equal volumes of the starch–iodine solution and a solution of purified penicillinase (e.g. from *Bacillus cereus,* 1000 units/ml). Additional pale spots appear at the site of penicillins whose β-lactam ring is opened by the penicillinase (*B.J.* **79,** 513 (1961)). Sensitivity with benzylpenicillin 1 μg/cm² (*Nature, Lond.* **191,** 1161 (1961)). 2:6-Dimethoxyphenylpenicillin (methicillin) is revealed less readily owing to its relative stability to penicillinase and the method is not applicable to cephalosporin C. *p*-Hydroxybenzylpenicillin absorbs iodine before treatment with penicillinase owing to iodination of the phenolic side-chain.

(ii) In a variation of this method the paper is sprayed with 0·5N-NaOH and dried for 10–15 min (to open the β-lactam ring) before spraying with a starch–iodine solution in aqueous acetic acid (*Nature, Lond.* **191,** 1161 (1961)). This procedure has been used with both the penicillins and cephalosporin C.

The starch–iodine method is more sensitive than the hydroxamic acid method (*Analyst* **75,** 651 (1950)) and the iodoplatinic acid method (*Science* **108,** 506 (1948)) for components with potential sulphydryl groups. It is similar in sensitivity to the iodine–azide spray (*J.B.C.* **175,** 67 (1948)).

6-AMINOPENICILLANIC ACID (6-APA)

3. *Bioautographs*

6-APA is first converted on paper to its *N*-phenylacetyl derivative (benzylpenicillin). The paper is sprayed with 5% (w/v) aqueous $NaHCO_3$ (*Proc. R. Soc.* B **154,** 490 (1961)) or with M-pyridine in 50% (w/v) acetone (*B.J.* **79,** 408 (1961)). It is then sprayed with 2–5% phenylacetyl chloride in acetone and again with $NaHCO_3$ solution or with pyridine in acetone. After drying for a short time in air the paper is placed on plates seeded with *Micrococcus pyogenes* var *aureus* or *Bacillus subtilis.* Sensitivity 0·5 μg.

4. *Starch–iodine*

As described in 2. When penicillinase is used to open the β-lactam ring the sensitivity is about 5 μg/cm² (*B.J.* **79,** 408 (1961)).

7-AMINOCEPHALOSPORANIC ACID (7-ACA)

5. *Bioautographs*

7-ACA is converted on paper to its *N*-phenylacetyl derivatives as described for 6-APA and the paper placed on plates seeded with *Micrococcus pyogenes* var. *aureus.* Sensitivity 1 μg.

6. *Starch–iodine*

As described in 2 (ii).

7. *Ultraviolet absorption*

A dark spot is observed when the paper is viewed in ultraviolet light. Sensitivity, 5 μg. Cephalosporin C and other *N*-acyl derivatives of 7-ACA may be detected similarly (*B.J.* **79,** 408 (1961)).

STREPTOMYCIN

8. *Bioautographs*

On plates seeded with *Micrococcus pyogenes* var *aureus* (*J.A.C.S.* **70,** 3333 (1948)) or *Bacillus subtilis* (*J.A.C.S.* **72,** 3598 (1950)).

9. *Sakaguchi reaction*

Spray with (*a*) 0·5N-NaOH. Then spray with (*b*) 0·25% α-naphthol. Dry at R.T. for 2 min. Finally spray with (*c*) 5% NaOCl soln. Streptomycin gives red bands (*J. Bact.* **55,** 231 (1948)). *See also* Amino acids, 22.

KANAMYCIN

10. *Bioautographs*

On plates seeded with *Bacillus subtilis* (*J. Antibiot., Tokyo* Ser. A, **10,** 228 (1957)).

NEOMYCINS

11. *Starch–iodide following N-chlorination*

Acetylate with acetic anhydride in 4·5M-sodium acetate or 3M-K_2HPO_4. Acetylated neomycins are detected on paper by the method of Rydon and Smith, giving deep blue spots against a colourless background (*Analyt. Chem.* **28,** 836 (1956)).

CHLORAMPHENICOL (CHLOROMYCETIN)

12. *Bioautographs*

On plates seeded with *E. coli* (*J. Bact.* **57,** 315 (1949)), *Sarcina lutea* or *Bacillus subtilis* (*Analytical Microbiology*, p. 273, Academic Press (1963)).

13. *Reduction–diazo reaction*

Spray with (*a*) 15% titanous chloride in N-HCl, diluted 1 in 10, to reduce the nitro group to —NH_2. While still damp hang in an atmosphere of Br_2 for a few minutes to oxidize excess titanous reagent. Then spray with (*b*) butyl nitrite: *n*-BuOH: CH_3COOH = 10:5:1. Finally, after 2 min, spray with (*c*) 0·1% *N*-(1-naphthyl)ethylenediamine dihydrochloride in *n*-BuOH:2N-HCl = 95:5. Pink spots are given by compounds which have an aromatic nitro group (*J.B.C.* **183,** 679 (1950)).

14. *Reduction–Ehrlich reagent*

Spray with (*a*) 15% $SnCl_2$:conc. HCl:H_2O = 3:15:180, freshly prepared. Dry at R.T. Spray with (*b*) a soln. of 1 g *p*-dimethylaminobenzaldehyde in EtOH:conc. HCl:*n*-BuOH = 30:30:180. Chloramphenicol gives a yellow spot. Decomposition compounds containing an aryl amino group instead of the nitro group of chloramphenicol react with (*b*) without previous reduction (*Arch. B.B.* **28,** 1 (1950)).

TETRACYCLINES

15. *Fluorescence*

Examine the paper under a strong source of ultraviolet light (*Antibiotics Chemother.* **7,** 292 (1957); *J. Chromat.* **11,** 62 (1963)). Tetracyclines and their epimers appear as yellow fluorescent spots. The fluorescence is greatly enhanced by exposure of the paper to NH_3 vapour. Sensitivity 0·5 μg.

16. *Ehrlich reagent*

Spray with 2% *p*-dimethylaminobenzaldehyde in 1·2N-HCl and keep for 5 hr at R.T. Aureomycin gives a dirty yellow colour and terramycin a blue-green colour. Sensitivity 5 μg (*Arch. B.B.* **43,** 236 (1953)).

17. *Starch–iodide following N-chlorination*

The method described is a modification of that of Rydon and Smith. (1) Spray with dilute sodium hypochlorite and air dry. (2) Dip into 95% ethanol and air dry. (3) Spray with starch–iodide (1% soluble starch and 1% KI (1:1 by vol.)) (*Arch. B.B.* **43,** 236 (1953)).

MACROLIDES

18. *Bioautographs*

Place papers on plates seeded with *Micrococcus pyogenes* var *aureus* (*J.A.C.S.* **76,** 570 (1954)) or *Bacillus subtilis* (*J. Chromat.* **5,** 126 (1961)) for erythromycin and oleandomycin.

19. *Coloration with hot* 10% H_2SO_4

After thin-layer chromatography on silica gel G (Merck) spray with 10% H_2SO_4 and heat at 80° for 5 to 10 min. Spots are brownish-green (erythromycin), purple (oleandomycin), reddish-brown (spiramycin), pink (picromycin), and blue (carbomycin) (*J. Antibiot., Tokyo* Ser. A, **16,** 56 (1963)).

ACTINOMYCINS

20. *Colorimetric*

Actinomycins appear as yellow bands after circular chromatography on paper. Elute with water and measure optical densities at 440 mμ (*Appl. Microbiol.* **5,** 95 (1957); *Antibiotics Chemother.* **5,** 409 (1955)).

ANTIMYCINS

21. *Bioautographs*

On plates seeded with the fungus *Glomerella cingulata* (Stonem) Spauld & v. Schrenk. Paper strips are removed from the agar 6–12 hr before zones are read so that inhibition of growth beneath can be detected (*Phytopathology* **44,** 438 (1954)).

AZASERINE

22. *Bioautographs*

On plates seeded with *Kloeckera brevis* (*J.A.C.S.* **76,** 2878 (1954)).

NOVOBIOCIN

23. *Bioautographs*

On plates seeded with *Micrococcus pyogenes* var *aureus.*

24. *Ultraviolet light*

The substance has been visualized by use of u.v. absorption scanner. Sensitivity 5 μg (*Antibiotics Annual* **1956–7**, p. 1035).

CYCLOSERINE (OXAMYCIN)

25. *Bioautographs*

On plates seeded with *Micrococcus pyogenes* var *aureus* (*Antibiotics Chemother.* **5,** 183 (1955)).

26. *Ninhydrin*

A characteristic brown-yellow colour is obtained when the paper is sprayed with ninhydrin.

---

6. CARBOHYDRATES

Revised by R. W. BAILEY (*Plant Chemistry Division, D.S.I.R., Palmerston North, New Zealand*)

For the separation and identification of the components in sugar mixtures, partition chromatography on paper sheets is generally satisfactory. A wide range of solvents is available (see *Chromat. Rev.* **4,** 114 (1962); *Methods in Carbohydrate Chemistry*, vol. 1, p. 21 (1962); *Meth. biochem. Anal.* **1,** 205 (1954); *B.J.* **67,** 253 (1957) (heptoses); *B.J.* **72,** 479 (1959) (aminosugars and their *N*-acetyl derivatives)). Solvents (1)–(3) form a useful range of acidic, basic, and neutral solvents suitable for most work:

(1) Ethyl acetate–acetic acid–formic acid–water (9:1·5:0·5:2); single phase; fast (14–24 hr).

(2) Ethyl acetate–pyridine–water (2:1:2); top phase; fast (14–24 hr).

(3) *n*-BuOH–EtOH–water (4:1·1:1·9); single phase; slow (2–3 days).

The separation of mono- and di-saccharides by solvent (2) is not affected by the ions normally present in enzyme digests containing McIlvaine's phosphate-citrate buffers. Two-dimensional chromatography is normally only necessary for the resolution of complex mixtures of monosaccharides; see Fig. 1. Identity of a sugar should only be assigned on the basis of movement in several solvents and reaction with a variety of the sprays listed. Spray no. 1 is recommended as the primary locating spray (it does react, however, with non-sugar compounds) and sprays 1, 7, 8, 9, 10, 23 ((i) or (ii)), 24, 27, 28, 37, and 52 represent a selection of well-tried sprays which cover most needs. The chromatographic identification of oligosaccharides should, in general, be confirmed by some chemical study of a small portion of isolated sugar. Sprays 8, 9, 10, 11, 32, 35, 41, and 52 are useful in that they give colour reactions dependent on the position of the glycosidic link at the reducing end of an oligosaccharide.

Identity may be further confirmed by paper ionophoresis. Many of the sprays listed may be used with ionophoretograms although the anions present often interfere. For a useful range of special sprays for this type of chromatogram see *Aust. J. Chem.* **12,** 65 (1959).

Thin-layer chromatography has been applied to sugars and particularly to derivatives such as acetates (see *J. Chromat.* **5,** 351 (1960); **9,** 278, 283 (1962); *Analyt. Chem.* **34,** 1736 (1962)). Many of the sprays listed may be applied to this method and other special ones have been developed and are listed.

As many of the reagents listed may be hazardous it is often preferable to dip papers rather than to spray them. Sprays may be used as dipping reagents provided they contain a solvent, such as acetone, in which sugars are not very soluble. See also *Analyt. Chem.* **28,** 849 (1956) for a number of special dipping reagents.

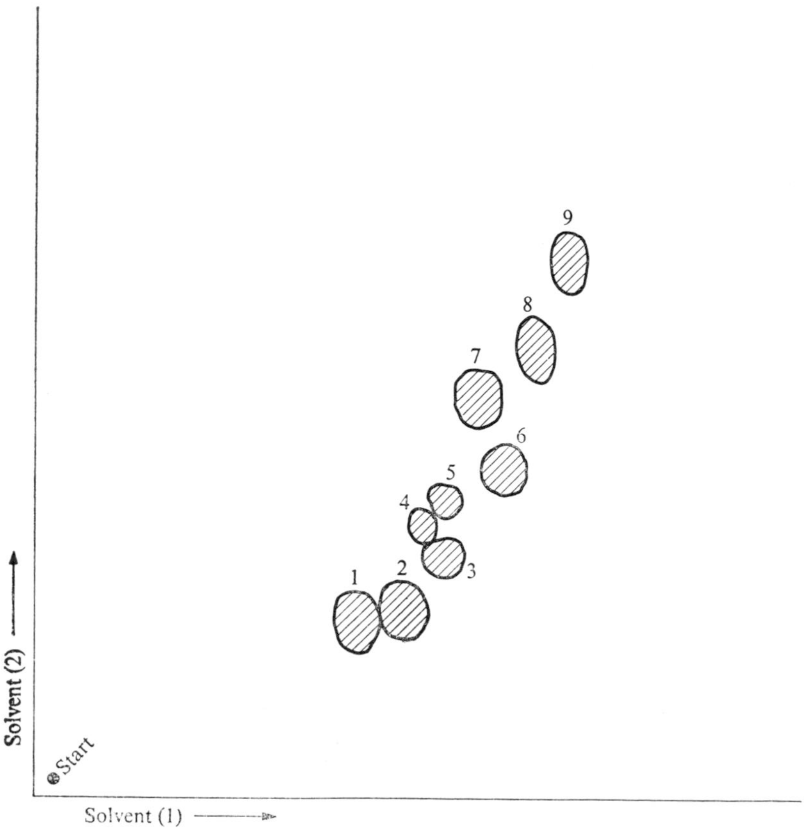

FIG. 1. *Two-dimensional chromatogram of mixture of common monosaccharides*

Solvent (1) followed by solvent (2) (*see* p. 539).

1, Galactose; 2, Glucose; 3, Mannose; 4, Fructose; 5, Arabinose; 6, Xylose; 7, Fucose; 8, Ribose; 9, Rhamnose.

Spots 3, 4, and 5 are not clearly distinguished from one another by a spray such as $AgNO_3$; they are differentiated by the more specific sprays.

GENERAL METHODS

1. *Silver nitrate–sodium hydroxide*

Dip in $AgNO_3$ (0·1 ml saturated aq. soln. diluted to 20 ml with acetone and water added dropwise until $AgNO_3$ redissolves), dry, and spray with 0·5N-NaOH in aq. EtOH (made by diluting saturated aq. NaOH with EtOH). Reducing substances appear immediately, at R.T., as black spots (sensitivity, 1–2 μg), and non-reducing substances (including non-reducing oligosaccharides, methyl glycosides, hexitols, and glycerol; sensitivity, 2–10 μg) appear more slowly (*Nature, Lond.* **166**, 444 (1950)). Better control and differentiation of reducing and non-reducing substances are obtained by using the above $AgNO_3$ solution at half-strength, when reducing substances appear in under 1 min and non-reducing compounds in 5–10 min. Papers may be fixed by dipping in strong aq. NH_3, washing well in water, and drying. This spray has largely replaced the older *Ammoniacal silver nitrate* (spray with 0·1N-$AgNO_3$:5N-NH_3 = 1:1; heat at 105° for 5–10 min) which gives similar reactions with reducing and non-reducing carbohydrates (*B.J.* **42,** 238 (1948); **47,** 437 (1950); *Nature, Lond.* **161,** 720 (1948); **165,** 400 (1950)). A modification of this spray has been used for locating sugar derivatives on thin-layer chromatograms (*J. Chromat.* **9,** 283 (1962)).

2. *Alkaline potassium permanganate*

Spray with 1% aq. $KMnO_4$ containing 2% Na_2CO_3. Dry at R.T. or rapidly at 100°. Yellow spots on a purple ground, then grey spots on a brown ground are given by sugar alcohols, glycosides, reducing and non-reducing sugars (*Science* **110,** 446 (1949)). Not given by methyl or acetyl sugars. Used for locating sugars by streaking on an extruded developed column (*J.A.C.S.* **67,** 527 (1945)).

3. *Periodate–potassium permanganate*; *periodate–p-anisidine*

(*a*) Spray with 2% aq. Na metaperiodate:1% $KMnO_4$ in 2% aq. Na_2CO_3 = 4:1, freshly mixed. Wash in H_2O after the spots develop. Brown spots on a white ground are produced. Sensitivity for glucose, 3 μg; mannitol, 3-methyl glucose, 5–8 μg; substances which reduce periodate only slowly, e.g. sucrose and trehalose, need 10–15 μg, and 40–60 min may be necessary for the colour to appear (*Analyt. Chem.* **26,** 920 (1954)).

(*b*) Spray with 0·01M-Na metaperiodate, and after 2 min spray with 1% *p*-anisidine ·HCl in BuOH. White spots appear on a pink ground with polyols or any substance reacting with periodate. Sensitivity 25 μg (*J.C.S.* **1958,** 4050).

4. *Iodine*

Expose for 15 min to I_2 vapour. Brown spots are given by sugar mercaptals and alcohols, glycosides, hexonic acids, *N*-acylamino sugars, neutral and acidic polysaccharides (*Research* **6,** 65 (1953)). Do not use this method after solvents containing pyridine, collidine, or other *N*-compounds. *See* Amino acids, 4; Steroids, 35; Amines, 8.

5. *p-Aminodimethylaniline*

Spray with a 0·3% soln. of the $ZnCl_2$ double salt of *p*-aminodimethylaniline in EtOH. General reagent for reducing and non-reducing mono- and oligo-saccharides, giving various colours (*Naturwissenschaften* **39,** 160 (1952)).

6. *Ultraviolet light*

Bright yellow fluorescence is shown by tetroses in u.v. light (*J.B.C.* **212,** 811 (1955)).

REDUCING SUGARS

7. *p-Anisidine*

3% *p*-anisidine hydrochloride in BuOH–EtOH–H_2O (4:1:1) plus a trace of $SnCl_2$. Spray and heat at 100–110° for 3–5 min. Aldohexoses and methyl pentoses, green to brown; ketohexoses, brilliant lemon yellow; uronic acids, red-brown; pentoses, cherry red; methylated aldohexoses, brown; methylated aldopentoses, intense red (*J.C.S.* **1950,** 1702). Sensitivity 1–5 μg. Reducing oligosaccharides react as their reducing unit.

Non-reducing substances, except acid-labile oligosaccharides such as sucrose and raffinose, do not react. *p*-Anisidine phosphate (0·5 g *p*-anisidine in 2 ml H_3PO_4 (Sp. G. 1·75)+EtOH to 50 ml) may also be used to give essentially similar reactions (*Nature, Lond.* **169,** 330 (1952)). Also used in conjunction with u.v. to detect sugar sulphates (*Nature, Lond.* **185,** 309 (1960)).

8. *Aniline–diphenylamine*

Reagent: aniline (4 ml), diphenylamine (4 g), and syrupy H_3PO_4 (20 ml) in EtOH or acetone (200 ml), freshly prepared. Spray or dip (acetone) and heat for 5 min at 60–65° (pentoses) or 80° (all other sugars). Aldohexoses, grey to brown; ketoses, yellow-brown; methyl pentoses, orange; aldoheptoses, bright purple; uronic acids, bright red-brown; pentoses, green-blue. A split version of the reagent can also distinguish between fructose and sorbose (*J. Chromat.* **4,** 206 (1960)). Oligosaccharides give similar colours except those containing a 1→4 linked reducing aldohexose (maltose), bright blue (*Science* **123,** 543 (1956)), or 1→2 linked reducing aldohexose (sophorose), orange.

9. *Triphenyltetrazolium chloride* (TTC)

Spray with 2% aq. TTC:N-NaOH = 1:1, freshly mixed. Heat at 40° in a damp atmosphere for 20 min. Red spots on a white ground are given by reducing sugars, especially fructose and xylose (5 μg) (*Naturwissenschaften* **37,** 491 (1950)). Reducing oligosaccharides also react except those with a 2-substituted reducing aldohexose or 1-substituted reducing fructofuranose (*B.J.* **64,** 351 (1956)). Alternatively, 0·5% TTC in $CHCl_3$ can be used with the dipping technique followed by a spray with alcoholic NaOH (*Nature, Lond.* **166,** 444 (1950)).

10. *Benzidene**

Spray with 0·5 g benzidene in 20 ml glacial CH_3COOH+80 ml EtOH. Heat at 100–5° for 15 min. Pentoses give chocolate brown spots in 5 min; lactose, maltose, galactose, glucose, fructose, dark brown spots in 10 min. Sensitivity 5 μg. Ascorbic acid gives a pale brown spot after 10 min. Sensitivity 10 μg (*Lancet* **1949** (1), 1042). Inositol, and other polyols, sucrose, and raffinose do not react (*Analyt. Chem.* **24,** 1371 (1952)). Sensitivity and specificity are extended if the spray contains HCl or H_3PO_4 (*Nature, Lond.* **192,** 69 (1961)).

A modification giving brown spots with 1 μg glucose (free or combined) is a spray containing 0·5 g benzidine in 10 ml CH_3COOH+10 ml 40% aq. trichloroacetic acid+80 ml EtOH. Yellow colours are given with free or combined fructose but the reaction is much less sensitive than with glucose (*B.J.* **48,** 114 (1951)). Disaccharides with an aminosugar reducing unit give different colours depending on the position of the glycosidic link (*Nature, Lond.* **181,** 117 (1958)).

* Warning: Benzidine is carcinogenic.

11. *p-Anisidine–diphenylamine*

Mix equal vols. of 2% diphenylamine and 2% *p*-anisidine, each in acetone containing 10% (v/v) conc. H_3PO_4, shake well, spray, and heat 2–3 min at 90–95°. Aldopentoses and aldohexoses, green to blue-green; methyl pentoses, pale yellow; uronic acids, red-brown; ketohexoses, yellow-brown; ketoheptoses, bright red-brown. Disaccharides with a reducing aldose unit give similar colours but those with a reducing ketose unit give different colours according to the position of the glycosidic link (*J. Chromat.* **8,** 57 (1962)).

12. *Acid potassium permanganate*

Spray with 0·03 to 0·15N-$KMnO_4$ containing 3% H_2SO_4. Organic compounds give white or light yellow spots. If this spray is applied after aniline oxalate (which gives brown spots with fructose, glucose, and maltose, *see* 23) and the paper heated at 90°, the paper loses its background colour, fructose, sucrose, and melizitose turn grey-black, and glucose and maltose remain brown (*Naturwissenschaften* **38,** 478 (1951)).

13. *p-Aminophenol*

Reagent: 0·5 g *p*-aminophenol+2 g H_3PO_4+50 ml 96% EtOH. Filter. Spray and then heat at 105–10° for 5 min. Glucose gives dark brown spots; fructose, lemon yellow; sucrose and maltose, brownish-yellow; raffinose, light brown (*C.A.* **48,** 506 (1954)).

14. *m-Phenylenediamine*

Spray with 0·2M-*m*-phenylenediamine dihydrochloride in 76% EtOH. Heat at 105° for 5 min. Bright fluorescent spots are given in u.v., yellow with glucose, orange with ribose. Sensitivity 10 μg (*J.B.C.* **175,** 67 (1948)). Pentoses give pink-brown spots; disaccharides yellow (*J.A.C.S.* **77,** 1196 (1955)); uronic acids pink (*Chem. Listy* **46,** 450 (1952)). Phenol, morpholine, diethylene glycol, and dioxan interfere with the fluorescence.

15. *p-Aminohippuric acid*

Spray with 0·3% *p*-aminohippuric acid in EtOH. Heat at 140° for 8 min. In u.v. most hexoses and pentoses give orange fluorescent spots. Sensitivity 1 μg (*Analyt. Chem.* **24,** 1862 (1952)).

16. *Phthalic acid*

Spray with 3% phthalic acid. Detects 0·25 μg glucose, 1 μg fructose by fluorescence in u.v. In visible light four to five times these amounts give orange-red spots. Also detects reducing disaccharides and acid-labile non-reducing oligosaccharides. 4-Aminoantipyrene may be used in place of phthalic acid but it has slightly lower sensitivity and the paper must be heated at 150° for 10 min (*Analyt. Chem.* **24,** 1862 (1952)).

17. *α-Napthylamine*

Spray with a 2% soln. of α-naphthylamine in BuOH–MeOH (1:1), containing 5% trichloroacetic acid. General spray for sugars giving a variety of colours (*J.C.S.* **1950,** 1702).

18. *β-Naphthylamine*

Reagent: 0·1 g pure β-naphthylamine in 50 ml EtOH+50 ml *n*-BuOH+0·4 ml 3·8N-HCl+0·2 ml H_2O+1 drop 10% ferric sulphate. Spray and heat at 160–70° for 10 min. Fructose gives a yellow colour at first, later turning yellow-brown; the same results are given with oligosaccharides which give fructose on hydrolysis; methylpentoses give duller yellow spots; pentoses, bright pink-red; aldoses, light brown (*Nature, Lond.* **166,** 745 (1950)).

19. *Dinitrosalicylic acid*

Spray with 0·5% 3:5-dinitrosalicylic acid in 4% NaOH. Reducing sugars give brown spots on a pale yellow ground (*Analyt. Chem.* **23,** 415 (1951)).

20. *Dinitrobenzoic acid*

Spray with 1% 3:4-dinitrobenzoic acid in 2N-Na_2CO_3. Heat 5 min at 100°. Reducing sugars give blue spots turning brown. Ketoses react faster than aldoses; ascorbic acid reacts in the cold. Sensitivity 1 μg (*Ber.* **83,** 405 (1950)).

21. *Ammonium molybdate*

Reagent: 20 ml 10% NH_4 molybdate is mixed with 3 ml HCl. Then 5 g NH_4Cl is added. Spray the paper. Any inorganic phosphate or readily hydrolysable organic phosphate gives yellow spots immediately. Heat at 75° for 15 min. Reducing substances give blue spots on a white ground due to reduction of molybdate to molybdenum blue. Sensitivity for glucose, 2 μg. Ketoses are more easily detected than aldoses. Sucrose also gives a positive reaction (*Arch. B.B.* **28,** 424 (1950)).

22. *Cysteine*–H_2SO_4 *and thioglycollic-β-aminonaphthalide*–H_2SO_4

For use on glass-fibre chromatograms. Reagent: 0·75 g cysteine·HCl in 20 ml 50% (v/v) aq. EtOH; add 5 ml conc. H_2SO_4 with cooling. Spray and dry at 70°. Pentoses, red; aldohexoses, violet to brown; fructose, blue. A similar reagent containing 0·1 g thioglycollic-β-aminonaphthalide gives grey to brown colours with aldohexoses. Neither reagent reacts with uronic acids or aminosugars (*B.B.R.C.* **2,** 358 (1960)).

ALDOSES

23. *Aniline*

Many variations of this reagent have been reported, the most useful being the following:

(i) Spray with 0·93 g aniline + 1·66 g phthalic acid in 100 ml water-saturated *n*-BuOH. Heat at 105° for 5 min. Aldopentoses give bright red spots, with red fluorescence in u.v.; aldohexoses, deoxysugars, and uronic acids give various shades of green and brown with yellow fluorescence (*Nature, Lond.* **164,** 443 (1949)). The colour given by ketoses is very weak. Oligosaccharides need longer heating. Sensitivity for maltose is 10 μg; maltotriose, 20 μg; glucose, 2 μg (*B.J.* **56,** 86 (1954)).

(ii) Spray with a mixture of equal vols. of 0·1M-aniline and 0·1M-H_3PO_4, each in water-saturated *n*-BuOH. Heat as in (i) (*B.J.* **67,** 643 (1957)). Detects a wider range of sugars and is more sensitive, particularly for reducing oligosaccharides.

(iii) Aniline hydrogen oxalate spray is prepared by shaking 100 ml 0·1M-oxalic acid with 0·9 ml aniline. Pentoses (5 μg) bright red in 5 min; glucose brown in 10 min (*Lancet* **1949** (2), 1042). In u.v. light tetroses (1 μg) show a bright fluorescence. Aldopentoses and hexoses also give this but not ketohexoses or dihydroxyacetone (*J.B.C.* **201,** 161 (1953)).

(iv) Spray with 2·5% aniline trichloroacetate in glacial acetic acid. This gives coloured spots with methylated aldohexoses (brown), pentoses (brown), ketohexoses (brown), and uronic acids (red), but not with polyols. Sensitivity 1–5 μg (*J.C.S.* **1950,** 1702).

(v) Dip ionophoretograms in acetone containing 0·1M-aniline and 0·2M-picric acid and heat at 100°. Sugars develop as dark brown spots on a yellow ground (*Chemy Ind.* **1956,** 578).

(vi) Any of the following aromatic bases in conjunction with HCl, HCOOH, trichloroacetic or toluene sulphonic acids, give colours with methylated sugars after heating at 100–103°: aniline; *p*-aminodimethyl-(or diethyl-)aniline; the colours with these depending on the degree of methylation and position of methyl group on the sugar; *p*-phenylenediamine; *N*-(1-naphthyl)-ethylenediamine; the latter is useful for methyl derivatives of ketoses (*Nature, Lond.* **166,** 520 (1950)).

24. *Benzylamine–ninhydrin*

Essentially a combined spray reagent–rate of movement test for oligosaccharides with a reducing aldose unit. Apply to sugar spot at start line 1–2 spots of 1% benzylamine in MeOH, dry (cold air), and heat the paper for 1 min at 80°. Develop with the top phase of *n*-BuOH–EtOH–H_2O–0·880NH_3 (40:10:49:1) for 15–20 hr, dry, and spray with 0·25% ninhydrin in EtOH to locate the *N*-benzyl glycosylamines; these appear slowly as yellow turning to purple-blue spots. Monosaccharides run just behind the solvent front but very good resolutions of the amines of di- and tri-saccharides with a reducing aldose group are obtained. With other versions of the solvent the reaction may be extended to higher oligosaccharides or increased in resolving power (*Nature, Lond.* **171,** 385 (1953)). The rate of formation of the coloured spots distinguishes these and other *N*-glycosylamines from amino acids, although a control with no benzylamine should always be run.

25. *Diphenylamine*

Spray with 2% diphenylamine in BuOH–MeOH (1:1), containing 5% trichloroacetic acid. Heat at 100° for 10 min. Aldohexoses give brown spots; aldopentoses, purple (*J.C.S.* **1950,** 1702).

26. *Alkaline hypoiodate*

With this spray aldoses give white to yellow spots on a brown ground; ketoses do not react (*Naturwissenschaften* **39**, 160 (1952)).

KETOSES AND PENTOSES

27. *Naphthoresorcinol*

Spray with 0·2% naphthoresorcinol in EtOH–2% aq. trichloroacetic acid (1:1), mixed just before use. Heat at 100° for 5–10 min. Fructose, sorbose, sucrose, raffinose give red colours; pentoses, uronic acids, blue on standing; aldoses, non-reactive. α-Naphthol and resorcinol are also used (*B.J.* **42**, 238 (1948)).

An alternative procedure is to spray with 1% of any of the above phenols in EtOH–2N-HCl (1:9). Heat at 90° for 10 min. Ketohexoses give red and brown colours. Sensitivity 10 μg (*Nature, Lond.* **161**, 239 (1948)).

Phosphoric acid can also be used as the acid, detecting a wider range of sugars and attacking the paper less. In this spray a 0·2% soln. of resorcinol, naphthoresorcinol, α-naphthol, phloroglucinol, or orcinol in EtOH is mixed with 0·1 vol. H_3PO_4 (sp. gr. 1·85) (*Nature, Lond.* **167**, 864 (1951)). The naphthoresorcinol version of this spray is very sensitive and excellent for locating higher sucrose oligosaccharides. Used also on thin-layer chromatograms (*J. Chromat.* **9**, 278 (1962)). A modification of the spray is 1% α-naphthol in EtOH–H_3PO_4 (10:1). Spray and air-dry for 30 min. Then heat at 90° for 5 min. Used for detecting raffinose, 2 μg (*Analyst* **75**, 454 (1950)).

28. *Urea or anthraquinone*

(i) To 100 ml of 1M-H_3PO_4 in water-saturated *n*-BuOH add 3 g of urea then 5 ml of EtOH to eliminate the water phase which forms when the urea dissolves, spray and heat at 100–110° (*Analyt. Chem.* **27**, 33 (1955)). Free or acid-labile bound ketoses (sucrose, etc.), bright blue, highly sensitive; acid-stable oligosaccharides with a reducing fructopyranose, grey-brown (*J.A.C.S.* **78**, 2514 (1956)). Aldoses only react, brown, if present in very high concentration.

(ii) 3% urea or anthraquinone in 5% HCl in EtOH give similar reactions (*J.C.S.* **1950**, 1702). If applied after aniline-phthalic acid (*see* 23 (i)) glucose turns brown-red; fructose and fructosans green-black (*Bull. Soc. Chim. biol.* **34**, 144 (1952)).

29. 2:5-*Diphenyl-3-p-styrylphenyltetrazolium chloride*

Dissolve 20 mg of the above substance in 10 ml EtOH. Mix, immediately before spraying, with an equal vol. of 0·1N-NaOH. After a few minutes at R.T. or slight warming free ketoses and oligosaccharides with a reducing ketose (not sucrose) appear as purple spots on a yellow ground. Sensitivity 5 μg. Aldoses only react if the paper is heated strongly (*B.J.* **73**, 507 (1959)).

30. *Phloroglucinol*

Spray with 0·2 g phloroglucinol in 80 ml 90% EtOH+20 ml 25% aq. trichloroacetic acid. Heat at 110°. Ketoses (5 μg) give orange-brown spots; pentoses (20 μg), green-blue after long heating; aldoses, no reaction (*Lancet* **1949** (1), 1042).

31. *Orcinol*

Spray with water-saturated *n*-BuOH containing 0·5% orcinol and 15% trichloroacetic acid. Heat at 105° for 20 min. Specific for ketoheptoses, sedoheptulose and mannoheptulose, which give bluish-green spots; ketohexoses, yellow; no colour with aldoheptoses or hexoses (*Arch. B.B.* **34**, 225 (1951)). If followed by aniline–phthalic acid with no further heating, D-xylulose, gives a purple colour; D-ribulose, pink; aldopentoses, negative (*B.B.A.* **16**, 292 (1955)). A modification is the spray 3% orcinol in 5% HCl in EtOH. Ketoses and methyl ketoses give red colours (*J.C.S.* **1950**, 1702).

32. *Urea–diphenylamine*

Mix equal vols. of 1% diphenylamine in acetone containing 10% H_3PO_4 and 3% urea in water-saturated *n*-BuOH also containing 10% H_3PO_4. Spray and heat 2–3 min at 90°, observe colours immediately and 1 hr after heating. Fructose and sorbose, brown to grey-black; mannoketoheptose, purple-blue. Disaccharides with a reducing ketose give colours which are dependent on the position of the glycosidic link (*J. Chromat.* **8,** 57 (1962)). If the diphenylamine is increased to 2% and the papers heated for 4–5 min at 95–100° most aldoses give bright red or pink colours.

33. *Anthrone*

Spray with 300 mg anthrone in 10 ml warm glacial acetic acid and 20 ml EtOH+3 ml H_3PO_4 (sp. gr. 1·6)+1 ml H_2O. Heat at 108° for 5–6 min. Mono- di-, tri-, and polysaccharides containing ketohexoses give bright yellow spots; ketopentoses, purple; ketoheptoses, orange-yellow. In u.v., ketoses, brown; aldoses may show a light blue fluorescence. Stronger acid conditions, e.g. H_2SO_4, give green spots with both aldo- and keto-sugars (*Nature, Lond.* **172,** 956 (1953)).

34. 2:4-*Dinitrophenylhydrazine*

Spray with a saturated soln. of 2:4-dinitrophenylhydrazine in 95% EtOH containing 1% conc. HCl. Heat at 70° for 3–5 min. Fructose, sucrose, and raffinose give orange spots on a light yellow ground (*Science* **115,** 129 (1952)).

35. *Diazouracil*

Dissolve 15 mg diazouracil in 10 ml 0·1N-NaOH. Spray paper immediately, partly dry at 60–80° for 3 min, dip in 2% aq. $MgCl_2$ and dry by blotting. Sucrose and substituted sucroses (e.g. raffinose) appear as blue spots provided that the sucrose is not substituted on the fructose portion. Sensitivity 100 μg. Aldoses and monosaccharides do not react (*B.J.* **66,** 462 (1957)).

KETOSE-AMINO ACIDS

36. *Ferricyanide–ferric sulphate*

Spray with (*a*) 0·1% K ferricyanide in 80% EtOH:10% NaOH in 80% EtOH = 10:1, mixed just before use. Leave at R.T. for 5 min. Then spray with (*b*) ferric sulphate–gum ghatti–H_3PO_4 soln. (Prep. in *J.B.C.* **83,** 115 (1929)). Dark blue spots on a colourless or light blue ground are given by ketose-amino acids. Sensitivity 10 μg (*J.B.C.* **215,** 111 (1955)).

SUGAR ALCOHOLS, GLYCOLS, DEOXY-SUGARS, AND GLYCALS

See also Inositol *in* Vitamins.

37. *Potassium periodocuprate*

Dissolve 12·5 g $CuSO_4 \cdot 5H_2O$ in 400 ml boiling water, add 23 g K periodate plus a conc. aq. soln. of 56 g KOH followed by 20 g K persulphate (in small portions at 1 min intervals). Boil 20 min, dilute to 500 ml and add 500 ml 2N-KOH. Stable. Spray. Sugars, polyhydric alcohols, esters, and other non-reducing substances appear as white spots on a brown ground. Highly sensitive (*Chemy Ind.* **1960,** 345).

38. *Vanillin*

Spray with 1% vanillin in EtOH:3% aq. perchloric acid = 1:1, mixed just before use. Heat at 85° for 3–4 min. Polyhydric sugar alcohols give pale blue spots, turning lilac then pale grey-blue on a sandy ground. Sensitivity, hexitols, 15 μg; pentitols, 20 μg; erythritol, 25 μg; glycerol, 30 μg. Inositol, dihydroxyacetone, aldopentoses, and aldohexoses do not react except rhamnose (20 μg) which gives a brick red spot; sorbose and fructose (5 μg) give deep grey-green spots. Phenols and some indolic compounds react (*Nature, Lond.* **174,** 134 (1954)). A greater range of compounds may be detected by examining the sprayed, heated, paper under u.v. light (*Analyt. Chem.* **29,** 1449 (1957)).

39. *Indicators*

Spray with 0·04% bromocresol purple in 95% MeOH containing 0·1% boric acid+7·5 ml 1% borax soln. per 100 ml. Sugar alcohols give yellow spots on a blue ground. Reaction given by *cis*-diols. Fructose but not aldoses react (*Nature, Lond.* **166,** 264 (1950)).

Another indicator spray is 0·05N-Na borate buffer (pH 9·18):0·2% phenol red in EtOH (just alkaline with NaOH):MeOH = 1:2:7. Yellow spots on a purple ground are given by polyols. Sensitivity 25–50 μg. Reducing monosaccharides also react (*Nature, Lond.* **171,** 982 (1953)).

40. *Periodate oxidation–nitroprusside–piperazine*

Spray with (*a*) saturated aq. Na metaperiodate:H_2O = 1:2. Leave at R.T. for 10 min and then spray with (*b*) saturated Na nitroprusside: H_2O:EtOH saturated with piperazine = 1:3:20. Methylpentoses, deoxysugars and glycals give blue spots in 5–10 min, later fading (*J.C.S.* **1952,** 3631).

The following reaction is not given by methylpentoses. After oxidation with periodate, spray with (*b*) 1% *p*-nitraniline in EtOH–conc. HCl (4:1). Deoxysugars and glycals give deep yellow spots on a pale yellow ground and, in u.v., a yellow fluorescence on a brown ground. Then spray with (*c*) 5% NaOH in MeOH. The spots turn green.

41. *Periodate oxidation–Schiff's reagent*

Spray with (*a*) 2% aq. Na metaperiodate. Heat at 60° for 7 min in an atmosphere of N_2 then place in an atmosphere of SO_2 to reduce iodate and excess periodate. Then spray with (*b*) Schiff's reagent (prepared by dissolving 1 g rosaniline in 50 ml H_2O followed by decolorization with SO_2; the solution is treated with charcoal, filtered and diluted to 1 l with H_2O). Heat at 60° for 10 min. Aldehydes arising during oxidation give blue and purple spots. Sensitivity is 10 μg of all 1:2-glycols tested. Carbohydrates containing the 1:2:3 triol-system are distinguished from 1:2-diols because they also give HCOOH on periodate oxidation; the latter gives a brown iodine stain with 5% KI, sprayed after excess periodate is destroyed with 10% aq. ethylene glycol (*J.C.S.* **1950,** 3162).

Reducing oligosaccharides containing a 1→2 linked reducing unit (e.g. kojibiose, sophorose) give a specific yellow colour with the periodate-rosaniline spray reagent (*B.J.* **87,** 54 (1963)).

42. KIO_4–$MnSO_4$–*aromatic base*

Spray with (*a*) 0·5% KIO_4. Leave for 1–5 min. Then spray with (*b*) 15% aq. $MnSO_4$: saturated soln. di-(*p*-dimethylaniline)methane in 2N-CH_3COOH = 1:1. α-Glycols give white spots on a blue ground. Sensitivity 5–50 μg (*J. chem. Soc. Japan*, Pure Chem. Sect. **73,** 18 (1952)). Other sprays of this type for detecting reducing and non-reducing sugars are periodate–permanganate–benzidine and periodate–ferricyanide–benzidine (*Analyt. Chem.* **28,** 1037 (1956); **29,** 1560 (1957)).

43. *Lead tetra-acetate oxidation*

Spray with xylene. Immediately spray with 1% Pb tetra-acetate in benzene, the reagent being decolorized with charcoal and filtered if necessary before spraying. White spots on a brown ground are given by all 1:2-glycols (10 μg), α-hydroxyacids, pyruvic acid, and dihydroxyacetone (*J.C.S.* **1950,** 3162). For locating sugar alcohols on ionophoretograms sensitivity is improved by subsequently spraying with rosaniline (*Chemy Ind.* **1961,** 82).

44. *Hydrochloric acid*

Spray with conc. HCl:EtOH = 1:4. Heat at 90°. Glycals give pink spots turning brown. If alcoholic $FeCl_3$ soln. is used instead of the HCl spray, sensitivity is slightly less (*J.C.S.* **1952,** 3631).

45. *Cysteine*

Used to detect deoxyribose and deoxyribosides (*Nature, Lond.* **168,** 1091 (1951)). *See* Purines, 14. A modification of this spray is 0·12% carbazole in EtOH:1·5% cysteine·HCl:EtOH:25N-H_2SO_4 = 1:1:5:0·2. Heat at 65–70° for 5 min. Xylulose and ribulose give violet spots turning grey (3 μg) or black (15 μg) on a colourless ground; xylose (15 μg) gives a very faint colour (*J.A.C.S.* **77,** 1663 (1955)). Also given by glycals. *See also* Purines 15.

46. *p-Dimethylaminobenzaldehyde*

Spray with 1% *p*-dimethylaminobenzaldehyde in EtOH:conc. HCl = 4:1. Heat at 90° for 30 sec. Deoxypentoses, deoxypentosides, D-ribal give bluish- or purplish-grey spots; deoxyhexoses, deoxyhexosides, glucal, galactal, pinkish-grey. After 2 min, xylose and arabinose give grey spots (*J.C.S.* **1952,** 3631); acetylglucosamine, violet (*C.A.* **47,** 5310 (1953)). Ninhydrin may be substituted for *p*-dimethylaminobenzaldehyde, giving more bluish colours.

47. *Periodate–thiobarbiturate*

Spray with (*a*) 0·02 M-Na periodate. After 15 min spray with (*b*) ethylene glycol:acetone:conc. H_2SO_4 = 50:50:0·3 and, after 10 min, spray with (*c*) aq. 6% Na-2-thiobarbiturate. Heat at 100° for 5 min when 2-deoxy-sugars give red spots. Sensitivity 0·5 μg (*Nature, Lond.* **186,** 237 (1960)).

SUGAR ACIDS

48. *o-Phenylenediamine*

Spray with 2% *o*-phenylenediamine dihydrochloride in 80% EtOH. Heat at 100° for several min. 2-Ketohexonic acids (50 μg) give greenish-grey spots; 10–20 μg detected by fluorescence in u.v. light. Some aldoses may react but give different colours (*J.B.C.* **189,** 109 (1951)).

A spray of 0·05% *o*-phenylenediamine in 10% aq. trichloroacetic acid has also been used for uronic acids but *m*-phenylenediamine as described in 14 is more sensitive, although it may not be as specific as *o*-phenylenediamine (*Chem. Listy* **46,** 450 (1952)).

49. *Hydroxylamine–ferric chloride*

Spray with (*a*) N-NH_2OH·HCl in MeOH:1·1N-KOH in MeOH = 1:1, freshly prepared. Leave at R.T. for 10 min. Then spray with (*b*) 1–2% $FeCl_3$ in 1% aq. HCl. Esters, lactones, or ester lactones give blue or mauve spots. Also given with certain amides and methylamides of sugar acids and most esters (*J.A.C.S.* **73,** 5859 (1951)). *See* Amines, 12.

A modification of this spray in which soln. (*b*) is strongly acid $Fe(NO_3)_3$ gives purple colours with sugar acetates and inositol acetates on thin-layer chromatograms (*Can. J. Chem.* **40,** 1043 (1962)).

50. *Bromophenol blue*

Spray thoroughly dried paper, with bromophenol blue (50 mg bromophenol blue in 100 ml 95% EtOH adjusted to pH 6·5 with 0·1N-NaOH). Excellent for uronic acids and oligouronides (*Arch. B.B.* **51,** 114 (1954)).

SUGAR ACETATES

51. *Diethylaminomethanol*

Expose the paper to an atmosphere of diethylaminomethanol at 50°. Acetates are saponified and free sugars can be detected with $AgNO_3$, *see* 1 (*Naturwissenschaften* **39,** 380 (1950)).

HEXOSAMINES

52. *Acetylacetone–p-dimethylaminobenzaldehyde*

Component solutions of first spray: (*a*) 0·5 ml acetylacetone in 50 ml *n*-BuOH, (*b*) 50% aq. KOH:EtOH = 5:20. (*a*):(*b*) = 10:0·5, mixed just before use and a few drops 50% EtOH added to redissolve any crystals. Spray. Heat at 105° for 5 min. Spray with (*c*) 1 g *p*-dimethylaminobenzaldehyde in 30 ml EtOH+30 ml conc. HCl+180 ml *n*-BuOH. Heat at 90° for 5 min. Free hexosamines give cherry red spots (*B.J.* **42,** 238 (1948)) except fructosamine, red-purple and sialic acids, salmon pink (*B.J.* **72,** 479 (1959)). *N*-Acetylglucosamine gives an intense purple-violet colour with (*c*) alone, without previous treatment with acetylacetone; cf. 46. With the complete reagent 1→6 and 1→3 linked disaccharides with an *N*-acetyl aminosugar reducing unit give a purple colour but similar 1→4 linked compounds do not react (*Nature, Lond.* **181,** 117 (1958)).

53. *Ninhydrin*

Spray with 0·05% ninhydrin in *n*-BuOH. Heat at 105–110° for 10 min (*Arch. B.B.* **52,** 1 (1954)). Aminosugars give red colours. This spray may be followed by aniline hydrogen oxalate (*see* 23 (iii)) for free sugars (*Naturwissenschaften* **38,** 478 (1951)).

A spray of 2% ninhydrin in 95% EtOH, containing 4% pyridine, has also been used for aminosugars (*Arch. B.B.* **52,** 373 (1954)). See *Meth. biochem. Anal.* **6,** 294 (1958), for the separation of hexosamines as pentoses after degradation by ninhydrin.

54. *Periodate thiobarbiturate*

Spray 47 with a modified (*a*) reagent, 0·05M-Na metaperiodate in 0·05N-H_2SO_4, gives a red colour with sialic acids after heating for 10 min at 100°. Sensitivity 3 μg (*Nature, Lond.* **186,** 237 (1960)).

POLYSACCHARIDES

55. *Copper sulphate–phosphomolybdate*

Spray with (*a*) 40 g Na_2CO_3 (anhyd.)+20 g $NaHCO_3$+25 g Rochelle salt+7·5 g $CuSO_4\cdot 5H_2O$+H_2O to 1 l. Heat at 105° for 5 min. Then spray with reagent (*b*) prepared by dissolving 150 g molybdic acid+75 g Na_2CO_3 (anhyd.) in 500 ml H_2O; heat and filter; add 300 ml 85% H_3PO_4+H_2O to 1 l. Reducing polysaccharides give blue spots on a white ground (*J.A.C.S.* **72,** 5150 (1950)).

Periodate–Schiff's reagent (41), alkaline permanganate (2) and, on glass-fibre ionophoretograms, 5% naphthol in 10N-H_2SO_4 have also been used (*Nature, Lond.* **194,** 573 (1962); **178,** 154 (1956)).

56. *Toluidine blue*

For acidic mucopolysaccharides, fix polysaccharides by dipping in EtOH–ether (95:5). Dry. Then dip in 0·06% toluidine blue 0 in 0·5% aq. CH_3COOH. Finally rinse in 2% aq. CH_3COOH (*Stain Technol.* **29,** 257 (1954)). Heparin gives a bright pink colour; chondroitin sulphate and hyaluronate, purple, on a light blue ground (*Science,* **122,** 924 (1955)); dextran sulphate gives purple colour on a light blue ground (*B.J.* **58,** 532 (1954)). Azure blue (0·05%) is also used as a metachromatic stain for sulphated acid mucopolysaccharides (*B.J.* **53,** 79 (1953)). Other stains used for acidic polysaccharides are Alcian blue, mucicarmine, and azur A7 (*Nature, Lond.* **194,** 573 (1962)).

57. *Carmine*

Stock solution: 1 g carmine+0·5 g anhyd. $AlCl_3$+2 ml H_2O are heated in a porcelain crucible for 2–3 min. Dissolve in 100 ml 50% EtOH. Filter after 24 hr. Store at 5°. Spray with the mixture, stock solution:EtOH:H_2O = 5:17:3. Rinse in H_2O containing a small amount of CH_3COOH. Both acid and neutral mucopolysaccharides give bright pink spots on a very light pink or colourless ground (*Science* **122,** 924 (1955)).

GLYCOSYLAMINES

58. *Ninhydrin*

Detected with the ninhydrin reagent of spray no. 24, and distinguished from amino acids by heating at 85° for 1–2 min when glycosyl derivatives turn brown before developing the normal purple colour. Spots begin to appear in 1 hr and are fully developed in 12 hr (*Nature, Lond.* **171,** 385 (1953)).

---

7. HORMONES

ADRENALINE, *see* Catecholamines *in* Amines

AUXINS AND OTHER INDOLE DERIVATIVES

By J. A. MOWAT (*Marine Laboratory, Aberdeen*)

Indole derivatives are important in medicine, chemistry, and plant physiology. Most of the naturally occurring auxins (a group of plant hormones) are indole compounds. The most important recent reviews giving details of chromatography, suitable solvents and R_F values, bio-assays, and chemical determination are:

J. A. Bentley, *Meth. biochem. Anal.* **9,** 75–125 (1962). Analysis of plant hormones, including extraction, purification, chemical determination, and methods of biological assay.

J. B. Jepson, *Chromatographic and Electrophoretic Techniques*, ed. I. Smith, 2nd ed., vol. 1, Heinemann, London (1960). Chapter on indoles and related Ehrlich reactors of mainly medical interest, pp. 183–211. Cited in this section as *Chromatographic Techniques*.

E. V. Truter, *Thin Film Chromatography*, Cleaver-Hume Press, London (1963). Section on analysis of indole derivatives and metabolites, pp. 149–52.

Z. Prochazka, V. Sanda, and K. Macek, *J. Chromat.* **3,** D30 (1960). Table 43, giving R_F values of 74 indole derivatives in 7 solvents.

Other recent relevant reviews and a symposium are:

F. Wightman (ed.), *Biochemistry and Physiology of Plant Growth Substances*, Runge Press, Ottawa (1968).

E. M. Shantz, *A. Rev. Pl. Physiol.* **17,** 409 (1966).

J. A. Bentley, 'Chemistry of the native auxins', p. 484; 'Extraction and purification of auxins', p. 501; 'Chemical determination of auxins', p. 513. *Handb. PflPhysiol.* **14** (1961)

Methods of extraction of auxins from plant tissues depend on whether 'free' auxins such as 3-indolylacetic acid (IAA) are being examined, or 'bound' complexes such as indole glycosides and indole peptides. Compounds may be labile in certain solvents, e.g. glucobrassicin (*Annls Acad. Sci. Fenn.* A **107,** 3 (1961)) and 3-indolylpyruvic acid (*B.J.* **64,** 44 (1956)) in ammoniacal solvents. IAA is slowly decomposed by light and acids. The best solvent to use depends on the type of compound being examined, e.g. whether neutral or acidic, 'free' or a complex. When analysing unknowns it is imperative to use a range of solvents including both acidic and alkaline.

BIOLOGICAL ASSAY

Auxins are a group of compounds defined by their biological activity in promoting various aspects of growth and development in plants. To establish biological activity or to detect compounds in too small a concentration to be determined by chemical methods, a method of bio-assay must be employed. Solutions eluted from segments of the chromatogram are tested for their effect on growth of various plant tissues. The most-used methods are (*a*) *Avena* coleoptile section growth. Minimum detectable IAA, 0·02 μg in 2 ml solution. Full details of test in *Meth. biochem. Anal.* **9,** 75 (1962). Gibberellins show low activity, not rising to a maximum at optimum concentration. (*b*) *Avena* internode test—approximately same sensitivity (*Pl. Physiol.* **31,** 94 (1956)). For a critical comparison of the main methods of auxin bioassay see Table V in *Meth. biochem. Anal.* **9,** 75 (1962).

CHEMICAL REACTIONS

1. *Ehrlich's reagent*

Gives stable pink, purple, or blue colours with indole derivatives, except some hydroxy-indolyl acetic acids.

(*a*) *Paper chromatograms.* (i) Spray with 2% (w/v) *p*-dimethylaminobenzaldehyde (DMAB) in conc. (12·1N-) HCl. After 2–3 min, spray with 1% (w/v) $NaNO_2$ in H_2O. Indole compounds appear as deep blue spots immediately (except indican, orange-brown). Colours persist 4–8 weeks without fading (*J. Chromat.* **3,** 97 (1960)). (ii) Dip in 10% (w/v) *p*-DMAB in conc. HCl:acetone = 1:4. Sensitivity, 0·05 μg IAA. Can be applied after a ninhydrin reaction (*Chromatographic Techniques*, p. 193).

(*b*) *Thin-layer chromatograms.* Dissolve 1 g *p*-DMAB in 50 ml HCl (24%) and 50 ml ethanol (96%). Use 10 ml soln. to each 20×20 cm plate. Warm to 50° for 20 min, then expose to vapours of *aqua regia.*

2. *Acidic oxidizing reagent*

One drop of a fresh, sat. soln. of potassium persulphate, 10 ml conc. HCl and 40 ml acetone are freshly mixed as required and the chromatogram dipped. The acetone is blown off and paper allowed to dry for 1 hr, or dried in a stream of warm air, in which the colours develop immediately (*Chromatographic Techniques*, p. 195). IAA, stable pink; 3-indolylacetonitrile (IAN) blue purple. Indolylacetyl derivatives of amino acids, violet, developing slowly. Tryptophan and tryptamines, very slow, yellow.

3. *Prochazka reagent*

(*a*) *Paper chromatograms.* Spray with 40% formaldehyde:conc. HCl:water = 1:1:2. Heat to 70°. 3-Indolylcarboxylic acid gives a red spot in ordinary light. Other indoles fluoresce yellow or yellow-orange in u.v. light (*Flora, Jena* **153,** 54 (1963)).

(*b*) *Thin-film chromatograms.* 35% Formaldehyde soln. (10 ml) is diluted with 25% HCl (10 ml) and 96% ethanol (20 ml). Spray heavily (10 ml of reagent) and after 5 min heat to 100°. Indole derivs. form yellow brown spots with orange fluorescence in u.v. Exposure of sprayed films to vapours of *aqua regia* causes intensification of fluorescence.

Truter (*Thin Film Chromatography*, Cleaver-Hume Press, 1963) gives R_F values of simple indole derivatives (Table 13) and tryptophan metabolites (Table 14) on neutral, unbuffered silica gel G films, using this reagent or the Ehrlich reagent.

4. *p-Dimethylaminocinnamaldehyde*

2 g *p*-Dimethylaminocinnamaldehyde in 6 N-HCl (100 ml) and ethanol (100 ml) used as a spray (*B.J.* **69,** 60P (1958)). More sensitive than the Ehrlich reagent but less specific. Used as a dip with acetone instead of ethanol it has approximately the same sensitivity as the Ehrlich reagent with IAA and IAN, but the colours come up more rapidly in the cold. Useful for detecting serotonin and certain indoles which do not react with Ehrlich reagent (e.g. β,β-dimethyltryptamine) but generally the Ehrlich reagent is preferable because of its higher selectivity for indoles.

5. *Nitrous–nitric acids*

1 g KNO_2+20 ml HNO_3+80 ml 95% EtOH (*Physiologia Pl.* **7,** 98 (1954)) is used as a spray. As a dip, 5 vol. conc. HNO_3, 45 vol. acetone, 1 vol. 5% aqueous $NaNO_2$ (added last) are mixed and used within 2 min. IAN, grey-blue or olive-green with

intense green u.v. fluorescence. Other indoles, faint yellow or brown colours (*Chromatographic Techniques*, p. 198).

6. *Alkaline silver nitrate*

Test for enols and oxidizable phenols. Used as a dip: 1 drop sat. $AgNO_3$ in water is added to 10 ml acetone and the paper dipped. It is then dipped in 0·5% NaOH in 80% EtOH. Indolylpyruvic acid, *immediate* dark brown. Other indoles take several minutes to react (*Chromatographic Techniques*, p. 198).

7. *Ninhydrin—acetic acid reagent*

Specific test for certain tryptamines. 0·2% ninhydrin in acetone (9 vol.)+glacial acetic acid (1 vol.) are freshly mixed and used as a dip. Heat at 110° for 2 min. Susceptible tryptamines show intense greenish-blue fluorescence in u.v. light (*Chromatographic Techniques*, p. 196).

PHYSICO-CHEMICAL DETERMINATIONS

8. *Ultraviolet fluorescence*

Some indole auxins have a characteristic fluorescence in u.v. light (Hanovia Chromatolite, 2537 Å transmitted). IAA and IAN, purple; 3-indolylpyruvic acid, bright blue (Table IV in *Meth. biochem. Anal.* **9**, 75 (1962)).

9. *Spectrophotofluorometry*

A precise and sensitive means of indole identification. Sensitivity comparable to the *Avena* bio-assay, but impurities interfere severely, and must be removed by gas or thin layer chromatography (*Pl. Physiol.* **37S**, xxxiv (1962)).

GIBBERELLINS

By J. A. MOWAT (*Marine Laboratory, Aberdeen*)

Evidence is accumulating that the gibberellins, a relatively recently discovered group of plant hormones, play as important a role in the regulation of plant growth and development as the auxins. It is likely that large-scale screening of substances for gibberellin-like activity will take its place in routine research on plant growth regulators, in addition to the analysis of plants for occurrence of natural gibberellins.

For biological activity (oat-leaf test) and R_F values of gibberellins A_1 to A_9 in benzene–acetic acid–water (4:2:1) and *n*-butanol–1·5N-ammonia (3:1) see *Ann. Bot.* **30**, 165 (1966). Thin-layer chromatographic data in five solvent systems are given in *Phytochemistry* **6**, 867 (1967), and permit the separation of the seventeen known gibberellins. All seventeen can be separated and identified by gas–liquid chromatography (same ref.).

BIOLOGICAL ASSAY

Relative activity of the gibberellins in a number of different bio-assays have been examined by Brian *et al.* (*Nature, Lond.* **193**, 946 (1962)). Bio-assays fall into two categories:

(1) Assay with isolated plant tissues—rapid, lasting only a day or two, and large numbers of tests can be carried out in the laboratory. Most used are growth of first leaf of oat or wheat seedlings (*Meth. biochem. Anal.* **9**, 113 (1962); *Phyton, B. Aires* **16**, 97 (1961); *Acta Soc. Bot. Pol.* **30**, 553 (1961)). Tests are specific for gibberellins and sensitive down to concentrations of GA_3 (gibberellic acid) of around 10^{-9} g/ml. Good activity is shown in the oat leaf test by all the gibberellins (except A_2 and A_8, which have low or no activity in all bio-assays), and it is therefore a useful scanning test.

(2) Assay using entire plants—these demand greenhouse facilities and sometimes

a fairly long preparatory growing period. They are therefore not so convenient for routine laboratory scanning investigations.

(*a*) Dwarf pea seedlings (*Nature, Lond.* **191,** 684 (1961)) A_1 and A_3 show high activity; A_9 is inactive. Different pea varieties differ considerably in activity, with optima from 0·001–0·1 μg GA_3.

(*b*) Growth of leaf sheath of dwarf mutant maize (*Plant Growth Regulation*, ed. R. M. Klein, p. 489, Iowa State University Press, 1961). Variety d_1—A_1, A_3, A_4, A_7 good activity, A_9 low; Variety d_3—A_5, A_7, A_9 good activity; Variety d_5—A_3, A_5, A_7 good activity. A_6 and A_8 low activity in all varieties. Note difference in response to A_9 between varieties d_1 and d_3.

(*c*) Lettuce hypocotyl growth (*Nature, Lond.* **185,** 255 (1959); 9*th Ann. Rep. Scott. Hort. Res. Inst.* Dundee, 1961–2). A_3 and A_7 highly active $> A_1, A_4, A_9 > A_5 > A_6$, and A_8 practically inactive.

(*d*) Cucumber hypocotyl growth (*Nature, Lond.* **189,** 74 (1961)). A_4, A_7, and A_9 good activity, A_6 and A_8 practically inactive.

Thus, gibberellins A_1–A_9 show considerable specificity in the different tests. In studies of endogenous plant gibberellins, it is advisable to combine a rapid scanning method (e.g. oat first leaf) with an assay based on a response of the plant under examination.

PHYSICO-CHEMICAL DETERMINATION

Fluorescence in u.v. light (*Nature, Lond.* **197,** 790 (1963))

(*a*) Ethanol:conc. H_2SO_4 = 95:5 is used with paper or thin-layer chromatograms. Spray and heat at 120° for 10 min. Examine under u.v. light. Gibberellins A_1, A_3, A_5, A_6, A_8, blue fluorescence; gibberellins A_2, A_4, A_7, A_9, purple fluorescence.

(*b*) Water:conc. H_2SO_4 = 30:70 is used with thin-layer chromatograms. Gibberellins A_3, A_7, yellow-green fluorescence without heating; gibberellins A_1, A_3, A_6, A_8, green-blue fluorescence after heating; gibberellins A_2, A_4, A_9, blue-purple fluorescence after heating; gibberellins A_5 and A_7, light yellow and brown fluorescence respectively after heating.

Sensitivity of both sprays ranges from 0·00025 μg A_3 to 0·01 μg A_6. These tests are very much more sensitive and specific than other sprays for gibberellins (70% perchloric acid and heat, 0·5% potassium permanganate). Combined with thin-layer chromatography, they offer a technique of separation and determination of gibberellins which is as sensitive as the bio-assays.

THYROXINE AND RELATED COMPOUNDS

By J. R. TATA (*National Institute for Medical Research, Mill Hill, London*)

The thyroid hormones, L-thyroxine and 3:5:3′-triiodo-L-thyronine, and their halogenated analogues are still commonly separated by paper chromatography. R_F values in three solvent systems of the biologically important compounds have been summarized (Pitt-Rivers & Tata, in *The Thyroid Hormones*, Pergamon Press, London (1959)). Since 1958, other methods of separation of thyroxine and related compounds, especially in biological media, have been developed. These include separation by (*a*) paper electrophoresis (*Clinica chim. Acta* **4,** 427 (1959); *Endocrinology* **70,** 679 (1962)); (*b*) combination of partition chromatography and paper electrophoresis (*Arch. B.B.* **99,** 1 (1962)); (*c*) chromatography on columns of anion-exchange resins (*Bull. Soc. Chim. biol.* **40,** 369 (1958); *Bull. Soc. Chim. biol.* **40,** 609 (1958); *B.J.* **82,** 111 (1962)); (*d*) gel filtration on dextran ('Sephadex') gel columns (*Mikrochim. Acta* **1961,** 296; *Scand. J. clin. Lab. Invest.* **14,** 285 (1962); *Clinica Chim. Acta* **7,** 183 (1962)). Some of the methods of detection on paper, described below, can be adapted to the newer methods of separation on columns. However, it is recommended that aliquots of eluates be characterized by paper chromatography in the presence of markers of known compounds.

21. Detection of Biochemical Compounds

1. *Ninhydrin*

Spray with 0·2% ninhydrin in *n*-BuOH saturated with H_2O, containing 5% CH_3COOH. *See* Amino acids, 1. Sensitivity for thyroxine, 20 μg (*B.B.A.* **11,** 215 (1953)). This spray is suitable for iodothyronines and iodotyrosines but unsuitable for the deaminated analogues or when amino acid contamination is high.

2. *Pauly reaction*

(i) *Diazotized sulphanilic acid. See* Amino acids, 14 (*P.S.E.B.M.* **84,** 240 (1953)).

(ii) *Diazotized N′, N′-diethylsulphanilamide.* Mix equal vols. cold 0·05M-*N′*, *N′*-diethylsulphanilamide in 9% HCl and cold 4% $NaNO_2$. Let stand for 10 min at 4°. Spray and let stand 5 min. Then spray with 10% aq. Na_2CO_3. Purple colours are given with compounds containing diphenolic ethers (e.g. thyroxine) and orange with compounds possessing a single benzene ring (e.g. diiodotyrosine) (*Brit. med. Bull.* **10,** 218 (1954)). Sensitivity for iodothyronines and analogues is 20–30 μg and 10–15 μg for iodotyrosines. The Pauly reaction is particularly suitable for the deaminated analogues and for iodothyronines and iodotyrosines in the presence of large amounts of amino acids. Unsuitable for phenolic conjugates, i.e. β-glucoronides and sulphate esters.

3. *Ceric sulphate–arsenious acid*

(i) Component solutions of the spraying reagent: (*a*) 10 g $Ce(SO_4)_2 \cdot 4H_2O$ is suspended in 100 ml N-H_2SO_4 at 0–5°. Filter after 1 hr. (*b*) 5 g Na arsenite in 100 ml N-H_2SO_4 at 0°. (*a*):(*b*) = 1:1, mixed just before use. The reagent is applied by thoroughly wetting a blank paper on a glass plate; the chromatogram is then placed on top and covered with another glass plate for 30 min. Dry in an I_2-free atmosphere. Iodine containing compounds give white spots on a yellow ground. If photographed in u.v. these show as black spots on a white ground. Sensitivity for KI, 0·01 μg; diiodotyrosine, 0·02 μg; thyroxine and triiodothyronine, 0·1 μg (*B.J.* **59,** 93 (1955)). To prevent fading of the background colour due to traces of I_2 in the atmosphere, spray with (*c*) 1% aq. *o*-phenylenediamine before drying in air. A stable chocolate-coloured ground is produced by the reaction of excess ceric sulphate with the amine (*Nature, Lond.* **175,** 730 (1955)).

(ii) Modification of Robbins (*C.r. Trav. Lab. Carlsberg* **32,** 233 (1961)).

Stock solutions: (*a*) 10 g $Ce(SO_4)_2.4H_2O$ in 100 ml 10% (v/v) H_2SO_4; (*b*) 5 g $NaAsO_2$ in 100 ml H_2O; (*c*) 0·025M-aq. *o*-phenanthroline ferrous sulphate ('Ferroine'). One part of solution (*a*) is added to 6 parts of solution (*b*), giving a clear orange-yellow solution. One part of 'Ferroine' solution (*c*) is then added giving a turbid, dark green suspension which is kept shaken. The dried chromatogram paper is sprayed lightly on each side (about 8 ml of reagent to spray 30×30 cm). Spots of iodine-containing substances turn orange at a rate depending on their concentration. The green background is unstable, first turning orange and then decolorized. Storage in dark increases stability. Sensitivity 0·2 μg for iodothyronines and 0·02 μg for iodotyrosines.

4. *Ferric chloride–ferricyanide–arsenite*

Stock solutions: (*a*) 2·7 g $FeCl_3 \cdot 6H_2O$ in 100 ml 2N-HCl. (*b*) 3·5 g $K_3Fe(CN)_6$ per 100 ml H_2O. (*c*) 5 g $NaAsO_2$ in 30 ml 1N-NaOH (under cooling) and then add 65 ml 2N-HCl under vigorous stirring. Store in a cool, dark place. Before use, mix (*a*):(*b*):(*c*) = 5:5:1. Dried paper chromatograms are sprayed evenly from both sides and placed between 2 glass plates for 15 min under dim light or in a dark room. The paper is then washed well in distilled H_2O and dried. Iodide, iodotyrosines and iodothyronines give blue spots which can be quantitated photometrically (Zeiss filter FE-54). Sensitivity is 0·01–0·07 μg for the above compounds (*Acta chem. scand.* **13,** 1469 (1959)).

5. *Starch-iodate*

Dried papers are first sprayed with 1% starch solution and then with 1% KIO_3 or $KBrO_3$ solution. While still wet, the paper is exposed for 3–4 min to u.v. light. Positions of iodinated substances appear as blue spots which later fade away. Sensitivity 0·5 μg for thyroxine, 0·05 μg for diiodotyrosine (*Analyt. Biochem.* **4,** 185 (1962)).

6. *Neutron activation*

Thyroxine and other iodinated compounds are separated by paper chromatography. The iodinated compounds are detected and quantitated by activation of ^{127}iodine by thermal neutrons (flux of $1–4 \times 10^{12}$ n/cm^2/sec for 30–50 min). The ^{128}I formed is separated radiochemically from other radioactive products formed by the activation of paper. Limit of detection is 0·0015 μg of thyroxine or triiodothyronine/cm^2 of paper (*Atomkernenergie* **6,** 408 (1961); *Nature, Lond.* **197,** 446 (1963)).

---

8. LIPIDS

Revised by J. OLLEY (*Torry Research Station, Aberdeen*)

The chromatography of lipids in general on laminates (TLC), paper and glass paper have been reviewed in *J. Am. Oil chem. Soc.* **38,** 708, 565, 582 (1961). The advantages of the individual techniques are discussed at length and solvent systems and sprays listed. Neutral lipids may be separated into individual components according to the nature of the fatty acids by impregnation of TLC plates with silver nitrate (*Chemy Ind.* **1962,** 1050). Lipoproteins are often stained prior to electrophoresis (*J. Lab. clin. Med.* **54,** 291 (1959)). Paper chromatography of phospholipids has been reviewed (*J. Lipid Res.* **3,** 1 (1962)) and three papers specifically deal with one and two-dimensional TLC of phospholipids (*B.Z.* **334,** 175 (1961); *J. Lipid. Res.* **3,** 467, 471 (1962)). A new technique on anion exchange paper (*B.B.R.C.* **5,** 422 (1961)) separates phospholipids and glycolipids in a different order. The use of a non-polar antioxidant such as BHT (3:5-di-*t*-butyl-4-hydroxytoluene) is recommended in the solvent especially for two way chromatograms which have to be dried between runs.

GENERAL SPRAYS OR DIPS

1. *Sulphuric acid*

Spray TLC plates or glass papers with conc. or 50% H_2SO_4 or sat. chromic–H_2SO_4. Heat on hot plate, diagnostic colours appear with increasing temperature. Most non-volatile compounds eventually give black spots. As little as 0·1 μg lipid is detected by the charring technique (*J. Am. Oil chem. Soc.* **38,** 708 (1961)).

2. *Dichlorofluorescein*

0·2% 2′:7′-dichlorofluorescein in 95% ethanol. View under u.v. at 366 mμ (*J. Am. Oil chem. Soc.* **38,** 609 (1961)).

3. *Phosphomolybdic acid*

10% phosphomolybdic acid in absolute ethanol. Heat chromatogram to 160–180°. Spray immediately on removal from oven. Intense blue spots appear immediately (*J. Lipid Res.* **3,** 391 (1962)).

4. *Rhodamine 6G or Rhodamine B*

0·001% aq. Rhodamine 6G in 0·25M-K_2HPO_4. View wet under u.v. light. Purple, blue, and yellow spots against rose background. Length of time of immersion in stain varies with compound and type of chromatogram. A few seconds to 2–3 min for paper chromatograms, 5–15 min for glass paper chromatography (*J. Am. Oil chem. Soc.* **38,** 565 (1961)).

5. *Iodine vapour*

Detects lipids, nitrogenous compounds, non-reducing carbohydrates. Compounds recovered unchanged after detection. Expose to crystals of I_2 in closed chamber, or dip in 0·2% I_2 solution in ether. Test the day chromatograms are developed. Ultraviolet light enhances feeble staining. If the chromatography solvent contained acid it must first be removed from chromatograms in a vacuum dessicator or with NH_3 (*J. Chromat.* **1,** 385 (1958); **8,** 75 (1962)).

SPECIFIC SPRAYS OR DIPS

6. *Ninhydrin*

For lipids containing free amino groups.

(i) Spray or dip in 0·25% solution of ninhydrin in acetone-lutidine (9:1). Develop at R.T. for several hours (*J. Lipid Res.* **3,** 1 (1962)).

(ii) Stock ninhydrin in *n*-butanol (1 mg/ml) diluted with 2:4-lutidine (20% by volume) immediately before use. Develop at 120° for 5 min. Intensify colour by dipping chromatogram in 2N-HCl for 2 min, washing and drying before spraying with reagent (*J. Am. Oil chem. Soc.* **38,** 14 (1961)).

7. 2:4-*Dinitrophenylhydrazine*

For aldehydogenic lipids. Dry chromatogram washed three times in distilled water. Immerse 1–2 min in 2:4-dinitrophenylhydrazine (0·15% in 3N-HCl). Wash thoroughly to remove excess reagent. View wet or dry under u.v. at 366 mμ (*J. Lipid Res.* **3,** 1 (1962)).

8. *Periodate–Schiff reagent*

For phosphatidylglycerol, inositol phosphatides, and cerebrosides. Wash chromatogram with distilled water and dry. Immerse in 2% aqueous sodium periodate for 1 min. Rinse with water, immerse in 2% aqueous sodium bisulphite for 25 min. Dip in Schiff's reagent (1% *p*-rosaniline decolorized with SO_2 and filtered through charcoal) for 30 sec. Purple spot develops in 10–15 min (G. V. Marinetti, personal communication).

9. *Dragendorff's reagent*

To detect choline. Mix 4 ml solution (*a*), 1 ml solution (*b*), and 20 ml distilled water. Solution (*a*) 1·7 g $Bi(NO_3)_3 \cdot 5H_2O$ diluted to 100 ml with 20% (v/v) acetic acid. Solution (*b*) 40 g KI in 100 ml water. Dry at R.T. Free choline, purple spot; choline containing compounds, orange spots (*B.Z.* **334,** 175 (1961)). *See also* Amines 10, 11.

10. *Bial's orcinol*–$FeCl_3$–HCl *reagent*

For glycolipids. Heat chromatograms for 1½ hr at 80° in HCl atmosphere. Treat with Bial's reagent and replace in HCl vapour at 80°. Violet spots develop on a white background (*B.Z.* **334,** 175 (1961)). Bial's reagent: 40·7 ml conc. HCl, 0·1 g orcinol, 1 ml 1% $FeCl_3$, and distilled water to 50 ml.

11. *Molybdate-perchloric acid*

For phospholipids; *see* Phosphate esters, 1. This spray is not specific for phospholipids on TLC and gives blue or brownish-blue colours with all lipids.

12. *Molybdenum blue* (*Zinzadze*) *reagent*

Specific for phosphate containing compounds.

Solution 1. 40·1 g of MoO_3 boiled in 1 litre of 25N-H_2SO_4 until dissolved.

Solution 2. 1·78 g of powdered molybdenum is added to 500 ml of solution 1. Mixture boiled gently for 15 min. Cool and decant any residue. Mix equal volumes of solutions 1 and 2 and dilute with two volumes of water. Final solution should be greenish-yellow. Spray plates with solution. Phosphate containing compounds appear immediately as blue spots on a white ground (*J. Lipid Res.* **5,** 126 (1964)).

13. *Sudan black*

For lipoproteins and histochemistry.

Dissolve 0·1 g of Sudan black B in 1 ml ethyl acetate at R.T. Dilute after solution with 9 ml propylene glycol. Stain for 15 min. Ratio stain: lipoprotein = 1:5 (*Analyt. Biochem.* **2,** 178 (1960)).

---

9. NATURAL PIGMENTS

CAROTENOIDS AND CHLOROPHYLLS

A review of the paper chromatography of chloroplast pigments is given by Sestak in *J. Chromat.* **1,** 293 (1958). See also *Modern Methods of Plant Analysis*, vol. 3, p. 272 (1955) (carotenoids) and vol. 4, p. 142 (1955) (chlorophylls). The R_F's of many pigments in the solvents, (i) 4% propanol in light petroleum (B.p. 60–80°); (ii) 30% chloroform in light petroleum, are reported in *B.J.* **80,** 336 (1961). Separations on thin layers by either adsorption or partition chromatography are reviewed by Randerath, *Thin-layer Chromatography*, pp. 152–6, Academic Press, New York (1963).

Detection

Carotenoids and chlorophylls are detected by their colour in visible light and fluorescence in u.v. (*Naturwissenschaften* **39,** 88 (1952)).

PORPHYRINS

Revised by R. J. PORRA (*Division of Plant Industry, C.S.I.R.O., Canberra*)

Porphyrins, free and esterified, are recognized on paper chromatograms as intense red fluorescent spots when viewed under u.v. light; sensitivity, 0·1–3 μg. To obtain the best results the following considerations should be taken into account.

1. To prevent decomposition of porphyrin:
   (*a*) Remove peroxides from organic solvents.
   (*b*) Run chromatograms in dark to prevent photodecomposition.
   (*c*) Read and mark spots under u.v. light even before drying the paper; spots fade rapidly. Spraying with *iso*-octane or kerosene may intensify fluorescence of spots.

2. To obtain well-defined spots:
   (*a*) Avoid overloading the spot at the origin.
   (*b*) Remove lipids from samples from biological sources. Repeated ether–HCl fractionation is therefore advisable.
   (*c*) Avoid presence of high salt concentrations in the porphyrin solution applied to the paper.

Porphyrins are normally applied on Whatman No. 1 paper as ether solutions or dissolved in dil. NH_4OH. The esters are applied dissolved in $CHCl_3$. The spot on the origin should not exceed 1 cm diameter; this is best achieved by drying paper with a hair-dryer after application of each drop.

Procedure for examining unknown porphyrins

The following order of paper chromatographic investigations is suggested. It is essential to use markers and not rely on R_F values. *See* Reviews in *J. Chromat.* **5,** 277 (1961) and *Meth. biochem. Anal.* **8,** 221 (1960). More recently, thin-layer chromatography has been used successfully (*J. Chromat.* **25,** 373 and 380 (1966); **27,** 180 (1967)).

Free carboxyl groups. This is indicated by chromatograms of the free porphyrin with 2:6 lutidine–H_2O solvent (*B.J.* **48**, 306 (1951)). The higher the R_F the lower the number of carboxyl groups; uroporphyrin III (8COOH), coproporphyrin III (4COOH), and mesoporphyrin IX (2COOH) are commonly used as markers. One can determine COOH number before and after hydrolysis to estimate number of esterified COOH.

Side chain substituents. The nature of the side chain substituents can sometimes be determined by paper chromatography of the methyl esters using the following five solvent systems.

(1) Kerosene–chloroform (*J.B.C.* **190**, 643 (1951)).

(2) Kerosene–*n*-propanol (*J.B.C.* **190**, 643 (1951)).

Further information and R_F values in these 2 systems in *Nature, Lond.* **183**, 1185 (1959), where a technique using the above two solvent systems to detect hydroxyl groups in side chains of porphyrin esters is used.

(3) Kerosene–tetrahydropyran–methyl benzoate (*J.B.C.* **208**, 537 (1954)).

(4) Water–acetonitrile–*n*-propanol–pyridine (*J.B.C.* **208**, 537 (1954)).

(5) Water–acetonitrile–dioxan (*J.B.C.* **208**, 537 (1954)).

To detect isomers. Coproporphyrins I, II, and III are distinguished by a lutidine–H_2O solvent system (*B.J.* **63**, 87 (1956)), and the esters distinguished by kerosene–chloroform, and kerosene–*n*-propanol solvent systems (*J.B.C.* **190**, 643 (1951)). Thin-layer chromatography has also been used to separate coproporphyrins I and III (*J. Chromat.* **10**, 236 (1963)).

Uroporphyrins I and III have been distinguished after esterification using various 2-dimensional techniques (*B.J.* **55**, 101 (1953); *J. Chromat.* **10**, 141 (1963)). Uroporphyrin isomers may also be decarboxylated to the corresponding coproporphyrin isomers by the method of Edmondson & Schwartz (*J.B.C.* **205**, 605 (1953)) and then chromatographically distinguished as above.

Mesoporphyrin I and IX have been distinguished using a 2:6-lutidine–H_2O solvent system (*J. Chromat.* **6**, 350 (1961)).

---

10. PHENOLS AND RELATED COMPOUNDS

By T. SWAIN (*Low Temperature Research Station, Cambridge*)

Although some chemically simple phenols are involved in animal metabolism, the widest variety of phenolic compounds which occur in Nature are found in plants (i.e. flavonoid compounds, cinnamic acids, coumarins, and tannins) usually in a combined form (e.g. glycosides). The majority of the phenolic compounds or their derivatives (e.g. glucuronides) which are present in normal urine arise from these two sources, but administration of drugs and other foreign organic compounds containing an aromatic nucleus can lead to the formation of phenols even though the original substance contained no phenolic groups (R. T. Williams, *Detoxication Mechanisms*, Chapman & Hall, London (1959)). Thus there is a wide range of compounds of different reactivities and polarities included in the term phenolic, ranging from nitrophenols (*B.J.* **78**, 262 (1961)) to complex tannins (*J. Chromat.* **1**, 537 (1958)) and the choice both of solvent for separation and of reagent for detection depends therefore on the class of compounds under examination.

By far the most useful solvents for the separation of less polar compounds (i.e. simple phenols) are combinations of benzene (or toluene or chloroform), acetic (or formic) acid and water (e.g. Bz–HAc–H_2O, 125:72:3). Such water-poor solvents are usually temperature sensitive, and also require pre-equilibration. A wide variety of other solvents, may however, be used (*Meth. biochem. Anal.* **1**, 27 (1954); *J. Chromat.* **1**, 338, 374 (1958); **4**, 458 (1960)).

For the more polar compounds (i.e. the majority of those present in plant extracts and the phenolic derivatives in urine) the most useful solvents are those based on combinations of alcohols, water, and acetic (or formic) acid (e.g. *n*-BuOH–HAc–H_2O, 6:1:2; *n*-BuOH–EtOH–H_2O, 4:1:2·2; 2% aqueous HAc; HAc–conc. HCl–H_2O, 30:3:10) (*Modern Methods of Plant Analysis*, vol. 3, p. 450 (1955); *J. Chromat.* **1,** 473 (1958); **2,** 581 (1959)). Basic solvents (e.g. *iso*PrOH–5M-NH_3, 20:3) have been used for separating certain classes (especially phenolic acids), but since many phenols are readily oxidized at high pH, such solvents should be avoided if possible. Pre-treatment of the paper, for example with formamide for alkyl phenols (*J. Chromat.* **5,** 408 (1961); **6,** 475 (1961)), or with buffers and chelating agents for a wide variety of plant phenols (*J. Chromat.* **2,** 605 (1959); **4,** 369 (1960); **6,** 467 (1961)) is sometimes of advantage both in separation and the detection of structural groups. In some cases also the preparation of derivatives of the phenols (e.g. azo dyes) prior to chromatography is advantageous.

As mentioned earlier, most of the compounds encountered both in plants and in urine are present in a combined form, and it is desirable in these cases to examine the extract before and after hydrolysis (with acid, base (usually in an atmosphere of N_2) or an enzyme). Methods have been elaborated for the quantitative determination of, and the partial or complete elucidation of the structure of, many phenolic compounds. These utilize a combination of chromatographic, spectral, and chemical techniques and are especially useful for the examination of plant extracts (*J. Chromat.* **1,** 473 (1958); **2,** 581 (1959); *Phytochemistry* **2,** 85 (1963)).

Methods of detection

The methods used for the location of phenolic compounds, other than those that are coloured in visible light or fluorescence in u.v. are dependent either on the enhanced reactivity of aromatic rings containing phenolic groups to substitution by electron-seeking reagents (e.g. diazonium salts), or to the susceptibility of phenols to oxidation, or to their ability to form chelates with metals and other ligands.

DETECTION BY COLOUR OR FLUORESCENCE

1. *Colour in visible light and fluorescence in u.v.*

The vast majority of phenolic compounds occurring in plant extracts are either coloured or more usually fluoresce strongly under a long wave u.v. lamp ($\sim$ 300 mμ). Both visible colour and the ability to fluoresce are dependent on the presence of an extended system of conjugated double bonds in the molecule, and simple phenols are therefore both colourless and non-fluorescent. They may, however, be detected by their absorption (i.e. appear dark) when examined under short wave u.v. ($\sim$ 250 mμ).

The major classes of compounds which are coloured are anthocyanins (orange to mauve), flavonols and some nitrophenols (pale yellow), and chalkones and aurones (deep yellow). The shade and depth of colour changes with increase in the number of suitably oriented phenolic groups. Fluorescence is usually brown (flavones, flavonol-3-glycosides, and chalkones), varying shades of yellow (flavonols and aurones) or varying shades of blue or purple (cinnamic acids, coumarins, methylated flavones, and stilbenes), but there is a wide overlap depending on orientation or substitution of the phenolic hydroxyl groups (*J. Chromat.* **1,** 473 (1958); **2,** 581 (1959); *Phytochemistry* **2,** 85 (1963); *J. Chromat.* **1,** 338, 374 (1958); **4,** 458 (1960)).

When the chromatogram is exposed to NH_3 vapour (best) or sprayed with base (0·1 to 2N-aq. Na_2CO_2 is suitable) usually both the visible colour and fluorescence undergo characteristic changes due to the ionization of phenolic hydroxyl groups and subsequent increase in conjugation. It can generally be taken that a reversible change in colour or fluorescence on exposure to ammonia indicates the presence of a phenolic compound. Anthocyanins go to bluer shades, and flavonols, etc., deeper yellow. Some compounds, colourless before exposure to alkaline pH (e.g. chlorogenic acid), may also appear yellow. Exposure to base also induces oxidation of certain compounds leading to the formation of permanent brown spots. Changes in the fluorescence colour in the presence of base are usually to longer wavelengths (i.e. blue → green → yellow).

Absence of change in visible or fluorescence colour probably indicates methylation or other forms of substitution of the phenolic groups.

SUBSTITUTION REAGENTS

2. *Diazotized amines*

All compounds containing phenolic hydroxyl groups which have a free *para* or *ortho* position and which do not contain strongly deactivating substituents or sterically hindering groups react with diazotized amines at a suitable pH to give coloured azo dyestuffs. Imidazoles also react. Many different amines have been used for the coupling reaction but the most useful is *p*-nitroaniline since the azo dyes produced often show variation of colour with pH.

(i) *Diazotized p-nitroaniline*

(*a*) A solution of the amine (5 ml, 0·5% w/v) in 2N-HCl is mixed with aq. sodium nitrite (0·5 ml, 5% w/v), and sodium acetate (15 ml, 20%) added. (*b*) Na_2CO_3 (20% w/v). The two sprays are used successively, the colour reaction with each being noted (*B.J.* **53,** 200 (1953)). If required a further overspray with 0·1N-NaOH can be used. In all cases spraying with the first reagent should be light and even, or excessive background develops. Alternatively the spray can be made up with sodium carbonate instead of acetate (carefully, because of effervescence). The concentration and volumes of reagents used here, as with other diazo reagents, are not critical. *See* Amines, 17 (ii).

(ii) *Diazotized sulphanilic acid and benzidine*

Both these amines are used at 0·5% w/v in 2N-HCl and after diazotization the first is made alkaline with sodium carbonate solution (3 vol. 20% w/v). For the colours given by simple phenols *see J. Chromat.* **1,** 338 (1958); **4,** 458 (1960). *See also* Amines, 17 (i).

Other substitution reagents

The most useful reagents from the number of others which have been used are 2:6-dibromoquinone-4-chloroimide, *p*-dimethylaminobenzaldehyde, vanillin and toluene-*p*-sulphonic acid, and nitrous acid. The first reagent reacts only with phenols that have a free *para* position; the next two react most strongly with *meta* substituted dihydric undeactivated phenols and thus can be used to detect catechins and leuco-anthocyanins in the presence of other compounds. Nitrous acid, on the other hand, reacts with many phenolic compounds but the nitroso phenols produced do not all give coloured quinonoid salts with base.

3. 2:6-*Dibromoquinone*-4-*chloroimide**

The reagent (0·5%) in ethanol is sprayed first, followed by a spray of any suitable base (~ pH 10) or exposure of the paper to ammonia (*J. Chromat.* **1,** 338 (1958); **4,** 458 (1960)). Blue colours are formed with most phenols that react; some other compounds also react (e.g. thiol-imidazoles).

* Warning: This compound can be an explosive risk at temperatures of 50° C and above.

4. *p-Dimethylaminobenzaldehyde*

A solution of *p*-dimethylaminobenzaldehyde (10% w/v) in conc. HCl is diluted fivefold with acetone or EtOH. If the reagent is dissolved in acetic anhydride instead of conc. HCl it is somewhat selective for aryl glycines (e.g. hippuric acid) which give orange or red colours; some organic acids also react (*J.B.C.* **206,** 695 (1954)). Catechins and similar compounds give magenta spots either slowly in the cold or on heating. Indoles, pyrroles and aromatic amines react more readily but may be differentiated from phenols with other groups.

5. *Vanillin–p-toluenesulphonic acid*

The aldehyde (2 g) and acid (1 g) are dissolved in EtOH (100 ml), and after spraying the paper is heated to 100° for 10 min. Catechins and related compounds give pink to violet-red colours (*J. Chromat.* **4**, 65 (1960)).

6. *Nitrous acid*

Sodium nitrite (1%) in N-acetic acid is sprayed first, followed by 0·1N-NaOH (*Arch. B.B.* **33**, 299 (1951)). This reagent gives red colours with many phenols including chlorogenic acid.

OXIDIZING AGENTS

Most phenols, except those which are highly substituted, are readily oxidized, especially at high pH, but compounds containing vicinal di- or tri-hydric groups are the most reactive.

Although certain phenols may be detected, usually as brown spots, either by allowing them to autoxidize after spraying with base (*see above*) or spraying with a crude phenolase preparation (*Arch. B.B.* **56**, 97 (1955)), the most usual mode of detection is by selecting reagents which themselves change colour. The most useful is the ferric chloride–potassium ferricyanide reagent (*Nature, Lond.* **170**, 249 (1952)), which is fairly specific for phenolic compounds. Monohydric phenols, however, react very slowly. Alkaline silver nitrate can also be used but it reacts with a wide variety of other compounds. Advantage can be taken of autoxidation of vicinal di- or tri-hydric phenols at high pH by condensing the quinones formed with ethylenediamine.

7. *Ferric chloride–potassium ferricyanide*

Aqueous 1% solutions of each salt (AR quality) are mixed in equal proportions before spraying or dipping (the solution should be orange-brown with no trace of blue). Reactive phenols give blue spots immediately in the cold. After development the paper must be washed with 0·1N-HCl followed by water if a permanent record is required.

8. *Alkaline silver nitrate*

(*a*) Silver nitrate (1 ml 10% w/v) is diluted with acetone (20 ml).

(*b*) Sodium hydroxide solution (10 ml, 5% w/v) is diluted with ethanol (90 ml). The paper is dipped in solution (*a*), dried, and dipped in solution (*b*). Reactive compounds give black spots on a brown ground in a few minutes in the cold. The paper is finally washed with ammonia and water to clear the background (*Nature, Lond.* **166**, 444 (1950)).

9. *Ethylenediamine*

Equal volumes of ethylenediamine (10% v/v) and 1N-Na_2CO_3 are mixed, and after spraying the paper is heated to 100° for 5 min (Swain, unpub.). This spray gives more consistent results than the one described earlier (*J. Sci. Fd Agric.* **5**, 593 (1954)). Vicinal tri-hydroxy compounds give immediate colour of various shades which go brown on heating and usually have a yellow fluorescence; *ortho*-dihydroxy compounds give either dark colours on heating or yellow spots with a blue fluorescence.

CHELATING AGENTS

These reagents are rather insensitive but have the advantage that the phenols can be recovered after use. The formation of all the chelates is pH-dependent.

10. *Ferric salts*

Phenols having two or more vicinal hydroxy groups, or *ortho* (or *peri*) hydroxy-carbonyl groups, give coloured chelates with ferric salts. The chelates with di-hydroxy compounds are usually green, those with tri-hydroxy compounds blue, and others brown or red. Ferric ammonium sulphate (0·2%) or ferric chloride (2%) are suitable reagents (*J. Chromat.* **1,** 338 (1958); **4,** 458 (1960)).

11. *Aluminium salts*

Aluminium salts (e.g. 1% ethanolic aluminium chloride) form coloured or fluorescent chelates with flavonols, and other compounds (*J. Sci. Fd Agric.* **5,** 593 (1954); *Chemy Ind.* **1954,** 1389). Blueing of anthocyanin colours by aluminium salts indicates the presence of vicinal hydroxy groups (*J. Chromat.* **1,** 473 (1958)).

12. *Molybdates*

Molybdates (e.g. 0·1M-sodium molybdate) give yellow-coloured chelates in the cold, with vicinal di- and tri-hydroxy phenols (*J. Chromat.* **2,** 605 (1959)).

SPECIAL SPRAYS

Two special sprays are worthy of mention for the detection of leuco-anthocyanins and flavanones.

13. *p-Toluenesulphonic acid*

A solution (3%) in ethanol is sprayed and the paper heated to 100° for 5–10 min. Leuco-anthocyanins give orange to dark red colours (*J. Chromat.* **4,** 65 (1960)).

14. *Sodium borohydride*

$NaBH_4$ (0·1 g) is dissolved in the minimum quantity of water and made up to 10 ml with *iso*-PrOH. After spraying the paper is exposed to conc. HCl fumes. Flavanones give red colours (*Arch. B.B.* **68,** 501 (1957)).

---

11. PHOSPHATE ESTERS

Revised by H. ROSENBERG (*Department of Biochemistry, Australian National University, Canberra*)

The large number and variety of methods for phosphate ester chromatography preclude complete coverage and the reader is referred to some excellent recent reviews or review-like articles. Hettler (*Chromat. Rev.* **1,** 225 (1959)) deals with the chromatography of inorganic phosphates and polyphosphates up to P_8, and metapolyphosphates up to P_4. A large number of the biologically important phosphate compounds have been dealt with by Wood (*J. Chromat.* **6,** 142 (1961)), and the chromatography, in combination with electrophoresis, of nucleotides in particular received much study from Bergkvist. In one of his more recent publications he described the complete separation of the mono-, di-, and tri-phosphates of adenosine, guanosine, cytosine, and uridine, as well as of NAD and NADP (*Acta chem. scand.* **12,** 752 (1958)). The method of Eggleston and Hems (*B.J.* **52,** 156 (1952)) also affords excellent separation of the adenosine nucleotides, including the tetraphosphate (*Bull. Soc. Chim. biol.* **44,** 751 (1962)).

The methods in general involve chromatography in mixtures of aqueous and organic solvents or electrophoresis, or both, on paper. Chromatography is the slower of the two methods, while electrophoresis at high voltage may be accomplished in about 30 min. A recent innovation (*J. Chromat.* **10,** 236 (1963)), however, offers a novel means of chromatography on polyethyleneimine cellulose, using 1M-NaCl as a solvent, and affords the separation of 5′-mononucleotides in about 30 min.

For the chromatography of thionophosphates such as various insecticides and related compounds, see *J. Chromat.* **9,** 111, 307 (1962).

The *detection* of phosphates on paper varies with the compounds studied, since in some cases (viz. u.v. absorption of nucleotides) the non-phosphate moiety of the compound may afford a rapid and, what is more important, a non-destructive means of detection. The various methods are discussed in the relevant section.

1. *Molybdate–perchloric acid*

This method depends on the hydrolysis of phosphate esters to inorganic phosphate in the presence of molybdic acid followed by the reduction of the phosphomolybdate so formed to give blue spots. Many variations both of the reagent and of the subsequent method of reducing the phosphomolybdate spots have been used. The following are the most useful:

(i) Spray with the mixture 60% (w/v) perchloric acid:N-HCl:4% ammonium molybdate:H_2O = 5:10:25:60. Inorganic phosphate gives a yellow spot. Dry the paper at 85° for 1 min. Glucose-1-phosphate and other readily labile phosphate esters give yellow spots. Expose the paper to u.v. radiation. All organic phosphates, including those hydrolysed with difficulty (e.g. phosphoglyceric acid), now give blue spots. Inorganic phosphate, yellow-green. Citric acid may give a blue spot. Remove background colour by exposing the paper to NH_3 vapour (*J.B.C.* **193,** 405 (1951)).

(ii) Spray with molybdate–perchloric acid. Heat at 85° for 5 min. Autoclave paper for 2 min at 8–10 lb pressure. The paper is now uniformly blue. When treated with NH_3 vapour, background blue disappears while colour due to phosphomolybdate blue remains (*J.B.C.* **193,** 405 (1951)).

(iii) Spray with molybdate–perchloric acid. Heat at 85° for 7 min. Hang in moist H_2S gas for 10 min. Phosphate esters give blue spots on a faint buff ground. Stable esters, glucose-6-phosphate, and 3-phosphoglyceric acid, give only faint spots (*Nature, Lond.* **164,** 1107 (1949)). The water in the molybdate spray can be replaced by acetone so that papers can be dipped (*Nature, Lond.* **170,** 800 (1952)).

(iv) Spray with molybdate–perchloric acid. Heat at 85° for 10 min. Then spray with a fresh soln. containing 3 vol. 60% perchloric acid and 1 vol. reducing agent (1 g *p*-methylaminophenol sulphate+3 g Na bisulphite in 100 ml H_2O). Sugar phosphates give blue spots on a white ground (*J.B.C.* **201,** 161 (1953)).

(v) Spray with molybdate–perchloric acid. Heat at 85° for 7 min. Then spray with a mixture of 2·5 g Rhodol+146 g Na bisulphite+5 g Na sulphite in 50 ml 60% EtOH (*Bull. Soc. chim. Fr.* **19,** 874 (1952)). This gives more stable colours than by the use of H_2S (iii).

(vi) Spray with 2·5% NH_4 molybdate in 2N-H_2SO_4. Then spray with 0·25% aq. ascorbic acid (*Helv. chim. Acta* **34,** 931 (1951)).

(vii) Dip in mixture of 3 ml 5% w/v ammonium molybdate, 7 ml 5N-HCl, and 90 ml acetone. Air-dry. Then dip in mixture of 10 ml of 1% vanadyl chloride in 1·0N-HCl and 90 ml acetone. The mixture is freshly reduced by shaking with 0·2 g of Zn powder. Orthophosphate, phosphite, pyrophosphate, and a number of phosphate esters and phosphonates produce spots varying from green to purple on a white background (*J. Chromat.* **2,** 487 (1959)).

(viii) Spray with a mixture of 0·5 g NH_4 molybdate in 400 ml H_2O+0·05 g basic quinine sulphate in 100 ml H_2O+4 ml HNO_3. Phosphate esters form quinine phosphomolybdate which gives a dark spot on a fluorescent ground in u.v. light. Sensitivity for orthophosphate is 10 μg (*Bull. Soc. chim. Fr.* **17,** 868 (1950)).

(ix) Alkaline phosphomonoesterase has been used to liberate phosphate before detection (*Nature, Lond.* **171,** 838 (1953)).

(x) If the paper is first sprayed with aniline phthalate (*see* 3) and heated, glucose-6-phosphate and fructose-1:6-diphosphate give brown spots, which turn blue on subsequent spraying with molybdate–perchloric acid (*Can. J. Chem.* **30,** 653 (1952)).

(xi) For the detection of some aromatic phosphate esters which are not hydrolysed and therefore not detected under the standard Hanes & Isherwood procedure, the following (*J. Chromat.* **9,** 121 (1962)) is suggested: Spray paper with 5% $FeSO_4$, follow with 5M-H_2O_2, dry, and leave overnight in atmosphere of ammonia. Follow with Hanes & Isherwood spray (i).

Note. When highly stable phosphates require destructive techniques beyond the durability of the paper, thin-layer chromatography should be tried.

2. *Ferric chloride–salicylsulphonic acid*

Spray with (*a*) 0·1% $FeCl_3 \cdot 6H_2O$ in 80% EtOH. Dry at R.T. Ferric ion is fixed by phosphate esters. Then spray with (*b*) 1% salicylsulphonic acid in 80% EtOH, which reacts with free iron. Phosphate esters give white spots on a pale mauve ground (*Nature, Lond.* **171,** 529 (1953)).

3. *Aniline hydrogen phthalate*

This spray detects aldose phosphates (*J.B.C.* **194,** 199 (1952)). *See* Carbohydrates, 23 (i).

4. *Naphthoresorcinol*

Spray with the mixture 0·2% naphthoresorcinol in EtOH:2% trichloroacetic acid:60% perchloric acid = 4·75:4·75:0·5. Heat at 85° for 8 min. Fructose phosphates give cherry red spots on a pale mauve ground (*B.J.* **49,** xxi (1951)). Cf. Carbohydrates, 27.

---

12. PURINES, PYRIMIDINES, NUCLEOSIDES, AND NUCLEOTIDES

Revised by P. WHITFELD (*Division of Plant Industry, C.S.I.R.O., Canberra*)

The separation and identification of these compounds using paper chromatographic techniques has been reviewed by Wyatt in *The Nucleic Acids*, eds. Chargaff and Davidson, vol. 1, Academic Press, New York (1955) and Markham in *Modern Methods of Plant Analysis*, eds. Paech and Tracy, vol. 4, Springer-Verlag, Berlin (1955); also *Meth. Enzymol.* **3,** 743 (1957). More recently (*J. Chromat.* **10,** 236 (1963)) a method of chromatography on polyethyleneimine cellulose, using M-NaCl as solvent, affords good separation of 5′-mononucleotides in about 30 min.

Ion-exchange chromatography (e.g. Cohn, *Meth. Enzymol.* **3,** 724 (1957)), paper electrophoresis (e.g. Smith in *The Nucleic Acids*, vol. 1 (1955)), and thin-layer chromatography (e.g. Randerath, *Thin-layer Chromatography*, Academic Press (1963)) are also useful methods for separating nucleotides and their derivatives.

The purification and separation of purines is described by Bergmann and Dikstein (*Meth. biochem. Anal.* **6,** 79 (1958)). The products resulting from the digestion of RNA with pancreatic ribonuclease may be conveniently identified by the two-dimensional mapping procedure of Rushizky and Knight (*Virology* **11,** 236 (1960)). Characterization of small oligonucleotides can be achieved by use of the approach outlined by Schmidt (*Meth. Enzymol.* **3,** 747 (1957)).

Identification of purine and pyrimidine bases is usually achieved by comparing the R_F values of the unknown in a number of solvents with those of marker compounds or with published data, such as can frequently be obtained by reference to the *Journal of Chromatography*. Comparison of the u.v. absorption spectrum of the chromatographically purified compound with that of appropriate reference compounds should as a rule give fairly conclusive identification.

GENERAL METHODS

1. *Absorption in ultraviolet light*

Purine and pyrimidine derivatives show as dark spots on the faintly fluorescing paper background when viewed under u.v. light (*Nature, Lond.* **163,** 216 (1949)). This is the most sensitive method of detection (1 μg) and permits location of the compound without chemically modifying it. A suitable light-source has been described by Markham (*Modern Methods of Plant Analysis*, vol. 4 (1955)), or a commercial lamp which has its maximum emission at 2537 Å (e.g. Mineralite) may be used. The compounds may be directly visualized or photographed by contact printing (Markham, ibid.). If phenol or collidine solvents have been used they must first be removed by exhaustive washing with ether. A preliminary spray of 0·5N-NaOH is used for barbituric acids (*Nature, Lond.* **170,** 845 (1952)). To increase background fluorescence and thereby the contrast, a spray of 0·005% fluorescein in 0·5N-NH_3 may be used (*Angew. Chem.* **63,** 511 (1951)). This is not recommended, however, if the compound is to be subsequently eluted from the paper for spectrophotometry.

Caution should be taken not to expose the naked eyes to the u.v. light.

2. *Fluorescence in ultraviolet light*

Certain purine and pyrimidine derivatives may fluoresce when exposed to u.v. light. This may be seen directly or photographed by contact print (Markham in *Modern Methods of Plant Analysis*, vol. 4). A sheet of nitrocellulose film (0·08 mm) placed between the chromatogram and the photographic paper excludes the u.v. light but permits the transmission of the visible fluorescent light. The compound is thus shown as a black spot on a grey-white background. Sensitivity 0·1 μg.

PURINES

3. *Silver chromate*

Spray with (*a*) 2% $AgNO_3$. Then dip in (*b*) 0·5% Na dichromate. This gives a red Ag chromate precipitate. Dip in (*c*) 0·5N-HNO_3. In this bath the red precipitate slowly dissolves leaving red deposits (purine–Ag chromate complexes) at the purine positions. Remove from the HNO_3 while the background is still slightly pink. Wash in H_2O. 0·5 μg guanine or adenine is detected. Pyrimidines do not react (*J.A.C.S.* **72,** 5781 (1950)).

4. *Mercury salt*

Spray with (*a*) 0·25% mercuric acetate in 95% ethanol containing a few drops of glacial acetic acid. Air-dry and spray with (*b*) 0·05% diphenylcarbazone in 95% ethanol. Purines containing one ionizable hydrogen will react. Sensitivity 5 μg. Spots should be immediately obvious but will stand out more after 24–48 hr (*Meth. biochem. Anal.* **6,** 88 (1958)). If phenol or pyridine solvents have been used they must first be removed by washing the paper in ether.

5. *Bromine*

Expose paper to Br_2 vapour for 2 min and then to steam over a boiling water bath for 1 min. Dry paper for 5 min at 110°. A rose pink spot which becomes reddish-purple when exposed to NH_3 is given by caffeine, theobromine, and theophylline. Sensitivity 10–20 μg (*Nature, Lond.* **198,** 783 (1963)).

PYRIMIDINES

6. *Mercury salt*

Immerse the paper for 30 sec in (*a*) 0·1M-mercuric acetate:M-Na acetate:H_2O = 1:3:6. Then immerse for exactly 20 sec in slowly renewed water. Finally dip in (*b*) ammonium sulphide soln. Uracil and cytosine (5 μg) and thymine (10 μg) give black spots (*J.B.C.* **176,** 703 (1948)).

7. *p-Dimethylaminobenzaldehyde*

Spray with 2% *p*-dimethylaminobenzaldehyde in 30% HCl. Yellow-orange spots are given with sulphapyrimidines (*C.A.* **47,** 4796 (1953)).

BARBITURIC ACIDS

8. *Cobaltous acetate*

Spray with a 0·1 saturated soln. of cobaltous acetate in pyridine. Pentobarbital and its derivatives give dull purple spots. Specificity and sensitivity not reported (*J.B.C.* **214,** 807 (1955)).

Thio-derivatives of barbituric acids

9. *Ammoniacal silver nitrate*

Spray with 0·1N-$AgNO_3$:10% NH_3 = 1:1. Heat at 95° for 15 min. Barbiturates may appear as white spots (Ag salts) on a yellow background and thio-derivatives not at all on first spray. Repeat spray. Heat at 95° for 5 min. Thio-barbiturates give black spots (*J. Pharm. Pharmac.* **4,** 98 (1952)).

10. *Copper sulphate–diethylamine*

Spray with 10% diethylamine in methanol:saturated soln. of anhyd. $CuSO_4$ in 90% methanol (1:1). Green spots are given. This is fairly specific for thio-barbiturates (*J. Pharm. Pharmac.* **4,** 98 (1952)).

Other derivatives of barbituric acids

11. *Potassium permanganate*

Spray with 0·02N-$KMnO_4$. Derivatives containing —C═C— in open chain give yellow spots on a red background immediately; derivatives containing the hexenyl group give this colour in 3 min (*J. Pharm. Pharmac.* **4,** 98 (1952)).

12. *Mercuric oxide*

5 g HgO in 100 ml H_2O+20 ml H_2SO_4 is diluted with an equal vol. H_2O. Dip paper in this soln. Saturated derivatives give white spots (*J. Pharm. Pharmac.* **4,** 98 (1952)).

RIBONUCLEOSIDES

13. *Periodate oxidation–Schiff's reagent*

Ribonucleosides and 5′-ribonucleotides after periodate oxidation of the *cis*-glycol groups give Schiff's reaction for dialdehydes; *see* Carbohydrates, 41. Sensitivity for ribonucleotides, 20–50 μg (*J.C.S.* **1950,** 3162).

DEOXYRIBONUCLEOSIDES

14. *Cysteine hydrochloride*

Spray with 0·5% cysteine·HCl in 3N-H_2SO_4. Heat at 85° for 5–10 min. Deoxyribose and deoxyribosides give pink spots. Sensitivity, 10–20 μg. Purine compounds react more quickly than pyrimidines. Not given by ribose or the ribonucleosides (*Nature, Lond.* **168,** 1091 (1951)).

15. *Dische reaction*

Reagent: 1% diphenylamine in glacial acetic acid to which 2·75% by vol. H_2SO_4 has been added is diluted with 0·5 vol. H_2O. Spray. Clamp the paper between glass and heat at 90°. Purine deoxyribonucleosides (10 μg) give purplish blue-spots in 5–10 min; pyrimidine deoxyribonucleosides (50–100 μg) give blue spots in 25–30 min. Deoxyribose reacts (*J.C.S.* **1950,** 3162). Sensitivity of the pyrimidine derivatives increased 4-fold by bromination with Br_2:water:acetic acid = 1:50:10 prior to diphenylamine reaction (*J. Chromat.* **1,** 291 (1958)).

16. *Feulgen reaction for purine deoxyribonucleosides*

Spray with Schiff's reagent as in Carbohydrates, 41, made 0·1N with respect to H_2SO_4. Heat at 60° for 6 min, then leave at R.T. for 24 hr. Purine deoxyribonucleosides give purple colours; sensitivity 10 μg (*J.C.S.* **1950,** 3162).

17. *Bioautograph*

Promotion of growth zones of *Lb. lactis* on agar plate is shown by certain deoxyribonucleosides and nucleotides, which can replace Vitamin B_{12} (*J.A.C.S.* **73,** 867 (1951)).

NUCLEOTIDES

18. *Molybdate-perchloric acid, etc.*

See Phosphate esters, 1.

19. *Uranyl acetate-ferrocyanide*

Dip in (*a*) 0·15% aq. uranyl acetate. Wash 20 sec in H_2O, then dip in (*b*) 3% aq. K ferrocyanide, made acid with HCl. Nucleotides give brown spots (*Bull. Soc. chim. Fr.* **19,** 844 (1952)).

PYRIDINE NUCLEOTIDES

(*See also* Nicotinic acid *in* Vitamins)

20. *Ultraviolet light*

Fluorescence in u.v. light is shown by reduced pyridine nucleotides. Sensitivity 3 μg. (A spray of 2% $Na_2S_2O_4$:4% $NaHCO_3$ = 1:1 will reduce NAD and NADP to dihydroforms) (*Arch. B.B.* **48,** 184 (1954)).

21. *Ultraviolet light-potassium cyanide*

The paper is streaked with M-KCN from a pipette. Addition compounds with intense fluorescence under u.v. light are formed by oxidized pyridine nucleotides, nicotinamide mononucleotide, and nicotinamide riboside (*Arch. B.B.* **48,** 184 (1954)).

22. *Sulphuric acid*

For use on thin-layer chromatograms. Spray with 50% H_2SO_4 and heat at 200° for about 10 min until charring occurs (*Analyt. Biochem.* **5,** 291 (1963)). *Iodine vapour* is used for transitory location on TLC if it is required to elute the spots for estimation.

FLAVINS

The paper chromatography and electrophoresis of flavins is discussed in a review on the chemical determination of flavins by Yagi (*Meth. biochem. Anal.* **10,** 319 (1962)).

23. *Ultraviolet light*

Yellow-green fluorescence is shown by flavins, especially after spraying with 0·05N-NaOH. Sensitivity, 0·01 μg. Remove any residual phenol solvent from the paper with an ether wash since it quenches fluorescence (*Nature, Lond.* **161,** 349 (1948)).

Coenzyme A—see Pantothenic acid *in* Vitamins

---

13. STEROIDS

Revised by R. W. H. EDWARDS (*Hospital for Sick Children, Great Ormond Street, London*)

Steroids vary in properties from the lipid-like, monofunctional cholesterol to the hydrophilic sapogenins and corticosteroids. Both adsorption and partition chromatographic procedures have been widely used to separate out the individual steroids but the use of adsorption is frequently precluded by the occurrence of decomposition of the polyoxygenated derivatives. Whilst conventional partition procedures are generally satisfactory, reversed phase conditions are required for the monofunctional steroids (*Science* **114,** 299 (1951)).

Wide experience has established the following solvent pairs in partition systems: (i) light petroleum *v.* aqueous methanol, with benzene added to suit the more highly oxygenated steroids (*B.J.* **50,** 370 (1952)); (ii) various solvents *v.* formamide (*J.A.C.S.* **72,** 8328 (1950)) or glycols (*J.B.C.* **193,** 749 (1951); *Helv. chim. Acta* **35,** 276 (1952)); light petroleum *v.* formic acid with benzene additive (*J. Chromat.* **12,** 212 (1963)). Each procedure was established for the sheet paper chromatography technique and is directly applicable to cellulose TLC† and, with suitable arrangements for the take-up of stationary phase, for celite TLC. Ionized steroids and steroid conjugates and derivatives have been separated by electrophoresis (*Acta endocr., Copenh.* **13,** 19 (1953)).

These procedures are described in detail in the following volumes which are largely devoted to the practical aspects:

R. W. H. Edwards, in *Chromatographic and Electrophoretic Techniques*, ed. Ivor Smith, 3rd ed., vol. 1, chap. 23, Heinemann, London (1969).
R. Neher, *Steroid Chromatography*, Elsevier, Amsterdam (1964).
I. E. Bush, *Chromatography of the Steroids*, Pergamon Press, London (1961).

See also reviews in *Meth. biochem. Anal.* **1,** 171 (1954) (chromatographic separation of the steroids of the adrenal gland); *J. Chromat.* **1,** 461 (1958); **3,** 483 (1960) (chromatography of steroids on fully acetylated paper); *Chromat. Rev.* **1,** 99 (1959) (chromatography of sterols, steroids, and related compounds; columns and paper); *J. Chromat.* **8,** 2 (1962) (paper chromatography of oestrogens); *J. Chromat.* **8,** 449 (1962); **9,** 81 (1962) (demonstration of steroidal functional groups).

The location procedures described in this section may be assumed to be satisfactory for both paper and TLC procedures unless otherwise stated because it is not possible to review this matter completely at this stage of the history of TLC. It is, however, simple enough to test each reaction under the circumstances under which it will be used, and this is doubly necessary because reactions may be upset by both adsorbants and binders.

The criterion used in deciding the order of layout of this section has been specificity in the detection of functional groups but following a simple order of the groups. The miscellaneous section at the end consists mainly of unclassifiable reactions. Most of the reactions described have been used at one time or the other by the author or his immediate colleagues, and hitherto unpublished procedures are indicated (Au), as are modifications to the cited procedures. (Mr. D. J. H. Trafford's name is frequently coupled with that of the author and his help is gratefully acknowledged.)

It may be assumed that esters of the steroid alcohols react in the same way as do the unesterified steroids unless otherwise stated. The sensitivity of the reactions has been indicated 'Sens. *X*' and this should be taken to mean that approximately X $\mu g/cm^2$ may just be discerned against the background. This is a subjective assessment aimed at helping the choice of reagent when sensitivity is at premium. Sensitivity may frequently be increased two- to tenfold by contact photographic processes using an appropriate colour filter, as detailed below.

The photography of coloured zones on chromatograms

The coloured zones formed during many location reactions are transitory and photography will be required to obtain a permanent record. The following is an outline of the basic procedures which may be used in a dark-room that is not absolutely light-tight.

Reagents: Johnson's Universal Developer diluted 1+7 with water (enough for 20 photographs). Johnson's Fix-sol acid hardener. Ilford Reflex document paper, No. 50.

Apparatus: Flat pad of clean cotton wool. Sheet of plate glass to weight the film into good contact with the chromatogram. Alternatively, and the only way to manage u.v. photographs, a heavy brass frame is constructed in a rectangle bigger than the chromatogram being used. Cross wires (preferably of steel wire) are run from side to side in both directions and soldered in position. A suitable distance between the wires provides a lattice on the chromatogram approximately marking tens of percentage

† The following abbreviations will be used in this section; TLC = thin-layer chromatography, PC = paper chromatography; St = steroid; keto = oxo; ol = hydroxy; al = aldehyde; 3ol = 3α- and/or 3β-hydroxy.

units of R_F. Coloured plastic filters for increasing the contrast between spots and background may be chosen from the wide range of plastic 'Cinemoid gels' used for stage lighting and supplied by Strand Electric (250 Kennington Lane, London, S.E.11).

(*a*) Contact recording procedure: Prepare the developer, rinse water, and fixer, and work under safe lighting (Ilford 910 v.s. 2 orange filter). Lay the following in order on the cotton wool pad; (i) the document paper with sensitive side up, (ii) the chromatogram (dry or sandwiched between polythene plastic sheets), and (iii) the weighting frame or glass. Make the exposure (see next paragraph), place the document paper face downward in the developer, and agitate. After 10 sec turn it over and continue developing until the image is suitably contrasted. Remove to the wash solution for 10 sec, fix for 10 min, wash in running tap-water for 30 min, and dry.

Suitable exposure times with a 75 W pearl lamp at 1 m from the papers are: BTT (procedure 18) 15–20 sec; 17-ketogenic (25) 25 sec; phosphomolybdate (35) 30 sec; Zimmerman (3) 15–20 sec; dilute sulphuric (40) 30–40 sec. 4-en-3-ones (2) require 20 sec exposure from a Chromatolite 254 mμ u.v. source at 1 m.

(*b*) Recording fluorescent emissions: A camera must be used in a completely light-tight dark-room; fluorescing objects must be removed from the dark-room including detergent-washed lab. coats and shirts. Ultraviolet light must not enter the camera and is filtered out by attaching a Wratten 2B filter to the lens system. Illuminate the chromatogram by the u.v. lamp at 45° to the perpendicular to the plane of the paper. A hypersensitive panchromatic film will require $1\frac{1}{2}$–2 min exposure from a Hanovia Sunlamp (365 mμ) at 2 m at f 8.

Some location procedures may very conveniently be superimposed on one another to increase the information gained from each chromatogram. Those used by the author will be indicated 'after Y' = in sequence after using procedure Y; 'before Z' = in sequence before use of procedure Z. Procedure 2 will be indicated when it follows other procedures but, as it is purely physical, it may precede all the others and it will not then be designated. It is so simple to carry out that it should routinely always precede use of other location procedures, even if only to locate the solvent front.

UNSATURATED CENTRES

1. *Osmic acid*

Expose to the vapours from a 1% aq. soln. of osmic acid (very toxic!). Grey to black spots are produced with unsaturated steroids; 9(11)-ene, sens. 10; 5-ene, sens. 5; 4-en-3-one, sens. 2. Oestrogens, negative (*Endocrinology* **48,** 114 (1951)).

2. *Ultraviolet light (for conjugated double bonds)*

(i) Absorption of 254 mμ u.v. light (*B.J.* **50,** 370 (1952)). The weak fluorescence of the paper is quenched by absorption centres consisting of two or more double bonds in conjugation, e.g. 3:5 and 5:7 dienes; 4-en-3-one, 5-en-7-one, 16-en-20-one, 4-ene-3:6-dione, etc., sens. 0·5. The sensitivity is increased five-fold by photography on document paper (*B.J.* **45,** 294 (1949)) or by impregnating the paper with a fluorescing substance, e.g. 0·01% anthracene (Au) in light petroleum (40–60°). The anthracene is inert and does not interfere with subsequent operations.

(ii) Absorption of 360 mμ u.v. light. A similar quenching of fluorescence is shown by three or more double bonds in conjugation (but not aromatic centres), e.g. 4-ene-3:6-dione, sens. 5. The increased sensitivity on anthracene treatment is available as above.

KETONES

3. *Alkaline m-dinitrobenzene (Zimmerman reaction)*

(i) Reagents: (*a*) Dilute 1 vol. of stock 15N-KOH (80 g KOH+60 ml H_2O) with 5 vol. ethanol, mix well (N_2 stream). (*b*) 2% ethanolic *m*-dinitrobenzene. Dip through (*a*), blot, dip through (*b*), blot, and warm gently with a hair drier (*J.B.C.* **202,** 457 (1953) & Au). Procedures have been described using mixtures of (*a*) and (*b*) but the sensitivity is less and the background colour is worse.

17-one (no 15, 16 or 18-oxy) and 6-ol-4-en-3-one purple, sens. 1; 3-one blue, sens. 5;

4-en-3-one blue, sens. 2; 4-ene-3:6-dione yellow (*see* procedure 5 (i)) becoming black, sens. 0·5; 20-one brown, sens. 10; 21-deoxy-17-ol-20-one red, sens. 2. Butenolides of the digitalis series (*Helv. chim. Acta*, **34,** 108 (1951)), blue or purple, sens. 1 to 5.

(ii) An all-aqueous procedure using hyamine to stabilize the *m*-dinitrobenzene solution (*J. clin. Endocr. Metab.* **23,** 355 (1963)) is as sensitive but has not the variation of colour which is so useful diagnostically, although it is very valuable for quantitative work.

4. 2:4-*Dinitrophenylhydrazine*

Dip through 0·3% dinitrophenylhydrazine in 0·3% HCl (v/v) in methanol. Heat 5 min at 90°. Wash by drawing through 2N-NaOH in water, water, and 2N-HCl (*J. Chromat.* **1,** 205 (1954); **8,** 449 (1962)).

Most ketones give yellow spots, sens. 2 to 5; but 4-en-3-ones give orange spots, sens. 1. Proposed intensification reactions provide little advantage (Au) except reduction with 1% $SnCl_2$ in N-HCl followed by coupling with 0·5% *p*-dimethylaminobenzaldehyde (Ehrlich's reagent) in 1% HCl (v/v) in ethanol. After 3.

5. *Alkali*

(i) Dip through N-NaOH. 4-ene-3:6-dione gives yellow colour, sens. 2, and yellow fluorescence under 365 mμ u.v. light, sens. 0·5. 4-en-3-one-6-ol gives this reaction weakly on standing for some hours.

(ii) A yellow fluorescence, and weaker colour, appearing after warming, indicates 4-en-3-one, usually with three or more oxygen functions (*B.J.* **50,** 370 (1952)). Use of 50% methanolic NaOH with the paper sandwiched between glass plates to avoid evaporation makes the results more reliable (*J. Endocr. Metab.* **18,** 1 (1959)), sens. 0·5. Inclusion of a tetrazolium derivative suppresses background fluorescence and thus increases sensitivity. After 18 or 19.

6. *Nitroprusside (for aceto-derivatives)*

Reagent: Make a paste as follows in a quantity proportional to the area of the dish. Mix 0·5 g Na nitroprusside, 10 g Na_2CO_3 and 10 g NH_4 acetate with 10 ml methanol for each 100 cm² area of the dish to be used. Spread the paste to cover the floor of the dish, lay the chromatogram on the paste, and gently press into contact. The spots appear in 5 to 10 min, and intensify in the course of 1 hr. Methyl-ketones give violet spots; 21-deoxy-20-one, progesterone, sens. 2. 17- and other hydroxylic substituents do not interfere but 16-ene or 16-one does (*J. Chromat.* **8,** 449 (1962)).

ALDEHYDES

7. *Schiff's reaction*

Reagent: Dissolve 1 g basic fuchsin ('for histology') in 100 ml boiled-out distilled water, cool to 60°, add 2 g K metabisulphite, mix to dissolve, and slowly add 20 ml N-HCl. Stopper, leave overnight, add animal charcoal, mix, and filter. This reagent remains colourless if stored in the dark at 4°.

Dip, blot, heat at 60° for 10 min, and suspend in a tank gassed out with SO_2. This preserves the colours; alternatively enclose between glass or polythene sheet to keep out the air. Free aldehydes react quickly, sens. 2; some involved in hemi-acetal condensation may react slowly (*J.C.S.* **1950,** 3162 & Au).

ALCOHOLS

Most reagents described in the earlier literature for the location of 'sterols' also detect 'sterones' and are largely unspecific. They are, of course, none the less useful and will be found in the miscellaneous section.

8. *Tert-butyl chromate oxidation (for β:γ-unsaturated alcohols)*

Reagent: Add 5 g CrO_3 to a cold mixture of 10 ml *tert*-butanol and 10 ml CCl_4, stir 10 min, add 65 ml CCl_4, and filter through 10 g Na_2SO_4 (anhyd.) on a sintered filter.

Store at 4° over Na_2SO_4; keeps 2 months or more (*B.J.* **84**, 195 (1962)). Immediately before use dilute 1 ml with a mixture of 80 ml xylene and 20 ml pyridine; shake the cloudy solution well (*J. Chromat.* **21**, 275 (1966)).

Procedure: Spray evenly, heat at 100±5° for 5 min. Dip through N-NaOH and dry at 100°. 3β-ol-5-enes give yellow colours, sens. 5, and yellow fluorescences under 360 mμ u.v. lamp, sens. 1, due to conversion to 4-ene-3:6-diones which also react if originally present. The colour and fluorescence may be slow to develop if the oxidation was incomplete, resulting in the 6-ol instead of the 6-one.

2α-Hydroxy-testosterone gives a yellow colour during the heating with *tert*-butyl chromate, sens. 5, which fades on treatment with alkali. 7-keto-dehydro*epi*androsterone gives a blue fluorescence on alkali treatment.

9. *Tert-butyl chromate oxidation (for α-substituted ethanols)*

Use the *tert*-butyl chromate oxidation described in procedure 8. After heating at 100° proceed as for procedure 6. Violet spots appear from 17:21-deoxy-20-ols, sens. 10; the 20-one also reacts and must be differentiated using procedure 6 without the oxidation (*J. Chromat.* **8**, 449 (1962)).

10. *Phenol red (for α-glycols)*

Reagent: Dilute 2 ml of 0·1% phenol red in ethanol, and 1 ml of 0·15M-H_3BO_3 with 20 ml methanol. Titrate with 0·1N-NaOH to pH 11 on the pH meter. Spray the paper; yellow spots appear on a pink ground from acids and *cis*-α-diols. 16:17 diols, sens. 5; N.B. 2-ol-3-one-4-ene, sens. 10. Pregnane side-chain diols are negative (*J. Chromat.* **9**, 81 (1962)).

ACIDS

11. *Indicators*

pH indicator reagents which locate the long-chain fatty acids work well provided that neutral solvents were used in the chromatography (*B.J.* **69**, 38 (1958)).

Reagent: To 0·1% bromocresol green in ethanol add 0·1N-NaOH until bluish-green. Dilute 1:4 with acetone for use. Dip or spray. The background is green upon which the acids appear as yellow spots, sens. 2; bases are blue. The spots are more stable if immediately covered with plastic film to keep out CO_2.

12. *Salt formation*

Dip through 1% ammoniacal $AgNO_3$. Wash well with distilled water, irradiate with u.v. light for 10–20 sec, and immerse in photographic developer. Silver salts give black spots, sens. 2, which may be preserved by the photographic fixing process. Reducing substances do not interfere unless the paper is heated.

ESTERS AND LACTONES

13. *Hydroxamic reaction*

Reagents: (*a*) 14 g $NH_2OH \cdot HCl$ in 100 ml CH_3OH; (*b*) 3·5N-KOH in CH_3OH; (*c*) 2 g $FeCl_3$ in 100 ml 10% HCl (v/v). Mix (*a*):(*b*) = 5:4, shake, and filter off the KCl. Spray (not dip), stand 10 min, and spray with (*c*). If brown $Fe(OH)_3$ appears, leave to dry and spray again with (*c*). Acetates and propionates, but not formates, of steroid alcohols, methyl and ethyl esters of steroid acids, and steroid lactones give purple spots, sens. 2.

14. *Nitroprusside (for α:β-unsaturated lactones)*

Legal's reagent: 1% nitroprusside in 50% ethanolic N-NaOH. Dip; the cardenolides with α:β-unsaturated lactone rings give red to violet colours, e.g. digitonin, sens. 5 (*Helv. chim. Acta* **35**, 276 (1952)).

PHENOLS

These are all general reagents for phenols and thus care must be taken in interpreting the results purely in terms of phenolic steroids, the oestrogens.

15. *Diazo reaction*

Reagent: (*a*) 0·5% Brentamine Fast Blue B base (ICI Ltd.) in water. (*b*) 1% $NaHCO_3$ adjusted to pH 9·0 (pH meter) with 10% NaOH. These are stable indefinitely if kept cold. For use mix equal volumes of (*a*) and (*b*). Dip and blot. All phenols give orange to red spots. Oestrogens, sens. 5–10 (Braunsberg, unpublished).

16. *Sodium p-phenolsulphonate*

Spray with 2% Na *p*-phenolsulphonate in 85% H_3PO_4. Oestrogens give light green or orange colours, with blue-green, violet-pink, or yellow-orange fluorescence in u.v. light, sens. 10 (*J.B.C.* **201,** 59 (1953)).

17. *Millon's reagent*

Reagent: 1 part by weight Hg is dissolved in 2 parts conc. HNO_3 and 2 vol. H_2O are added. On spraying, oestrogens give yellow-brown spots showing purple-brown fluorescence in u.v. light, sens. 15 (*J.B.C.* **201,** 59 (1953)).

REDUCING CENTRES

The principal reducing centre of the steroids is the α-ketol although α:β-unsaturated ketones also react weakly.

18. *Blue tetrazolium*

Reagents: (*a*) stock BTT, 0·2% dianisole-bisdiphenyl-tetrazolium chloride (only the Merck reagent is reliable—Au) in water. (*b*) 2N-NaOH. Mix (*a*):(*b*):EtOH = 3:10:5 immediately before use. Dip and blot. Blue spots appear without warming. If the room temperature is low, warm very gently with a hair dryer (*Fed. Proc.* **10,** 377 (1951); *J. Endocr. Metab.* **18,** 1 (1959)). Clearer blue spots on a yellow ground are obtained if styryl tetrazolium (M & B 1767) is used (*J. Chromat.* **14,** 263 (1964)).

Blue spots appear immediately for 21-ol-20-one, 16-ol-17-one, sens. 1. 2-ol-3-one reacts slowly, sens. 1. 4-en-2-one reacts slowly on warming, sens. 10. Before 44.

The background does not develop and the spots are preserved by washing in 5% acetic acid in water.

19. *Triphenyltetrazolium chloride*

Reagent: 0·2% triphenyltetrazolium chloride (TPT) in water. Mix 2 vol. with 1 vol. 10% NaOH. Dip or spray and warm with a hair dryer. Red spots appear on a pink ground from 21-ol-20-ones, sens. 5 (*J.B.C.* **188,** 763 (1951)).

To differentiate 17-hydroxylated side chains precede the above by dipping through N-NaOH. Lay on a sheet of glass, cover with another sheet of glass, and heat at 100° for 5 min. The 17-ols are destroyed by this procedure so that only 17-deoxy-21-ol-20-ones give the reddish spots (*J.A.C.S.* **75,** 4074 (1953)).

20. *Ammoniacal silver nitrate*

Spray with 0·1N-$AgNO_3$:conc. NH_3:10% NaOH = 100:5:50, mixed just before use. After 5–10 min fix the spots in a bath of 25 g $Na_2S_2O_3$+15 g $KAl(SO_4)_2 \cdot 12H_2O$ in 1·5 l H_2O. After 30 min rinse for 30 min in H_2O. Dry at R.T. Black or dark brown spots after benzene–formamide solvent and reddish-brown after toluene–propylene glycol solvent are given by cardiac aglycones containing the α:β-unsaturated lactone ring. Sens. 2–25 (*J.B.C.* **194,** 703 (1952)). This test is also given by the α-ketol group on C_{17} characteristic of the corticosteroids. Sens. 10–15 (*J.B.C.* **188,** 763 (1951)). α-Keto-aldehydes also give brown spots, but glycols do not (*Mem. Soc. Endocr.* **2,** 9 (1953)).

21. *Arsenomolybdate*

Reagent: 25 g NH_4 molybdate in 450 ml H_2O is mixed with 21 ml conc. H_2SO_4, and a solution of 3 g $Na_2HAsO_4 \cdot 7H_2O$ in 25 ml H_2O is added. Incubate at 37° for 48 hr. Filter the solution and store in the dark. This reagent cannot be sprayed directly onto the paper. The method for applying it by means of a moistened cloth attached to an X-ray film which is wrapped around a glass plate is described in the reference given. The paper is kept between humidified glass plates and incubated at 70° for 30–60 min. Reducing steroids of adrenal cortex having an α-ketol side chain or an α:β-unsaturated 3-keto structure give a blue colour. Sens. for deoxycorticosterone, 1–2 (*B.J.* **53,** 148 (1953)).

'OGENIC REACTIONS

This group consists of reactions for the conversion of one chemical type into another for detection by one of the above reactions, or for detection of a small molecular fragment. The reactions for steroid moieties should be carried out on duplicate chromatograms, with and without the 'ogenic conversion, so that a distinction may be drawn between the preformed and formed reactors.

22. *Formaldehydogenic*

Reagent: Dissolve 15 g NH_4 acetate in 85 ml of 80% methanol. Add 1 ml acetylacetone, 0·3 ml gl. acetic acid, and 0·1 ml HIO_4 (50% aq. solution). Prepare the reagent and use it in diffuse light. Dip and blot. After 10 min the greenish-yellow fluorescent spots appear, becoming most intense after an hour when yellow colours will have developed. 21-ols with 20-ol or 20-one react, sens. 5 by colour and 1 by fluorescence. The reagent is generally specific for α-substituted primary alcohols. It is ineffective on chromatograms prepared by impregnation with glycols (*J. Chromat.* **9,** 81 (1962) & Au).

23. *Acetaldehydogenic*

Reagents: (*a*) Dilute 5 ml of 50% aqueous HIO_4 solution with 5 ml water and 90 ml *tert*-butanol. (*b*) 2 g Na nitroprusside and 15 ml piperidine diluted to 100 ml with methanol. Dip through (*a*), blot, hang up for 5–10 min to react. Spray with (*b*). After 10 min blue spots appear on the pale yellow ground where acetaldehyde has been liberated. Among the steroids, only pregnane-17:20-diols react, sens. 2. This procedure is not applicable after a chromatographic run involving impregnation of the paper with a glycol (*J. Chromat.* **9,** 81 (1962)).

An extension of the above procedure is as follows. Reagent: Freshly prepared 0·1% solution of Na (or K) BH_4 in 0·01N-NaOH in methanol (dilute aqueous N-NaOH). Dip, blot, hang in the room atmosphere 30 min to react, and proceed as above. 21-deoxy-17-ol-20-ones now react in addition to the 17:20-diols, sens. 10.

24. *Specific* 17-*ketogenic*

Reagents: Freshly prepared 2·5% lead tetra-acetate in warm gl. acetic acid containing 10% acetic anhydride (rather lachrymatory). Dip, blot, and hang in free air for 15 min. Blow off the excess acid with air from a hair dryer and detect the ketones by procedure 3 (i) (*B.J.* **59,** xiv (1955)). The reagent is positive for the ketones listed under 3 (i) and with 17:20-diols, sens. 5 and 17:20-diol-20-ones, sens. 20. After 18 and 19.

An alternative oxidizing agent is 1% HIO_4 and 1% H_2SO_4 in 75% ethanol. Hang for 30 min to react and use procedure 3 (i) as described above. This reaction is sometimes accompanied by iodine liberation and the spots diffuse more than with $PbAc_4$.

25. *Non-specific* 17-*ketogenic*

(i) Use *tert*-butyl chromate oxidant as described in procedure 8. Follow with procedure 3 (i) to detect ketones. Ketones listed under 3 (i) are detected together with all 17-ols, with or without the side chain, sens. 2. Side chains without 17-ol, sens. 5 to 20, mainly by detection of blue reacting 3-substituent (Au & DJHT).

(ii) Use of 0·2% CrO_3 in acetic anhydride and warming is rather similar to the above but rather difficult to control the destruction of ketones by the excess CrO_3 (*Analyt. Chem.* **27,** 1308 (1955)).

26. *Aldehydogenic*

Dip through reagent (*a*) of procedure 23 and blot. Hang to react for 10 min, then suspend in an SO_2 atmosphere 15 min. Apply the aldehyde reagent of procedure 7. Steroid aldehydes present before oxidation and formed on oxidation give red to blue colours. 17-deoxy-20:21-diols, sens. 10; 17:20:21-triol, negative due to further oxidation. 16:17-diol, oestriol, sens. 5 (*J. Chromat.* **9,** 81 (1962) & Au).

27. *Acidogenic*

Reagent: 1 vol. 0·7% KIO_4 in water diluted with 3 vol. ethanol. Dip, blot, and hang for an hour. Spray with reagent 11 for acids. Yellow spots indicate acids formed on oxidation or present before oxidation. 17-deoxy-21-ol-20-ones, sens. 5; 17:21-diol-20-ones, sens. 10; 16-ol-17-one, sens. 5; but 2-ol-3-one-4-ene, negative. Does not work on chromatograms impregnated with glycols (*J. Chromat.* **9,** 81 (1962) & Au).

NITROGENOUS DERIVATIVES

28. *Hydrazones*

Reagents: 5% $PtCl_4$ in N-HCl, diluted for use with 30 vol. 3% KI. Dip, and wash the background out with water. Purple spots from trimethylaminoacetohydrazones (Girard-T derivatives), brown with semi-carbazones. A blue to purple reaction is obtained with steroid or other alkaloids (*J.B.C.* **177,** 109 (1949)).

SAPOGENINS

29. *Haemolysis*

Spray with 2% suspension of guinea pig blood cells in physiological saline. Haemolysis by sapogenins causes lighter or darker spots on a tan ground. Sensitivity is less than 60 μg (*J.B.C.* **197,** 47 (1952)).

CONJUGATES

Steroid conjugates are compounds of steroids with another moiety and are formed during metabolism. Products of synthesis are not included in this term. The steroid portion may be detected by the steroid reagents provided that the position of conjugation does not block the reaction. Reactions for the non-steroid portion may be dependent on hydrolytic liberation from combination with the steroid. Whilst the conjugates are acidic in themselves, indicator reagents (procedures 11 and 12) are rarely of use since acidic solvents are used in the chromatographic procedure.

30. *Naphthoresorcinol* (*for glucuronides*)

Reagent: To 100 ml of 0·2% naphthoresorcinol in ethanol add 10 ml phosphoric acid. Dip, blot, and hang in warm air ½–1 hr. Heat at 90°, 5 min. Glucuronides give blue spots, sens. 10 (free glucuronic acid, sens. 1).

The procedure is rendered more sensitive (Au) by using glucuronidase hydrolysis. 5000 units per ml glucuronidase at a suitable pH is used as a dip (of the commercial preparations, the limpet enzyme from Baylove, Musselburgh, Midlothian, Scotland is the most potent and economical; use in pH 4·5, 0·1M-acetate buffer). After hanging in an incubator for an hour at 37°—preferably in a moist atmosphere—dry and apply the naphthoresorcinol reagent. Proceed directly to the 90° heating. Glucuronides give blue spots, sens. 2, but they are rather more diffuse after the enzymic hydrolysis.

31. *Rhodizonic acid test* (*for sulphate*)

Reagents: (*a*) 20 ml conc. HCl diluted with 180 ml dioxan. (*b*) 20 mg $BaCl_2$ in 100 ml 75% methanol. (*c*) 12 mg K rhodizonate in 15 ml water, diluted with 10 ml 0·880 ammonia and 25 ml ethanol. Suspend the chromatogram in an enclosed chamber saturated with the vapours from (*a*) for 3 hr. Dry in an air stream in the fume cupboard for 1 hr. Dip through (*b*), dry in the air stream for 10 min. Dip through (*c*) and blot. Sulphates appear as yellow spots on a pink ground; sens. 10 for $DHASO_4$. This reaction is specific for all organic sulphates (*J.B.C.* **222**, 787 (1956)).

32. *Methylene blue test* (*for sulphate*)

Reagent: 20 mg methylene blue (922) histological stain and 5 g Na_2SO_4 are dissolved in 100 ml water, and 1 ml conc. H_2SO_4 is carefully added immediately before use. Dip and blot. Suspend in chloroform and agitate gently for 1–2 min. Large quantities of sulphate appear as pinkish-white zones on the blue ground before the $CHCl_3$ wash. Small quantities appear as white zones during the wash; sens. 1 for $DHASO_4$. This reaction is positive for all organic sulphates and also for organic phosphates but steroid phosphates have not yet been tried (*Revue fr. Étud. clin. Biol.* **5**, 284 (1960) and Au).

Counterstaining by 0·01% rhodamine-6G in chloroform produces reddish spots on a blue ground and a yellow fluorescence under 360 mμ u.v. light; sens. 0·1 (Au).

33. *Phosphate*

Reagent: Add 1 g NH_4 molybdate to 8 ml water. Dissolve and add 3 ml conc. HCl and 3 ml perchloric acid (sp. gr. 1·72). Dilute with 86 ml acetone for use. Dip, and leave to dry. Blue spots appear on irradiation with 360 mμ u.v. light for at least 30 min (*Acta endocr., Copenh.* **30**, 93 (1959)). Greater sensitivity is obtained by leaving overnight but it is then necessary to bleach out the blue background by exposure to ammonia vapour.

MISCELLANEOUS

All the following are unspecific procedures and care must be taken in interpreting the results since very different steroids may produce the same reaction and non-steroidal substances likewise.

34. *Phosphotungstic acid*

Reagent: 15% phosphotungstic acid in ethanol. Dip, blot, and heat in an oven at 80°. A variety of colours are produced, especially from cholestane derivatives. 3β-ol-5-enes produce pink colours, sens. 3.

35. *Phosphomolybdic acid*

Reagent: 10% *dodeca*-molybdophosphoric acid in *n*-propanol (Bush, *Chromatography of the Steroids*, Pergamon, 1962), filter if cloudy (reject if not almost entirely dissolved). Use within an hour. Dip, blot, and heat—'Infra-red lamps' are very suitable heaters because the paper may be removed before the background develops. Otherwise use an oven at 100–140° *whilst watching* (a glass door is essential). Blue spots on a yellow ground indicate substances such as steroids with a low degree of oxygenation (*Arch. B.B.* **35**, 346 (1952); *Acta chem. scand.* **8**, 339 (1954)). All steroids with mono- or di-oxygenated nuclei react; trioxygenated nuclei react on quick heating in the oven, sens. 2 to 5. Red colours are given by *cis*-testosterone and the 17-alkyl-testosterone derivatives. Does not work on adsorption TLC.

36. *Iodine*

(i) Dip in a saturated soln. of I_2 in pet. ether (60–80°) to detect many steroids (*B.J.* **50**, 370 (1952)). Sensitivity for oestrogens, 1 μg. Yellow or brown spots given.

(ii) Spray with 0·3% I_2 in 5% aq. KI, followed by a H_2O rinse. Δ^4-3-Ketones (20–50 μg) give yellow spots; cortisone (15 μg), a blue spot (*J.B.C.* **188**, 763 (1951)).

(iii) Spray with a cold saturated soln. of I_2 in EtOH. This gives a blue colour with cholic acid (*Mh. Chem.* **84**, 99 (1953)). It should be noted, however, with reference to the above three reagents that KI solution and organic solvents have been reported to dissociate blue steroid–iodine complexes (*B.J.* **48**, xlviii (1951)).

(iv) Stock reagent: Hydriodic acid (sp. gr. 1·5) saturated with I_2. This solution is diluted ten times with tap-water just before use. Immerse the paper. Rinse with tap-water until the background is free of colour. Functional groups giving a reaction with this reagent are α:β-unsaturated ketones, 17-ketones, and C_3-hydroxyl groups on a molecule containing a methyl ketone or α-ketol side chain. Brown, orange, and blue colours are given. Sens. 8–20 (*J.B.C.* **205**, 173 (1953)).

Of these procedures (i) is the most satisfactory if other reagents are to be applied in sequence. The other procedures give colours with a wider variety of steroids and may be most satisfactory in particular problems.

37. *Bromine*

Spray with a saturated aq. soln. of Br_2. A crimson spot is given by the non-steroid diethylstilboestrol. Sens. 5 (*J.B.C.* **201**, 59 (1953)).

A modified method for detecting sterols is as follows. Expose to Br_2 vapour for 30 sec. Spray with (*a*) saturated KI in MeOH. Then spray with (*b*) 20% starch soln. Sterols give dark blue spots on a colourless or light blue ground. Sens. 10 (*P.S.E.B.M.* **75**, 799 (1950)).

For conjugated bile acids, chlorination, then the KI–starch reagent (as for Amino Acids, 5) has been used (*Acta chem. scand.* **8**, 339 (1954)).

38. *Potassium permanganate*

Spray with 0·2% $KMnO_4$ in 5% Na_2CO_3. Rinse in H_2O until the background is colourless. Corticosteroids give brown colours. Groups which react with this spray are 4-en-3-one, α-ketol, 17:20:21-triol. Sens. 30–70 (*J.B.C.* **188**, 763 (1951)).

39. *Strong sulphuric acid*

Concentrated H_2SO_4 is applied in a thin layer to a glass plate and the filter paper is laid on this. Vivid green fluorescence is shown with compounds containing an 11-hydroxyl group, especially compound F (*J.B.C.* **187**, 411 (1950)). The reaction is useful for characterization of $C_{19}O_3$ steroids (*J.B.C.* **208**, 579 (1954)).

An alternative method using (15% SO_3) fuming H_2SO_4 gives orange-yellow to red-brown colours with oestrogens in visible light and yellow-green or red-brown fluorescence in u.v. light. Sensitivity, 5 μg (*J.B.C.* **201**, 59 (1953)). This method is sensitive, but non-specific for C_{19} and C_{21} steroids. Sensitivity range: pregnanediols (orange spots), 5 μg; androstanedione (pink), 50 μg (*J.B.C.* **205**, 173 (1953)).

40. *Dilute sulphuric acid*

Reagent: 1% H_2SO_4 in ethanol. Dip, blot, and heat at 100–20°. Watch carefully and remove from the oven at the first signs of charring. 4-en-3-ones give red colours with orange fluorescence, sensitivity 1 μg; most steroids react, e.g. THE yellow and THF blue fluorescence, sensitivity 2 μg (Au & DJHT).

41. *Strong phosphoric acid*

Dip through 70% H_3PO_4 in water, lay on a glass plate, and heat at 90°. A great variety of colours are produced including purples from pregnanetriols, sens. 1 to 2. 360 mμ u.v. light produces various fluorescent emissions (*J.B.C.* **234**, 1693 (1959)). 85% ethanolic H_3PO_4 has been used for bile acids (*J.A.C.S.* **74**, 4713 (1952)).

42. *Dilute phosphoric acid*

Dip through 20% H_3PO_4 in water and heat at 90° for 20 min (*Helv. chim. acta* **39**, 1664 (1956)). Most steroids give colours which differ from those of procedure 40 above.

43. *Hydrochloric acid*

Dip through conc. HCl, lay on a glass sheet and heat at 60° for 5 min. 17 α-alkylated steroids give characteristic colours and fluorescence emissions (*Steroids* **1**, 395 (1963) and Au).

44. *Formic acid*

Dip through cold formic acid (98–100%). A green colour changing to blue is produced after a few minutes by 7 α-hydroxydehydro*epi*androsterone (Au).

45. *Trichloroacetic acid*

(i) Reagent: 10 g TCA in 20 ml ethanol. Dip, blot, and heat at 70° for 10 min. Many steroids give yellow or pink fluorescences (360 mμ u.v. light) but the pregnane-3:17:20-triols give characteristic blue fluorescences, sens. 2 (*J. Endocr.* **14**, 164 (1956)). After 18 or 19.

(ii) 25% TCA in $CHCl_3$ heated at 100° for 20 min gives colours and fluorescences with cardiac glycosides (*J.B.C.* **194**, 703 (1952)) and sapogenins (*J.B.C.* **197**, 47 (1952)).

46. *Liebermann-Burchard reaction*

Reagent: Add 5 ml conc. H_2SO_4 slowly and with agitation to 20 ml ice cold acetic anhydride (this reagent is highly lachrymatory). Dip through rapidly and lay out on a glass sheet. Alternatively, lay on a glass sheet and spread the reagent with the aid of a glass rod used as a roller. Cover with another glass or plastic sheet. Within a few minutes green colours appear from cholesterol or its esters, sens. 5. The spots slowly change to blue (*B.B.A.* **19**, 187 (1956)).

47. *Phosphomolybdotungstic acid*

Spray with Folin's phenol reagent, freshly diluted with 5 vol. H_2O. Preparation is given in Table 25, Preparation of biochemical reagents, p. 618. Expose to NH_3 vapour for 5 min. Oestrogens (0·5 μg) give blue spots. Other steroids with an α-ketol side chain give intense blue colours (*B.J.* **56**, 690 (1954)).

48. *Aniline phthalate*

See Carbohydrates, 23 (i). Yellow, orange, or brown spots on a white ground are given by steroids with a Δ^4-3-keto group in the A ring. Sensitivity is increased 10 times when *p*-phenylenediamine is substituted for aniline in the spray. Sensitivity, 2–3 μg. α- or β-Naphthylamine may also be substituted for aniline, and oxalic acid for phthalic acid (*Nature, Lond.* **175**, 729 (1955)).

49. *Aromatic aldehydes*

Spray with 0·5 ml anisaldehyde in 50 ml CH_3COOH+1 ml conc. H_2SO_4. Heat at 90° for 2–5 min. Corticosteroids give coloured spots (*Helv. chim. acta* **34**, 2278 (1951)).

The following method has been used for detecting steroidal sapogenins. Spray with (*a*) 1% soln. in EtOH of one of the aldehydes mentioned below. Dry for 5 min. Then spray with (*b*) acetic anhydride: conc. H_2SO_4 = 12:1. Heat at 85–90° until spots appear. Vanillin, anisaldehyde, cinnamic aldehyde, and salicylic aldehyde give rise to yellow spots on a white-grey ground with steroid sapogenins; *p*-dimethylaminobenzaldehyde gives rise to rose spots on a yellow ground; 4-acetoxy-2-naphthaldehyde is the most sensitive reagent giving red spots with sapogenins (*C.r. hebd. Séanc. Acad. Sci.* **233**, 1670 (1951)). Suitable for TLC (*J. Chromat.* **14**, 269 (1964)).

Of 130 steroids examined by D. J. H. T., 110 gave spots varying widely in brightness and differing in colour; none showed fluorescent emission. Androstane derivatives were least reactive but other structural correlations were not possible.

50. *Antimony trichloride*

This reagent is very poisonous.

Spray with 10–20% $SbCl_3$ in $CHCl_3$. Heat at 70–90° for 4 min. Various colours in visible and u.v. light are given by corticosteroids (*Helv. chim. acta* **34,** 2278 (1951)), oestrogens (brown, yellow, and pink spots) (*Nature, Lond.* **171,** 42 (1953)); C_{19} and C_{21} steroids containing an —OH group (20–50 μg) (*J.B.C.* **205,** 173 (1953)); *Digitalis* glycosides (< 0·5 μg) (*Nature, Lond.* **170,** 415 (1952)); sterols: ergosterol (0·5 μg) and cholesterol (5 μg) (*P.S.E.B.M.* **75,** 799 (1950)); and steroidal sapogenins (mainly yellow or reddish orange spots; sens. 2–5) (*C.r. hebd. Séanc. Acad. Sci.* **233,** 1670 (1951)).

Modifications include the following sprays:

(i) Spray with 25 g anhyd. $SbCl_3$ in 5 ml nitrobenzene. This has been used as a general spray for non-ketonic, hydroxylated steroids. Sens. 1·5 (*Arch. B.B.* **44,** 1 (1953)).

(ii) A fresh solution of 380 g $SbCl_3$ in 100 ml acetic anhydride is sprayed after exposing the paper for 20 min to an atmosphere of Cl_2. Heat at 90–100° to dry the paper. Spots both fluorescent and non-fluorescent in u.v. light are obtained. Sens. 0·5–5 except cortisone (75) (*Arch. B.B.* **37,** 186 (1952)).

(iii) Spray with 50% $SbCl_3$ in gl. acetic acid. Heat at 90–96° for 3–5 min. Rose, purple, and yellow colours are given by bile acids (*J.B.C.* **210,** 181 (1954)).

51. *Antimony pentachloride*

This reagent is very poisonous.

Spray with 20–40% $SbCl_5$ in $CHCl_3$ (*Arch. B.B.* **34,** 346 (1952)). Various colours, mainly brown and red, are given by oestrogens (15 μg) (*J.B.C.* **201,** 59 (1953)); vitamin D sterols; ergosterol (0·5 μg); cholesterol (5 μg) (*J.A.C.S.* **74,** 4483 (1952)).

52. *Ferric chloride*

Spray with 2% $FeCl_3$ in MeOH. Oestrogens give purple spots. Sens. 20 (*J.B.C.* **201,** 59 (1953)). Alternatively a spray containing 1% $FeCl_3$+1% K ferricyanide may be used. Oestrogens, corticosteroids, and androgens give blue spots. A permanent record is obtained by washing the paper in 0·1N-HCl and then in H_2O (*Nature, Lond.* **171,** 750 (1953)).

53. *Zinc chloride*

(i) Spray with 30% anhyd. $ZnCl_2$ in MeOH. Heat at 130° for 1 hr. Various colours in visible light and fluorescence in u.v. light are given by hydroxysteroids, sens. 2–10 (*Arch. B.* **29,** 219 (1950)).

(ii) A modification of this spray is 40% $ZnCl_2$ in gl. CH_3COOH:benzoyl chloride: $CHCl_3$ = 5:7:12. Heat at 90° for 5 min. Mainly orange, pink, or brown colours with yellow or pink fluorescence in u.v. are given by corticosteroids (*Helv. chim. acta* **35,** 276 (1952)) and oestrogens, sensitivity 5 μg (*J.B.C.* **201,** 59 (1953)). Suitable for TLC (*J. Chromat.* **14,** 269 (1964)).

(iii) Reagent: 4 g $ZnCl_2$ mixed with 0·5 ml water. Slowly add 25 ml acetyl chloride with careful mixing. Use within an hour. Dip through the reagent, lay on a glass plate, and heat at 100°. A great variety of colours are produced by a wide range of steroids, sens. 2 to 5 (*Arch. B.B.* **89,** 105 (1960)).

54. *Stannous chloride*

Reagent: Dissolve 0·3 g $SnCl_2$ and 4 g urea in 10 ml 40% H_2SO_4. Dip, blot, and heat on glass at 80°. Fluorescent emissions (360 mμ u.v. light) are produced by oestrogens, sens. 2 to 5, and corticosteroids, sens. 10 (*Arch. B.B.* **89,** 105 (1960)).

14. VITAMINS

FAT-SOLUBLE VITAMINS

Revised by J. GREEN (*Vitamins Ltd., Tadworth, England*)

GROUP SEPARATION AND IDENTIFICATION

Individual members of the group of fat-soluble vitamins and the provitamins A (carotenes) can be separated by *thin-layer chromatography* on alumina (Brockman III/IV), using two or three different solvents (*J. Chromat.* **7**, 204 (1962)). Spray with 70% perchloric acid or 98% H_2SO_4: coloured spots appear as follows, with the stated sensitivities: Vitamin A, violet, 2 μg; vitamin D_2, orange-brown, 3 μg; vitamin E (α-tocopherol only, q.v.), brown, 400 μg; vitamin K, yellow-brown, 140 μg; carotenes, blue, 2 μg.

Vitamin A and α-tocopherol can be separated by *paper partition chromatography* (silicone oil/acetonitrile-water) (*Analyt. Chem.* **25**, 774 (1953)). Several of the methods of paper chromatography referred to below under individual vitamins can be used to separate fat-soluble vitamins from each other.

VITAMINS A, PROVITAMINS A (CAROTENES) AND CONGENERS

This group includes vitamins A_1 and A_2, their esters, their respective aldehydes (retinenes or retinals), the anhydrovitamins, the neo-vitamins A (*cis*-forms), vitamin A_1 acid, and the various carotenoids with biological activity (especially β-carotene). For a general review, *see* Moore, *Vitamin A*, Elsevier, Amsterdam (1957).

Separation

(i) Vitamin A alcohol can be separated from vitamin A palmitate by direct phase chromatography (1:1 isopropanol–water; Munktell 20 paper) (*Arch. B.B.* **63**, 118 (1956)).

(ii) Reversed phase circular chromatography (90% methanol against vaseline) for 4–5 hr separates vitamins A_1 and A_2, their palmitates, their acetates, respective anhydro-vitamins and aldehydes and vitamin A_1 acid. These compounds give fluorescent spots of various colours in u.v. light (*J. Chromat.* **8**, 535 (1962)).

(iii) Separation of some of these substances is possible by adsorption on alumina-impregnated paper, using light petroleum as mobile phase (*B.J.* **44**, xliii (1949)).

Detection

Vitamin A and its derivatives react with many acidic reagents, yielding easily detected colours.

1. *Antimony trichloride*

This reagent is the most specific one known for vitamin A. Spray with a saturated solution of $SbCl_3$ in $CHCl_3$. Blue colours are given by vitamin A, its esters, retinene, and anhydro-vitamin A (*Nature, Lond.* **164**, 673 (1949); *B.J.* **44**, xliii (1949)).

2. *Ultraviolet light*

Vitamin A fluoresces with a bright, golden-brown colour under short-wave light (256 mμ) (*Br. J. Nutr.* **17**, 199 (1963)).

Provitamins

The carotenoids may constitue a considerable part of the total vitamin A activity of many foodstuffs. The α-, β-, and γ-carotenes can be separated from each other and from other plant pigments by circular chromatography on alumina-impregnated paper, with light petroleum as mobile phase (*Acta chem. scand.* **14**, 205 (1961)). They are easily observed in visible light.

Assay

Vitamin A is determined by spectroscopic measurement at 325 mμ (*Br. Pharmacopaeia*, 1963, p. 1149; *U.S. Pharmacopaeia*, 16th Revision, 1960, p. 938) or colorimetrically at 620 mμ (*Biol. Symp.* **12,** 13 (1942)) after reaction with $SbCl_3$. Bio-assay is by the growth test (*Biol. Symp.* **12,** 1 (1942)). Determination of low levels of vitamin A in animal tissues needs special techniques (*Br. J. Nutr.* **3,** 50 (1949); *B.J.* **67,** 208 (1960); *Br. J. Nutr.* **17,** 199 (1963)). Carotenes are measured colorimetrically after special chromatographic techniques (*Biol. Symp.* **12,** 38 (1942)).

VITAMINS D

There are several substances with vitamin D activity for birds and mammals and they have closely related structures derived (by opening of ring B on irradiation) from certain steroidal dienes, the so-called provitamins D. The only important ones are vitamin D_2 (ergocalciferol) derived from ergosterol and vitamin D_3 (cholecalciferol) derived from 7-dehydrocholesterol. They apparently never occur together in natural products and their separation is of academic interest only.

Separation

(i) Vitamin D can be separated from vitamins A and E (α-tocopherol) by direct phase chromatography (light petroleum against water-saturated paper) (*Helv. chim. acta* **45,** 1275 (1962)).

(ii) Vitamins D_2 and D_3 are separable from each other and other steroids on 'Quilon'-impregnated paper (*J.A.C.S.* **74,** 4483 (1952)).

(iii) Vitamin D is separated from vitamin A and other steroids by reversed phase chromatography (95% methanol against paraffin) (*B.J.* **57,** xii (1954)).

(iv) Thin-layer chromatography (silica gel using $CHCl_3$ and other solvents) separates vitamin D_2 from the pro-vitamins D and the intermediate products of irradiation (*Analyt. Chem.* **35,** 1247 (1963)).

Detection

1. *Potassium permanganate*

On silica gel layers, spray with alkaline $KMnO_4$ to give brown spots (*Analyt. Chem.* **35,** 1247 (1963)).

2. *Ultraviolet light*

On paper chromatograms, vitamins D show as dark spots on a fluorescent ground under short-wave light (256 mμ) (*B.J.* **57,** xii (1954)). Under long-wave light (365 mμ), vitamins and provitamins appear fluorescent (*J. Chromat.* **5,** 500 (1961)).

3. *Antimony trichloride*

Spray with 24% $SbCl_3$ in $CHCl_3$ and heat the paper (*B.J.* **57,** xii (1954)). Vitamins D give brown spots, whereas provitamins D and cholesterol have a violet tinge (*J. Chromat.* **5,** 500 (1961)).

4. *Other colour reactions*

Vitamins D give well-defined colours with many acidic reagents, most of them non-specifically. Antimony pentachloride (20% in $CHCl_3$) is very sensitive for chromatographic detection (brown-blue colours) (*J. Chromat.* **5,** 500 (1961)).Brown colours are also given with 33% bismuth trichloride in ethanol, or 15% silicotungstic or phosphotungstic acid in ethanol. Dimethyl-*p*-phenylene-diamine in water gives a blue colour (*J. Chromat.* **5,** 500 (1961)). After being sprayed with the appropriate reagent, the chromatograms are generally heated for some time at 60°. 1 μg quantities are detectable.

Assay

Because of the exceptionally high potency of the vitamins D (40×10^6 i.u./g for the rat), physiological amounts can only be measured by bio-assay (*Biol. Symp.* **12,** 409, 435

(1942)). Higher potency fish oils and irradiation products can be measured chemically. The provitamins are separable by digitonin precipitation. The best and most specific colour reaction is with a saturated solution of $SbCl_3$ in ethylene dichloride, containing acetyl chloride (*J. Am. pharm. Ass.* **47,** 385 (1958)), followed by measurement of the extinction at 500 mμ. Another good reagent is glycerol 1,3-dichlorhydrin in the presence of acetyl chloride (*Ind. Engng Chem.* (*Anal.*) **18,** 117 (1945)). Vitamin A interferes with both procedures and must be removed chromatographically.

VITAMINS E (TOCOPHEROLS)

Eight tocopherols are known to occur in materials of vegetable origin. Four are methylated derivatives of tocol, and four are corresponding methylated derivatives of tocotrienol. They differ considerably in vitamin E activity. α-Tocopherol is the main source of vitamin E for animals, although other tocopherols may be observed in tissues (*Br. J. Nutr.* **15,** 253 (1961)).

Separation

(i) Adsorption on $ZnCO_3$-impregnated paper separates the complex into three groups depending on the number of methyl groups adjacent to the OH group (*J. Sci. Fd Agric.* **6,** 274 (1955)).

(ii) Partition chromatography separates the tocopherols into different groups, according to their molecular weight and the saturation or unsaturation of the side chain. A suitable system is liquid paraffin against 75% ethanol (*J. Sci. Fd Agric.* **4,** 569 (1953)), or 92% methanol (*B.J.* **84,** 444 (1962)). All eight substances are separable by two-dimensional chromatography of the tocopherols and their nitrosoderivatives (*Analyst* **84,** 304 (1959)).

(iii) Thin-layer chromatography separates all the tocopherols, some of them with difficulty, by a combination of different adsorbents and solvents. Examples are silica gel/$CHCl_3$, alumina/benzene, sec. magnesium phosphate/light petroleum (*Vitams Horm.* **20,** 407 (1962)). Impregnation of the layers with a fluorescent compound such as sodium fluorescein enables the tocopherols to be seen as dark spots under short-wave light (256 mμ). As little as 0·2 μg is visible. Individual identification is possible by spraying with $SbCl_5$ (q.v.). β- and γ-Tocopherol are especially difficult to separate by normal chromatographic procedures, but are separable on Kieselgel G (Merck) layers, using as mobile phase a mixture of light petroleum (40–60°), isopropyl ether, acetone, ethyl ether, and glacial acetic acid (85:12:4:1:1). Development takes 70 min (*Arch. B.B.* **103,** 42 (1963)). For recent developments in tocopherol chemistry and thin-layer separation, *see B.B.R.C.* **17,** 542 (1964).

(iv) In spite of their high boiling points, the tocopherols can be separated by gas-liquid chromatography. Suitable systems are: (*a*) silicone polymer SE-30 on Celite at 250° (*B.J.* **84,** 524 (1962)); (*b*) polyethylene glycol adipate on Celite at 250° (*B.J.* **84,** 524 (1962)); (*c*) Apiezon N on Celite at 260° (*Vitams Horm.* **20,** 407 (1962)).

Detection

1. *Dipyridyl-ferric chloride*

Spray with a freshly-prepared mixture of 2:2′-dipyridyl (0·5%) and $FeCl_3 \cdot 6H_2O$ (0·2%) in EtOH. Tocopherols give bright red spots (*Analyst* **84,** 356 (1959)). Sensitivity 2–5 μg. The sensitivity of the reagent can be considerably increased by the use of other Fe^{++}-complexing reagents instead of 2:2′-dipyridyl (*Vitams Horm.* **20,** 407 (1962)). 4:7-Diphenyl-1:10-phenanthroline is especially effective, increasing the depth of colour 2½ times (*Analyt. Chem.* **33,** 849 (1962)). Its use as a spray reagent has not been described, however.

2. *Ultraviolet light*

If $ZnCO_3$-impregnated paper contains a few ppm of sodium fluorescein, tocopherols can be observed as dark spots on a fluorescent ground under short-wave light (256 mμ) (*Analyst* **84,** 356 (1959)). Spraying chromatograms with an aqueous solution of sodium fluorescein is also effective.

3. *Potassium ferricyanide*

Spray with (*a*) 2% HCl in EtOH. Dry and then spray with (*b*) 0·05% aq. $K_3Fe(CN)_6$. Tocopherols give deep blue colours. Sensitivity 1 μg. Wash in H_2O and dry in the dark (*C.r. hebd. Séanc. Acad. Sci.* **235,** 1295 (1952)).

4. *Furter-Meyer Reaction*

On being heated for 3 min with 20% HNO_3 in EtOH, α-, β-, γ-tocopherol and β-tocotrienol give intense red colours. δ-Tocopherol and γ-tocopherol give red colours when reacted with 4% HNO_3 in $CHCl_3$ at room temperature (*J. Sci. Fd Agric.* **7,** 493 (1956)).

5. *Diazo reaction*

Spray with an excess of 2% Na_2CO_3, followed by 0·5% diazotized *o*-dianisidine. Tocopherols lacking a methyl group at C-5 give blue or violet colours, readily distinguishable from each other. Tocopherols lacking a methyl group at C-7 give pale reddish-amber spots. Fully substituted tocopherols give no reaction (*Analyst* **84,** 356 (1959)).

6. *Nitrosation*

Tocopherols lacking a methyl group at either C-5 or C-7 form distinctive yellow nitroso-derivatives. React 10–1000 μg in 5 ml of EtOH, containing 0·2 ml acetic acid, with 3 ml of 2% $NaNO_2$. Add an excess of KOH after 60 sec (*J.B.C.* **175,** 605 (1948)). The nitroso-derivatives are readily characterized chromatographically and by their spectra (*Analyst* **84,** 304 (1959)).

7. *Gibbs' reagent**

Spray with 2% Na_2CO_3 solution, followed by a solution of Gibbs' reagent (2:6-dichloro-*p*-benzoquinone-4-chloro-imine). Blue-green colours are given by γ-, η-, and δ-tocopherol (*Analyst* **84,** 297 (1959)).

* Warning: Closely related compounds are explosive above 50° C.

8. *Antimony pentachloride*

Spray thin-layer chromatograms with 20% $SbCl_5$ in $CHCl_3$ and observe after 3 min. The known tocopherols give widely differing colours, which depend also on the adsorbent being used (*Vitams Horm.* **20,** 407 (1962)). Limit of detection, 2 μg. Optimal colours with 20–50 μg.

9. *Physical data*

Individual tocopherols can be identified by their infrared and ultraviolet spectra (*Vitam. Horm.* **20,** 407 (1962)).

Assay

Specific bio-assay is by the rat gestation-resorption method (*Biol. Symp.* **12,** 549 (1942)). Various chemical methods are available, depending on chromatographic separation followed by colorimetric reaction with $FeCl_3$-dipyridyl (*Analyst* **84,** 356 (1959); *Acta chem. scand.* **15,** 783 (1961)). Special procedures are available for determination of tocopherols in animal tissues (*B.J.* **76,** 563 (1960); **79,** 91 (1960)) and plant tissues (*J. Sci. Fd Agric.* **12,** 251 (1961); *Analyt. Biochem.* **5,** 531 (1963)). A chick liver-storage bio-assay is available (*J. Nutr.* **75,** 165 (1961)).

Tocopherolquinones

These quinones are physiological oxidation products of the tocopherols and are of especial importance during the separation and identification of the total quinone mixture of chloroplasts (*B.B.R.C.* **10,** 237 (1963)). They are separated from other quinones and each other by thin-layer chromatography on silica gel, with 15% ethyl acetate in benzene as mobile phase, and are identified by their typical u.v. spectra (*B.B.R.C.* **10,** 237 (1963)). They give the reactions of quinones, described under the vitamins K (q.v.).

α-Tocopherolquinone is separated by adsorption on $ZnCO_3$-impregnated paper (*B.B.A.* **29,** 456 (1958)), by reversed phase partition chromatography (75% EtOH against liquid paraffin) (*B.J.* **76,** 563 (1960)), or by thin-layer chromatography on silicic acid with 2% methanol in benzene as mobile phase (*B.J.* **90,** 7P (1964)). It is readily identified by a bicuspid peak at 262 and 269 mμ, which is replaced by a peak at 287 mμ on addition of sodium borohydride and restored on adding anhydrous silver oxide (*B.J.* **90,** 7P (1964)).

VITAMINS K

The main members of this series are vitamin $K_{1(20)}$ and vitamin $K_{2(35)}$, found respectively in green plants and microorganisms. *See* the Review in *Vitams Horm.* **17,** 54 (1959). The substances are extremely labile and their detection is often difficult unless careful precautions are taken.

Separation

Vitamins K_1 and K_2 are easily separable by partition paper chromatography. System: 95% ethanol against liquid paraffin (*J. Chromat.* **10,** 158 (1963)). Full differentiation of vitamin K_1 from other lipid constituents can be achieved by two-dimensional chromatography (*B.J.* **84,** 444 (1962)). Reversed phase paper chromatography on silicone impregnated paper is used for separating various ubiquinones (Coenzyme Q), plastoquinone and vitamin K (*J.B.C.* **234,** 672 (1959)). For a method of thin-layer chromatography separating vitamins E and K, β-carotene and ubiquinone 50, see *J. Chromat.* **7,** 213 (1962). Column chromatography on deactivated alumina and separation of vitamin K from the ubiquinones involves special techniques (*B.J.* **83,** 606 (1962)). The system butanol–butyl acetate–acetic acid–water (59:4·5:12:24·5) against soft white paraffin is useful (*B.J.* **83,** 606 (1962)).

Detection

1. *Ultraviolet light*

Vitamins K show as dark spots on a fluorescent ground under short-wave light (*J. Chromat.* **10,** 158 (1963)).

2. *Diazo reaction*

Spray with a mixture of *p*-nitroaniline (0·4% in 0·33N-HCl), $NaNO_2$ (1% in H_2O), urea or ammonium sulphamate (5% in H_2O) and H_2O in the following proportions, 1:1:1:7. Vitamin K gives a reddish spot (*Chem. Listy* **45,** 76 (1951)).

3. *Leucomethylene blue*

The reagent is prepared by dissolving 100 mg of methylene blue in 100 ml of EtOH, adding 1 ml of acetic acid and 1 g of zinc dust, and swirling until the blue is discharged (*J.A.C.S.* **81,** 4007 (1959)). Vitamins K give blue spots (about 1 μg detectable) when sprayed with the reagent, but the reaction is given by many other quinones, especially the ubiquinones and plastoquinones (*J. Scient. ind. Res.* **20C,** 69 (1961)).

Assay

Both isolation and determination are difficult. When sufficient quantities are present (as in bacterial extracts), chromatography followed by measuring the typical absorption peak at 249 mμ (ε 19 000) may be used (*B.J.* **83,** 606 (1962)). For most other types of extract, only bio-assay is possible: this is based on determining blood coagulation times in vitamin-deficient chicks (*Biol. Symp.* **12,** 508 (1942); *Acta physiol. scand.* **22,** 238 (1951)).

WATER-SOLUBLE VITAMINS

By D. C. ELLIOTT (*School of Biological Sciences, Flinders University of South Australia*

THIAMIN AND DERIVATIVES

Some applications of chromatography to thiamin analysis are detailed in a review by

Mickelsen and Yamamoto on the determination of thiamin (*Meth. biochem. Anal.* **6,** 242 (1958)). Siliprandi and Siliprandi (*B.B.A.* **14,** 52 (1954)) have used various methods of paper and column chromatography and electrophoresis for the separation of thiamin and its phosphoric esters. See also *J. Chromat.* **1,** 545 (1958) for the use of ion-exchange resins with these compounds.

As with the chromatography of other phosphate esters, washing of the paper with EDTA (0·2% EDTA at pH 8·5, followed by thorough washing with water) or 8-hydroxyquinoline (successive washing with 4N-HCl, a saturated solution of oxine in 50% EtOH and finally with 50% EtOH) is important for the successful separation of thiamin and its phosphoric esters. Solvents which have been used include: *n*-PrOH–H_2O–1M-acetate buffer, pH 5 (70:20:10), *p*-toluenesulphonic acid–*tert.*-amyl alcohol–H_2O (2:60:30), *n*-BuOH–ethylene glycol–0·1N-HCl (4:1:1). For improved separation of the triphosphate, Kiessling has recommended *iso*butyric acid–N-ammonia–0·1M-EDTA (100:60:1·6) (*Acta chem. scand.* **10,** 1356 (1956)).

Detection

1. *Ultraviolet light*

Strong absorption is shown by thiamin and its derivatives at 250–60 mμ. Chromatographic solvents which absorb u.v. cannot be used, e.g. phenol, *p*-toluenesulphonic acid (*B.J.* **56,** 379 (1954)).

2. *Potassium ferricyanide*

Spray with 2·5% $K_3Fe(CN)_6$:10% NaOH:55% EtOH = 0·1:5:5. Thiamin and its esters are oxidized to thiochromes which have a blue fluorescence in u.v. light. Sensitivity 0·5 μg (*Science* **116,** 711 (1952)).

3. *Cyanogen bromide*

This can be used instead of 2 for oxidation to thiochrome. Spray with (*a*) 10% NaCN added to H_2O saturated with Br_2 until the colour of the Br_2 has just disappeared. Heat at 70° for 5–10 min. Then spray with (*b*) 5% NaOH in *n*-BuOH, saturated with H_2O. Thiamin gives a fluorescence; thiamin-cysteine, weak. If the paper is given a preliminary spray of reducing agent (0·4% aq. cysteine hydrochloride) and heated at 70° for 15–30 min, then thiamin cysteine and thiamin disulphide also fluoresce (*Science* **118,** 109 (1953)).

4. *Bioautograph*

This technique, using *S. lactis*, *E. coli*, *Kloeckera brevis*, *L. viridescens*, or *A. aerogenes* as test organism, has been employed in various problems of thiamin metabolism (*J.B.C.* **199,** 873 (1952); **235,** 2404 (1960); **236,** 2099, 2768 (1961)).

5. *Potassium bismuth iodide*

Reagent: 5 g K bismuth iodide is added to 100 ml H_2O containing 0·5 ml conc. HCl. Boil and filter when cold. On spraying with this reagent thiamin derivatives give red-purple to orange spots. Remove background colour by washing in ether saturated with H_2O. Sensitivity 0·1 μg (*B.J.* **56,** 379 (1954)). *See* Amines, 7.

6. *Dipicrylamine*

Spray with 0·2 ml 0·5N-Mg dipicrylamine in 100 ml 50% MeOH containing 1 ml conc. NH_3. Dry at room temperature. Red spots on a yellow ground are given by quaternary ammonium bases (*B.Z.* **323,** 265 (1952)).

7. *Molybdate-perchloric acid* (*for thiamin phosphates*)

This spray may be applied after 5. *See* Phosphate esters, 1 (*B.J.* **56,** 379 (1954)).

8. *Azide-iodine*

This method is used for S-containing amino acids and thiamin (*Science* **118,** 109 (1953)). *See* Amino acids, 18.

Riboflavin—see Purines, pyrimidines, nucleosides, and nucleotides.

PYRIDOXINE

See the references given below for solvents used in the separation of pyridoxine, pyridoxamine, and pyridoxal on paper. For thin-layer chromatography of these compounds see *Naturwissenschaften* **47,** 279 (1960); *Dt. ApothZtg.* **101,** 268 (1961).

1. *Ultraviolet light*

Pyridoxine absorbs at 297 mμ in u.v. light (*Analyt. Chem.* **24,** 1952 (1952)).

2. *Bioautograph*

The bioautograph technique with *S. carlsbergensis* has been used for pyridoxine (*P.S.E.B.M.* **67,** 513 (1948)). Full details for the technique are given in this reference.

3. 2:6-*Dichloroquinone chloroimide* (*Gibbs' reagent*)*

Spray with 0·1% 2:6-dichloroquinone chloroimide in benzene. Then expose the paper to NH_3 vapour. A blue spot is given by vitamin B_6. Sensitivity 1 μg (*Arch. B.B.* **46,** 465 (1953)).

* Warning: Closely related compounds are explosive above 50° C.

4. *Ferric chloride*

Spray with a dilute soln. of $FeCl_3$. Pyridoxine gives a brown colour (*Bull. Soc. Chim. biol.* **34,** 196 (1952)).

5. *Phenylhydrazine*

Spray with a saturated soln. of phenylhydrazine in 95% EtOH containing 10% CH_3COOH (*Arch. B.B.* **46,** 465 (1953)). A yellow spot is given with pyridoxine (1 μg). *See* Carbohydrates, 34.

6. *Diazotized p-aminoacetophenone*

Component solutions of spraying reagent: (*a*) 3·18 g *p*-aminoacetophenone in 45 ml conc. HCl diluted to 1 l with H_2O. (*b*) 2·25% $NaNO_2$. (*c*) 25% Na acetate. Spray with (*a*):(*b*):(*c*) = 2:10:10, freshly mixed. Heat at 50–60° for 10 min. Pink, orange, and yellow colours are given by pyridoxine, pyridoxal, and pyridoxamine and their phosphates (*B.B.A.* **14,** 212 (1954)).

7. *Ehrlich's and Ekman's reactions*

These sprays have been used to detect pyridoxamine. *See* Amino acids, 11; Amines, 18 (i).

NICOTINIC ACID AND RELATED COMPOUNDS

Separation of these compounds has been achieved by paper chromatography (see references to sprays below). Paper electrophoresis (*J. Chromat.* **2,** 531 (1959)) and more recently thin-layer chromatography (*Naturwissenschaften* **47,** 279 (1960); *Dt. ApothZtg.* **101,** 142 (1961)) have also been used.

1. *König reaction*

Hang the paper in a closed vessel over cyanogen bromide crystals (or a solution of CNBr; *see* Thiamine 3) for 30–60 min. *iso*Nicotinic acid hydrazide, nicotinic acid hydrazide, and *iso*propyl*iso*nicotinic acid hydrazide give a specific blue fluorescence in u.v. light (*B.J.* **52,** xxxiv (1952)). Follow the CNBr treatment by spraying with one of the following aromatic amines:

(i) Spray with 2 g *p*-aminobenzoic acid in 75 ml 0·75N-HCl diluted to 100 ml with 96% EtOH. Nicotinic acid gives a yellow spot; nicotinamide, deep yellow; nicotinuric acid, orange; diethylnicotinamide (coramine), pink. Sensitivity 0·1 μg. Little or no colour is given with *iso*nicotinic derivatives (*Nature, Lond.* **168,** 475 (1951)).

(ii) Spray with 0·25% benzidine in 50% EtOH. Nicotinic acid gives a red-violet spot; *iso*nicotinic acid, grey-lavender; nicotinamide, red-violet; coramine, violet. Sensitivity 5 μg (*Nature, Lond.* **167,** 119 (1951)). Warning: Benzidine is carcinogenic.

(iii) Spray with 1% *p*-aminoacetophenone in 50% EtOH. Sensitivity > 10 μg. Colours tend to fade.

(iv) Spray with a saturated aq. soln. of 3-methyl-1-phenylpyrazol-5-one. Sensitivity 5 μg (*B.J.* **55,** 669 (1953)).

(v) Spray with 0·5% *N*-(1-naphthyl)-ethylenediamine dihydrochloride in EtOH. Yellow spots are given by nicotinic acid and its derivatives. Sensitivity 40 μg (*J.A.C.S.* **75,** 2971 (1953)).

(vi) Aniline (*Naturwissenschaften* **38,** 333 (1951)) and β-naphthylamine (*Arch. B.B.* **43,** 269 (1953)) have also been used for nicotinic acid in connexion with tobacco alkaloids.

2. *Picryl chloride*

Dip in 1·5% picryl chloride in EtOH. Dry. Hang in NH_3 vapour. Red spots are given with pyridine, nicotinic acid, *iso*nicotinic acid, nicotinamide, and *iso*nicotinamide, but only the red-purple spots of *iso*nicotinic acid hydrazide, nicotinic acid hydrazide, and *iso*propyl*iso*nicotinic acid hydrazide remain after exposure to acetic acid vapour. Sensitivity 5 μg (*B.J.* **52,** xxxiv (1952)).

3. 1-*Fluoro*-2:4-*dinitrobenzene*

Spray with (*a*) 2% 1-fluoro-2:4-dinitrobenzene in EtOH. Heat at 110° for 10–15 min. Then spray with (*b*) 5% NaOH. *iso*Nicotinic acid gives a violet spot; nicotinic acid gives a red-brown colour which fades in 3 min; pyridine, violet; β-picoline, rust-brown; γ-picoline, green-black (*Angew. Chem.* **65,** 342 (1953)). Characteristic red, purple, yellow, or green colours are given by various *iso*nicotinic acid hydrazide metabolites, the colours developing more slowly than with 2 (*B.J.* **55,** 669 (1953)).

4. 1-*Chloro*-2:4-*dinitrobenzene*

Spray with (*a*) 1% 1-chloro-2:4-dinitrobenzene in EtOH. Yellow-orange spots are given by hydrazides but this spray is not as sensitive as 2. Heat at 100° until the paper turns yellow. Nicotinamide (5 μg) gives an intense purple spot. Then spray with (*b*) 0·7% KOH in EtOH. Yellow-brown spots develop in a few hours with nicotinic acid. Sensitivity 10 μg (*B.J.* **55,** 669 (1953)).

5. *Diazotized p-nitraniline*

See Amines, 17 (ii), for preparation of this reagent. Spray with diazotized *p*-nitraniline, then with 20% Na_2CO_3. Hydrazides give yellow spots, fading in a few hours (*B.J.* **55,** 669 (1953)).

6. *Sodium hypobromite—diazo reaction*

Reagent (*a*): 4 ml 2·5N-NaOH is diluted to 45 ml, 2 ml Br_2 is added and the volume made up to 50 ml with H_2O. Spray and leave at room temperature for 15 min. Then heat at 100° for 5 min. Carbonamide groups of acid amides are converted to —NH_2. Then spray with (*b*) 2·4N-HCl:0·1% $NaNO_2$ = 1:1. After 1 min spray with (*c*) 0·5% NH_4 sulphamate:0·1% *N*-(1-naphthyl)-ethylenediamine dihydrochloride = 1:1. This method detects *N*-methyl-2-pyridone-5-carbonamide which the König reaction (1) does not (*B.J.* **56,** 513 (1954)).

7. *Sodium carbonate–sulphonic acid*

Stock solution: 0·1 g $Na_2S_2O_4$ in a few ml H_2O+1 ml 10% Na_2CO_3+0·1 g 1-amino-2-naphthol-4-sulphonic acid diluted to 100 ml with H_2O. Keep in the dark under toluene. Spray with (*a*) 20% trichloroacetic acid: 30% Na_2CO_3:H_2O = 1:1:2. Heat at 50° for 2 min. Then spray with (*b*) stock solution:H_2O:30% Na_2CO_3 = 1:2:1. A red spot is given with *iso*nicotinic acid hydrazide (*C.A.* **47,** 10604 (1953)).

8. *Potassium iodate–starch*

Spray with a soln. of KIO_3-starch in dilute H_2SO_4. *iso*Nicotinic acid hydrazide gives a blue spot; *iso*nicotinic acid, no reaction (*B.J.* **61,** 128 (1955)).

9. *p-Dimethylaminobenzaldehyde*

Spray with 2% *p*-dimethylaminobenzaldehyde in 5% HCl; orange-yellow colours are given after 24 hr at room temperature by hydrazides (*B.J.* **55,** 669 (1953)).

10. *Ultraviolet light*

Contact photography in u.v. light (260 mμ) gives white spots on a black ground (*Bull. Soc. Chim. biol.* **34,** 196 (1952)). If the material has been developed on a chromatogram as a band, and a strip is then streaked with 20% KOH, a purple colour on the edge of the alkali-treated area is shown in u.v. light by NAD, NADP, nicotinamide mononucleotide, *N′*-methylnicotinuric acid betaine and *N′*-methylnicotinamide (*J.A.C.S.* **75,** 2971 (1953)).

11. *Fluorescein*

Spray with 0·05% fluorescein in EtOH. In u.v. light pyridine carboxylic acids and aldehydes give dark spots on a fluorescent ground. Sensitivity 25 μg (*Angew. Chem.* **65,** 342 (1953)).

12. *Methylethyl ketone–ammonia*

Hang the paper over a mixture of methylethyl ketone:conc. NH_3 = 1:1 for 1 hr. Quaternary pyridine compounds with the side chain CO—NH—R in the β-position show bluish-white fluorescence in u.v. light. Sensitivity 0·05 μg (*Nature, Lond.* **168,** 475 (1951)).

PANTOTHENIC ACID AND DERIVATIVES (COENZYME A)

For solvents used in the separation of these compounds see references given for the sprays below. More recently calcium pantothenate has been separated from other water-soluble vitamins by thin-layer chromatography (*Naturwissenschaften* **47,** 277 (1960)).

1. *Ninhydrin*

See Amino acids, 1. Pantoic acid derivatives give purple spots. Pantothenic acid, no colour (*J.B.C.* **175,** 483 (1948)).

2. *β-Naphthoquinone-4-sulphonate* (*Folin's reagent*)

See Amino acids, 7 (i). Spray with 0·5% β-naphthoquinone-4-sulphonate, adjusted to pH 9·2 to 9·4 with Na tetraborate. Heat at 100° for 10 min. Pantothenic acid gives an intense yellow spot; β-alanine, reddish orange. Allow to stay in the light for several hours to bleach the background (*Archs int. Physiol.* **56,** 189 (1948)).

3. *Bioautograph*

The bioautograph technique using *Lactobacillus helveticus* 80, has been used for pantethine and naturally occurring *Lb. bulgaricus* factors (*J.B.C.* **198,** 375 (1952)).

4. *Ultraviolet light*

Quenching of the natural fluorescence of the paper is shown by CoA and acetyl-CoA due to the adenine constituent (*J.B.C.* **196,** 535 (1952)).

5. *Nitroprusside*

Spray with (*a*) 3% NaOH in 95% MeOH. Then spray with (*b*) nitroprusside reagent, Amino acids, 19 (*a*). This gives a positive test for the —SH group of alkyl mercaptans (*J.B.C.* **196,** 535 (1952)).

An alternative method is to spray with (*a*) 5% NaCN and 5% Na_2CO_3 in 25% EtOH, then after a few minutes spray with (*b*) 2% Na nitroprusside in 75% EtOH. This method detects the —S—S— link of oxidized CoA, etc. (*J.A.C.S.* **74,** 4017 (1952)).

BIOTIN

1. *Bioautograph*

The bioautograph technique using *Lb. casei* has been employed for detecting biotin (*Analyst* **76,** 77 (1951)).

2. *Potassium permanganate*

Spray with 1% aq. $KMnO_4$. Biotin (and many other organic compounds) gives a yellow spot on a purple ground. Sensitivity 4 μg (*Current Sci.* **22,** 209 (1953)).

3. *Potassium iodoplatinate*

For use on thin-layer chromatograms: spray with 10% KI:5% platinic chloride: water = 45:5:50. Biotin forms a white spot on a pink ground. Some other vitamins also give colours: B_1, grey; nicotinamide, pale yellow; C, yellow (*Naturwissenschaften* **47,** 277 (1960)).

FOLIC ACID

1. *Bioautograph*

Using the bioautograph technique acceleration of the growth of *Leuconostoc citrovorum* is shown by pteroylglutamic acid and citrovorum factor (CF) (*Arch. B.B.* **40,** 205 (1952)); inhibition of the growth of *Strep. faecalis* is shown by 4-amino antagonists (*J.B.C.* **205,** 361 (1953)).

Conjugated forms of CF are detected by including chick pancreas conjugase in the medium to split conjugates (*J.B.C.* **200,** 223 (1953)).

The biosynthesis of folic acid has been followed using the bioautograph technique (*J.B.C.* **236,** 2534 (1961)). The papers are soaked in sodium ascorbate (6 mg/ml, pH 7·0) and dried. The developing solvent (ascending technique) is 0·1M-phosphate, pH 7·0, containing 6 mg/ml sodium ascorbate. The ascorbate serves as an antioxidant to prevent destruction of dihydro- and tetrahydro-forms of pteroate and folate.

2. *Ultraviolet light*

Blue or green fluorescence in u.v. light is given by pterins. Leucopterin gives a pale blue fluorescence; xanthopterin, yellowish-green; rhizopterin, bright blue (*Nature, Lond.* **163,** 31 (1949)), pteroylglutamic acid (PGA), blue (*Ber.* **84,** 579 (1951)). Dark spots on a fluorescent ground are given by pteridines (*J.C.S.* **1951,** 474).

3. *Titanous chloride—diazo reaction*

Spray with (*a*) 10% $TiCl_3$ in conc. HCl mixed with 15% Na citrate. Destroy excess titanium chloride by air oxidation. Then spray with (*b*) 0·2% $NaNO_2$ in 0·1N-HCl. Finally spray with (*c*) 0·2% 1-naphthylamine or *N*-(1-naphthyl)-ethylenediamine. Used for the detection of folic acid (*Chem. Listy* **47,** 1877 (1953)).

COBALAMIN

Various solvents have been employed with success to separate the factors in the B_{12} group (*see references below*). Water-saturated *sec.*-BuOH with either 1% acetic acid or 1% ammonia added is favoured by many (cf. Kon in 'The biochemistry of vitamin B_{12}', *Biochem. Soc. Symp.* no. **13**, p. 17, Cambridge University Press (1955); see also *J. Chromat.* **7,** 86 (1962)). It is necessary to work in the presence of HCN vapour to keep the factors in their cyano-coordination states, and also to carry out all operations in a dim light.

Detection

1. *Bioautograph*

Cobalamin may be detected by the bioautograph technique using *E. coli* (*B.J.* **59,** 86 (1955)) and the addition of a reducing agent (ascorbic, thioglycollic, or mercapto-succinic acids) to the medium (*Can. J. Technology* **30,** 265 (1952)).

Lb. lactis has also been used to detect vitamin B_{12} (*J.B.C.* **183,** 569 (1950)). Purine and pyrimidine nucleosides (especially thymidine) will also support growth (*B.J.* **44,** v (1949)). *Lb. leichmannii* has been used for vitamin B_{12} and related bacterial growth factors (*J.B.C.* **181,** 109 (1949)). Sensitivity of these methods, 0·005–0·1 μg. *See also* Purines, 17.

2. *Colour*

The red colour of B_{12} is visible in quantities of 10 μg (*B.J.* **44,** v (1949)).

INOSITOL

Revised by R. W. BAILEY (*Division of Plant Chemistry, D.S.I.R., Palmerston North, New Zealand*)

1. *Alkaline silver nitrate*

Detected as a non-reducing substance by either the acetone $AgNO_3$–alcoholic NaOH or ammoniacal $AgNO_3$ reagents (Carbohydrates, 1) (see also *Analyst* **77,** 416 (1952)). As these sprays, and those listed under 2 (below) react with other sugar compounds their use must be coupled with the known rate of movement of inositol in various solvents (*see* refs. to reviews on solvents under Carbohydrates, also *J.A.C.S.* **75,** 648 (1953); *J.B.C.* **228,** 1 (1957)). Failure of the suspected $AgNO_3$-inositol spot to react with the specific sprays for various classes of reducing sugars will at least eliminate these types of compounds.

2. *Other carbohydrate sprays*

Many of the more general carbohydrate sprays, particularly those based on reagents such as periodate will detect inositol. These include the following sprays listed in section 6; 2, 3, 37, 41, 42, and 43 (see also *Analyt. Chem.* **28,** 849 (1956)).

3. *Rhodizonic acid reaction*

Reagents: (*a*) 10 ml conc. HNO_3 in 90 ml EtOH. (*b*) *n*-BuOH:glacial acetic:10% (w/v) aq. Ba acetate:$CaCl_2$ = 40:10:10:0·5 g. (*c*) 5% (w/v) $CaCl_2$ in 50% aq. EtOH. Dip in (*a*), heat 95–100° 10 min, expose to NH_3 vapour 1–2 sec then dip in (*b*). Inositol gives an orange colour on a white ground; sensitivity 8–10 μg (*Nature, Lond.* **181,** 1730 (1958)). For greater sensitivity, spray with (*c*) and heat at 95–100° for 2 min; orange spots turning pink; sensitivity 1 μg. A modification will also detect inositol phosphate. Amino acids and aldohexoses do not interfere and the reagent may be used following ninhydrin detection of amino acids.

Another version of this spray is as follows: (*a*) 10 g mercuric oxide+10 g HNO_3 diluted to 200 ml with H_2O. Dilute 1 in 3 before use. Spray and heat at 85–100° for 10 min. Spray again and heat for a further 5 min. Then spray with (*b*) 10% aq. Ba acetate:CH_3COOH = 15:85. Dry for 2 min at 85–100°. Respray with (*b*). Repeat the drying and spraying up to 4 or 5 times depending on the concentration of inositol. A rose salmon spot on a white ground is given by 5–10 μg inositol (*Bull. Soc. Chim. biol.* **35,** 537 (1953)). This spray may be followed by *p*-anisidine phosphate (*see* Carbohydrates, 7), when the characteristic spot for inositol is retained as well as the characteristic colours of the sugars developed by the second reagent (*Analyt. Chem.* **28,** 1216 (1956)).

4. *Ferricyanide–ferric sulphate*

Spray with (*a*) 0·4% aq. K ferricyanide:1·6% aq. Na_2CO_3 containing 0·025% NaCN = 2:1. Dry in warm air. Then spray with (*b*) 0·5% $Fe_2(SO_4)_3$ in 6·5% aq. H_3PO_4 (*J.B.C.* **205,** 1007 (1953)). This method has been used for *l*-deoxyinositol which gives a blue spot. Sugars which reduce Benedict's solution only after being heated do not give coloured spots.

5. *Bioautograph*

This method has been used for the detection of inositol and inositol phosphate. *Saccharomyces carlsbergensis* is the test organism (*Analyt. Biochem.* **3,** 124 (1962)).

ASCORBIC ACID

Revised by R. W. BAILEY (*Division of Plant Chemistry, D.S.I.R., Palmerston North, New Zealand*)

1. *Alkaline silver nitrate*

Detected by the various alkaline $AgNO_3$ spray reagents (*see* Carbohydrates, 1). Other carbohydrate sprays shown to react with ascorbic acid include nos. 2, 3, 10, 20, and 42 (see also *Analyt. Chem.* **28,** 849 (1956)). As all of these sprays react with various classes of sugars they must be used in conjunction with rate of movement studies in various solvents (*see* reviews on solvents in section 6, also *B.J.* **55,** 821 (1953); *J. Ass. off. agric. Chem.* **36,** 1127 (1953); and references to the spray reagents listed below).

2. 2:6-*Dichlorophenol indophenol* (*Tillmann's reagent*)

Reagent: 0·8 g 2:6-dichlorophenol indophenol is dissolved in 1 l H_2O and diluted with an equal volume of EtOH. Spray. Ascorbic acid and related dienols give colourless spots on a dark blue ground. Sensitivity 1–2 μg (*Nature, Lond.* **164,** 479 (1949)).

3. *Ferric salt–o-phenanthroline*

Spray with 0·15% ferric ammonium sulphate:2% *o*-phenanthroline HCl = 1:9. Dry at 80–100°. Uric acid (0·5 μg) and ascorbic acid reduce Fe^{3+} to Fe^{2+}, which reacts giving a red spot (*Nature, Lond.* **170,** 501 (1952)).

4. *Ferric chloride–ferricyanide*

Reagent: 1% aq. $FeCl_3$:1% aq. K ferricyanide = 1:1, freshly mixed. Spray. Ascorbic acid gives a pink spot in the cold (*Analyt. Chem.* **33,** 1446 (1961)). Many other substances react, generally to give a blue colour.

5. *Ammonium molybdate*

Spray with 15% $(NH_4)_2MoO_4$ in 1% NH_4OH. Heat at 75° for 15 min. Ascorbic acid gives a blue spot on a white ground (*C.A.* **48,** 2812 (1954)).

6. *Cacotheline*

Spray with 2% aq. cacotheline. Heat at 110° for several min. Ascorbic acid (5 μg) gives a violet spot (*Z. Naturf.* **8B,** 373 (1953)).

7. *p-Aminobenzoic acid*

Spray with 1% *p*-aminobenzoic acid in 10% CH_3COOH. A yellow colour is given with reductone but not with ascorbic acid (*Ark. Kemi* **3,** 11 (1950)).

8. *Reagents depending on organic acid reaction*

Spray with either (*a*) 0·04% bromophenol blue in 95% EtOH adjusted to pH 6·7; or (*b*) 10% (v/v) acetic anhydride in pyridine, heat at 100° for 5 min (ascorbic acid gives a yellow spot, many other acids do not react); or (*c*) saturated aq. NH_4 vanadate (ascorbic acid blue-grey turning grey, most other acids yellow) (*Analyt. Chem.* **24,** 489 (1952)). *See also under* Acids, section 1. Fluorescence with *o*-phenylenediamine has been used to detect 5 μg of dehydroascorbic acid in the presence of ascorbic acid which does not react (*C.A.* **47,** 4042 (1953)).

22. Ion Exchangers and Gel Filtration Media

Revised by N. K. BOARDMAN (*C.S.I.R.O., Division of Plant Industry, Canberra, A.C.T.*)

ION EXCHANGERS

ION-EXCHANGE RESINS

An ion-exchange resin consists essentially of a cross-linked polymeric structure to which are attached ionized or ionizable groups. The original synthetic ion-exchange resins were formed by condensation processes, but these resins have limited use for chromatographic purposes, since they behave as mixtures of ionizable groups. They suffer also from the practical disadvantage of limited chemical stability.

The most useful resins for laboratory purposes are the polystyrene resins. These are formed by copolymerizing styrene and divinylbenzene (or some other compound with two unsaturated bonds), and ionic groups are attached to confer the property of ion-exchange. Another useful resin is cross-linked polymethacrylic acid formed by copolymerizing methacrylic acid and divinylbenzene (DVB). The properties of the ion-exchange resins vary with the nature of the ionizable group, cross-linkage, and particle size.

CHEMICAL STABILITY

The polystyrene resins and the polymethacrylic acid resins are very stable and although the free base forms of the anion-exchange resins should not be used above 60° C, the salt forms, as well as the salt and hydrogen forms of the cation-exchange resins are stable up to 120° C. The resins resist all but the strongest oxidizing agents.

CROSS-LINKING

The degree of swelling of an ion-exchange resin is dependent on the amount of cross-linking which in turn depends on the DVB content. The useful range of cross-linking varies between 20% and 1%, the pore size varying from about 5 Å to 35 Å or larger. For the chromatography of small ions, an ion-exchange resin with a DVB content of 8–10% is commonly used. Resins of low cross-linkage (1–4% DVB) are suitable for the chromatography of larger molecules such as polypeptides or antibiotics; these resins show a decreased physical stability.

PARTICLE SIZE

As the particle size of an ion-exchange resin is decreased, the time required to reach equilibrium is decreased, leading to an increased efficiency of a given volume of resin and sharper separations. The sharpness of the separation depends also on the range of particle sizes of the resin. For column operation 100–200 mesh or finer particles are recommended, while 100–200 mesh or coarser particles are recommended for batch operations. For desalting, particle size is not critical.

EXCHANGE CAPACITY

The exchange capacity of an ion-exchange resin is dependent not only on the concentration of ionizable groups in the resin but also on the nature of the ionizable groups. Thus if a resin contains only the strongly acidic sulphonic acid group, the capacity of the resin for a simple ion is constant and independent of pH above pH 3. In contrast, a resin containing only carboxyl groups has a lower capacity in neutral and acid solutions than in alkaline ones. Below pH 5 the exchange capacity decreases rapidly.

Similarly, the capacity of a resin containing basic quaternary nitrogen groups is constant over a wide range of pH, but resins containing weakly basic groups exhibit low capacities at pH values above 8.

22. Ion Exchangers and Gel Filtration Media

CHROMATOGRAPHIC GRADE ION-EXCHANGE RESINS

A. *Cation-exchange resins*

Designation	*Type of polymer*	*Functional group*	*Acidity*	*Supplier*	*Particle size Dry mesh range*
Dowex 50–X1(AG50W–X1)	Styrene	ϕ-SO_3^-	Strong	*a*, *b*	50–100
Dowex 50–X2(AG50W–X2)	,,	,,	,,	,,	50–100, 100–200, 200–400
Dowex 50–X4(AG50W–X4)	,,	,,	,,	,,	20–50, 50–100, 100–200, 200–400, minus 400
Dowex 50–X5(AG50W–X5)	,,	,,	,,	,,	Minus 400
Dowex 50–X8(AG50W–X8)	,,	,,	,,	,,	20–50, 50–100, 100–200, 200–400, minus 400
Dowex 50–X12(AG50W–X12)	,,	,,	,,	,,	50–100, 100–200, 200–400, minus 400
Dowex 50–X16(AG50W–X16)	,,	,,	,,	,,	20–50, 50–100, 100–200, 200–400
Zeo Karb 225	,,	,,	,,	*c*	
Zeo Karb 225	,,	,,	,,	,,	
Zeo Karb 225	,,	,,	,,	,,	
Zeo Karb 225	,,	,,	,,	,,	
Zeo Karb 225	,,	,,	,,	,,	
Zeo Karb 225	,,	,,	,,	,,	
IR–120 C.P.	,,	,,	,,	*d*	
IR–120 C.P.	,,	,,	,,	,,	
IR–120 C.P.	,,	,,	,,	,,	
IR–120 C.P.	,,	,,	,,	,,	
IR–120 C.P.	,,	,,	,,	,,	
IR–120 AR	,,	,,	,,	,,	
CG 120 AR[1]	,,	,,	,,	,,	100–200
CG 120 AR[1]	,,	,,	,,	,,	200–400
CG 120 AR[1]	,,	,,	,,	,,	400–600
Bio-Rex 70	Acrylic acid	R_1-COO^-	Weak (pH 4–14)	*b*	
Bio-Rex 62	Styrene	ϕ-POO^-	Intermediate	,,	
Bio-Rex 63	,,	ϕ-POO_2^-	Strong & weak	,,	
Bio-Rex 40	,,	ϕ-O^-; R-$CH_2SO_3^-$	Strong & very weak	,,	
Chelex 100	,,	ϕ-$N(CH_2COO^-)_2$		,,	
Zeo Karb 226	Methacrylic acid	R_2-COO^-	Weak (pH 5–14)	*c*	
Zeo Karb 226	,,	,,	,,	,,	
IRC–50 C.P.	,,	,,	,,	*d*	
IRC–50 AR	,,	,,	,,	,,	
CG–50 AR[1]	,,	,,	,,	,,	100–200, 200–400, 400–600
XE-89 C.P.	Acrylic acid	R_1-COO^-	Weak (pH 4–14)	,,	

See notes on p. 598.

Particle size Wet mesh range	*Cross-linkage (% di-vinyl-benzene)*	*Maximum tempera-ture (°C)*	*Water† regain*	*Exchange capacity dry (m-equiv./g)*	*wet (m-equiv./ml)*
20–50	1	150		5·0	0·4
20–50, 50–100, 80–200	2	,,		5·2	0·7
20–50, 40–80, 60–140, 100–200, 200–400	4	,,		5·2	1·2
200–400	5	,,		5·2	1·3
20–50, 40–80, 60–140, 100–230, 230–400	8	,,		5·1	1·7
40–80, 60–140, 140–230, 230–400	12	,,		5·0	2·3
20–50, 40–80, 60–140, 140–230	16	,,		4·9	2·6
14–52, 52–100, 100–200, < 200	1		6–12	4·5–5·0	
,,	2		3–5	,,	
,,	4·5		1·5–2	,,	
,,	8		0·9–1·1	,,	
,,	12		0·6–0·9	,,	
,,	20		0·4–0·6	,,	
20–50	1	100		4·2	0·3
,,	5	120		4·3	1·2
,,	8	,,		4·4	1·9
,,	10	,,		4·3	2·1
,,	12	,,		4·0	2·1
,,	8	,,		5·0	1·9
	8	120		4·5	
	8	120		4·5	
	8	,,		4·5	
20–50, 50–100, 100–200, 200–400, minus 400	10	100		10·2	3·5
20–50, 50–100, 100–200, 200–400	5·5	100		6·0	2·8
20–50, 50–100, 100–200, 200–400	5·5	100		6·0	3·1
20–50, 50–100, 100–200, 200–400		40		2·9	1·2
50–100, 100–200, 200–400		75		Divalent ions held selectively	
14–52, 52–100, 100–200, < 200	2·5		0·8–1·0	9–10	
,,	4·5		0·6–0·8	9–10	
20–50	5	120		10·0	3·5
,,	,,	,,		,,	,,
	,,	,,		10·0	
20–50		,,		11·0	

B. *Anion-exchange resins*

Designation	*Type of polymer*	*Functional group*	*Basicity*	*Supplier*	*Particle size Dry mesh range*
Dowex 1–X1(AG1–X1)	Styrene	ϕ-CH_2N^+-$(CH_3)_3$	Strong	*a, b*	50–100
Dowex 1–X2(AG1–X2)	,,	,,	,,	,,	50–100, 100–200, 200–400
Dowex 1–X4(AG1–X4)	,,	,,	,,	,,	20–50, 50–100, 100–200, 200–400
Dowex 1–X8(AG1–X8)	,,	,,	,,	,,	20–50, 50–100, 100–200, 200–400, minus 400
Dowex 1–X10(AG1–X10)	,,	,,	,,	,,	50–100, 100–200, 200–400, minus 400
Dowex 21K(AG–21K)[2]	,,	,,	,,	,,	
Dowex 2–X4(AG2–X4)	,,	ϕ-CH_2N^+-$(CH_3)_2$-C_2H_4OH	,,	,,	20–50
Dowex 2–X8(AG2–X8)	,,	,,	,,	,,	20–50, 50–100, 100–200, 200–400
Dowex 2–X10(AG2–X10)	,,	,,	,,	,,	50–100, 100–200, 200–400
De-Acidite FF	,,	ϕ-CH_2N^+-$(CH_3)_3$	,,	*c*	
De-Acidite FF	,,	,,	,,	,,	
De-Acidite FF	,,	,,	,,	,,	
IRA–401 AR	,,	,,	,,	*d*	
IRA–402 C.P.	,,	,,	,,	,,	
IRA–400 C.P.	,,	ϕ-CH_2N^+-$(CH_3)_3$	,,	,,	
IRA–400 AR	,,	,,	,,	,,	
CG–400 AR	,,	ϕ-CH_2N^+-$(CH_3)_3$	,,	,,	100–200, 200–400
IRA–410 C.P.	,,	ϕ-CH_2N^+-$(CH_3)_2$-CH_2OH	,,	,,	
Dowex 3–X4(AG3–X4)	,,	Polyamine	Weak	*a, b*	20–50, 100–200, 200–400
IR–45 AR	,,	,,	,,	*d*	
De-Acidite G	,,	ϕ-CH_2N^+-$(C_2H_5)_2$	,,	*c*	
De-Acidite G	,,	,,	,,	,,	
De-Acidite G	,,	,,	,,	,,	
De-Acidite H	,,	Mixed base, tertiary amine & quaternary ammonium	Strong and weak	,,	
De-Acidite H	,,	,,	,,	,,	
De-Acidite H	,,	,,	,,	,,	
Bio-Rex 5	Alkyl-ene-amine	,,	,,	*d*	

See notes on p. 598.

Particle size *Wet mesh range*	*Cross-linkage (% divinylbenzene)*	*Maximum temperature (°C)*	*Water† regain*	*Exchange capacity dry (m. equiv./g)*	*wet (m.equiv./ml)*
20–60	1	50 (OH^- form) 150 (Cl^- form)		3·2	0·4
20–60, 60–140, 80–200	2	,,		3·5	0·8
20–50, 40–80, 60–140, 100–230	4	,,		3·5	1·2
20–50, 40–80, 80–140, 140–325, <230	8	,,		3·2	1·4
40–80, 60–140, 140–325, <230	10	,,		3·0	1·5
16–20, 20–50, 50–100		,,			1·3
20–50	4	30 (OH^- form) 150 (Cl^- form)		3·2	1·2
20–50, 40–80, 60–140, 140–325	8	,,		3·2	1·4
40–80, 60–140, 140-325	10	,,		3·0	1·5
14–52, 52–100, 100–200, < 200	2–3		1·5–2·0	4·0	
,,	3–5		1·0–1·5	4·0	
,,	7–9		0·6–1·0	4·0	
20–50	4	75		3·4	0·8
,,	6	,,		4·3	1·2
,	8	,,		3·3	1·2
,,	,,	,,		,,	,,
	8	,,		3·3	
20–50	8	,,		3·3	1·3
16–40, 60–140, 140–325	4	65		5·5	2·5
20–50		75		5·0	2·0
14–52, 52–100, 100–200, < 200	2–3		1·5–2·0	4·0	
,,	3–5		1·0–1·5	,,	
,,	7–9		0·6–1·0	,,	
	2–3		1·5–2·0	3·8	
,,	3–5		1·0–1·5	,,	
,,	7–9		0·6–1·0	,,	
20–50, 50–100, 100–200, 200–400				8·7 (salt splitting capacity 2·0)	

Notes to Table 1

[1] Chromatographic grade resins milled from AR beads.
[2] Because of its novel cross-linking, this resin has many of the properties of a lower cross-linked resin (X4) but its volume changes are comparable to an 8% cross-linked resin.

† *Water regain* defined as:
Cation resins: The weight of water associated with 1·0 g dry hydrogen resin, measured by drying the resin after centrifuging to remove interstitial water.
Anion resins: The weight of water associated with 1·0 g dry resin chloride, measured by drying the resin after centrifuging to remove interstitial water.

Suppliers. *a.* Dow Chemical Company, Midland, Mich., U.S.A. (Dowex series of resins).
b. Bio-Rad Laboratories, Richmond, California, U.S.A. (analytical grade resins, processed from Dowex resins, AG series of resins).
c. Permutit Company Ltd., Chiswick, London, England.
d. Mallinckrodt Chemical works, New York, U.S.A. (Amberlite resins manufactured by Rohm & Haas).

Mixed bed resins

These resins are a mixture of equivalent amounts of a strongly acidic resin in the H^+ form and a strongly basic resin in the OH^- form. Mixed bed resins are normally used for complete deionization of solutions and are supplied as 20–50 mesh beads. In some preparations, a dye has been incorporated into the anion exchanger to give a visual indication of exhaustion.

ION-EXCHANGE CRYSTALS[1]

These are inorganic microcrystalline aggregates with ion-exchange capacities and properties similar to those of ion-exchange resins. They show extremely high selectivities for alkali metals and alkaline earths. They will withstand temperatures up to 300° C and high levels of radiation without breakdown, but they are stable over limited pH ranges only. Their special applications are to alkali metal and alkaline earth separation.

Designation	*Type*	*Composition*	*Particle size*	*Stability range*	*Capacity m-equiv./g*	*Bed volume (ml/g)*
ZP–1	Cation exchanger	Zirconium phosphate	50–100, 100–200	Strong acid to pH 13	1·9	1·4
ZT–1	,,	Zirconium tungstate	50–100, 100–200	pH 1–pH 6	0·6	0·7
ZM–1	,,	Zirconium molybdate	50–100, 100–200	pH 1–pH 5	0·6	1·2
AMP–1	,,	Ammonium molybdo-phosphate	microcrystals	Strong acid to pH 6	1·2	..
HZO–1	Anion-exchanger in acidic media. Cation-exchanger in basic media	Hydrous zirconium oxide	50–100, 100–200	pH 1 to 5N-base	1·5[2]	1·2

[1] *Supplier*: Bio-Rad Laboratories, Richmond, California, U.S.A.
[2] Anion exchange capacity: $Cr_2O_7^{2-}$ uptake at pH 1.

22. Ion Exchangers and Gel Filtration Media

CELLULOSE ION-EXCHANGERS†

The ion-exchange celluloses are widely used for the separation and purification of substances of high molecular weight, including proteins, nucleic acids, and acidic polysaccharides. Acidic or basic groups are incorporated into cellulose by reacting it with appropriate chloro-compounds. The ion-exchange celluloses usually have maximum capacities in the range 0·2–0·9 m-equiv./g. The definition of particle size is somewhat arbitrary because of the rod-like shape of the cellulose particles.

Prolonged exposure to solutions more acid than pH 4 should be avoided, although brief contact with 1 N hydrochloric acid is not harmful.

Designation	*Chemical type*	*Manufacturer*	*Acidity*	*Remarks*
A. *Cation-exchangers*				
CM-Cellulose	Carboxymethyl ($-O\cdot CH_2\cdot CO_2H$)	*a, b, c, d, f*	Weak	Useful for the fractionation of neutral and basic proteins.
P-Cellulose	Phosphorylated ($-O\cdot PO_3H_2$)	*a, b, c, f*	Strong and weak	Dibasic; binds basic proteins strongly.
SE-Cellulose	Sulphoethyl	*a, b*	Strong	
Hydroxylapatit-cellulose	Calcium phosphate	*a*	. .	Hydroxylapatit in combination with cellulose gives faster flow rates than those obtained with hydroxylapatit alone.
B. *Anion-exchangers*			*Basicity*	
DEAE-Cellulose	Diethylamino-ethyl $-O\cdot C_2H_4N(C_2H_5)_2$	*a, b, c, d, e, f*	Moderately Strong	Widely used for the chromatography of acidic and neutral proteins
TEAE-Cellulose	Triethylamino-ethyl	*a, b*	Strong	Probably contains some strongly basic quaternary amine groups. Absence of carboxylic groups (masked as esters) may result in sharper separation.
AE-Cellulose	Aminoethyl $-O\cdot C_2H_4\cdot NH_2$	*a, c*	Weak	
ECTEOLA-Cellulose	Mixed amines	*a, b, c, d, f*	Inter-mediate	Used for the chromatography of nucleic acids.
PAB-Cellulose	Para-aminobenzoyl $-O\cdot CH_2\cdot C_6H_4NH_2$	*a, b*	Weak	Applicable to the chromatography of high molecular weight nucleic acids. Amino group can be diazotized and coupled with proteins to yield specific adsorbents.
GE-Cellulose	Guanidoethyl $-OC_2H_4\cdot NH\cdot C-(NH_2):NH_2^+Cl^-$	*a*	Strong	

a. Serva-Entwicklungslabor, Heidelberg, Germany
b. Bio-Rad Laboratories, Richmond, California, U.S.A.
c. Whatman (H. Reeve Angel & Co. Ltd., 9 Bridewell Place, London)
d. Brown Company, 550 Main Street, Berlin, New Hampshire, U.S.A.
e. Eastman Organic Chemicals, Rochester 3, New York, U.S.A.
f. Mann Research Laboratories, 136 Liberty St., New York 6, U.S.A.

† Cellulose ion-exchangers in the form of paper are available from Whatman. Preparations suitable for thin-layer chromatography are available from Serva and Bio-Rad.

SEPHADEX AND BIO-GEL ION-EXCHANGERS†

Designation	*Functional group*	*Particle size (mesh)*	*Maximum exchange capacity (m-equiv./g)*	*Haemoglobin capacity‡ (g/g)*	*Bed volume (ml/g dry gel)*
Cation-exchangers					
CM-Sephadex C-25	$—O—CH_2—COOH$	40	4·5±0·5	0·4 at pH 6·5	. .
CM-Sephadex C-50	"	"	"	7 "	15–20§
SE-Sephadex C-25	$—O—C_2H_4—SO_3H$	"	2·5±0·2	0·2 "	. .
SE-Sephadex C-50	"	"	"	3 "	15–20§
Bio-gel CM2	—COOH	100–200	6·0±0·3	trace at pH 7	5·6‖, 5·5††
Bio-gel CM30(1)	"	"	"	2·4 at pH 7	68‖, 35·5††
Bio-gel CM30(2)	"	"	1·0±0·3	1·6 "	50‖, 40††
Bio-gel CM100	"	"	6·0±0·3	4·0 "	124‖, 45††
Anion-exchangers					
DEAE-Sephadex A-25	$—O—C_2H_4—\overset{+}{N}H(C_2H_5)_2$	40–120	3·5±0·5	0·5 at pH 8·8	. .
DEAE-Sephadex A-50	"	"	"	3 "	15–20§
Bio-gel DE2	$—COO—C_2H_4—\overset{+}{N}H(C_2H_5)_2$	100–200	2·0±0·5	. .	. .
Bio-gel DM2	$—CONH—CH_2—\overset{+}{N}H(C_2H_5)_2$	"	4·5±0·5	trace at pH 7	7‡‡
Bio-gel DM30(1)	"	"	"	0·3 at pH 7	25–30‡‡
Bio-gel DM30(2)	"	"	1·5±0·3	0·1 "	20‡‡
Bio-gel DM100	"	"	4·5±0·5	0·4 "	50‡‡

† Sephadex ion-exchangers are derivatives of Sephadex G-25 and G-50. Owing to their porous structure and high degree of substitution, they have a high capacity even for large molecules. Bio-gel exchangers are derivatives of Bio-gel P polyacrylamide gels.

‡ For highest adsorption capacity C-25 and A-25 should be used for substances with a molecular weight up to about 10 000 and C-50 and A-50 for larger molecules (Sephadex range).

§ 0·2M-phosphate buffer, pH 7.

‖ 0·01M-phosphate buffer, pH 7.

†† 0·4M-phosphate buffer, pH 7.

‡‡ 0·01M-Tris-HCl buffer, pH 8·8.

GEL FILTRATION MEDIA

SEPHADEX AND BIO-GEL FILTRATION MEDIA

Sephadex, manufactured by Pharmacia, Uppsala, Sweden, is a cross-linked dextran. It is available in different degrees of cross-linking which determines the pore size and hence its accessibility to molecules of large size. Large molecules are prevented from entering the gels, but small molecules may diffuse relatively freely throughout the network structure in the gel beads. This is the principle of the method of gel filtration for separating molecules of different sizes. Sephadex gels are insoluble in water, salt solutions, bases, weak acids, and dilute solutions of strong acids, but are hydrolysed by strongly acid solutions.

The Bio-gel P range, manufactured by Biorad Laboratories, Richmond, California, are a series of porous polyacrylamide beads with closely controlled pore size. The beads are hydrophilic and swell readily in water or buffer solutions.

Type	*Approx. exclusion limit (M. wt.)*	*Fractionation range (M. wt.)*	*Water regain (g water/g dry gel)*	*Bed volume*† *(ml/g dry gel)*	*Particle size (microns)*	*Wet density/g*
‡Sephadex G–10	700	up to 700	1·0±0·1	2–3	40–120	..
‡Sephadex G–15	1500	up to 1500	1·5±0·2	2•5–3·5	40–120	..
‡Sephadex G–25	5000	100–5000	2·5±0·2	5		
Fine					20–80	1·12
Coarse					100–300	..
‡Sephadex G–50	10 000	500–10 000	5·0±0·3	10		
Fine					20–80	1·06
Coarse					100–300	..
‡Sephadex G–75	50 000	1000–50 000	7·5±0·5	12–15	40–120	1·03
‡Sephadex G–100	100 000	5000–100 000	10·0±1·0	15–20	40–120	..
‡Sephadex G–150	150 000	5000–150 000	15·0±1·5	20–30	40–120	..
‡Sephadex G–200	200 000	5000–200 000	20·0±2·0	30–40	40–120	..
§Sephadex LH–20		100–4000 in EtOH 100–2000 in $CHCl_3$	2·1 (H_2O) 1·8 ($CHCl_3$, EtOH)	4 (H_2O) 3–3·5 ($CHCl_3$, EtOH)	25–100	1·3
Bio-gel P–2	1600	200–2000	1·5	3·8	Range 50–100, 100–200, minus 400 available in all; 200–400 in P–2, P–4, P–6, P–10.	
Bio-gel P–4	3600	500–4000	2·4	5·8		
Bio-gel P–6	4600	1000–5000	3·7	8·8		
Bio-gel P–10	10 000	5000–17 000	4·5	12·4		
Bio-gel P–30	30 000	20 000–50 000	5·7	14·8		
Bio-gel P–60	60 000	30 000–70 000	7·2	19·0		
Bio-gel P–100	100 000	40 000–100 000	7·5	19·0		
Bio-gel P–150	150 000	50 000–150 000	9·2	24·0		
Bio-gel P–200	200 000	80 000–300 000	14·7	34·0		
Bio-gel P–300	300 000	100 000–400 000	18·0	40·0		

† Volume of 1 g dry material when in equilibrium with an excess of water.
‡ Data refer to the bead form of Sephadex and not the original crushed powders.
§ Produced by alkylation of Sephadex G–25 and can be used to fractionate substances dissolved in organic solvents.

AGAROSE GEL FILTRATION MEDIA

Agarose is the non-ionic component of agar. It is a linear polysaccharide with alternate residues of D-galactose and 3,6-anhydro-L-galactose units. Agarose gels are particularly suitable for separating very large molecules such as viruses and the higher molecular weight proteins. Sepharoses are stable only between pH 4–9 and 0–40° but are unaffected by exposure to M-NaCl and 2M-urea.

Designation†	*Particle size (swollen) microns*	*Exclusion limit (M. wt.)*	*Fractionation range (M. wt.)*	*Approx. agarose conc. (%)*
Bio-Gel A—0·5m	50–100, 100–200	$0{\cdot}5 \times 10^6$	$< 10\,000$–$0{\cdot}5 \times 10^6$	10
Bio-Gel A—1·5m	,,	$1{\cdot}5 \times 10^6$	$< 10\,000$–$1{\cdot}5 \times 10^6$	8
Bio-Gel A—5m	,,	5×10^6	$10\,000$– 5×10^6	6
Bio-Gel A—15m	,,	15×10^6	$40\,000$– 15×10^6	4
Bio-Gel A—50m	,,	50×10^6	$100\,000$– 50×10^6	2
Bio-Gel A—150m	,,	150×10^6	1×10^6–150×10^6	1
Sagavac 10	66–142	$2{\cdot}5 \times 10^5$	10^4–$2{\cdot}5 \times 10^5$	10
Sagavac 8	66–142	7×10^5	$2{\cdot}5 \times 10^4$– 7×10^5	8
Sagavac 6	66–142	2×10^6	5×10^4– 2×10^6	6
Sagavac 4	66–142	15×10^6	2×10^5– 15×10^6	4
Sagavac 2	66–142	150×10^6	5×10^5– 15×10^7	2
Sepharose 4B	40–190	..	$300\,000$– 3×10^6	4
Sepharose 2B	60–250	..	2×10^6– 25×10^6	2

† The Bio-Gel A series of agarose gels are manufactured by Bio-Rad Laboratories, California, U.S.A. Sepharose is produced by Pharmacia, Uppsala, Sweden, and Sagavac by Seravac Laboratories, Maidenhead, England.

POLYSTYRENE GEL FILTRATION MEDIA

Bio-Beads S, manufactured by Bio-Rad Laboratories, California, U.S.A., are a series of cross-linked, non-ionic, polystyrene polymers. They are suitable for the separation by gel filtration of low molecular weight, hydrophobic materials. The gels are swollen in organic solvents, and organic solvents are used as eluting solvents. Bio-Beads SM function in aqueous media.

Designation	*Particle size (mesh)*	*Approx. exclusion limit (M. wt.)*	*Medium*
Bio-Beads S–X1	200–400	3500	Non-aqueous
Bio-Beads S–X2	,,	2700	,,
Bio-Beads S–X3	,,	2100	,,
Bio-Beads S–X4	,,	1700	,,
Bio-Beads S–X8	,,	1000	,,
Bio-Beads SM–1	20–50	200 Å	Aqueous
Bio-Beads SM–2	,,	90 Å	,,

23. Isotopic Data

DEFINITIONS

Curie (*milli-*, *micro-*). The quantity of radon in radioactive equilibrium with 1 g of radium. Equivalent to the amount of an isotope undergoing $3{\cdot}7 \times 10^{10}$ nuclear disintegrations per second ($2{\cdot}22 \times 10^{12}$ per minute).

Atom per cent excess. The concentration of an isotope in a sample of the element expressed as the difference between the per cent of the atoms existing as the isotope in the sample and the per cent of the atoms existing as the isotope in the element found in its natural state.

Specific activity. The radioactivity of an element per unit mass of the element.

Carrier-free isotope. Theoretically the isotope under consideration free from all other isotopes of the same element.

Electron volt (eV, *or* MeV $= 10^6$ eV). The energy acquired by an electron when accelerating across a potential gradient of 1 volt $= 1{\cdot}6 \times 10^{-12}$ ergs.

Half-value thickness. The depth of material which reduces the intensity of a radiation beam by one-half.

Röntgen (r). That quantity of X or gamma radiation such that the associated corpuscular emission per 0·001293 g of air produces, in air, ions carrying 1 electrostatic unit of quantity of electricity of either sign (1 ml air at 0°, dry, 760 mm Hg). 1 r corresponds to the absorption of $5{\cdot}24 \times 10^{13}$ eV of energy or 83·8 ergs per g of air.

Röntgen-equivalent physical. The dose of radiation which produces, when absorbed in tissue, the same amount of energy dissipation per g of tissue as the absorption of 1 r in 1 g of dry air, i.e. 83·8 ergs per g of tissue.

Relative biological effectiveness (RBE) of a particular radiation dose is the ratio of the body damage it causes to that produced by the same dose of X-rays with an average specific ionization of 100 ion pairs/micron of water.

The *rad* is a unit of absorbed dose. 1 rad is an absorbed dose of 100 ergs/g of tissue.

The *rad equivalent man* (rem) is defined as (dose in rem) = (dose in rad) × (RBE).

Electron charge, $e = 1{\cdot}6 \times 10^{-19}$ coulombs.

Beta-ray absorption half thickness $= \dfrac{\text{max. range}}{7}$ approx.

FORMULAE, ETC.

Dead time correction

$$N = \frac{N_0}{1 - N_0 t}, \qquad \text{or} \qquad N - N_0 = N_0\{N_0 t + (N_0 t)^2 + (N_0 t)^3 + \ldots\},$$

where N = true counting rate,
N_0 = observed counting rate,
t = dead time of the counter (period during which the counter is insensitive to incoming pulses).

(This correction is subject to an error of the order $\frac{1}{2}N_0(N_0 t)^2$.)

Statistical formulae

Standard deviation (%) of a count $= \pm\sqrt{(10^4/N_t)}$, where N_t = total number of counts recorded. For example, if 10^4 counts are recorded, the probability of the error being less than ±1% is 2 to 1, and less than ±2% 19 to 1.

Standard deviation (SD) of the difference between two counts

$$= \pm\sqrt{\{(SD_1)^2 + (SD_2)^2\}}.$$

Therefore the accuracy of background counting will only be of importance when the counting rate of the sample is low.
The difference between two counting rates (N_1, N_2) is obtained with maximum accuracy by counting for times t_1 and t_2 such that

$$\frac{t_1}{t_2} = \sqrt{\left(\frac{N_1}{N_2}\right)}.$$

Autoradiography

The response of an emulsion to a series of exposures to X-rays or electrons is given by $a = A(1-e^{-\epsilon r})$, where

a = number of developed grains,
A = total number of grains per unit area,
r = exposure in röntgens or number of electrons,
ϵ = factor of proportionality depending on the emulsion.

As a rough guide a satisfactory autoradiograph may be obtained with 10^7 β-particles/cm² or 2×10^6 α-particles/cm².

Radioactive decay correction

$$\log_{10}\frac{N_0}{N_t} = 0{\cdot}3010(t/h).$$

$$\text{Percentage isotope remaining} = \frac{100}{\text{antilog}\{0{\cdot}3010(t/h)\}},$$

where t = time of decay,
h = half-life or time taken for radioactivity to decay to 50% of original activity,
N_0 = radioactivity at zero time,
N_t = radioactivity at time t.

^{24}Na (*half-life* 14·8 *hr*)		^{32}P (*half-life* 14·3 *days*)		^{35}S (*half-life* 87·1 *days*)		^{42}K (*half-life* 12·4 *hr*)		^{131}I (*half-life* 8·1 *days*)	
Time (hr)	*% activity remaining*	*Time (days)*	*% activity remaining*	*Time (days)*	*% activity remaining*	*Time (hr)*	*% activity remaining*	*Time (days)*	*% activity remaining*
1	95·4	1	95·3	2	98·4	1	94·6	0·2	98·3
2	91·1	2	90·8	5	96·1	2	89·5	0·4	96·6
3	86·9	3	86·5	10	92·3	3	84·5	0·6	95·0
4	82·9	4	82·4	15	88·7	4	80·0	1·0	91·8
5	79·1	5	78·5	20	85·3	5	75·6	1·6	87·2
6	75·5	6	74·8	25	82·0	6	71·5	2·3	81·2
7	72·1	7	71·2	31	78·1	7	67·6	3·1	76·7
8	68·7	8	67·8	37	74·5	8	63·9	4·0	71·0
9	65·6	9	64·7	43	71·0	9	60·5	5·0	65·2
10	62·6	10	61·5	50	67·0	10	57·2	6·1	59·3
11	59·7	11	58·7	57	63·6	11	53·9	7·3	53·4
12	57·0	12	55·9	65	59·6	12	51·2	8·1	50·0
13	54·4	13	53·2	73	56·0	12·4	50·0		
14	51·9	14	50·7	81	52·5				
14·8	50·0	14·3	50·0	87·1	50·0				

Some Radioactive Isotopes used in Biochemical Investigations

Element (mass no.)	Radiation	Half-life	Energy of radiation (MeV) particles	γ-rays
^{3}H	β^-	12·1 yr	0·0185	. .
^{11}C	β^+	20·5 min	0·95	. .
^{14}C	β^-	5100 yr	0·156	. .
^{22}Na	β^+, γ	2·6 yr	0·58	1·3
^{24}Na	β^-, γ	14·8 hr	1·39	1·38, 2·76
^{28}Mg	β^-	21·4 hr	0·459	. .
^{31}Si	β^-	170 min	1·8	. .
^{32}P	β^-	14·3 days	1·71	. .
^{35}S	β^-	87·1 days	0·169	. .
^{36}Cl	β^+, κ, β^-	2×10^6 yr (β^-)	0·64	. .
^{38}Cl	β^-, γ	38·5 min	1·19 (36%) 2·70 (11%) 5·20 (53%)	1·60 (43%) 2·12 (57%)
^{42}K	β^-, γ	12·4 hr	2·04 (25%) 3·58 (75%)	1·4, 2·1
^{45}Ca	β^-	152 days	0·260	. .
^{51}Cr	κ, γ	28 days	. .	0·323, 0·237
^{52}Mn	β^+ (35%) κ (65%)	5·8 days	0·58	1·0, 0·73 0·94, 1·46
^{54}Mn	κ, γ	310 days	. .	0·835
^{55}Fe	κ only	2·94 yr	. .	. .
^{59}Fe	β^-, γ	46·3 days	0·46 (50%) 0·26 (50%)	1·3 (50%) 1·1 (50%)
^{57}Co	γ	270 days	. .	0·136 (10%) 0·122 (88%)
^{58}Co	β^+ (14·5%), γ	72 days	0·472	0·805
^{60}Co	β^-, γ	5·3 yr	0·31	1·16, 1·32
^{64}Cu	κ (54%) β^- (31%) β^+ (15%) $\gamma+\kappa$ (1·5%)	12·8 hr	0·57 (β^-) 0·66 (β^+)	1·35 (2·5%)
^{65}Zn	β^+ (1·3%) κ (98·7%)	250 days	0·32	1·14 (46% of κ)
^{76}As	β^-, γ	26·8 hr	3·04 (60%) 2·49 (25%) 1·29 (15%)	1·705 1·20 0·55
^{75}Se	κ, γ	125 days	. .	0·076–0·405
^{82}Br	β^-, γ	34 hr	0·465	0·547, 0·787 1·35
^{86}Rb	β^-, γ	19·5 days	1·822 (80%) 0·716 (20%)	1·081
^{89}Sr	β^-	53 days	1·46	. .
^{90}Sr	β^-	25 yr	0·61	. .
^{99}Mo	β^-, γ	68 hr	1·3	0·75, 0·24
^{125}Sb	β^-, γ	2·7 yr	0·3 (65%) 0·7 (35%)	0·55
^{125}I	γ	60 days	. .	0·035
^{131}I	β^-, γ	8·1 days	0·605 (86%) 0·25 (14%)	0·637, 0·363 0·282, 0·08

Attenuation of β-rays

The attenuation of β particles depends on the density of the shielding material and is largely independent of its atomic weight.

		Thickness of material in mm required to reduce intensity by one-half		
Energy β particles (MeV)	*Weight material/cm² to reduce intensity by one-half (mg)*	*Water*	*Glass* ($d = 2{\cdot}5$)	*Lead*
0·1	1·3	0·013	0·005	0·0011
1·0	48	0·48	0·192	0·042
2·0	130	1·3	0·52	0·115
5·0	300	3·0	1·2	0·265

Attenuation of γ-rays

Energy of γ-rays (MeV)	*Thickness of material in inches required to attenuate broad beam of γ-rays by a factor of* 10			
	Water	*Aluminium*	*Iron*	*Lead*
0·5	21·5	8·0	2·4	0·7
1·0	24	10·0	3·2	1·5
2·0	30	12·5	4·3	2·3
3·0	35	14·5	4·7	2·5
4·0	38	15·5	5·0	2·45
5·0	42	17·2	5·1	2·40

24. Manometry

1. REFERENCES

For detailed discussion of methods of employing manometers in biochemical investigations see:

M. Dixon, *Manometric Methods*, 3rd ed., Cambridge University Press (1951);
W. W. Umbreit, R. H. Burris, and J. F. Stauffer, *Manometric Techniques*, 4th ed., Burgess (1964).

2. EQUATION FOR WARBURG MANOMETER CONSTANTS

$$k = \frac{V_g(273/T) + V_f \alpha}{P_0}$$

V_g = volume of gas space in μl;
T = temperature in °K (absolute);
V_f = volume of liquid in manometer vessel in μl;
α = absorption coefficient of gas to be measured in liquid in manometer vessel;
P_0 = standard pressure in mm of fluid in the manometer (760 mm for mercury or 10 000 mm for Krebs's or Brodie's fluids).

Values of k for O_2 and CO_2 can be read directly from the nomograms given on pages 612 and 613. Values for H_2 and N_2 differ insignificantly from those for O_2.

3. ABSORPTION COEFFICIENTS OF GASES

The Bunsen coefficient (α) is employed. It is defined as the volume of gas in ml reduced to 0° and 760 mm pressure dissolved in 1 ml of water (or other fluid) when the gas pressure is 760 mmHg.

(*a*) IN WATER

Temp. (°C)	O_2	H_2	N_2	CO_2
0	0·049	0·021	0·024	1·713
5	0·043	0·020	0·021	1·424
10	0·038	0·020	0·019	1·194
15	0·034	0·019	0·017	1·019
20	0·031	0·018	0·015	0·878
25	0·028	0·018	0·014	0·759
30	0·026	0·017	0·013	0·665
35	0·024	0·017	0·013	0·592
37	0·024	0·017	0·012	0·567
38	0·023	0·017	0·012	0·550
40	0·023	0·016	0·012	0·530
45	0·022	0·016	0·011	0·479
50	0·021	0·016	0·011	0·436

(*b*) IN SALT SOLUTIONS, ETC.

(1) Values of α for O_2, N_2, and H_2 in dilute salt solutions, e.g. Ringer's solution, are substantially the same as those for water given above. In more concentrated solutions the value of α falls, e.g. α_{O_2} at 25°: in 2N-H_2SO_4, 0·023; in 2M-NaCl, 0·015. Even these changes in α alter the values of k by amounts which are insignificant except for work of the very highest accuracy.

(2) Carbon dioxide. Van Slyke *et al.*—*J.B.C.* **78**, 765 (1928)—give values for α_{CO_2} at

38° in various salt solutions, including the following (compared with α_{CO_2} at 38° in water = 0·546):

Conc.	NaCl	KCl	Na lactate	KH_2PO_4	NaH_2PO_4
0·15M	0·529	0·532	0·522	0·516	0·510
0·30M	0·511	0·520	0·500	0·490	0·480

α_{CO_2} at 38° in Ringer's soln., 0·537; in serum, 0·510.

The effects of individual ions are additive, at least in solutions below 0·5M, and Van Slyke *et al.* give the following figures for the **decrease** in α_{CO_2} at 38° per unit molar concentration of the ion present in the solution:

H^+	Na^+	K^+	Cl^-	$H_2PO_4^-$	$Lactate^-$	$HC_2O_4^-$
0·0	0·085	0·053	0·029	0·137	0·066	0·026

α_{CO_2} in H_2SO_4 at **25°**: 0·5N-H_2SO_4, 0·727; 1N-H_2SO_4, 0·705; 2N-H_2SO_4, 0·669.

Further figures for α_{CO_2} in solutions of salts, acids, and non-electrolytes, mainly at 25° and 40°, are given in: *J.B.C.* **78,** 765 (1928); *International Critical Tables*, vol. 3, p. 279 (1928); *J.A.C.S.* **63,** 449, 1165 (1941); *J.A.C.S.* **65,** 2030 (1943).

4. CALIBRATION OF MANOMETERS

The most accurate method of calibrating manometers and vessels is by filling them with mercury and then weighing the mercury. Convenient methods of doing this have been described by:

O. Schales, *Arch. B.* **3,** 475 (1944), modified in *Science* **109,** 491 (1949) and *Science* **110,** 403 (1949);
S. Grisolia in *Manometric Techniques*, 4th ed., p. 47;
A. Lazarow, *J. Lab. clin. Med.* **34,** 1702 (1949), **38,** 767 (1951).

Less accurate methods which are satisfactory for most purposes are:

1. filling with water by the techniques above;
2. evolution of CO_2 from bicarbonate solution by the addition of sulphuric acid. The bicarbonate solution should be standardized using a manometer and vessel of which the volume is accurately known by other methods;
3. evolution of N_2 upon mixing standard potassium ferricyanide solution with saturated hydrazine sulphate solution under alkaline conditions—see *Manometric Techniques*, 4th ed., p. 49.

Density of mercury and water

Temp. (°C)	*Density of mercury* (*g per ml*)	*Density of water* (*g per ml*)
0	13·596	0·99987
5	13·583	0·99999
10	13·571	0·99973
12	13·566	0·99952
14	13·561	0·99927
16	13·556	0·99897
18	13·551	0·99862
20	13·546	0·99823
22	13·541	0·99780
24	13·536	0·99732
26	13·532	0·99681
28	13·527	0·99626
30	13·522	0·99567
35	13·510	0·99406
40	13·497	0·99224

5. MANOMETER FLUIDS

(*a*) Krebs, *B.J.* **48,** 240 (1951)

Density 1·033 at 20°, P_0 = 10 000

NaBr (anhyd.)	44 g
'Stergene'	1·0 ml
Evans blue	0·3 g

Dissolve in water and dilute to 1 l. If necessary, filter through sintered glass, not paper.

Notes. The NaBr is dried at 110° before use. 'Stergene' may be replaced by 'Lissapol-N', 'Triton X-100', 'Triton-A20', or other detergents which do not form stable foams. Only 0·3 g of the 'Triton' detergents should be used since these are almost water-free, while 'Stergene' and 'Lissapol-N' are obtained commercially as 30% solutions in water.

This manometer fluid is preferable to the original Brodie's fluid.

(*b*) BRODIE'S FLUID

Density 1·033 at 20°, P_0 = 10 000

NaCl	46 g
Sodium choleate	10 g
Evans blue	0·3 g

Dissolve in water and dilute to 1 l.

(*c*) CLERICI SOLUTION

Density about 4, P_0 = about 2500

Thallium formate	7 g
Thallium malonate	7 g
Water	1 ml

6. NOMOGRAMS FOR WARBURG MANOMETER CONSTANTS

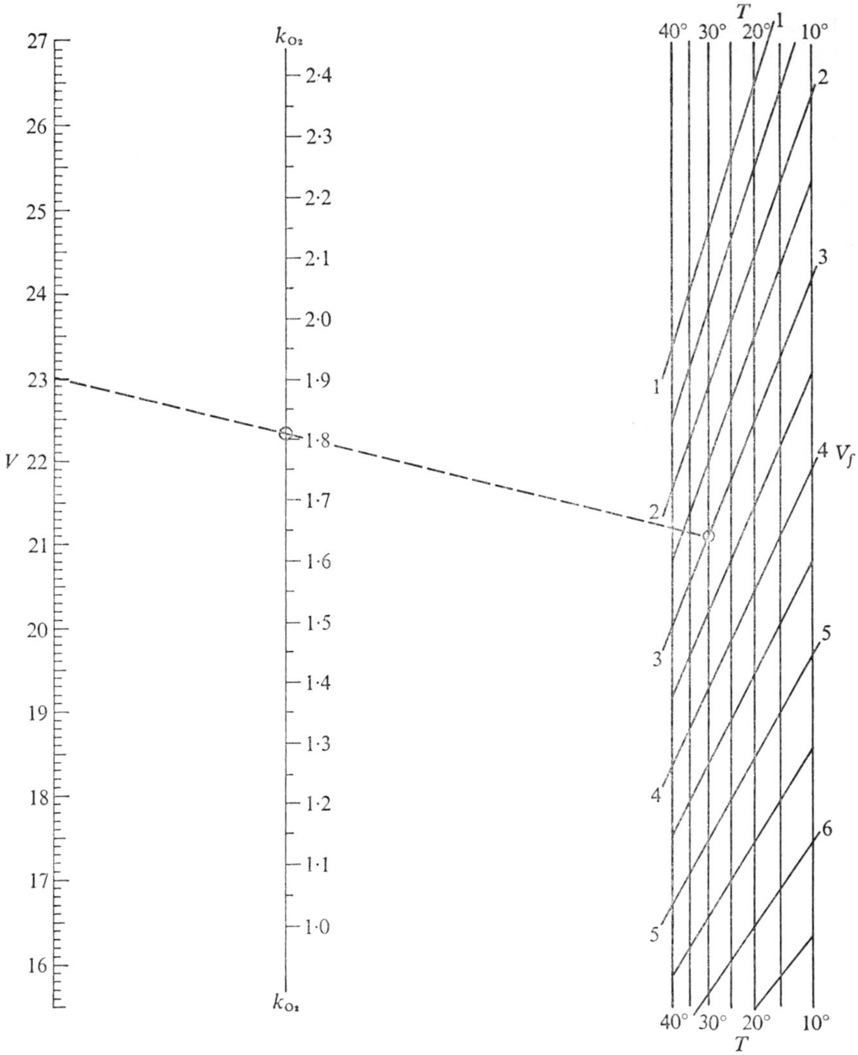

FIG. 1. k_{O_2} for Warburg manometers. Stretch a fine black thread across the nomogram so as to connect the given value of V with the point of intersection of the lines for V_f and T, and read off k_{O_2}. Intermediate values can readily be estimated visually. The example indicated shows that a manometer with a 23 ml vessel containing 3 ml of liquid has a k_{O_2} of 1·81 at 30°.

(From M. Dixon, *B.J.* **48**, 575 (1951). Reproduced by kind permission of Professor M. Dixon, F.R.S., and the Biochemical Society.)

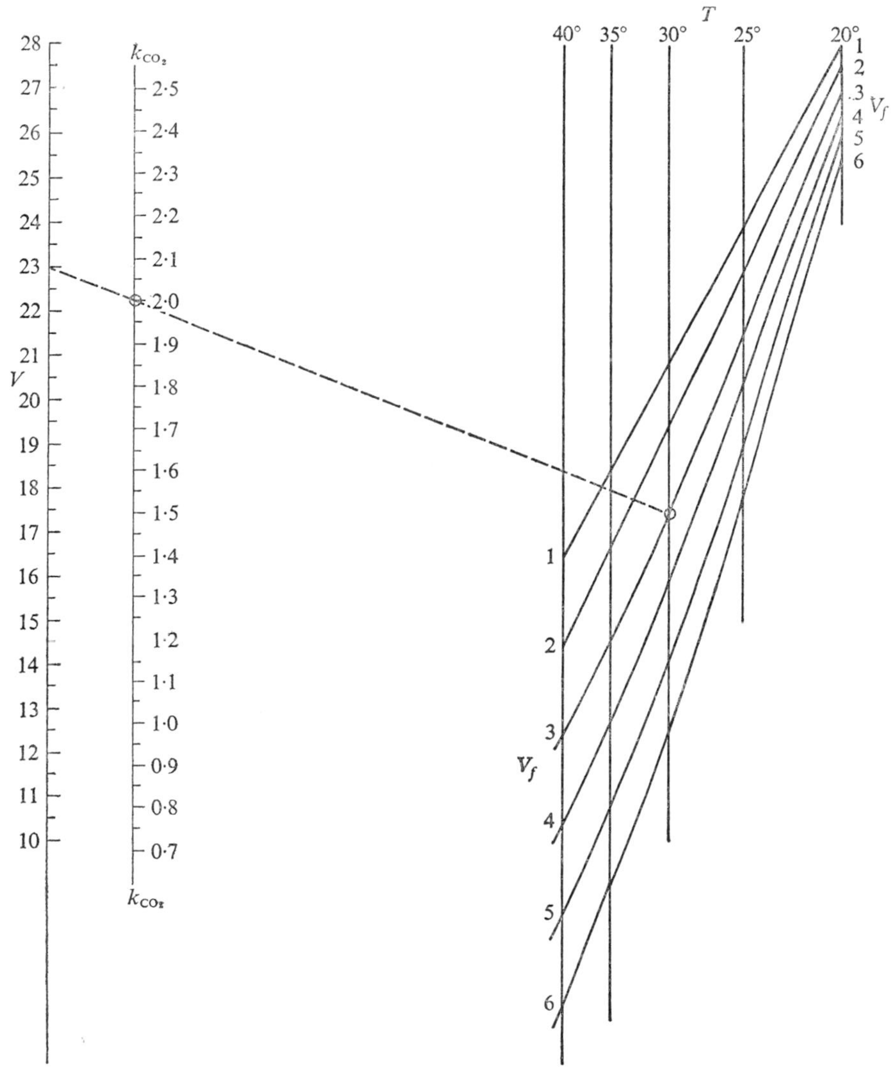

FIG. 2. k_{CO_2} for Warburg manometers. To be used in the same way as previous figure.

(From M. Dixon, *B.J.* 48, 575 (1951). Reproduced by kind permission of Professor M. Dixon, F.R.S., and the Biochemical Society.)

25. Preparation and Composition of Biochemical Reagents

1. REAGENTS USED IN PROTEIN FRACTIONATION

(*a*) AMMONIUM SULPHATE

Nomogram for ammonium sulphate additions

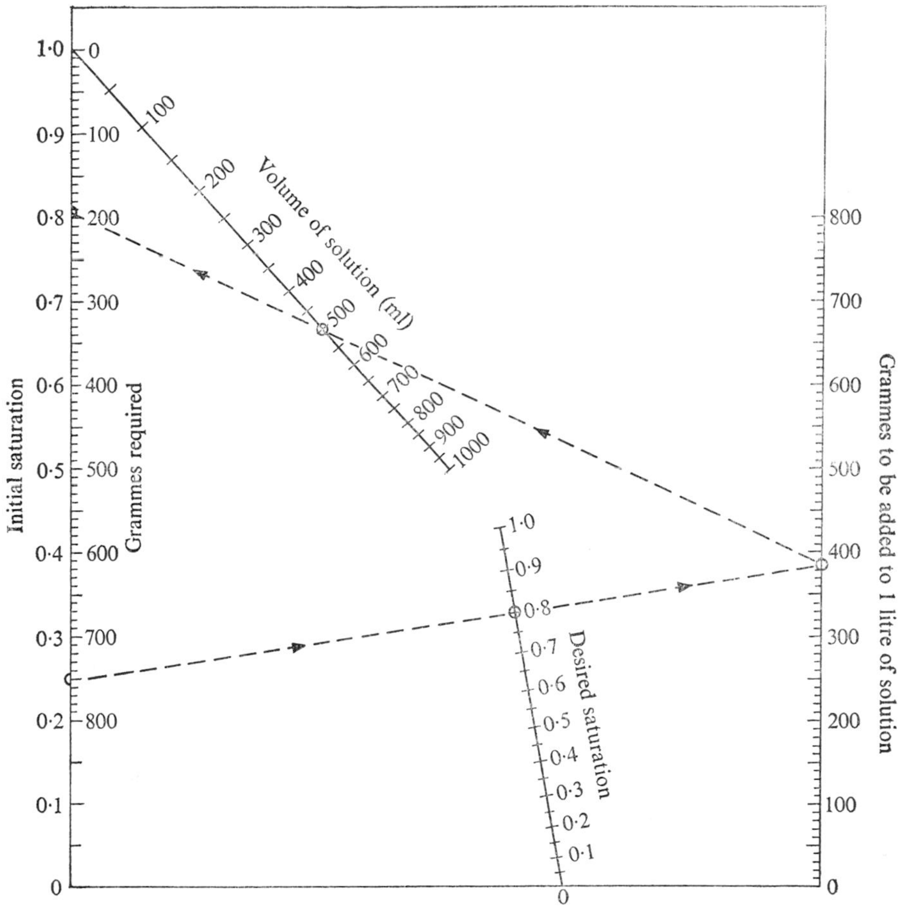

A straight line through the initial saturation and the desired saturation gives the amount of solid $(NH_4)_2SO_4$ to be added to 1 l of the solution. A line from this point passing through the volume of the solution gives the amount required. **All saturations are relative to full saturation at room temperature** (760 g to 1 l of water).

From M. Dixon, *B.J.* **54**, 457 (1953). Reproduced by kind permission of Professor M. Dixon, F.R.S., and the Biochemical Society.)

Chart for ammonium sulphate additions

The chart shows the amount of solid $(NH_4)_2SO_4$ required to bring a solution of known initial saturation to a desired final saturation. In this case, **the saturation is relative to full saturation at 0°.** A similar chart based upon saturation at 25° is given in *Meth. Enzymol.* **1,** 76 (1955).

	Final concentration of ammonium sulphate—% saturation at 0 °C																
Initial concentration of ammonium sulphate, % saturation	20	25	30	35	40	45	50	55	60	65	70	75	80	85	90	95	100
	g solid ammonium sulphate to add to 100 ml of solution																
0	10·6	13·4	16·4	19·4	22·6	25·8	29·1	32·6	36·1	39·8	43·6	47·6	51·6	55·9	60·3	65·0	69·7
5	7·9	10·8	13·7	16·6	19·7	22·9	26·2	29·6	33·1	36·8	40·5	44·4	48·4	52·6	57·0	61·5	66·2
10	5·3	8·1	10·9	13·9	16·9	20·0	23·3	26·6	30·1	33·7	37·4	41·2	45·2	49·3	53·6	58·1	62·7
15	2·6	5·4	8·2	11·1	14·1	17·2	20·4	23·7	27·1	30·6	34·3	38·1	42·0	46·0	50·3	54·7	59·2
20	0	2·7	5·5	8·3	11·3	14·3	17·5	20·7	24·1	27·6	31·2	34·9	38·7	42·7	46·9	51·2	55·7
25		0	2·7	5·6	8·4	11·5	14·6	17·9	21·1	24·5	28·0	31·7	35·5	39·5	43·6	47·8	52·2
30			0	2·8	5·6	8·6	11·7	14·8	18·1	21·4	24·9	28·5	32·3	36·2	40·2	44·5	48·8
35				0	2·8	5·7	8·7	11·8	15·1	18·4	21·8	25·4	29·1	32·9	36·9	41·0	45·3
40					0	2·9	5·8	8·9	12·0	15·3	18·7	22·2	25·8	29·6	33·5	37·6	41·8
45						0	2·9	5·9	9·0	12·3	15·6	19·0	22·6	26·3	30·2	34·2	38·3
50							0	3·0	6·0	9·2	12·5	15·9	19·4	23·0	26·8	30·8	34·8
55								0	3·0	6·1	9·3	12·7	16·1	19·7	23·5	27·3	31·3
60									0	3·1	6·2	9·5	12·9	16·4	20·1	23·9	27·9
65										0	3·1	6·3	9·7	13·2	16·8	20·5	24·4
70											0	3·2	6·5	9·9	13·4	17·1	20·9
75												0	3·2	6·6	10·1	13·7	17·4
80													0	3·3	6·7	10·3	13·9
85														0	3·4	6·8	10·5
90															0	3·4	7·0
95																0	3·5
100																	0

Formulae for ammonium sulphate additions

For the addition of saturated $(NH_4)_2SO_4$ solutions, the volume changes on mixing are negligible. The volume (V) of saturated $(NH_4)_2SO_4$ (in ml) which has to be added to 100 ml of solution of initial saturation S_1 to produce a final saturation S_2 is given by the equation

$$V = \frac{100\,(S_2 - S_1)}{1 - S_2}.$$

S_1 and S_2 are expressed as fractions of the saturated solution, e.g. $S_1 = 0{\cdot}5$ and $S_2 = 0{\cdot}7$.

Other formulae for calculating the required quantities of solid $(NH_4)_2SO_4$ or of a saturated solution are given in *J.B.C.* **208,** 149 (1954), *J. gen. Physiol.* **35,** 423 (1952), and *The Proteins*, eds. Neurath and Bailey, 1st ed., vol. 1, part A, p. 55, Academic Press (1953). A chart based upon the formulae in the first reference and expressing $(NH_4)_2SO_4$ concentration as a molarity is given in *Manometric Techniques*, eds. Umbreit *et al.*, 4th ed., p. 158, Burgess (1964).

Saturated ammonium sulphate solutions at various temperatures

Temperature (° C)	0	10	20	25	30
Moles $(NH_4)_2SO_4$ per 1000 g H_2O	5·35	5·53	5·73	5·82	5·91
Percentage by weight	41·42	42·22	43·09	43·47	43·85
g $(NH_4)_2SO_4$ required to saturate 1000 ml H_2O	706·8	730·5	755·8	766·8	777·5
g $(NH_4)_2SO_4$ per 1 of saturated solution	514·8	525·2	536·5	541·2	545·9
Molarity of saturated solution	3·90	3·97	4·06	4·10	4·13

(*b*) PREPARATION OF ALUMINA Cγ GEL

Willstätter and Kraut, *Ber.* **56,** 1117 (1923); see also *Meth. Enzymol.* **1,** 97 (1955); **2,** 823 (1957); **6,** 169 (1963).

Dissolve 300 g $(NH_4)_2SO_4$ in 6·5 l of water, heat to 60°, and add 420 ml of 20% (w/w) NH_3 (this contains 77·5 g NH_3 which provides a small excess necessary to keep the fluid slightly alkaline during the addition of $Al_2(SO_4)_3$). Maintaining the temperature at not less than 60° and stirring vigorously, rapidly pour a hot solution of 500 g $Al_2(SO_4)_3 \cdot 18H_2O$ in 1 l of water into the $(NH_4)_2SO_4$–NH_3 solution. Continue stirring for 15 min after the addition is complete, still keeping the temperature at not less than 60°. When the initial voluminous precipitate becomes flocculent dilute to 40 l with water. Allow the precipitate to settle and decant (or siphon off) the supernatant. Repeat the washing of the gel and on the fourth wash add 80 ml 20% NH_3 to the water to precipitate any residual $Al_2(SO_4)_3$. Between the 12th and 20th washes the wash water will remain turbid. After this point is reached wash twice more; these washings generally require a period of 2 days.

The gel should be free from sulphate when tested with HCl and $BaCl_2$. It is usual to allow the gel to stand for 3 months before use in order to convert the Cα form into the Cγ form.

(*c*) PREPARATION OF CALCIUM PHOSPHATE GEL

Keilin and Hartree, *Proc. R. Soc.* **B124,** 397 (1938).

Dilute 150 ml calcium chloride solution (132 g $CaCl_2 \cdot 6H_2O$ per l) to 1600 ml with tap water and add 150 ml trisodium phosphate solution (152 g $Na_3PO_4 \cdot 12H_2O$ per l) with vigorous stirring. Adjust the mixture to pH 7·4 with dilute acetic acid and wash the precipitate three or four times by decantation with 15–20 l of water. Finally wash the precipitate with distilled water in a centrifuge. Suspend the gel in a small volume of distilled water and preferably keep for at least a month before use. Store at 5° in the dark.

(*d*) PREPARATION OF HYDROXYLAPATITE

Levin, *Meth. Enzymol.* **5,** 28 (1962). Preparations on a larger scale are described in *Arch. B.B.* **65,** 132 (1956) and *Biochem. Preps.* **9,** 83 (1962).

Two litres of 0·5M-$CaCl_2$ and 2 l of 0·5M-Na_2HPO_4 are allowed to run at equal rates (12–15 ml per min) into a 5-l beaker and the mixture stirred constantly. The resulting precipitate is allowed to settle and the supernatant sucked off with a water pump. The precipitate is washed four times with 3-l quantities of water, complete settling being allowed each time. The final suspension is diluted to 3 l with distilled water and 100 ml of freshly prepared 40% (w/v) NaOH solution added with stirring. Bring the mixture to the boil over about 45 min and boil gently for 1 hr, stirring slowly throughout. Allow to settle for 5 min and suck off the very turbid supernatant. The precipitate is then washed four times with 3-l quantities of water as before, allowing 5 min settling each time. Add 4 l of 0·01M-sodium phosphate buffer, pH 6·8, to the precipitate and heat the suspension just to boiling with stirring. Allow to settle for 5 min and then suck off supernatant. Repeat this procedure twice with 0·01M- and twice with 0·001M-sodium phosphate buffer, pH 6·8, but allowing 15 min boiling each time. Make up the final suspension in 0·001M-buffer. It is stable for at least a year. Slow stirring and gentle boiling are essential to give a product which is sufficiently coarse-grained to allow reasonable rates of flow through columns.

2. QUALITATIVE AND QUANTITATIVE REAGENTS

ALKALINE PYROGALLOL FOR OXYGEN ABSORPTION

Dissolve 320 g KOH in 260 ml water. After cooling, dissolve 10 g pyrogallol in 200 ml of the KOH solution. This solution evolves small quantities of carbon monoxide, and will absorb carbon dioxide in addition to oxygen.

AMMONIACAL SILVER NITRATE

Dissolve 2·6 g silver nitrate in 50 ml water and add ammonium hydroxide until the brown precipitate initially formed just redissolves. Excess ammonia should be avoided. Dilute to 100 ml. The solution should **NOT** be stored since an explosive precipitate may be formed, especially in sunlight.

BARFOED'S REAGENT

Dissolve 66 g copper acetate and 10 ml glacial acetic acid in water, and dilute to 1 l.

Alternatively, dissolve 24 g copper acetate in 450 ml of boiling water. Add 25 ml of 8·5% lactic acid solution. Cool, dilute to 500 ml, and if necessary, filter.

Gives a precipitate of cuprous oxide on boiling with reducing monosaccharides, but not with reducing disaccharides.

BENEDICT'S QUALITATIVE REAGENT

Dissolve 173 g sodium citrate and 100 g anhyd. Na_2CO_3 in water and make up to 850 ml. Add to this, with rapid stirring, a solution prepared by dissolving 17·4 g $CuSO_4 \cdot 5H_2O$ in 100 ml water. Dilute the reagent to 1 l. Can be stored indefinitely.

Gives a red or yellow precipitate of cuprous oxide on boiling with reducing sugars. Not reduced by uric acid.

BIAL'S REAGENT

Dissolve 0·15 g $FeCl_3$ (anhyd.) in 430 ml conc. HCl and 70 ml water. Dissolve 1 g orcinol in the solution.

Gives a green colour on boiling with solutions containing pentoses. Glucuronides give the reaction on prolonged boiling.

BIURET REAGENT

Quantitative reagent of Gornall *et al.*, *J.B.C.* **177**, 751 (1949).

Dissolve 1·5 g $CuSO_4 \cdot 5H_2O$ and 6 g sodium potassium tartrate (Rochelle salt, $NaKC_4H_4O_6 \cdot 4H_2O$) in 500 ml water. Add, mixing thoroughly, 300 ml of 10% (w/v) sodium hydroxide solution (carbonate free). Potassium iodide (1 g) may also be added if the reagent prepared without it deposits a precipitate of cuprous oxide. Make up to 1 l with water and store in a waxed or plastic bottle.

To estimate protein, mix 4 ml of reagent with 1 ml of protein solution containing 1–10 mg protein and allow the mixture to stand at room temperature for 30 min. Read the optical density at 540 to 560 mμ. Ammonium salts interfere with the estimation.

As a qualitative test a violet or pink coloration is obtained with proteins or polypeptides.

2,4-DINITROPHENYLHYDRAZINE REAGENT

Dissolve 100 mg 2,4-dinitrophenylhydrazine in 100 ml 2N-HCl. Solution takes some time and requires gentle warming. Filter.

Forms 2,4-dinitrophenylhydrazones with aldehydes and ketones (incl. keto-acids).

FEHLING'S SOLUTION

Solution A: 34·65 g $CuSO_4 \cdot 5H_2O$ dissolved in water and diluted to 500 ml.

Solution B: 173 g sodium potassium tartrate (Rochelle salt, $NaKC_4H_4O_6 \cdot 4H_2O$) and 125 g KOH dissolved in water and diluted to 500 ml.

Mix equal volumes of solutions A and B immediately before use.

Gives a red, brown, or yellow precipitate of cuprous oxide on boiling with reducing sugars. Also reduced by uric acid and creatinine.

FOLIN–CIOCALTEU PHENOL REAGENT

Dissolve 100 g sodium tungstate ($Na_2WO_4 \cdot 2H_2O$) and 25 g sodium molybdate ($Na_2MoO_4 \cdot 2H_2O$) in 700 ml water. Add 100 ml conc. HCl and 50 ml 85% phosphoric acid, and reflux the mixture for 10 hr in an all-glass apparatus. Add 150 g of lithium sulphate, 50 ml water, and a few drops of Br_2. Boil for 15 min to remove excess bromine, cool, dilute to 1 l, and then filter. The reagent should be golden-yellow in colour and should be stored in the refrigerator. If the reagent acquires a greenish tint it is unsatisfactory for use, but may be regenerated by boiling with a few drops of Br_2. Care must be taken to boil away all the excess bromine.

Dilute this concentrated reagent with 2 vol. water before use.

Estimation of protein with Folin–Ciocalteu reagent by the method of Lowry *et al.*, *J.B.C.* **193,** 265 (1951).

Solution A: 2% Na_2CO_3 in 0·1N-NaOH.

Solution B: 0·5% $CuSO_4 \cdot 5H_2O$ in 1% sodium or potassium tartrate.

Solution C: Mix 50 ml of reagent A with 1 ml of reagent B. Renew daily.

Solution D: Folin–Ciocalteu reagent prepared as above and diluted with water to make it 1N in acid.

Use a protein sample containing 25–500 μg protein in 1·0 ml. Add to it 5 ml of solution C, mix well, and allow to stand 10 min or longer at room temperature. Add 0·5 ml of solution D rapidly with immediate mixing. Stand for 30 min and then read optical density at 750 mμ (low protein concs.) or 500 mμ (high protein concs.). Multiples or fractions of these quantities may be used.

FOLIN'S URIC ACID REAGENT

Dissolve 100 g molybdate-free sodium tungstate ($Na_2WO_4 \cdot 2H_2O$) (for purification see *J.B.C.* **106,** 311 (1934)) slowly in 31 ml 85% phosphoric acid in 150 ml water. Boil the mixture for 1 hr under reflux, add 0·1 ml Br_2, and then drive off excess bromine by boiling without a condenser. Cool and dilute to 500 ml.

An improved reagent for quantitative work has been devised by Brown, *J.B.C.* **158,** 601 (1945). Dissolve 100 g sodium tungstate (molybdate-free) and 20 g Na_2HPO_4 in about 150 ml water. Dilute 25 ml conc. H_2SO_4 with 75 ml water and pour the warm solution into the Na_2WO_4–Na_2HPO_4 solution. Boil gently under reflux for 1 hr. Cool and dilute to 1 l with water. It is *not* necessary to decolorize with bromine.

Either reagent in the presence of NaCN gives a blue colour with solutions containing uric acid.

FOUCHET'S REAGENT FOR BILIRUBIN

Dissolve 1 g ferric chloride and 25 g trichloroacetic acid in water and dilute to 100 ml.

To 0·15 ml serum or plasma add 0·15 ml reagent. The white precipitate turns green or blue if bilirubin is present in amounts greater than 1·5 mg/100 ml.

MILLON'S REAGENT

Dissolve 10 g Hg metal in 10 ml fuming nitric acid. Add 40 ml H_2O and decant the clear solution after standing.

Gives a white precipitate with proteins; on boiling this turns brick red or dissolves to form a red solution.

NESSLER'S SOLUTION

There is a bewildering variety of ways of preparing this reagent, of which the following are three.

(i) To 50 g potassium iodide dissolved in 50 ml water, add saturated mercuric chloride solution until a permanent precipitate just forms. Add 200 ml 5N-NaOH and dilute to 1 l. Decant clear liquid after standing.

(ii) Dissolve 4 g KI and 4 g HgI_2 in 25 ml water. Grind 1·75 g gum ghatti (select light-coloured pieces) in a mortar, add the powder to 750 ml boiling water, and boil under reflux until dissolved. Add the KI–HgI_2 solution to the gum ghatti solution, dilute to 1 l, and filter.

(iii) Dissolve 22·5 g I_2 in a solution of 30 g KI in 20 ml H_2O. Put aside 1–2 ml of this solution and to the remainder add 30 g mercury. Shake well, keeping the solution cool under running cold water, until the supernatant fluid has lost all yellow colour due to iodine. Test a few drops of the supernatant for iodine with 1% starch solution. If the test is negative, add small quantities of the original I_2–KI solution until a faint blue colour is obtained indicating a slight excess of I_2. Dilute to 200 ml and decant from the mercury. Add this solution to 975 ml of accurately 10% (w/v) NaOH (carbonate free) and mix well. Allow any precipitate to settle and use the clear supernatant fluid.

ROTHERA'S TEST FOR ACETONE AND KETONE BODIES

With blood, deproteinize with tungstic acid and test the supernatant; urine may be tested directly. To a 2 ml sample add 1 g powdered $(NH_4)_2SO_4$ followed by 0·1 ml freshly prepared 5% sodium nitroprusside solution (or a small pinch of powdered solid) and 0·4 ml 0·880 NH_3. Mix. Ketone bodies (incl. acetone) slowly produce a purplish-pink to deep purple coloration, which is maximal after 10–15 min.

SCHIFF'S REAGENT

Dissolve 9 g sodium bisulphite and 0·5 g acid fuchsin in 490 ml water. Add 10 ml conc. HCl and mix carefully. Store in the dark under N_2 or in a well-stoppered bottle.

Gives a pink colour with aldehydes but not with ketones.

SELIWANOFF'S REAGENT

Dissolve 50 mg resorcinol in 33 ml conc. HCl and dilute to 100 ml with water. Gives an intense red colour immediately on boiling with solutions containing fructose or free ketoses. Glucose, lactose, and pentoses give a positive test after boiling for 5–10 min. Sucrose gives a colour only after hydrolysis by the HCl in the reagent.

STARCH SOLUTION

(i) Make a paste from 1 g soluble starch and 5 ml H_2O and pour the suspension into 200 ml boiling water; boil 1 min, cool, and preserve with a little chloroform.

(ii) Make a paste from 3 g soluble starch and 20 ml cold H_2O. Add 500 ml saturated NaCl solution and 80 ml glacial acetic acid. Bring the solution to the boil. On cooling, the mixture will keep indefinitely.

3. REAGENTS FOR TOTAL NITROGEN DETERMINATIONS

DIGESTION MIXTURES

It is difficult to choose among the many digestion mixtures that have been employed, but the following general points may help to guide the choice of a suitable one and ensure that it is used to the best advantage. For fuller discussion see *Chem. Rev.* **27,** 331 (1940), *Adv. Protein Chem.* **3,** 142 (1947), *Analyt. Chem.* **22,** 354 (1950), *Analyt. Chem.* **26,** 185 (1954), *Meth. Enzymol.* **3,** 984 (1957), and *Meth. biochem. Anal.* **13,** 241 (1965).

(1) Most mixtures consist of H_2SO_4, one or more catalysts to speed the digestion, and frequently a salt, most commonly K_2SO_4, to raise the temperature of the digestion.

(2) There must always be a considerable excess of H_2SO_4 present in the mixture, remembering that H_2SO_4 is consumed in the digestion of organic matter and in the conversion of K_2SO_4 to $KHSO_4$. Too large a proportion of K_2SO_4 to H_2SO_4 causes serious losses of N.

(3) The addition of phosphoric acid speeds digestion, especially of proteins.

(4) The best recoveries of N from proteins are obtained with a mercury catalyst, but this has the disadvantage that it hinders the release of NH_3 in the subsequent distillation. This may be overcome by the addition of Zn dust (*J.B.C.* **176,** 1401 (1948)) or $Na_2S_2O_3$ (*B.J.* **61,** 210 (1955)) to the distillation.

(5) Somewhat lower recoveries are obtained with selenium and copper catalysts and digestion is slower than with mercury. Selenium in high concentrations causes loss of N.

(6) The use of oxidizing agents, e.g. H_2O_2, $K_2S_2O_8$, is not advised since it tends to cause loss of N.

(7) Heating of the digestion mixture should be even and only sufficient to produce the desired boiling of the mixture. Overheating causes inconsistent results.

(8) Clearing of the digest is not a criterion of completion of the digestion process. Digestion should be continued at least 1–2 hr (with Hg catalysts) or 8–12 hr (with Se–Cu catalysts) after clearing.

(9) Oxidized forms of nitrogen, such as nitrates, nitrites, nitro compounds, azo compounds, hydrazones, etc., are not completely converted to NH_3 by the standard digestion procedures. In these cases the inclusion of an organic compound, such as sucrose, salicylic acid, or pyrogallol, in the digestion mixture, or prior reduction with HI, is advisable.

A selection of well-tried digestion mixtures is given below:

(i) Mix equal volumes of conc. H_2SO_4 and saturated $KHSO_4$ solution. Dissolve 0·2 g SeO_2 per 100 ml of mixture. Up to 0·1 g $CuSO_4{\cdot}5H_2O$ per 100 ml may also be added (Conway, *Microdiffusion Analysis and Volumetric Error*, 5th ed., Crosby Lockwood (1962)).

(ii) 18N-H_2SO_4 containing 0·1–1% SeO_2 and 0·1–1% $CuSO_4{\cdot}5H_2O$ (Borsook and Dubnoff, *J.B.C.* **131**, 163 (1939); Tompkins and Kirk, *J.B.C.* **142**, 477 (1942)).

(iii) Dissolve 10 g $CuSO_4{\cdot}5H_2O$ and 10 g SeO_2 in a mixture of 750 ml conc. H_2SO_4 and 250 ml syrupy H_3PO_4 (Campbell and Hanna, *J.B.C.* **119**, 1 (1937)).

(iv) Solid catalyst prepared by grinding together 80 g K_2SO_4, 20 g $CuSO_4{\cdot}5H_2O$, and 0·34 g sodium selenate. Mix sample with conc. H_2SO_4 and start digestion. When charring commences, add 1 g solid catalyst per 2 ml conc. H_2SO_4 (Chibnall *et al.*, *B.J.* **37**, 354 (1943)).

(v) 100 g K_2SO_4, 200 ml conc. H_2SO_4, 100 ml $HgSO_4$ solution made by dissolving 10 g red HgO in 100 ml 4·4N-H_2SO_4 (Van Slyke *et al.*, *J.B.C.* **176**, 1401 (1948)).

(vi) 0·625% (w/w) yellow HgO in 9N-H_2SO_4. After water has boiled off add 100 mg K_2SO_4 per ml digestion mixture (Weil-Malherbe and Green, *B.J.* **61**, 210 (1955)).

CONWAY'S BORATE BUFFER

Dissolve 10 g boric acid in 200 ml ethanol plus about 700 ml distilled water. Add 10 ml mixed indicator and mix. Adjust colour to the desired end-point colour (faint reddish) and make up to 1 l.

If large amounts of ammonia are to be collected use 2% or even 5% boric acid.

Mixed indicator:

Bromocresol green	33 mg
Methyl red	66 mg
Ethanol	100 ml

Keeps indefinitely. Acid colour, red; alkaline colour, green; midpoint colour, grey.

Addition of phenol red (66 mg per 100 ml) gives a more readily seen brownish colour at the mid point.

TASHIRO'S INDICATOR

Mix 200 ml of 0·1% ethanolic solution of methyl red and 50 ml of 0·1% ethanolic methylene blue. Store in a darkened bottle; keeps indefinitely. Acid colour, purple; alkaline colour, bright green; midpoint colour, grey-blue.

4. PROTEIN PRECIPITANTS

TUNGSTIC ACID

J.B.C. **38**, 81 (1919); **182**, 29 (1950).

Solution A. 10% (w/v) sodium tungstate ($Na_2WO_4{\cdot}2H_2O$) in water.

Solution B. 0·67N-H_2SO_4.

Homogenize tissue sample with water to required dilution, then add tungstate solution, followed by an equal volume of sulphuric acid dropwise with thorough mixing. Alternatively equal volumes of solution A and solution B may be mixed before adding to the sample. The mixed reagent is not stable; it should be kept not more than two weeks and renewed if any precipitate appears. The filtrate obtained by tungstic acid precipitation has a pH of approx. 6·5.

Approximate amounts required for complete precipitation of protein (rat tissues):

Tissue	*Amount*	*Homogenize with (ml H_2O)*	*Solution A*	*Solution B*
Whole blood	1 ml	7 ml	1 ml	1 ml
Plasma	1 ml	8 ml	0·5 ml	0·5 ml
Liver	1 g	7·5 ml	0·75 ml	0·75 ml
Brain	1 g	3·4 ml	0·3 ml	0·3 ml
Muscle	1 g	2·8 ml	0·6 ml	0·6 ml
Spleen	1 g	8·1 ml	0·45 ml	0·45 ml

ZINC SULPHATE–ALKALI

J.B.C. **86,** 655 (1930); **160,** 69 (1945).

Cadmium sulphate may be used in place of $ZnSO_4$, but offers no particular advantage as a protein precipitant.

(i) For blood

Solution A. 10% $ZnSO_4 \cdot 7H_2O$
Solution B. 0·5N-NaOH

10 ml A diluted with 70 ml H_2O should require approx. 11 ml B when titrated using phenolphthalein (permanent pink).

Dilute 1 ml whole blood to 8 ml, add 1 ml solution A, mix, add 1 ml solution B, mix and filter. Quantities for other tissues similar to those for tungstic acid.

(ii) For blood and tissues

Solution A. 12·5 g $ZnSO_4 \cdot 7H_2O$ plus 125 ml 0·25N-H_2SO_4. Dilute to 1 l.
Solution B. 0·75N-NaOH

50 ml A should require 6·7–6·8 ml B when titrated using phenolphthalein (permanent pink).

Mix 1 ml whole blood with 8 ml solution A. Add 1 ml solution B, mix, and filter.

(iii) For plasma, semen, urine, muscle, liver, etc.

Solution A. 5% $ZnSO_4 \cdot 7H_2O$
Solution B. 0·3N-$Ba(OH)_2$

10 ml A diluted with 100 ml H_2O should require 10 ml B when titrated using phenolphthalein (permanent pink).

Dilute 1 ml whole blood with 5 ml H_2O. Add 2 ml solution A, mix, and then add 2 ml solution B. Mix and filter. Use same proportions for other tissues.

TRICHLOROACETIC ACID

For blood, mix 1 ml blood with 9 ml 10% (w/v) trichloroacetic acid and then centrifuge or filter. For tissue extracts, enzyme incubation mixtures, etc., a final concentration of 3–5% (w/v) is normally sufficient to ensure complete precipitation of proteins. Non-protein N remains in the supernatant. After removal of the protein precipitate, the trichloroacetic acid can be largely removed from the supernatant by extracting several times with water-saturated ether.

PERCHLORIC ACID

For tissue extracts, enzyme incubation mixtures, etc., add sufficient perchloric acid to give a final concentration of 3–5%. After centrifuging, excess perchloric acid may be precipitated as the potassium salt by neutralizing the supernatant with KOH, K_2CO_3, or K_3PO_4 solution, and then cooling to 0° before removing the precipitate of $KClO_4$ by centrifuging. Do not allow the mixture to warm up during centrifuging, since $KClO_4$ is appreciably more soluble at room temperature than at 0°.

ETHANOL

Add sufficient ethanol to give a final concentration of 75–80% (v/v), heat the mixture (preferably to boiling for 1–2 min), cool, centrifuge, and decant the supernatant. Ethanol may be removed, together with lipid material, by the addition of 3 volumes of $CHCl_3$. Mix thoroughly and centrifuge. The ethanol becomes dissolved in the $CHCl_3$ (lower) layer.

5. ACID–BASE INDICATORS

Indicator (*common name*)	*Preparation* 0·1 *g in* 250 *ml of*	*Acid colour*	*Basic colour*	pH *range*
Cresol red (acid range)	water containing 2·62 ml 0·1N-NaOH	red	yellow	0·2–1·8
m-Cresol purple (acid range)	water containing 2·72 ml 0·1N-NaOH	red	yellow	1·0–2·6
Thymol blue (acid range)	water containing 2·15 ml 0·1N-NaOH	red	yellow	1·2–2·8
Tropaeolin OO	water	red	yellow	1·3–3·0
Methyl yellow	90% EtOH	red	yellow	2·9–4·0
Bromophenol blue	water containing 1·49 ml 0·1N-NaOH	yellow	purple	3·0–4·6
Tetrabromophenol blue	water containing 1·0 ml 0·1N-NaOH	yellow	blue	3·0–4·6
Congo red	water or 80% EtOH	violet	reddish-orange	3·0–5·0
Methyl orange	free acid: water Na salt: water containing 3 ml 0·1N-HCl	red	orange-yellow	3·1–4·4
Bromocresol green (blue)	water containing 1·43 ml 0·1N-NaOH	yellow	blue	3·6–5·2
Methyl red	Na salt: water free acid: 60% EtOH	red	yellow	4·2–6·3
Chlorophenol red	water containing 2·36 ml 0·1N-NaOH	yellow	violet-red	4·8–6·4
Bromocresol purple	water containing 1·85 ml 0·1N-NaOH	yellow	violet	5·2–6·8
Azolitmin (litmus)	water	red	blue	5·0–8·0
Bromothymol blue	water containing 1·6 ml 0·1N-NaOH	yellow	blue	6·0–7·6
Phenol red	water containing 2·82 ml 0·1N-NaOH	yellow	red	6·8–8·4
Neutral red	70% EtOH	red	orange-brown	6·8–8·0
Cresol red (basic range)	water containing 2·62 ml 0·1N-NaOH	yellow	red	7·2–8·8
m-Cresol purple (basic range)	water containing 2·62 ml 0·1N-NaOH	yellow	purple	7·6–9·2
Thymol blue (basic range)	water containing 2·15 ml 0·1N-NaOH	yellow	blue	8·0–9·6
Phenolphthalein	70% EtOH (60% cellosolve)	colourless	pink	8·3–10·0
Thymolphthalein	90% EtOH	colourless	blue	9·3–10·5
Alizarin yellow	EtOH	yellow	red	10·1–12·0
Tropaeolin O	water	yellow	orange	11·1–12·7

It is usual to adjust the pH of indicators to an intermediate colour shade using 0·1N-NaOH or 0·1N-HCl.

26. Definitions, Formulae, and General Information

1. APPROXIMATE MOLARITIES AND SPECIFIC GRAVITIES OF CONCENTRATED ACIDS AND AMMONIA

	Percentage by weight	*Approx. molarity* M	*ml per l to prepare* M-*soln.*	*Sp. gr.*
Acetic acid	99·6	17·4	57·5	1·05
Ammonia	25	13·3	75·1	0·91
	35	18·1	55·2	0·88
Formic acid	90	23·6	42·4	1·205
	98	25·9	38·5	1·22
Hydrochloric acid	36	11·6	85·9	1·18
Nitric acid	70	15·7	63·7	1·42
Perchloric acid	60	9·2	108·8	1·54
	72	12·2	82·1	1·70
Phosphoric acid	90	16·0 (N = 48·1)	62·4 (N = 20·8)	1·75
Sulphuric acid	98	18·3 (N = 36·7)	54·5 (N = 27·3)	1·835

2. PROTEIN ESTIMATION BY EXTINCTION AT 260 mμ AND 280 mμ

Method of Warburg and Christian, *B.Z.* **310,** 384 (1941).

Measure the extinction of an appropriately diluted protein solution at both 260 mμ and 280 mμ, and calculate the ratio E_{280}/E_{260}. Using this ratio, the proportion of nucleic acid in the protein solution and a factor for the calculation of the protein concentration can be read off from the table on p. 626 or from a graph constructed from those figures. The protein concentration is given by:

$$\text{Protein concentration (mg/ml)} = \text{Extinction at 280 m}\mu \times \text{Factor} \times 1/d,$$

where d = length of light path in cm.

The figures in the table have been calculated from the extinctions of crystalline yeast enolase (E_{260} = 1·18, E_{280} = 2·06 for solutions containing 1 mg/ml) and pure yeast nucleic acid (E_{260} = 50·8, E_{280} = 24·8; concentration 1 mg/ml). The method is liable to error in so far as other proteins and nucleic acids have different extinctions.

E_{280}/E_{260}	*Nucleic acid* (%)†	*Factor*
1·75	0	1·118
1·60	0·30	1·078
1·50	0·56	1·047
1·40	0·87	1·011
1·30	1·26	0·969
1·25	1·49	0·946
1·20	1·75	0·921
1·15	2·05	0·893
1·10	2·4	0·863
1·05	2·8	0·831
1·00	3·3	0·794
0·96	3·7	0·763
0·92	4·3	0·728
0·90	4·6	0·710
0·88	4·9	0·691
0·86	5·2	0·671
0·84	5·6	0·650
0·82	6·1	0·628
0·80	6·6	0·605
0·78	7·1	0·581
0·76	7·8	0·555
0·74	8·5	0·528
0·72	9·3	0·500
0·70	10·3	0·470
0·68	11·4	0·438
0·66	12·8	0·404
0·64	14·5	0·368
0·62	16·6	0·330
0·60	19·2	0·289

† Nucleic acid is expressed as a percentage of the total (protein + nucleic acid).

3. RELATIVE CENTRIFUGAL FORCE (g)

NOMOGRAM FOR COMPUTING RELATIVE CENTRIFUGAL FORCE

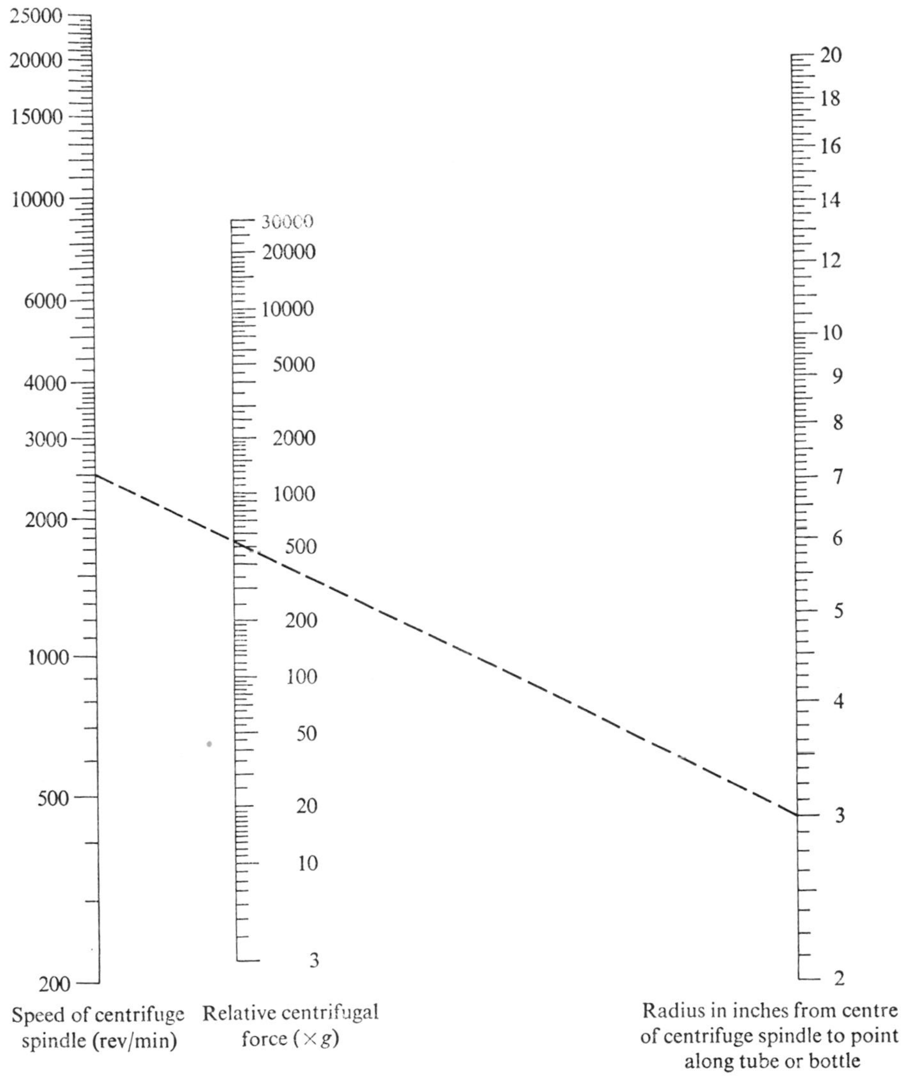

To calculate the RCF value at any point along the tube or bottle being used in the centrifuge, measure the radius in inches from the centre of the centrifuge spindle to the particular point. A straight line connecting the value of the radius on the right of the nomogram with the centrifuge speed on the left will enable the RCF value to be read off on the centre column.

(Reproduced by kind permission of Measuring & Scientific Equipment Ltd., London.)

FORMULAE

$$\text{RCF value (g)} = 1118 \times 10^{-8} \times R \times N^2,$$

where R = radius in **cm** from the centre of the rotor to the point at which the RCF value is required, and N = speed of centrifuge in revolutions/min.

$$\text{RCF value (g)} = 284 \times 10^{-7} \times R \times N^2,$$

where R = radius in **inches** from the centre of the rotor to the point at which the RCF value is required, and N = speed of centrifuge in revolutions/min.

4. PRESSURE–TEMPERATURE CONVERSION TABLE FOR AUTOCLAVES

Pressure (*lb/in²*)	*Temperature* °C	°F	*Pressure* (*lb/in²*)	*Temperature* °C	°F
0	100·0	212·0	16	122·0	251·6
1	101·9	215·4	17	123·0	253·4
2	103·6	218·5	18	124·1	255·4
3	105·3	221·5	19	125·0	257·0
4	106·9	224·4	**20**	**126·0**	**258·8**
5	**108·4**	**227·1**	25	130·4	266·7
6	109·8	229·6	30	134·5	274·1
7	111·3	232·3	35	138·1	280·6
8	112·6	234·7	40	141·5	286·7
9	113·9	237·0	45	144·6	292·3
10	**115·2**	**239·4**	**50**	**147·6**	**297·7**
11	116·4	241·5	60	153·0	307·4
12	117·6	243·7	70	157·8	316·0
13	118·8	245·8	80	162·1	323·8
14	119·9	247·8	90	166·2	331·2
15	**121·0**	**249·8**	100	169·9	337·8

5. SPECTROPHOTOMETRIC TERMS

The following definitions are recommended by I.U.P.A.C.:

$$A \equiv E = -\log_{10} T = \log_{10} I_0/I = \epsilon lc,$$

where A = absorbance,
E = extinction,
T = transmittance (transmission),
I_0 = intensity of incident light,
I = intensity of transmitted light,
ϵ = molar absorptivity (molar extinction coefficient),
c = concentration (moles/litre),
l = length of optical path (cm).

Under this definition ϵ is the absorbance (extinction) of a 1M-solution (i.e. 1 mole/litre) using a 1-cm light path. It has the dimensions litre mole^{-1} cm^{-1} or M^{-1} cm^{-1} (*not* cm^2 mole^{-1}) and, for substances which absorb visible or u.v. light strongly, e.g. purines, pyrimidines, flavins, porphyrins, nicotinamide nucleotides, etc., is of the order of magnitude 10^3 to 10^5.

An alternative definition, also widely employed, expresses c (concentration) in moles/ml. In this case, ϵ is the absorbance of a solution containing 1 mole/ml using a 1-cm light path; it has the dimensions cm^2 mole^{-1} and is of the order of magnitude 10^6 to 10^8.

6. OPTICAL ROTATION

$$[\alpha] = 100\alpha/lc,$$

where $[\alpha]$ = specific rotation, defined as the rotation of a 10-cm thickness of a solution containing 1 g of solute/ml. Temperature is denoted by a superscript and the wavelength of light used by a subscript (D indicates the D line of sodium at 589 mμ),
α = observed rotation,
l = length of light path in decimetres,
c = concentration in g/100 ml solution.

$[M]$, the molar rotation, is the rotation of a 10-cm thickness of a solution containing 1 mole of solute in 100 ml. It is calculated from the equation

$$[M] = (\text{M.wt.}/100)[\alpha],$$

where M.wt. = molecular weight.

7. DISSOCIATION CONSTANTS OF ACIDS AND BASES

For an acid dissociating thus:

$$HA \rightleftharpoons H^+ + A^-,$$

the thermodynamic dissociation constant, K_a, is defined by the equation

$$K_a = \frac{a_{H^+} \times a_{A^-}}{a_{HA}}$$

$$= \frac{c_{H^+} \times c_{A^-}}{c_{HA}} \times \frac{f_{H^+} \times f_{A^-}}{f_{HA}}$$

and

$$pK_a = -\log_{10} K_a,$$

where a = activity,
c = concentration,
f = activity coefficient,

in each case of the molecular or ionic species indicated by the subscript.

For a base dissociating thus:

$$BH^+ \rightleftharpoons B + H^+,$$

$$K_a = \frac{a_{H^+} \times a_B}{a_{BH^+}}.$$

If the activity coefficients are neglected, the classical or stoicheiometric dissociation constant, K_c (but frequently denoted by K_a in biochemical literature), is obtained:

$$K_c = \frac{c_{H^+} \times c_{A^-}}{c_{HA}} = \frac{[H^+][A^-]}{[HA]},$$

where square brackets denote the concentration of the species indicated within the brackets.

In biochemical literature a clear distinction is not always made between values of the thermodynamic dissociation constant, which may be obtained by extrapolation of determined values of K_c to zero ionic strength ($I = 0$), and 'practical' values of the dissociation constant, obtained at finite ionic strengths. Where 'practical' values are quoted, the conditions of measurement, particularly the ionic strength, should be given. Note that 'practical' values may differ appreciably (in some cases by as much as 3-fold, i.e. 0·5 pK unit) from the thermodynamic dissociation constants.

8. OXIDATION-REDUCTION POTENTIAL

The oxidation-reduction potential is the electrode potential of a half-cell containing a mixture of oxidized and reduced forms of an oxidation-reduction system,

$$E = E_0 + \frac{RT}{nF} \ln \frac{a_{ox}}{a_{red}},$$

where E = observed potential,
E_0 = the standard potential, defined as the potential of the system when all the reactants are present at unit activity,
R = gas constant,
T = absolute temperature,
n = number of equivalents involved in the reaction,
F = the faraday (96 494 coulombs),
a_{ox} = activity of the oxidized form of the oxidation-reduction system,
a_{red} = activity of the reduced form of the system.

In practice, E_0 is often taken to be the electrode potential when the concentrations of oxidized and reduced forms are equal, and not necessarily unity.

Note that, for reactions involving a proton, E_0 is the standard electrode potential at unit activity of hydrogen ions, i.e. pH 0. For such reactions the term E_0' is used to indicate measurements made at stated pHs other than 0. In biochemical work this pH is usually 7.

9. ENZYME UNIT

One unit (U) of any enzyme is defined as that amount which will catalyse the transformation of 1 micromole (1 μmole) of substrate per minute, or, where more than one bond of each substrate molecule is attacked, 1 micro-equivalent of the group concerned per minute, under defined conditions. Where two identical molecules react together, the unit is the amount which catalyses the transformation of 2 μmoles of substrate per minute. The temperature should be stated; a temperature of 30 °C is recommended where practicable. Other conditions, such as pH and substrate concentration, should, where practicable, be optimal; if they are not, this should be stated.

10. STEM CORRECTION IN MELTING POINT DETERMINATIONS

Stem correction (in degrees) = $KL(T_1-T_2)$,

where K = apparent expansion coefficient of mercury in glass,
L = length (in degrees) of the exposed mercury column of the thermometer,
T_1 = the observed temperature,
T_2 = the temperature recorded by a second thermometer with its bulb placed at the middle of the exposed mercury column.

K for Pyrex glass = $1{\cdot}64\times10^{-4}$ at 100°, $1{\cdot}65\times10^{-4}$ at 150°, $1{\cdot}67\times10^{-4}$ at 200° $1{\cdot}70\times10^{-4}$ at 250°, $1{\cdot}74\times10^{-4}$ at 300°, $1{\cdot}78\times10^{-4}$ at 350°.

11. SOLUTIONS USED IN FORMING DENSITY GRADIENTS

Sucrose

Conc. of sucrose % (*w/w*)	*g/l of soln.* (*at* 20°)	*Density* (*g/ml*) *at* 0°	*at* 20°	*Viscosity* (*centipoises*) *at* 0°	*at* 5°	*at* 20°
5	50·9	1·020	1·018			1·14
10	103·8	1·041	1·038			1·33
15	158·9	1·063	1·059			1·59
20	216·2	1·085	1·081	3·82	3·17	1·95
25	275·9	1·109	1·104			2·45
30	338·1	1·133	1·127			3·19
35	402·9	1·158	1·151			4·32
40	470·6	1·183	1·176	14·8	11·6	6·17
45	541·3	1·210	1·203			9·38
50	614·8	1·238	1·230			15·4
55	691·9	1·266	1·258			28·1
60	771·9	1·296	1·286	238	156	58·5
65	855·6	1·326	1·316			147

More extensive tables are given in

Prog. Biophys. biophys. Chem. **9,** 357 (1959),
International Critical Tables, vol. 2, p. 343 (1927),
F. J. Bates, *Polarimetry, Saccharimetry and the Sugars*, U.S. Department of Commerce, National Bureau of Standards, Washington, D.C. (1942).

Caesium chloride (CsCl)

Conc. of CsCl % (*w*/*w*)	*g*/*l of soln.* (*at* 20°)	*Density* (*g*/*ml*) *at* 0°	*at* 20°
5	51·9	1·040	1·038
10	108·0	1·084	1·080
15	168·9	1·131	1·126
20	235·2	1·181	1·176
25	307·7	1·236	1·231
30	386·4	1·296	1·288
35	473·2	1·361	1·352
40	568·8	1·432	1·422
45	675·0	1·511	1·500
50	793·0	1·598	1·586
55	924·5	1·695	1·681
60	1073	1·804	1·789
65	1241		1·910

The concentration of caesium chloride solution corresponding to any desired density may be calculated from the formula

$$W(\%) = 137{\cdot}48 - 138{\cdot}11(1/\rho_{25}),$$

where ρ_{25} is the desired density at 25°.

Similar formulae for other salts are given in *Fortschr. Chem. org. NatStoffe* **20,** 372 (1962).

Ficoll

A polymer of sucrose, weight-average M. wt. = 400 000, $[\alpha]_D$ +56·5.

Conc. of Ficoll % (*w*/*v*)	d_4^{20}	*Viscosity* (η_{rel} *at* 20°)
10	1·033	5
20	1·068	20
30	1·103	60
40	1·138	180
50	1·171	600

27. Atomic Weights

INTERNATIONAL ATOMIC WEIGHTS, 1961

J.A.C.S. **84**, 4175 (1962); *Nature, Lond.* **194**, 621 (1962).

There is now a single scale of atomic weights based upon $^{12}C = 12$ as standard. Values on the new scale are 43 parts per million lower than those on the old chemical scale (based on O = 16).

Name	*Symbol*	*Atomic number*	*Atomic weight*
Aluminium	Al	13	26·9815
Antimony	Sb	51	121·75
Argon	Ar	18	39·948
Arsenic	As	33	74·9216
Barium	Ba	56	137·34
Beryllium	Be	4	9·0122
Bismuth	Bi	83	208·980
Boron	B	5	10·811
Bromine	Br	35	79·909
Cadmium	Cd	48	112·40
Caesium	Cs	55	132·905
Calcium	Ca	20	40·08
Carbon	C	6	12·01115
Cerium	Ce	58	140·12
Chlorine	Cl	17	35·453
Chromium	Cr	24	51·996
Cobalt	Co	27	58·9332
Copper	Cu	29	63·54
Dysprosium	Dy	66	162·50
Erbium	Er	68	167·26
Europium	Eu	63	151·96
Fluorine	F	9	18·9984
Gadolinium	Gd	64	157·25
Gallium	Ga	31	69·72
Germanium	Ge	32	72·59
Gold	Au	79	196·967
Hafnium	Hf	72	178·49
Helium	He	2	4·0026
Holmium	Ho	67	164·930
Hydrogen	H	1	1·00797
Indium	In	49	114·82
Iodine	I	53	126·9044
Iridium	Ir	77	192·2
Iron	Fe	26	55·847
Krypton	Kr	36	83·80
Lanthanum	La	57	138·91
Lead	Pb	82	207·19
Lithium	Li	3	6·939
Lutetium	Lu	71	174·97
Magnesium	Mg	12	24·312

27. Atomic Weights

Name	*Symbol*	*Atomic number*	*Atomic weight*
Manganese	Mn	25	54·9380
Mercury	Hg	80	200·59
Molybdenum	Mo	42	95·94
Neodymium	Nd	60	144·24
Neon	Ne	10	20·183
Nickel	Ni	28	58·71
Niobium	Nb	41	92·906
Nitrogen	N	7	14·0067
Osmium	Os	76	190·2
Oxygen	O	8	15·9994
Palladium	Pd	46	106·4
Phosphorus	P	15	30·9738
Platinum	Pt	78	195·09
Potassium	K	19	39·102
Praseodymium	Pr	59	140·907
Rhenium	Re	75	186·2
Rhodium	Rh	45	102·905
Rubidium	Rb	37	85·47
Ruthenium	Ru	44	101·07
Samarium	Sm	62	150·35
Scandium	Sc	21	44·956
Selenium	Se	34	78·96
Silicon	Si	14	28·086
Silver	Ag	47	107·870
Sodium	Na	11	22·9898
Strontium	Sr	38	87·62
Sulphur	S	16	32·064
Tantalum	Ta	73	180·948
Tellurium	Te	52	127·60
Terbium	Tb	65	158·924
Thallium	Tl	81	204·37
Thorium	Th	90	232·038
Thulium	Tm	69	168·934
Tin	Sn	50	118·69
Titanium	Ti	22	47·90
Tungsten	W	74	183·85
Uranium	U	92	238·03
Vanadium	V	23	50·942
Xenon	Xe	54	131·30
Ytterbium	Yb	70	173·04
Yttrium	Y	39	88·905
Zinc	Zn	30	65·37
Zirconium	Zr	40	91·22

ATOMIC WEIGHT MULTIPLES

	Carbon C = 12·01115	*Hydrogen* H = 1·00797	
1	12·01	1·01	1
2	24·02	2·02	2
3	36·03	3·02	3
4	48·04	4·03	4
5	60·06	5·04	5
6	72·07	6·05	6
7	84·08	7·06	7
8	96·09	8·06	8
9	108·10	9·07	9
10	120·11	10·08	10
11	132·12	11·09	11
12	144·13	12·10	12
13	156·14	13·10	13
14	168·16	14·11	14
15	180·17	15·12	15
16	192·18	16·13	16
17	204·19	17·14	17
18	216·20	18·14	18
19	228·21	19·15	19
20	240·22	20·16	20
21	252·23	21·17	21
22	264·25	22·18	22
23	276·26	23·18	23
24	288·27	24·19	24
25	300·28	25·20	25
26	312·29	26·21	26
27	324·30	27·22	27
28	336·31	28·22	28
29	348·32	29·23	29
30	360·33	30·24	30
31	372·35	31·25	31
32	384·36	32·26	32
33	396·37	33·26	33
34	408·38	34·27	34
35	420·39	35·28	35
36	432·40	36·29	36
37	444·41	37·29	37
38	456·42	38·30	38
39	468·43	39·31	39
40	480·45	40·32	40
41	492·46	41·33	41
42	504·47	42·33	42
43	516·48	43·34	43
44	528·49	44·35	44
45	540·50	45·36	45
46	552·51	46·37	46
47	564·52	47·37	47
48	576·54	48·38	48
49	588·55	49·39	49
50	600·56	50·40	50
60	720·67	60·48	60
70	840·78	70·56	70
80	960·89	80·64	80
90	1081·00	90·72	90
100	1201·11	100·80	100

27. Atomic Weights

	Oxygen O = 15·9994	*Nitrogen* N = 14·0067	
1	16·00	14·01	1
2	32·00	28·01	2
3	48·00	42·02	3
4	64·00	56·03	4
5	80·00	70·03	5
6	96·00	84·04	6
7	112·00	98·05	7
8	128·00	112·05	8
9	143·99	126·06	9
10	159·99	140·07	10
11	175·99	154·07	11
12	191·99	168·08	12
13	207·99	182·09	13
14	223·99	196·09	14
15	239·99	210·10	15
16	255·99	224·11	16
17	271·99	238·11	17
18	287·99	252·12	18
19	303·99	266·13	19
20	319·99	280·13	20
21	335·99	294·14	21
22	351·99	308·15	22
23	367·99	322·15	23
24	383·99	336·16	24
25	399·98	350·17	25
26	415·98	364·17	26
27	431·98	378·18	27
28	447·98	392·19	28
29	463·98	406·19	29
30	479·98	420·20	30
40	639·98	560·27	40
50	799·97	700·33	50
60	959·96	840·40	60

	Phosphorus P = 30·9738	*Sulphur* S = 32·064	
1	30·97	32·06	1
2	61·95	64·13	2
3	92·92	96·19	3
4	123·90	128·26	4
5	154·87	160·32	5
6	185·84	192·38	6
7	216·82	224·45	7
8	247·79	256·51	8
9	278·76	288·58	9
10	309·74	320·64	10
20	619·48	641·28	20
30	929·21	961·92	30
40	1238·95	1282·56	40
50	1548·69	1603·20	50

	Chlorine Cl = 35·453	*Sodium* Na = 22·9898	*Potassium* K = 39·102	
1	35·45	22·99	39·10	1
2	70·91	45·98	78·20	2
3	106·36	68·97	117·31	3
4	141·81	91·96	156·41	4
5	177·26	114·95	195·51	5
6	212·72	137·94	234·61	6
7	248·17	160·93	273·71	7
8	283·62	183·92	312·82	8
9	319·08	206·91	351·92	9
10	354·53	229·90	391·02	10

	Ammonium NH_4 = 18·03858	*Hydrogen chloride* HCl = 36·46097	
1	18·04	36·46	1
2	36·08	72·92	2
3	54·12	109·38	3
4	72·15	145·84	4
5	90·19	182·30	5

	Water H_2O = 18·01534				
1	18·02	11	198·17	30	540·46
2	36·03	12	216·18	40	720·61
3	54·05	13	234·20	50	900·77
4	72·06	14	252·21		
5	90·08	15	270·23		
6	108·09	16	288·25		
7	126·11	17	306·26		
8	144·12	18	324·28		
9	162·14	19	342·29		
10	180·15	20	360·31		

Index*

* Figures in *italics* refer to entries in the section on 'Methods for the Detection of Biochemical Compounds'.

Index